HIGH POLYMERS

Vol. I: **Collected Papers of W. H. Carothers on High Polymeric Substances.**
Edited by H. Mark and G. S. Whitby

Vol. II: **Physical Chemistry of High Polymeric Systems.**
Second Edition. By H. Mark and A. V. Tobolsky

Vol. III: **Mechanism of Polymer Reactions.**
By G. M. Burnett

Vol. IV: **Natural and Synthetic High Polymers.**
Second Edition. By K. H. Meyer

Vol. V: **Cellulose and Cellulose Derivatives** (in three parts).
Second Edition. Edited by Emil Ott, H. M. Spurlin, and M. W. Grafflin

Vol. VI: **Mechanical Behavior of High Polymers.**
By Turner Alfrey, Jr.

Vol. VII: **Phenoplasts: Their Structure, Properties, and Chemical Technology.**
By T. S. Carswell

Vol. VIII: Replaced by Vol. XVIII.

Vol. IX: **Emulsion Polymerization.**
By F. A. Bovey, I. M. Kolthoff, A. I. Medalia, and E. J. Meehan

Vol. X: **Polymer Processes.**
Edited by Calvin E. Schildknecht

Vol. XI: Replaced by Vol. XX.

Vol. XII: **Analytical Chemistry of Polymers** (in three parts).
Edited by Gordon M. Kline

Vol. XIII: **Polyethers** (in three parts).
Edited by Norman G. Gaylord

Vol. XIV: **Polyesters** (in two parts).
Edited by Norman G. Gaylord

Vol. XV: **Radiation Chemistry of Polymeric Systems.**
By Adolphe Chapiro

Vol. XVI: **Polyurethanes: Chemistry and Technology** (in two parts).
By J. H. Saunders and K. C. Frisch

Vol. XVII: **Configurational Statistics of Polymeric Chains.**
By M. V. Volkenstein. Translated by Serge N. Timasheff and M. J. Timasheff

Vol. XVIII: **Copolymerization.**
Edited by George E. Ham

Vol. XIX: **Chemical Reactions of Polymers.**
Edited by E. M. Fettes

Vol. XX: **Crystalline Olefin Polymers** (in two parts).
Edited by R. A. V. Raff and K. W. Doak

HIGH POLYMERS

A SERIES OF MONOGRAPHS ON THE CHEMISTRY, PHYSICS, AND TECHNOLOGY OF HIGH POLYMERIC SUBSTANCES

VOLUME XIX

CHEMICAL REACTIONS OF POLYMERS

Edited by E. M. FETTES

Koppers Company
Monroeville, Pennsylvania

INTERSCIENCE PUBLISHERS

a division of John Wiley & Sons

NEW YORK • LONDON • SYDNEY

Library of Congress Catalog Card Number: 64-17054

PRINTED IN THE UNITED STATES OF AMERICA

PREFACE

The chemical reactions of polymers, a subject currently of scientific as well as industrial importance, is not a recent development. Even before the pioneering work of Staudinger which led to the still fairly recent concepts of polymer chemistry, various chemical modifications of natural polymers were carried out. The nitration of cellulose, first described in 1845, led to the first synthetic plastic, celluloid, in 1870. The chlorination of rubber to produce a hard plastic was described in 1859.

In spite of this antiquity (in terms of polymer chemistry), the general subject of chemical reactions has never been treated separately in a book. Separate portions of the field, in particular, the derivatives of cellulose, have been well covered, while books on natural rubber have dealt with its chlorination, hydrochlorination, and cyclization. The purpose of this book is to attempt to fill this gap by covering the various types of chemical reactions that have been carried out with diverse polymeric substances. This book is designed to survey critically rather than exhaustively the various types of chemical reactions in which at least one of the reacting species is polymeric. To cover in complete detail all of the published information on all of the reactions of all polymers is certainly difficult and probably impossible in a volume of any reasonable size.

The broad scope of the field, the wide diversity of the types of polymers, and the necessity of groupings for which suitable authors could be found led inevitably to a hybrid system. Reactions which are common to most polymers, such as thermal degradation, oxidation, or effects of radiation, are the subjects of separate chapters or sections of chapters on that reaction. On the other hand, the reactions undergone by cellulose and proteinaceous polymers are sufficiently different that these polymers are each handled in separate chapters.

The chief difficulty (at least as judged by reviews) in books with a number of contributors is securing a balanced treatment. As the manuscripts started to come in, I was concerned about the differences in approach, in style, and in length. I finally decided that this was an inevitable result of dealing with over thirty different individuals. Moreover, who is the best judge of the proper treatment and length of a subject—the editor, the reviewer, or the specialist in the particular field? The subjects themselves, admittedly arrived at somewhat arbitrarily, differ greatly in scope, in amount of published information, and in stages of industrial development. One can therefore rationalize the results as still being preferable to the only alternative, that of having a book written completely by one person and losing the advantage of personal familiarity with the subject.

The applicability of polymers, whether elastomers, plastics, or fibers, to end uses such as fabrics, coatings, films, molded articles, or foams can be broadened in scope by using chemical reactions to crosslink a polymer, to combine different polymers, or to modify the structure and thus the properties of a given polymer. The stability of a polymer to its environment can be best understood and improved by a knowledge of the pertinent chemical reactions involved in exposure to heat, oxygen, ozone, or radiation. The many chemists and engineers involved in these fields of activity should find this book of value, as should the graduate student specializing in the chemistry of polymers. A general knowledge of the properties and structure of polymers is assumed to have been already acquired by the reader.

To make the bibliographies of the chapters more useful, the reference to *Chemical Abstracts* is inserted for all abstracted patents, for most references in foreign journals, and for journals which are not always immediately available in the smaller companies.

The planning of this volume was aided greatly by discussions with and/or suggestions from: T. Alfrey, R. F. Boyer, E. Immergut, H. Mark, C. G. Overberger, W. B. Reynolds, H. M. Spurlin, V. Stannett, R. F. Tuckett, and W. F. Watson. The background and experience of R. A. V. Raff in projects of this nature was drawn upon as well as the invaluable assistance of Mrs. Elizabeth Lyle in the actual editing. The advice and aid of E. P. Meckly, Manager of the Technical Information Group at Koppers, was greatly appreciated. Thanks are also due to Mrs. Majorie Radzwill for the secretarial assistance rendered.

E. M. FETTES

AUTHORS

T. ALFREY, JR., *The Dow Chemical Co., Midland, Michigan*

F. S. ANG, *Molloy Catholic College for Women, Rockville Center, New York*

D. J. ANGIER, *Esso Research and Engineering, Linden, New Jersey*

M. B. BERENBAUM, *Thiokol Chemical Corp., Trenton, New Jersey*

E. E. BOSTICK, *General Electric Co., Schenectady, New York*

P. J. CANTERINO, *W. R. Grace & Co., Polymer Chemicals Division, Clifton, New Jersey*

W. G. CARSON, *Rohm & Haas Co., Research Laboratories, Bristol, Pennsylvania*

D. CRAIG, *B. F. Goodrich Research Center, Brecksville, Ohio*

T. DAVIES, *Imperial Chemical Industries, Ltd., Fibres Division, Research Department, Harrogate, Yorkshire, England*

K. C. FRISCH, *Wyandotte Chemical Corp., Industrial Chemicals Division, Wyandotte, Michigan*

N. G. GAYLORD, *Gaylord Associates, Inc., Newark, New Jersey*

R. GOBRAN, *Thiokol Chemical Corp., Trenton, New Jersey*

M. A. GOLUB, *Stanford Research Institute, Menlo Park, California*

N. GRASSIE, *Department of Chemistry, The University, Glasgow, Scotland*

F. P. GREENSPAN, *FMC Corp., Plastics Department, New York, New York*

J. D. GUTHRIE, *Southern Regional Research Laboratory, United States Department of Agriculture, New Orleans, Louisiana*

W. L. HAWKINS, *Bell Telephone Laboratories, Inc., Murray Hill, New Jersey*

G. D. JONES, *The Dow Chemical Co., Physical Research Laboratory, Midland, Michigan*

J. LE BRAS, *Institut Français du Caoutchouc, Paris, France*

G. E. MEYER, *Goodyear Tire & Rubber Co., Research Division, Akron, Ohio*

A. J. MORAK, *The Institute of Paper Chemistry, Appleton, Wisconsin*

H. MORAWETZ, *Polytechnic Institute of Brooklyn, Department of Chemistry, Brooklyn, New York*

M. MORTON, *Institute of Rubber Research, University of Akron, Akron, Ohio*

R. W. MURRAY, *Bell Telephone Laboratories, Inc., Murray Hill, New Jersey*

R. PAUTRAT, *Institut Français du Caoutchouc, Paris, France*

R. M. PIERSON, *Goodyear Tire & Rubber Co., Research Division, Akron, Ohio*

C. P. PINAZZI, *Institut Français du Caoutchouc, Paris, France*

D. A. S. RAVENS, *Imperial Chemical Industries, Inc., Fibres Division, Harrogate, Yorkshire, England*

W. A. REEVES, *Southern Regional Research Laboratory, United States Department of Agriculture, New Orleans, Louisiana*

E. E. RENFREW, *Minnesota Mining and Manufacturing Co., St. Paul, Minnesota*

J. Scanlan, *Rubber and Plastics Research Association of Great Britain, Shawbury, Shrewsbury, Shropshire, England*

L. Segal, *Southern Regional Research Laboratory, United States Department of Agriculture, New Orleans, Louisiana*

A. R. Shultz, *Polymer and Interface Studies Section, General Electric Research Laboratory, Schenectady, New York*

J. E. Sisley, *Imperial Chemical Industries, Ltd., Fibres Division, Harrogate, Yorkshire, England*

G. J. Smets, *University of Louvain, Louvain, Belgium*

P. R. Story, *Bell Telephone Laboratories, Inc., Murray Hill, New Jersey*

D. Taber, *Armour Grocery Products Co., Chicago, Illinois*

L. B. Tewksbury, *Goodyear Tire & Rubber Co., Research Division, Akron, Ohio*

H. E. Tiefenthal, *Armour Industrial Chemical Co., Chicago, Illinois*

H. C. Vogt, *Wyandotte Chemical Corp., Wyandotte, Michigan*

K. Ward, Jr., *The Institute of Paper Chemistry, Appleton, Wisconsin*

W. L. Wasley, *Western Regional Research Laboratory, United States Department of Agriculture, Albany, California*

W. F. Watson, *Rubber and Plastics Research Association of Great Britain, Shawbury, Shrewsbury, Shropshire, England*

R. E. Whitfield, *Western Regional Research Laboratory, United States Department of Agriculture, Albany, California*

F. H. Winslow, *Bell Telephone Laboratories, Inc., Murray Hill, New Jersey*

J. Wicklatz, *General Mills, Inc., Polymer Research Department, Minneapolis, Minnesota*

M. Wismer, *Pittsburgh Plate Glass Co., Pittsburgh, Pennsylvania*

CONTENTS

Chapter I

GENERAL CONSIDERATIONS

A. REACTIVITY OF FUNCTIONAL GROUPS ON POLYMERS

T. ALFREY, JR.

Dow Chemical Co.

1. Introduction

How does the chemical reactivity of an organic functional group on a polymer molecule compare with the reactivity of the same group on a low molecular weight analogue?

In the answer to this question, we encounter a fascinating paradox of polymer chemistry.

On the one hand, the postulate of *equal* reactivity is one of the cornerstones of polymerization kinetics. The classic investigation of polyesterification reactions by Flory (1,2) established that the rates of reaction of carboxyl and hydroxyl groups do not depend upon the sizes of the polymer chains to which they are attached. Furthermore, Flory (3) has developed firm theoretical arguments supporting the principle of equal reactivity for a broad range of polymeric reactions.

On the other hand, it is well known that some organic reactions involving high polymers are orders of magnitude slower or orders of magnitude faster than analogous reactions of small molecules. For example, the (heterogeneous) catalytic hydrogenation of an unsaturated polymer in solution can be much slower than the hydrogenation of an analogue of low molecular weight. Enzymatic reactions commonly exhibit extremely high rates at low concentrations, and similar effects have been observed with synthetic polymers. For example, Morawetz and co-workers (4) have found that copolymers of acrylic acid and *p*-nitrophenyl methacrylate are hydrolyzed many orders of magnitude more rapidly than the *p*-nitrophenyl ester of a monocarboxylic acid.

In this chapter, we must resolve the above paradox in a manner which will permit us to retain the powerful and valuable principle of equal reactivities while recognizing certain definite limitations to its applicability.

One central theme of the chapter is this: We can confidently expect a functional group on a polymer to exhibit essentially the same reactivity as the same group in a low molecular weight homologue, if the following conditions are met: (*1*) the reaction occurs in a homogeneous, fluid medium, all reactants, intermediates, and products being soluble in the medium; (*2*) each elementary step of the reaction involves *no more than one* polymer-attached functional group, all other reacting species being small and mobile; and (*3*) the choice of a low molecular weight "homologue" is made with sufficient care, attention being given to the steric hindrances that can arise in the immediate vicinity of a polymer chain. The above are advanced as sufficient conditions for equal reactivity of a polymer and its small homologue. Essentially equal reactivity *may* be observed in cases where one or another of these conditions is not met.

The term "fluid" in condition (*1*) deserves some comment. The real requirement here is a high diffusional mobility of the low molecular weight reactants. The macroscopic viscosity of the polymer solution can be extremely high without resulting in diffusion-controlled kinetics, as long as the small molecules are mobile. Even in a three-dimensional network polymer, with zero macroscopic shear fluidity, the small molecules will often exhibit sufficient mobility to meet this requirement. On the other hand, at very high concentrations of polymer, the multicomponent system can be in a glassy state which immobilizes even the small molecules. This, however, is a most extreme situation, not normally encountered in kinetic studies. The point is that the reacting medium can be extremely viscous and yet retain the characteristic of "fluidity" in the sense of condition (*1*) above. The reader is referred to Flory (3) for a more detailed discussion of this point.

2. Concerted Nucleophilic Displacement Reactions (and Related Polar Reactions)

Flory (1,2) observed that polyesterification kinetics followed the same third-order pattern as that found in simple esterification. When a strong acid catalyst is employed, the rate is proportional to organic acid, to alcohol, and to catalyst concentration:

$$\text{Rate} = k[\text{RCOOH}][\text{R'OH}][\text{H}^+] \tag{1}$$

When no strong acid is employed, the organic acid must play two roles—reactant and catalyst. This leads to the following kinetic pattern:

$$\text{Rate} = k[\text{RCOOH}]^2[\text{R'OH}] \tag{2}$$

Such third-order kinetics (and by implication termolecular mechanisms) are often encountered in polar organic reactions. If three molecules participate in a reaction, their actions may be sequential, or concerted; uncertainty with respect to this feature often exists in the analysis of individual reaction mechanisms. In this section, we shall arbitrarily select *concerted nucleophilic displacement reactions* for discussion.

Following Swain (5,6), we shall picture concerted nucleophilic displacement reactions as termolecular processes involving a nucleophile (N:), a substrate (S), and an electrophile (E). These respective roles might be played by Me_3N:, $C_6H_5CH_2Cl$, and CH_3OH, as in reaction (3). The rate of

$$\begin{array}{ccccc} & C_6H_5 & & & \\ & | & & & \\ (CH_3)_3N: & CCl & HOCH_3 & \rightarrow \text{Transition state} \rightarrow & \text{quat. } Cl^- \\ & | & & & \\ & H_2 & & & \\ N: & S & E & & \end{array} \tag{3}$$

this reaction would be proportional to the product of the concentrations of the three participating species:

$$\text{Rate} = k[\text{N:}][\text{S}][\text{E}] \tag{4}$$

Let us now examine polymer reactions of this type. If no more than one reacting species is attached to the polymer, we are faced with the three possibilities illustrated in Scheme I, where

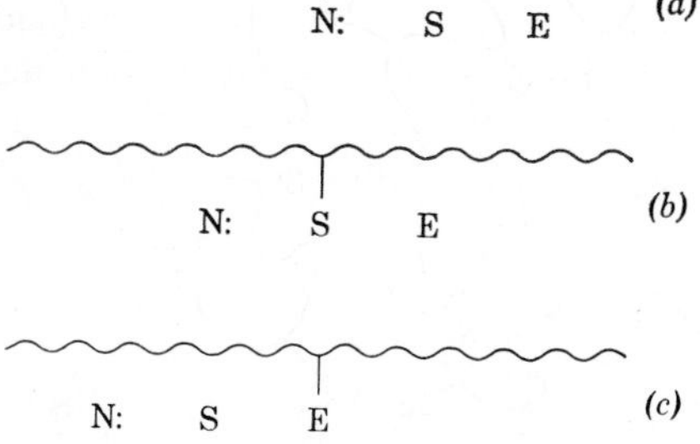

Scheme I

(*a*) N: is poly-4-vinylpyridine, S is benzyl chloride, and E is ethyl alcohol; (*b*) N: is 4-methylpyridine, S is poly-*p*-chloromethylstyrene, and E is ethyl alcohol; or (*c*) N: is 4-methylpyridine, S is benzyl chloride, and E is poly(hydroxyethyl methacrylate). In cases (*a*) and (*b*), the polymer molecule is converted to a quaternary pyridinium chloride; in case (*c*), the polymer is not involved in the reaction stoichiometry but is involved kinetically in the formation of a low molecular weight product. Assuming that the solvent medium is kinetically inert, but that all reactants and products are soluble, we would expect that in all three cases the reaction rate would follow the third-order equation:

$$\text{Rate} = k\,(\text{molar concn. of N: groups})\,(\text{molar concn. of S groups}) \times (\text{molar concn. of E groups}) \quad (5)$$

and further, that the effective rate constant, k, would be of the same order of magnitude as that for the prototype reaction (methylpyridine; benzyl chloride; ethanol).

In each case, two of the three kinetically active species are small and mobile. Hence, even if the functional group attached to the polymer were completely immobilized, the frequency of termolecular collisions (N:, S, E) would not be greatly reduced. Furthermore, the functional groups in poly-4-vinylpyridine, poly-*p*-chloromethylstyrene and poly(hydroxyethyl methacrylate) are all set out well away from the chain, and would probably be accessible to small molecules in solution.

Let us now consider a number of cases where two of the functional groups are attached to polymer chains. First, consider the reaction of poly-4-vinylpyridine, poly-*p*-chloromethylstyrene, and ethyl alcohol in a moderately dilute solution.

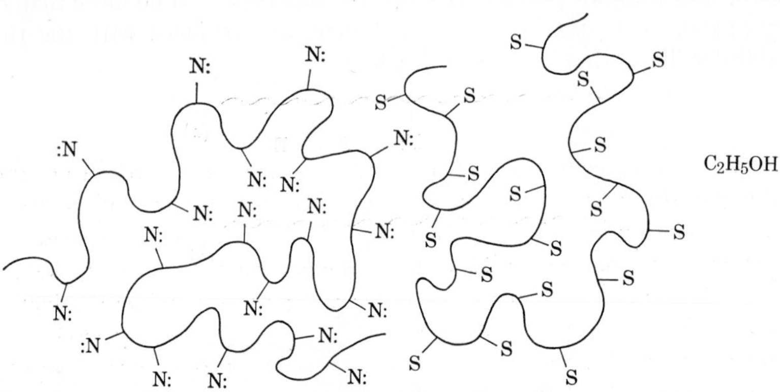

Scheme II

These reactants are indicated in Scheme II. Ordinarily, we would encounter phase separation in such a system, even though the solvent was completely miscible with each individual reactant. Even if a homogeneous phase were established, the chemical reaction could not be expected to follow the kinetic pattern of the prototype of low molecular weight. A three-dimensional gel structure would form at a low degree of conversion, and further reaction would become more and more difficult. Even after a very long reaction time, there would be many attached N: groups which were "trapped" in regions of the gel where no S groups could be reached, and vice versa. Potentially, these trapped pyridine groups are essentially as reactive as the prototype (4-methylpyridine); if a substrate of low molecular weight were diffused into the gel, these trapped groups could react in a normal manner. However, in the actual situation they would be unable to diffuse to the trapped chloromethyl groups, and consequently they would display a markedly depressed effective reactivity.

In the case of a polymeric electrophile assisting the attack of a polymeric nucleophile upon a low molecular weight substrate, the problem of gelation would not arise (Scheme III). If such a reaction were carried out in dilute

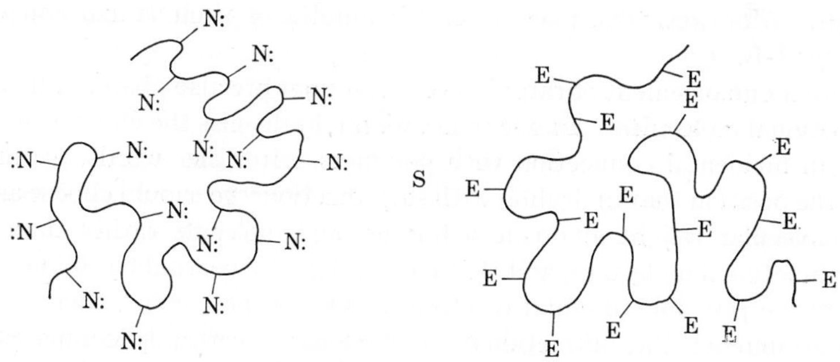

Scheme III

solution, the rate would presumably fail to follow the simple third-order kinetic expression (in terms of the concentrations of N:, S, and E groups), because of the limited extent of interpenetration of the random coils. At high concentrations, we would often encounter phase separation, resulting in anomalous reaction kinetics. If phase separation did not occur, the kinetics at high concentration might well turn out to be "normal"—i.e., first-order in the concentrations of N:, S, and E groups, with a rate constant comparable to that for analogues of low molecular weight.

Finally, if two of the kinetically significant groups are attached to the same (copolymer) chain, the kinetic consequences can be large, and most diverse. Three general cases suggest themselves, as illustrated in Scheme IV. It is readily apparent that striking deviations from "normal" third-

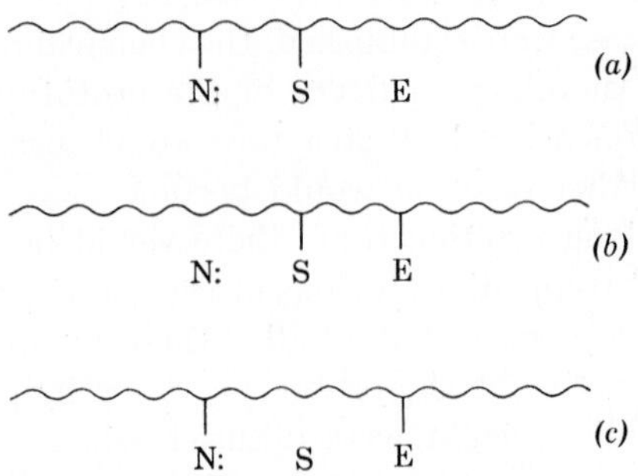

Scheme IV

order kinetics can be anticipated in such reactions. Many of the possible effects have been discussed by Swain (5,6) and by Morawetz (4). Of particular interest is the possibility of strong enhancement of reaction rate, resulting from a favorable geometric arrangement of the two polymeric groups. Morawetz discusses several examples of such enhancement in Chapter I-B.

Similar enhancement of rates in polar reactions are also observed in small bifunctional molecules. In one sense, we might dismiss the effect as having only an incidental connection with polymers. In other words, we might take the position that in dealing with such reactions we should choose as our low molecular weight analogue a bifunctional molecule rather than two monofunctional molecules, and that having done so we would automatically restore the principle of equal reactivity. On the first point, there can be little argument; the bifunctional small molecule certainly simulates the chemical behavior of a copolymer such as (*a*), (*b*), or (*c*) more closely than does a pair of monofunctional molecules. However, as Morawetz points out, the rates of reaction of the copolymers are extremely sensitive to configuration and specific steric effects, and "it will be difficult to simulate in small molecules the conformational restraints which must necessarily exist in polymer chains." Consequently, it will often be impossible, in practice, to provide an adequate low molecular weight analogue of these abnormally reactive polymer systems.

Returning to the case where two functional groups, on separate polymer molecules, must participate in the reaction, we should emphasize that "normal" kinetics are often observed, in spite of the fact that condition (*2*) (having no more than one functional group attached to a polymer) is not met. A classic example is provided in ordinary polyesterification kinetics. Flory (2) has pointed out that even if the frequency of binary encounters is markedly reduced because of attachment to large polymer chains, the rate of chemical reaction is not necessarily depressed. The same diffusional retardation which makes binary encounters infrequent causes the encounters which do occur to be of long duration. Once two functional groups diffuse close to one another, they stay near one another for a long time, with many repeated collisions. Only a very small fraction of the collisions leads to chemical reaction. As long as this fraction multiplied by the average number of collisions per encounter, is small compared to unity, the reaction rate is normal. In the following part, we shall see that in free radical reactions, where the probability of a collision resulting in reaction may be considerably larger, abnormal kinetics are more likely to result from failure of condition (*2*).

3. Free Radical Chain Reactions

In contrast to the polar reactions of the previous section, the most common propagation steps of free radical chain reactions are mainly bimolecular reactions between a radical and a substrate molecule, as shown in eqs. (6)–(8). These propagation steps determine the chemical composition

Addition to C=C:

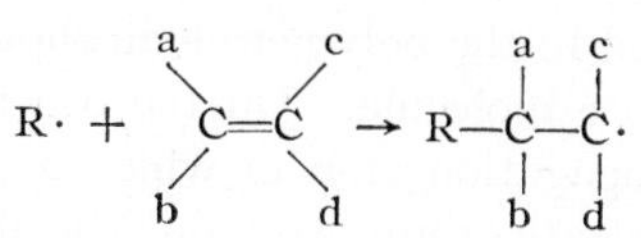

(6)

Chain transfer:

$$R\cdot + XR' \rightarrow R\text{—}X + R'\cdot \tag{7}$$

Addition to O_2:

$$R\cdot + O_2 \rightarrow RO_2\cdot \tag{8}$$

of the reaction product, in the case of long kinetic chain length, but the absolute rate of reaction is influenced by initiation and termination steps as well. We will assume here that initiation is understood and controllable, and does not involve polymeric species. Termination reactions are normally bimolecular, involving either one or two free radicals:

$$R\cdot + T \rightarrow \text{Inert} \tag{9}$$

$$R\cdot + R'\cdot \rightarrow \text{Inert} \tag{10}$$

The overall reaction may include a number of different propagation steps, involving several different radicals ($R_1\cdot$, $R_2\cdot$, $R_3\cdot$) and several different substrate molecules (S_1, S_2, S_3). For example, the free radical addition of RX to an olefin involves (at least) the steps:

$$R\cdot + C{=}C \rightarrow R{-}C{-}C\cdot \tag{11}$$

$$RCC\cdot + XR \rightarrow RC{-}C{-}X + R\cdot \tag{12}$$

and the autoxidation of RH involves the propagation steps:

$$ROO\cdot + RH \rightarrow ROOH + R\cdot \tag{13}$$

$$R\cdot + O_2 \rightarrow ROO\cdot \tag{14}$$

In each of these examples, two different radicals and two different substrate molecules are involved.

Our question is this: Given a free radical reaction with a long kinetic chain length involving small radicals and small substrate molecules, to what extent can we expect the reaction pattern and reaction kinetics to carry over to polymeric reactants?

Consider first the propagation steps. If each bimolecular radical-substrate reaction involves no more than one polymeric species, we would expect a reasonably "normal" pattern of reaction. Thus a small, mobile free radical (R·) should be able to attack a substrate group which is attached to a polymer chain at a normal rate, i.e., a rate similar to the attack on a properly chosen small substrate molecule. Likewise, a free radical which is attached to the polymer chain should react normally with a small, mobile substrate molecule. On the other hand, if a postulated reaction involves a propagation step in which a polymeric radical must attack a polymeric substrate group, we should be alert to the possibility of strong departures of the polymer reaction from the pattern set by the low molecular weight analogue. Such reaction anomalies, if such they may be called, can provide either depression or enhancement of the reaction step in question. When competitive propagation steps are involved, this can lead to a marked alteration of the product composition.

A similar consideration applies to termination steps. We can expect termination rates to be "normal" if they involve two small radicals, one small radical and one small terminator molecule, one polymeric radical and one small radical, or one polymeric radical and one small terminator molecule. On the other hand, bimolecular termination between two polymeric radicals is very likely to be abnormal. In particular, the bimolecular termination of free radicals attached to a network polymer can be strongly depressed, leading to an abnormally high concentration of long-lived free radicals.

In all these cases, we can consider the potential reactivity of a free radical which is attached to a polymer chain to be similar to that of a small analogue radical, but the actual rate of reaction, with a polymeric substrate or with a second polymeric radical, may be very low because of geometrical restraints (particularly in network polymers). In some cases, the geometrical constraint may be favorable to reaction, e.g., the strong tendency toward intramolecular cyclization in the copolymerization of certain difunctional monomers such as diallylamine (7) or acrylic anhydride (8,9).

If the condition of having no more than one functional group attached to a polymer is not met in a free radical reaction, a deviation in reaction kinetics from the analogous low molecular weight pattern is more likely to be encountered than in a polar reaction of the type considered above. This follows from the fact that the degree of deviation in rate of an elementary reaction involving two polymeric groups depends upon the reaction probability associated with an individual collision. In many elementary reactions of a free radical, this reaction probability is much higher than that associated with a binary collision of two of the three groups involved in a polar displacement reaction. Consequently, a much lower degree of diffusional retardation is required to influence the reaction rate in the former case.

B. EFFECT OF GROUP INTERACTIONS ON REACTIVITY

H. MORAWETZ

Polytechnic Institute of Brooklyn

1. Introduction

The reactivity of functional groups attached to polymer chains is, in many cases, similar to the reactivity of such groups in small molecules. This generalization was first enunciated by Flory, who used it to explain the character of the kinetics of polyesterification reactions (10). In a similar manner, the rate of the hydrolytic degradation of cellulose has been treated successfully on the assumption that the reactivity of the glucosidic linkage is independent of the size of the molecule in which it occurs (11,12). However, in the present discussion, we shall be interested in the exceptions from this generalization, where functional groups attached to a high polymer have reactivities deviating to a significant extent from those of monofunctional analogues.

The phenomena with which we shall deal in this discussion may be placed into four categories.

(*1*) The effect of an electrostatic charge carried by the polymer will often extend over a considerable distance, and it will exert a profound effect on reactions involving charged reagents.

(*2*) A neighboring group effect, modifying the reactivity of a functional group of a polymer, would be expected to be qualitatively similar to an effect in a bifunctional analogue. Such effects may be expected to be important only if the interaction of two neighboring functional groups may lead to a five- or six-membered cyclic transition state.

(*3*) Interactions of functional groups spaced further apart along the polymer chain may become important because of chain flexibility and the large number of such functional groups which are constrained to occupy the limited volume of the swollen polymer coil. The reactivity of a dilute polymer solution may, therefore, approximate that to be expected in a system containing droplets of concentrated solution separated by long distances of pure solvent.

(4) Functional groups which would have little chance of interacting with each other if the polymer backbone to which they are attached were randomly coiled, may be forced into mutual proximity by specific chain folding. This situation is highly characteristic of the reactivity of globular proteins.

2. Reaction Equilibria

a. Ionization Equilibria

It is unfortunate that very little experimental evidence is available which would indicate to what extent the equilibria of reactions involving polymeric reagents deviate from analogous equilibria involving small molecules. The neglect of this field is undoubtedly due in part to the difficulty of finding systems in which reaction equilibrium is easily attained and in which both the polymeric reagents and the polymeric reaction products are soluble in the same reaction medium.

The most fully investigated equilibria of reactions involving polymeric reagents are the ionization equilibria of polymers carrying weakly ionizing groups. A typical material of this nature is poly(acrylic acid) (I):

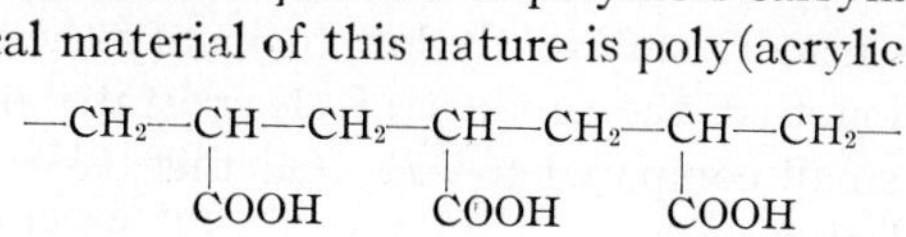

(I)

If we interpret titration curves of this polymeric acid in terms of the apparent ionization constant K_{app} defined by

$$K_{app} = [H^+]\alpha/(1 - \alpha) \tag{15}$$

where α is the fraction of the carboxyl groups which have been ionized, then it is found that K_{app} decreases sharply with increasing α. This variation in K_{app} may be interpreted in terms of an "electrical free energy of ionization" ΔF_{el}^i, representing the electrical work required to increase by one the number of ionized groups of the polyion. This additional work requirement reduces K_{app} as compared to K_0, the ionization constant of an analogous monocarboxylic acid, according to

$$K_{app} = K_0 \exp\{-\Delta F_{el}^i/kT\} \tag{16}$$

In the absence of simple electrolytes and in dilute solutions, K_{app}/K_0 may be as low as 10^{-4}. If neutral salts are added to polyelectrolyte solutions, ΔF_{el}^i is sharply reduced, but it cannot be entirely eliminated if the polymer chain carries a high density of ionized groups. Experimental data of the

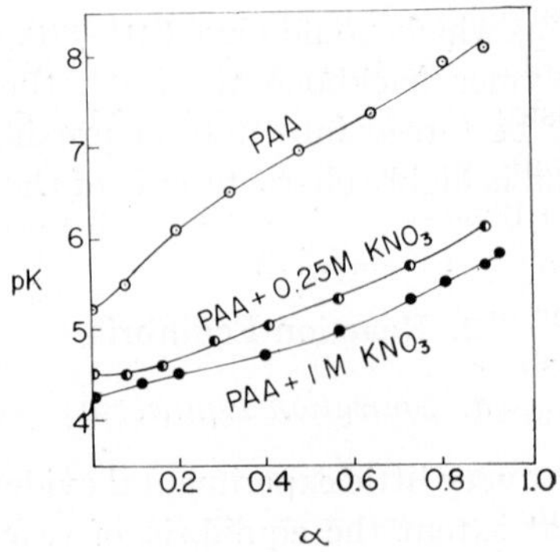

Fig. I-1. Titration of poly(acrylic acid); concentration $0.015N$. (Taken from ref. 16.)

dependence of ΔF_{el}^{i} on the degree of ionization, polyelectrolyte concentration and the amount of added salts have been reported by a number of investigators (13–16), and various theoretical treatments of ΔF_{el}^{i} have been proposed. For globular proteins ΔF_{el}^{i} may be estimated by using as a model for the protein molecule a sphere of uniform surface charge. The charge density is usually sufficiently low to justify the use of the Debye-Hückel assumption that the product of electrostatic potential and electronic charge is small compared to kT. On this basis ΔF_{el}^{i} is estimated (17) from the relation

$$\Delta F_{el}^{i} = (q^2/D)\{(1/a) - [\chi/(1 + \chi b)]\} \tag{17}$$

where a is the radius of the protein carrying a charge q, b the closest distance of approach of the protein and the small ions, D the dielectric constant of the medium, and χ is the Debye-Hückel parameter which has the significance of the reciprocal mean thickness of the counterion atmosphere.

The theoretical treatment of ΔF_{el}^{i} with flexible chain polyions with high charge density presents much greater problems, and suggested solutions (18,19) must be considered as being very approximate. The high local charge densities in these systems preclude the use of the Debye-Hückel approximation. In addition, one has to consider the expansion of the polyion due to the mutual repulsions of the fixed charges, the possibly high extent of ion-pair formation between fixed charges of the polyion and counterions, and the uncertainty of the effective value of the dielectric constant in the region occupied by the polyion coil. The range of the experimental variation of K_{app} with α and the dependence of this variation on the concentration of added salts is illustrated in Figure I-1 on data obtained by Kotliar (16) for poly(acrylic acid). Under certain conditions ΔF_{el}^{i} may be largely determined by neighboring group interactions, i.e., a given group will be hard to ionize if a neighboring group is ionized, while the state of ionization of more distant groups has little influence. Under such conditions a theoretical analysis shows that K_{app} should change most rapidly at half-ionization (20)—a behavior which has been observed to be typical of polyvinylamine and poly(ethylene imine) (21).

Anomalous behavior of some of the ionizable groups is commonly met with in the case of globular proteins. In these materials the polypeptide chain to which the various ionizable groups are attached is folded in a highly specific manner, and side chains which would be far from each other if the polymer backbone were extended are forced into very close proximity to one another. This may affect ionization equilibria for three distinct reasons.

(*a*) If an ionizable function is constrained to lie close to a negatively charged group, the effective value of $\Delta F_{el}{}^{i}$ for this function will be much higher than that estimated on the basis of an assumed uniform surface charge of the protein molecule. The reverse effect will be observed with groups forced into the vicinity of cationic centers.

(*b*) The ionization constant may be modified due to the formation of a hydrogen bond. For instance, if a carboxyl group lies close to the phenolic group of a tyrosine residue the ionization equilibria may be represented by

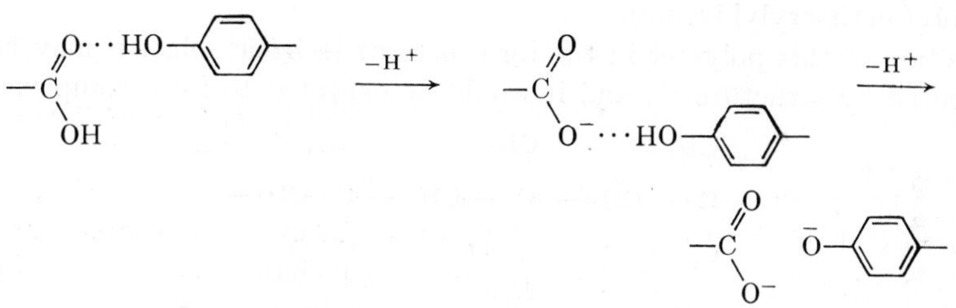

(18)

It may be seen that a hydrogen bond has to be broken in the ionization of the phenolic group and this group should, therefore, be less acidic than normally. In addition, since it may be assumed that the hydrogen bond involving the carboxylate is stronger than that of unionized carboxyl, the acidity of the carboxyl group should be enhanced. Both effects have been observed in the enzyme ribonuclease (22,23) and have been interpreted as indicated above (24). A detailed theoretical analysis of the effect of hydrogen bonding on ionization equilibria has been published by Laskowski and Scheraga (25).

(*c*) Finally, the specific folding of the polypeptide chains may "bury" ionizable groups in nonpolar regions. The low local value of the dielectric constant would then render ionization extremely difficult. This may be the cause of the observation that some of the phenolic groups in egg albumin (26) and in the enzymes papain (27) and ribonuclease (22,28) cannot be ionized without an irreversible destruction of the specific folding of the molecule.

The supposition that the specific folding of the protein molecule is responsible (for any of the reasons outlined above) for observed abnormalities in the titration behavior was greatly strengthened by the demonstration that these abnormalities disappear, if the titration is carried out after disruption of the native protein structure (28–30).

b. Chelate Formation

The enhancement of the stability of complex ions brought about by the use of multifunctional complexing agents is well known. In such reagents the spacing of the ligand groups is critically important, since only the formation of five- or six-membered rings is possible without undue strain. However, when a polymeric material carrying a large number of ligand groups is the complexing reagent, the stability of the complex ions indicates that very large rings make an essential contribution. This fact was demonstrated most clearly in a study (31) of the complexation of Cu(II) with poly(methacrylyl lysine).

A section of this polymer in the form present in basic solution may be represented by structure II, and it would be expected to form complexes

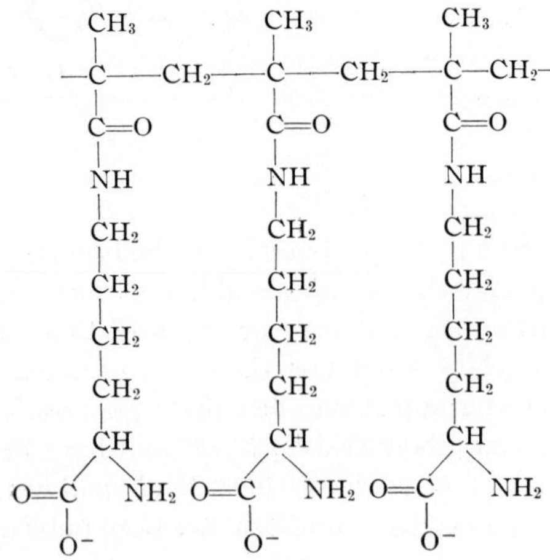

(II)

with Cu(II) in the manner characteristic of α-aminoacids as shown in eq. (19). The complexes containing one and two amino acid residues, respec-

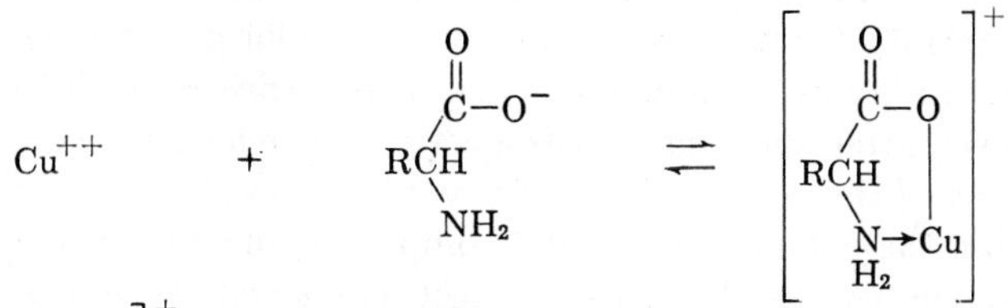

(19a)

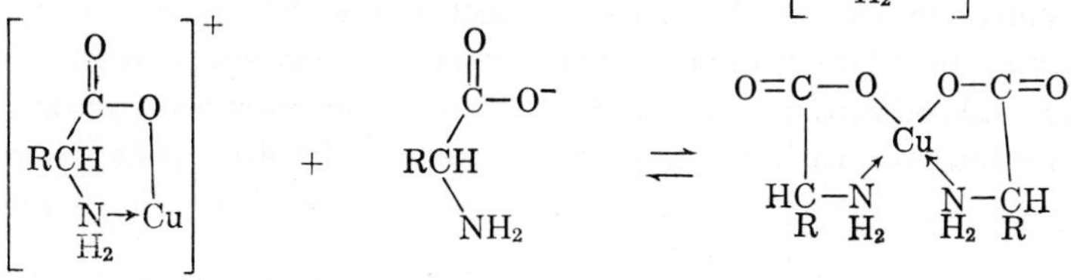

(19b)

tively, per Cu(II) ion have characteristic spectra, and it is possible, therefore, to determine quantitatively the concentration of each type of complex in a solution containing Cu(II) and the polymer. It was found in this manner that the polymer favors the formation of the higher complex even at a relatively low pH, where little of this complex forms in solutions containing monomeric amino acid. This observation may be understood if each polymer coil is thought of as a droplet of concentrated amino acid solution. Although any chelate formation necessitates the formation of rings of at least 20 members—and a given ring of that size has a very low probability—there is a very large number of ligand groups which may participate in ring formation and the aggregate probability of forming any one of these rings is high. The system behaves as if the local amino acid concentration in the regions occupied by the polymer coils were of the order of $1M$.

Similar results were obtained in an investigation of the formation of hydrogen-bonded dimers from carboxyl groups in styrene–methacrylic acid copolymers (32). The extent of hydrogen bonding was found to be quite independent of the polymer concentration, indicating that it involved mostly interactions of carboxyl groups attached to the same macromolecule. A comparison with the dimerization behavior of a monocarboxylic acid allowed the estimation of the "effective carboxyl concentration" within the swollen polymer coil. This "effective concentration" was, for instance, $0.3M$ in a copolymer containing 15 mole-% of methacrylic acid.

Extensive studies of the complexation of Cu(II) with poly(acrylic acid) and poly(methacrylic acid) have been reported (16,33,34). The very high affinity of the polymeric acid for the cation is partially accounted for by their mutual electrostatic attraction. This effect may be estimated since the electrostatic free energy corresponding to the dissociation of the doubly charged Cu(II) ion from the polyanion is twice as large as the $\Delta F_{el}{}^{i}$ for the dissociation of a hydrogen ion, which can be obtained from titration data. However, even after allowing for the electrostatic effect, the complexation characteristics of the polymer reflect the very high local density of carboxyl groups within the polymer coil, and a comparison of absorption spectra of the polymer–copper complex with the spectra of acetate complexes suggests that four carboxylate groups of the polymer are coordinated with a Cu(II) ion (35). Data obtained at varying polymer concentrations show clearly that coordination with several groups carried by the same polyion is favored overwhelmingly over coordination with groups belonging to different chains.

Just as our earlier discussion showed that anomalous titration equilibria in globular proteins may be the result of a specific chain folding, so this folding may also bring into favorable juxtaposition groups which participate in cation chelation equilibria. This concept must be invoked to explain the very high affinities with which activating cations are frequently found to be bound to enzymes. For instance, the association constant of 3300 for the complexation of magnesium ion with enolase at pH 7.2 (36) is surprising for an ion which has very little affinity for either carboxylate or amine groups, and can only be understood by assuming that several favorably spaced functions participate in chelation. The fact that the activating ion may protect an enzyme against denaturation (i.e., unfolding by hydrogen-bonding reagents) (37) is further indication that the groups participating in chelate formation are close to each other only as long as the protein molecule exists in its specifically folded form.

c. Other Reaction Equilibria

The group interaction effects enumerated in the discussion of ionization equilibria would be expected to affect also the position of thermodynamic equilibrium in other types of reactions. Such effects have been considered in particular for the case of the thermodynamic stability of a peptide bond in a protein molecule (38). If the hydrolysis of such a peptide bond leads to the loss of a fragment involving the dissociation of a number of hydrogen bonds, then it has been estimated that the apparent equilibrium constant for the hydrolysis of the peptide bond is reduced by a factor of 2 for each hydrogen bond which must be broken (39). Experimental data on an equilibrium of this type have been obtained on fibrinogen, a protein which is involved in the blood clotting process. The first step in fibrinogen clotting involves the hydrolysis of a specific peptide bond with the release of a small peptide fragment and this step may be reversed, so that the position of the equilibrium can be determined. It was found (39) that the equilibrium concentration of the peptide fragment corresponds to a stability of the sensitive peptide bond exceeding that of a "normal" peptide bond by four orders of magnitude. However, it seems that the real bond stability is very close to normal and that the low apparent equilibrium constant for the reaction is due to a very high association constant of the two fragments formed from the original protein. This would indicate that the breaking of the hydrogen bonds is not required for the solvolysis of the peptide bond, but is a process which takes place only after its completion. A similar conclusion may be reached from experiments on the enzyme ribonuclease. Here it is also possible to hydrolyze specifically a single peptide bond, which breaks a chain of twenty amino acid residues from the remainder of the protein (40). However, once again the fragments of the reaction are held together extremely tightly (dissociation constant below 10^{-8}), presumably by hydrogen bonds and various secondary valence forces which remain undisturbed when the peptide bond is broken.

3. Rates of Reaction

a. Electrostatic Effects on the Reactivity of Polyions

Reactions involving two charged species have been studied for a long time. As would be expected, reactions are slowed down if the reagents carry charges of the same sign and are accelerated if a positively and a negatively charged species react with each other. Additions of electrolyte tend to reduce the long-range forces between charged reagents so that reactions involving species with charges of the same sign are accelerated, while those between oppositely charged reagents are slowed down. These phenomena are quantitatively well understood and have been ably summarized (41).

When one of the reagents is a polymer carrying a large number of ionic groups, these effects would be expected to be greatly magnified, and this has been found to be the case. A typical example of this class of reactions is the hydroxyl ion catalyzed hydrolysis of pectins, the partially esterified derivatives of polygalacturonic acid which are widely distributed in plants. The polymer may be represented schematically by III, and it was found (42) that the apparent second-order rate constant for its basic hydrolysis falls off rapidly with the progress of the reaction due to the increasing

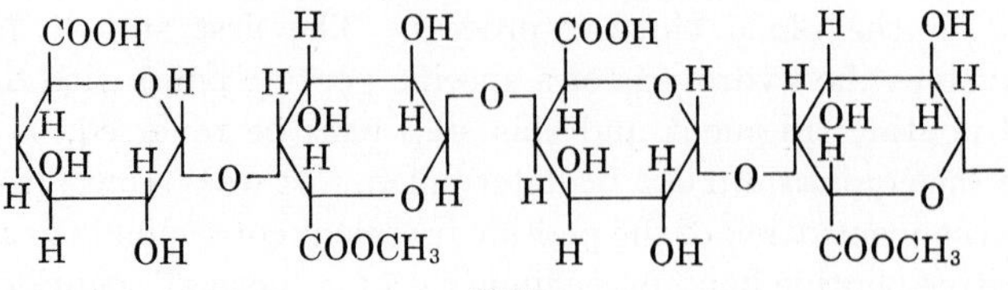

(III)

charge of the chain carrying ionized carboxyl groups. It was also confirmed that the inhibition of the reaction in its later stages may be counteracted by addition of neutral salts (42,43). A similar effect of polymer charge on reactivity was observed in a study of bromine displacement by the carboxylate groups of partially ionized poly(methacrylic acid)

$$R-\overset{O}{\overset{\|}{C}}-O^- + R'-Br \rightarrow [R\text{---}\overset{O}{\overset{\|}{C}}\overset{-\delta}{-}O-R'\text{---}\overset{-\delta}{Br}] \rightarrow R\overset{O}{\overset{\|}{C}}OR' + Br^- \quad (20)$$

It was found that bromide was liberated from the uncharged α-bromoacetamide, but not from the negatively charged bromoacetate ion (44).

A somewhat different phenomenon was observed in the basic hydrolysis of polymethacrylamide. It was found that not all of the amide groups could be hydrolyzed, and the effect was ascribed to a complete loss of reactivity of amide residues flanked by two carboxylate groups (45). This assumption was later tested by determining the fraction of amide groups which could be hydrolyzed from copolymers of methacrylamide and methacrylic acid (46). It was found that the fraction of reactive amide groups decreased with the amide content of the copolymer and the results

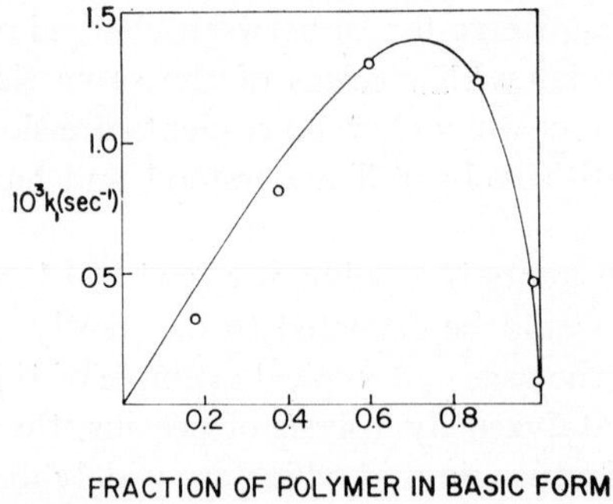

Fig. I-2. Solvolysis of 3-nitro-4-acetoxybenzenesulfonate in 0.01N poly-4-vinylpyridine solution (50% ethanol, ionic strength 0.04, temperature 36.8°C.). (Taken from ref. 48.)

were in close quantitative agreement with those predicted on the basis of a model in which all amide groups were assumed to be equally reactive, except for the totally inert amide groups lying between two carboxylates. If this is the correct explanation of the phenomenon, then we are dealing with an electrostatic effect operating only over the distance of neighboring chain residues. Since the hydrolysis was carried out in 4*N* sodium hydroxide, the restriction of the electrostatic effect to neighboring groups would be expected.

Two studies have also been reported in which a polyion reacts with a reagent of opposite charge. This is the situation in the reaction of partially ionized poly-4-vinylpyridine with bromoacetic acid (47):

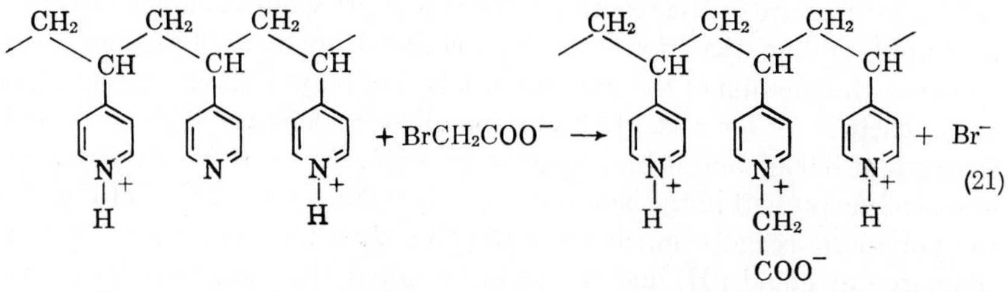

(21)

where the electrostatic interaction of the reagents favors the reaction. The addition of neutral salts has, therefore, an inhibiting effect. Another demonstration of the high reactivity of polycations with anionic reagents concerns the catalysis of the hydrolysis of 3-nitro-4-acetoxybenzenesulfonate in solutions of partially ionized poly-4-vinylpyridine (48). This reaction may be represented by

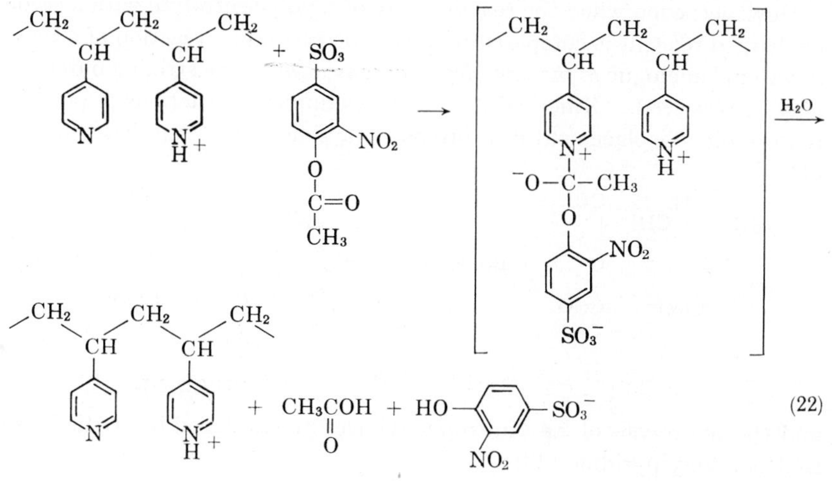

(22)

The magnitude of the effect of the electrostatic interaction of the polycation and the sulfonic acid is shown in Figure I-2. It may be seen that the reaction rate passes through a maximum when about one quarter of the pyridine residues of the polymer are ionized. This is clearly the result of the powerful attraction of the polyion and the sulfonic acid which forces the ester groups into the neighborhood of the catalytically active unionized pyridine groups.

In the last two cases cited, the reactive function of the polymer participates also in an ionization equilibrium. Since only the basic form of the pyridine residues is reactive and since the ionization of these groups is hindered by the high positive charge of the chain, the fraction of these residues which are in the reactive form at low pH values is much larger for polyvinylpyridine than for its monofunctional analogue 4-picoline. For instance, the fraction of the pyridine residues of poly-4-vinylpyridine which are in their basic form at pH 3 was found to be 0.45 and 0.15 at an ionic strength of 0.0065 and 0.15, respectively, while the corresponding fraction of 4-picoline present in the basic form is only 0.006 (47). This factor makes the polymeric reagent much more reactive than its analogue if they are compared at equal pH, and it should be noted that this consideration is applicable also when the second reagent is uncharged. These considerations apply also to the reaction of proteins involving various ionizable groups such as carboxyl, amino, thiol, etc. Since the reactivity of these groups depends on their state of ionization, the effect of the protein charge on the ionization equilibria has to be considered in the interpretation of kinetic data. For a summary of this field, the reader is referred to a review by Putnam (49).

However, even when the reaction rate of a polyelectrolyte with a second uncharged reagent is compared with the corresponding reaction of a monofunctional analogue *at the same degree of ionization*, some striking differences may be observed. Kinetic data for two examples of reactions of polyions, the bromide displacement in α-bromoacetamide by poly(methacrylic acid) (44):

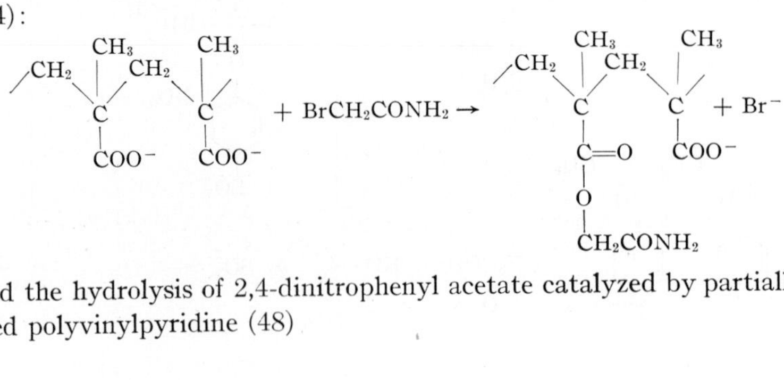

(23)

and the hydrolysis of 2,4-dinitrophenyl acetate catalyzed by partially ionized polyvinylpyridine (48)

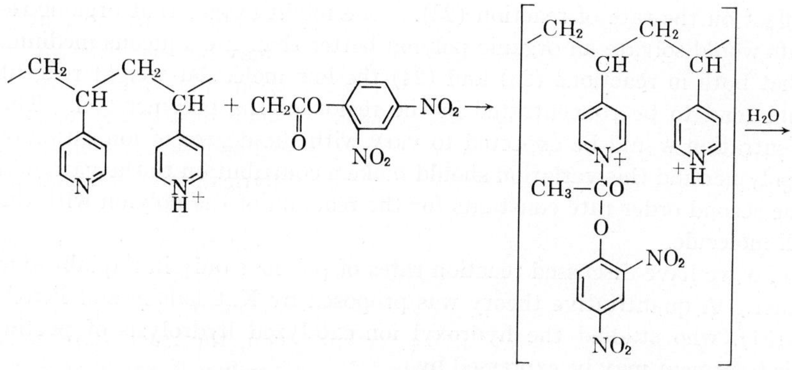

(24)

are illustrated in Figure I-3. In both cases the apparent second-order rate constant for the reaction of the low molecular weight reagent with the basic groups in the polymer varies markedly with the degree of ionization of the polyion. However, in one case k_2 decreases and in the other it increases with the fraction of the ionizable groups present in the form of the conjugate base. The effect can, therefore, not be interpreted by the concepts underlying the Brønsted catalysis law which predicts a linear relation between the pK of a base and the logarithm of its catalytic rate coefficient (50) and would, therefore, require poly(methacrylic acid) to become a more efficient nucleophile as its ionization is increased. It was also found (44) that an increase in ionic strength which produces an eightfold increase in the apparent ionization constant of half-ionized poly(methacrylic acid) has

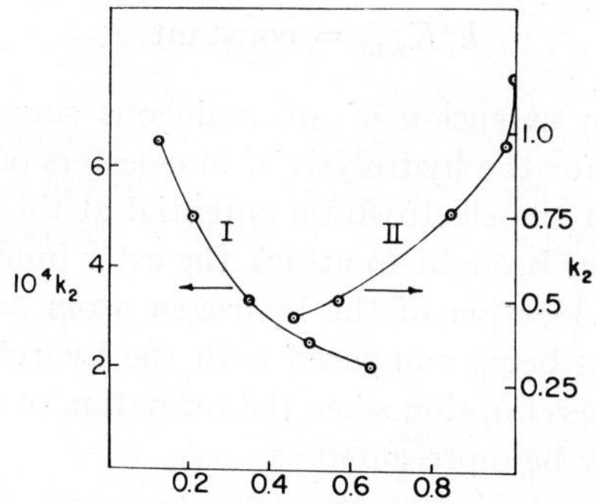

Fig. I-3. Reactions of polyions with neutral molecules: (*I*) poly(methacrylic acid) with α-bromoacetamide (ionic strength 0.148, temperature 50°C.); (*II*) poly-4-vinylpyridine with 2,4-dinitrophenyl acetate (50% ethanol, ionic strength 0.04, temperature 36.8°C.). (Taken from refs. 44 and 48.)

no effect on the rate of reaction (23). One might expect that organic reagents would solvate an organic polyion better than the aqueous medium, so that both in reactions (23) and (24) the low molecular weight reagent should tend to be concentrated in the region of the polymer coil. The concentration would be expected to vary with the degree of ionization of the polymer and this variation should make a contribution to the variation in the second order rate constants for the reaction of the polyion with the small molecule.

So far we have discussed reaction rates of polyions only in a qualitative manner. A quantitative theory was proposed by Katchalsky and Feitelson (51), who studied the hydroxyl ion catalyzed hydrolysis of pectin. Their treatment may be expressed by

$$k = k_0 \exp \{ -\Delta F_{\text{el}}^{\ddagger}/kT\} \tag{25}$$

where k is the observed second-order rate constant and k_0 the rate constant which would characterize the hydrolysis of an uncharged ester. The electrical free energy of activation $\Delta F_{\text{el}}^{\ddagger}$ required to bring the catalyzing hydroxyl ion to the ester group against the repulsion of the polyanion charge is assumed to be equal to the electrical free energy required to remove a hydrogen ion from a carboxyl group against the field of the polyanion,

$$\Delta F_{\text{el}}^{\ddagger} = \Delta F_{\text{el}}^{i} \tag{26}$$

so that, by comparison of eqs. (16), (25), and (26)

$$k/K_{\text{app}} = \text{constant} \tag{27}$$

This treatment is an extension of an analogous suggestion made many years ago by Ingold for the hydrolysis of monoesters of dicarboxylic acids (52). It implies that the electrostatic potential at the point to which the hydroxyl ion has to be brought to attack the ester function is the same as the potential at the location of the hydrogen atom of a carboxyl whose ionization constant is being compared with the hydrolytic rate constant. This is a reasonable assumption since the formation of the transition state in the hydrolysis may be represented as

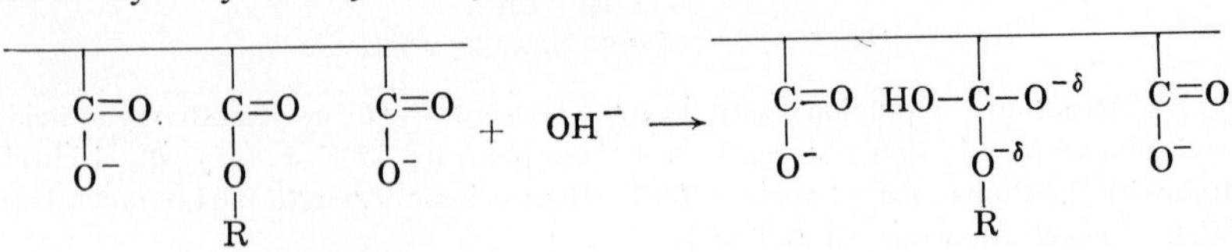

(28)

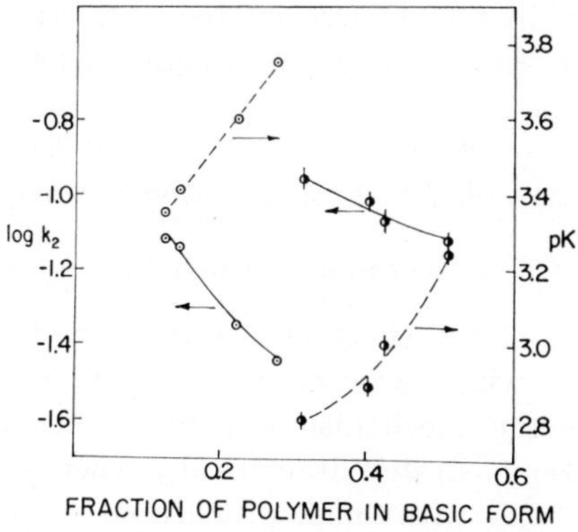

Fig. I-4. Reaction rate of poly-4-vinylpyridine with bromoacetate (temperature 50°C.): (◐) ionic strength 0.003; (⊙) ionic strength 0.034. (Taken from ref. 47.)

However, in other cases of reactions of polyions with small ionized species $\Delta F_{el}^{\ddagger}$ need not be equal to ΔF_{el}^{i}. For instance, in the reactions represented by eqs. (21) and (22) the anionic charge of the second reagent is not brought nearly as close to the backbone of the polymer as a hydrogen ion associating with the nitrogen of a pyridine residue. It would then be expected that $\Delta F_{el}^{\ddagger}$ should be appreciably smaller than ΔF_{el}^{i}, and this expectation is in accord with experimental data (47) which show that the effect of polyion charge on reaction rates is distinctly less than on ionization equilibria (Fig. I-4).

If we consider in detail the reaction of a polyion with an uncharged species, then we may distinguish two cases, depending on whether a charged or an uncharged group in the polymer is the reaction site. We may exemplify these reaction types by the nucleophilic displacement of bromide from a C—Br bond by a carboxylate (eq. 20) and the attack of a pyridine residue on the carbonyl carbon of an ester function (eq. 24), respectively. In the first case, the transition state represents a dispersal of the carboxylate charge over a larger volume. This should lead to a reduction of the electrostatic energy due to interactions with other fixed charges of the chain molecule, but the effect of charge dispersal will be very much smaller than the effect of bringing a charged species into the neighborhood of the polyion. In the second case a dipole is created in the transition state, and the free energy of activation should, therefore, contain a term representing the electrostatic energy due to the interaction of this dipole with the fixed charges of the chain. Since dipole–charge interactions fall off with distance much more rapidly than charge–charge interactions, we might expect that only neighboring group charges would affect rates of reactions of this type.

b. Specific Effects of Neighboring Groups

(1) Effect of a Neighboring Carboxyl on Solvolysis

The considerations of the effect of electrostatic charge on the rate of reactions of polyions, which were discussed in the previous section, presuppose that the reaction mechanism remains unchanged. This need not be the case as was demonstrated dramatically when it was found that copolymers of acrylic acid with small proportions of *p*-nitrophenyl methacrylate are hydrolyzed many orders of magnitude more rapidly than the *p*-nitrophenyl ester of a monocarboxylic acid (53,54). Since the experiments were carried out under conditions where the hydrolytic rate would be normally controlled by hydroxyl ion catalysis, the high reactivity of an ester group attached to a polyanion was just the opposite of the expected effect. The cause of the discrepancy was found in a change of the reaction mechanism; the ester hydrolysis is not due to the action of hydroxyl ions but to the attack of a neighboring ionized carboxyl on the carbonyl carbon of the ester group. It was later demonstrated (55) that the first product of the reaction is an acid anhydride, so that the reaction may be represented by the sequence (29):

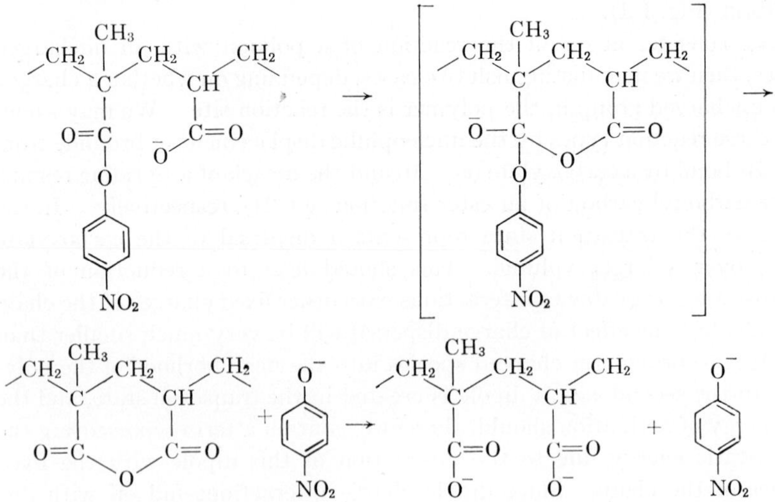

(29)

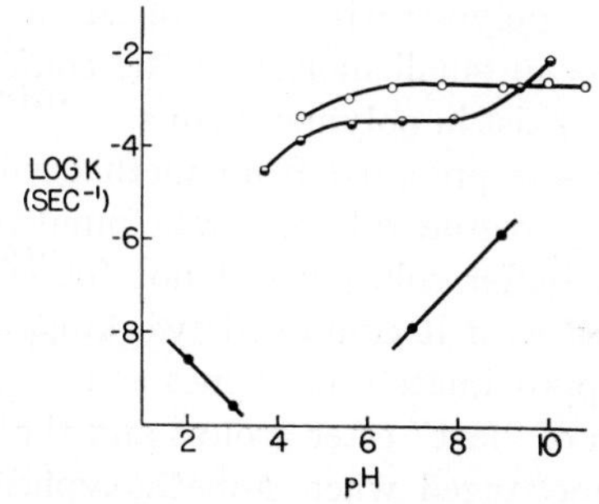

Fig. I-5. Hydrolysis of *p*-nitrophenyl esters at 0°C.; (O) methacrylic acid–*p*-nitrophenyl acrylate copolymer; (◒) *p*-nitrophenyl acid glutarate; (●) *p*-nitrophenyl trimethylacetate. (Taken from ref. 55a.)

As would be expected, this reaction mechanism is operative not only with copolymers, but also with phenyl monoesters of dicarboxylic acids. The rate of such reactions has a characteristic pH dependence of the shape shown in Figure I-5 (55a). In the pH range of 3–6 the experimentally observed rates may be shown (56) to be strictly proportional to the degree of ionization of the neighboring carboxyl so that the pK of the catalyzing neighboring group may be calculated from kinetic data. At pH values above 7, hydroxyl ion catalysis makes a contribution to the hydrolysis rate of the succinic monoester. In the case of the polyion, hydroxyl ions are so powerfully repelled that they make no contribution to the rate at least up to pH 10.

As would be expected, the effectiveness of the neighboring carboxylate in catalyzing the solvolysis of a phenyl ester group is critically dependent on the spacing of the two groups from each other. Succinic acid monoesters are 120–200 times more reactive than glutaric acid monoesters (56). Moreover, steric restraints which force the carboxyl and ester groups into close proximity to one another may have an enormous effect on the reaction rate. For instance, the substance IV was found to hydrolyze 230 times as rapidly as the anion of the corresponding monoester of succinic acid (57). It is important to keep this factor in mind in comparing the interactions of

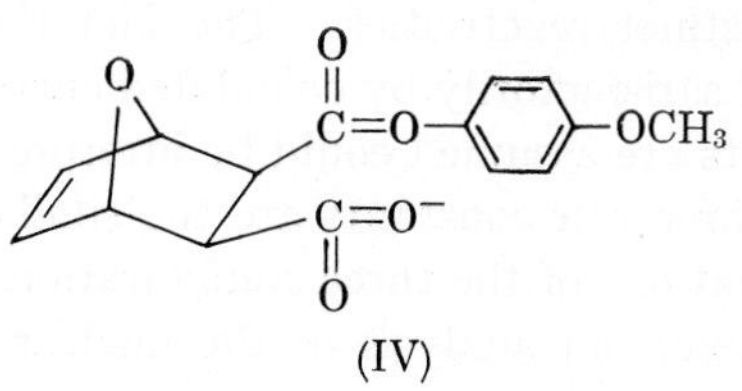

(IV)

neighboring groups in a polymer with those of an "analogue," since it will be difficult to simulate in small molecules the conformational restraints which must necessarily exist in polymer chains.

When a copolymer was prepared from methacrylic acid with a small amount of *p*-nitrophenyl methacrylate, it was found that the hydrolysis of the ester groups in a buffer solution did not follow first-order kinetics. The substance behaved as if it contained two kinds of ester groups with about 20% of them approximately ten times as reactive as the remainder (58,59). The fraction of "fast" ester groups and the ratio of the two rate constants remained unchanged when *p*-methoxyphenyl were substituted for the *p*-nitrophenyl esters. This behavior has been ascribed to the stereoisomerism of the polymer, in which the asymmetric carbons carrying the ester and the catalyzing carboxylate, respectively, may have either the same or opposite steric configurations. With two neighboring carboxylates flanking each ester group, there are three possible steric relationships as indicated by V, VI, and VII.

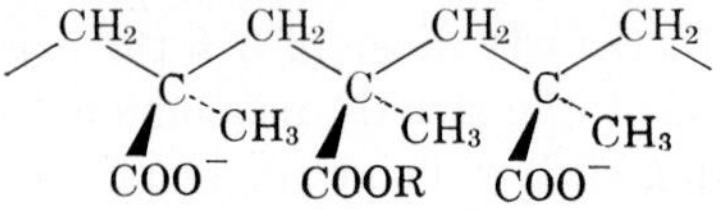

(V) (isotactic)

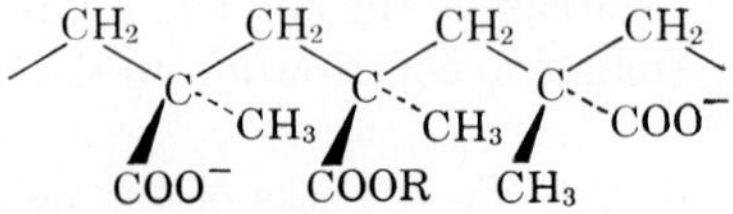

(VI) (heterotactic)

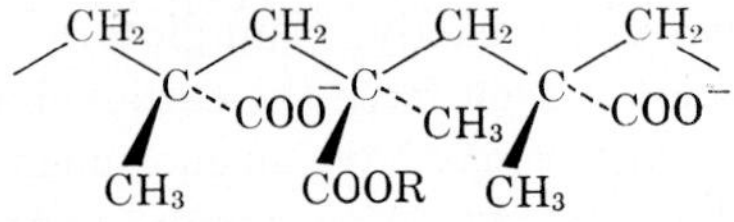

(VII) (syndiotactic)

One might therefore expect, *a priori*, that the chain should contain ester groups with three distinct reactivities. The fact that the experimental kinetic data are fitted satisfactorily by calculated curves in which only two different rate constants are assumed could be interpreted either as signifying that two of the three rate constants are too similar to be resolved by this method or else that one of the three configurations exists only in small concentration. However, an analysis of the nuclear magnetic resonance spectra of poly(methacrylic acid), prepared under similar conditions as the copolymer, indicates that 11% of triplets of monomer residues have the isotactic, 32% heterotactic, and 57% the syndiotactic configuration (60). It must be conceded that it is hard to see how this distribution could be reconciled with the kinetic data unless it is assumed that in copolymerization the relative probability of the three steric configurations in the immediate vicinity of an ester monomer residue is substantially different from that characterizing homopolymerization of methacrylic acid.

It was found that similar deviations from first order kinetics are characteristic of the solvolysis of substituted phenyl acrylates copolymerized with methacrylic acid (59). We find therefore that the reactivity of both acrylic and methacrylic ester residues is sensitive to stereoisomerism if they are copolymerized with methacrylic acid, while first-order kinetics are observed in the solvolysis of both types of ester when copolymerized with acrylic acid. This is a rather remarkable result, since one might have expected that in the methacrylic acid-acrylic ester (VIII) and in the acrylic acid–methacrylic ester copolymers (IX) the attack of the neighboring carboxylate on the ester group

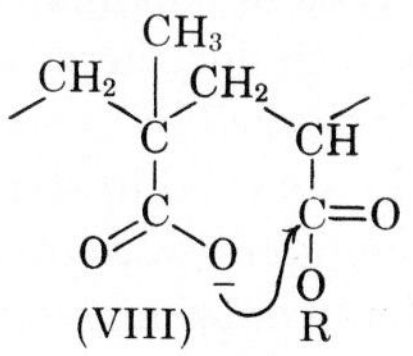

(VIII)

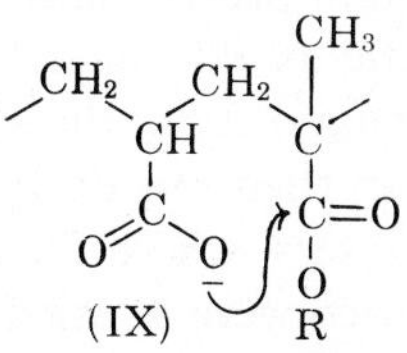

(IX)

would be subject to similar steric restraints. The fact that these two materials differ so strikingly in their sensitivity to stereoisomerism proves that it is the rigidity of the methacrylic chain as a whole and not the substituents in the immediate neighborhood of the reaction site which are of decisive importance.

The attack of neighboring carboxylate is much less efficient in promoting hydrolysis of neighboring alkyl esters. Nevertheless, it was proved conclusively by experiments on methyl hydrogen phthalate (61) that a neighboring carboxylate accelerates, by a very large factor, the hydrolysis rate of the methyl ester and it was similarly found that the ester residues in partially neutralized methyl methacrylate–methacrylic acid copolymers are about a hundred times more reactive than in copolymers of methyl methacrylate with vinylpyrrolidone (62). A strange and unexplained feature of these experiments was a suggestion that the hydrolytic rate is a maximum when one quarter of the carboxyl groups are ionized.

We have seen previously that the deviation of the hydrolysis of methacrylic acid–*p*-nitrophenyl methacrylate copolymers in buffer solution from first-order kinetics was interpreted in terms of the stereoisomerism of the polymer chain. While this interpretation was based on indirect evidence, a much more conclusive proof of the importance of stereoisomerism on the rate of ester hydrolysis is possible with methyl methacrylate–methacrylic acid copolymers. Methyl methacrylate can be polymerized under different conditions to yield preponderantly isotactic or syndiotactic chains. It was found that the hydrolysis in strong acid or strong base (63,64) as well as the hydrolysis catalyzed by neighboring carboxylate groups (65) proceeds much more rapidly with the isotactic than with the syndiotactic or atactic polymer.* The isotactic species was also found to have the highest reactivity in partially methylated poly(acrylic acid) (65a). The analysis of the kinetic data in this system is, however, much more difficult than in the case of phenyl esters. When a phenyl ester is hydrolyzed, the reaction is accompanied by a pronounced shift in the ultraviolet spectrum, and this enables the investigator to follow it very accurately at very high dilution. It is this analytical sensitivity which made it possible to obtain precise data for the hydrolysis of copolymers containing initially as little as 1% phenyl ester groups. Under these conditions the overwhelming majority of the ester residues is flanked by two carboxyls and any variation in their reactivity may be safely assigned to stereoisomerism. With methyl esters, where the analytical techniques were much less sensitive, the kinetics were studied on copolymers containing relatively large concentrations of ester, so that the reactivity of the ester might have been affected by the chemical nature of its nearest neighbors as well as by steric factors.

The hydrolysis of amide groups is also subject to neighboring group catalysis. This was proved unambiguously in a kinetic study of the hydrolysis of phthalamic acid (66) which showed that the unionized form of the neighboring carboxyl is catalytically active in this case. The same pattern of behavior was observed in copolymers of acrylamide and acrylic acid (67). Data obtained on the hydrolysis of a copolymer of acrylyl *p*-nitrophenylanilide with acrylic acid (68) are more ambiguous. The dependence of the reaction velocity on the degree of ionization of the polymer indicated that the rate was proportional to the fraction of nitroanilide residues flanked by at least one unionized carboxyl, a result which could be

* Smets and De Loecker (65) assigned the tacticity of their samples on the basis of a faulty previous analysis and reached, therefore, the incorrect conclusion that the syndiotactic polymer is more reactive.

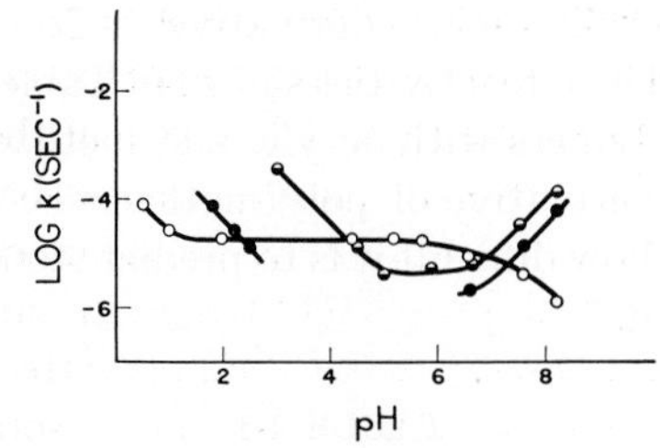

Fig. I-6. Hydrolysis of *p*-nitroanilides at 135.4°C.: (O) acrylic acid–*p*-nitroacrylanilide copolymer; (●) *p*-nitrotrimethylacetanilide; (◒) mono-*p*-nitroanilide of glutaric acid. (Taken from ref. 68.)

interpreted either in terms of an acceleration by an unionized neighboring carboxyl or an inhibition by two ionized carboxyl neighbors. In any case, it is instructive to note (Fig. I-6) that the pH dependence of the hydrolysis of mono-*p*-nitroanilide of glutaric acid (X)

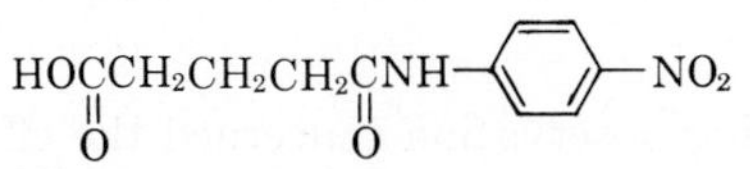

(X)

gives no evidence of a neighboring group effect, such as characterizes the pH dependence of the hydrolysis rate of the copolymer (XI).

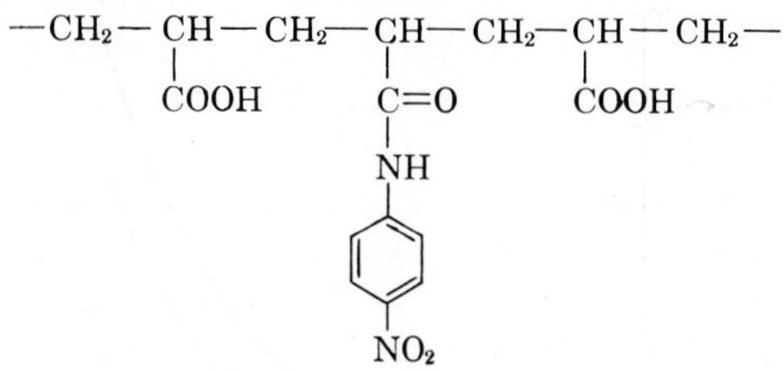

(XI)

We may ascribe the difference either to the presence of two neighboring carboxyl groups in the copolymer, or to steric restraints in the polymer chain not present in the glutaric acid derivative.

Some unexpected effects were also found in studying the hydrolysis in strongly basic solution of the four copolymers obtained from acrylic or methacrylic acid with their *p*-nitroanilides (68). It had long been known that derivatives of poly(methacrylic acid) are much more inert than the corresponding poly(acrylic acid) derivatives. It came therefore as a surprise to find the order of reactivities shown in Table I-1. The data show that the "mixed" copolymers with acrylic and methacrylic units are much less reactive than the derivative of poly(methacrylic acid). This demonstrates very strikingly how difficult it is to predict steric relations in a highly hindered polymer chain.

TABLE I-1
Rates of Hydrolysis of Copolymers[a,b]

Copolymer		$10^5 k_2$,
p-Nitroanilide	Acid	l.-mole^{-1}-sec.$^{-1}$
Acrylic	Acrylic	9.2
Acrylic	Methacrylic	0.12
Methacrylic	Acrylic	0.07
Methacrylic	Methacrylic	2.2

[a] At 84.4°C. in 1.02N sodium hydroxide.
[b] Taken from ref. 68.

A second interesting observation concerned the effect of the addition of relatively low concentrations of barium ion on the reaction rate (68) The data plotted in Figure I-7 show that the very large acceleration of the hydrolytic rate brought about by less than 0.01M Ba^{++} was not diminished

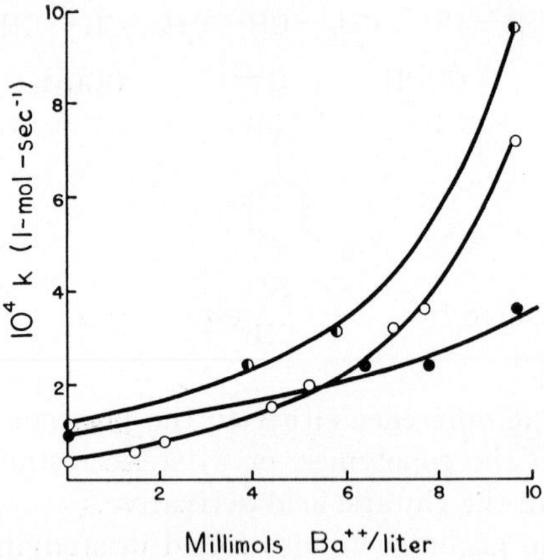

Fig. I-7. Effect of Ba^{++} on the base-catalyzed hydrolysis of an acrylic acid–*p*-nitroacrylanilide copolymer at 84.4°C.: (◐) 0.4N NaOH + 0.6N NaCl; (○) 0.4N NaOH; (●) 1.0N NaOH. (Taken from ref. 68.)

by addition of NaCl, but was strongly reduced when the NaOH concentration was raised from 0.4*N* to 1*N*. Moreover, the catalytic effect of Ba^{++} was approximately proportional to the square of its concentration. The data could be accounted for very well by assuming that the effect is due to a chelate formation of two Ba^{++} ions with a pair of carboxylate groups on either side of the nitroanilide (XII).

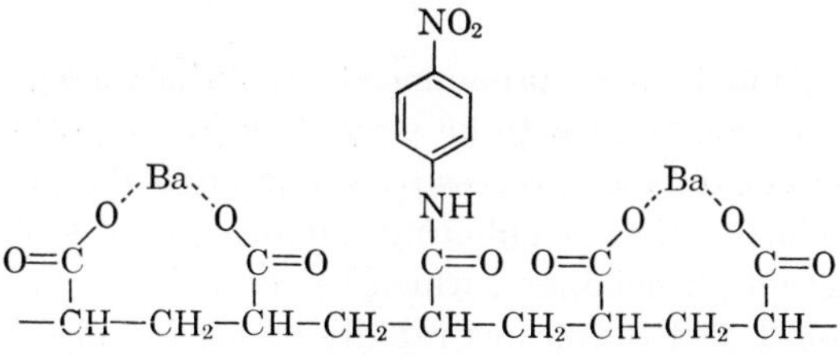

(XII)

These carboxylates are responsible for the low reactivity of the nitroanilide residues on the copolymer, and their elimination by chelating produces, therefore, the observed acceleration.

An intramolecular amide interchange has been reported in acid solutions of poly(α-acetamidoacrylic acid) (70). The reaction may be represented by eq. (30):

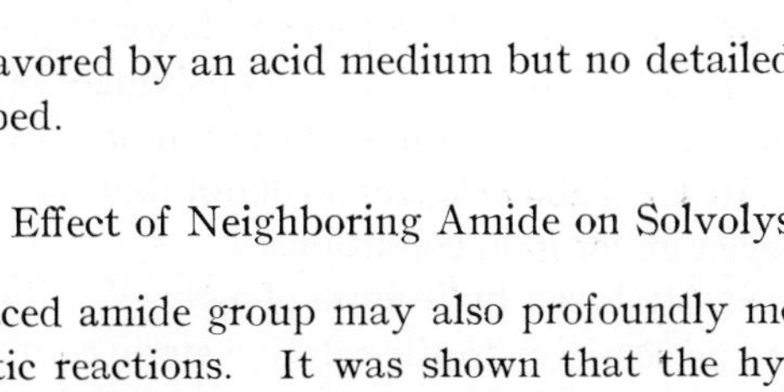

(30)

This reaction is favored by an acid medium but no detailed kinetic studies have been described.

(2) Effect of Neighboring Amide on Solvolysis

A properly spaced amide group may also profoundly modify the mechanism of solvolytic reactions. It was shown that the hydrolysis of succinamide, which is surprisingly rapid, proceeds through an imide intermediate (69). The mechanism of the hydroxyl ion catalyzed reaction is probably that shown in eq. (31).

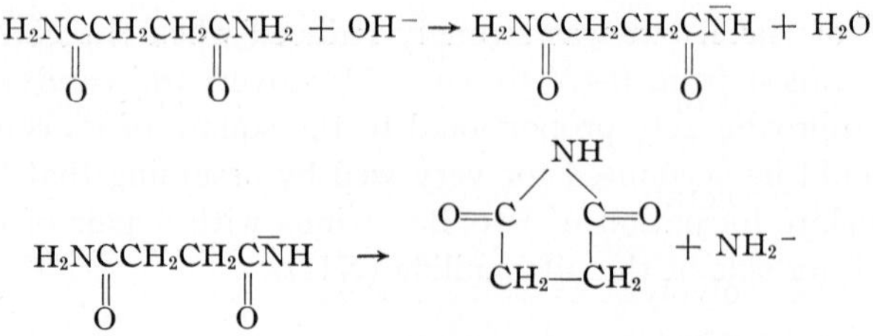

(31)

The effect is much more pronounced in phthalamide, where the two amide groups are constrained to lie very close to each other and both the acid and the base-catalyzed process passes through the phthalimide intermediate. Similarly, the neighboring amide group labilizes the ester function in methyl phthalamate, which has been found to be destroyed in neutral solution 3×10^6 times as rapidly as methyl benzoate (71). The mechanism of this reaction has been shown to be

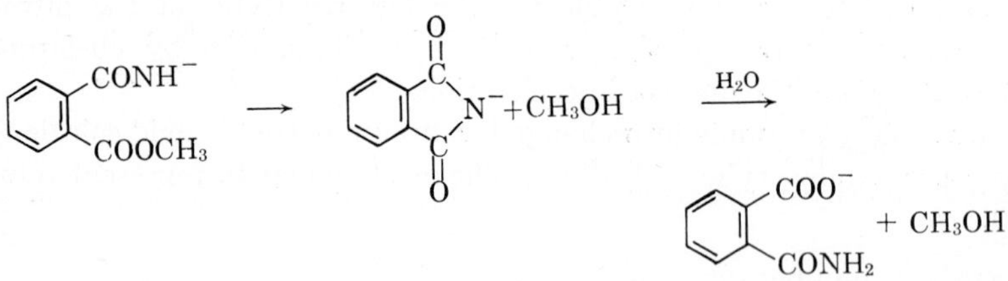

(32)

From these data obtained on small molecules one would be led to expect that imide formation should also proceed easily in solutions of polyacrylamide and this has been found to be the case (72), particularly if the solution is acidic. The mechanism of this reaction could involve either two neighboring amide groups or an amide with a neighboring carboxyl formed previously by hydrolysis. The data seem to favor the second alternative. The breakdown of ester groups in, e.g., copolymers of acrylamide with acrylic esters, does not appear to have been studied, but the behavior of methyl phthalamate cited above leaves no doubt that the ester groups would be highly labile even under mild conditions.

The rate of acid catalyzed hydrolysis of poly-*N*,*N*-dimethylacrylamide has been found to be sensitive to the relative steric configuration of neighboring asymmetric centers in the same manner as the ester hydrolysis discussed in the preceding section. Here it has also been established that the isotactic polymer is the more reactive species (73).

(3) Effect of Neighboring Hydroxyl on Solvolysis

The enhancement of the rate of ester solvolysis which may be produced by properly spaced hydroxyl groups has been demonstrated clearly on steroid diol monoacetates in which the acetoxy and the hydroxy groups have the 1,2 or the 1,3 diaxial relation (74,75). An analogous effect should occur during the solvolysis of poly(vinyl acetate), and this appears to be the case. An investigation of the infrared spectra of partially saponified poly(vinyl acetate) and of poly(vinyl alcohol) acetylated to the same acetyl content has revealed striking differences in the region of the carbonyl and hydroxyl stretching vibrations (76). The carbonyl band lies at 1732 $cm.^{-1}$ for the partially saponified and at 1723 $cm.^{-1}$ for the acetylated samples, the corresponding hydroxyl peaks are at 3290 and at 3470 $cm.^{-1}$, respectively. These results may be understood on the assumption that the alcoholic hydroxyl produced in the hydrolysis of an ester group enhances the hydrolysis rate of neighboring ester groups, so that there is a tendency for continuous sequences of ester groups to be eliminated during hydrolysis. By contrast, in the acetylation of poly(vinyl alcohol) the reaction proceeds essentially at random. The difference in the absorption peaks of the carbonyl and hydroxyl group may then be characterized as due to the difference in the extent of hydrogen bonding in a material in which ester and hydroxyl groups tend to be segregated or randomly interspersed.

Recently, a number of investigations have been concerned with the effect of stereoregularity of the polymer chain on reactions which appear to be activated by neighboring hydroxyl groups. It was found that the acid hydrolysis of poly(vinyl acetal) was much faster if the polymer was derived from syndiotactic poly(vinyl alcohol) (76a) and that the acetalization equilibrium was also somewhat dependent on the tacticity of the chain (76b). In the hydrolysis of poly(vinyl acetate), the syndiotactic polymer was distinctly more reactive than the isotactic species (76c); the activation by neighboring hydroxyl was here clearly apparent from the kinetics of the reaction (76c,76d). Finally, we should mention a study of the kinetics of base catalyzed hydrolysis of the alternating vinyl acetate–maleic acid copolymer (76e). In this case the polymer behaves as if the first half of the ester groups were an order of magnitude more reactive than the second half. This effect is difficult to account for, since the vinyl acetate groups are relatively distant from one another, being separated by the maleic acid residues, which are not altered during the reaction. The authors of this study believe that the ester hydrolysis might be catalyzed by carboxylate groups which are inactivated by hydrogen bonding with the hydroxyl groups.

(4) Intramolecular Bifunctional Catalysis

It was proposed by Swain and Brown (77) that a bifunctional reagent carrying a nucleophilic and an electrophilic group which may attack simultaneously a reactive center should be a particularly powerful catalyst. This principle is of special interest because it is believed that it is the basis of the high catalytic activity of enzymes.

Bifunctional catalysis may be intramolecular if the reactive center and the attacking nucleophile and electrophile are all in a favorable steric relationship to one another. This seems to be the case in the condensation product of a methacrylic acid–maleic anhydride copolymer with *p*-nitroaniline, in which the anilide group is placed between two carboxyl neighbors. It was found (54,68) that this anilide group condenses easily with one of the carboxyl neighbors to an imide, the rate of the reaction being a maximum when one of the neighboring carboxyls is ionized and the other unionized. The proposed mechanism of the process (68) is shown in eq. (33).

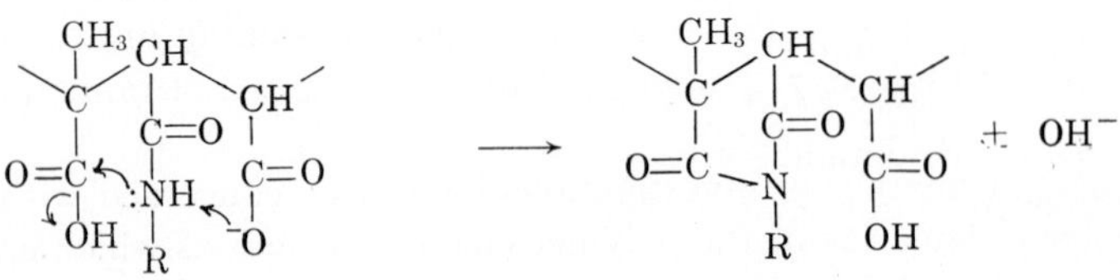

(33)

Another example of intramolecular bifunctional catalysis was found in succinylsalicylic acid (XIII),

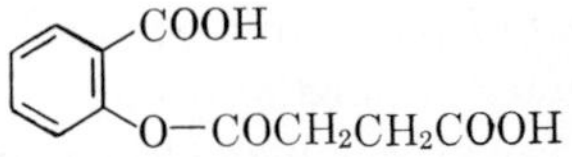

(XIII)

which was also found to hydrolyze most rapidly with one of the carboxyls in the acid and the other in the basic form (78). An analogous situation seems to exist in copolymers of acrylic acid with ethyl ethacrylate, which has been reported to hydrolyze at the highest rate when half of the carboxyl groups are ionized (65a). It has also been found recently (78a) that similar intramolecular bifunctional catalysis is obtained in the hydrolysis of an amide with two neighboring carboxyls one of which is ionized (XIV).

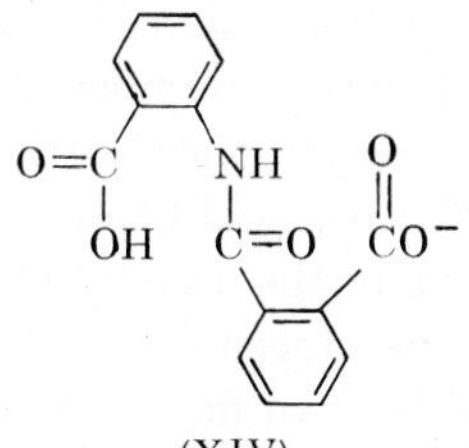

(XIV)

(5) Group Interaction Effects on Oxidation Rates

The sensitivity to oxidizing reagents is much higher in 1,2-glycols than in other polyhydroxylic compounds. This difference in reactivity has been utilized (79) to characterize the extent of head-to-head addition in the polymerization of vinyl acetate. The polymer is saponified and the poly(vinyl alcohol) is treated with periodate or lead tetraacetate. Wherever head-to-head addition had taken place, the chain was broken, so that the number-average molecular weight of the poly(vinyl alcohol) decreases from M_n^0 to M_n. It can then easily be shown that the average number x of 1,2-diol sequences per poly(vinyl alcohol) chain is given by

$$x = (M_n^0 - M_n)/M_n^0 \tag{34}$$

It has also been found that the oxidation rate of thiol groups attached to polymeric chains may be significantly different from the rates observed in simple thiols. A detailed investigation of this effect (80) showed that hydrolyzed poly(*p*-vinylphenyl thiolacetate) (XV)

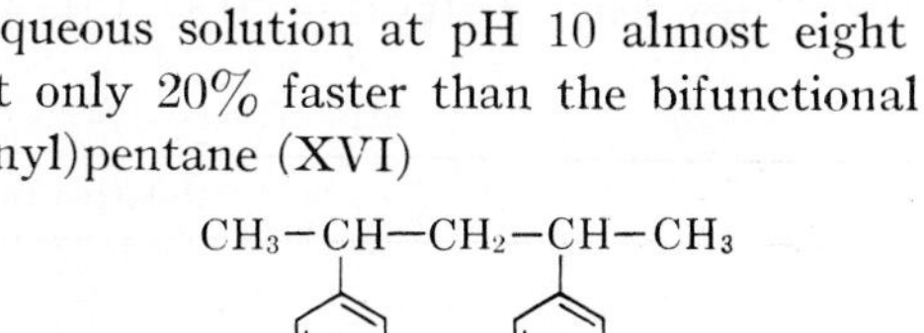

(XV)

is oxidized in aqueous solution at pH 10 almost eight times as fast as *p*-thiocresol, but only 20% faster than the bifunctional analogue 2,4-di-(*p*-mercaptophenyl)pentane (XVI)

(XVI)

The similar reactivity of the polymer and the bifunctional analogue may, however, be partly accidental, since a number of factors must be involved. Since the polymer is a polyelectrolyte, the electrical free energy of ionization will tend to decrease the effective acidity of the thiol groups. A larger fraction of these groups will be in the unionized form, which is involved in the oxidation reaction, in the polymer than in the analogue. The polymer has each thiol group flanked by two neighbors at a spacing at which the analogue has only one such group. Finally, more distant pairs of thiols might have been expected to make some contribution to the reaction rate. In view of these factors the polymer might have been expected to exceed the reactivity of the bifunctional analogue by a larger factor, and it might be surmised that some steric restraints present in the polymer but not in the analogue work in the opposite direction.

A similar study, in which hydrolyzed poly(vinyl thiolacetate) (XVII)

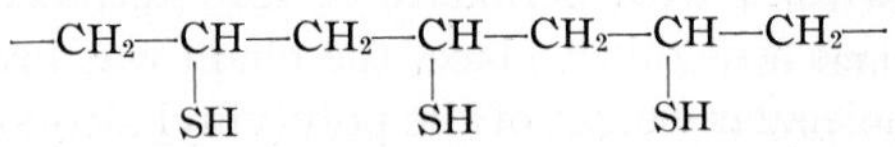

(XVII)

was compared with 2,4-pentanedithiol (XVIII)

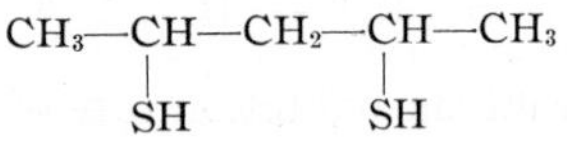

(XVIII)

was carried out in dimethylformamide solution (81) and avoided, therefore, uncertainties in the interpretation due to the state of ionization of the polymer. The polymer was found to be almost ten times as reactive as the bifunctional analogue, indicating clearly that interactions of pairs of thiol groups other than those of nearest neighbors make a contribution to the reaction rate. The sensitivity of the reaction rate to the spacing of the

TABLE I-2

Relative Oxidation Rates of $CH_3CH(SH)—(CH_2)_n—CH(SH)—CH_3$[a]

n	Relative rate
3	1.0
2	11.9
1	28.7
0	61.2

[a] Taken from ref. 81.

—SH groups in a dithiol is shown in the data compiled in Table I-2 obtained in dimethylformamide solution with sodium 2,6-dichlorobenzeneoneindophenol as the oxidizing agent.

It may be noted that the spacing of the interacting thiol groups is much less critical than, e.g., the spacing of the ester and the activating neighboring carboxylate discussed previously.

The wide variation in the reactivity of thiol groups in proteins has been the subject of extended investigations (82,83). These differences are undoubtedly a result of specific interactions of functional groups held in juxtaposition by the folding of the polypeptide chain in the native protein molecule. Denaturation reagents which disrupt this specific folding are commonly observed to eliminate the variations in the reactivity of thiol groups. These effects are probably determined by factors similar to those which were discussed in connection with the ionization equilibria.

A result of unusual interest has been obtained in studies of the enzyme ribonuclease. This protein has four disulfide bonds, which may be fully reduced to eight thiol groups. Under proper conditions, the reduced protein has been reoxidized with a recovery of 62% of the original catalytic activity (84). Since there are 105 ways in which 8 thiol groups can combine to form 4 disulfide bonds, and since enzymatic activity is associated, undoubtedly, only with one of these possible forms, it appears that this form possesses a large advantage of thermodynamic stability over the other forms.

(6) Reactions of Neighboring Groups Induced by Friedel-Crafts Catalysts

A number of reactions in which Friedel-Crafts catalysts were used to introduce cyclic units into chain polymers were investigated by Smets and his collaborators. When poly(vinyl chloride) was treated with aluminum trichloride in the presence of benzene, the primary product (equivalent to a copolymer of styrene and vinyl chloride which is difficult to prepare by copolymerization) reacted further to form by intramolecular cyclization poly-1,3-methyleneindans (85)

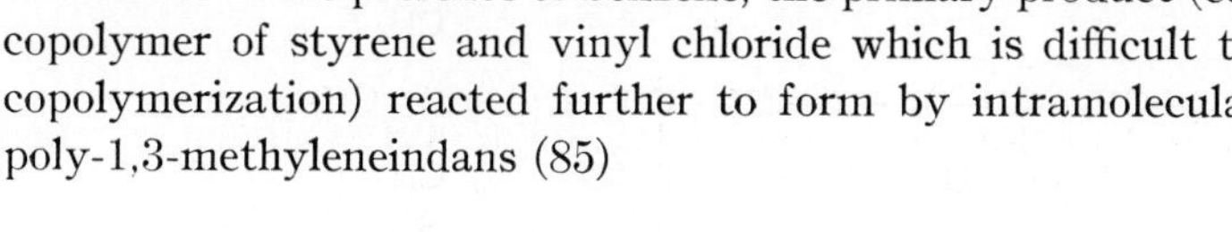

(35)

In an analogous manner, copolymers of styrene with acrylic acid, acrylyl chloride, or methyl acrylate were found to condense in the presence of aluminum trichloride to form methylenetetralone units (86):

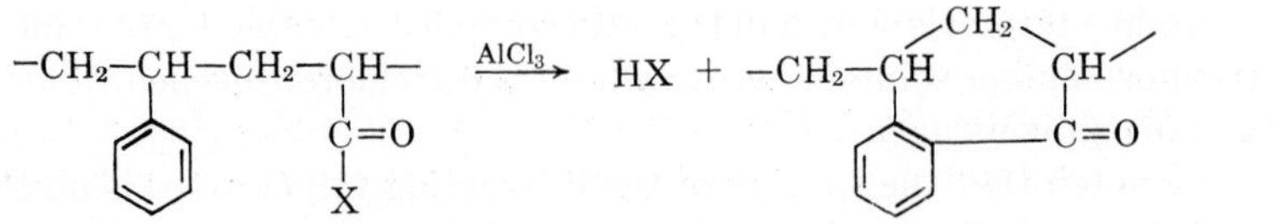

(36)

The evidence suggested that the condensation process could continue as indicated by eq. (37).

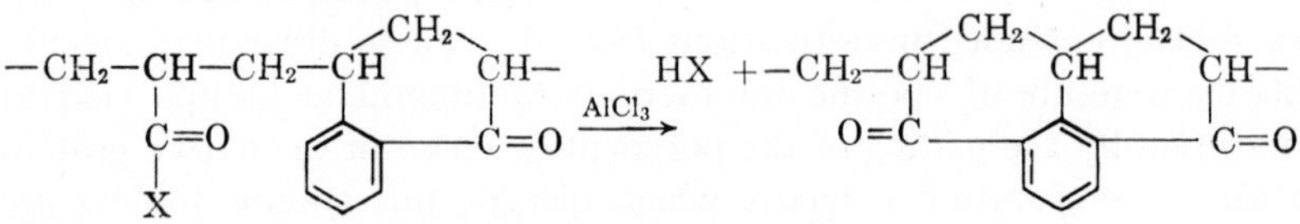

(37)

When, however, poly(ethyl α-chloroacrylate) was treated with benzene and $AlCl_3$, the aromatic nucleus was not incorporated into the polymer as might have been expected. Instead, a bicyclic lactone was formed (87):

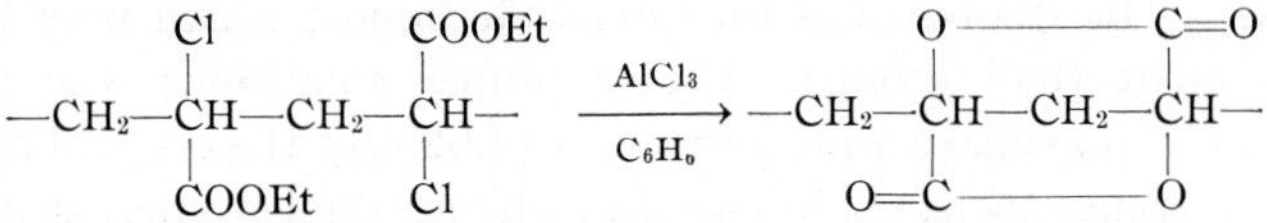

(38)

Similar lactone formation from poly(methyl α-bromoacrylate) and poly(methyl α-chloroacrylate) has been observed when the polymer in a dioxane–methanol–water solution was treated with sulfuric acid (88).

(7) Group Interactions in the Thermal Degradation of Polymers

In a number of thermal degradation processes of chain polymers the product of the decomposition catalyzes the reaction of the neighboring unit. An interesting example of such a process is the pyrolysis of poly(*tert*-butyl acrylate) (89):

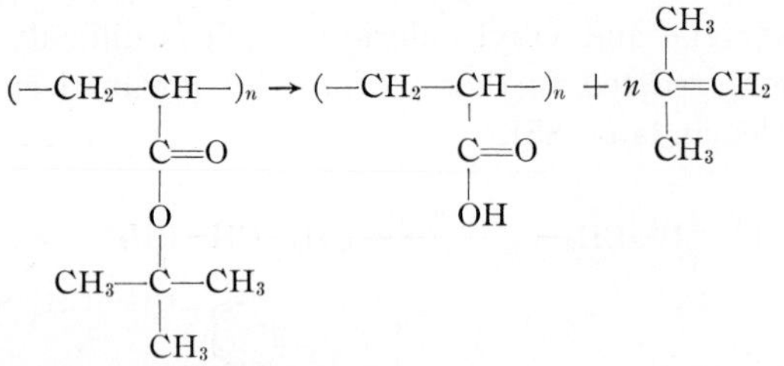

(39)

This reaction was found to be proceeding at a constant rate up to about 10% decomposition. At this point a rapid acceleration to a second, much higher constant rate is observed. The ratio of the rates observed in the two phases of the thermal degradation was, under some conditions, above

40. It is very difficult to formulate a plausible mechanism which would account for the shape of the kinetic curve, but there is no question that an activation of the ester by a neighboring carboxyl is involved in some fashion. This interpretation is also borne out by the extremely high thermal degradation rate of partially hydrolyzed poly(*tert*-butyl acrylate).

The activation of the dehydrochlorination of poly(vinyl chloride) by the double bond formed in the elimination of hydrogen chloride from a neighboring monomer unit (eq. 40)

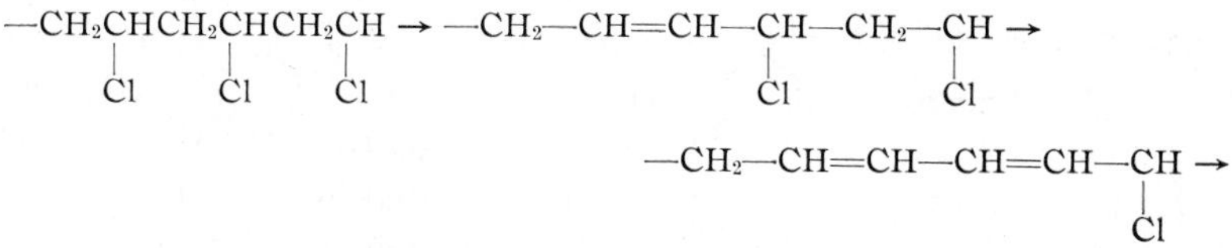

(40)

has long been recognized to be an important factor in this reaction. It is also believed to be the cause of the deep color produced at relatively low degrees of degradation, suggesting a preferential formation of long conjugated double bond sequences. Detailed investigations have indicated that the degradation starts at branch points or double bonds produced at the chain ends during the polymerization process (90). Spectroscopic data have shown, rather surprisingly, that degradation induced by ionizing radiation leads to absorption bands which change in intensity but not in location during the degradative process (91). The significance of this observation is not clear at the present time.

A similar tendency for thermal degradation to proceed along a continuous sequence of monomer residues in the polymeric chain has been reported for polymethacrylonitrile (92). The process is initiated by carboxyl group in the chain, and the mechanism is believed to be that shown in reaction (41),

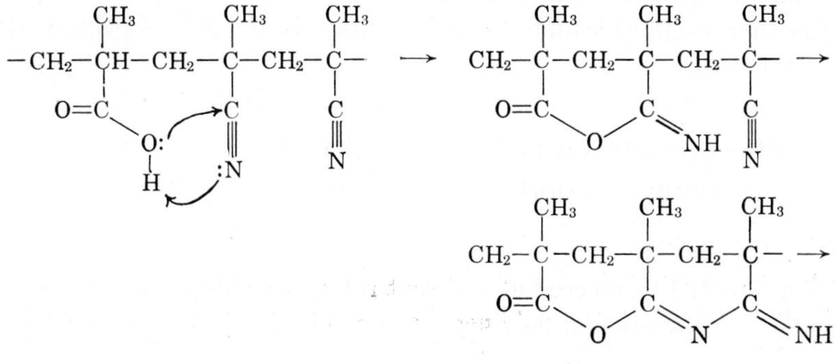

(41)

resulting in the formation of long conjugated sequences of the type (—C=N—)$_n$ which are responsible for the observed color development. The initiating acid need not be incorporated in the chain, since added carboxylic acids and phenols produce the same effect, with the catalytic efficiency increasing with the pK of the acid (93). The mechanism of reaction (41) is also supported by the observation of the instability of *o*-cyanobenzoic acid which tends to rearrange to phthalimide (94,95). The mechanism of this reaction is presumably as shown in eq. (42).

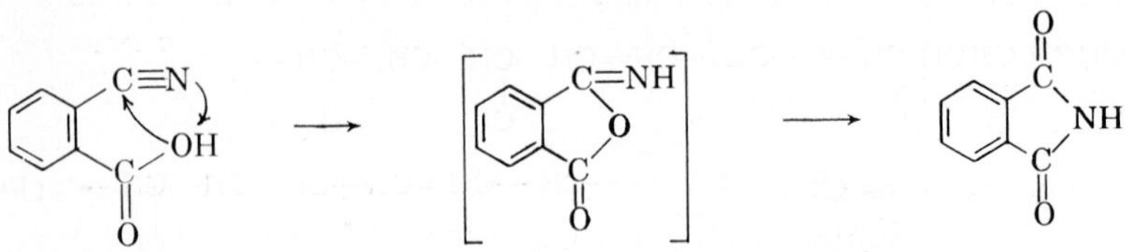
(42)

The decomposition of polyacrylonitrile follows a similar mechanism, except that in this case the chain may be initiated even if acrylic acid units are rigorously excluded. It was suggested (96) that the initiation of the process may be represented by

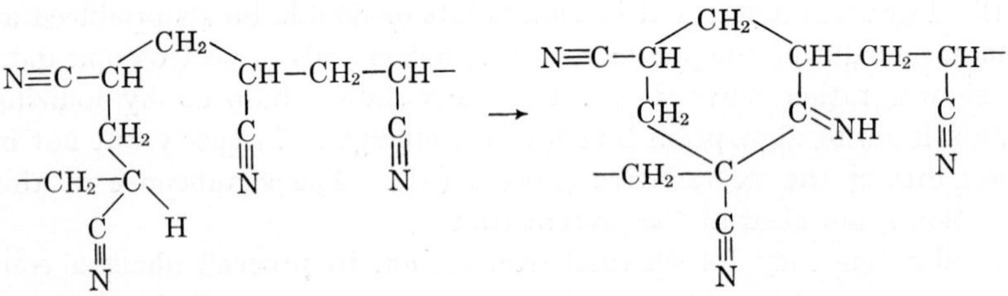
(43)

As would be expected, the incorporation of inert units into the chain by copolymerization with, e.g., styrene, reduces the length of the degradative reaction chain and improves the stability of the polymer (96).

Neighboring groups of the polymer chain may also participate in typical condensation reactions leading to cyclic units. In the case of poly(acrylic acid) the reaction

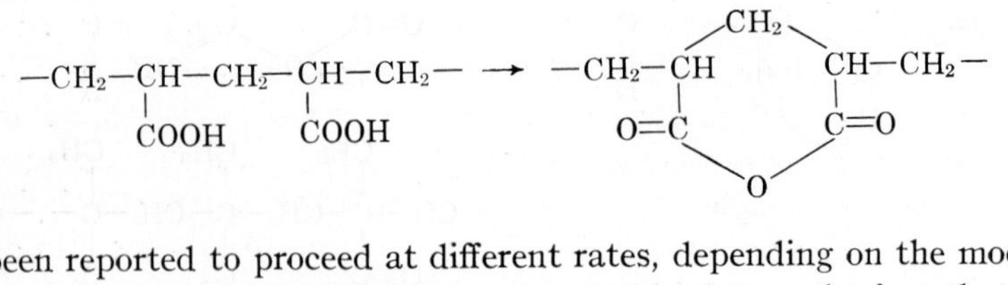
(44)

has been reported to proceed at different rates, depending on the mode of preparation of the original polymer, presumably due to the fact that it is sensitive to the stereoisomerism of the polymer backbone (70). A similar study of cyclic anhydride formation when poly(methacrylic acid) is heated (97) did not concern itself with the effects of stereoisomerism in this process. Effects of stereoisomerism were also noted in reaction (39), and are also probably a complicating feature in other cases, where they have not been clearly recognized.

The formation of bicyclic units from poly(α-acylaminoacrylic acid) shown in reaction (30) may take place not only in solution under the influence of acidic catalysts but also by thermally induced condensation of the polymer in bulk (98).

(8) Kinetic Patterns Characteristic of Chain Molecules with Reactivities Subject to Neighboring Group Effects

Frequently a chain molecule carries a large number of chain substituents, whose reactivity depends on whether its nearest neighbors have reacted. We have then, in general, three rate constants to consider: k_1 characteristic of groups with two unreacted neighbors, k_2 for groups lying next to one reacted and one unreacted residue, and k_3 describing groups lying between two reacted residues of the chain molecule. The mathematical analysis of the kinetic pattern resulting from such a situation is quite difficult, even if additional complications such as might result from effects due to the stereoisomerism of the chain molecule are neglected. Solutions to the general problem have recently been formulated by a number of workers (99a–e).

Let us consider in a rough qualitative fashion certain features of some typical cases. In the first case a given reactive group is strongly activated by the functional group resulting from the reaction of a similar neighboring group, so that $k_2 \approx k_3 \gg k_1$. A typical case of this kind is the carboxyl-catalyzed pyrolysis of poly(*tert*-butyl acrylate) already discussed. We may then regard the slow reaction of a residue in the middle of an unreacted sequence as a "nucleation" process, which is followed by a rapid "chain reaction" of a series of residues, each activated by the reaction of the preceding unit. If the ratio k_2/k_1 exceeds greatly the number of reactive residues in the chain, then all the reactive groups in any one chain will react rapidly as soon as one such group has reacted. In polymer samples consisting of chains of identical length, the reaction will then be first order; for polydisperse samples, the kinetics will reflect the chain length distribution. If the number of reactive groups in a chain is much larger than k_2/k_1, effects due to the finite lengths of the chains may be neglected. We may then form several "nuclei" for the reaction in any one chain, the concentration of nuclei being, in the initial stages, proportional to the reaction time. Since the reaction rate is approximately proportional to the number of reacted sequences, the extent of reaction will be initially proportional to the square of the reaction time.

The second case of interest is the one in which a reactive group is deactivated by the reaction of one or both nearest neighbors. A case in point is the quaternization of polyvinylpyridine by *n*-butyl bromide dissolved in tetramethylene sulfone (99f,99g). Kinetic data obtained for this reaction may be interpreted quantitatively (99h) on the assumption that $k_1 = k_2$ and $k_1/k_3 = 0.32$. An extreme case of deactivation by the product of the reaction of neighboring groups was cited in referring to the base catalyzed hydrolysis of polymethacrylamide (45,46) where an amide residue flanked by two ionized carboxyl groups appeared to be unable to hydrolyze. If we represent this case by $k_1 = k_2$, $k_3 = 0$, then theory predicts (99c,99d) that one third of the amide residues should eventually be between two carboxyl groups and the reaction should stop at that point.

Unfortunately, most systems in which neighboring group effects are to be expected cannot be investigated kinetically over the entire range of the reaction in a single solvent medium, since the solubility properties of the polymeric reaction product are usually quite different from those of the polymeric reagent. Thus, poly(vinyl acetate) is not soluble in solvents for poly(vinyl alcohol); poly(methyl acrylate) is insoluble in solvents for poly(acrylic acid), etc.

c. *Catalytic Effect of Non-Neighboring Groups*

When studying neighboring group effects on reaction mechanisms of compounds with a low molecular weight, it may be safely assumed that only such group interactions need be considered which lead in the transition state to cyclic structures containing not more than six atoms. This restriction does not necessarily hold with polyfunctional macromolecular reagents. We have seen already in discussing group association equilibria of such reagents that it is most realistic to compare the region occupied by the macromolecular coil to a droplet of a concentrated solution of a monofunctional reagent. This reasoning applies also to cases where the polymer contains reactive centers and other groups along the chain which may exert a catalytic action.

The only example of this situation which seems to have been described in the literature concerns the condensation of a methyl methacrylate–maleic anhydride copolymer with *p*-toluidine (99). The reaction is catalyzed by carboxyl groups, and the velocity of the process involving the polymeric reagent was found to be much higher than that of an analogue of low molecular weight under similar conditions. The data may be, however, understood, if the local carboxyl concentration within the swollen macromolecular coil, rather than the much lower bulk average carboxyl concentration, is taken to determine the catalytic efficiency.

It should be pointed out that this effect will become apparent only when the catalytic activity of substituents of the polymer chain is fairly high. The kinetic studies of the solvolysis of phenyl succinate and phenyl glutarate (56) show that the neighboring carboxylate in these two compounds is 8000 times and 60 times, respectively, as effective in attacking the ester bond as a molar acetate solution. By contrast, the chelation behavior of poly(*N*-methacrylyl lysine) could be interpreted in terms of a local amino acid concentration within the polymer coil of the order of 1*M* (31) and the carboxyl dimerization in a copolymer of styrene containing 15 mole-% methacrylic acid indicated a local effective carboxyl concentration of 0.3*M* (32). We can see then that a functional group attached to the polymer coil at some distance from the reaction center has to be several orders of magnitude more reactive than a neighboring group to produce a similar effect.

C. EFFECT OF MORPHOLOGY ON REACTIVITY

LEON SEGAL

Southern Utilization Research & Development Division, U. S. Department of Agriculture

1. Introduction

The reactivity of a chemical compound is the ability of the compound to react with another. With highly reactive compounds this occurs rapidly, and the system is said to have a high reaction rate. Compounds that do not react, or do so only poorly, are called inert, or nearly inert. One knows that compounds are reactive because the molecule of that compound possesses active centers; these may be hydroxyl or carboxyl groups, halogen atoms, multiple valence bonds, and the like. In any of these cases there are electron cloud distributions surrounding the atoms of the group, and these distributions have great influence. In organic chemistry with relatively simple molecules, the electron cloud distributions give rise to the inductive effect, the field effect, the various induced dipole effects, and such. It is well known how these affect the chemical reactivity of molecules. It is also well known that a molecule may contain one or more reactive centers and yet be nearly inert because of steric hindrance. Reviewing briefly, steric hindrance does not arise from any electronic influences. A sterically hindered molecule is inactive for physical reasons: the active group or groups cannot be reached by reactants because of the size, number, and close proximity of other substituents on the molecule. Thus, molecular structure enters into the concept of reactivity. Perhaps steric hindrance in organic chemistry is not as important as the other factors affecting reactivity but, as will be discussed, it or something closely akin to it operates quite frequently with polymers.

Polymers, of course, are formed when simple polyfunctional molecules react and may contain two monomer units or thousands. If the monomer originally contained reactive groups which were not involved in the formation of the polymer and were not affected by the reaction, these will still be found in the repeating units of the polymer chain. They are still reactive in their own right, meaning that the parent polymer would be capable of further chemical reaction. Reaction capability, however, for the parent molecule implies reactivity, but this is not necessarily true. One needs only to recall the previously mentioned steric hindrance of simple molecules to realize this. Great differences have been observed in reactivity among samples of polymers that appear to be chemically identical but differ in physical structure. This is the effect of morphology on reactivity, a sort of steric hindrance that will be elaborated on with examples taken from recent literature.

It must be pointed out first that the polymers to be considered in this light are necessarily limited to the linear high polymers, because it is among these that the morphological effect on reactivity is most frequent and most pronounced. The linear high polymers, for example, cellulose, polyethylene, poly(ethylene terephthalate), are commonly found in the form of films and fibers, but these forms are only two facets in the area of the morphology of the polymers. These are actually the ultimate in the gross structure, which is that which can be seen with the naked eye and in the optical microscope. Below this lies the fine structure extending down to the molecular level, and in this region one begins to find the effects which are similar to the steric hindrance encountered in the simpler molecules of organic chemistry.

The term morphology, then, means more than merely the type of structure recognized by botanists. In addition to the form and structure of the fiber and film, morphology of polymers includes factors of fine structure such as fibrils and micelles, accessible and nonaccessible regions, amorphous and crystalline areas, and other supramolecular agglomerations. Obviously, these factors can exist only when the polymer is in the solid state, so therefore considerations of the effect of morphology on the reactivity of polymers is restricted to heterogeneous systems. By heterogeneous systems is meant those systems of reactions in which the gross structure of the polymer starting material is retained, whether it be fiber or film; there are at least two phases always present, a factor which complicates kinetic studies. The various basic chemical reactions of the polymer, the organic chemistry of the basic molecule, will be dealt with elsewhere.

On becoming acquainted with the two-phase, heterogeneous systems under discussion, one immediately encounters trouble in semantics; the terms "reactivity" and "accessibility" are used to describe the ease with which polymers can react. More properly, however, reactivity is the ability of the polymer chain molecule to react with other molecules, while accessibility defines the ease by which the functional groups of the polymer molecule can be reached by the reactant molecules. Strictly speaking, then, this discussion would seem to deal mostly with accessibility, the steric hindrance effect of the gross and fine structure when a polymer is exposed to reactive molecules. The functional groups of a polymer molecule retain their own individual reactivities; for example, the primary hydroxyl groups of cellulose are more reactive than secondary in most cases, but secondary groups may be reacted before the primary if the latter are rendered nonaccessible because of their stereo relationships in the fine and gross structures of the cellulosic material. When a polymer molecule contains functional or substituent groups, it enters into the usual reactions of organic chemistry, e.g., esterification, etherification, saponification, the various aspects of which will be discussed in other chapters. The products of these reactions generally enhance the usefulness of a polymer because more desirable properties are obtained. But in all cases where the polymer remains as a solid phase in the reaction system, one must keep in mind that the extent of these reactions may be dictated by the morphology of the form in which the polymer molecules exist in the solid state.

Desirable properties do not always result, as in the case of solvolysis, which breaks the linkages between the monomeric units, thereby causing decomposition of the polymer chain. With some polymers only a short period of hydrolysis is needed to break enough linkages so that the material is useless. Hydrolysis can be carried out even to an extent that the monomer is the principal product. Solvolysis is useful in polymer chemistry, though, because by it much information is obtained regarding the fine structure of the polymer. Indeed, solvolysis, particularly hydrolysis, is highly sensitive to polymer morphology, such that various aspects of solvolysis, for example reaction rates, are taken as indices of accessibility, reactivity, or crystallinity.

Of all the high polymers, one in particular, cellulose, furnishes such a large variety of striking illustrations of the effect of morphology on reactivity that it is an almost ideal example for the purpose of this discourse.

2. Cellulose

a. General Considerations

Pure cellulose is an unbranched linear polymer of β-D-glucose where the chain molecule has the structure (I). The number of glucose residues or anhydroglucose units usually runs into several thousands in natural cellulose and is of the order of several hundreds in cellulose that has been degraded in one way or another. The Haworth formula (I) is an incomplete picture of the molecular structure because it fails to display the spatial

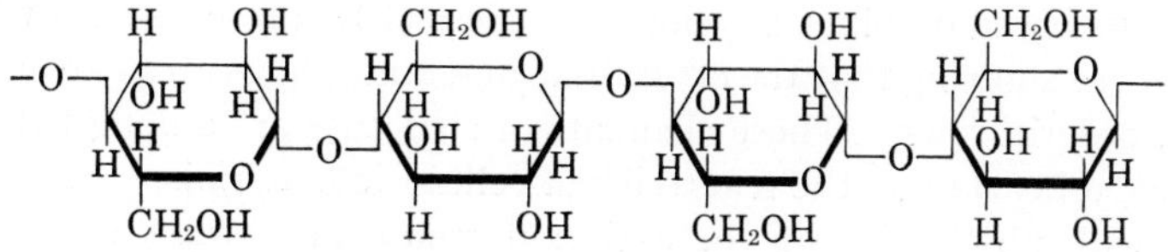

(I)

arrangements of the atoms of the glucose units, the true configuration of the pyranose ring, and the spatial arrangement of the hydroxyl groups. These factors which play highly important roles in the morphology of cellulose and its effects on cellulose reactivity are more properly considered when the molecule is diagrammed as in structure II, where the chair configuration of

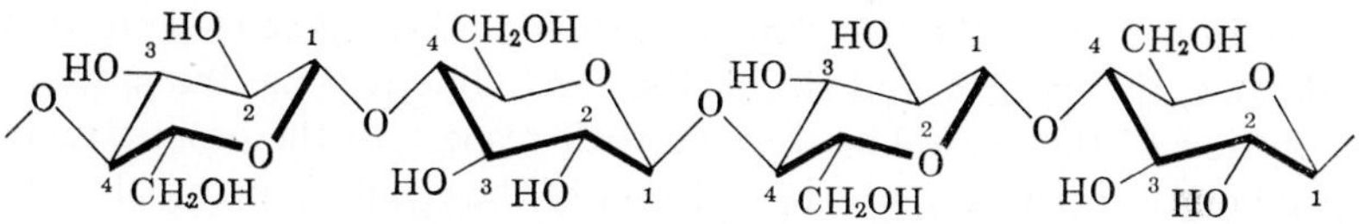

(II)

the glucose unit is displayed as well as the axial and equatorial positions of the hydroxyl groups. For more detailed information on this and other considerations of cellulose molecular structure, one is referred to the extensive reviews given in the volumes edited by Ott and Spurlin (100) and by Honeyman (101).

With its three hydroxyl groups per anhydroglucose unit and the chair configuration of the glucose rings, cellulose has the capability of forming many hydrogen bonds along the length of the polymer chain. These bonds, combined with other secondary valence forces (principally the Van der Waals attraction), bind together portions of the molecular chains into various degrees of lateral order, ranging from perfect geometrical packing of the crystal lattice to random conditions. In the former (the crystalline regions), the chains are parallel or nearly so. In the latter (the amorphous areas), the chain molecules separate and even cross one another. These regions, above the molecular level constituting the smallest units of the so-called fine structure, are not sharply defined but gradually merge into one another. One chain molecule, because of its length, passes through one, and then another of these regions several times along its length. Studies of the crystalline structure have been reviewed in great detail by Howsmon and Sisson (102), and such studies are still continuing. Frey-Wyssling (103) questions the directions of hydrogen bonding assumed in the presently accepted crystal lattice of cellulose, claiming that it does not fit in with conclusions based on plant physiology. Hess (104) presents data which he interprets as showing that the crystalline and amorphous areas are arranged in neat, orderly rows. These elements of structure are among the factors that have a bearing on the reactivity of cellulosic materials.

Chemical substitution on the hydroxyl groups and attack on the glucosidic linkages which connect monomer units is restricted according to their location in the overall morphology. Thus, those groups located in the amorphous regions react readily in all chemical reactions, being in a highly accessible environment. In the crystalline regions where there is close packing and strong interchain bonding, these groups are not readily accessible to reactant molecules, and, indeed, are completely inaccessible to some (105).

Certain factors of the fine structure, such as the degree of perfection of the lattice, the number and size of the crystalline regions, the position or orientation of the crystalline regions with respect to the gross structure, depend on the origin and previous history of the cellulosic material. Other elements of the fine structure, for example the crystal lattice type, are influenced by chemical treatments. There are at present at least four accepted crystalline modifications of cellulose, designated as celluloses I, II, III, and IV (106,107).

As with any chemical compound that exhibits polymorphism, these materials are the same insofar as the constituent molecule is concerned; there is only unmodified cellulose present. They differ from one another in that the planes of the anhydroglucose units of one chain molecule in the regions of close parallel alignment lie at different positions. These differences in position are evidenced by x-ray diffraction. Infrared absorption spectroscopy also differentiates the polymorphic forms (106), because group vibrations are affected by changes in the positions of the anhydroglucose units and of the chain molecules. Cellulose I is the modification found in the natural vegetable fibers, bacterial tissues, and some forms of animal life, hence the term "native cellulose lattice." Cellulose II, the "hydrate lattice," is obtained after the application of various reagents described as swelling agents for cellulose such as solutions of sodium hydroxide or inorganic acids. It is also obtained when dissolved cellulose is regenerated from its solutions, and when cellulose xanthate solutions are decomposed (these are the regenerated celluloses, such as viscose rayon). Cellulose III, which results from applications of liquid ammonia or anhydrous ethylamine, has no technical importance at present. Cellulose IV, originally obtained by high temperature treatments but now also by certain methods of decomposition applied to solutions of cellulose zinc xanthate, seems to have some significance in tire-cord rayons. Although these crystalline modifications differ in the parameters of their crystalline unit cells, as shown by x-ray diffraction, there is no direct experimental evidence showing clearly that the crystal lattice type *per se* has significant influence on the chemical reactivity of cellulose or on the accessibility of the reactive groups concerned. In all cases where lattice transformations are involved and where enhancement of reactivity or accessibility are observed, particularly in the case of cellulose II, such enhancement is more closely connected with a reduction of the size of the crystallites, an increase in the amorphous areas, and a decrease in the density of the gross structure which always accompanies such transformations. There is some evidence that chain length, or degree of polymerization, however, influences reactivity.

By virtue of the fact that the molecular chains pass through crystalline and amorphous regions, the next element of fine structure—the micelles or fibrils—are generated (108). These structures, visible under the electron microscope, have been studied extensively by Rånby (109–111) and by Rollins, Tripp, and Moore (112). The published electron micrographs at this level of structure display to a marked extent visible evidence of chemical reaction which is not usually apparent in the gross structure.

It is the gross structure that is most familiar to everyone: the cotton, linen, and ramie fibers, the rayon filament, cellophane film, wood pulp, and other forms. These are all varied among themselves. The cotton fiber is a single cell but complex, being built up of many layers which spiral around one another in opposite directions. In some respects, the gross structure of the cell is much like plywood, or more closely, the built-up, wire-wound artillery pieces of pre-World War II. The long ramie fiber, like linen and wood pulp, is not a single cell, but is built up of many small cells with much intercellular matter present. In all of these fibers, single-cell cotton or multicell ramie, many micellar strands are associated to form layers (113, 114). In rayons, on the other hand, where cellulose has been dissolved and regenerated, the structure is not as complex. The crystalline and amorphous regions are still present, but with more of the latter and with smaller crystalline regions. In viscose rayon, a skin and core develop, but all-skin and all-core rayon can be produced by proper control in the manufacturing process. Richardson (115) has reviewed this subject very thoroughly. Hock (116) has reviewed the fiber structure of some of the more important sources of cellulose, while Rollins (117) has dealt in detail with the cotton fiber. The reader is referred to these reviews because the subject matter is pertinent to this discourse, but the extensiveness of the subject precludes going into details of it here.

When native cellulose, i.e., cotton and ramie fibers, bacterial and animal membranes, purified wood pulp, and the like, is mercerized, not only are there changes in fine structure (in crystal lattice, crystallite size, and degree of crystallinity) but there are marked changes in gross structure (117). A mercerized cellulosic fiber, therefore, is of different total morphology from the fiber prior to mercerization (118,119), and this affects reactivity. Cellulosic fibers and film are swollen by water and other reagents (120,121). Changes in chemical reactivity are still observed when only the morphology is changed.

b. *Reactivity of Cellulose*

(1) Etherification and Esterification

The literature on the reactivity of cellulose is quite extensive (100) and is summarized in Chapter V. In a recent review (122), Cumberbirch brought forward many cases where the morphology of the cellulosic material had marked effects on the extent of chemical reactions, as for example the work of Sitch (123,124), who reported that when cotton, mercerized cotton, cuprammonium rayon, hydrocellulose, and a cotton ground in a ball mill were methylated with ethereal diazomethane, methoxyl contents of 7.0, 14.9, 18.6, 5.9, and 20.6%, respectively, were obtained. Sitch concluded that the degree of methylation produced is greatly affected by the crystallinity of the cellulose. Sitch's results confirmed earlier work of Reeves and Thompson (125) with native and mercerized cottons. Reeves and Sisson (126) also applied diazomethane to air-dry cottons and related the methoxyl contents with the fine structure as revealed by x-rays. Whereas Sitch used celluloses of mixed prehistory, i.e., given various chemical treatments and subjected to a physical process, Reeves and Sisson resorted only to one cellulosic material given several chemical treatments. Changes in fine structure were induced by treatment with solutions of sodium hydroxide at various temperatures, giving partially and completely mercerized cottons (crystal lattices of celluloses I and II and of cellulose II only, respectively). With native cotton, 5.6–7.9% methoxyl was obtained, with partially mercerized cotton, 8.7–9.8%, and with mercerized cotton, 10.7–12.6%. The application of boiling water or heated glycerol to never-dried, caustic-treated cotton resulted in what was described as a reversion to the native state, but these conditions are those which are recognized today as productive of crystalline cellulose IV. Nevertheless, Reeves and Sisson found that the methoxyl contents of cottons treated with hot glycerol (nearly all converted) were in the range 6.3–7.4%; with boiling water (partially converted), 9.2–9.9%.

There is no simple correlation of extent of reaction with type of crystalline lattice. Reeves and Sisson did not report to what extent the crystalline lattice was influenced by the methylation, but there is little reason to expect ethereal diazomethane to penetrate the crystalline regions of cellulose. What is of significance here, but apparently not considered, is the reduction of crystallinity (or increase of accessibility), the reduction of crystallite size, and the increase in fiber cross-sectional area as related to the treatments. Valko (118) has commented on this at great length. The loss of reactivity as a result of the drying and the heat treatment is a consequence of the treatment, not the lattice conversion. This is the "hornification" effect discussed by Spurlin (127), which arises from the formation of stronger bonds between the mobile cellulose chains of the swollen structure as it collapses in drying. Heuser (128) discusses the deleterious effect of drying on the reactivity of cotton which has been mercerized in order to enhance reactivity. Loeb and Segal (129) compared the reactivity of cotton decrystallized with anhydrous ethylamine with that of untreated and mercerized cottons, using the degree of acetylation as the criterion of reactivity. They, too, found that full reactivity could be sustained only if drying was avoided after the initial treatments which in their systems employed nonaqueous solvents.

Because of the commercial importance of cellulose acetate, a staggering amount of work has been done to establish optimum conditions for the acetylation of cellulose. All results point to the fact that the reactivity of the cellulose is a function of the accessibility of the hydroxyl groups under the conditions used for esterification. Some of the evidence for this is discussed by Heuser (130) and Happey (105). In the acetylation of cellulose, a factor of prime importance to reactivity is the moisture content of the material. Water does not play a part in the acetylation reaction at all; indeed, water is not wanted, and the conditions are such as to remove it from the system as fast as it is formed. Water affects the morphology of the cellulosic material in both the fine and gross structures to render the hydroxyl groups of the cellulose more accessible to the reactants. Water does not affect the crystalline material, whereas other reagents, e.g., ethylamine, affect both amorphous and crystalline cellulose. As pointed out earlier, intermolecular hydrogen bonding through the hydroxyl groups effectively crosslinks chains to form the fine structure. Water, ethylamine, the aliphatic diamines, and other compounds (the so-called swelling agents) supply the necessary energy to break the hydrogen bonds but not enough to bring the cellulose molecule into solution. This bond reforms with the swelling agent. What happens afterwards depends on the strength of the hydrogen bond in the particular system involved, and what is done to the system.

Urquhart has studied the cellulose–water system very extensively, and in his latest review (131) explains clearly the manner in which the swelling agent affects the morphology of the cellulose. In industrial practice it has long been known that in order to preserve high reactivity, swollen cellulose must not be allowed to dry, and where wet water-free cellulose is needed, water is removed by means of other solvents. In acetylation, for example, acetic acid is commonly used The classic work of Staudinger and co-workers (132,133) well illustrates in several ways the effect of morphology on reactivity of the polymer molecule. In these studies the following changes in morphology are encountered: (*1*) native fibers of different gross morphology (cotton, ramie, linen, and hemp); (*2*) native fibers mercerized and dried; and (*3*) both dried native and dried mercerized fibers made to "include" various solvents. This latter is accomplished by thoroughly wetting the fiber with water, and then completely extracting the water with the desired solvent from which the fiber is redried. Solvent exchange is resorted to when a water-immiscible solvent is to be the final solvent. The dry "inclusion" cellulose normally contains several per cent of the final solvent which can be removed only by rewetting with water or some other swelling solvent.

In Table I-3 are given acetylation data for "acetic acid-included" cellulose taken from Staudinger's work. The variation of acetyl contents in column 2 shows an effect of the original gross structure. The reduced acetyl contents of column 3 illustrate the deactivation or "hornification" effect of drying a swollen cellulose structure. The data in columns 4 and 5 show that inclusion of solvents markedly reactivates the polymer. The expected increased reactivity of mercerized cellulose is found in the data of column 5. Data of this sort are even more dramatic when milder acetylating conditions are used, as shown in Table I-4 for "pyridine-inclusion" cellulose. A simplified explanation of these effects can be gathered from the pictorial presentation of Figure I-8. The closely bonded chains of native cellulose are loosened by the mercerization process to give the reactive, never-dried, water-wet mercerized cellulose (Fig. I-8*A*). Reactivity is lost when the structure is dried because strong bonding is restored (Fig. I-8*B*). Wetting with water breaks the bonds again but only in the noncrystalline regions. The space between the chains occupied by the water molecules is taken up by the solvent molecules on inclusion, and some of these solvent molecules are trapped in the fine and gross structure, separating the polymer chain molecules when the solvent is dried off (Fig. I-8*C*). The inclusion cellulose is reactive by virtue of the chain separation which hinders the reformation of hydrogen bonding, thereby keeping the hydroxyl groups of the cellulose molecule in a more accessible condition for the entering reactant.

TABLE I-3
Acetylation of Cellulose Fibers with Benzene–Acetic Anhydride–Sulfuric Acid Reagent for 24 hr. at 60°C.[a]

	Acetyl content, %			
			Dry acetic acid-included	
Fiber	Dried native	Dried mercerized	Native	Mercerized
Cotton	2.0	0.9	41.8	44.9
Ramie	2.1	1.5	40.3	43.6
Linen	1.2	2.2	38.9	41.4
Hemp	3.3	2.3	40.3	41.3

[a] Taken from ref. 132.

TABLE I-4
Acetylation of Cellulose Fibers with Pyridine–Acetic Anhydride Reagent for 24 hr. at 60°C.[a]

	Acetyl content, %			
			Dry pyridine-included	
Fiber	Dried native	Dried mercerized	Native	Mercerized
Cotton	4.3	0.7	7.9	14.2
Ramie	2.1	0.9	7.2	15.6
Linen	1.3	0.4	7.6	15.7
Hemp	1.4	0.6	9.2	16.3

[a] Taken from ref. 132.

Sebille-Anthoine (134) prepared a benzene-included cellulose from mercerized, bleached cotton linters where the distention of the structure by the benzene was such that a translucent mass was obtained. With this inclusion cellulose and the anhydrides of acetic, propionic, or butyric acids, triesters were obtained in about 30 min. With the dry, mercerized linters there was practically no reaction. Sharkov, Dmitrieva, and Potapova (135) noted the same thing on acetylation of benzene-included cellulose, but found no differences in reactivity on solvolysis between this cellulose and the original material,

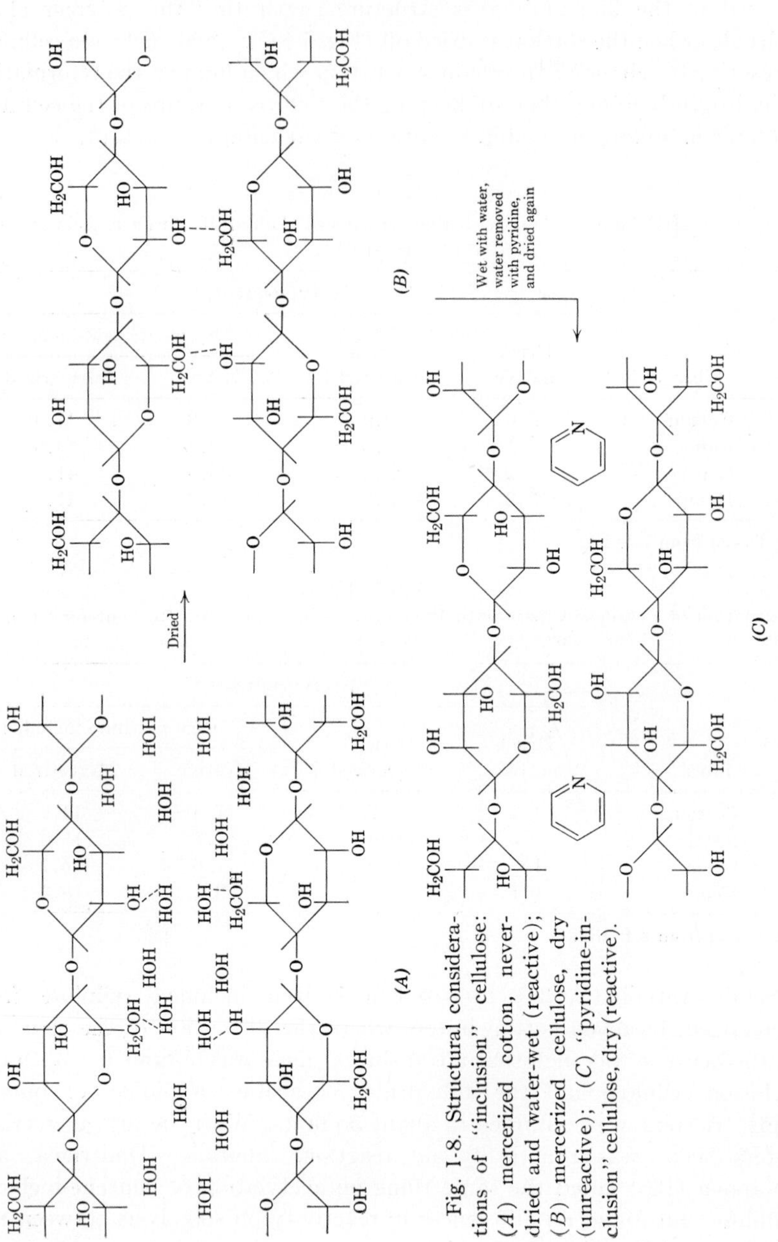

Fig. I-8. Structural considerations of "inclusion" cellulose: (*A*) mercerized cotton, never-dried and water-wet (reactive); (*B*) mercerized cellulose, dry (unreactive); (*C*) "pyridine-inclusion" cellulose, dry (reactive).

One of the most striking demonstrations of the effect of morphology on reactivity of cellulose has been given by Demint and Hoffpauir (136), also using acetylation (acetic anhydride–acetic acid–perchloric acid reagent).

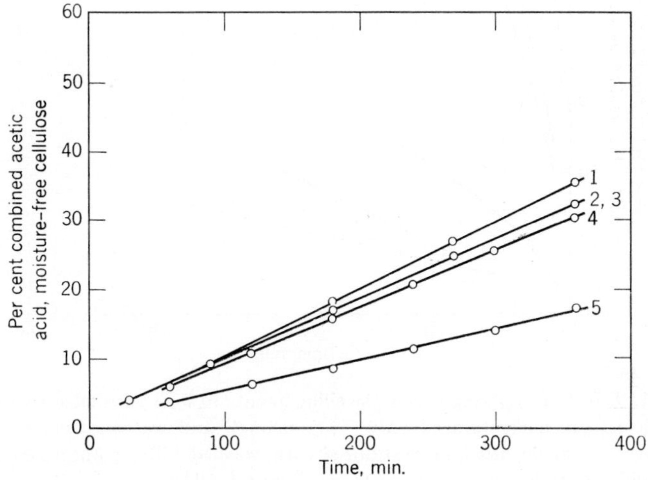

Fig. I-9. Effect of textile form on rate of acetylation: (*1*) 7s/3 yarn; (*2*) sliver lap, (1-in. cut); (*3*) 34s/2 yarn; (*4*) fabric, (*5*) ground sliver lap. (Taken from ref. 136.)

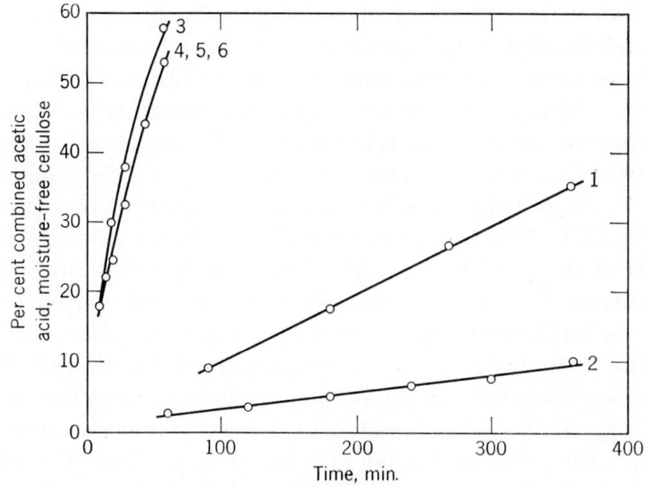

Fig. I-10. Effect of wetting of 7s/3 yarn on rate of acetylation after drying: (*1*) raw; (*2*) excessively dried; (*3*) wet by Soxhlet extraction, 1st cycle; (*4*) rewetted, 6th cycle; (*5*) rewetted, 12th cycle; (*6*) wet by soaking. (Taken from ref. 136.)

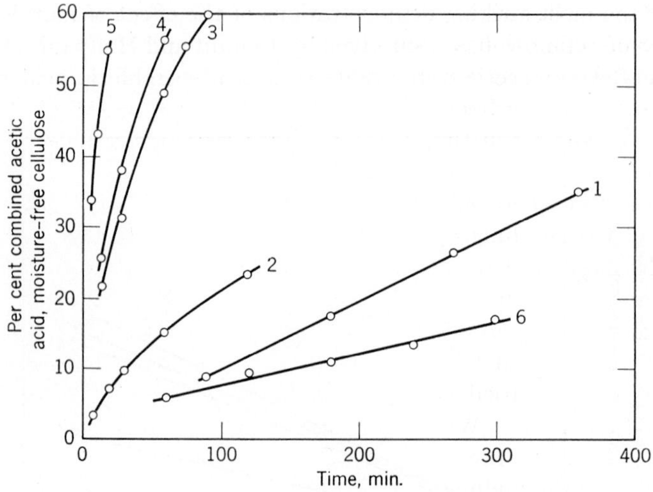

Fig. I-11. Effect of applying various swelling agents to 7s/3 yarn prior to acetylation: (*1*) raw yarn; (*2*) decrystallized yarn; (*3*) alcohol- and water-extracted yarn; (*4*) scoured yarn; (*5*) never-dried, decrystallized yarn, washed with ice water and exchanged to acetic acid; (*6*) mercerized yarn. (Taken from ref. 136.)

In their study the effect of gross and fine structures is separated, i.e., they acetylated sliver lap (a web of fibers before spinning), ground sliver lap, yarn, and fabric, all from the same lot of cotton in one series of experiments; in another series the yarn alone was subjected to various treatments before acetylation. Thus, in the first series only gross structure is changed, while in the second the fine structure is influenced. The effects of gross structure are observed in the data of Figure I-9. In Figures I-9, I-10, and I-11, per cent acetyl as shown in the original has been changed to per cent combined acetic acid (137). The faster rate shown by the heavier 7s/3 yarn and the slower rate of the ground sliver lap (relative to the other three forms) has been postulated as possibly arising from greater retention of heat of reaction by the bulkier structures so that the acetylation proceeds at a higher temperature (136), but there has been no experimental proof of this.

Much more impressive changes in rate are observed when fine structure is affected (Fig. I-10). The hornification effect previously mentioned in connection with mercerized cellulose is markedly evident even when only exposure to water is involved (curve *2*). The drastic drying conditions, forcing out more water from between the chains, cause extensive bonding which reduces accessibility of the hydroxyl groups. On the other hand, water-wetting followed by air-drying enhances reactivity (curves *3–6*), because chain separation is maintained by water molecules. The cellulose–HOH–cellulose bonding is more easily broken by the entering reactant than the cellulose–cellulose bond. The effect on cellulose of repeated wetting by water and drying in the nitration of dewaxed cotton linters has been studied by Brown and co-workers (138–140), whose work confirms this marked behavior where only the noncrystalline regions are first involved.

The effects of swelling agents other than water are apparent in Figure I-11. The data plotted here show without question what a tremendous effect distention of the fine structure has on reactivity of the polymer by making the hydroxyl groups more accessible. Curve *1* here is the same as that in Figure I-9 and I-10. Of the five pretreated yarns here in Figure I-11, four were air dried before acetylation (curves *2–6*), while one was never dried (curve *5*). Where the same swelling pretreatment is involved, but drying conditions are different (curves *2* and *5*), Demint and Hoffpauir have confirmed the findings of earlier workers (129) regarding retention of reactivity on keeping the fine structure distended with a solvent. Their findings, however, also pose a question as to why the dry, mercerized yarn should be so much more unreactive than the raw yarn (curve *6* versus curve *1*). The structures of both yarns have been subjected to high degrees of swelling, such that the degree of crystallinity, as well as the crystallite size, of each pretreated yarn has been reduced from that of the raw yarn. The explanation probably lies in differences that exist between the two swelling systems; differences that cause the fine structures to be affected differently. Thus, in mercerization which is carried out in an aqueous system with sodium hydroxide, the presently accepted concept holds that the sodium ion with its sheath of water molecules penetrates the fine structure, enters the crystalline regions, and forms new crystalline compounds there. It is the energy content of this highly hydrated ion that causes the extensive changes. Removing the sodium hydroxide is accomplished with water which remains in the crystalline regions, so that water completely permeates the entire polymer system. When the water molecules are removed on drying the collapse of the swollen structure is far-reaching. With the cellulose chains rearranged because of the extent of swelling, thus relieving strains, more hydrogen bonds form between the chains to "lock up" the fine structure more tightly than it was prior to mercerization.

Decrystallization, on the other hand, is accomplished with anhydrous ethylamine. There is no hydrated ion or molecule penetrating the fine structure. In the absence of water, an entirely different crystalline com-

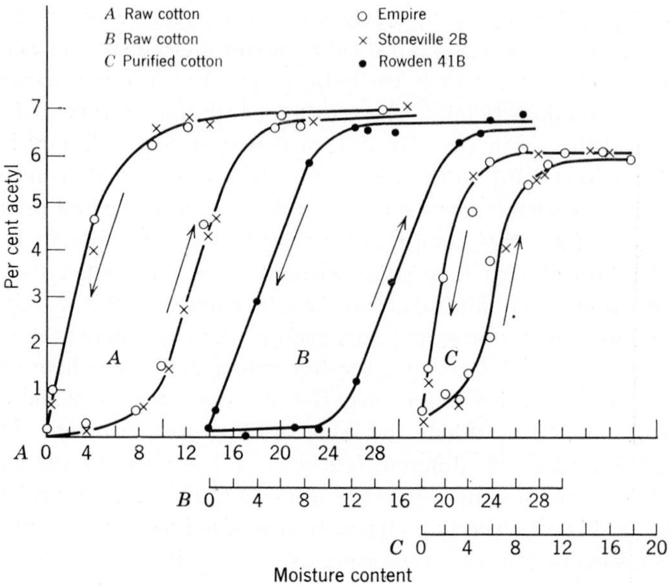

Fig. I-12. Influence of moisture and previous sorption history on extent of acetylation. (Taken from ref. 141.)

plex is present. Breaking this complex by removing the ethylamine with cold water, as was done with the cellulose in Demint and Hoffpauir's work, does not follow the same scheme as in mercerization. The amine diffuses from the crystalline regions to the water in the amorphous regions and to that external to the gross structure, while the swollen structure simultaneously shrinks. Water does not occupy space in the crystalline regions; consequently, when the swollen structure collapses on drying completely, the extent and type of hydrogen bonding set up between the cellulose molecules is not like that in the mercerized cellulose.

The changes in morphology brought about by water in the amorphous regions alone have marked influence on reactivity: not only the amount of water present but also the prehistory of the sample. Here prehistory means whether the cellulose is drying out or absorbing moisture, and whether the cellulose was purified or not. This effect can be seen in Figure I-12, where acetylation data of Blouin, Reeves, and Hoffpauir (141) are shown. Whether water is leaving or entering the cellulosic structure is of most importance on the extent of reaction. Thus, from Figure I-12 one readily concludes that, for the same moisture content, the cellulose is more accessible for reaction if the water molecules are leaving the cellulosic structure. This follows from what has already been discussed, because until the water molecules have broken the cellulose–cellulose hydrogen bonds (in the noncrystalline regions) the entering reactant finds strong cellulose–cellulose bonds present. There is some evidence in Figures I-12*A* and I-12*B* that botanical morphology has an influence on chemical reactivity of the polymer chain. Thus the data in Figure I-12*B* were obtained from a much coarser fiber than those in Figure I-12*A*. The difference has been postulated as possibly due to the smaller surface area per gram and the greater diameter of the coarser cotton fiber which requires more extensive swelling for reaching a given degree of accessibility. Removal of waxes and non-cellulosic constituents from cotton fiber markedly changes the picture also; less moisture in the fiber is required in order to attain the same level of substitution as in the raw fiber (Fig. I-12*C*).

Blouin and co-workers have indicated that botanical morphology has an effect when only cottons are involved. Other workers have found differences in a variety of aspects when celluloses from different sources were investigated. Petitpas (142) reported that different concentrations of sodium hydroxide are required to obtain x-ray diagrams characteristic of mercerized cellulose when cotton, ramie, and wood pulp are treated with sodium hydroxide solutions. Rånby (143,144) found similar results with animal cellulose (tunicin), cotton cellulose, and wood cellulose, where animal cellulose required a more concentrated caustic solution and wood cellulose the least. Peculiarly enough, Rånby found bacterial cellulose (from *Acetobacter xylinum*) to have properties very similar to cotton cellulose. The behavior of tunicin (animal cellulose) is a matter of degree rather than of kind. Tunicin enters into all cellulosic reactions, but these are governed by differences in accessibility caused by the morphological structure of the tunicin (145).

(2) Hydrolysis

When cellulose is heated with aqueous mineral acids, the polymer chain is attacked at the glucosidic oxygen atoms connecting the glucose units; the polymer is ultimately converted completely to the monomer, glucose. However, morphology was found to influence the rate of reaction very highly in easily distinguishable and characteristic ways in the early stages of this reaction (Figs. I-13 and I-14).

Nickerson and Habrle (147) concluded that their curves (Fig. I-14*A*) showing the amount of cellulose hydrolyzed by boiling 2.5*N* sulfuric acid indicate that all the materials used may represent molecular order ranging

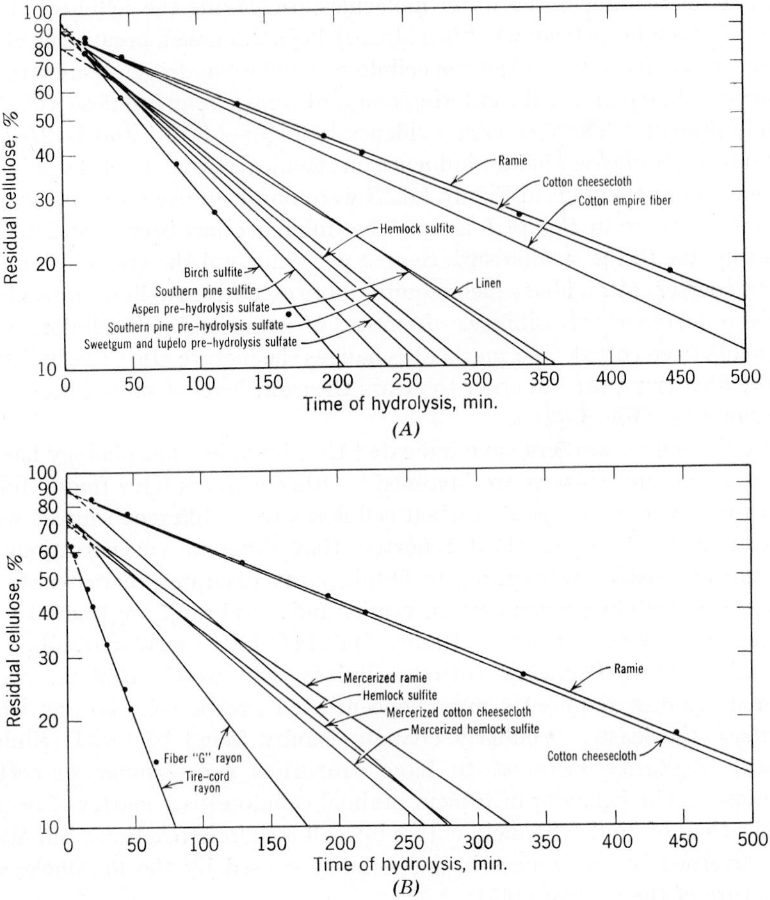

Fig. I-13. Response of various cellulosic materials to constant-boiling hydrochloric acid: (*A*) native celluloses; (*B*) native, mercerized, and regenerated celluloses. (Taken from ref. 146.)

from highly disordered and readily accessible to well-ordered and less readily hydrolyzed fractions. Philipp, Nelson, and Ziifle (149) further pursued this conclusion to develop a method for estimating the relative proportions of crystalline and amorphous cellulose present in any one cellulosic material. The heart of that method is the hydrolysis rate curve obtained for cellulosic materials, three of which are given in Figure I-15. The morphological parameters involved in this application of hydrolysis

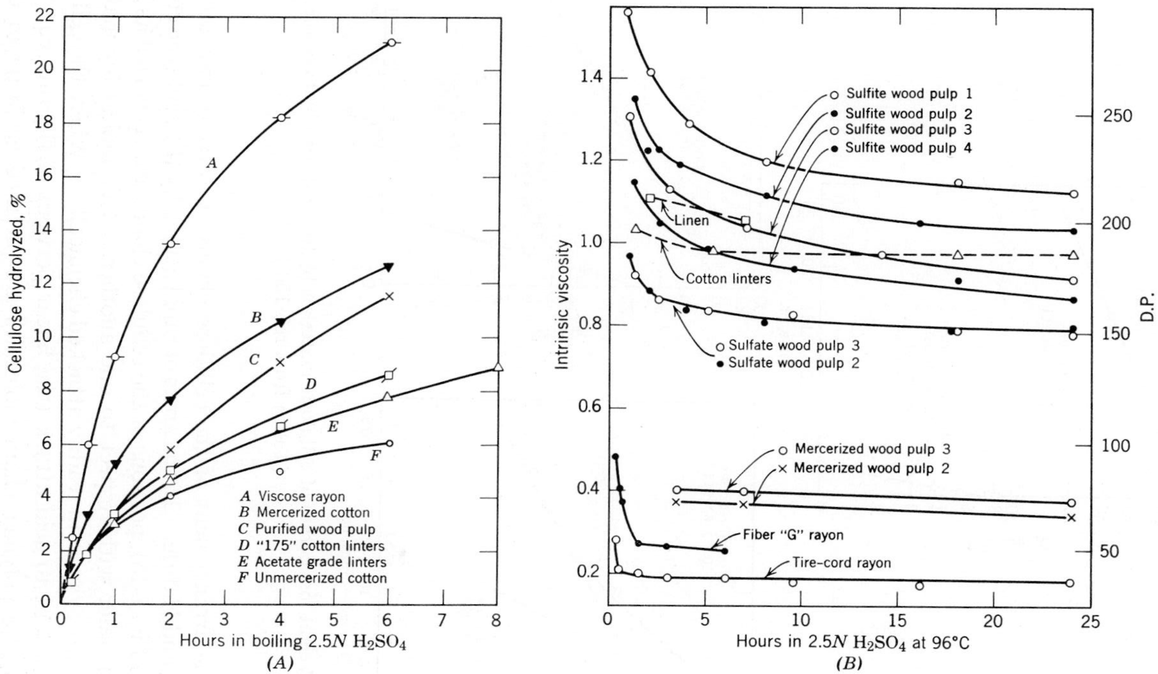

Fig. I-14. Response of various cellulosic materials towards boiling $2.5N$ sulfuric acid: (*A*) in terms of cellulose hydrolyzed; (*B*) in terms of viscosity or degree of polymerization of the residual material. (Taken from refs. 147, 148.)

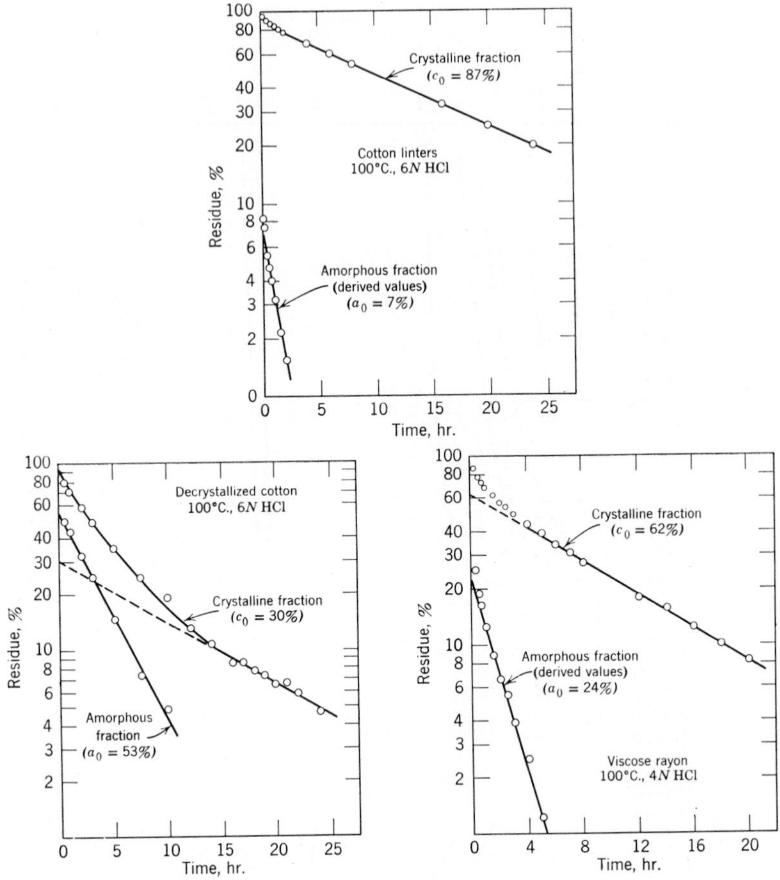

Fig. I-15. Weight loss curves of cellulosic materials hydrolyzed with hydrochloric acid. (Taken from ref. 150.)

concern the arrangement of the cellulose chains, as already indicated by Nickerson and Habrle. In the areas of rapid attack by the acid (the curved portions in Fig. I-15), portions of the cellulose chains are visualized as lying in random order with respect to one another. This makes for material amorphous to x-rays and readily attacked chemically. Where the cellulose is more resistant to acid attack (the linear portions of the rate curves in Fig. I-15), the polymer chain molecules are pictured as being in close-packed order. This material diffracts x-rays in characteristic patterns as does any crystalline material, and by virtue of this close packing is resistant

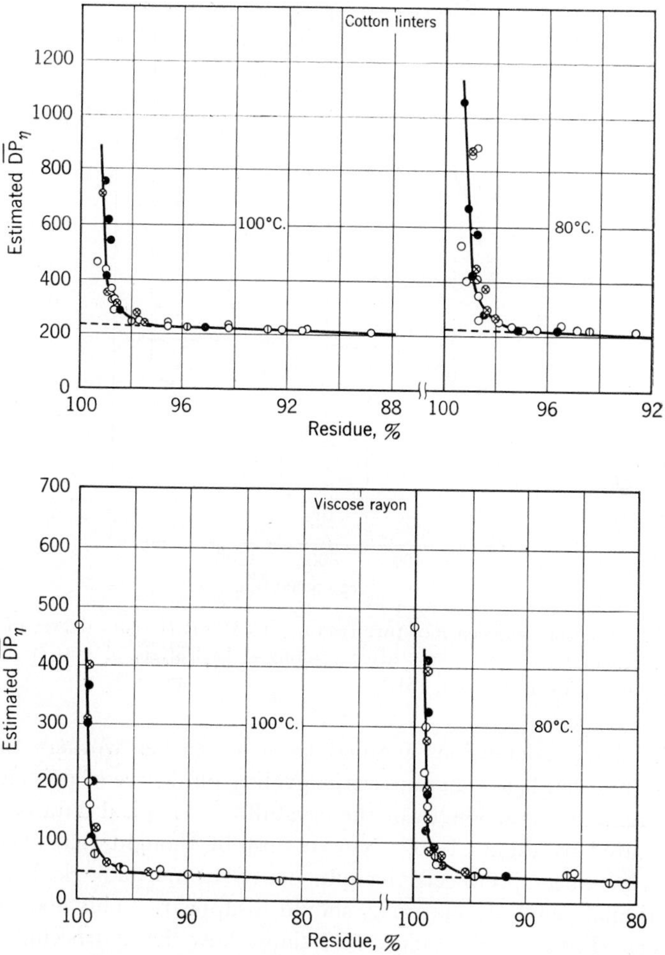

Fig. I-16. Relation between degree of polymerization and residual hydrocellulose after prolonged hydrolysis of cotton linters and viscose rayon. HCl values; ○ 2.5N, ⊖ 1.0N, ● 0.1N, ⊗ 0.01N. (Taken from ref. 151.)

to chemical attack. The chemically resistant hydrocellulose is only slowly attacked by continued prolonged exposure to strong acid. This is shown by the almost constant values of Roseveare's viscosity data in Figure I-14*B*. While Roseveare conducted hydrolysis for 24 hr., Nelson and Tripp (151) carried it up to 600 hr., using several acid concentrations and two temperatures to show how little the resistant hydrocellulose is

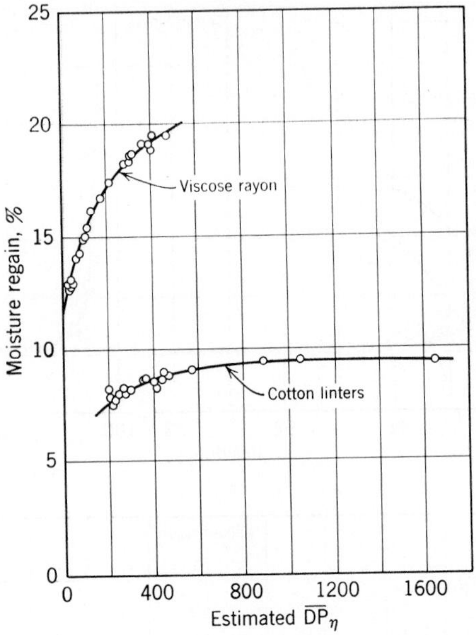

Fig. I-17. Relation between moisture regain (at 81% R.H.) and degree of polymerization of residual hydrocelluloses after prolonged hydrolysis of cotton linters and viscose rayon. (Taken from ref. 151.)

affected. Their conclusions verified those of earlier workers that each cellulosic material has a characteristic leveling-off degree of polymerization which is related to the length of the crystallite. Typical data of this sort are illustrated by Figure I-16. Now it may be thought that once hydrocelluloses have been produced, the influence of the morphological differences of the original cellulosic materials should disappear. This does not seem to happen. For example, Figure I-17 shows how the hydrocelluloses from cotton linters and viscose rayon retain the large difference in moisture sorption displayed by the initial materials. Millett and co-workers (146) also found that moisture sorption differences are retained by the hydrocelluloses (Fig. I-18). However, their experiments were carried to great length so that the fact could be seen that moisture sorption leveled off at limiting values for each cellulose used. Sharples (152) prepared hydrocelluloses from eight various cellulosic materials ranging from regenerated celluloses through ramie and cotton to bacterial and animal celluloses. Rate measurements made on the hydrocelluloses further exposed to hot hydrochloric acid showed that weight losses still followed the order expected

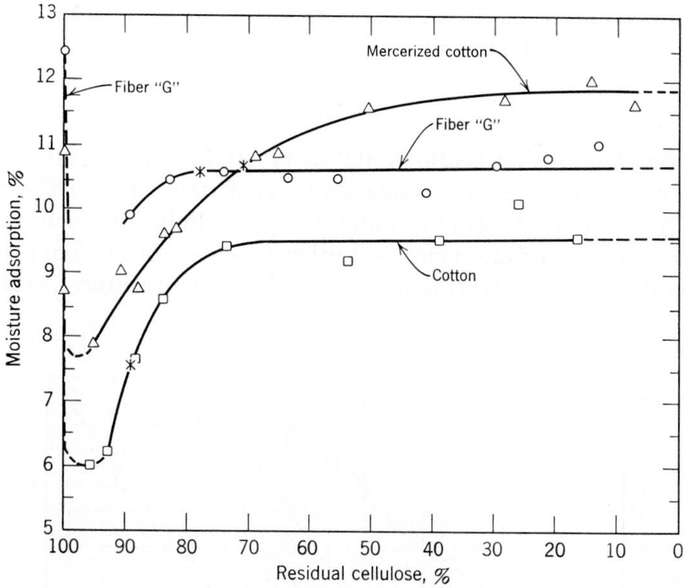

Fig. I-18. Moisture sorption (at 68.5% R.H.) of three cellulosic materials as a function of extent of hydrolysis. Asterisks indicate the point at which all easily hydrolyzable material has been removed. (Taken from ref. 146.)

on the basis of the crystallinity, crystallite size, and accessibility of the original unhydrolyzed material. One may conclude from Sharples' data that continued chemical attack on the hydrocelluloses occurs at the ends of the crystalline particles.

The attack of acid on crystalline cellulose is not without some anomalies. Segal, Loeb, and Creely (153) found that immersion of cotton cellulose III in boiling water for 2 hr. caused a reversion of its lattice to that of cellulose I. But, the same cellulose III exposed similarly to 6*N* hydrochloric acid was found by Segal and Nelson (154) to be still almost pure cellulose III. Somehow, the acid molecules present almost completely blocked the lattice conversion. Acid at somewhat lower concentrations was slightly less effective in preventing this reversion. Microscopic examination of the cellulose III hydrocelluloses after treatment with 2*N* acid showed fairly large, easily recognizable fiber fragments. Much smaller fragments, still identifiable as segments of fibers, remained after treatment with 6*N* acid. It is quite possible that these fiber sections, retaining morphological structure, are merely the framework of the original fiber, consisting of the more resistant portions of the structure, but to settle this is beyond the ability of present microscopic techniques.

(3) Heat

It is well known that heating cellulose in any form to elevated temperatures results in browning, charring, and loss of structure. This comes, of course, from the splitting out of water from the cellulose molecule as well as from oxidation, rearrangement, and other processes of organic chemistry, all beyond the scope of this discussion. At lower temperatures, below those

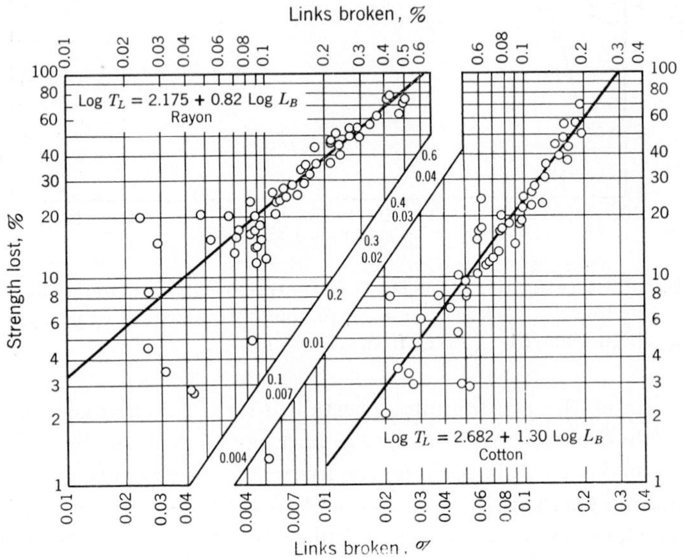

Fig. I–19. Relation between percentage of strength loss and percentage of cellulose chain links broken in thermally degraded cotton and rayon tire cords. (Taken from ref. 155.)

producing thermal decomposition, the effects of heat become manifest in more subtle ways, and there is some experimental evidence to show that the extent of such changes is influenced by morphology. These changes for the most part are hardly detected by the usual chemical means, but rather show up as changes in tensile strength and in the fluidity of cellulose solutions, or relatedly, in the degree of polymerization.

Conrad, Tripp, and Mares (155) made a very detailed study of the effect of heat alone on cotton and rayon tire cords at various stages of processing and in tire sections. Temperatures ranged as high as 150°C. for periods up to 1024 hr. with the oven atmosphere maintained at 40% R.H. Perhaps their most significant finding from the standpoint of the present discussion is given in Figure I-19. The difference in behavior of the cellulose molecules in the cotton and rayon tire cord used is clearly seen. Thus, for the cotton cord, 100% loss of strength would occur if 0.3% of the glucose links are broken, whereas the corresponding breakage for rayon would be 0.6%. Conrad concludes that the effect of heat on the degradation is shown more consistently and more sensitively by means of the computed percent of links broken and that on a percentage basis the rayon cords degraded generally much more than did the cotton cords. Exactly why there is a difference in behavior toward heat alone is not clear unless crystallite size, degree of crystallinity, accessibility, or lateral order distribution are the factors contributing to this effect. Similar evidence on cotton and rayon tire cords heated in a moist atmosphere was obtained by Waller, Bass, and Roseveare (156). This can be seen in the data of the last two columns in Table I-5.

The indicated trend found on heating in a moist atmosphere, however, was reversed when heating was carried out in the absence of moisture or oxygen; then the cotton cord degraded more than the rayon. Regardless of the heating conditions, these experimenters also consistently found a difference in behavior between cotton and rayon. Thermal degradation is principally attributed to oxidation, and it seems that the degree of accessibility conferred by morphology is the decisive factor contributing to the difference in behavior.

TABLE I-5

Loss in Oven-Dry Strength of Cotton and Rayon Tire Cords on Heat Aging[a]

Aging time, hr.	Strength loss, %					
	Continuous vacuum, 170°C.		Sealed, evacuated tubes, 170°C.		In air and moisture, 150°C.	
	Cotton	Rayon	Cotton	Rayon	Cotton	Rayon
4	—	—	—	—	4	9
8	—	—	—	—	11	39
16	—	—	—	—	23	46
24	14	4	21	10	41	100
46	21	7	43	20	—	—
72	29	6	67	30	—	—
96	31	9	—	—	—	—

[a] Taken from ref. 156.

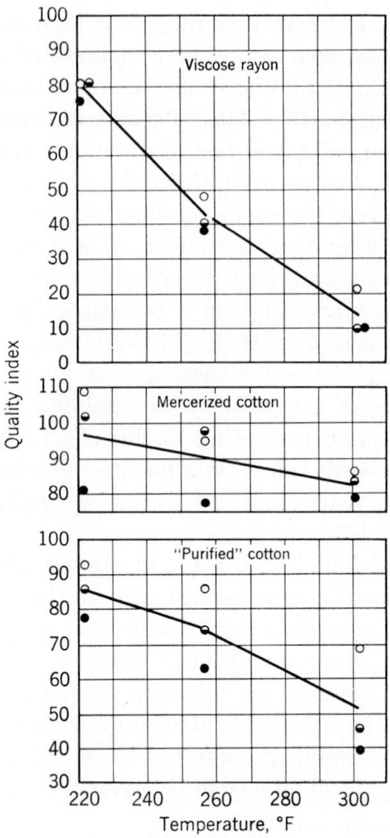

Fig. I-20. Effect on various cellulosic yarns of heat at (O) low, (◐) medium, and (●) high humidities. (Taken from ref. 157.)

Several different cellulosic yarns were investigated by Wiegerink (157) for their behavior toward drying. Wiegerink's interest was in establishing that temperature and humidity played a significant role in the deterioration of textile materials. In his data, however, one can see where significant differences exist among the celluloses of several different morphologies (Fig. I-20). The quality index, defined by Wiegerink as the product of the percentages of original breaking strength and original elongation retained after drying, seems to be more sensitive to differences arising from morphology than any of the other parameters reported. It is highly significant that mercerized cotton shows the lowest rate of change in index with temperature, for this is again illustrative of the previously mentioned hornification of mercerized cotton which reduces its chemical reactivity. This behavior of mercerized cotton is verified by the work of Lewis (158) who subjected rayon, cotton, and mercerized cotton tire cords to alternate heating (130°C. for 16 hr.) and cooling for a total of 48 cycles. Regardless of the test conditions, standard or oven-dry, the mercerized cotton cord showed the least loss in specific strength (tenacity). No significant conclusion can be drawn from the data obtained on the other cords because of variations in the test conditions.

Sharkov, Dmitrieva, and Potapova (135) found that inclusion cellulose as well as swollen celluloses are affected by heat. In their work, heat was applied by placing the material in kerosene heated to 200°C. for 3 hr., after which the sample was hydrolyzed. Hydrolysis of wood cellulose before heating gave a glucose yield of 7% which liquid ammonia treatment of the cellulose raised to 18% and sodium hydroxide treatment raised to 12%. After heating, the glucose yield of the original wood cellulose was 12%, 31% for the ammonia-treated, and 28% for the sample treated with sodium hydroxide. Inclusion cellulose prepared directly from the liquid ammonia-wet cellulose gave glucose yields of 16–22% before heating and 30–36% after heating, except for three samples which ran to 39, 49, and 57%. These three results were obtained with carbon tetrachloride, chloroform, and dichloroethane, respectively, and are attributed to an ability of these solvents to penetrate the ammonia-wet structure more deeply than the other solvents to retard subsequent close packing of the cellulose when it was dried. Inclusion cellulose prepared from samples treated with sodium hydroxide solutions gave glucose yields of 11% before heating, 24–39% after heating. All of this indicates that the stability of cellulose to heating has been lowered, which comes from loosening of the macromolecular packing of the chain molecules.

3. Polymers Other than Cellulose

a. General Considerations

The chemical reactivity of cellulose in its various morphological forms has become familiar because of long use, ease of conversion from one form to another, and much study. A search of the literature, however, reveals a dearth of similar studies on other polymers. Only recently have polymers such as poly(ethylene terephthalate) and polyethylene been subjected to such considerations, and in these studies many of the concepts and techniques of cellulose chemistry have been employed.

b. Poly(ethylene Terephthalate)

This polymer, being an ester, should be susceptible to hydrolysis and other familiar reactions. Those reactions which do occur are indeed affected by differences in morphology. Ravens (159) studied the way the physical structure of the polymer influenced the rate of acid hydrolysis. The polymer was prepared in three forms: (a) unoriented, amorphous; (b) oriented, partially crystalline (30%); and (c) unoriented, partially crystalline (48%). Ravens found that form a is attacked faster than form c, while form c is attacked faster than form b. He attributed this to a higher solubility of hydrochloric acid in the amorphous regions of the structure and the smaller degree of ionization of the acid in oriented fibers. According to Ravens, hydrolysis occurs principally in the amorphous region. Orientation apparently had some effect on the reaction, as Ravens reported activation energies of 22 kcal./mole for forms a and c, 18 kcal./mole for form b.

Farrow, Ravens, and Ward (160) extended this study by degrading poly(ethylene terephthalate) with aqueous methylamine. The polymer was prepared in five forms: (a) amorphous, spun fiber; (b) crystalline, unoriented fiber (from sample a by heating at 200°C. for 30 min.); (c) drawn fiber of high orientation; (d) drawn fiber of high orientation and heat-crystallized; and (e) a sample of commercial poly(ethylene terephthalate) (Terylene) containing delustrant. Data on the residues after washing and drying are presented in Table I-6. There can be no question from these data that the morphology of the polymer has affected the rate of attack. The most striking illustration is given by sample d (the drawn fiber of high orientation and heat-crystallized), where no effects were observed after 16 hr. of reaction, a period of time which already afforded considerable degradation in the other samples of different morphologies. Their data show further that the rate of attack by methylamine occurs in three stages. The initial attack is in the amorphous regions, but little low molecular weight material is formed. In the second stage scission produces more low molecular weight material and gives rise to an increase in the degree of crystallinity of the polymer. A gradual decrease in the rate of reaction forms the third stage, where this effect is attributed to slower attack on both the amorphous and the crystalline regions. Note also from sample a that there is much induced crystallization which further complicates relating reactivity and structure. Although the results show that it is not possible in this polymer to separate crystalline and amorphous phases as is done with cellulose, the present data on degradation by amines confirm Ravens' data on acid hydrolysis (159). Thus, the order of reactivity of

TABLE I-6
Weight Loss and Crystallinity of Poly(ethylene Terephthalate) Degraded with Aqueous Methylamine[a]

Time, hr.	Weight loss, %					X-ray crystallinity, %				
	a	b	c	d	e	a	b	c	d	e
0	0	0	0	0	0	0	47	18	48	20
3	27.5	0.2	—	—	—	—	48	—	—	—
5	58	0.4	0	—	—	20	51	20	—	—
6	63	—	—	—	0.3	—	—	—	—	31
16	—	32.5	44	0	44	—	59	56	50	65
24	—	—	93	33	89	—	—	60	60	61
40	—	89.6	—	—	—	—	65	—	—	—
48	—	—	—	74	—	—	—	—	66	—

[a] Taken from ref. 160.

poly(ethylene terephthalate) is again shown to be: unoriented amorphous, unoriented crystalline, oriented crystalline.

Among the data reported by Ravens and Ward (161) on the hydrolysis and esterification reactions of poly(ethylene terephthalate) in the solid phase there is also an indication that crystallinity of the polymer affects its chemical reactivity. Thus, moisture content (over the range of relative humidities 0–10%) for the unoriented film or chip, amorphous, was given by (0.0125 ± 0.003) × relative humidity; for unoriented film or chip, heat-crystallized, by (0.0075 ± 0.003) × relative humidity.

c. Polyethylene

Polyethylene is usually considered to be highly inert, yet work at Bell Telephone Laboratories has indicated that under certain circumstances

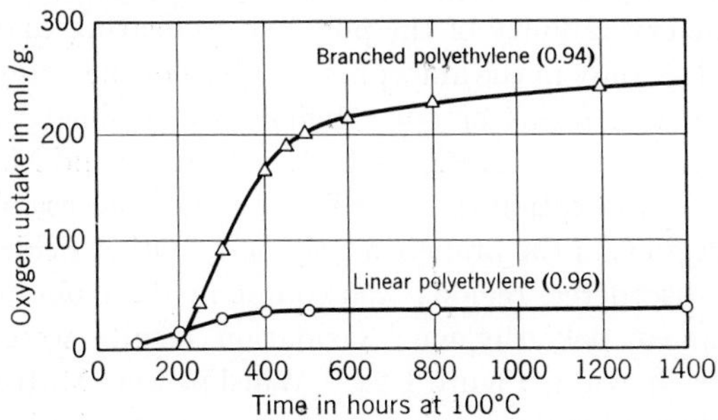

Fig. I-21. Effect of morphology on the oxidation patterns of a linear and a branched polyethylene. (Taken from ref. 164.)

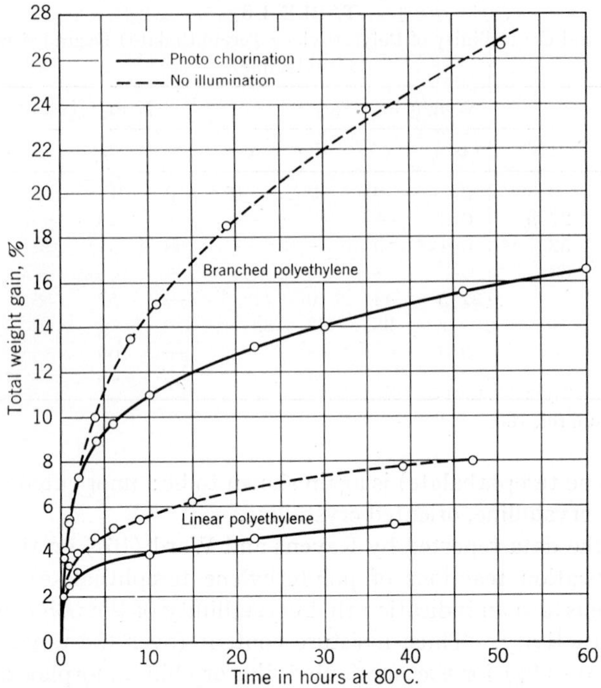

Fig. I-22. Chlorination of compression-molded polyethylene at 80°C. (Taken from ref. 164.)

this is not quite true (162). Branched polyethylene is more susceptible to oxidation than is the linear type (163), the former having an activation energy of 21.6 kcal./mole and the latter 26.0. These workers showed that the amount of oxygen reacting with solid polyethylene is inversely proportional to the crystallinity of the polymer, indicating that reaction with oxygen takes place only in the amorphous regions of the polymers. Oxygen uptake of these two forms of polyethylene, determined by Winslow and Matreyek (164), are shown in Figure I-21. Winslow and Matreyek further reported infrared absorption data confirming the inaccessibility of oxygen to crystalline regions in the branched polymer. Other evidence for oxygen attack in the disordered regions was found in data obtained after heat treatment of linear polyethylene. Oxidation results were confirmed by chlorination, as shown in Figure I-22. Winslow and Matreyek state that there is a marked advantage to using chlorine instead of oxygen as a reactant in studies with polyolefins. Oxidation alters the skeletal structure

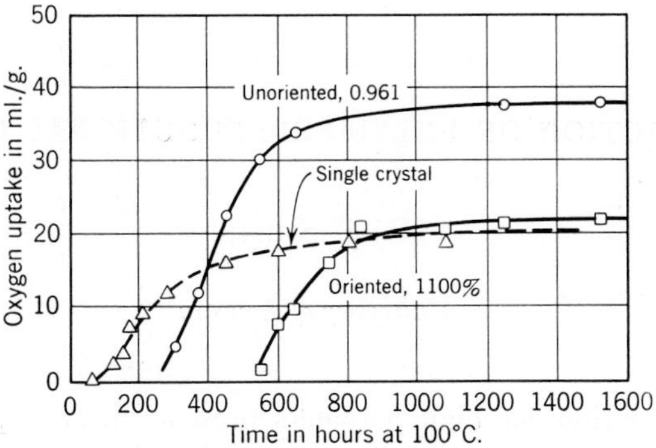

Fig. I-23. Effect of morphology on the thermal oxidation pattern of a linear polyethylene. (Taken from ref. 165.)

by removing carbon as an oxide, but chlorination involves only substitution of nonskeletal hydrogens by chlorine atoms.

It is conceded that comparison between branched and linear polyethylenes is not quite the same morphologically as comparison of various forms of either branched or linear polymer. However, Winslow, Hawkins, and Matreyek (165) have observed the effect of several forms of linear polyethylene on oxygen uptake. The linear polymer was (*a*) solution-crystallized to give single crystals, (*b*) compression-molded to give an unoriented sample, and (*c*) compression-molded and drawn to 1100% elongation to give an oriented sample. The oriented sample was reported also to be nearly completely crystalline, since its NMR spectrum and that of the solution-crystallized material showed no narrow line component. The effect on the reaction with oxygen of these changes in structure is shown in Figure I-23. Winslow et al. attribute the differences in the induction periods for the three modifications to the presence of a small amount of inhibiting impurity and the preparative techniques. Thus, crystallization removed the impurity, while cold-drawing concentrated it in regions accessible to oxygen. The curves in this figure, however, leave no question as to the effect of morphology on the reactivity of polyethylene towards oxygen.

D. REACTION OF POLYMERIC FUNCTIONAL GROUPS

G. J. SMETS

University of Louvain

Chemical reactions of high polymers present many important aspects which make their study especially attractive. From a practical point of view it is evident that transformation reactions make it possible to modify the properties of the polymers and adapt them to new technical uses. Sometimes transformations occur when the substances are exposed to air, light, or elevated temperature; they are then directly related with the phenomena of degradation, aging, or discoloration. The knowledge of the chemical nature of these modifications will permit us to prevent them and consequently to stabilize the material.

From the scientific point of view, these reactions occur in systems where the steric hindrance is strongly pronounced, where interaction between functional groups is favored, and where structural features may be dependent on the degree of conversion. Therefore the comparison of these reactions of high polymers with similar ones carried out on compounds of low molecular weight should take into account those effects which are eventually related to the macromolecular nature of the substances.

In the present section the fundamental aspects of the chemical transformations of high polymers are considered and illustrated with some typical examples. Its aim is not to present a general review of chemical reactions of high polymers, but to determine, in relation to the general principles of organic chemistry, the different fundamental principles on which these reactions are based.

Before discussion it must, however, be pointed out that chemical transformation reactions seldom proceed with a quantitative yield on account of changes of solubility and consequently changes in the accessibility of the functional groups when the degree of conversion increases. Consequently, a reaction product usually contains unchanged and transformed groups, as well as structural units resulting from interactions of neighboring groups, all together in one macromolecule. This fact is even more important for reactions carried out in heterogeneous systems, in which the reaction usually proceeds irregularly and depends on the degree of swelling of the polymer. In this case, the groups may be irregularly distributed along the macromolecule, and this distribution may vary with increasing degree of conversion.

A second preliminary remark concerns our lack of knowledge of the detailed chain structure of vinyl polymers as well as copolymers. Indeed it can be said that the problems of chain isomerism and stereoisomerism are for most polymers at least partly unsolved.

As a result of these considerations one must be extremely careful before drawing conclusions when attributing organic or kinetic effects to the polymeric nature of the substances, and especially to internal structural elements of the polymeric chain. With these restrictions in mind, the organic reactions of high polymers must be considered from the point of view of the reaction itself, i.e., its functionality, and from the point of view of the polymer, its internal structure (isomerism and stereoisomerism), and the location of the reactive sites.

1. Monofunctional Chemical Reactions

Generally a sharp distinction is made between monofunctional and di- or polyfunctional reactions, depending on the number, i.e., only one, two, or more, of functional groups directly involved in the modification.

Monofunctional polymeric reactions usually proceed through the same mechanism as reactions on similar low molecular weight compounds. Several examples are found in the literature, the methylation of poly(acrylic acid) with diazomethane to poly(methyl acrylate), the acetylation of poly(vinyl alcohol) with acetic anhydride to poly(vinyl acetate), the reduction of poly(methyl acrylate) with lithium aluminum hydride (166, 167) to poly(allyl alcohol), the acidolysis of poly-*N*-vinyl-*tert*-butylurethane with hydrobromic acid to poly(vinyl amine) (168a). Most of the "polymeranalog Umsetzungen" of Staudinger (168b) were monofunctional and reversible reactions of high yield; the transformation of a polymeric substance into its derivatives having completely different solubilities but with unchanged degree of polymerization has been considered as the final proof of the macromolecular structure of these substances.

The autoxidation of polypropylene (169) and of poly-*p*-isopropylstyrene (170) affords tertiary hydroperoxides; their reactivities and rates of decomposition are similar to those of *tert*-butyl and cumene hydroperoxide, respectively. The chlorination of atactic polypropylene attacks mainly tertiary hydrogen atoms, while that of poly(vinyl chloride) orients the halogen mainly on the methylenic CH_2-groups, and not on the carbon carrying the chlorine atom. These results are completely in agreement with those of the chlorination of aliphatic hydrocarbons. Usually the activation energies of these monofunctional reactions are equivalent to those for their homologues of low molecular weight, slight differences being generally compensated by steric effects. For example, Hiller (171) has shown by measuring the enthalpy and activation energy of the acetylation of cellulose, that this reaction as well as the reverse one of hydrolysis are similar to those carried out on ordinary alcohols and are both examples of general acid-catalyzed reactions.

In Table I-7 some data are given for the alkaline hydrolysis of polyvinylpyrrolidone derivatives and homologous substances.

In the case of polyvinylpyrrolidone, the increasing number of electric charges formed on the polymeric chain when the hydrolysis proceeds is without effect on the further hydrolysis, on account of the considerable distance between the carboxylate groups and the neighboring lactam unit (eight atoms). Moreover, the ionized carboxylate side groups are too far from each other to affect the overall shape of the molecule by reciprocal repulsion effect. As a result, the apparent first-order rate constants remain constant even up to 50% yield and more. In the case of the third and fourth substances in Table I-7, the presence of negatively charged maleic units in the neighborhood of a lactam unit causes a strong decrease of the effective collision frequency (log PZ) on account of the electrostatic repulsion between these negative charges and the hydroxyl ion; nevertheless the activation energy decreases appreciably on account of the strong negative inductive effect of the neighboring carboxylic groups.

The similarity between the reaction kinetics of a polymeric molecule and its corresponding low molecular homologous substance becomes disturbed if the electrical potential of the polymer molecules increases in the course of

TABLE I-7
Hydrolysis of Lactams[a]

Polymer	E_a, kcal./mole	log PZ
Poly-*N*-vinylpyrrolidone	25 ± 1	11.7
N-Isopropyl-2-methylpyrrolidone	27 ± 0.5	12.3
Poly(vinylpyrrolidone-*co*-maleic acid) (68/32)	16 ± 1	6.3
Pyrrolidone *N*-acetic acid	17 ± 0.5	7.3

[a] Taken from refs. 172,173.

the reaction, and if simultaneously the charged groups are carried by the main chain in the direct neighborhood of the reacting groups. Katchalsky and co-workers (174,175) have calculated the electrostatic potential of a macromolecule carrying a given number of charges distributed statistically along the chain as a function of the degree of ionization and the ionic strength of the solution, taking into account the end-to-end distances of the uncharged molecule and of the stretched ionized molecule. Katchalsky tested the validity of these predictions in the case of the alkaline hydrolysis of pectinic acids (176); this reaction is characterized by a strong decrease of the experimental rate "constant" as the reaction proceeds, and by an increase of it when the ionic strength of the solution is increased. Taking into account the variation of the electrical potential, he was able to assign an "intrinsic" rate constant for the hydrolysis, which remains valid even at very high degree of conversion (90%). This example is in fact a relatively simple case because the shape of the macromolecule remains unchanged during the reaction, being already stretched at very low degree of ionization on account of its polyhexuronic structure.

A similar case is the alkaline hydrolysis of polymethacrylamide (177–179) in which the accumulation of methyl side groups assures a stretched form of the macromolecule; the "intrinsic" velocity constant can be evaluated only at low degree of conversion and is similar to that of trimethylacetamide, its low molecular weight homologue (E_a = 16 and 15.7 kcal./mole and log PZ = 7.6 and 6.0, respectively). Again the reaction slows down progressively, and is practically limited to 72% of the hydrolysis on account of the electrostatic repulsions toward the hydroxyl ions. It was postulated that the methacrylamide units become resistant to hydrolysis when bordered by two methacrylate ions, and this interpretation was confirmed by hydrolyses carried out on methacrylic acid–methacrylamide copolymers.

The hydrolysis of polyacrylamide differs from the preceding one by the occurrence of two distinct steps, of which the second is about ten times slower than the first. By comparison with related copolymers (Table I-8) it is easy to demonstrate that the decrease of the reaction velocity at about 40–50% conversion results from the accumulation of electrostatic charges on the main chain; this provokes a change in the molecular shape from a statistical coiled system to a stretched molecule as soon as the density of charges becomes sufficiently high. It is also noteworthy that polyacrylamide unlike polymethacrylamide, can be hydrolyzed completely. In all the preceding examples the differences which may occur between polymer and their homologues result from a variation, during the course of the reaction, of the electrostatic potential of the chain; obviously such an effect is excluded for low molecular weight monofunctional compounds.

It must, however, be pointed out that if these phenomena modify strongly the course of the reactions, nevertheless these reactions remain strictly monofunctional; their rates decrease on account of increasing steric effects and may even become negligible at a given degree of conversion. However they do not call for a new reaction mechanism.

Very recently this comparison between polymers and low molecular weight homologues has been extended to the study of the formation and properties of electron-donor and acceptor complexes (EDA) (180). On the basis of spectrometric measurements poly-*p*-dimethylaminostyrene has

TABLE I-8

Alkaline Hydrolysis of Polyacrylamide and Acrylamide Copolymers[a]

Polymer	Rate constant k_1				E_a, kcal./mole	log PZ
	35°C.	50°C.	65°C.	80°C.		
Polyacrylamide, first step	0.44	1.2	2.5		14.16	5.63
Poly(vinylpyrrolidone-*co*-acrylamide) (58/42)	0.61	2.02	4.94		14.5	5.55
Isobutyramide					14.2	5.56
Polyacrylamide, second step		0.13	0.32	0.77	13.71	4.4
Poly(acrylic acid-*co*-acrylamide, (36/64)		0.14	0.27	0.89	13.75	4.1

[a] Taken from ref. 177.

been compared to *N,N'*-dimethylcumidine in relation to its ability for complex formation with electron acceptor molecules (trinitrobenzene, chloranil, tetracyanoethylene). Similar stoichiometric donor/acceptor compositions (1/1) of the complexes were found, i.e., the reaction is monofunctional, and the equilibrium constant of complex formation determined. Conversely, polydinitrostyrene was compared to dinitrocumene in its complexes with electron donor molecules, such as β-naphthylamine. Some data are summarized in Table I-9.

From Table I-9 it can be seen that only slight differences in behavior can be observed between the polymers and its homologues; consequently electronic effects between neighboring EDA-complex side groups must be very small.

The difference in behavior between polymers and simple substances becomes very important however, as soon as the reaction itself becomes multi-

TABLE I-9
EDA Complexes of Poly-*p*-dimethylaminostyrene and Its Homologues (λ_{max})[a]

Electron acceptor	Poly-*p*-dimethyl-aminostyrene	Dimethyl-aniline	*N,N'*-Dimethyl-cumidine
Chloranil	675 blue	650 660 ($CHCl_3$)	665
Dinitrobenzene	440 brown-red	—	—
Nitrobenzene	425	—	—
Trinitrobenzene[b]	515 violet	475	505 510 ($CHCl_3$)
ϵ_{max}	2350	1800	1510
c_K	0.39	0.62	0.36

[a] Taken from ref. 180.
[b] With trinitrobenzene (TNB). ϵ_{max} = molar extinction coefficient at λ_{max} absorption wavelength. c_K = concentration equilibrium constant of complex formation.

functional, for in this case it depends directly on the relative position and on the nature of the neighboring groups.

2. Polyfunctional Chemical Reactions

When two or more functions are affected by a chemical reaction, the relative positions of the reactive groups play an important role in the final degree of conversion which can be obtained. Indeed, assuming that the accessibility of all the functional groups is equivalent and remains constant in the course of the reaction, Flory (181) has shown on the basis of statistical calculations that the degree of conversion of a bifunctional polymeric reaction is limited to 86.5 and 81.6, respectively, depending on the alternating (—CH_2—CHX—CH_2—CHX—) or statistical internal structure of the polymer (—CH_2—CHX—CH_2—CHX—CHX—CH_2—CH_2—CHX—CH_2—CHX—), even if the reaction proceeds quantitatively for low molecular weight derivatives; only a regular vicinal structure (—CH_2—CHX—CHX—CH_2—) permits a theoretical 100% yield. Therefore, before discussing chemical transformations of polymers, the question arises whether monomer units are arranged in a head-to-tail fashion, or head-to-head, tail-to-tail. Generally it can be said that the main structure is predominantly head-to-tail for most vinyl polymers, such as poly(vinyl chloride), poly(vinyl acetate), polymethacrylates, and polystyrene; this structure results from the addition of the growing polymer to the methylene group of the monomer, giving a resonance-stabilized adduct radical. For monomers with low reactivities some head-to-head, tail-to-tail arrangements may be expected.

The influence of this chain isomerism can best be illustrated by the dechlorination reaction of poly(vinyl chloride) with zinc dust. If we consider, for instance, the reaction of zinc with poly(vinyl chloride), cyclopropane rings are formed at relatively high rate from 1,3 dichloride units, as in eq (45):

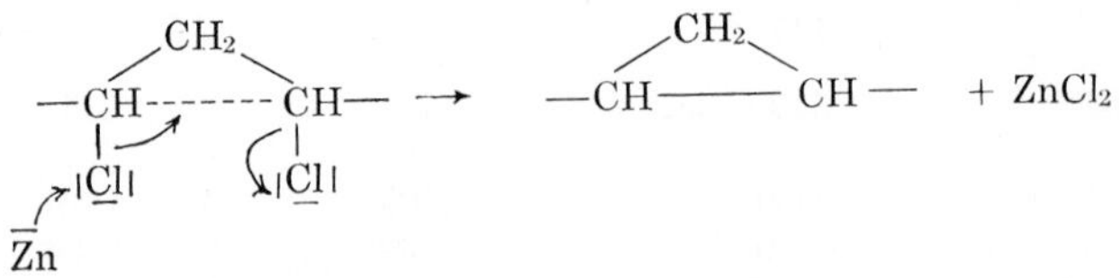

(45)

Evidently, cyclopentane and cycloheptane rings could also be formed (eq. 46), although at a slower rate, but when chlorine atoms are isolated between two cyclopropane rings steric effects prevent them from reacting to form larger rings, and the reaction levels off at 86% in agreement with theoretical predictions (182).

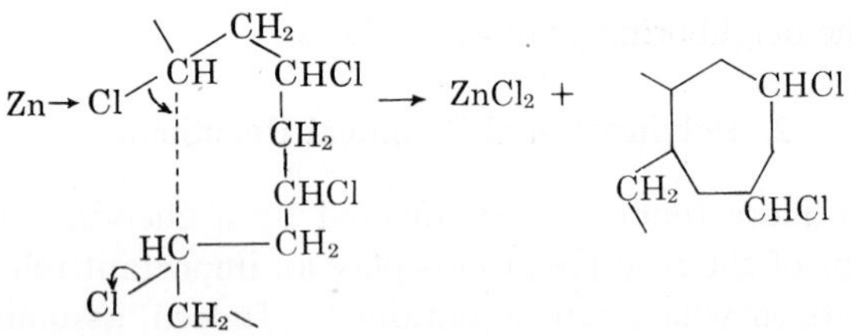

(46)

The time of reaction, however, plays a very important role in the final degree of conversion, and may attain 150–200 hr. Sometimes even 400 hr. is required for some vinyl chloride–vinyl acetate copolymers before the reaction levels off (183).

Zinc dechlorination of 1,2 vicinal units, if present, produces mainly double bonds instead of rings (eq. 47), and the presence of these double bonds enhances considerably further dehydrochlorination.

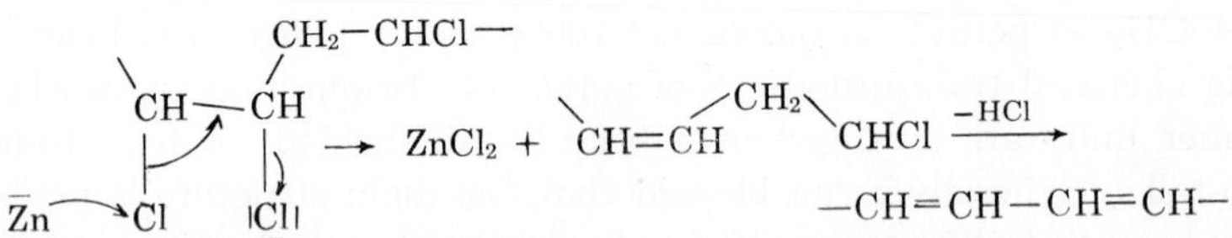

(47)

This reaction would be responsible for the shape of the curves of extent of reaction versus time, which suggests an autocatalytic reaction. It could, however, also be attributed to the zinc chloride formed during the dechlorination. If a polymer contains both structural units, both reactions will occur simultaneously, and the final degree of conversion will have no significance with respect to chemical structure; any kinetic interpretation will then be excluded.

Conversely, the dehydrochlorination of poly(vinyl chloride) (184,185) with aluminum chloride (eq. 48) is strongly enhanced by the presence of vicinal units, and produces polyvinylene much more easily than 1,3-poly-(vinyl chloride) does.

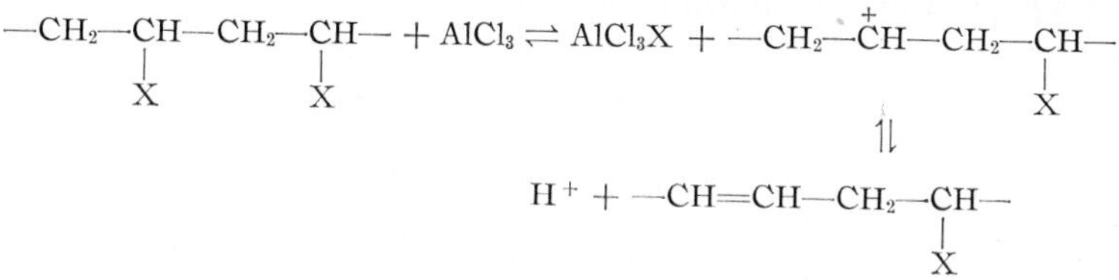

(48)

Similar polyvinylene compounds can be obtained by pyrolysis at 600–700°C. of poly(vinyl acetate), poly(vinyl alcohol), or poly(vinyl bromide) by splitting off acetic acid, water, or hydrobromic acid. In this first example, chain isomerism influences directly the nature of the reaction product as well as the final degree of conversion.

Very often, however, bifunctional reactions are accompanied by intramolecular cyclization, which results from interaction between neighboring reactive groups. These interactions may be concomitant with the polymerization itself; for example, the imidization of polymethacrylamide (186) during synthesis (eq. 49) when the temperature exceeds 65°C. In the presence of acids the splitting off of ammonia is increased, and the extent of imidization may attain 70%.

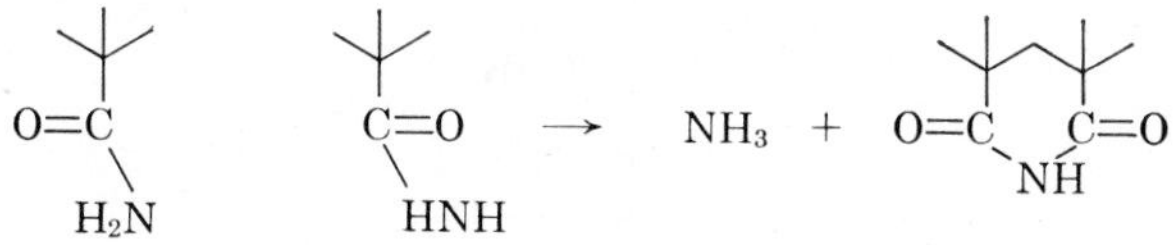

(49)

Similarly α-chloroacrylic acid (187,188) shows during its polymerization, partial lactonization and hydrolysis (eq. 50).

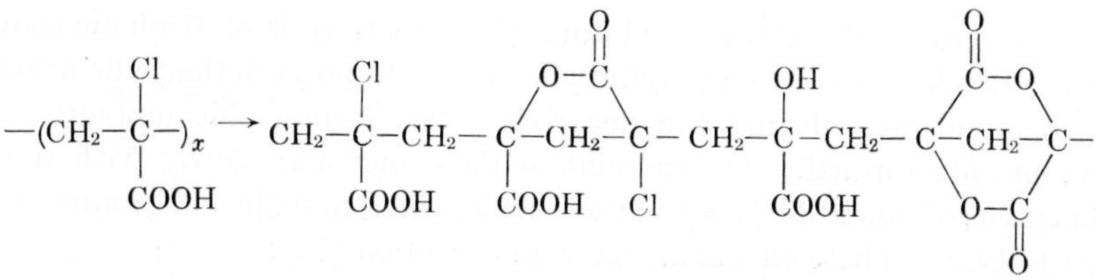

(50)

The abnormal viscometric behavior of poly(α-chlorovinylacetic acid) (189) is likely related to an analogous intramolecular condensation. These interactions are very often enhanced by the cyclization tendency, as the stability of the rings is a function of the nature and relative positions of the substituents. For instance, the copolymers of maleic anhydride and vinyl acetate (190) give on alkaline hydrolysis a polymeric hydroxydiacid; on acidification of the solution or acidic hydrolysis in alcoholic medium, internal lactonization occurs with the formation of five- and six-membered rings (about 42% lactone) as shown in eq. (51).

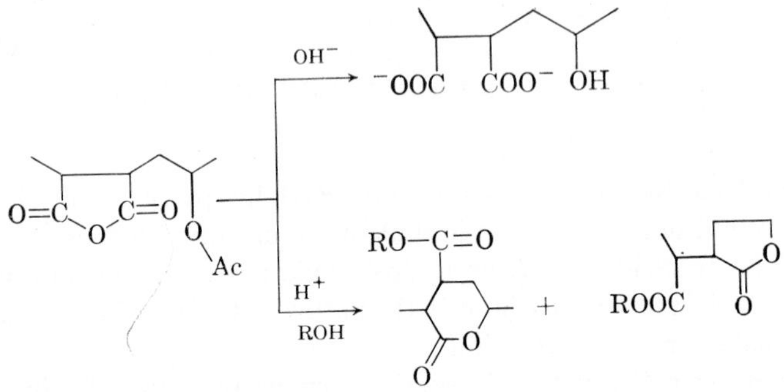

(51)

Similarly, when poly(α-chloroacrylic acid) is heated in alcohol, it undergoes esterification and lactonization, and the predominating groups are the lactone (42%) and ester groups (36.7%) (188). Similarly, copolymers of maleic anhydride and allylacetamide (191) yield on acid hydrolysis polymers containing the lactam unit of structure I.

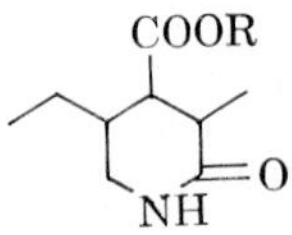

(I)

Lactone groups are also formed during the electrolysis of alcoholic solution of partially neutralized poly(acrylic acid) and poly(methacrylic acid). It was found that during the decarboxylation appreciable amounts of γ-lactones are formed. The amount of these increases slowly with time to an extent of about 35%, with ether, olefin, ester, and alcohol groups also present (192). These effects are shown in reaction (52):

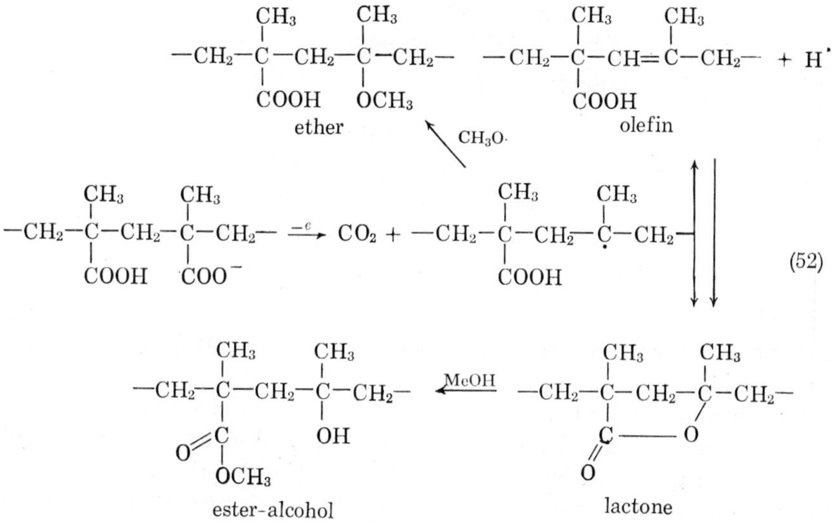

(52)

The opening of these intramolecular rings can usually be carried out in alkaline medium; sometimes it remains very limited on account of the accumulation of rings and consequently the important steric hindrance. Thus Van Dessel obtained by acid hydrolysis of poly(α-acetaminoacrylic acid) a polymer with a high content of single and double lactam rings (193) shown in eq. (53).

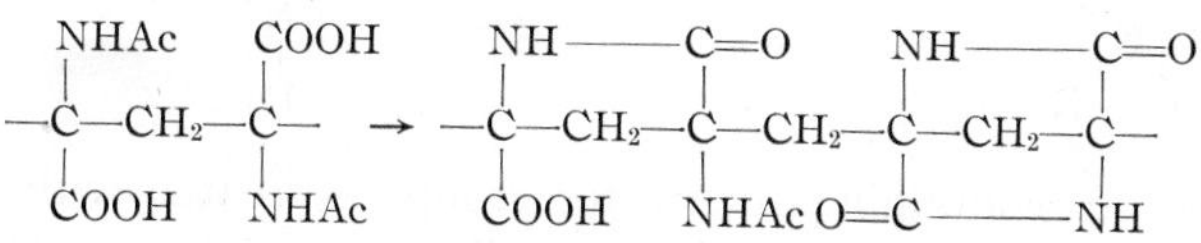

(53)

The ring opening, especially of the double lactams, is very difficult so that the amounts of free acid and amine groups remain still very low (10–20%).

Sometimes these interactions are responsible for an apparently unexpected course of the reaction: a typical example of it is given by the hydrolysis of poly(vinyl tosylate). It is well known that the hydrolysis of organic sulfonic esters proceeds through an alkyl-oxygen scission; consequently poly(vinyl sulfonate) would yield polyvinylamine when treated by primary or secondary amines. In fact, a polymer is obtained containing cyclic ether, alcohol, and substituted amino groups (194) as in eq. (54).

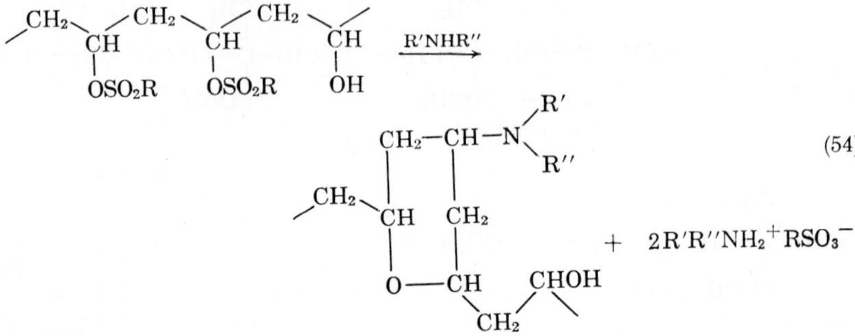

(54)

After reaction with piperidine, the polymer contains 50% vinylpiperidine units besides 38% ethers.

The intramolecular reaction between the alcohol and sulfonate groups is enhanced considerably by the presence of the amine, which binds the sulfonic acid formed during the condensation. With primary amines, an interaction between the sulfonate and the disubstituted amine group occurs also whereby cyclic tertiary amine units are formed (eq. 55).

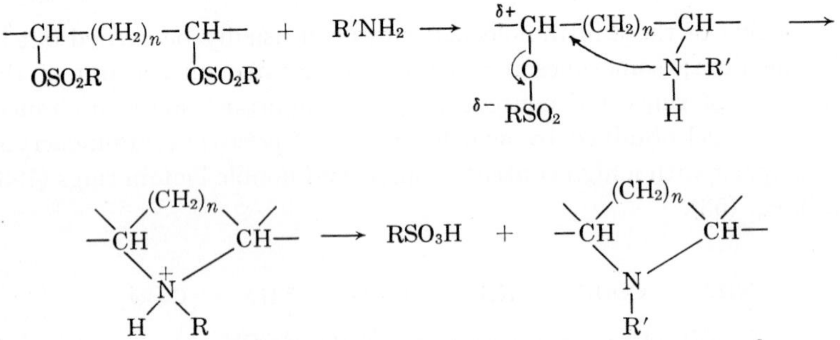

(55)

When a polymer containing such ester groups is treated with a tertiary amine, quaternization and formation of cyclic ethers of the tetrahydropyran occur together as shown in eqs. (56) and (57).

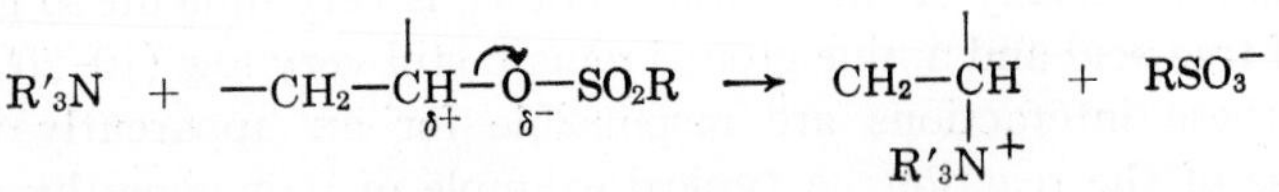

(56)

Such undesirable group interactions can be avoided if the alcohol and sulfonate groups are separated from each other by inert units; in this case the reaction again becomes monofunctional. This has been done by using styrene–allyl alcohol (72/28) copolymers obtained by reduction with lithium aluminum hydride of the corresponding styrene–ethyl acrylate co

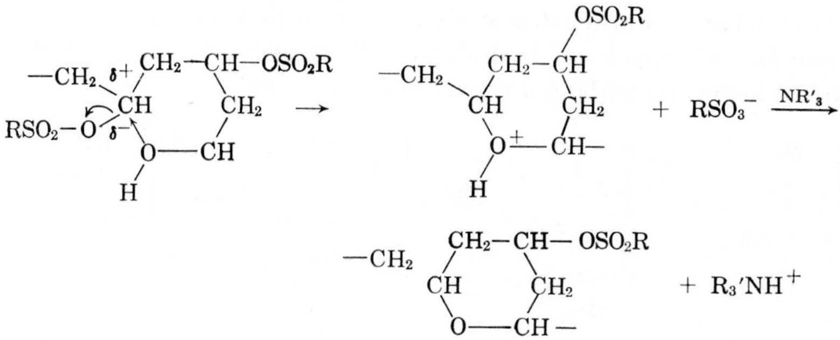
(57)

polymers; after tosylation they underwent aminolysis with diethylamine. Indeed, in this case 75% of the sulfonate groups can be replaced by diethylamino groups, and no cyclization occurs. However, small amounts of olefin are formed simultaneously by an elimination reaction (195) shown by eq. (58).

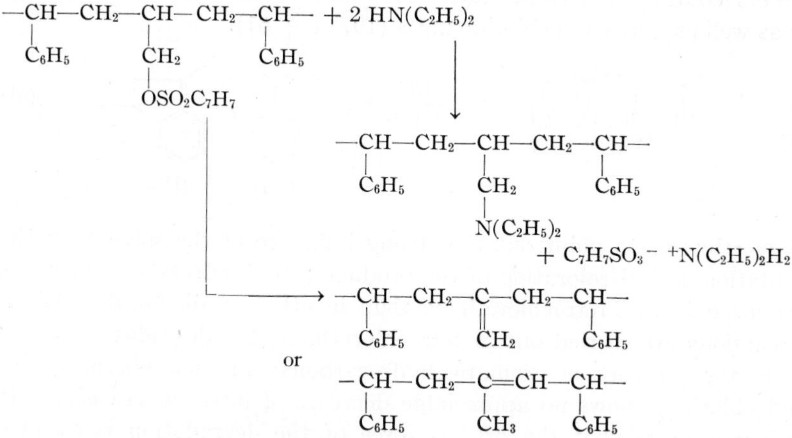
(58)

An unexpected course of the reaction has also been observed by carrying out the Arndt-Eistert diazomethane reaction on poly(methacrylyl chloride). Normally, a chain-lengthening reaction would occur with formation of poly(isopropenylacetic acid) on account of the rearrangement of the intermediate diazoketone:

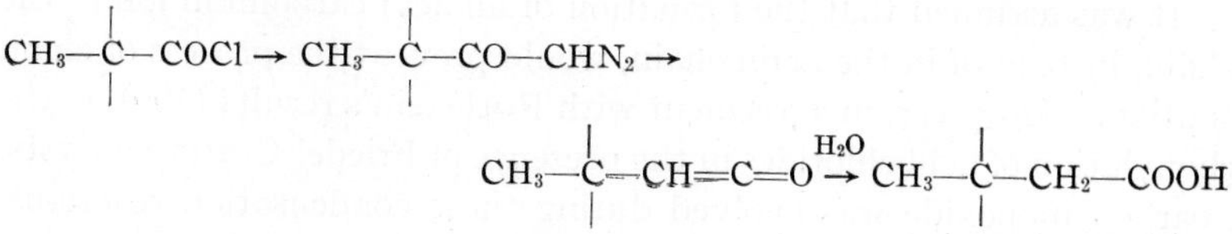
(59)

An analytical and spectrometric study has shown that β-keto-ketene rings (II) are formed, which on hydrolysis and decarboxylation yield five-membered keto rings without any acid properties (196).

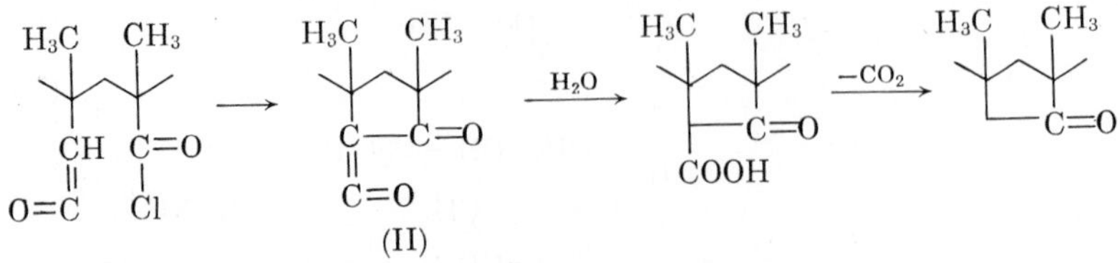
(60)

Functional interactions have been also used for the syntheses of new types of polymers generally not obtainable by direct synthesis. For instance, the Friedel-Crafts reaction makes it possible to build up into the main chain condensed aromatic rings; the condensation of poly(vinyl chloride) with aromatic hydrocarbons, e.g., benzene, toluene, *m*-xylene, mesitylene, gives polymers containing styrene units (III) and 1,3-methyleneindane rings (IV) as well as unreacted chloride units (197) (eq. 61).

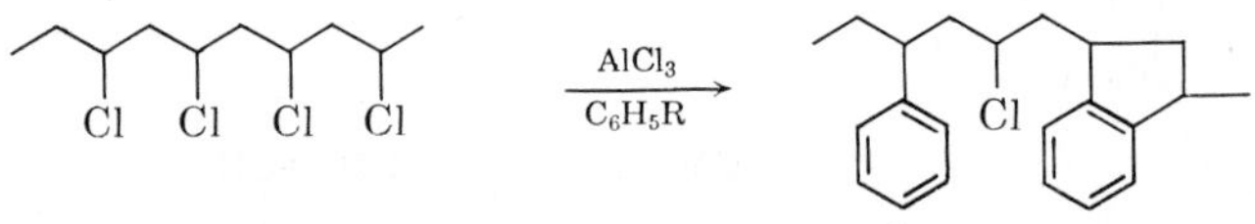
(61)

(III) (IV)

It is worthwhile to point out the strong influence of the solvent on the degradation and discoloration of the products; both effects are much less pronounced in *sym*-tetrachlorethane than in ethylene dichloride. When the reactions are carried out in tetrachlorethane, the degradation occurs only in the presence of aromatic hydrocarbons; in their absence poly(vinyl chloride) shows no appreciable decrease of intrinsic viscosity. It therefore appears that the driving force of the degradation is directly related to the resonance stabilization of the α-arylcarbonium ion.

Similarly Friedel-Crafts reactions were carried out on copolymers of styrene and methacrylic acid, methacrylyl chloride, or methacrylic ester, and from these methylene–tetralone units and rings of a higher degree of condensation were formed (198). The content of tetralone never exceeded 55%. It was assumed that the formation of an acyl carbonium ion in the side chain, instead of in the main chain, would prevent the process of chain degradation. However, in agreement with Rothstein's results (199) on the decarbonylation of acid chlorides in the presence of Friedel-Crafts catalysts, some carbon monoxide was evolved during these condensation reactions, and consequently an analogous degradation mechanism must be operating, which can be represented by reaction (62).

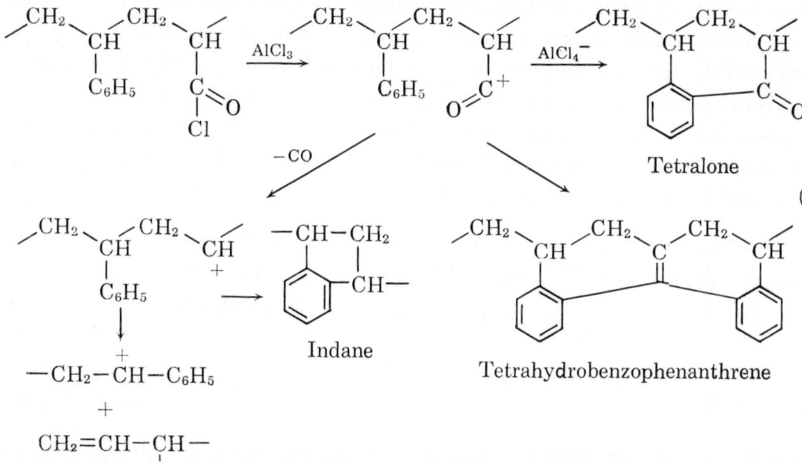

(62)

In the presence of polyphosphoric acid as a catalyst instead of aluminum chloride, the mixed anhydride which is formed gives much less degradation on cyclization, on account of the less polar character of the intermediate complex.

If finally the same Friedel-Crafts reaction is carried out on poly(ethyl α-chloroacrylate), no incorporation of aromatic rings occurs; the reaction consists in an intramolecular cyclization following the path of a nucleophilic substitution mechanism, with formation of lactone rings (eq. 63). The absence of carbonium ion on the chain, due to the change of mechanism, makes it possible to avoid practically any depolymerization, even at high degree of conversion. The lactone ring content in this case can be as high as 81% (200).

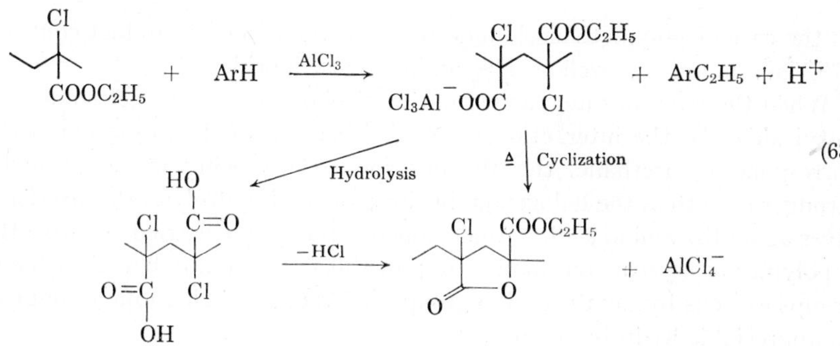

(63)

The interaction possibilities have also been used for the synthesis of polyampholytes, carrying amino and acid groups on the main chain, starting either from polyacrylic derivatives, or from styrene–maleimide copolymers, through the intermediate formation of high reactive isocyanic function. For example, by carrying out the reactions of Curtius and Lossen on poly-(acrylyl chloride), copolymers of vinylamine, acrylic acid, and lactam units are obtained. The lactam content attains usually 62–63%; their formation results from interactions of neighboring groups; these units can again be opened in strong alkaline medium (201) as in eq. (64).

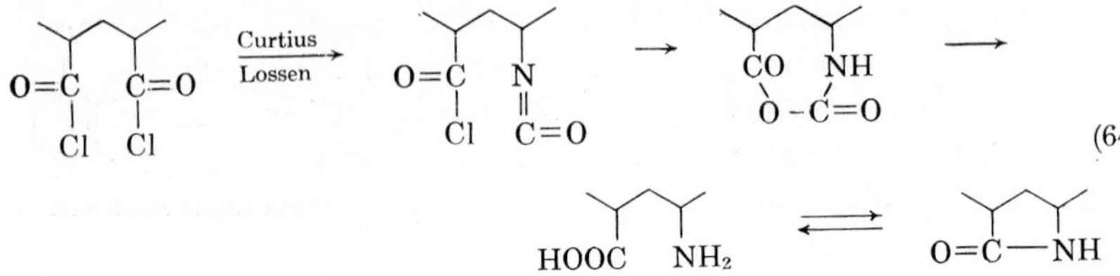

(64)

Similarly, polyacrylamides and polymethacrylamides also give polyamino acids by Hofmann degradation (202) (eq. 65).

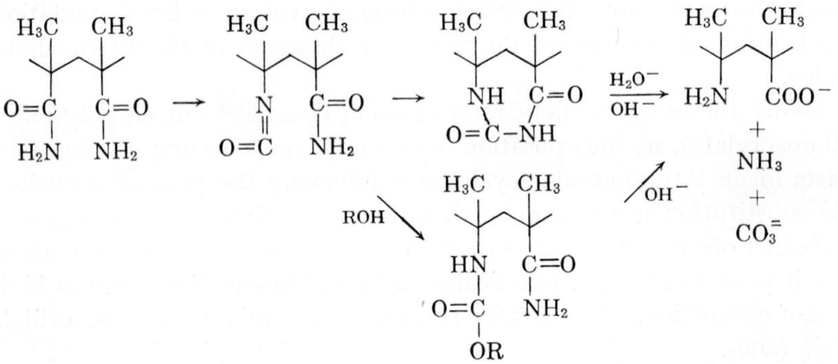

(65)

In the case of polymethacrylamide (eq. 65), the reaction product contains 57% lactam units as well as 28% amine hydrochloride.

When the reactions are carried out in alcoholic medium (methanol, *tert*-butyl alcohol), the interaction is avoided because of the formation of the corresponding urethane, the alkoxide ion (RO^-) being indeed a much stronger base than the halogenoimide ion; on acid hydrolysis this urethane gives again the amino acid. Analogous reactions were carried out with the copolymer of styrene and maleimide; in this case the number of carboxyl groups exceeds by far the amino groups (75 versus 20–25%) on account of an appreciable hydrolysis (203).

If one considers all these bifunctional reactions described above, it is found that the percentage of reaction is always appreciably lower than foreseen on the basis of theoretical calculations, even when side reactions seem to be absent. It suggests that another structural feature of the polymer, namely its stereochemical structure (microtacticity) also plays an important role; this influence will be considered further in this section in relation to the reaction velocity and the final degree of conversion.

Attention must be paid, however, to the several attempts made during recent years to obtain ladder polymers; very often they are based upon a polyfunctional reaction, in which adjacent side groups are linked together. A typical example of this type of polyfunctional reaction was described by Grassie and co-workers (204) on the thermal coloration reaction of polyacrylonitrile and polymethacrylonitrile, during which neighboring nitrile groups add to each other to form conjugated carbon–nitrogen sequences (eq. 66). The reaction is accelerated by nucleophilic reagents, such as acids either copolymerized into or external to the polymeric chains.

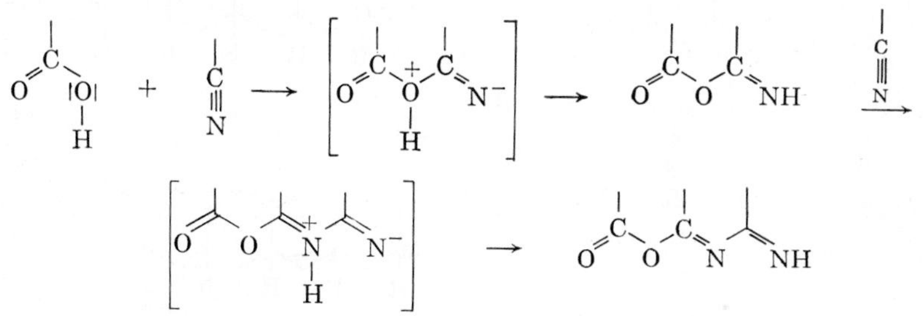

(66)

In the case of polyacrylonitrile the coloration develops much more easily than for polymethacrylonitrile on account of a self-initiating mechanism by the α-hydrogen atoms; moreover polyacrylonitrile insolubilizes rapidly while polymethacrylonitrile remains soluble. This is due to the successive linking up of nitrile groups of different polyacrylonitrile molecules to produce a structure (V) resulting from the stronger molecular packing in this polymer.

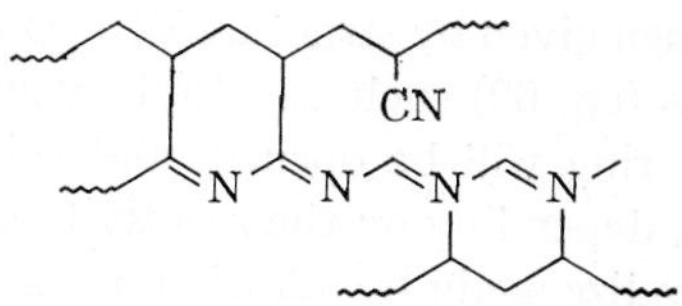

(V)

The inhibiting effect of incorporated foreign monomer on this coloration reaction results from the interruption of this propagating polyfunctional reaction. As indicated by the same authors, the coloration of poly(methyl vinyl ketone) and its copolymer with acrylonitrile on thermal degradation is based on similar condensation reactions with simultaneous elimination of water (205).

Gaylord and co-workers polymerized conjugated dienes to ladder cyclohydrocarbons with Ziegler-Natta type catalyst (206); the powdery cyclopolymers which still contained some amount of linear structure were completely cyclized by the action of sulfuric acid. It is suggested that in the initial stage of polymerization the reaction proceeds through 1,2 isotactic or 1,2-syndiotactic addition, and that the cyclization results from a reversal of the direction of polymerization through an intramolecular cyclopolymerized unit (eq. 67), or from the reaction of a side vinyl group with a growing chain (eq. 68).

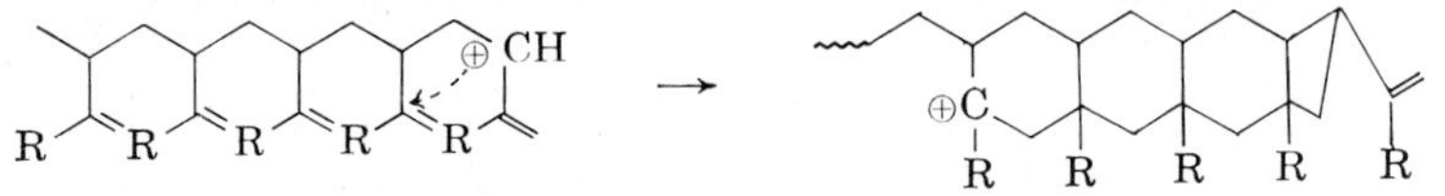

(67)

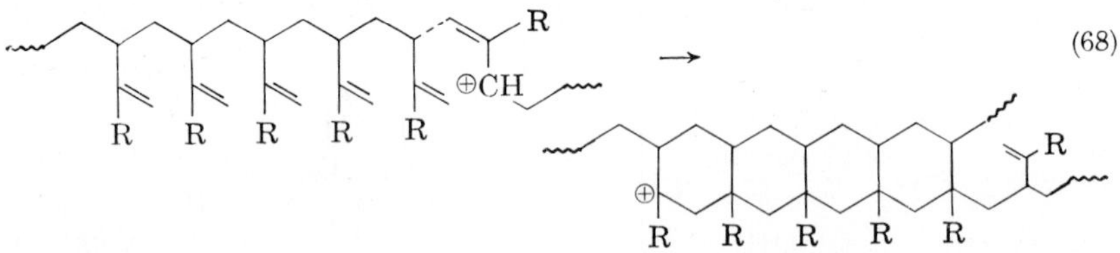

(68)

The ladder polymer shown from a 1,2 isotactic material is then essentially linear and made from fused cyclohexane rings. For a syndiotactic system the cyclopolymer would have a spiral ladder structure. Here again, the length of ladders inside a macromolecule is a function of the regularity of the ethylene isomeric units in the first polymerization step.

It should be also remembered that in agreement with Kern, Schulz, and co-workers (207–211) polyacrolein itself must be considered a ladder polyacetal containing only 5–10 mole-% free aldehyde groups or its hydrate. Its main structure is then given by structure VI. On reaction with reactive methylene compounds (eq. 69) such as ethyl cyanoacetate the terminal 2-oxytetrahydropyran ring will be opened, and this ring-opening process can eventually repeat, depending on the reactivity of the methylenic compound. It can also cyclize again by addition on the carbon-carbon double bond.

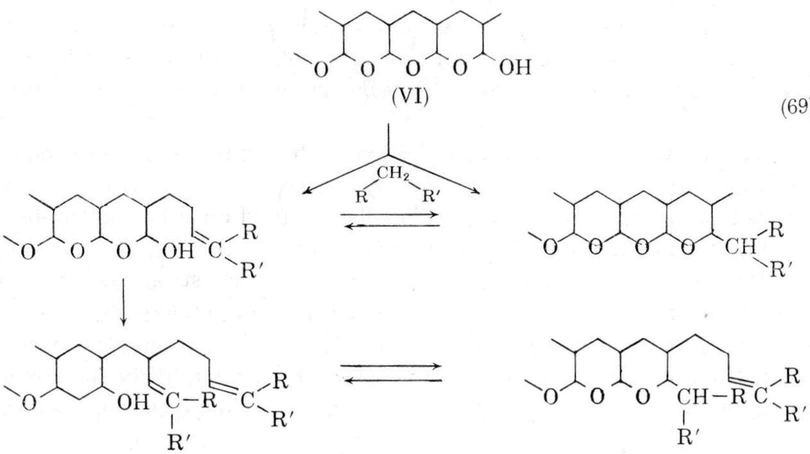

(69)

Depending on the nature of the condensation reagent, the reaction will only affect the endgroups of the ladder which remains intact, or else proceed stepwise with a progressive degradation of the ladder itself.

3. Stereoisomerism of the Polymeric Chain

The recent discovery of the synthesis of vinyl polymers differing only in the stereochemical position of the monomeric units has permitted correlation of chemical reactions with the tacticity of the high polymers. Simultaneously it became possible to interpret on the basis of specific group interactions some particular effects previously described as exceptional. Morawetz (212) showed that the incorporation of some methacrylic-*p*-nitranilide groups into a polyacid molecule stabilizes these groups by a factor of about a thousand times towards 1*N* sodium hydroxide if one compares them to the corresponding trimethylacetic and glutaric *p*-nitranilides. This stabilization was interpreted as a result of formation of intramolecular hydrogen bonding as shown in VII between the amide and the neighboring carboxylate groups, an increase of the steric effect, and an increase of the

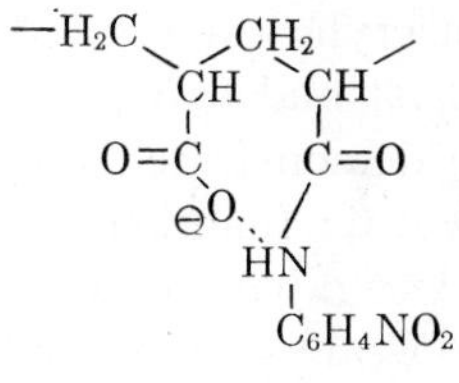

(VII)

electrostatic repulsion effect. This interpretation was corroborated by the accelerating effect due to the addition of small amounts of barium ions, which on chelating and binding carboxylate groups liberate the anilide function.

Similarly, (213) he found that the hydrolysis at pH 6 of *p*-nitrophenyl methacrylate units incorporated at 1–2% into a chain of poly(acrylic acid) proceeds at a rate about one million higher than that of *p*-nitrophenyl pivalate. This behavior was interpreted by Morawetz on the basis of a selective catalytic effect of the neighboring carboxylate ion, with the formation of an intermediate six-membered transition complex (eq. 70). This interpretation was confirmed by the similarity of behavior of the copolymer and the glutaric acid monoester, and makes unlikely the participation of a second neighboring carboxyl in the reaction of the copolymer.

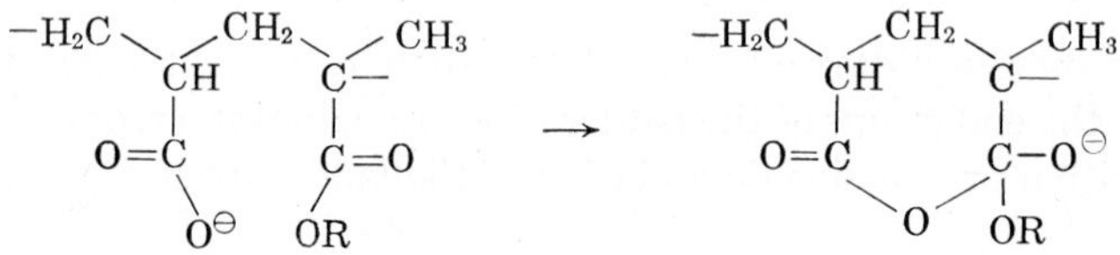
(70)

The difference of behavior is a consequence of the intramolecular mechanism involving an anhydride intermediate occurring in the polymers which is completely different from that of an ester of an usual carbonic acid, but which is directly related to the mechanisms described by Swain and Brown (214) and by Bender and co-workers (215–217). It is evident that the formation of such intramolecular cyclized intermediates must depend on the relative position of the carboxylate and ester groups towards each other, and consequently on the microtacticity of the system. Indeed, Morawetz (218) observed that a part of the ester groups was much more reactive (10 to 15 times) than the remainder, the fraction of fast ester groups being calculated to be about 18–28%.

This new aspect of polymeric reaction has been examined thoroughly by De Loecker and Smets (219) in the hydrolysis of several copolymers of methacrylic acid and methacrylic esters of different compositions (acid content: 28.8, 50, 60, 66, 72, 83, and 86.5%) and each at various degrees of neutralization. They have demonstrated the intramolecular mechanism of the reaction between the ester function on one side, and an unionized and/or an ionized carboxylic neighbor on the other side. In similar experimental conditions, the copolymers of methyl methacrylate and vinylpyrrolidone hydrolyzed only very slowly (about a thousand times slower), even in the presence of buffered acetic acid. Moreover, they showed that the occurrence of only one or of two successive steps of hydrolysis must be related not only to the chemical composition of the copolymers, but also to the stereospecificity of some interactions. An identity of chemical composition of two statistical copolymers is insufficient to ensure an equal reaction velocity; a copolymer C_{60} (containing 60% acid) hydrolyzed up to 72% hydrolyzes much more slowly than a copolymer C_{72} (containing 72% acid), obtained by direct copolymerization. For the same reason, the copolymer C_{72}, hydrolyzed at 83%, reacts much more slowly than a C_{83} copolymer. Starting from three samples of poly(methyl methacrylates) of different tacticities, De Loecker (220) was also able to obtain three methacrylic acid–ester copolymers (72% acid) of which the isotactic polymer (initiated with Grignard reagent) hydrolyzes ten to fifteen times more rapidly than the conventional one, and may attain in a rapid step a much higher degree of hydrolysis (40% instead of 20%).

These results confirm previous experiments reported by Glavis (222) concerning alkaline hydrolysis in heterogeneous medium of poly(methyl methacrylate) samples of various tacticities, where also the isotactic polymer hydrolyzes more rapidly and to a higher degree of conversion than the other types. These results agree also with the hydrolytic measurements carried out by Chapman (223) on tactic and atactic poly-*N*,*N*-dimethylacrylamide, when the tactic variety reacts about 6 to 7 times faster than the atactic one.

The influence of the microtacticity on the reaction velocity was also demonstrated with conventional and isotactic acrylic acid–methyl acrylate copolymer of about the same overall chemical composition. The isotactic copolymer was obtained by hydrolysis of isotactic poly(*tert*-butyl acrylate), followed by the partial methylation of the poly(acrylic acid) with diazomethane. The isotactic systems hydrolyze 3 to 5 times more rapidly than the conventional ones, and their final degree of conversion is much higher (224).

For acrylic acid–ethyl ethacrylate copolymers the rate of hydrolysis is highest when on the average half of the acid groups are neutralized; a concerted reaction mechanism has been therefore postulated.

For acrylic acid–acrylamide copolymers (225), the hydrolysis proceeds in two distinct steps, of which the first is about 50 to 100 times faster than the second, and results from an interaction between an amide group and an undissociated, directly neighboring acid group, which moreover must be present in a well determined stereochemical position. The second slow step corresponds practically to the hydrolysis of amide groups by external acid, the requirements of vicinality and stereospecificity being not satisfied for these residual amides.

For all these copolymers both the rate of reactions and the final degree of conversion are strongly dependent on the microtacticities of the chains.

Another interesting example of the dependence of chemical transformation on the tacticity of the chain is the ability of polymeric acids to cyclize to yield the corresponding polyanhydride. As expected, the copolymers of styrene–maleic acid can be rapidly transformed into styrene–maleic anhydride copolymers (five-membered rings). Atactic poly(acrylic acid) shows two successive distinct steps of dehydration reaction of which the first is 5 to 6 times more rapid than the second (226).

Syndiotactic poly(acrylic anhydride) prepared at 35°C. at low degree of conversion by cyclopolymerization (227,228) gives on hydrolysis the corresponding polymeric acid. This syndiotactic acid gives no anhydride on treatment with thionyl chloride; this means that it cannot revert to the original cyclopolymer. By carrying out the cyclopolymerization of the anhydride at higher temperatures or by heating the polyanhydride in the presence of pyridine, isomerization of the syndiotactic to the isotactic form occurs, presumably through the enolization of the α-hydrogen atoms (229). The corresponding isotactic polyacid, however, can be very easily transformed with thionyl chloride into the polyanhydride. These different transformations are represented in eqs. (71).

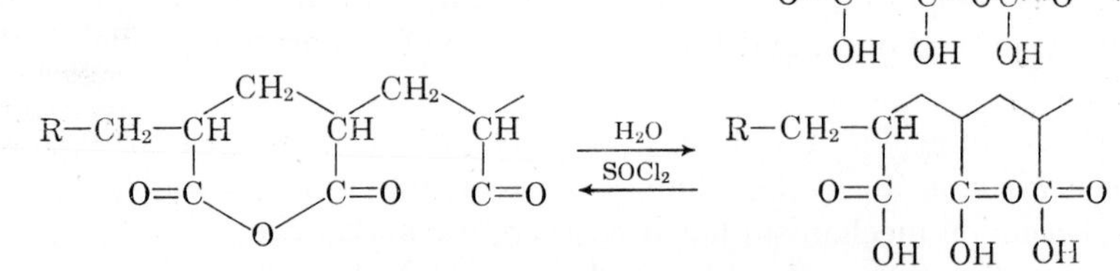

(71)

Poly(methacrylic anhydride) obtained by radical cyclopolymerization of methacrylic anhydride does not undergo this isomerization and shows a isotactic structure (230).

A last and typical example of group interactions and influence of chain microtacticity is given by the hydrolysis of poly(vinyl acetal) of different degrees of acetalization. In $N/3$ sulfuric acid the rate of hydrolysis is proportional to the acetal concentration and independent of the concentration of alcohol, the rate-determining step being the scission of the conjugated acid of the acetal into an unstable hemiacetal carbonium ion (eq. 72).

(72)

On the contrary, in more dilute solution ($N/200$), the hydrolysis is enhanced by neighboring hydroxyl groups (VIII), in such a manner that the rate of hydrolysis is highest for polymer with highest alcohol content, i.e., the rate increases autocatalytically with the degree of conversion, although the concentration of hydrolyzable groups decreases (231).

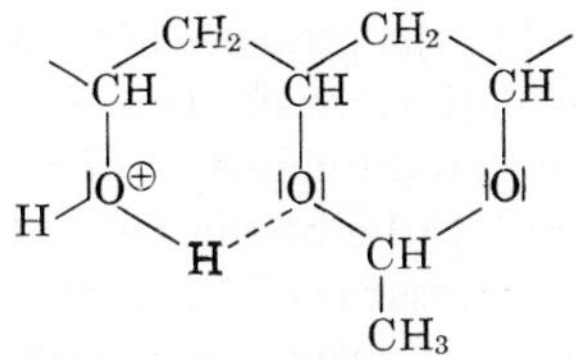

(VIII)

Recently Matsumoto and co-workers (232) reported on the rates of hydrolysis for poly(vinyl acetals) derived from poly(vinyl alcohols) of various tacticities, and showed that the acetal becomes more easily hydrolyzable when the syndiotactic content increases.

These phenomena must be compared to those described by Sakurada and Sakaguchi (233,234) concerning the hydrolysis of poly(vinyl acetate), where the rate of hydrolysis also increases autocatalytically with the degree of conversion, while the rate of acetylation decreases with an increasing degree of acetylation. Although both reactions are likely more complex on account of the well known association of poly(vinyl alcohol) groups, nevertheless these examples illustrate once more a passage from a mono- to a bifunctionality of hydrolysis in consequence of the polymeric nature of the substrate.

It may be worthwhile to mention that chain isomerism not only influences the organic transformations of high polymers but affects also fundamental physicochemical properties of these substances. For instance, the potentiometric behavior and consequently the acid dissociation constants of polymeric acids depend on the tacticity of the samples (235–238); sometimes, however, a similar effect can be due to a different positioning of the acid groups along the chain, depending on whether they are regularly distributed or else present in small blocks (239).

4. Site of Reaction

The reactions considered previously transform one or two functional groups independently of their location along the chain, and therefore occur statistically. Some reactions nevertheless exist in which only one particular reactive site is involved and are consequently very selective. This very peculiar aspect of the reactivity of high polymers can be very well illustrated by two examples: the first refers to the presence of a labile site in the macromolecule which is particularly sensitive to a radical attack, the second concerns the reactivity of some groups according as they are present as an endgroup or as side groups along the chain.

When a radical is formed in the presence of a saturated polymer molecule, such as a polyvinyl derivative, chain transfer reactions seldom occur; indeed, in the presence of equal quantities of monomer and polymer the frequency can be evaluated to be about 10^{-5} at 60°C. In fact, several polymeric molecules contain unsaturated endgroups the formation of which is due to the termination reaction by disproportionation. In the case of poly(methyl methacrylate) the hydrogen atoms in the α position with respect to the double bond react about five thousand times more easily than the internal groups (240–242), and consequently the frequency becomes 10^{-2}. If this radical attack occurs in the presence of a vinyl monomer, the activated endgroup adds new monomer units, giving rise to formation of block polymer (eq. 73).

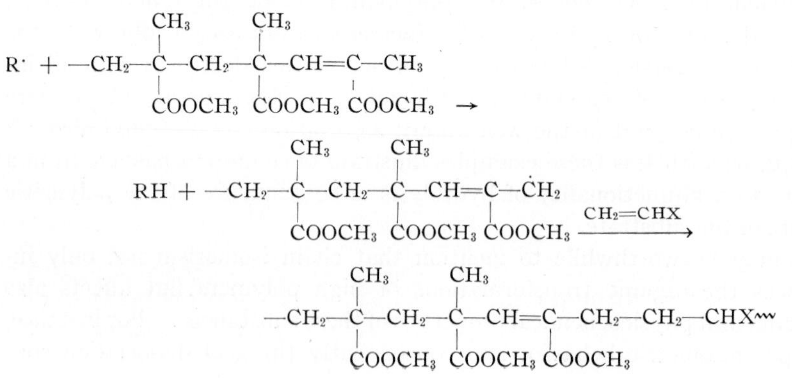

(73)

The influence of the location of a reactive group on its reactivity has been studied on polymers carrying *tert*-butyl perester groups, either at the end of the chain or as side groups. On decomposition in the presence of a vinyl monomer these perester groups give small amounts of *tert*-butyl oxide radicals, $C_4H_9O\cdot$, and macroradicals which add the second monomer, giving homopolymer and block (or graft) polymers, respectively. Depending on the accessibility of the reactive sites at the end (eq. 74) or on the side (eq. 75) of the macroradicals, monomer addition will be different, and consequently the block or graft efficiency is different. Indeed, it was found that when polystyrene carrying *tert*-butyl perester endgroups was heated in benzene with methyl methacrylate, the ratio of the amount of block polymer to homopolymer is only 0.15 to 0.17. This ratio is independent of the monomer concentration (243); in contrast, in copolymers of styrene–methyl acrylate-*tert*-butyl peracrylate (78/20/2) this ratio exceeds unity, and for monomer concentrations of 1.9–4.8 mole/l. varies from 1.52 to 1.15 (244).

This difference of behavior between both systems remains practically unchanged by changing from benzene to a poorer solvent in which the polymer chains are coiled up.

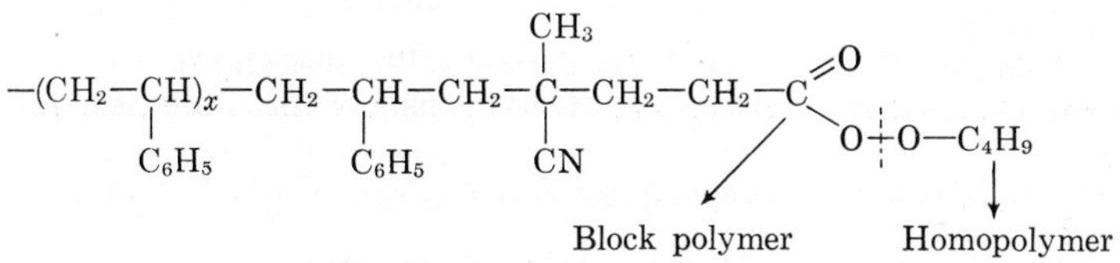

(74)

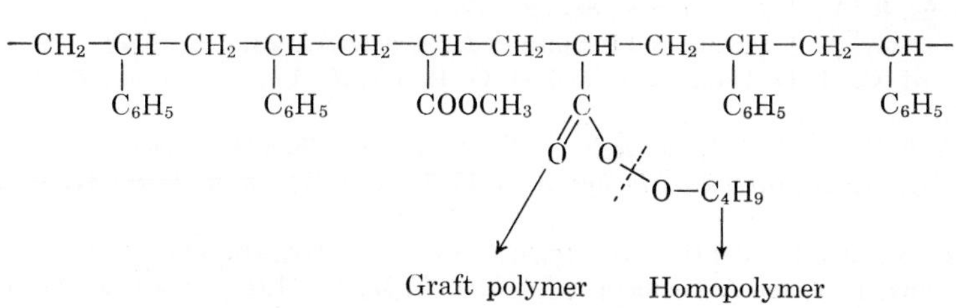

(75)

Although both systems differ slightly, e.g., in steric hindrance and intramolecular induced decomposition of perester groups, nevertheless it seems evident that these effects are due mainly to the difference in location of the reactive site in the macromolecule.

References

A. Reactivity of Functional Groups on Polymers

1. Flory, P. J., *J. Am. Chem. Soc.*, **61,** 3334 (1939).
2. Flory, P. J., *J. Am. Chem. Soc.*, **62,** 2261 (1940).
3. Flory, P. J., *Principles of Polymer Chemistry*, Cornell University Press, Ithaca, New York, 1953, chap. III.
4. Morawetz, H., and P. E. Zimmering, *J. Phys. Chem.*, **58,** 753 (1954); see also references of Section B of this chapter.
5. Swain, C. G., *J. Am. Chem. Soc.*, **70,** 1119 (1948).
6. Swain, C. G., *Record Chem. Progr.* (*Kresge-Hooker Sci. Lib.*), **12,** 21 (1951); *Chem. Abstr.*, **45,** 6906f (1951).
7. Butler, G. B., and R. J. Angelo, *J. Am. Chem. Soc.*, **79,** 3128 (1957).
8. Butler, G. B., and A. Crawshaw, *J. Am. Chem. Soc.*, **80,** 5464 (1958).
9. Jones, J. F., *J. Polymer Sci.*, **33,** 15 (1958).

B. Effect of Group Interactions on Reactivity

10. Flory, P. J., *J. Am. Chem. Soc.*, **61,** 3334 (1939).
11. Freudenberg, K., W. Kuhn, W. Dürr, F. Bolz, and G. Steinbrunn, *Chem. Ber.*, **63,** 1510 (1930).
12. Freudenberg, K., and G. Blomqvist, *Chem. Ber.*, **68,** 2070 (1935).
13. Oth, A., and P. Doty, *J. Phys. Chem.*, **56,** 43 (1952).
14. Arnold, R., and J. T. G. Overbeek, *Proceedings of the International Colloquium Macromolecules, Amsterdam,* **1949,** D. B. Centen, Amsterdam, 1950, p. 314.
15. Pals, D. T. F., and J. J. Hermans, *Rec. Trav. Chim.*, **71,** 513 (1952); *Chem. Abstr.*, **46,** 8468i (1952).
16. Kotliar, A. M., and H. Morawetz, *J. Am. Chem. Soc.*, **77,** 3692 (1955).
17. Scatchard, G., *Ann. N. Y. Acad. Sci.*, **51,** 660 (1949); *Chem. Abstr.*, **43,** 7519c (1949).
18. Overbeek, J. T. G., *Bull. Soc. Chim. Belges*, **57,** 252 (1948); *Chem. Abstr.*, **43,** 2073a (1949).
19. Katchalsky, A., and S. Lifson, *J. Polymer Sci.*, **11,** 409 (1953).
20. Marcus, R. A., *J. Phys. Chem.*, **58,** 621 (1954).
21. Katchalsky, A., J. Mazur, and P. Spitnik, *J. Polymer Sci.*, **23,** 513 (1957).
22. Tanford, C., J. D. Hauenstein, and D. G. Rands, *J. Am. Chem. Soc.*, **77,** 6409 (1955).
23. Tanford, C., and J. D. Hauenstein, *J. Am. Chem. Soc.*, **78,** 5287 (1956).
24. Scheraga, H. A., *Biochim. Biophys. Acta*, **23,** 196 (1957); *Chem. Abstr.*, **51,** 6732g (1957).
25. Laskowski, M., Jr., and H. A. Scheraga, *J. Am. Chem. Soc.*, **76,** 6305 (1954).
26. Crammer, J. L., and A. Neuberger, *Biochem. J.*, **37,** 302 (1943); *Chem. Abstr.*, **37,** 6288[3] (1943).
27. Glazer, A. N., and E. L. Smith, *J. Biol. Chem.*, **236,** 2948 (1961); *Chem. Abstr.*, **56,** 6365c (1962).
28. Blumenfeld, O. O., and M. Levy, *Arch. Biochem. Biophys.*, **76,** 97 (1958); *Chem. Abstr.*, **52,** 20318d (1958).
29. Sage, H. J., and S. J. Singer, *Biochim. Biophys. Acta*, **29,** 663 (1958); *Chem. Abstr.*, **53,** 1434a (1959).

30. Cha, C. Y., and H. A. Scheraga, *J. Am. Chem. Soc.*, **82,** 54 (1960).
31. Morawetz, H., and E. Sammak, *J. Phys. Chem.*, **61,** 1357 (1957).
32. Chang, S. Y., and H. Morawetz, *J. Phys. Chem.*, **60,** 782 (1956).
33. Gregor, H. P., L. B. Luttinger, and E. M. Loebl, *J. Phys. Chem.*, **59,** 34 (1955).
34. Wall, F. T., and S. J. Gill, *J. Phys. Chem.*, **58,** 1128 (1954).
35. Morawetz, H., *J. Polymer Sci.*, **17,** 442 (1955).
36a. Malmström, B. G., *Arch. Biochem. Biophys.*, **46,** 345 (1953); *Chem. Abstr.*, **49,** 8347d (1955).
36b. Malmström, B. G., *Arch. Biochem. Biophys.*, **58,** 381 (1955); *Chem. Abstr.*, **50,** 2709f (1956).
37. Gorini, L., and F. Felix, *Biochim. Biophys. Acta*, **10,** 128 (1953); *Chem. Abstr.*, **47,** 4384i (1953).
38. Laskowski, M., Jr., and H. A. Scheraga, *J. Am. Chem. Soc.*, **78,** 5793 (1956).
39. Laskowski, M., Jr., S. Ehrenpries, T. H. Donnelly, and H. A. Scheraga, *J. Am. Chem. Soc.*, **82,** 1340 (1960).
40. Richards, F. M., and P. J. Vithayathil, *J. Biol. Chem.*, **234,** 1459 (1959); *Chem. Abstr.*, **53,** 16252h (1959).
41. Bell, R. P., *Acid-Base Catalysis*, Oxford University Press, New York, 1941, pp. 21–35.
42. Deuel, H., K. Hutschneker, and J. Solms, *Z. Elektrochem.*, **57,** 172 (1953); *Chem. Abstr.*, **47,** 9523f (1958).
43. Lineweaver, H., *J. Am. Chem. Soc.*, **67,** 1292 (1945).
44. Ladenheim, H., and H. Morawetz, *J. Am. Chem. Soc.*, **81,** 4860 (1959).
45. Arcus, C. L., *J. Chem. Soc.*, **1949,** 2732.
46. Pinner, S. H., *J. Polymer Sci.*, **10,** 379 (1953).
47. Ladenheim, H., E. M. Loebl, and H. Morawetz, *J. Am. Chem. Soc.*, **81,** 20 (1959).
48. Leitsinger, R. L., and T. J. Savereide, *J. Am. Chem. Soc.*, **84,** 114 (1962).
49. Putnam, F. W., in *The Proteins*, H. Neurath and K. Bailey, eds., Vol. I, Part B, Academic Press, New York, 1953, p. 893.
50. Hammett, L. P., *Physical Organic Chemistry*, McGraw-Hill, New York, 1940, pp. 222–227.
51. Katchalsky, A., and J. Feitelson, *J. Polymer Sci.*, **13,** 385 (1954).
52. Ingold, C. K., *J. Chem. Soc.*, **1930,** 1375.
53. Morawetz, H., and P. E. Zimmering, *J. Phys. Chem.*, **58,** 753 (1954).
54. Zimmering, P. E., E. W. Westhead, Jr., and H. Morawetz, *Biochim. Biophys. Acta*, **25,** 376 (1957); *Chem. Abstr.*, **51,** 16617d (1957).
55. Bender, M. L., and M. C. Neveu, *J. Am. Chem. Soc.*, **80,** 5388 (1958).
55a. Zimmering, P. E., Ph.D. Thesis, Polytechnic Institute of Brooklyn, 1955.
56. Gaetjens, E., and H. Morawetz, *J. Am. Chem. Soc.*, **82,** 5328 (1960).
57. Bruice, T. C., and U. K. Pandit, *J. Am. Chem. Soc.*, **82,** 5858 (1960).
58. Morawetz, H., and E. Gaetjens, *J. Polymer Sci.*, **32,** 526 (1958).
59. Gaetjens, E., and H. Morawetz, *J. Am. Chem. Soc.*, **83,** 1738 (1961).
60. Morawetz, H., and I. D. Rubin, *J. Polymer Sci.*, **57,** 687 (1962).
61. Bender, M. L., F. Chloupek, and M. C. Neveu, *J. Am. Chem. Soc.*, **80,** 5384 (1958).
62. De Loecker, W., and G. Smets, *J. Polymer Sci.*, **40,** 203 (1959).
63. Glavis, F. J., *J. Polymer Sci.*, **36,** 547 (1959).
64. Smets, G., and W. De Loecker, *J. Polymer Sci.*, **41,** 375 (1959).

65. Smets, G., and W. De Loecker, *J. Polymer Sci.*, **45**, 461 (1960).
65a. Smets, G., and W. Van Humbeeck, *J. Polymer Sci.*, **A1**, 1227 (1963).
66. Bender, M. L., *J. Am. Chem. Soc.*, **79**, 1258 (1957).
67. Smets, G., and A. M. Hesbain, *J. Polymer Sci.*, **40**, 217 (1959).
68. Westhead, E. W., Jr., and H. Morawetz, *J. Am. Chem. Soc.*, **80**, 237 (1958).
69. Vigneron, B., P. Crooy, F. Kezdy, and A. Bruylants, *Bull. Soc. Chim. Belges*, **69**, 616 (1960); *Chem. Abstr.*, **55**, 16416d (1961).
70. Smets, G., *Makromol. Chem.*, **34**, 190 (1959).
71. Shafer, J. A., and H. Morawetz, *J. Org. Chem.*, **28**, 1899 (1963).
72. Moens, J., and G. Smets, *J. Polymer Sci.*, **23**, 931 (1957).
73. Chapman, C. B., *J. Polymer Sci.*, **45**, 237 (1960).
74. Henbest, H. B., and B. J. Lovell, *J. Chem. Soc.*, **1957**, 1965.
75. Kupchan, S. M., P. Slade, and R. J. Young, *Tetrahedron Letters*, **24**, 22 (1960).
76. Nagai, E., and N. Sagane, *Kobunshi Kagaku*, **12**, 195 (1955); *Chem. Abstr.*, **51**, 8606 (1957).
76a. Fujii, K., J. Ukida, and M. Matsumoto, *Makromol. Chem.*, **65**, 86 (1963).
76b. Fujii, K., J. Ukida, and M. Matsumoto, *J. Polymer Sci.*, **B1**, 693 (1963).
76c. Fujii, K., J. Ukida, and M. Matsumoto, *J. Polymer Sci.*, **B1**, 687 (1963).
76d. Minsk, L. M., W. J. Priest, and W. O. Kenyon, *J. Am. Chem. Soc.*, **63**, 2715 (1941).
76e. Dusek, K., I. Klaban, and J. Kopecka, *Vysokomolekul. Soedin.*, **4**, 1595 (1962); *Chem. Abstr.*, **58**, 14130a (1963).
77. Swain, C. G., and J. Brown, Jr., *J. Am. Chem. Soc.*, **74**, 2538 (1952).
78. Morawetz, H., and I. Oreskes, *J. Am. Chem. Soc.*, **80**, 2591 (1958).
78a. Morawetz, H., and J. A. Shafer, *J. Am. Chem. Soc.*, **84**, 3783 (1962).
79. Flory, P. J., and F. S. Leutner, *J. Polymer Sci.*, **3**, 880 (1948).
80. Overberger, C. G., and P. V. Bonsignore, *J. Am. Chem. Soc.*, **80**, 5431 (1958).
81. Overberger, C. G., and J. J. Ferraro, *J. Org. Chem.*, **27**, 3539 (1962).
82. Barron, E. S. G., in *Advances in Enzymology*, F. A. Nord, ed., Vol. 12, Interscience, New York, 1951, p. 201.
83. Benesch, R., R. E. Benesch, P. D. Boyer, I. M. Klotz, W. R. Middlebrook, A. G. Szent-Györgyi, and D. R. Schwartz, eds., *Sulfur in Proteins*, Academic Press, New York, 1959.
84. White, F. H., Jr., *J. Biol. Chem.*, **235**, 383 (1960); *Chem. Abstr.*, **54**, 13212a (1960).
85. Teyssié, P., and G. Smets, *J. Polymer Sci.*, **20**, 351 (1956).
86. Teyssié, P., and G. Smets, *J. Polymer Sci.*, **27**, 441 (1958).
87. Smets, G., and P. Flore, *J. Polymer Sci.*, **35**, 519 (1959).
88. Marvel, C. S., E. D. Weil, L. B. Wakefield, and C. W. Fairbanks, *J. Am. Chem. Soc.*, **75**, 2326 (1953).
89. Schaefgen, J. R., and I. M. Sarasohn, *J. Polymer Sci.*, **58**, 1049 (1962).
90. Baum, B., and L. H. Wartman, *J. Polymer Sci.*, **28**, 537 (1958).
91. Atchison, G. J., *J. Polymer Sci.*, **49**, 385 (1961).
92. Grassie, N., and I. C. McNeill, *J. Polymer Sci.*, **27**, 207; **30**, 37 (1958).
93. Grassie, N., and I. C. McNeill, *J. Polymer Sci.*, **39**, 211 (1959).
94. Sandmeyer, T., *Chem. Ber.*, **18**, 1496 (1885).
95. Rose, R. E., and W. Scott, Jr., *J. Am. Chem. Soc.*, **39**, 273 (1917).
96. Grassie, N., and J. N. Hay, *J. Polymer Sci.*, **56**, 189 (1962)

97. Grant, D. H., and N. Grassie, *Polymer*, **1**, 125 (1960).
98. Ivanov, S. S., and M. M. Koton, *Vysokomolekul. Soedin.*, **3**, 248 (1961); *Chem. Abstr.*, **55**, 26515i (1961).
99. Loucheux, M. H., and A. Banderet, *J. Polymer Sci.*, **48**, 405 (1960).
99a. Keller, J. B., *J. Chem. Phys.*, **37**, 2584 (1962).
99b. Keller, J. B., *J. Chem. Phys.*, **38**, 325 (1963).
99c. Alfrey, T., Jr., and W. G. Lloyd, *J. Chem. Phys.*, **38**, 318 (1963).
99d. Arends, C. B., *J. Chem. Phys.*, **38**, 322 (1963).
99e. Lazare, L., *J. Chem. Phys.*, **39**, 727 (1963).
99f. Coleman, B. D., and R. M. Fuoss, *J. Am. Chem. Soc.*, **77**, 5472 (1955).
99g. Fuoss, R. M., M. Watanabe, and B. D. Coleman, *J. Polymer Sci.*, **48**, 5 (1960).
99h. Arends, C. B., *J. Chem. Phys.*, **39**, 1903 (1963).

C. Effect of Morphology on Reactivity

100. Ott, E., and H. M. Spurlin, eds., *Cellulose and Cellulose Derivatives*, High Polymer Series, Vol. V, Part I, 2nd ed., Interscience, New York, 1954.
101. Honeyman, J., ed., *Recent Advances in the Chemistry of Cellulose and Starch*, Interscience, New York, 1959.
102. Howsmon, J. A., and W. A. Sisson, Ref. 100, pp. 231–346
103. Frey-Wyssling, A., *Biochim. Biophys. Acta*, **18**, 166 (1955); *Chem. Abstr.*, **50**, 562h (1956).
104. Hess, K., *Chim. Ind. (Paris)*, **80**, 129 (1958).
105. Happey, F., *J. Textile Inst.*, **41**, T381 (1950); *Chem. Abstr.*, **45**, 856h (1951).
106. Marrinan, H. J., Ref. 101, pp. 147–186.
107. Howsmon, J. A., and W. A. Sisson, Ref. 100, pp. 231–244.
108. Hock, C. W., *J. Polymer Sci.*, **8**, 425 (1952).
109. Rånby, B. G., *Tappi*, **35**, 53 (1952); *Chem. Abstr.*, **46**, 6825d (1952).
110. Rånby, B. G., *Svensk Papperstid.*, **57**, 9 (1954).
111. Rånby, B. G., Inaugural Dissertation, University of Uppsala, Sweden, 1952.
112. Rollins, M. L., and V. W. Tripp, *Forest Prod. J.*, **11**, 493 (1961); *Chem. Abstr.*, **56**, 3692g (1962).
113. Heuser, E., *Chemistry of Cellulose*, Wiley, New York, 1944, pp. 7–33.
114. Hermans, P. H., *Physics and Chemistry of Cellulose Fibres*, Elsevier, New York, 1949, pp. 163–172.
115. Richardson, W. A., *Rept. Progr. Appl. Chem.*, **41**, 366 (1956).
116. Hock, C. W., Ref. 100, pp. 347–392.
117. Rollins, M. L., *Anal. Chem.*, **26**, 718 (1954).
118. Valko, E. I., in *Cellulose and Cellulose Derivatives*, E. Ott, ed., High Polymer Series, Vol. V, 1st ed., Interscience, New York, 1946, pp. 324–340.
119. Hermans, P. H , Ref. 114, pp. 143–155.
120. Howsmon, J. A., and W. A. Sisson, Ref. 100, pp. 317–334.
121. Heuser, E., Ref. 113, pp. 42–85.
122. Cumberbirch, R. J. E., *Rept. Progr. Appl. Chem.*, **40**, 451 (1955).
123. Sitch, D. A., *J. Textile Inst.*, **44**, T407 (1953); *Chem. Abstr.*, **48**, 998c (1954).
124. Sitch, D. A., *Shirley Inst. Mem.*, **26**, 89 (1952–53).
125. Reeves, R. E., and H. J. Thompson, *Contrib. Boyce Thompson Inst.*, **11**, 55 (1939); *Chem. Abstr.*, **34**, 3923[4] (1940).

126. Reeves, R. E., and W. A. Sisson, *Contrib. Boyce Thompson Inst.*, **13,** 11 (1943); *Chem. Abstr.*, **37,** 4252[5] (1943).
127. Spurlin, H. M., in *Cellulose and Cellulose Derivatives*, E. Ott and H. M. Spurlin, eds., High Polymer Series, Vol. V, Part II, 2nd ed., Interscience, New York, 1954, pp. 695–696, 700.
128. Heuser, E., Ref. 113, pp. 101, 113, 246.
129. Loeb, L., and L. Segal, *Textile Res. J.*, **24,** 654 (1954).
130. Heuser, E., Ref. 113, pp. 240–243, 247–255.
131. Urquhart, A. R., *Textile Res. J.*, **28,** 159 (1958); *Chem. Abstr.*, **52,** 7688c (1958).
132. Staudinger, H., K. H. In den Birken, and M. Staudinger, *Makromol. Chem.*, **9,** 148 (1953).
133. Staudinger, H., and W. Dohle, *Makromol. Chem.*, **9,** 188, 190 (1953).
134. Sebille-Anthoine, J., *Compt. Rend.*, **252,** 3797 (1961); *Chem. Abstr.*, **55,** 20443a (1961).
135. Sharkov, V. I., O. A. Dmitrieva, and N. P. Potapova, *Zh. Prikl. Khim.*, **34,** 1133 (1961); *J. Appl. Chem. USSR (English Transl.)*, **34,** 1079 (1961); *Chem. Abstr.*, **55,** 21577a (1961).
136. Demint, R. J., and C. L. Hoffpauir, *Textile Res. J.*, **27,** 290 (1957); *Chem. Abstr.*, **51,** 9164h (1957).
137. Hoffpauir, C. L., personal communication.
138. Rosenthal, A., and R. K. Brown, *Pulp Paper Mag. Can.*, **51** (6), 99 (1950); *Chem. Abstr.*, **44,** 8639d (1950).
139. Brickman, W. J., H. B. Dunford, E. M. Tory, J. L. Morrison, and R. K. Brown, *Can. J. Chem.*, **31,** 550 (1953).
140. Yin, T. P., and R. K. Brown, *Can. J. Chem.*, **37,** 444 (1959).
141. Blouin, F. A., R. E. Reeves, and C. L. Hoffpauir, *Textile Res. J.*, **26,** 272 (1956); *Chem. Abstr.*, **50,** 8211a (1956).
142. Petitpas, T., *Mém. Serv. Chim. État (Paris)*, **37,** 271 (1952); *Chem. Abstr.*, **48,** 9682a (1954).
143. Rånby, B., *Arkiv Kemi*, **4,** 241 (1952); *Chem. Abstr.*, **46,** 8775c (1952).
144. Rånby, B., *Arkiv Kemi*, **4,** 249 (1952); *Chem. Abstr.*, **46,** 8365c (1952).
145. Krässig, H., *Makromol. Chem.*, **26,** 17 (1958).
146. Millett, M. A., W. E. Moore, and J. F. Saeman, *Ind. Eng. Chem.*, **46,** 1493 (1954).
147. Nickerson, R. F., and J. A. Habrle, *Ind. Eng. Chem.*, **39,** 1507 (1947).
148. Roseveare, W. E., *Ind. Eng. Chem.*, **44,** 168 (1952).
149. Philipp, H. J., M. L. Nelson, and H. M. Ziifle, *Textile Res. J.*, **17,** 585 (1947); *Chem. Abstr.*, **42,** 755f (1948).
150. Nelson, M. L., *J. Polymer Sci.*, **43,** 351 (1960).
151. Nelson, M. L., and V. W. Tripp, *J. Polymer Sci.*, **10,** 577 (1953).
152. Sharples, A., *Trans. Faraday Soc.*, **54,** 913 (1958).
153. Segal, L., L. Loeb, and J. J. Creely, *J. Polymer Sci.*, **13,** 193 (1954).
154. Segal, L., and M. L. Nelson, *J. Am. Chem. Soc.*, **76,** 4626 (1954).
155. Conrad, C. M., V. W. Tripp, and T. Mares, *Textile Res. J.*, **21,** 726 (1951); *Chem. Abstr.*, **46,** 745e (1952).
156. Waller, R. C., K. C. Bass, and W. E. Roseveare, *Ind. Eng. Chem.*, **40,** 138 (1948).
157. Wiegerink, J. G., *J. Res. Natl. Bur. Std.*, **25,** 435 (1940); *Textile Res. J.*, **10,** 493 (1940); *Chem. Abstr.*, **34,** 8288[8] (1940).
158. Lewis, W. S., *Textile Res. J.*, **17,** 431 (1947); *Chem. Abstr.*, **41,** 6725h (1947).

159. Ravens, D. A. S., *Polymer*, **1**, 375 (1960).
160. Farrow, G., D. A. S. Ravens, and I. M. Ward, *Polymer*, **3**, 17 (1962).
161. Ravens, D. A. S., and I. M. Ward, *Trans. Faraday Soc.*, **57**, 150 (1961).
162. Winslow, F. H., and W. L. Hawkins, in *Crystalline Olefin Polymers*, R. Raff and K. W. Doak, eds., High Polymer Series, Vol. XX, Part I, Interscience, New York, 1964, chap. 15.
163. Hawkins, W. L., W. Matreyek, and F. H. Winslow, *J. Polymer Sci.*, **41**, 1 (1959).
164. Winslow, F. H., and W. Matreyek, paper presented at the 141st Meeting of the American Chemical Society, Washington, D. C., Mar. 21–29, 1962.
165. Winslow, F. H., W. L. Hawkins, and W. Matreyek, paper presented at the 139th Meeting of the American Chemical Society, St. Louis, Mo., Mar. 21–30, 1961.

D. Reaction of Polymeric Functional Groups

166. Houel, B., *Compt. Rend.*, **246**, 2488 (1958); *Chem. Abstr.*, **52**, 15119d (1958).
167. Cohen, H. L., D. G. Borden, and L. M. Minsk, *J. Org. Chem.*, **26**, 1274 (1961).
168a. Hart, R., *J. Polymer Sci.*, **29**, 629 (1958).
168b. Staudinger, H., K. Frey, and W. Starck, *Ber.*, **60**, 1782 (1927).
169. Natta, G., E. Beati, and F. Severini, *J. Polymer Sci.*, **34**, 685 (1959).
170. Metz, D. J., and R. B. Mesrobian, *J. Polymer Sci.*, **16**, 345 (1955).
171. Hiller, L. A., Jr., *J. Polymer Sci.*, **10**, 385 (1953).
172. Conix, A., G. Smets, and J. Moens, Intern. Symp. Macromol. Chem. (IUPAC), Milan-Turin, 1954 [pub. as *Ric. Sci. Suppl.*, **25**, 200 (1955)].
173. Conix, A., and G. Smets, *J. Polymer Sci.*, **15**, 221 (1955).
174. Lifson, S., and A. Katchalsky, *J. Polymer Sci.*, **13**, 43 (1954).
175. Katchalsky, A., N. Shavit, and M. Eisenberg, *J. Polymer Sci.*, **13**, 69 (1954).
176. Katchalsky, A., and J. Feitelson. *J. Polymer Sci.*, **13**, 385 (1954).
177. Moens, J., and G. Smets, *J. Polymer Sci.*, **23**, 931 (1957).
178. Arcus, C. L., *J. Chem. Soc.*, **1949**, 2732.
179. Pinner, S. H., *J. Polymer Sci.*, **10**, 379 (1953).
180. Smets, G., V. Balogh, and Y. Castille, Intern. Symp. Macromol. Chem. (IUPAC), Paris, 1963; *J. Polymer Sci.*, **C4**, 1467 (1964).
181. Flory, P. J., *J. Am. Chem. Soc.*, **61**, 1518 (1939).
182. Marvel, C. S., G. D. Jones, T. W. Mastin, and G. L. Schertz, *J. Am. Chem. Soc.*, **64**, 2356 (1942).
183. Marvel, C. S., J. H. Sample, and M. F. Roy, *J. Am. Chem. Soc.*, **61**, 3241 (1939).
184. Bevington, J. C., and R. G. W. Norrish, *J. Chem. Soc.*, **1948**, 771.
185. Bevington, J. C., and R. G. W. Norrish, *J. Chem. Soc.*, **1949**, 482.
186. Crauwels, K., and G. Smets, *Bull. Soc. Chim. Belges*, **59**, 182 (1950); *Chem. Abstr.* **45**, 4480d (1951).
187. Marvel, C. S., J. Dec, H. G. Cooke, Jr., and J. C. Cowan, *J. Am. Chem. Soc.*, **62**, 3495 (1940).
188. Minsk, L. M., and W. O. Kenyon, *J. Am. Chem. Soc.*, **72**, 2650 (1950).
189. Kocher, R., and C. Sadron, *Makromol. Chem.*, **10**, 172 (1953).
190a. Minsk, L. M., G. P. Waugh, and W. O. Kenyon, *J. Am. Chem. Soc.*, **72**, 2646 (1950).
190b. Minsk, L. M., and W. O. Kenyon, *J. Am. Chem. Soc.*, **72**, 2650 (1950).
191. Smets, G., and F. Teugels, unpublished results.

192. Van der Borght, X., and G. Van Haeren, Dissertation, Univ. Louvain, 1963.
193. Van Dessel, R., Dissertation, Univ. Louvain, 1959.
194. Reynolds, D. D., and W. O. Kenyon, *J. Am. Chem. Soc.*, **72**, 1584, 1587, 1591 (1950).
195. Delheye, G., Dissertation, Univ. Louvain, 1963.
196. Rondou, S., G. Smets, and M. C. de Wilde-Delvaux, *J. Polymer Sci.*, **24**, 261 (1957).
197. Teyssié, P., and G. Smets, *J. Polymer Sci.*, **20**, 351 (1956).
198. Teyssié, P., and G. Smets, *J. Polymer Sci.*, **27**, 441 (1958).
199. Rothstein, E., *Chem. Ind. (London)*, **1954**, 403.
200. Smets, G., and P. Flore, *J. Polymer Sci.*, **35**, 519 (1959).
201. Vrancken, M., and G. Smets, *J. Polymer Sci.*, **14**, 521 (1954).
202. Mullier, M., and G. Smets, *J. Polymer Sci.*, **23**, 915 (1957).
203. Goethals, E., and G. Smets, *J. Polymer Sci.*, **40**, 227 (1959).
204. Grassie, N., and J. N. Hay, *J. Polymer Sci.*, **56**, 189 (1962).
205. Grassie, N., and J. N. Hay, *Makromol. Chem.*, **64**, 82 (1963).
206. Gaylord, N. G., K. Kossler, M. Stolka, and J. Vodehnal, paper presented at the 145th Meeting of the American Chemical Society, New York, Sept. 8–13, 1963.
207. Schulz, R. C., H. Cherdron, and W. Kern, *Makromol. Chem.*, **24**, 141 (1957).
208. Cherdron, H., R. C. Schulz, and W. Kern, *Makromol. Chem.*, **32**, 197 (1959).
209. Schulz, R. C., R. Holländer, and W. Kern, *Makromol. Chem.*, **40**, 16 (1960).
210. Schulz, R. C., and W. Passmann, *Makromol. Chem.*, **60**, 139 (1963).
211. Schulz, R. C., K. Meyersen, and W. Kern, *Makromol. Chem.*, **59**, 123 (1963).
212. Morawetz, H., and E. W. Westhead, Jr., *J. Polymer Sci.*, **16**, 273 (1955).
213. Morawetz, H., and P. E. Zimmering, *J. Phys. Chem.*, **58**, 753 (1954).
214. Swain, C. G., and J. F. Brown, Jr., *J. Am. Chem. Soc.*, **74**, 2538 (1958).
215. Bender, M. L., *J. Am. Chem. Soc.*, **79**, 1258 (1957).
216. Bender, M. L., Y. L. Chow, and F. Chloupek, *J. Am. Chem. Soc.*, **80**, 5380 (1958).
217. Bender, M. L., F. Chloupek, and M. C. Neveu, *J. Am. Chem. Soc.*, **80**, 5384 (1958).
218. Morawetz, H., and E. Gaetjens, *J. Polymer Sci.*, **32**, 526 (1958).
219. De Loecker, W., and G. Smets, *J. Polymer Sci.*, **40**, 203 (1959).
220. Smets, G., and W. De Loecker, *J. Polymer Sci.*, **45**, 461 (1960).
221. Smets, G., and W. De Loecker, *J. Polymer Sci.*, **41**, 375 (1959).
222. Glavis, F. J., *J. Polymer Sci.*, **36**, 547 (1959).
223. Chapman, C. B., *J. Polymer Sci.*, **45**, 237 (1960).
224. Smets, G., and W. Van Humbeeck, *J. Polymer Sci.*, **A1**, 1227 (1963).
225. Smets, G., and A. M. Hesbain, *J. Polymer Sci.*, **40**, 217 (1959).
226. Poot, A., private communication.
227. Jones, J. F., *J. Polymer Sci.*, **33**, 15 (1958).
228. Crawshaw, A., and G. B. Butler, *J. Am. Chem. Soc.*, **80**, 5464 (1958).
229. Mercier, J., and G. Smets, *J. Polymer Sci.*, **A1**, 1491 (1963).
230. Smets, G., P. Hous, and N. Deval, *J. Polymer Sci.*, to be published.
231. Smets, G., and B. Petit, *Makromol. Chem.*, **33**, 41 (1959).
232. Fujii, K., J. Ukida, and M. Matsumoto, *Makromol. Chem.*, **65**, 86 (1963).
233. Sakurada, I., and Y. Sakaguchi, *Kobunshi Kagaku*, **13**, 441 (1956); *Chem. Abrst.*, **51**, 17365g (1957).
234. Sakaguchi, Y., J. Nishino, and T. Nitta, *Kobunshi Kagaku*, **20**, 86 (1963).

235. Loebl, E. M., and J. J. O'Neill, *J. Polymer Sci.*, **45,** 538 (1960).
236. Miller, M. L., M. C. Botty, and C. E. Rauhut, *J. Colloid Sci.*, **15,** 83 (1960).
237. Sakurada, I., Y. Sakaguchi, Y. Osumi, and J. Nishino, *Kobunshi Kagaku,* **19,** 620 (1962).
238. Sakurada, I., Y. Sakaguchi, and O. Ohara, *Kobunshi Kagaku,* **19,** 704 (1962).
239. Sakurada, I., Y. Sakaguchi, K. Fukami, and K. Takashima, *Kobunshi Kagaku,* **20,** 81 (1963).
240. Henrici-Olivé, G., S. Olivé, and G. V. Schulz, *Makromol. Chem.*, **23,** 207 (1957).
241. Schulz, G. V., Henrici, G., and S. Olivé, *J. Polymer Sci.*, **17,** 45 (1955).
242. Schulz, G. V., Henrici, G., and S. Olivé, *Z. Elektrochem.*, **60,** 296 (1956); *Chem. Abstr.*, **50,** 1171f (1956).
243. Van Beylen, M., and G. Smets, *Makromol. Chem.*, **69,** 140 (1963).
244. Dysseleer, E., Dissertation, Univ. Louvain, 1963.

Chapter II

REACTIONS OF UNSATURATED POLYMERIC HYDROCARBONS

A. ISOMERIZATION

M. A. Golub

Stanford Research Institute

1. Isomerism in Polymers

Isomerism of macromolecules, as in the case of small molecules, occurs when materials having the same chemical formula possess different structures or configurations. Polymers exhibiting structural isomerism can be produced in a variety of ways: (*1*) by the polymerization of isomeric monomers, e.g., isoprene and 1,3-pentadiene, to form

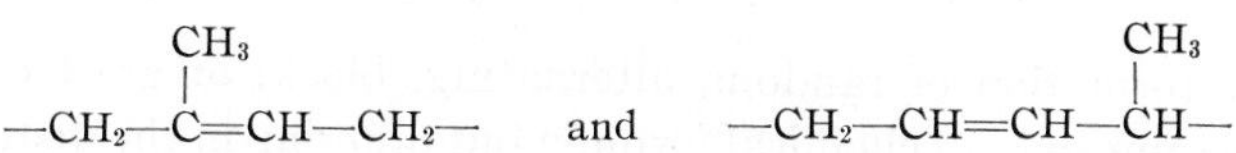

(*2*) by the polymerization of nonisomeric monomers, e.g., ethylene and any of its homologues, e.g., propylene, to produce *essentially* isomeric polymers:*

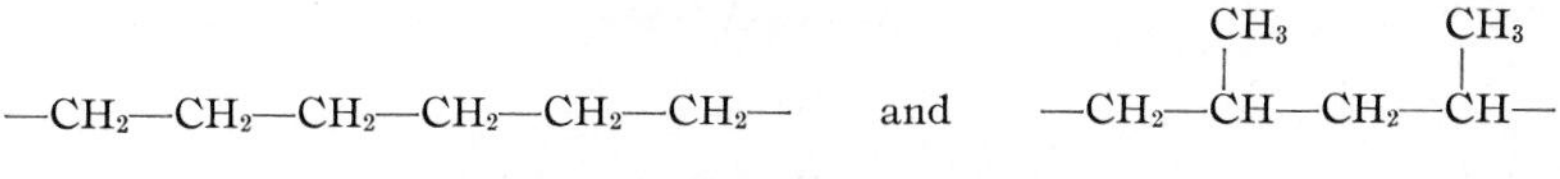

(*3*) by different polymerization techniques on diene monomers to produce 1,4-, 1,2-, or 3,4-addition polymerization units such as, in the case of isoprene, for example,

* Additional examples of isomeric polymers obtained from different monomers, as well as various other examples of isomerism in vinyl and related polymers, were considered by Schildknecht et al. (1).

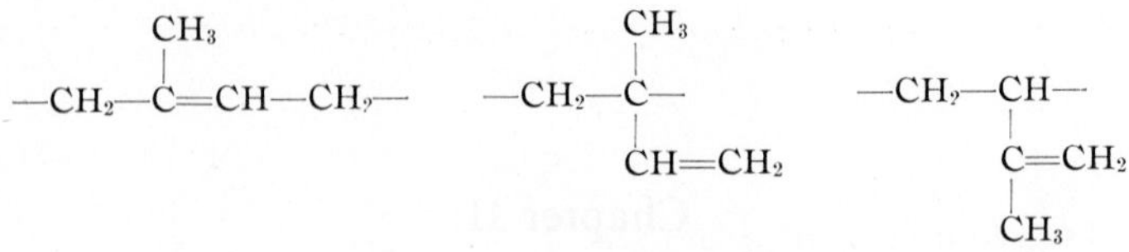

1,4 unit 1,2 unit 3,4 unit

(*4*) by the addition polymerization of asymmetric vinyl monomers, of the type $CH_2{=}CXY$, in a regular or random fashion. The former situation may involve the usual head-to-tail, or the less probable head-to-head, tail-to-tail, linkages:

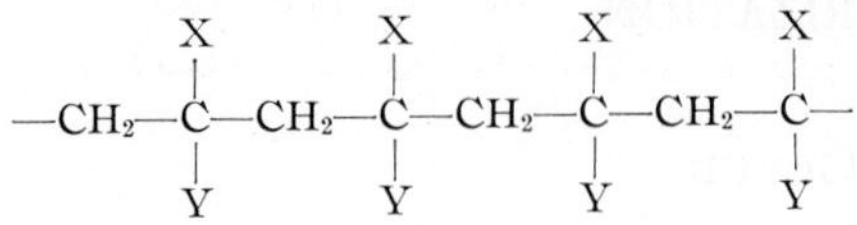

Head-to-tail

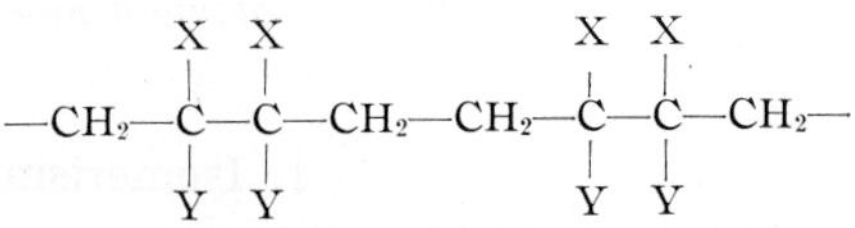

Head-to-head, tail-to-tail

while the latter may involve a random arrangement of such linkages:

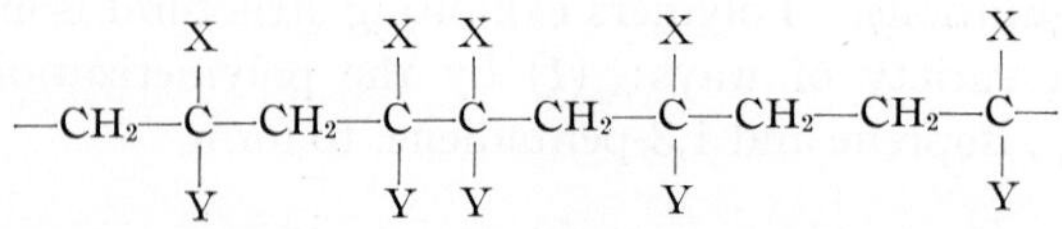

(*5*) by the formation of random, alternating, block, or graft copolymers having the same overall chemical formula but differing in the distribution of the comonomer units in the polymer chains:

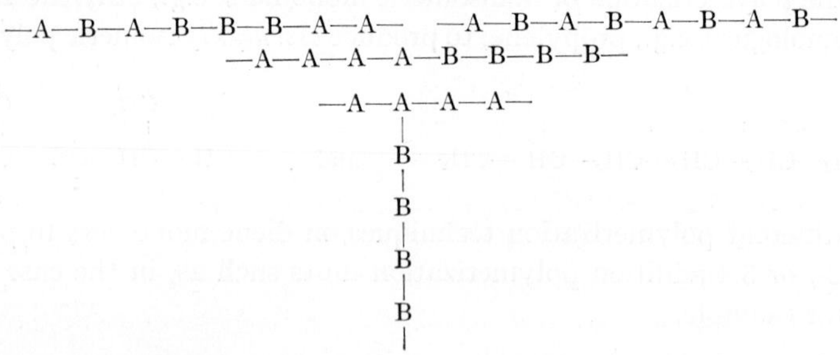

and (*6*) by the incidental formation of branched polymer in the course of polymerization:

$$—CH_2—CH_2—CH_2—CH_2—CH_2—$$

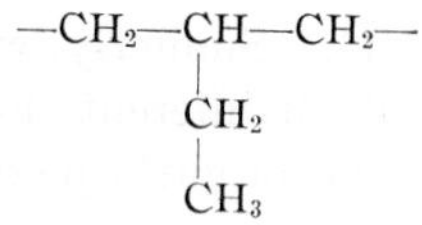

Many other examples of structural isomerism in polymers, drawn from among the condensation polymers, synthetic and natural polypeptides, etc., as well as functional isomerism

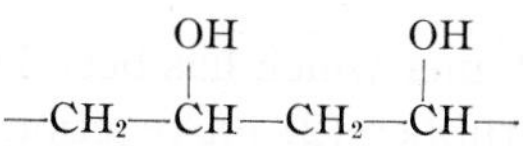 and $—CH_2—CH_2—O—CH_2—CH_2—O—$

can be mentioned, but the examples given above should suffice.

Configurational isomerism in high polymers may involve the existence of *cis* and *trans* forms of the 1,4 units which, in the case of polyisoprene,

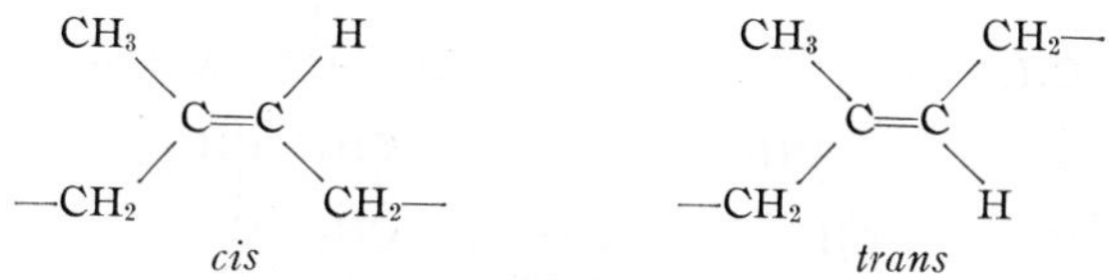

accounts for the microstructural differences between natural rubber (hevea) and balata (or gutta-percha). Other configurational differences in polymers may be obtained by means of various stereospecific polymerization techniques to produce isotactic or syndiotactic polymer structures as well as the random or atactic structures. Since the monomer units in the "tactic" structures have asymmetric carbon atoms, they can have the *d* or *l* configuration, depending upon the orientation along the chain. The various "tactic" as well as stereoblock polymers may be represented, therefore, by *dddddddddd* (or *lllllllll*), isotactic; *dldldldldl*, syndiotactic; *dlddldlldl*, atactic; *dddddlllll*, stereoblock.

Although there are many kinds of isomerism in high polymers, those which have lent themselves to isomerization processes are almost completely confined to polymers containing double bonds. While there are examples of structural rearrangements in saturated polymers, analogous to those occurring in simple saturated hydrocarbons, such as may be involved in intramolecular migration of groups, in branching, or in certain crosslinking reactions, these are more or less trivial instances of isomerization and need not be considered here. In accordance with the main theme of this chapter, the discussion will be restricted to a consideration of isomerization of unsaturated polymers. Thus, interchange reactions in polyesters, polyamides, polysulfides, and silicones, although involving isomerizations of a sort, will not be discussed in this section; they are, however, treated in

Chapter VII. Similarly, we shall pass over the phenomenon of polymorphism in which different modifications of a given crystalline structure, e.g., α and β forms of gutta-percha, may be interconverted.

2. Isomerization of Polymers

a. Cyclization Processes

An isomerization of an unsaturated high polymer which has been known for many years is the cyclization of natural rubber (2) on reaction with strong acids such as H_2SO_4, or with Lewis acids such as $SnCl_4$, BF_3, $TiCl_4$, and $FeCl_3$. This reaction, leading to the formation of a hard, nonrubbery

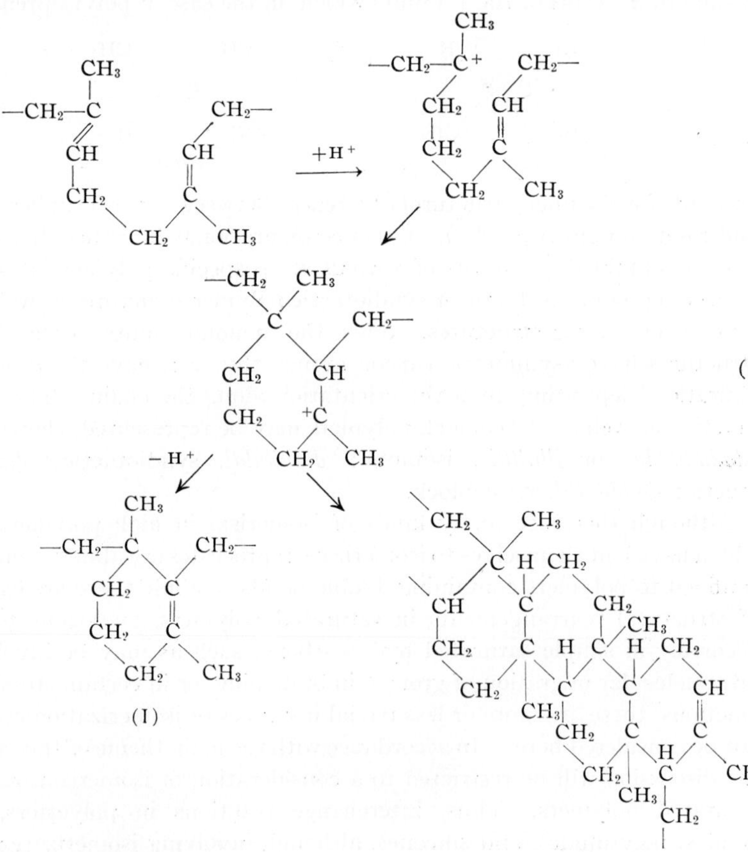

(1)

(I)

(II)

material with much less unsaturation than the original rubber, has been considered for some time to involve a carbonium ion mechanism (eq. 1), although there has been a controversy as to whether the product consists of monocyclic (I) (3–6) or polycyclic (II) (7,8,8a) ring structures. Recently, evidence has been obtained to support an average tricyclic structure for cyclized rubber (9,9a). Synthetic polyisoprenes also undergo this reaction but polybutadienes require fairly drastic conditions (10). This cyclization is examined in detail in Section B of this chapter.

Another cyclization which deserves to be mentioned here, since it is a potentially important reaction, is involved in the recent Soviet work on the heat treatment of polyacrylonitrile to produce a polymeric material having semiconducting properties (11,12).

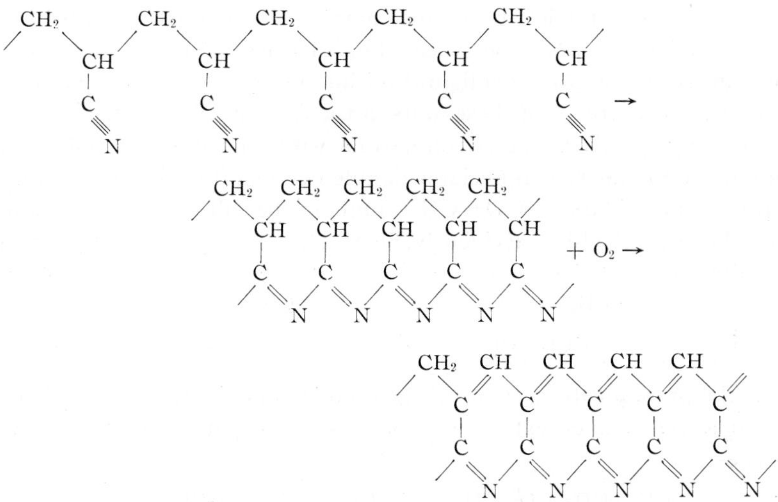

(2)

This reaction results in the formation of a fused ring structure which is in effect a "ladder" or double-chain polymer. The above cyclization in polyacrylonitrile and polymethacrylonitrile had been observed by other workers as well (13,14) and is discussed in Chapter VIII-B.

b. Double Bond Shifts

Another type of isomerization consists of a shift or migration of a double bond in the course of some reaction. This has been assumed to take place in the vulcanization of natural rubber (15) according to

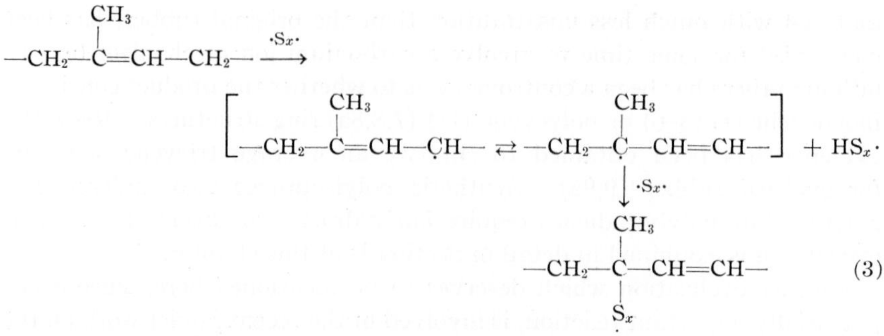

(3)

It was observed recently, however, that process (3) does not occur to any great extent during vulcanization with sulfur, nor is there any evidence for double bond shift to the left to produce new $—CH{=}C(CH_3)—$ units (16). Such units, if formed, would be expected on thermodynamic grounds to be predominantly of the *trans* configuration but infrared spectroscopic indications for the occurrence of these units in the rubber vulcanizate are completely lacking. This result is compatible with the observed failure of polybutadiene to undergo appreciable double bond shift as seen in the very small production of *trans* $—CD{=}CH—$ units in the sulfur vulcanization of polybutadiene-2,3-d_2 (16). Evidently, abstraction of a hydrogen atom from C_1 according to

$$\underset{1}{—CH_2}—\underset{2}{\overset{CH_3}{\overset{|}{C}}}{=}\underset{3}{CH}—\underset{4}{CH_2}— \rightarrow —\dot{C}H—\overset{CH_3}{\overset{|}{C}}{=}CH—CH_2— \quad (4)$$

which is the prerequisite for shift of the double bond from C_2–C_3 to C_1–C_2 occurs to a very minor extent, as does the analogous process in polybutadiene-2,3-d_2:

$$—CH_2—CD{=}CD—CH_2— \rightarrow —\dot{C}H—CD{=}CD—CH_2— \quad (5)$$

These observations are in line with the general view that abstraction of a hydrogen atom (17) from C_4 in polyisoprene proceeds about 3 to 4 times as readily as at C_1; thus, whereas a very small double bond shift occurs in polybutadiene, only a very slight shift according to eq. (3) can occur in polyisoprene. Nevertheless, such a shift of the double bond in the course of sulfur vulcanization of diene rubbers is real and constitutes an interesting although not very important example of isomerization in an unsaturated high polymer.

The occurrence of double bond shift in the case of the high temperature oxidation of polymers is, however, much more definite. Thus, methyl oleate, which may be regarded here as an olefinic model for an unsaturated high polymer, yields on autoxidation a mixture of 8-, 9-, 10-, and 11-hydroperoxides (18) in approximately equal proportions (19).

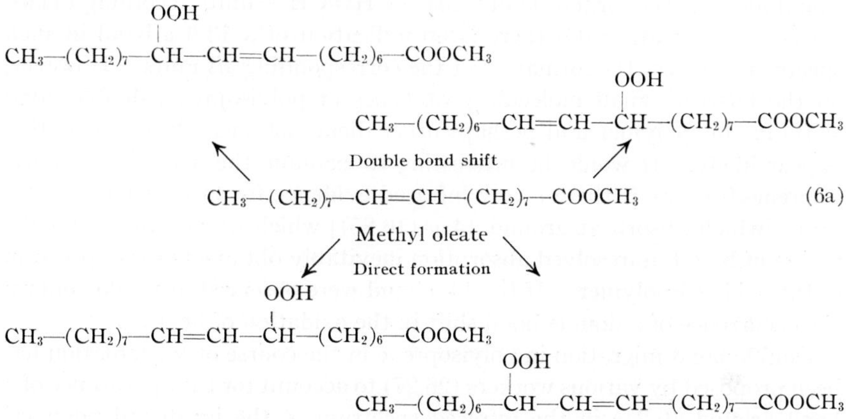

(6a)

The double bond shifts presumably occur through reactions of the type

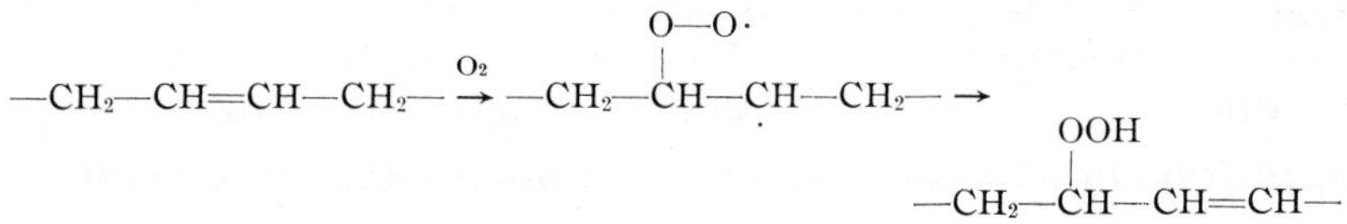

(6b)

Bevilacqua (20–22) has considered that a process analogous to eq. (6) is involved in the oxidation of hevea:

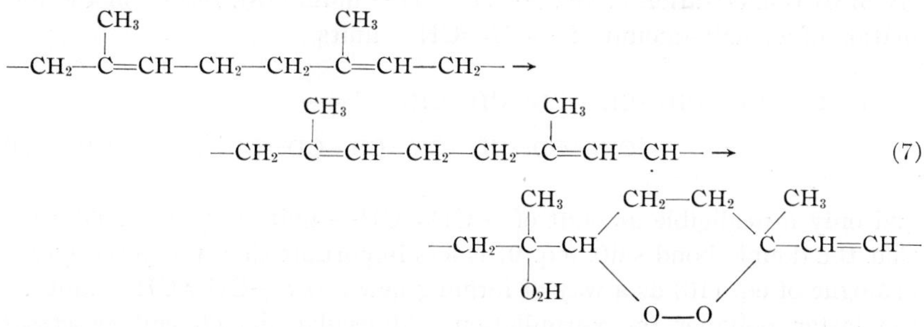

(7)

and that at temperatures of 150°C. and above the double bond shift

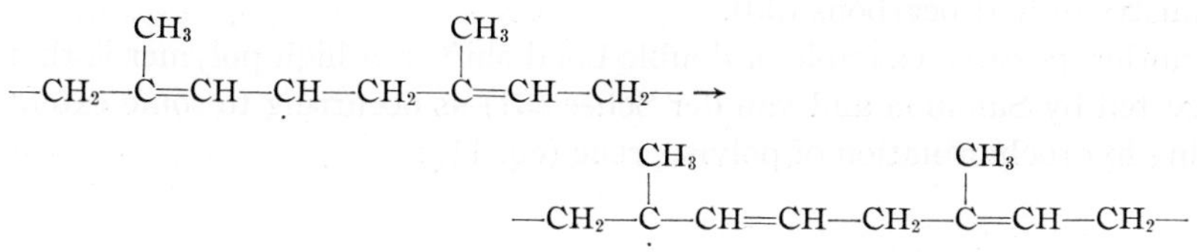

(8)

is substantially complete (23). Since the infrared spectra of oxidized natural rubber (24) show broad and intense absorption throughout the 7–11 μ region, it is impossible to say whether a 10.35 μ band may be present which would indicate the formation of *trans* —CH=CH— units according to eqs. (7) or (8). At any rate, there is no indication of a 13.6 μ band in such spectra to suggest the formation of the corresponding *cis* units. However, on the basis of small molecule prototypes of polyisoprene, double bond shifts in this polymer and perhaps other diene polymers during oxidation appear likely. It would be interesting to examine the oxidation of polyisoprene-d_8 to see if there is any infrared evidence for *trans* —CD=CD— units [which absorb at around 14 μ (16,25)] which would fall outside the region of broad, unresolved absorption inevitably obtained in the spectrum of the oxidized polymer. If the 14 μ band were observed, it would confirm the occurrence of a double bond shift in the oxidation of hevea.

Double bond migration in polyisoprene in the course of γ-irradiation has been proposed by various workers (26,27) to account for the appearance of a band around 10.2 μ in the infrared spectrum of the irradiated polymer. This has been assumed to be due to *trans* —CH=CH— units formed in the reaction

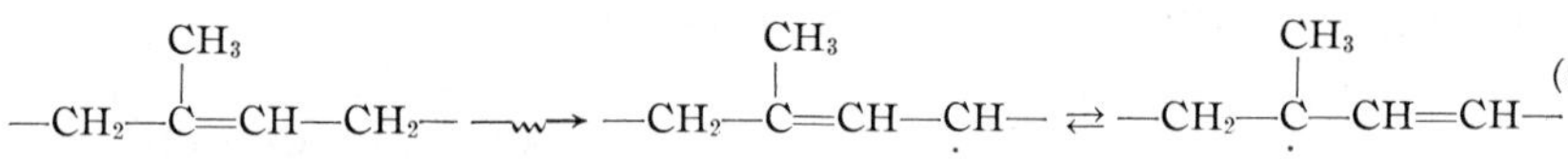
(9)

Since γ-irradiation of polybutadiene-2,3-d_2, apart from producing extensive *cis–trans* isomerization of the —CD=CD— units (28), results in the formation of a small amount of —CH=CH— units

$$\text{—CH}_2\text{—CD=CD—CH}_2\text{—CH}_2\text{—CD=CD—CH}_2\text{—} \rightsquigarrow \text{—CH}_2\text{—CD=CD—CH=CH—CD=CD—CH}_2\text{—} + \text{H}_2 \quad (10)$$

and only a negligible amount of —CD=CH— units (29), it would seem that the double bond shift (eq. 9) is less important than the polyisoprene analogue of eq. (10) as a way of forming new *trans* —CH=CH— units in the latter polymer on γ-irradiation. Molecular detachment processes such as eq. (10) are now regarded as important reactions in the radiation chemistry of hydrocarbons (30).

Another possible example of double bond shift in a high polymer is that suggested by Salomon and van der Schee (31) as occurring to some extent during hydrochlorination of polyisoprene (eq. 11):

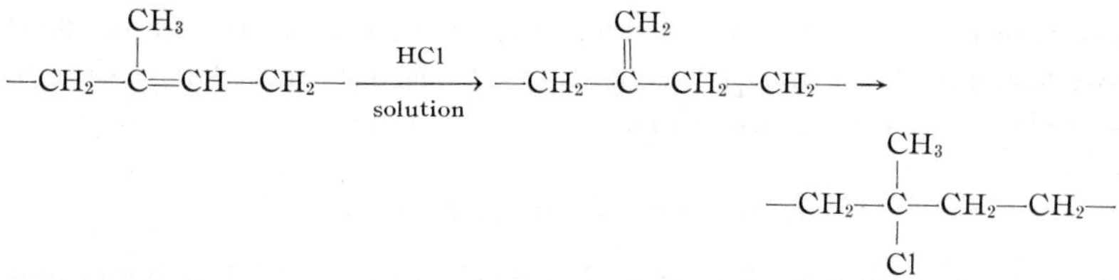

(11)

The production of exo-methylene or vinylidene units through partial isomerization of the internal double bonds has been invoked to account also for some of the spectroscopic changes observed on the γ-irradiation of polyisoprene (26):

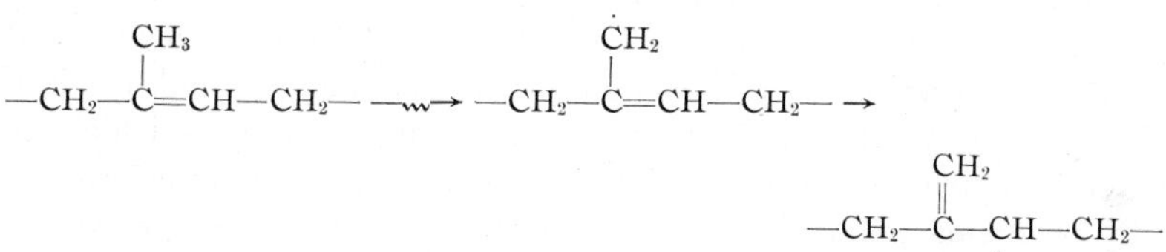

(12)

The formation of vinylidene units in irradiated rubber has been observed also by Hayden (27), but he has considered these units to arise through scission of the polymer chain rather than through double bond migration. Still another instance of the formation of pendant methylene groups by apparent isomerization is in the reaction of hevea or balata with $TiCl_4$ in benzene at about 80°C. where, in addition to pronounced cyclization, very small amounts of vinylidene units are produced (9). Interestingly, when a synthetic high-*cis*-polyisoprene containing a relatively large amount (~4.4%) of vinylidene units is likewise reacted with $TiCl_4$ the vinylidene content falls to the same level (about 2.5% of the *original* double bonds) reached on treatment of the natural *cis*- or *trans*-polyisoprenes (9). The mechanism of the isomerization,

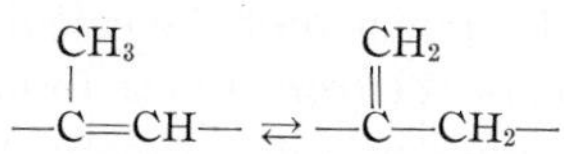

if real, is unclear, but there appears to be a definite equilibrium between these two structures which is far over to the left and which can be attained by treatment of various polyisoprenes with $TiCl_4$.

The various examples of double bond shifts presented above are not pure isomerizations, since they involve also the addition of new groups to the polymer chain, such as sulfur atoms in vulcanization or oxygen atoms in oxidation, or they are accompanied by other structural changes in the polymer molecule. They are considered here, however, because of their similarity to pure structural isomerizations involving migration of double bonds in simple olefinic compounds.

c. cis–trans *Isomerization*

Perhaps the most interesting type of isomerization of a high polymer and one which has received considerable attention recently is that involving the interconversion of *cis* and *trans* double bonds in diolefin polymers. The first attempt to effect such an isomerization was carried out by Meyer and Ferri (32), who irradiated a solution of hevea in cyclohexane with ultraviolet light with the aim of transforming it into gutta-percha, but without success. Later, Ferri (33) showed that treatment of both hevea and gutta-percha with certain chemicals, such as chlorostannic acid and titanium tetrachloride, led to the production of very similar materials which he considered had structures intermediate between the two isomeric forms of naturally occurring polyisoprene. The polymer products were, however, crosslinked in the course of chemical treatment and presumably also cyclized,* so that the changes observed by Ferri can certainly not be regarded as involving a genuine interconversion of *cis* and *trans* double bonds.

(1) Polybutadiene

The first successful transformation of the *cis* units into corresponding *trans* units in a high polymer, apart from the polyenes which are conjugated structures of quite low molecular weight (35), was accomplished by Golub (36,37). He found that a high-*cis*-polybutadiene could be isomerized to an equilibrium *cis/trans* ratio of about $^{5}/_{95}$ to $^{8}/_{92}$ by irradiation with ultraviolet light of a dilute solution of the polymer in the presence of a suitable sensitizer, such as an organic bromide, sulfide, disulfide, or mercaptan, or even elemental bromine. On the basis of a re-examination of the infrared spectra of the isomerizates and a revision of the calculations involving the use of a new value for the ratio of the *trans* to *cis* absorption coefficients (3.65, in place of the previous values of 1.63 to 1.89), the above value for the equilibrium *cis/trans* ratio in polybutadiene must be revised to a new value (29) of about 20/80. Recently, this same ratio was obtained in the photosensitized isomerization of a polybutadiene having initially about 95% *trans*-1,4 units (29,29a). The photoisomerization affords a convenient means for preparing a family of polymers with different *cis/trans* ratios which

* The pronounced cyclizing tendency of titanium tetrachloride and various generalized acids is discussed by Grassie (2) and Scanlan (34).

could be used in studies involving correlation of structure with properties. This technique was utilized by Trick (38,39) to investigate the rate of crystallization of polybutadiene as a function of its *cis* and *trans* content. The photoisomerization procedure has also been applied to the preparation of high-*trans* forms of various deuterated polybutadienes starting with the stereospecifically polymerized *cis* polymers (25,25a).

The mechanism of the photosensitized *cis–trans* isomerization of polybutadiene is considered to involve the formation of a composite radical structure from the polymer double bond, either *cis* or *trans*, and the bromine atom or thiyl radical formed in the photolysis of the organic bromine or sulfur compound employed as sensitizer. The transitory isomeric radicals thus formed can then interconvert (eq. 13). On release of

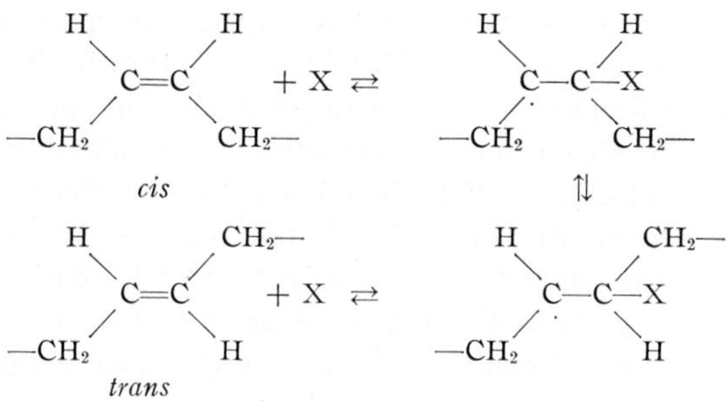

(13)

the attached radical X, representing either Br· or RS·, the double bonds are re-established with the thermodynamically more stable configuration, *viz.*, *trans*, being formed predominantly. The mechanism is thus basically the same as that depicted for the *cis–trans* isomerization of simple olefins involving the same types of sensitizers (40,41).

Following the discovery of the photosensitized *cis–trans* isomerization of polybutadiene, Golub (42,43) showed that an analogous reaction could occur when a benzene solution of polymer was irradiated with γ-rays in the presence of the same sensitizers as in the photoisomerization. A detailed kinetic study of the radiation induced isomerization showed that the mechanism of the reaction, which is first-order with respect to both the *cis* content of the polymer and the steady-state concentration of Br· or $C_6H_5S\cdot$, is essentially the same as that for the photoisomerization and can likewise be represented by the sequence of steps shown in eq. (13). The reaction is characterized by long kinetic chains in which the $C_6H_5S\cdot$ radical produced by radiation can isomerize about 1000–1300 *cis* double bonds (43a), and the Br· atom about 300–400 such double bonds, before being removed by some recombination or termination reaction. Similarly, in the case of the diphenyl disulfide photosensitized isomerization of polybutadiene, Seely (43b) found that each thiyl radical could isomerize about 370 polymer double bonds.

It was subsequently observed that polybutadiene could also undergo *cis–trans* isomerization on γ-irradiation in solution or in the solid state even in the absence of any deliberately added sensitizer (28). Starting with a nearly all-*cis*- or all-*trans*-polybutadiene, the "unsensitized" isomerization approaches a radiostationary equilibrium in which the *cis/trans* ratio in the polymer is about 33/67.* This value is in contrast to the thermodynamic equilibrium ratio of about 20/80 indicated above for the photo- or radiation-sensitized isomerization of polybutadiene. The rate of the radiation-induced "unsensitized" isomerization of this polymer in a 1% solution in benzene is about eight times the corresponding rate in the pure solid polymer, indicating considerable energy transfer from the solvent to the polymer molecules. Whether in solution or in the solid state, the isomerization is an efficient nonchain reaction when viewed from the standpoint of energy utilization. The initial G values for the *cis* → *trans* isomerization, i.e., the number of *cis* double bonds converted to *trans* per 100 e.v. absorbed by the polymer and the solvent, in the solution case, and by the polymer alone, in the solid state case, are about 0.66 and 8.0, respectively, while the corresponding G values for the reverse *trans* → *cis* reaction are about 0.33 and 4.0, respectively.†

The mechanism of the "unsensitized" isomerization is pictured as involving, in the solid state case, the direct as well as indirect excitation of the π-electrons of the double bonds through collisions between polymer molecules and the energetic electrons generated by the γ-rays. Energy acquired by the methylenic groups in the polymer is, to a large extent, transferred intramolecularly into the double bonds. These processes occur also in the solution case but are less important there than intermolecular energy transfer from excited or ionized solvent molecules to the polymer double bonds. In essence the double bond is excited to a higher energy level in which the π-electrons are no longer involved in bond formation (the so-called antibonding state), so that free rotation is then possible about the remaining single σ-bond connecting the carbon atoms of the original double

* This represents a change, based on revised infrared calculations (29), from the previously reported value (20/80) for the radiostationary equilibrium in polybutadiene (28).

† Here again, the specific values constitute revision of previous values (28) due to new infrared calculations for the *cis* and *trans* content in the polybutadienes (29).

bond. When the antibonding state drops to the ground state with release of its excitational energy the double bond is formed again, but with the *trans* configuration predominating, although not to quite the same extent as in the sensitized isomerization. The mechanisms for the two types of isomerization are, therefore, fundamentally different in that the sensitized reaction involves the formation of a transitory radical adduct whereas the unsensitized isomerization takes place via an excited state of the polymer double bond. This difference in mechanism may account for the fact that the ultimate *cis/trans* ratio in the unsensitized case (33/67) is higher than in the sensitized one (20/80). In the latter case thermodynamics must determine the value of this ratio, but in the former case the relative populations of the *cis* and *trans* forms in the higher energy levels presumably determine the final value of the *cis/trans* ratio (44). Thus, while the more stable form predominates in a thermodynamic equilibrium, the less stable form is often favored in a system exposed to strong illumination (45). A classical example of a system showing such differences in the *cis/trans* ratio for thermodynamic and photostationary equilibria is the maleic acid–fumaric acid interconversion (46,47), and it is entirely possible that this type of situation also exists for the thermodynamic and radiostationary equilibria in polybutadiene.

It is worth noting here that Charlesby (48), while studying the cross-linking produced in long chain olefins by ionizing radiation, found incidentally that molten *cis*- and *trans*-octadecenes isomerized to an equilibrium state with a *cis/trans* ratio of 65/35. The first-order rate constant for this reaction is of the same order of magnitude as that of the radiation-induced unsensitized isomerization of polybutadiene in solution (42), a fact which calls attention to the likely similarity between the two reactions.

cis–trans Isomerization of polybutadiene occurs also in the course of vulcanization with sulfur at 140–160°C. (16,49,50,50a), whereas polyisoprene does not isomerize under these conditions (16). This difference between the two polymers parallels the situation in the photosensitization case where polybutadiene isomerizes but polyisoprene either does not (36,37) or at most very slightly (see below). The methyl group attached to the double bond evidently has a stabilizing effect on the given configuration so far as isomerization is concerned which is in sharp contrast to the activating effect it has in the addition of hydrogen chloride across the double bonds. A polar mechanism has been suggested (16) for both *cis–trans* isomerization and vulcanization of polybutadiene when this polymer is heated with sulfur. According to the polar chain mechanism for sulfur–olefin reactions (51–53), addition to a double bond of a persulfenium ion, TS_a^+, where T is an alkyl or alkenyl group, results in the transitory structure

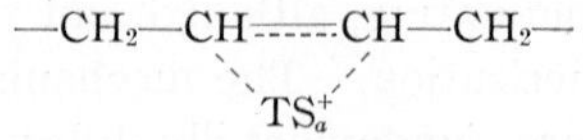

The TS_a ion is derived from the heterolysis of the polysulfide, $TS_a \cdot S_bT$, formed in the initial sulfuration of the olefin. In the subsequent steps leading to the formation of cyclic sulfide structures, this ion remains attached to the double bond in the polymer at all times. However, if this ion is easily detached, as may be the case with polybutadiene, the double bond could then re-form with the more stable or *trans* form predominating. Thus, isomerization would compete with formation of saturated ring structures in this polymer. In the case of polyisoprene, however, the persulfenium ion is presumed to be firmly attached to the double bond so that cyclic sulfide formation occurs to the exclusion of isomerization.

Bishop (50) has proposed a different mechanism for the sulfur-induced isomerization of polybutadiene involving the formation of a π-complex between sulfur, either in the form of S_8 rings or polysulfides, and the polymer double bond, which complex then decomposes successively to give a radical and then a triplet which are free to rotate about the resulting σ-bond (eq. 14). Although one involves polar groups and the other a

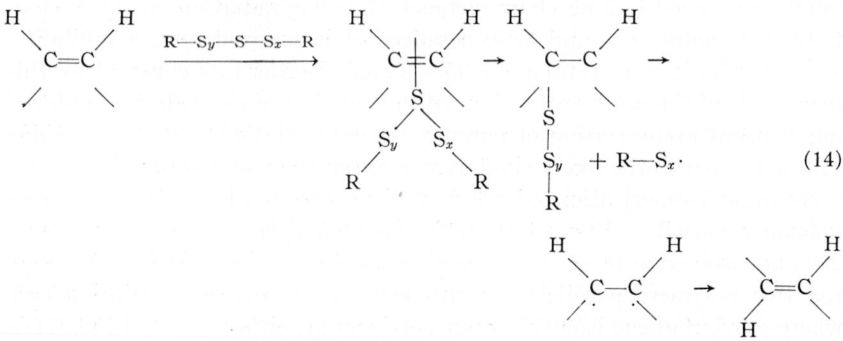

(14)

triplet intermediate, the two mechanisms have the common feature that they both assume some kind of complex formation between the double bond and part or all of the polysulfide. The sulfur-induced isomerization reaction was found (50) to obey first-order kinetics, with a rate constant proportional to the initial sulfur concentration, and to possess an activation energy of about 30 kcal./mole. The minimum *cis* content which could be obtained in polybutadiene on reaction with sulfur under vulcanizing conditions was reported to be about 35–36% (16,50). In contrast, a high-*trans*-polybutadiene, under these same conditions, as well as with ultraviolet light and diphenyl disulfide, was isomerized to approximately 22–23% *cis* content (29a,50). This compares well with the value indicated above (~20%) for the *cis* content in polybutadiene at thermodynamic equilibrium.

Bishop (50) reported also that polybutadiene undergoes *cis–trans* isomerization under the influence of peroxides through a process comparable to that shown in eq. (13) involving the addition of an RO· radical to the double bond followed by its release. Recently, nitrogen dioxide at elevated temperatures has been shown to induce the isomerization of polybutadiene in benzene (54), and it is quite possible that still other catalysts will be found for this reaction.

(2) Polyisoprene

Cunneen and co-workers (55–61) succeeded in bringing about a *cis–trans* isomerization in hevea and gutta-percha by treating these polymers with thiol acids, sulfur dioxide, butadiene sulfone, and various other reagents. This work developed in the course of efforts by these workers to retard low-temperature crystallization in natural rubber by the attachment of suitable side groups along the main polymer chain. Their observation that certain thiol acids produced a much greater reduction in the crystallization rate than could be accounted for by direct addition of these acids to the polyisoprene double bonds (55,56) led to the view that the reduced crystallization was the result of partial *cis–trans* isomerization. To support this view the British workers then showed that sulfur dioxide, which can add reversibly to olefinic double bonds above the "ceiling temperature" (62) for the given olefin, produced the same type of effect in natural rubber as did the thiol acids (57). Furthermore, the effect of these reagents on gutta-percha, which is partly crystalline at temperatures up to about 65°C., was to produce a polymer which is rubbery at room temperatures (58). The *cis–trans* isomerization picture was fully verified by showing not only that treatment of both hevea and gutta-percha with SO_2 gave products with identical infrared spectra but also that the spectrum of the product obtained from prolonged treatment of natural rubber, after compensating for the absorption of natural rubber itself, was identical with that of gutta-percha (59). The SO_2-catalyzed isomerization at 140°C. resulted in an equilibrium *cis*/*trans* ratio in polyisoprene of 43/57. Cunneen and co-workers showed further that this isomerization could also occur in squalene and in *cis*-polybutadiene as well as in *cis*- and *trans*-3-methyl-2-pentene (59). Butadiene sulfone is a convenient reagent for practical applications, since it can be milled into rubber and evolve SO_2 when the temperature is raised, thus initiating the isomerization and thereby producing a polymer with markedly lower rate of crystallization (60). Thus, for example, vulcanized rubber containing about 6% *trans* double bonds showed a 500- to 1000-fold reduction in the rate of crystallization at −26°C. compared to that of an ordinary natural rubber vulcanizate.

The mechanism of the isomerization in the case of the thiol acid (or acyl disulfide) can be depicted by a scheme analogous to eq. (13) where X would represent an RCOS· radical. The isomerization by SO_2 presumably occurs through a similar "on-off" reaction at the double bonds, but free radicals are not involved, since the rate of isomerization appears to be insensitive to free radical catalysts and inhibitors (61).

It should be mentioned that Cunneen and co-workers reported also the isomerization of milled natural rubber and gutta-percha by means of ultraviolet irradiation of benzene solutions of these polymers with dibenzoyl disulfide and thiolbenzoic acid as sensitizers (59). Diphenyl disulfide was also considered to be effective in bringing about a photoisomerization of milled rubber on the basis of a greatly reduced crystallization rate for the reaction product. However, the polymer resulting from the diphenyl disulfide treatment was crosslinked so that no infrared spectrum could be obtained. The previously reported failure of Golub (36) to observe photoisomerization of polyisoprene with diphenyl disulfide (in sharp contrast to polybutadiene) can be explained by assuming that this reagent produces no detectable spectroscopic change in hevea when employed at a concentration low enough to prevent extensive gelation of the polymer in the course of ultraviolet irradiation. On the other hand, at the rather high concentrations of diphenyl disulfide employed by Cunneen and co-workers (25% by weight) a definite although probably small amount of isomerization takes place, as indicated by a marked change in crystallization rate, but due to the crosslinking the extent of isomerization can not be determined. With regard to the action of thiol acids and acyl disulfides, it may be presumed that these reagents are more powerful than diphenyl disulfide in attacking the polymer double bonds and hence can promote a moderate amount of isomerization where diphenyl disulfide has little effect.

Polyisoprene can be made to undergo *cis–trans* isomerization by treating it in solution also with selenium at temperatures of about 180–200°C. (63). Starting with either hevea or balata (gutta-percha), a common structure was obtained having a *cis/trans* ratio estimated to be between 50/50 and 60/40. That this equilibrium ratio is somewhat higher than that obtained by Cunneen and co-workers (59) for the SO_2-treated polyisoprenes (43/57) may be a result of the different temperatures at which the respective reactions were carried out. Significantly, the infrared spectrum of the common isomerizate obtained in the selenium treatment is essentially the same as that obtained in the sulfur dioxide case. The mechanism of the former isomerization is believed to involve π-complexing of the polymer double bonds with selenium in the manner depicted for the selenium-catalyzed isomerization of oleic acid and stilbene (64,65). Polybutadiene also isomerizes with selenium to an equilibrium *cis/trans* ratio of about 26/74* at about 200°C.

Dolgoplosk and co-workers (66,67) claimed recently that treatment of natural rubber in solution at 80–90°C. with titanium tetrachloride, anhydrous hydrogen chloride, or various organometallic compounds results in extensive *cis–trans* isomerization of the polyisoprene hydrocarbon. However, kinetic and spectroscopic studies by Golub and Heller (9) have shown that the results obtained by the Soviet workers on the reaction of hevea with $TiCl_4$ can be accounted for entirely by cyclization. The pseudo first-order rate constants for the diminution of the 12 μ band in the infrared spectra of balata, associated with the —C(CH_3)=CH— units, whether *cis* or *trans*, were found to be approximately the same as those for the disappearance of this band in the spectra of hevea at comparable $TiCl_4$ concentrations. Since the two kinds of double bonds have different absorption coefficients at 12 μ, the rate data indicate that *cis–trans* isomerization makes a negligible contribution to the overall reaction of polyisoprene with $TiCl_4$.

Although Evans, Higgins, and Turner (26) suggest the possibility of *cis–trans* isomerization in polyisoprene on γ-irradiation, the slight changes in the infrared spectra noted by these workers are not sufficiently pronounced to provide definite support for that view. Unfortunately, the *cis* and *trans* double bonds in polyisoprene absorb at the same wavelength (12 μ), making it difficult to detect the presence of a small amount of *trans* units in a predominantly *cis* structure just from an examination of the absorption at this wavelength. This situation differs from that for polybutadiene, where the *cis* and *trans* units absorb at separate wavelengths. Subtle changes in the 8–10.5 μ region of the infrared may signify some *cis–trans* isomerization in polyisoprene, but one would have to obtain sharp differences in this region or other strong evidence in order to be certain that *trans* —C(CH_3)=CH— units have actually been formed in a reacted *cis*-polyisoprene. Since the radiation-induced isomerization of polybutadiene is assumed to proceed through an excited state of the double bond, it would seem, in principle, that a similar process could occur in polyisoprene. While this may be the

* Revision of previous reported value (63) (15/85) based on new infrared calculations (29).

case, the evidence presented to date (26) is inconclusive, and further work on this point would be of interest.

Note Added in Proof: Results have been obtained which show that *cis* and *trans* polyisoprenes, as well as squalene, indeed undergo radiation-induced *cis-trans* isomerization both in the pure state and in benzene solution (67a, 67b). The solid state yields for the two polyisoprenes have the same order of magnitude (G value for each, $\sim$10) as those given about for the *cis* and *trans* polybutadienes, *viz.*, 8.0 and 4.0, respectively.

B. CYCLIZATION

J. SCANLAN

Rubber and Plastics Research Association of Great Britain

1. Introduction

Natural rubber and some unsaturated synthetic rubbers can be transformed by acidic reagents and by Friedel-Crafts catalysts into resinous thermoplastic materials, which have found commercial application in adhesives and in printing inks. A variety of reagents has been used to bring about the reaction. Concentrated sulfuric acid was used originally by Harries and Kirchof.* Fisher (69), besides using this reagent with both solid rubber and rubber solutions, made successful trials of chlorosulfonic acid and a variety of organic sulfonic acids and sulfonyl chlorides. Gordon (70) and van Veersen (71) both adapted the use of sulfuric acid to rubber latex. Bruson, Sebrell, and Calvert (72) obtained similar products with halides of amphoteric metals, in particular, titanium tetrachloride, antimony chloride, ferric chloride, and stannic chloride, which latter material was also used by D'Ianni, Naples, Marsh, and Zarney (73) with synthetic polyisoprene. Similar products obtained from rubber hydrohalides by treatment with zinc dust were the subject of an early extensive investigation by Staudinger and co-workers (74,75).

2. Structure of Cyclized Rubber

The transformation from a rubber to a resin is accompanied by a partial loss of the original unsaturation without any change in the empirical formula, C_5H_8, for the polyisoprenes. While the molecular weight remains high, the product is still soluble in rubber solvents so that crosslinking of the chains cannot be important. It has been concluded that intramolecular bonds are formed leading to ring structures within the chain, and hence these products are called cyclized rubbers or cyclorubbers.

* Early developments have been reviewed by Dawson and Schidrowitz (68).

The mechanism (eq. 15) proposed by Bloomfield (76) for the cyclization of dihydromyrcene in sulfuric acid–acetic acid is the basis of all recent dis-

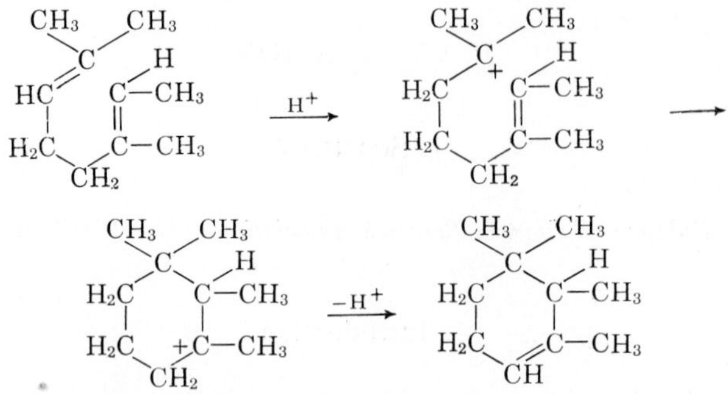

(15)

cussion of the mechanism of cyclization and the structure of the product. The similarity to ionic polymerization is obvious.

D'Ianni and his co-workers (73) proposed a very similar structure for cyclized polyisoprene in which pairs of adjacent isoprene units form six-membered rings:

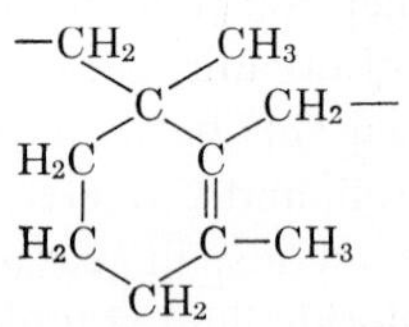

These workers quote in support of this structure the following changes on cyclization: increase in density and refractive index and the loss of about one half of the original unsaturation. Spectroscopic measurements indicated complete disappearance of trialkyl-substituted double bonds $R_1R_2C{=}CHR_3$.

Gordon (77,78) supported this structure of D'Ianni with an ingenious statistical argument. He pointed out that reaction of isoprene units in pairs would leave some units isolated with no reaction partners. Thus after cyclization of the two pairs of isoprene units I as indicated

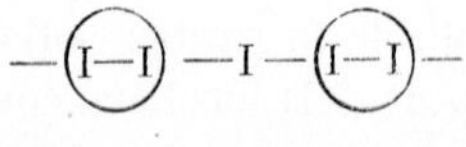

the central unit must always remain unreacted. Flory (79) had considered a similar problem in connection with the dehydration of poly(vinyl alcohol) and shown that such reactions occurring at random would leave a fraction

$1/e^2$ of the units unreaction. Gordon concluded therefore that the loss of unsaturation for a reaction of this type would be not 50% but only 43.2%. Fisher and McColm (80) gave the unsaturation in their fully cyclized rubbers as 57% of that originally present, and the close agreement with the theoretical value was taken as strong support for the proposed mechanism.

Other investigators have obtained lower values for the residual unsaturation after completion of the cyclization. Van Veersen (81), in particular, obtained results as low as 17% of the original and, while retaining the same type of reaction scheme, suggested the formation of polycyclic condensed ring structures by continuation of the cyclization reaction after formation of the cyclic carbonium ion with successive addition to the double bonds of adjacent isoprene units (eq. 16):

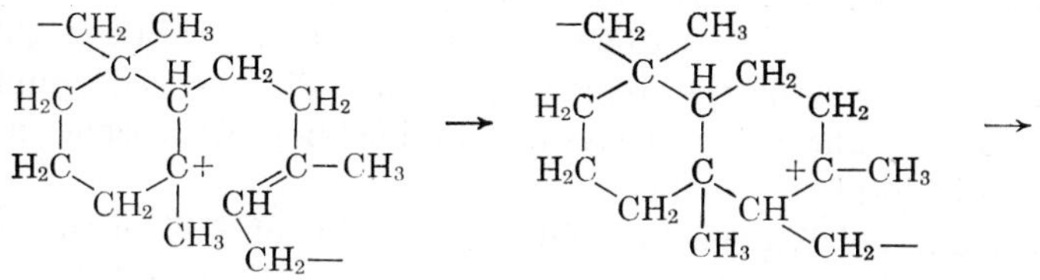

(16)

with a final deprotonation reaction giving one double bond to each ring system (eq. 17):

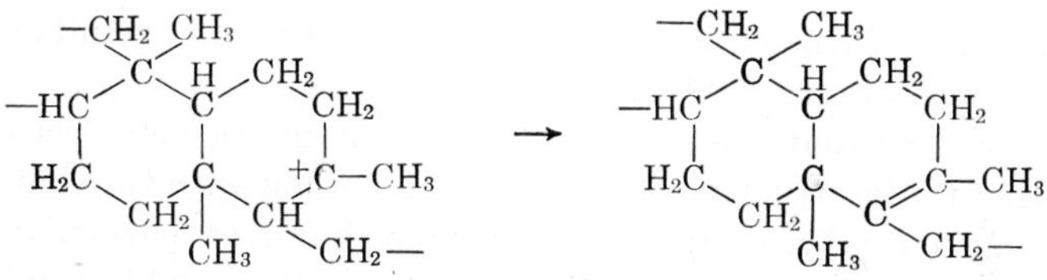

(17)

The determination of unsaturation in cyclized rubbers is of obvious importance. Bromine was the first analytical reagent used (74), but since then a whole series of reagents and procedures, iodine chloride (80), hydrogen chloride (81), phenyl iododichloride, ozone (83), and perbenzoic acid (83), has been advocated and each in its turn criticized. One principal difficulty has been reaction by substitution as well as addition, perhaps because, as van Veersen points out (81), his condensed ring structure has tertiary hydrogen atoms which would be expected to be labile under conditions favoring ionic reactions.

Lee, Scanlan, and Watson (83) have recently compared four of the methods of determination of unsaturation with iodine chloride, phenyl iododichloride, perbenzoic acid, and ozone with an uncyclized natural rubber and two samples cyclized with stannic chloride. With ICl, the reagent used by Fisher and McColm (80), high values of the unsaturation were apparently obtained, but substitution was clearly occurring as hydrogen chloride was evolved. The other three reagents gave lower values which were in approximate but not exact agreement. Ozone used in a manner following Barnard (84) did not give sharp endpoints, and bubbling of ozonized oxygen through solutions of the samples of cyclized rubber resulted in loss of ozone, even after the usual reaction with the double bonds must have been completed. A difficulty arose also with phenyl iododichloride. Cyclized rubber was found to be difficult to free from carbon tetrachloride, the solvent in which the reaction was carried out, a phenomenon noticed also by Fisher and McColm (80). As the method depends upon estimation of chlorine after reaction, errors are likely. Perbenzoic acid was, therefore, regarded as the most satisfactory reagent, but the value of 20% determined for the unsaturation remaining in the fully cyclized sample was considered to be confirmed by the results obtained both with ozone and with phenyl iododichloride.

Lee, Scanlan, and Watson (83) obtained a value of 36% of the original for the unsaturation remaining in a latex cyclized rubber, well below Gordon's theoretical limit. They also pointed out that Rao (82), who worked with a similar sample of cyclized rubber using phenyl iododichloride and who has claimed to have confirmed the theoretical value, had used an incorrect method of calculation. In fact, his experimental results correctly interpreted agreed reasonably well with theirs.

It is clear then that the condensed-ring structure of van Veersen must be preferred to the structure of D'Ianni and Gordon with the simple rings. The size of the condensed ring systems is not, however, particularly large, as the values of residual unsaturation for latex-cyclized rubber and stannic chloride-cyclized rubber give 1.5 and 4, respectively, for the average numbers of rings condensed, one less than the number of isoprene units per double bond in each case.

It was, in fact, always difficult to see why cyclization should cease after formation of a single ring, as molecular models do not indicate any marked steric hindrance. This is particularly the case if Gordon's conclusion (78) from kinetic evidence is accepted that deprotonization of the cyclized carbonium ion is slow. Even if, as appears more likely, the protonation equilibrium is weighted heavily on the side of unprotonated double bonds, the ring double bonds would be expected eventually to become reactivated by protonation and to react with any unreacted adjacent isoprene units. Isolated or widowed units would thus be removed with formation of condensed rings. The complete disappearance of the trialkyl unsaturation originally present in natural rubber noted by D'Ianni and confirmed by Lee and his co-workers argues against isolated units in any quantity and suggests that ring double bonds may indeed undergo a new proton attack.

3. Kinetics of Cyclization

Kinetic measurements were made by Gordon (77,78) on the sulfuric acid-catalyzed cyclization of natural rubber latex. The progress of the reaction was followed through the density of the polymer. Both direct measurement of the density of samples removed during the reaction and dilatometry were used, but no checks were made on unsaturation, it being assumed that this was linearly related to the density and that the limiting value of 57% of the original was eventually reached, in accordance with this author's statistical considerations. With acceptance of a polycyclic structure for cyclized rubber, the linear relation between density and extent of reaction is less plausible as the sizes of the condensed ring system being formed will change during the course of the reaction, and the residual unsaturation value used must be discarded. Gordon's investigations will not, therefore, be discussed in detail but an important finding was that the rates correlate well with Hammett's acidity function H_0, which is in accord with a protonation mechanism.

The kinetics of cyclization has also been investigated by Lee, Scanlan, and Watson (83) using perbenzoic acid to measure the unsaturation at varying times. Most of this work was carried out with the use of stannic chloride as a catalyst on solutions, but a small amount was also done with latex and sulfuric acid. The results were found to be in agreement with an ionic chain reaction of short chain length giving condensed rings after the van Veersen fashion.

Cyclization by reaction of only pairs of isoprene units necessitated allowance for the isolation of isoprene units which were thenceforward incapable of reaction, and Gordon showed, at least approximately, how such allowance could be made during the whole course of the reaction. The mechanism now preferred brings forward a new problem to which statistical methods must be applied. Ring systems are produced by growth along the polymer chain from one isoprene unit where a carbonium ion has been formed until there is a spontaneous termination or until the reaction chain encounters an already reacted unit or comes to the end of the polymer chain and can proceed no further. Thus for a given number of uncyclized units the rate of cyclization will depend on whether they are in a few long sequences or many short ones; in the former case, once initiation has occurred, cyclization will continue until loss of a proton or decomposition of the catalyst complex occurs spontaneously, but in the lattei the process will frequently be interrupted because no unreacted unit is available to carry it on.

In the theoretical treatment of Lee, Scanlan, and Watson a series of differential equations for the number n_x of sequences of unreacted isoprene units each containing x units was set up and a solution obtained for the case when the polymer chains are very long compared with the average size of the condensed ring systems formed.

Two parameters are involved in the treatment. k is the pseudo first-order rate constant for the formation of carbonium ions from the available double bonds (all double bonds being considered equally reactive). q is the probability of spontaneous reversion of carbonium ion to double bond, the alternative being a further cyclization step. q is assumed to be the same, regardless of the size of the cyclized sequence, and to remain constant throughout the reaction. q^{-1} is the average number of rings formed in each reaction chain in the absence of interference from already reacted units.

Thus at the start of the reaction the rate of formation of carbonium ions is kN_u, where N_u is the total number of isoprene or other monomer units, and each of these results in the formation of q^{-1} rings with loss of q^{-1} double bonds. The initial rate of reaction is then

$$kq^{-1}N_u \tag{18}$$

or if u is the fraction of the original unsaturation remaining at time t

$$(du/dt)_0 = -k/q \tag{19}$$

Thereafter the rate decreases, both because N_u is reduced and also because the reaction chains grow to length less than q^{-1}. The complete solution is found to be

$$u = 1 - \frac{1}{(1-q)} + \frac{qe^{-p}}{(1-q)(p+q-pq)} + \frac{qe^{q/(1-q)}}{(1-q)^2} \times \left[\mathrm{Ei}\left(-p - \frac{q}{1-q}\right) - \mathrm{Ei}\left(-\frac{q}{1-q}\right)\right] \tag{20}$$

where

$$p = 1 - e^{-kt} \tag{21}$$

and $-\mathrm{Ei}(-x)$ represents the tabulated exponential integral. The unsaturation remaining when reaction is complete, u_∞, is given by putting $p = 1$ and depends only on q so that its measurement determines q.

The complete disappearance of double bonds of the $R_1R_2C{=}CR_3H$ type indicates that re-formation of double bonds in the chain-termination process gives always completely substituted ones. On this assumption the fraction u^* of the double bonds remaining in the original form at time t can be obtained as

$$u^* = q(1 - p)e^{-p}/(p + q - pq) \tag{22}$$

The agreement of eqs. (20) and (22) with experimental data is good (Fig. II-1 shows a typical result) and confirms the general correctness of the assumed mechanism.

In reactions catalyzed by stannic chloride, both k and q were found to be independent of rubber concentration justifying further the assumptions, made in the theoretical treatment, that the rate of initiation of cyclization is first-order in the concentration of double bonds and that q is independent of this quantity and can be taken as constant throughout the reaction. Independence of q of the amount of unsaturation implies that transfer reactions are not important methods of termination of the growth of ring systems.

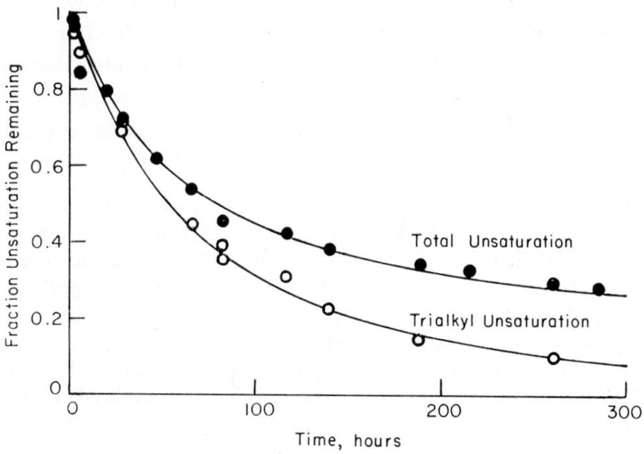

Fig. II-1. Remaining unsaturation against time for $SnCl_4$-catalyzed cyclization at 50°C. in toluene solution. Points represent experimental values for (●) total unsaturation and (O) unsaturation of the type $R_1R_2C{=}CHR_3$. The curves are theoretical ones calculated from eqs. (20) and (22) with $q = 0.2$ and $k = 2.7 \times 10^{-3}$ hr.$^{-1}$. (Taken from ref. 83.)

The parameter q was found also to be independent of the catalyst concentration although the complex pseudo constant k was strongly dependent on this quantity. It appears therefore that termination does not involve proton donation from a carbonium ion to a catalyst fragment but results from unimolecular decomposition of a catalyst–double bond complex or rearrangement of an ion-pair. In these experiments k was found to be proportional to the square of the catalyst concentration less a small constant correction which, it was thought, might be due to reaction of some stannic chloride with an impurity in the rubber.

The residual unsaturation was found to decrease with the temperature indicating that q increases and the size of the ring system decreases.

From the very limited amount of work carried out it seems that the kinetic equations are also obeyed for cyclizations of latex by sulfuric acid and that the reaction mechanism is very similar. The residual unsaturation of 36% quoted above indicates a value of q close to unity and may be contrasted with the value for q of 0.2 obtained in a stannic chloride-catalyzed reaction at the same temperature. With $q = 1$ each cyclization reaction involves just two isoprene units and then deactivation of the carbonium ion occurs. The ideas of D'Ianni and Gordon seem to have been correct for the latex cyclization in this respect. However, further reaction of the double bonds in the cyclized rings occurs with formation of small condensed systems, and this accounts for the fall in unsaturation to below 50%.

In general, a carbonium ion reaction giving polycyclic structures explains the results with both sulfuric acid and Friedel-Crafts cyclizations and is consistent with the known behavior of low molecular weight olefins. The chain structure of the rubber gives the reaction some special features, making possible the formation of large condensed ring systems.

Note Added in Proof: An account has recently appeared (84a) of an investigation of cyclized rubber by Golub and Heller. Infrared and NMR measurements were made on natural and synthetic polyisoprenes and on deuterated polyisoprenes cyclized by titanium tetrachloride in benzene at 80°C. The authors conclude that cyclized rubber consists essentially of bicyclic ring systems but it does not seem that their results would be inconsistent with a distribution of ring system sizes averaging about two. These results could then fit in well with the ideas expressed in this section. Wallenberger (84b) has also concluded on the basis of degradation studies that cyclized rubber has a polycyclic character.

C. ADDITION OF THIOLS

G. E. MEYER, L. B. TEWKSBURY, and R. M. PIERSON

Goodyear Tire and Rubber Co.

1. Introduction

The addition of thiols to olefinic double bonds of low molecular weight compounds has been known since the early work of Posner reported in 1905 (85). Either of two general mechanisms may be involved depending on the conditions of reaction. The acid- and base-catalyzed mechanisms, and particularly the free radical mechanism, have been discussed in detail by Walling (86) and Pryor (87). An interesting publication covering the addition of thiols to bridged bicyclic olefins (88) has appeared recently. The reaction of thiols with the olefinic bonds of polydienes has been the subject of various articles and patents resulting from work undertaken during the early part of the Government-sponsored synthetic rubber research and development program of 1941–1953.

Though various polymers contain olefinic double bonds which undoubtedly react with thiols under appropriate conditions, the present discussion will be limited to diene homopolymers and copolymers including natural rubber, emulsion-prepared polyisoprene, polybutadiene, and copolymers of butadiene with styrene and acrylonitrile. Presumably the reaction of thiols with polymers could occur by polar (ionic) mechanisms; however, only free radical reactions appear to have been reported. The type of product obtained depends on the nature of the principal ingredients, thiol and polymer, the type of initiator, and the conditions under which the reactions are carried out.

The topics discussed in this section are mechanism of reaction, the addition of alkanethiols, the introduction of reactive groups, isomerization of double bonds by thiols, and plasticization of rubbers by thiols.

2. Mechanism of Addition

The complete reaction for the formation of an adduct of a thiol and an olefin involves several steps and has been illustrated in several ways (86, 89–92).

$$\text{Initiator}\cdot + \text{RSH} \rightarrow \text{RS}\cdot + \text{Initiator H} \tag{23}$$

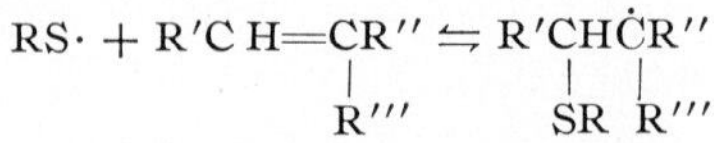
(24)

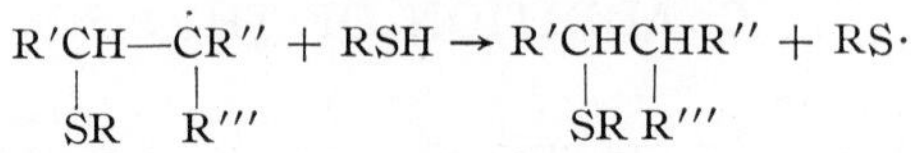
(25)

where R may be any of various monofunctional alkyl, aryl, acyl, etc., radicals which may in turn contain other substituents such as hydroxyl, carboxyl, ester, halide, etc.; R′, R″ and R‴ are portions of the polymer molecule attached to the doubly bonded carbon atoms of the original polymer. Where the double bond is in a side vinyl group, R′ and R″ are both H except for any 3,4 addition occurring in isoprene polymers, in which case R″ would be CH_3.

There is, of course, a termination step which may yield various products (92).

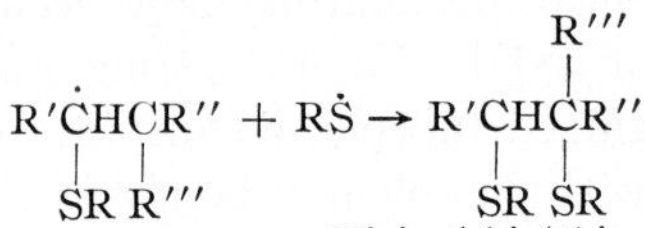
(26)

Vicinal bis(thioether)

$$2\text{RS}\cdot \rightarrow \text{RSSR} \tag{27}$$

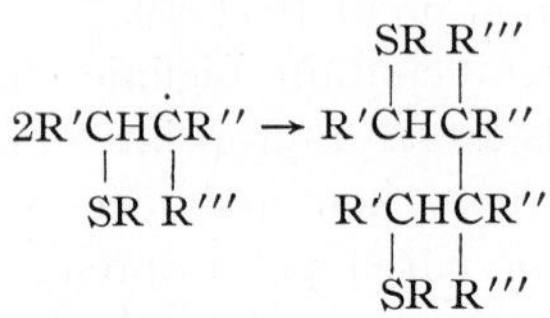
(28)

Crosslinked polymer

The termination step must normally be that represented by either step (26) or (27), or both, though crosslinked products have been reported in certain cases (93,94) when air was present during the reaction. The mechanism pictured by eq. (28) may not be the correct one under the special circumstances where the reaction mixture is in contact with oxygen.

Another reaction between thiols and polydienes that might occur would be the substitution of allylic H by RS· in the manner shown in eqs. (29) and (30). The initiator in eq. (29) could be RS· or whatever initiator is used

$$\text{Initiator} + \text{—CH}_2\text{—CH=CH—CH}_2 \rightarrow \text{—}\dot{\text{C}}\text{H—CH=CH—CH}_2\text{—} + \text{Initiator H} \tag{29}$$

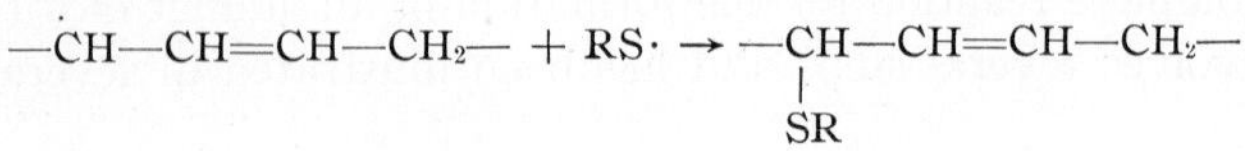
(30)

for the reaction. In the light of the discussion by Walling (86) this type of reaction has a rather good chance of occurring.

The allylic thioether shown in eq. (30) could, in turn, add a thiol at the double bond, a reaction which would result in a sulfur content higher than could be accounted for in the normal adduct. As mentioned later, saturation levels of 97–98%, based on content of sulfur, have been obtained in addition of methanethiol to polybutadiene, but higher sulfur contents have not been obtained. The test for allylic thioethers (95) with methyl iodide has given only negative results; therefore, it is believed the substitution reactions occur, if at all, to only a negligible extent.

3. Addition of Alkanethiols

The higher alkanethiols (approx. C_{12}–C_{16}) have been used extensively as chain transfer agents (modifiers) in emulsion polymerizations (96,97) with monomers such as butadiene, styrene, acrylonitrile, and chloroprene. Efforts to determine the various reactions by which alkanethiols were consumed in these systems generated much of the information on gross addition of thiols to diene polymers. Although much of the early work on synthesis and evaluation of the resulting products was done in research sponsored by and reported in communications to the Government during the period of 1943 to 1948, most of the significant data have been included in technical publications and patents (96,98–102).

Reactions of alkanethiols with polymers and copolymers of butadiene were carried out in both emulsion and solution. The studies included many of the thiols over the range of ethyl to octadecyl. It was observed that the products, as well as the extents of the reactions, depended on conditions used and whether or not oxygen was present in the reaction mixture. Certain combinations cause crosslinking. In either case, both scission and crosslinking undoubtedly occur simultaneously, to at least some extent, but the environment causes one reaction or the other to be predominant. Some attention, therefore, must be given to the conditions under which thiol–adduct reactions are carried out. The reaction was normally carried out in latex at temperatures from ambient to about 50°C., with air or oxygen as the initiator. Although residual persulfate from the initial polymerization may have been present, some results (101,102) indicate higher levels of persulfate as the initiator did not aid the reaction.

In the absence of oxygen, Serniuk, Banes, and Swaney (101,102) found that the quantity of ethanethiol reacting at 50°C. with SBR (styrene–butadiene rubber) appeared to reach a limiting value of about 25% saturation after about 6 hr. with latices short-stopped at low conversions. It was suggested this reaction took place when a particular type of structure was present in the polymer. Since the side vinyl groups resulting from 1,2 polymerization of butadiene would be expected to be the most reactive, the extent of the reaction with thiol was thought to be a measure of the quantity of this structure in the original polymer. Saturation levels as high as 89.9% were obtained when oxygen (air) was present during the addition. Later work in our own laboratory (92) has indicated the addition of alkanethiol is not sufficiently selective to give an accurate measure of the vinyl groups resulting from the 1,2 addition. Infrared absorption spectra of adducts of methanethiol with polybutadiene prepared by initiation with free radicals in the absence of oxygen show a significant absorption peak for the vinyl groups (11.0 μ) up to about 80% of total saturation. The higher primary and the secondary thiols appear to be somewhat more selective than methanethiol; however, the adduct of isopropanethiol still shows some vinyl absorption at 47% of complete saturation.

Fryling (98) observed that the presence of oxygen during the adduct reaction of alkanethiols with SBR caused cleavage of the polymeric chains resulting in low molecular weight "syrupy" products. He suggested using these products as plasticizers for diene polymers and copolymers. Since the plasticizers would be only partially saturated, it was hypothesized that they would be cured into the structure of the final compound, thus serving as vulcanizable plasticizers.

When prepared in the absence of oxygen, the number-average molecular weight of the product appears to be that calculated from the original molecular weight of the polymer, plus the quantity of added thiol. It has been shown (92) that the adduct reaction can be carried to essentially complete saturation by the use of appropriate initiators. Though 89.9% is the highest saturation reported in the presence of oxygen (101,102), it is believed that essentially complete saturation could be achieved but the product, however, would be highly degraded in a manner similar to Fryling's material. Kharasch, Nudenberg, and Mantell (103) and Oswald (104) have reported the formation of hydroxylated sulfoxides when thiols reacted with simple olefins in the presence of oxygen. The mechanism proposed by Kharasch does not provide for cleavage of the olefin.

Mechanisms for the degradation of polymers by the combined effects of oxygen and other chemical agents have been discussed by Grassie (105) and, more recently, by Foxley (106). After a hydroperoxide has been formed by oxidative attack on the α-methylene group, Foxley summarizes the reactions that lead to cleavage of polymers, in the presence of thiols, in the manner shown in eqs. (31)–(33). The reaction terminates by the combination of two RS· to form RSSR.

$$\mathrm{R'{-}CH{=}CH{-}CH(OOH)R'' \rightarrow R'{-}CH{=}CH{-}CH(O\cdot){-}R'' + \cdot OH} \qquad (31)$$

$$\mathrm{R'{-}CH{=}CH{-}CH(O\cdot)R'' \xrightarrow{\text{Chain scission}} R'{-}CH{=}CH{-}CHO + R\cdot''} \qquad (32)$$

$$\mathrm{R\cdot'' + RSH \rightarrow R''H + RS\cdot} \qquad (33)$$

A somewhat different mechanism appears possible under the conditions that exist during the addition of a relatively large amount of thiol to a polymer. Since the thiol–adduct and chemical–scission reactions would be occurring simultaneously, the steps in the cleavage might be as shown in eqs. (34)–(36). This hydroperoxide would then decompose by reactions

$$\mathrm{RS\cdot + R'CH{=}CHR'' \rightarrow R'CH(SR)\dot{C}HR''} \qquad (34)$$

$$\mathrm{R'CH(SR)\dot{C}HR'' + O_2 \rightarrow R'CH(SR)CH(OO\cdot)R''} \qquad (35)$$

$$\mathrm{R'CH(SR)CH(OO\cdot)R'' + RSH \rightarrow R'CH(SR)CH(OOH)R'' + RS\cdot} \qquad (36)$$

similar to eqs. (31)–(33) yielding RS· radicals which would participate in a continuation of the chain reaction.

The reactions represented by eqs. (34), (35), and (36) follow the concept proposed by Kharasch, Nudenberg, and Mantell (103) which eventually lead to the production of hydroxylated sulfoxides. Whether or not any of the latter type of material forms under the conditions being considered here is not known. The experimental evidence presently available does not provide any relationship between the amount of oxygen consumed and the number of chain scissions that occur. These authors report a high yield of the hydroxylated sulfoxide from the reaction of styrene, propanethiol, and oxygen carried out in hexane. In the absence of solvent, as well as when the organic reactants were in an aqueous emulsion, somewhat lower yields of the major product were obtained. The reaction of 1-octene, propanethiol, and oxygen in hexane gave a much lower yield of the corresponding hydroxylated sulfoxide. On the other hand, some of the usual olefin–thiol addition products were obtained in the reaction mixture with 1-octene but not with styrene. No products corresponding to those expected from a cleavage reaction were reported.

None of the literature cited prior to 1953 mentions the reaction of methanethiol with diene polymers. When this thiol was investigated by Pierson et al. (92), it was found to be similar to the higher members of the homologous series of thiols in many ways, but its differences in certain respects made it appear worthy of considerable study. The unique properties of the methanethiol as the first member of the series, namely, lower boiling point, higher sulfur content, and higher reactivity permit the preparation of adducts having properties which are noticeably different in degree from the products of the higher molecular weight mercaptans.

The structure of the partially saturated methanethiol-polybutadiene adducts appeared to be the expected polythioether, with unreacted double bonds scattered randomly in the polymer molecule. A typical segment of the chain would be

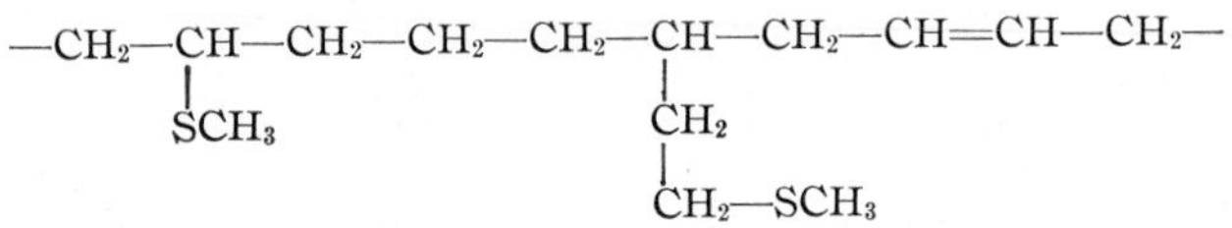

Evidence for this was derived from infrared analyses which showed the gradual reduction in intensity of absorption for olefinic double bonds and increase in absorption of CH_3S groups as the reaction of the polybutadiene with methanethiol progressed. Also, as in reactions with simple olefins, addition of methanethiol to the polyene was promoted with very small amounts of azobisisobutyronitrile (AIBN) or alkyl hydroperoxides. When large molecular excesses of methanethiol over olefinic double bonds were occasionally used, the reaction was found never to result in adducts with more than the theoretical quantity of sulfur (i.e., saturation of the double bonds was never over 97–98%). These highest saturated adducts show, by infrared, virtually no residual unsaturation; further, they cannot be adequately vulcanized by the usual sulfur-containing recipes and are very resistant to attack by oxygen or ozone.

It appears that all the primary alkanethiols up to at least dodecyl react sufficiently to yield highly saturated adducts of polybutadiene and copolymers, all of which would be expected to have greatly enhanced stability toward oxygen, ozone, and heat compared to the original unsaturated polymer. Little work has been reported on evaluation of the many possible adducts except for those prepared with methanethiol (92,107,108).

An indication of the reactivity of methanethiol with polybutadiene is the fact that adducts in the range of 97–98% saturation may be readily prepared. These saturation values are calculated from sulfur analyses assuming there was one double bond per original segment in the polybutadiene. Though various initiators such as AIBN, persulfate, and hydroperoxides yield highly saturated adducts, none has been found as convenient as γ-irradiation for small-scale laboratory preparations. With 20–50% excess methanethiol in freshly prepared, stripped but unshort-stopped, polybutadiene latex, 2–3 Mreps exposure to γ-radiation at room temperature appears to yield a product with maximum sulfur content. If the exposure to radiation is continued up to 5 or 6 Mreps, a slight but significant decrease in sulfur content occurs and the product becomes insoluble in benzene.

In the addition of thiols to styrene, it was found that relative reaction rates followed the order: primary > secondary > tertiary (103). A few experiments performed in our laboratory indicate this same order applies to the adduct reaction with diene polymers. The rate of reaction appears also to decrease as the molecular weight of the alkanethiol increases.

By use of the same procedure in emulsion found effective for polybutadiene, methanethiol adducts of natural rubber and emulsion polyisoprene were also prepared. The reaction, however, proceeded at a much lower rate for both these polymers than for polybutadiene. Adducts of the higher molecular weight alkanethiols with natural rubber and polyisoprene were not attempted.

4. Introduction of Reactive Groups

The earliest reported effort to react thiols with a polymer appears to be that of Holmberg (109,110), who obtained a material having a composition very close to that expected for a product containing 1 mole of thioglycolic acid per segment of isoprene in natural rubber. This product was prepared by soaking pale crepe in thioglycolic acid for a period of 16 months. Cunneen (111–113), on the other hand, obtained very low levels of reaction between thioglycolic acid and natural rubber under conditions thought to be favorable for the reaction. Serniuk, Banes, and Swaney (101,102) reported they were able to carry the reaction to 18.8% saturation in solution in benzene cements. Later, Cunneen, Moore, and Shephard (93) pursued the study of the properties of natural rubber crosslinked by the reactions of groups previously introduced by the addition of thiol compounds containing the desired reactive groups. In reaction mixtures containing sufficient thiol ester to saturate 13.6% of the double bonds in natural rubber, up to 91% of the ethyl thioglycolate reacted. The higher esters of thioglycolic acid as well as the ethyl esters of higher molecular weight thiol acids reacted to lower extents. These reactions were carried out in latex for 7 days at 0°C. and pH 1–2 with 2 mole-% *p*-menthanehydroperoxide as the initiator. Considerable gel was reported present in the adduct from ethyl thioglycolate. Whether or not gel was present in the other adducts is not indicated. The description of their procedure indicates the reaction mixture was exposed to air during the reaction period. In view of later results (to be described) air may have caused the formation of gel.

Both Serniuk (114) and Brown (115,116) have reported the introduction of carboxylic acid groups by the addition of thioglycolic and other mercaptoacids to polymers and copolymers of butadiene. Organic peroxides and hydroperoxides were found to be good free radical initiators for the reaction.

Marvel and co-workers (94) used the thiol adduct reaction to introduce polar groups such as nitrile, hydroxy, thioester, and carboxylic acid into polybutadiene. The additions of the water-soluble substituted thiols, 2-mercaptoethanol, 1-thiosorbitol, and mercaptoacetic acid were carried out in solution in dioxane with AIBN as the initiator. They observed the formation of gel if oxygen was not excluded from the reaction mixture. This result is quite different from the degradative effect of air on the addition of alkanethiols to polybutadiene and copolymers of butadiene already described.

5. Isomerization by Thiols

The catalysis of *cis–trans* isomerization of olefinic double bonds by a variety of agents has been recognized for a long time. Recent observations have established that thiols produce isomerization by a free radical process (91). A detailed treatment of the isomerization by thiols and other reagents is presented in the preceding section of this chapter. Thiols that form relatively stable thiyl radicals such as thiophenol, thiolbenzoic acid, and the naphthyl homologues cause isomerization with a low level of actual adduct formation. By using the combination of ultraviolet light and various chemicals, including thio-2-naphthol, Golub (117) converted 1,4-polybutadiene having a high *cis* content to an equilibrium mixture of the *cis* and *trans* forms. Though intermediate free radical addition products were believed to be part of the isomerization mechanism, no evidence for the presence of the completed adduct (i.e., thioether) was found in the isolated product.

Ritter (118) suggested an isomerization resulting from the shifting of double bonds in the rubber molecules, but efforts to establish this by infrared absorption spectra were not successful.

Some semiquantitative work in our own laboratory has shown that isomerization of *cis*-1,4-polybutadiene proceeds rapidly and simultaneously with the adduct reaction of methanethiol. In solution in benzene at 50°C. with 2% AIBN on the polymer and sufficient methanethiol to completely saturate, considerable change in *cis/trans* ratio of the residual double bonds was indicated by infrared absorption spectra at low levels of adduct reaction. Starting with a polybutadiene having over 90% *cis* double bonds, the residual double bonds appeared to have about a 20/80 *cis/trans* ratio by the time the polymer had become 15% saturated with methanethiol.

6. Plasticization of Elastomers by Thiols

Certain aromatic thiols (119–121) have been widely used industrially as plasticizing agents for rubbers, both natural and synthetic, and have received some attention in the reclaiming of rubber (122). Plasticization, as considered here, results from cleavage of the polymer molecules yielding lower molecular weight materials. Mastication is perhaps a more appropriate title for much of the experimental work for which data are available since the shearing action of rubber processing machinery is an important part of the process. On the other hand, Hastings (123) has shown that xylenethiol, dispersed in natural rubber latex prior to coagulation of the rubber, causes plasticization during the mild heating (ca. 60–75°C. for about 4 days) required for the preparation of smoked sheet. Both Kheraskova (124) and Montu (125) have studied the effect of aromatic thiols on the plasticization of natural rubber in solution. In general, at a particular temperature, the rate and extent of plasticization were found to be proportional to the amount of aromatic thiol used. Kheraskova's results indicated that nearly all the thiol consumed in the plasticization was converted to the disulfide; therefore, he, as well as Montu, concluded the aromatic thiols merely accelerated the oxidative cleavage of rubber.

The mastication of rubber has been studied over a period of years by Watson and co-workers (126,127). They conclude that the plasticizing action of thiols results from the "radical acceptor" nature of the thiols. The free radicals on the terminals of the polymer fragments, formed by the disruptive shearing action of the milling process, are so effectively scavenged through reaction with the thiols that there is prevented much of the normal combination of radicals to form large molecules which are the same as or similar to the original polymer chains. The subject of mastication and ensuing chemical reactions is discussed in Chapter XIV.

D. HALOGENATION

PETER J. CANTERINO

W. R. Grace & Co.

The chemistry of the halogenation of rubber is complex. Several reactions occur simultaneously. The halogenation technology for synthetic polymers is different from that for natural rubber. It is not surprising then that, although chlorinated rubber represents one of the earliest chemical modifications of a polymer, even now it is difficult to present a complete description of the reactions and mechanisms involved in its preparation.

1. Chemistry of the Chlorination Process

a. Natural Rubber

The early investigators were concerned chiefly with the elucidation of the chemical structure of natural rubber. Using the chlorination of rubber as a method of learning about its structure, they obtained unstable, complex chlorinated products whose analyses were difficult to interpret. It was not until the 1930's that serious attention was given to the chlorination reaction itself. An historical review of the work up to that period has been given by Marchionna (128). A good summary of the views of that time concerning the nature of the chlorination of rubber is reported by Clark (129), who presents the view of Kirchhoff in eq. (37). One and two molecules of

$$(\text{—CH}_2\text{—CH}{=}\underset{\displaystyle\text{CH}_3}{\underset{|}{\text{C}}}\text{—CH}_2\text{—})_x + (\text{Cl}_2)_x \rightarrow (\text{—CH}_2\text{—CHCl—CCH}_3\text{Cl—CH}_2\text{—})_x \tag{37}$$

hydrochloric acid would then split off giving the following compounds:

$$(\text{—CH}{=}\text{CH—}\underset{\displaystyle\text{CH}_3}{\underset{|}{\text{C}}}\text{Cl—CH}_2\text{—})_x \text{ and } (\text{—CH}{=}\text{CH—}\underset{\displaystyle\text{CH}_3}{\underset{|}{\text{C}}}{=}\text{CH—})_x$$

Addition of chlorine to the double bonds resulted in trichloro and tetrachloro derivatives.

It is interesting to note that even recently (130) little was generally understood regarding the nature of the chlorination reaction although various investigators had already published work on the substitutive and additive nature of the chlorination reaction accompanied by cyclization (131–134).

The best picture available now as to the reactions involved in the chlorination of natural rubber is based on the work of many investigators with important contributions by Bloomfield (132,133), Staudinger and Staudinger (131), Ramakrishnan, Raghunath, and Pande (135,136), and Troussier (137). During chlorination four reactions may occur: substitutive chlorination, additive chlorination, cyclization, and crosslinking. The solvent and halogenating agent influence the extent and order of these reactions.

With chlorine as the halogenating agent for rubber dissolved in carbon tetrachloride, these four reactions proceed as shown in eqs. (38)–(41).

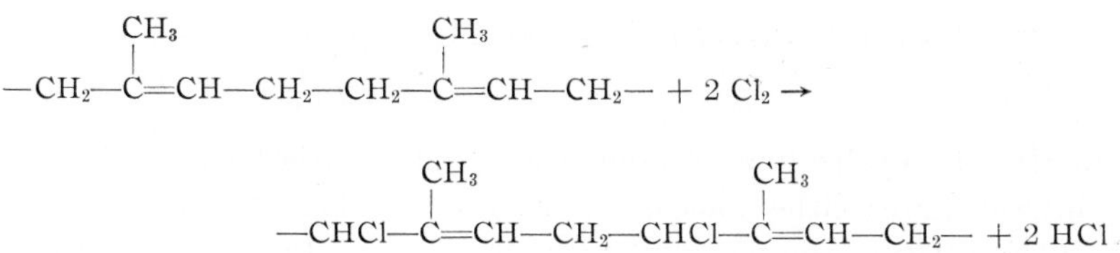

(38)

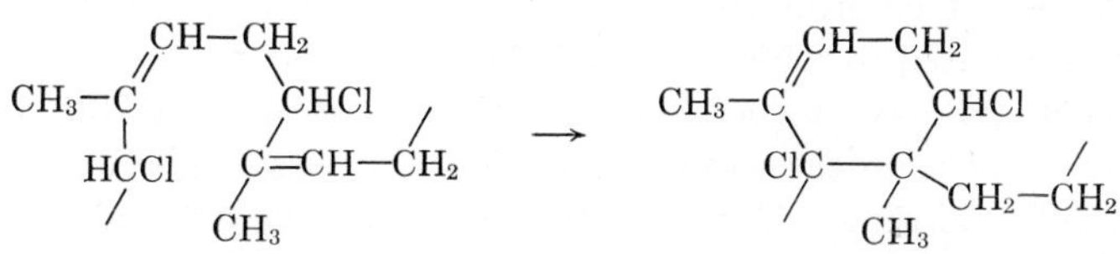

(39)

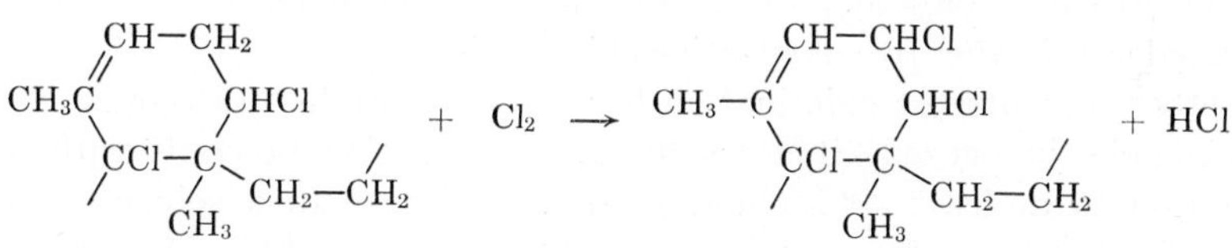

(40)

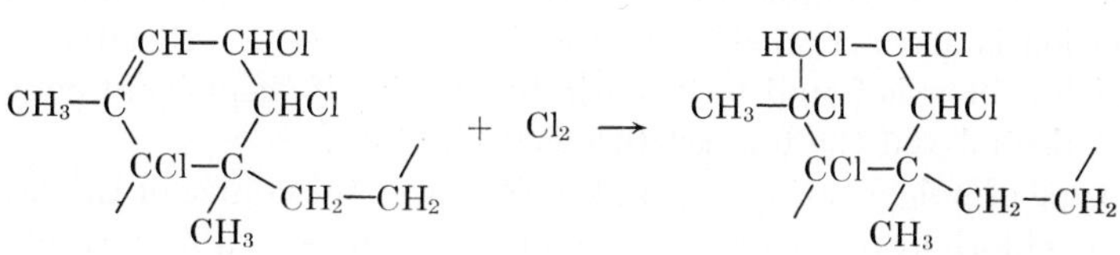

(41)

From the experimental data available, the mechanism for reactions (38)–(40) is not definitely characterized. For example the substitution reaction is probably ionic (137a), as in eq. (42).

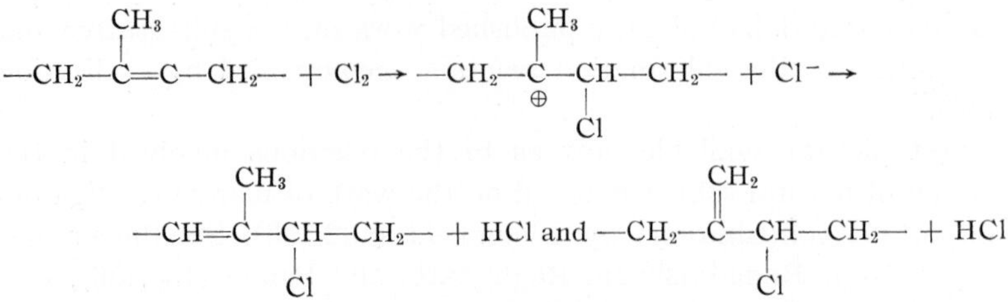

(42)

However, it could also be free radical, as shown in eq. (43), resulting in the same evolution of hydrogen chloride and the same residual unsaturation:

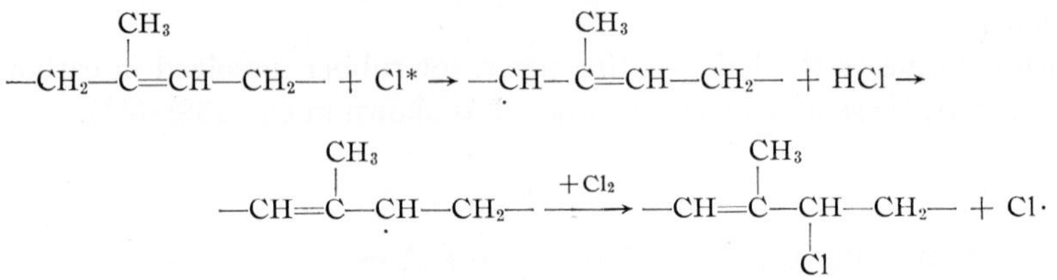

(43)

Similarly, the cyclization reaction could follow either path. The reactive intermediates, either ionic or free radical, could react with the double bond on the adjacent isoprene unit to result in cyclization and addition of a chloride ion or chlorine free radical; alternatively, an allylic hydrogen could be eliminated to reform a double bond.

The reactions may proceed concurrently, but it appears (135–137) that the two stages of substitution and cyclization occur first to give a product containing 35% chlorine. Then, further substitution and addition occur according to eqs. (40) and (41). Beyond this the chlorination can be continued still further by substitutive chlorination.

In other solvents the chlorination has not been studied so thoroughly. For example, in benzene it appears that the reaction proceeds without cyclization to at least 30% chlorine content (138). In a solvent composed of 60% by volume of methylcyclohexane and 40% of benzene, chlorination is accompanied by a crosslinking reaction. Reaction of bromine with rubber is found to be entirely additive if the solvent contains a trace of alcohol and the temperature is 0°C. (132).

The type of halogenating agent also influences the course of the reaction. Additive chlorination reactions are obtained when rubber reacts with chlorine from phenyl iododichloride or sulfuryl chloride in the presence of a peroxide (133). Ramakrishnan, Raghunath, and Pande studied the reaction of phenyl iododichloride with natural rubber in more detail (136). It was confirmed that the reaction between the chlorine liberated from the phenyl iododichloride and rubber dissolved in carbon tetrachloride proceeded by an additive reaction as revealed by the decrease in unsaturation during chlorination. Cyclization also occurs. It was observed that for the first 25 chlorine atoms introduced per 100 isoprene units, about 23 double bonds were lost. The next 105 chlorine atoms introduced caused a further decrease of about 53 double bonds—one double bond per two chlorine atoms. Only very small quantities of hydrogen chloride were formed in the first stages. This led these investigators to postulate as one of the possibilities that the radical adduct formed by addition of a chlorine atom to a double bond could stabilize itself by the loss of a hydrogen atom from the carbon next to the remaining double bond as in eq. (44).

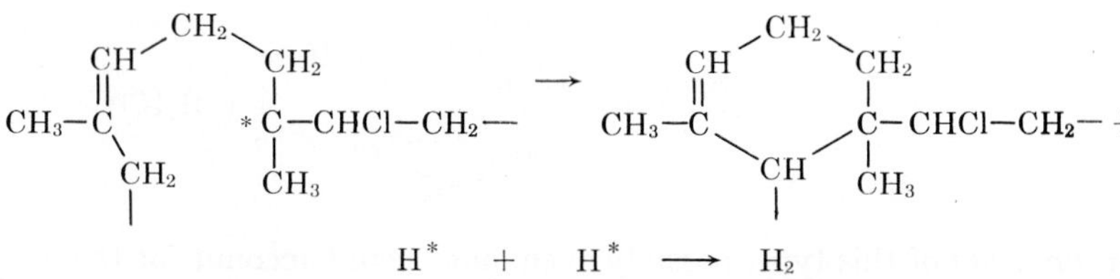

(44)

Bloomfield showed that *N*-bromosuccinimide gives a substitutive halogenation accompanied by cyclization as shown in eq. (45).

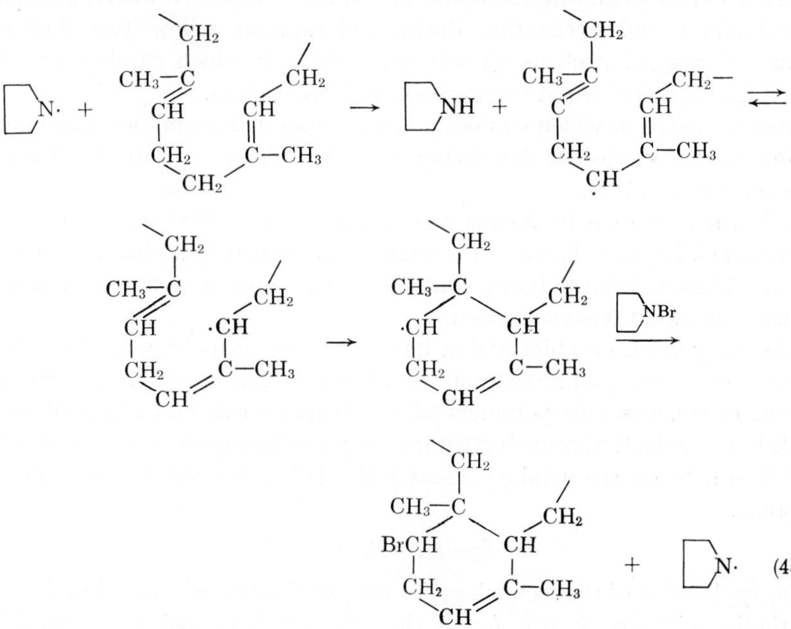

(45)

In view of this result, it is more likely that the reaction with phenyl iododichloride proceeds as in eq. (46).

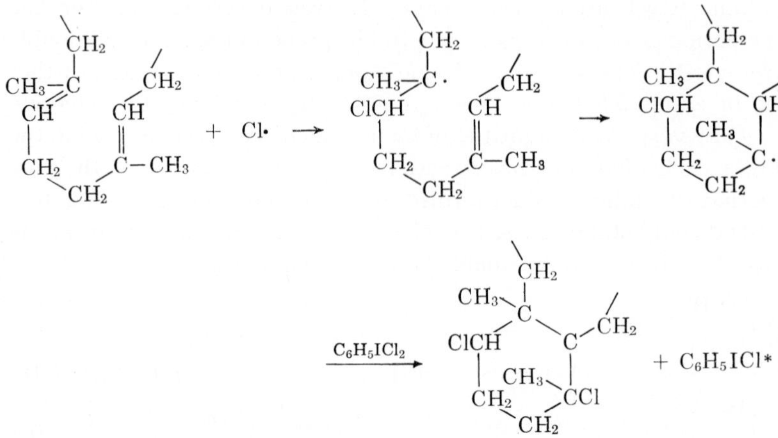

(46)

A mechanism of this type, possibly even ionic, could account for the disappearance of one double bond per chlorine atom.

Under certain conditions gelation occurs during chlorination. This has been attributed to an intermolecular cyclization (137). However, gelation (crosslinking) and cyclization during chlorination follow two distinct paths. A reagent such as phosphorus trichloride which catalyzes cyclization during chlorination suppresses crosslinking (138).

Another reaction which can occur during chlorination is the addition of hydrogen chloride to the double bonds of the rubber. There is evidence that this occurs (135).

It has been shown by Kraus and Reynolds (134) that emulsion-polymerized polyisoprene behaves the same as natural rubber during chlorination. The emulsion polymer contained 10% vinyl branching and hence showed somewhat less cyclization.

The early work on chlorination has been done on polymers whose fine structure was not well known and could not be varied. With the recent advent of stereospecific polymers whose structure can be fairly well controlled, it may be that some further investigations using these new polymers will shed light on the nebulous areas still existing in chlorination of polyisoprene.

b. Synthetic Polymers

On application of the technology for the chlorination of natural rubber to synthetic polymers, it was found that the synthetic polymers behaved differently. For example, chlorination of rubbery polymers and copolymers of butadiene dissolved in carbon tetrachloride normally resulted in the irreversible precipitation of polymer during chlorination (131,139, 140). To avoid this, various investigators took different approaches. Some highly modified polymers (141,142), as well as those subjected to a disaggregation process (143), gave soluble products. It was also possible to obtain soluble products by using solvents other than carbon tetrachloride, such as benzene, chloroform, ethylene dichloride, or mixtures of solvents (140,141).

In general, the chlorination of butadiene polymers differs from that of the polyisoprenes in that no cyclization reaction occurs, while the crosslinking reaction is much more pronounced. A study of the chlorination of polybutadiene compared to natural rubber has been made (138).

The chlorination of polybutadiene in solution in benzene proceeds by addition. Little hydrogen chloride is evolved until all the double bonds are saturated. In carbon tetrachloride some substitutive chlorination occurs, but very little in the early stages. A crosslinking reaction is prominent, but there is no evidence of cyclization.

The mechanism for the chlorination reaction, considering the addition of chlorine to olefins in nonpolar solvents, may be represented as in eq. (47). The crosslinking reaction in unsaturated polymers then occurs by the reaction of the positively charged intermediate of eq. (47) with a double bond in an adjacent polymer chain. With a polymer of high molecular weight, this reaction represented by eq. (48) gives a three-dimensional network even if it occurs to only a limited extent.

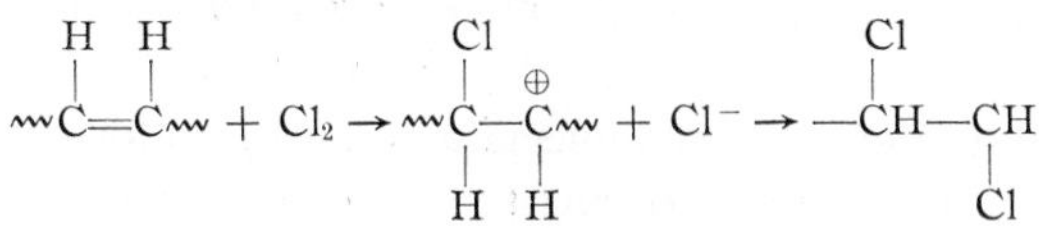
(47)

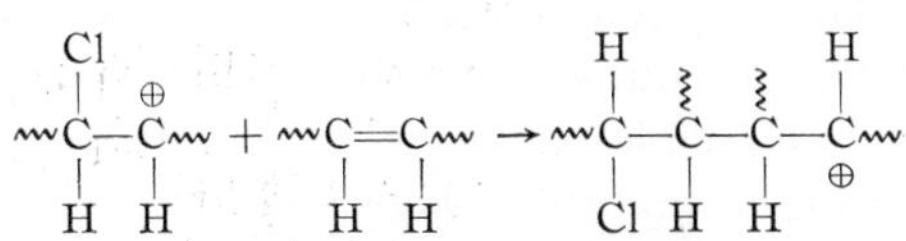
(48)

Bartlett has shown that in halogenations conducted in a reactive solvent the positively charged intermediate of eq. (48) may react with the solvent as shown in eq. (49):

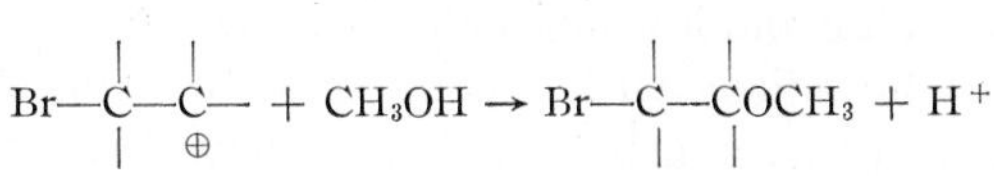
(49)

The crosslinking reaction during the chlorination of butadiene in carbon tetrachloride may then be eliminated by having present a reagent which can furnish a nucleophilic group, and thus decrease the possibility of the occurrence of the reaction according to eq. (48). When the reagent present is phosphorus trichloride or pentachloride, a chloride group is available so that the product contains only chlorine. With other polar compounds present, as for example methanol, the product also contains methoxy groups (144).

When an unsaturated copolymer contains polar functional groups, these groups will lead to crosslinking. For example, in chlorinating a copolymer of butadiene and acrylic acid crosslinking would occur as shown in eq. (50).

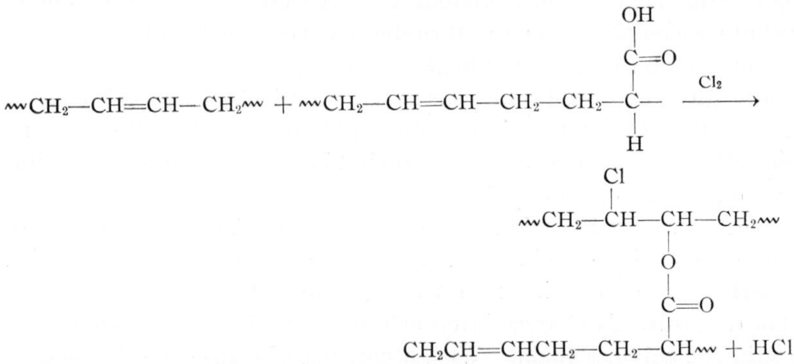

(50)

This reaction may be minimized to the point where no gelation occurs by halogenation in a solvent to which is added another reactive solvent, such as alcohol or acetic acid; soluble chlorinated copolymers are thereby obtained.

When a polybutadiene of low molecular weight is chlorinated, the crosslinking reaction, although still occurring, is not extensive enough to bring about incipient gelation. It is possible then to prepare in carbon tetrachloride a chlorinated polybutadiene resin which is not crosslinked. However, the products are friable resins of low molecular weight. By simultaneously chlorinating a mixture of high and low molecular weight resins it is still possible to avoid incipient gelation (145). A product of any desired viscosity with corresponding physical properties may thus be obtained by varying the ratio of high to low molecular weight polymer. These products are, in effect, chlorinated graft homopolymers between polybutadienes of high and low molecular weight.

Copolymers of butadiene with styrene give the same results as polybutadiene. Many other synthetic polymers have been chlorinated, and attempts to obtain soluble chlorinated products from polymers and copolymers of diolefins are the subjects of a voluminous patent literature.

c. Hydrohalogenation

When in solution, the polyisoprenes readily add hydrogen chloride. According to the study made by Staudinger (131), the addition of the hydrogen chloride is accompanied also by cyclization. This is likely to come about by splitting off hydrogen chloride to give a cyclic structure; another way for the cyclization to occur is shown in eq. (51). The other hydrogen halides add similarly to natural rubber.

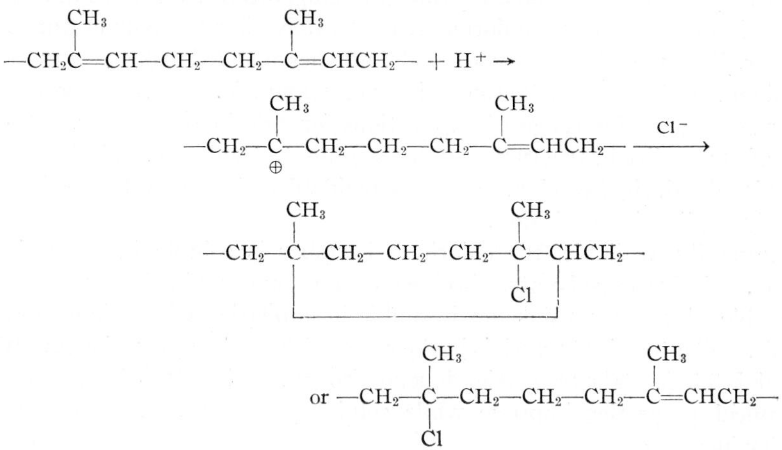

(51)

2. Manufacture and Uses

a. Chlorinated Rubber

The process for the chlorination of rubber consists essentially of dissolving the rubber in carbon tetrachloride, injecting chlorine into the solution, and continuing the chlorination until the rubber contains approximately 66% and higher chlorine. The solution is then passed into an aqueous alkaline bath or into hot water. Detailed descriptions of the process have been made (129,146).

The main problems encountered in the chlorination of rubber have been the stability of the product and control of its solution viscosity. The former has been achieved by carefully controlling the chlorination temperature, the degree of chlorination and by the methods of processing of the product. Using vessels from nickel for coagulation (147) is an example of the precautions taken. Stabilizers, such as epoxides, are used with the finished product. The viscosity of the product is usually controlled by mastication of the rubber before chlorination or the introduction of oxygen during chlorination.

Since chlorination of dilute solutions of rubber is expensive, attempts have been made to carry out the chlorinations of rubber in the latex form (148–150). Cationic or nonionic stabilizers are used to stabilize the latex. The latex is usually strongly acidified. After coagulation, washing, and drying, a product containing 65–68% chlorine is obtained as a white powder. A 20% solution in toluene gives a viscosity of 20 cpoise and higher.

Chlorinated rubber is stable at ambient temperatures, but decomposes with evolution of hydrogen chloride at moderately elevated temperatures. However, it has good stability to acids, alkalies and oxidizing agents at normal temperatures. Furthermore, it is nonflammable. These properties have suggested a wide range of applications for chlorinated rubber. Because of its cyclized structure and high content of chlorine, chlorinated rubber is a hard, rigid product not easily moldable. Hence in its uses it is generally applied from solution.

As generally available, the chlorinated rubber is soluble in aromatic solvents, chlorinated solvents, alkyl esters, and many plasticizers; it is compatible with many resins and insoluble in aliphatic hydrocarbons and alcohols. The tensile strength is in the range of 4000–4500 psi; elongation at break is 3.5%. The properties depend also on the viscosity of the resin. Mechanical properties improve while solubility becomes poorer as the viscosity increases.

The five most common viscosities (measured on a 20% resin solution in toluene) manufactured are 5, 10, 20, 125, and 1000 cpoise. The lower viscosity materials have found wide application in chemically resistant paints, and printing inks; the higher viscosity resins in paper and textile coatings, adhesives and other special finishes (130,151). The materials obtained by chlorination of polyisoprene (152) and polybutadiene (138) have similar properties.

b. Rubber Hydrochloride

The process for the preparation of rubber hydrochloride has been described by Polson (146) based on Calvert's patent (153). Rubber is dissolved in chloroform to give a 6% solution, and anhydrous hydrogen chloride is introduced until the product is essentially saturated. Excess acid is neutralized, and the product is recovered. In practice, stabilizers.

plasticizers and other additives are introduced into the rubber hydrochloride solution, the solution is filtered and cast onto a moving belt to give a film of the resin as the product. The film is tough, tear resistant, and flexible. Its main use has been (Pliofilm, The Goodyear Tire and Rubber Company) in packaging for a variety of products, especially foodstuffs. It has been replaced by other flexible plastics such as polyethylene and poly(vinylidene chloride) in many applications chiefly because of cost.

E. EPOXIDATION

Frank P. Greenspan

FMC Corporation

1. Epoxidation Reactions

Unsaturated compounds can be oxidized in a variety of ways to give oxiranes (1,2-epoxides) and/or 1,2-glycols (154–156). These reactions are known as epoxidation and hydroxylation, respectively. They are conveniently considered together because of the structural relationship of the respective products, the similarity of preparative methods, and the ease of transition from 1,2-epoxy compounds to the corresponding glycols. Many of these reactions have assumed the status of unit processes and are employed for the manufacture of tonnage organic chemicals (155–157).

a. Air Oxidation

Vapor-phase oxidation by air with a silver catalyst is widely employed for lower olefins (158), as ethylene. This process accounts for the bulk of ethylene oxide and ethylene glycol manufactured today. Reaction efficiencies fall off with increasing carbon chain length.

b. Hypochlorous Acid

Reactions of olefinic hydrocarbons with hypochlorous acid, followed by dehydrochlorination, proceeds well with lower olefins. This process accounts for the bulk of propylene oxide and propylene glycol manufactured today (158).

c. Hydrogen Peroxide and/or Peracids

Hydrogen peroxide reacts with olefinic material under well defined conditions to give epoxy compounds and/or glycols. Alkaline hydrogen peroxide (159,160) uniquely reacts with double bonds conjugate with carbonyl groups (α,β-unsaturated aldehydes or ketones) to give epoxides in good yields. The preparation of glycidaldehyde and α-methylglycidaldehyde from acrolein and methacrolein, respectively, with this type of reagent has recently been described (161–163). The reaction of hydrogen peroxide with olefins upon exposure to light has been described by Milas, Kurz, and Anslow (164). Milas and Sussman (165) discussed the reaction of olefins with hydrogen peroxide in solution in anhydrous tertiary alcohols in the presence of osmium tetroxide.

The use of hydrogen peroxide to react with olefin materials in the presence of aliphatic acids represents one of the preferred epoxidation-hydroxylation procedures. This reaction proceeds through the intermediate formation of an organic peracid and is further discussed later. Epoxidation of olefins with hydrogen peroxide in the presence of the acids or acid salts of heavy metals of Group VI of the Periodic Table has been described in the patent literature (166–169). Tungsten is a preferred catalyst. These methods have assumed commercial significance for the production of synthetic glycerine. The reaction probably proceeds through the intermediate formation of an inorganic peracid of the heavy metal catalyst employed and may be considered as a special type of *in situ* peracid reaction.

d. Organic Peracids

The reaction of organic peracids with double bonds, originally discovered by Prileschajew (170) in 1909 has assumed major preparative importance in recent years in the manufacture of epoxy fatty acid ester plasticizers (171), epoxy insecticides (172), hydroxy steroids (173), olefin and terpene epoxides (174,175), and epoxy resins (176). It is convenient to delineate those reactions carried out by the use of a preformed peracid and those utilizing an *in situ* peracid technique.

(1) Preformed Peracid

The reaction of organic peracids with unsaturated compounds is general for compounds with isolated double bonds. Reactivity of a given olefinic material with a peracid is dependent upon the specific peracid employed and the nature and extent of substituent groups neighboring the double bonds. Swern (177) has presented an excellent interpretation of this reaction mechanism. Electron attracting groups, e.g., carboxy, keto, aldehyde, attached to or near the nucleophilic double bonds slow down or prevent the reaction of a peracid (electrophilic peroxide oxygen) with the double bond. By contrast, electron-releasing groups, e.g., alkyl attached to or in close proximity to a double bond, increase the speed of reaction. Table II-1 illustrates neighboring group influences on the kinetics of the epoxidation of specific olefins.

TABLE II-1
Specific Reaction Rates for the Reaction of Olefins with Peracids

Olefin	Peracid	Temp., °C.	$K \times 10^3$, mole/l./min.	Reference
Ethylene	Peracetic	25.8	0.19	218, 219, 220
Propylene	Peracetic	25.8	4.2	218, 219, 220
1-Pentene	Peracetic	25.8	4.3	218, 219, 220
2-Pentene	Peracetic	25.8	93–95	218, 219, 220
2-Butene	Peracetic	25.8	93	219, 220
2-Methyl-1-propene	Peracetic	25.8	92	218, 219, 220
2-Methyl-2-butene	Peracetic	25.8–26.4	980–1240	218, 219, 220
Cyclopentene	Peracetic	25.8	185–195	218, 219, 220
Cyclohexene	Peracetic	25.8	129	217, 218, 219, 220
1-Methylcyclopentene	Peracetic	25.8	2220	218, 219, 220
Oleic acid	Peracetic	18	36	222, 223
Elaidic acid	Peracetic	18	23	222, 223
Ricinoleic acid	Peracetic	18	26	222, 223
Sorbic acid	Perbenzoic	20	0.2	221
Styrene	Peracetic	25.8	11.3	218, 219, 220
Allylbenzene	Peracetic	25.8–26.1	1.9–2.0	218, 219, 220

Classically, aromatic peracids, perbenzoic (170) and perphthalic (178), were employed in the laboratory for synthesis of a variety of epoxides. These peracids are generally prepared immediately before use by reaction of the corresponding organic peroxide with sodium methylate (179). For isolated double bonds, reactions are frequently quantitative. Smit (180) has proposed the use of a dilute solution of peracetic acid in solvent as a reagent for quantitative determination of unsaturation instead of iodine number or bromine number. In recent years the aliphatic peracids, performic and peracetic, have achieved dominant importance as epoxidizing reagents. Because of instability (181), performic acid is generally employed via an *in situ* process rather than being preformed in a separate reactor for subsequent use.

Stable equilibrium solutions of peracetic acid can readily be prepared by reaction of acetic acid and concentrated hydrogen peroxide in the presence of a strong acidic catalyst (181). A 40% peracetic acid made in this way has been available commercially for many years (182). These solutions of peracetic in acetic acid find application in the bleaching of synthetic textile fibers (183), as an industrial bactericide-germicide (184), as well as in epoxidation-hydroxylation reactions.

An anhydrous peracetic acid can be made by interaction of acetic anhydride with hydrogen peroxide (180,185). The reaction is vigorously exothermic and difficult to control. Special techniques (186) have been developed for safe preparation of concentrated anhydrous solutions of peracid.

More recently, air oxidation of acetaldehyde has assumed commercial importance for the preparation of peracetic acid solution for captive use. Phillips and colleagues have described the liquid-phase air oxidation of acetaldehyde at low temperatures (187,188) to an acetaldehyde peracetate which is then pyrolyzed to give a solution of peracetic acid. These authors have described a wide variety of reactions carried out with both the intermediate acetaldehyde peracetate and the peracetic acid solution derived therefrom (189–192). Bludworth (193) has described an alternate vapor-phase oxidation of acetaldehyde to peracetic acid. This process has attracted renewed interest and a number of refinements have been described in recent patent literature (194,195).

(2) *In Situ* Peracid

Epoxidation reactions can likewise be carried out without a preformed peracid, by utilizing conditions that allow concurrent formation and consumption of peracid within the reaction medium. These processes are known as "*in situ* reactions." Most commonly, an *in situ* epoxidation employs hydrogen peroxide as the oxidant in the presence of an aliphatic acid solution of the olefinic material to be epoxidized. Under well defined conditions, peracid formation and concurrent consumption by the olefin can be carried out with good efficiency. *In situ* processes of this type account for the bulk of industrial epoxidation reactions carried out at this time with peroxides. The reaction is schematically illustrated in eq. (52).

$$H_2O_2 + RCOOH \overset{H^+}{\rightleftharpoons} RCOOOH + H_2O$$

$$RCOOOH + -\overset{|}{C}=\overset{|}{C}- \rightarrow -\overset{|}{C}\underset{\diagdown O \diagup}{—}\overset{|}{C}- + RCOOH \qquad (52)$$

Neiderhauser and Koroly (196) have described *in situ* epoxidation with formic acid. Greenspan and Gall (197–200) have described *in situ* epoxidation procedures with acetic acid. Generally, the mole ratios of acetic acid to ethylenic unsaturation must be carefully controlled. A strong acidic catalyst such as sulfuric acid (197–199), an alkanesulfonic acid, or a sulfonic acid type of cation exchange resin (200) is employed with the *in situ* peracetic acid process. Reaction conditions are set so as to maximize formation of the desired epoxide and minimize epoxy ring opening (hydroxylation reaction). Solvents are found beneficial in repressing ring opening reactions. Many modifications of this process have been described in the literature. Adaptation of this reaction to continuous epoxidation procedures has been described (201–203), as have *in situ* epoxidations with acetic anhydride and hydrogen peroxide (204,205).

2. Epoxidation of Polymers

The epoxidation of unsaturated polymers is best carried out by use of organic peracids particularly the lower aliphatic peracids. Requirements of the reaction place some limitation on the molecular weight of the poly-

TABLE II-2

Unsaturated Polymers Converted to Epoxides by Oxidation with Peracids and/or Hydrogen Peroxide

Polymer or copolymer from	Description	Type of polymerization	Reference
Butadiene	Liquid	Sodium	224
Butadiene	Rubber	Free radical	224
Isoprene	Liquid rubber	Free radical	224
Piperylene			225
Butadiene–styrene	Liquid	Sodium	226
Butadiene–styrene	Solid	Free radical	226
Butadiene–acrylonitrile	Liquid		226
Butadiene–styrene	Rubber	Free radical	226
Butadiene–styrene	Rubber	Sodium	223
Butadiene–xylene	Liquid	Sodium	227
Cyclopentadiene	Solid	Thermal	228
Methylcyclopentadiene	Solid	Thermal	228
Hydrocarbon resins	Liquid and solid		229
Isoprene–styrene	Solid	Free radical	226
Isoprene–isobutylene	Liquid	Ionic	234
Isoprene–styrene–acrylonitrile	Solid		226
Cyclopentadiene–styrene–methylstyrene	Solid	Free radical	226
Alkenyl aromatic hydrocarbons		Alkylation with dienes	230
Propadiene–ethylene		Coordination catalyst	231
Vinyl chloride	Partially dehydrochlorinated		232
Rubber (depolymerized)	Liquid		234

mer. In general, the unsaturated polymer should be liquid or a solid readily soluble in suitable solvents, although the epoxidation of polymer latices has recently been reported (206). Steric factors are important in that the double bonds in the polymer must be accessible to the peracid. Neighboring groups play an important role, influencing the speed of the double bond reaction, as well as the tendency toward ring opening of the formed epoxide. Thus, highly alkyl-substituted double bonds will react much faster than will isolated double bonds. In turn, the more highly alkylated double bond structures will give rise to epoxides which in turn will have greater tendency toward ring opening and/or isomerization under the conditions for epoxidation.

The epoxidation of a wide variety of polymers has been described in the literature. These include homopolymers and copolymers of dienes such as butadiene, isoprene, and cyclopentadiene. Epoxidized polybutadienes are available commercially as Oxiron* resins. The polymers used have been prepared by thermal, free radical, sodium, ionic, and stereospecific techniques. A representative grouping of polymers that have been epoxidized are illustrated in Table II-2.

A number of secondary reactions of epoxides can occur under the conditions of epoxidation. These include ring opening to the glycol derivative, isomerization to aldehydes or ketones and unsaturated alcohols, and polymerization with another epoxide or hydroxyl group to give ether linkages.

In general, epoxidation of an unsaturated polymer results in a product that may include one or more of the epoxide secondary reaction products noted above, along with the expected epoxide. Reaction conditions are generally chosen to optimize epoxide formation and minimize secondary ring-opening reactions. These conditions are favored by carrying out the reaction under mild conditions at relatively low temperatures. The presence of organic solvents depresses ring opening. In turn, large amounts of aliphatic acids, the presence of strong acid catalysts, high temperatures, and prolonged times of reaction are all deleterious to the survival of the epoxide. Thus, if reactions are carried out with large excesses of aliphatic acids, hydroxylation occurs. The double bonds may be partially or completely reacted, dependent upon the molar ratios of hydrogen peroxide or peracid employed. The initial reactions are quite rapid, falling off with time. In practice, it is found that the oxirane values obtained are somewhat below theoretical. At high levels of oxirane oxygen, further formation of epoxide is counterbalanced by destruction of epoxide through

* Registered trade mark of FMC Corp.

secondary reactions. In general, preformed peracids give higher efficiencies in conversion of double bonds than do *in situ* processes. Following will be found representative procedures for the epoxidation of polybutadiene with preformed peracetic acid or by the *in situ* method with hydrogen peroxide.

a. Epoxidation of Polybutadiene by Preformed Peracetic Acid Method

A 300 g. portion of liquid polybutadiene with a viscosity of 15 poise at 25°C., is dissolved in 300 g. of toluene, 6.0 g. of sodium acetate is added; to this mixture is added, slowly over a period of 1 hr., 372 g. of peracetic acid (41%) (corresponds to 50% of the stoichiometric amount required for complete oxidation of the double bonds present). The mixture is maintained at 30°C. for $4^1/_2$ hr. The product is washed with water, neutralized with aqueous sodium hydroxide, again washed with water, and finally distilled free of solvent and residual water at 80–150°C. under vacuum (1–10 mm.). A product analyzing 6.6% oxirane oxygen is thus obtained.

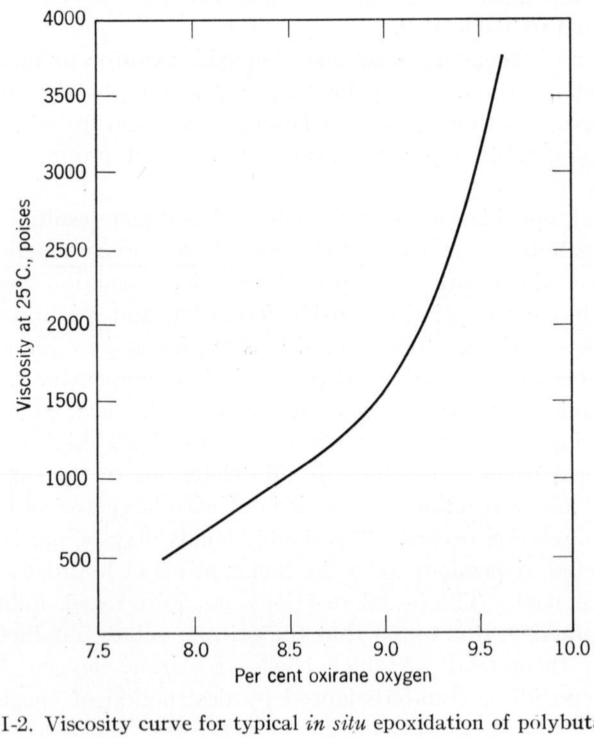

Fig. II-2. Viscosity curve for typical *in situ* epoxidation of polybutadiene.

b. Epoxidation of Polybutadiene by In Situ *Method*

A 300 g. portion of liquid polybutadiene with a viscosity of 10 poise at 25°C., is dissolved in 300 g. of benzene. Acetic acid (48 g.) is then added followed by 62 g. of ion exchange resin, (Dowex 50W-X12) and the whole heated to 80°C. with agitation. Then 210 g. of hydrogen peroxide (50%) is added over the course of 1–2 hr., care being taken to maintain the temperature at 60–70°C. The reaction is allowed to continue until analysis of an aliquot sample shows 9.0% oxirane oxygen. An additional 300 g. of benzene is then added, and the resin catalyst removed by filtration. The catalyst is washed with additional benzene, which is then combined with the reaction mixture. The latter is washed with water, neutralized with aqueous sodium hydroxide, water washed again, and then distilled free of solvent and residual water at 80–100°C. under vacuum (1–10 mm). A product analyzing 9% oxirane oxygen is thus obtained.

Viscosity increases with oxidation, becoming pronounced at high levels of oxirane oxygen, and is dependent not only on the mode of epoxidation, but the specific unsaturated polymer employed.

Variation of viscosity with oxirane oxygen is illustrated in Figure II-2 for a representative *in situ* epoxidation of a polybutadiene.

3. Chemistry of Epoxidized Polymers

a. Structure

Structural characterization of polymers resulting from the epoxidation of unsaturated polymers has been in the main limited to work with polymers and copolymers of butadiene. In general, it can be noted that the structure of epoxy polymers is dependent upon the microstructure of the unsaturated polymer employed and the reaction conditions used in epoxidation.

The backbone structure of the epoxy polymer will correspond to that of the precursor unsaturated polymer. Molecular weights for an epoxidation carried out under controlled reaction conditions will correspond closely to those calculated, indicating a minimum of intermolecular condensation. The functional groups present in the final polymer will include not only the expected oxirane oxygen and double bonds but may include small amounts of hydroxyl, acyloxy, ether, keto, and aldehyde groups resulting from secondary reactions of the epoxide. The presence or absence of these reaction products are greatly influenced by the degree of substitution at the double bond, as well as conditions of reaction. In Table II-3 are noted the

TABLE II-3
Possible Products of Epoxidation

Functional group	Origin	Conditions favoring formation
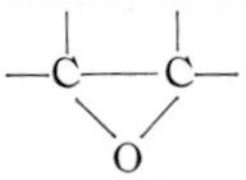	Initial product of peracid reaction with double bond	Isolated double bonds, low temperature, low H^+ concentration, low aliphatic acid concentration
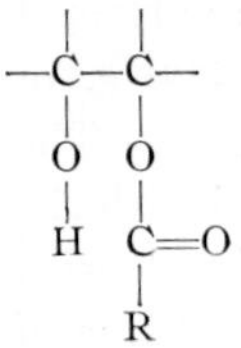	Ring opening of epoxide	H^+, high temperature, long reaction times, high concentration of aliphatic acid
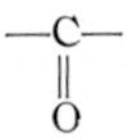	Isomerization of epoxide	H^+, high alkyl substitution on double bond
—CHO	Isomerization of terminal epoxide	H^+, high alkyl substitution on double bond
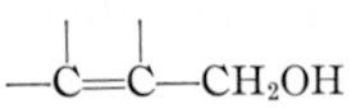	Isomerization of epoxide	H^+, high alkyl substitution on double bond
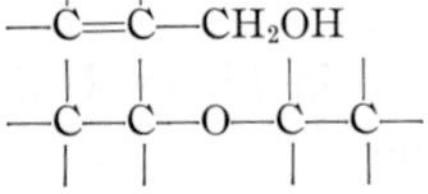	Polymerization of epoxide	H^+, high oxirane oxygen concentration, high temperature

various functional groups that may be present in the final oxidized polymer, along with their origins and conditions favoring their formation.

Table II-4 shows a typical analysis of an epoxidized polybutadiene. Infrared spectra for polybutadiene (*A*) and epoxidized polybutadiene (*B*) are shown in Figure II-3. The 995 and 967 cm.$^{-1}$ absorption maxima are used for the determination of 1,2-(vinyl) and *trans*-1,4 addition, respectively. No single wavelength can be applied to this *cis*-1,4 vibration. No positive band assignments due to epoxy groups can be made. Weak

TABLE II-4
Typical Properties of Uncured Epoxypolybutadiene[a]

Viscosity at 25°C., poise	1800
Active ingredients, %	100
Specific gravity	1.01
Epoxy (oxirane oxygen), %	9.0
Epoxy equivalent	177
Molecular weight (number-average)	1200–1500
Iodine number	185

[a] Taken from ref. 207.

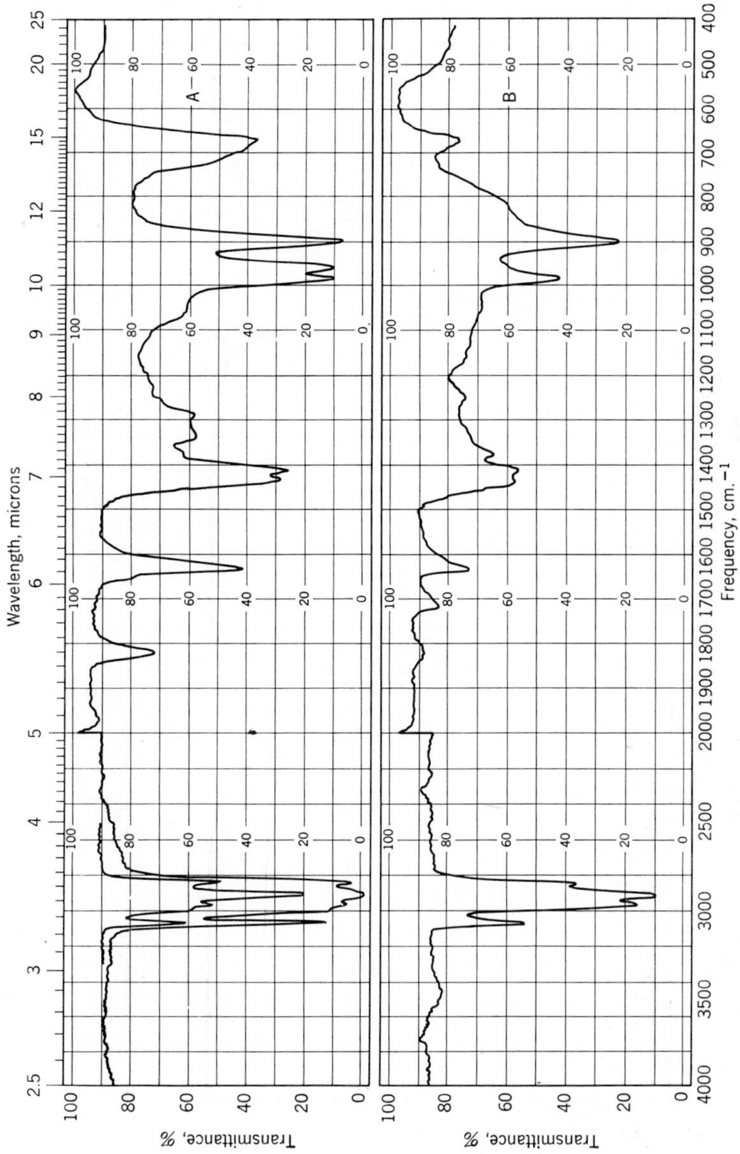

Fig. II-3. Infrared spectra of (*A*) polybutadiene and (*B*) epoxidized polybutadiene.

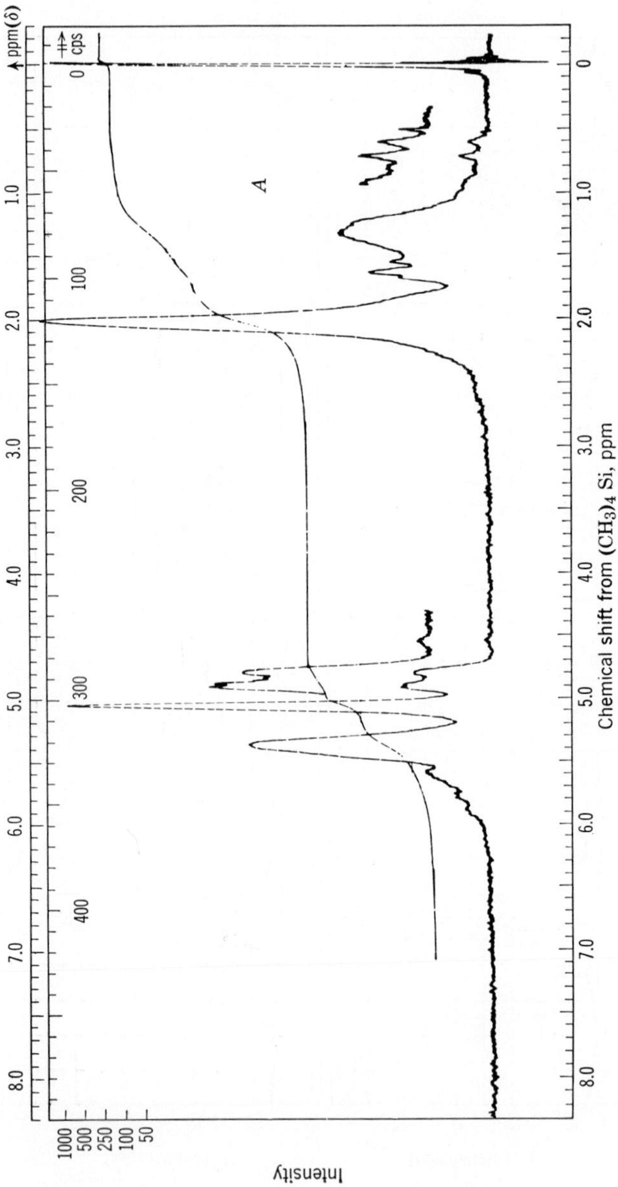
ppm(δ)
cps
Intensity
A
Chemical shift from $(CH_3)_4$ Si, ppm

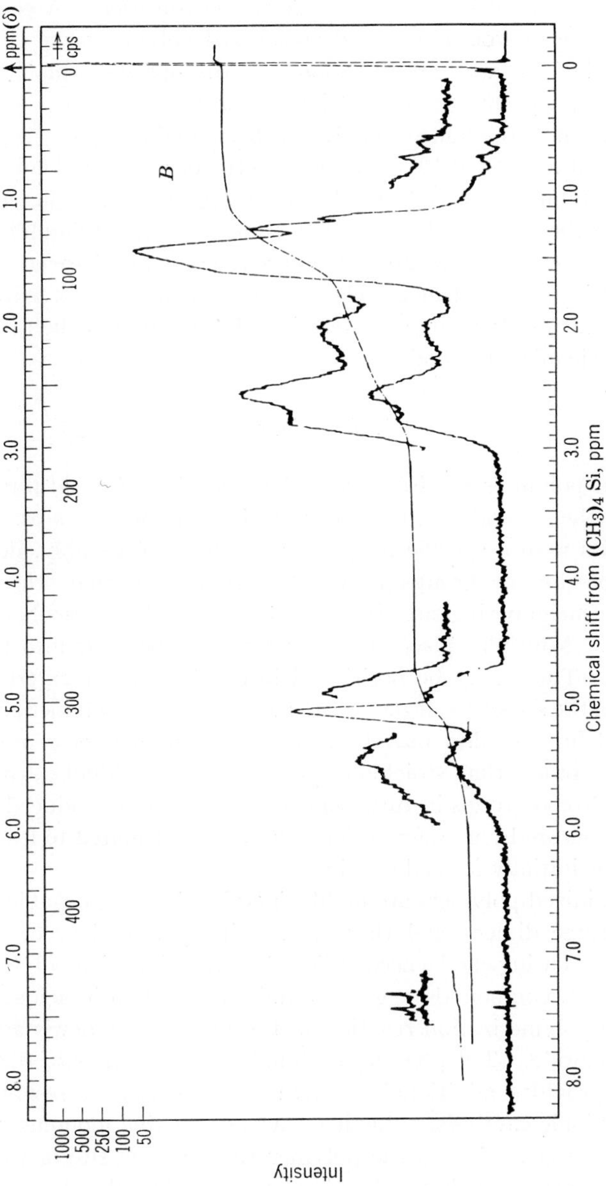

Fig. II-4. NMR spectra of (*A*) polybutadiene and (*B*) epoxypolybutadiene.

oxirane oxygen bands probably appear in the region of 800–950 cm.$^{-1}$ masked by or combined with bands due to unsaturation. A comparison of the spectra of polybutadiene and epoxidized polybutadiene (Fig. II-3) shows that the 1,4-*trans* unsaturation has disappeared and 1,2-(vinyl) bands remain in the specific epoxidation illustrated.

Nuclear magnetic resonance (NMR) has been used to study the structure of epoxypolybutadienes (210). NMR spectra of polybutadiene (*A*) and epoxidized polybutadiene (*B*) are shown in Figure II-4. The curves recorded above the main NMR spectrum designate higher amplification of the same spectrum. The S-type curves are the integrated areas. Durbetaki (210) has shown excellent correlation between the ratio of oxirane oxygen to the total unsaturation as determined by NMR and the ratio as determined by chemical methods.

b. Reactions

Epoxidized polymers resulting from the oxidation of unsaturated polymers exhibit the general reactions characteristic of epoxy groups. The reaction kinetics with a specific reagent may vary considerably, dependent upon the type of epoxy groups present (external or internal), the presence and nature of neighboring substituent groups, and the stereochemistry of the polymer. Multiple epoxy groups can readily be built into the polymeric chain. These may be positioned internally and/or externally, depending upon the structure of the precursor unsaturated polymer employed. Double bond functionality may be incorporated in the epoxy polymer if desired by use of less than stoichiometric amounts of oxidant during epoxidation. Hydroxyl groups in turn may be deliberately introduced into the polymeric structure by use of reaction conditions calculated to lead to ring opening of the initially formed epoxides.

These epoxidized polymers are highly functional resins, capable of being cured to a three dimensional thermoset resin by a variety of reagents. Crosslinking or curing can be accomplished by reaction with polyfunctional active hydrogen compounds, e.g., polyamines and dibasic acids, or by a condensation-polymerization reaction in the presence of Lewis acids such as boron trifluoride. The presence of double bonds, as in epoxidized polybutadienes, provides additional reactive sites capable of responding to peroxide and ionic catalysis. Further, various reactive monomers such as styrene may be grafted onto the polymer chain at the site of the double bond. The presence of double bonds in the epoxidized polymer likewise makes it possible to coreact the resins with other unsaturated polymers

TABLE II-5

Reactivity of Epoxypolybutadienes

Curing Agent	Feature	Reference
1. Epoxy Functional Group		
Polyamines	Long pot life, rapid cure at elevated temperatures; phenol-catalyzed, sluggish with secondary amines and polyamides	235
Anhydrides Anhydride-glycols Polybasic acids	Flexible to hard, rigid, enhanced reactivity over conventional resins, some low temperature cure systems; glycols or aliphatic side chain anhydrides impart flexibility; can be used in conjunction with peroxide curing; catalyzed by tertiary amines and acids	224
Phenolic resins Polyphenols	High temperature cures; hard, rigid materials, high performance coatings	236
Polymercaptans	Flexible	237
Hydrazine–carbon disulfide		238
Ionic (e.g. BF_3)	Rapid reaction at low temperatures; frequently used in conjunction with other cure systems; promotes etherification	211
2. Double Bond Functional Group		
Organic peroxides (free radical initiators)	Most frequently used with anhydride or anhydride glycol cure; gives highly thermoset resin, excellent electrical and high temperature properties	207
Monomers	Monomer copolymerizes with polymer under peroxide or ionic catalysis; most frequently used with anhydride cure; use of unsaturated anhydride provides additional site for copolymerization	211
Unsaturated polymers (polyesters, rubbers)	Copolymerizes under peroxide catalysis with double bonds of unsaturated polymer; can also be sulfur vulcanized in modification of rubbers	208, 209
Ionic	Rapid cure at low temperatures; also used in conjunction with other cure systems.	211

such as rubbers and polyesters. General reaction characteristics of epoxidized polybutadienes are described in Table II-5.

4. Properties of Epoxidized Polymers

The epoxidized polymers vary from liquids of low viscosity to elastomers or crystalline solids, dependent upon their structure and molecular weight. Epoxidation of polybutadienes of low molecular weight gives liquid products while polybutadienes of high molecular weight yield derivatives that are elastomeric solids. The physical properties of a representative commercial liquid epoxypolybutadiene (uncured) are described in Table II-4.

Properties of the final cured polymer reflect not only the structure of the epoxy polymer itself, but the curing agent employed. The cured epoxy polymer contains a considerable amount of the types of linkages and structures characteristic of the curing agent itself. The epoxy group, as such, is no longer present except where less than stoichiometric amounts of curing agents are employed. Properties can vary widely even within a general class of curing agents. Thus, long chain dibasic acids give rubbery flexible thermoset polymers with epoxidized polybutadiene, while short chain dibasic acids and anhydrides produce hard brittle solids.

a. Physical Properties

The physical properties of epoxypolybutadiene cured by amines, dibasic acids, anhydrides, and boron trifluoride are illustrated in Table II-6.

Epoxypolybutadienes can be cured to give resins with excellent high temperature properties (207). Extremely high heat distortion points, flat

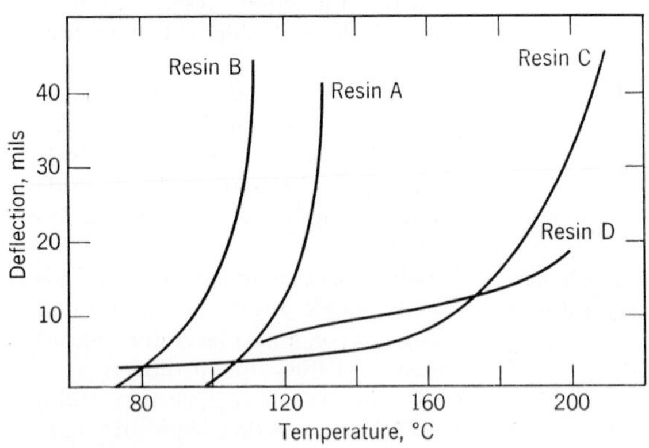

Fig. II-5. Heat distortion curves of epoxy resins. (Taken from ref. 207.)

nonbreaking heat distortion curves, and low creep or stress relaxation as well as excellent electrical performance are obtained. Figure II-5 illustrates heat distortion curves reported for several cured epoxypolybutadienes (resins B, C, D) compared to an epoxy from epichlorohydrin–bisphenol (resin A). A saturated anhydride such as hexahydrophthalic anhydride, used with the epichlorohydrin–bisphenol or epoxypolybutadiene resin shows a rapid break in the heat distortion curve as soon as a critical temperature is reached. When an organic peroxide is incorporated into the epoxypolybutadiene formulation (resin C), the deflection curve flattens somewhat, indicating crosslinking through double bonds of the polymer. When

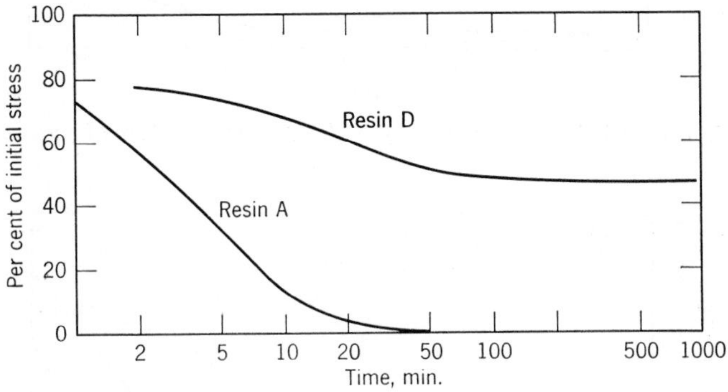

Fig. II-6. Stress relaxation of epoxy resins at 155°C. Both resins initially stressed to 1680 psi. (Taken from ref. 207.)

an unsaturated anhydride such as maleic is employed, high heat distortion materials result with extremely flat curves (resin D).

Similarly, stress relaxation data have been reported comparing similar formulations. These are illustrated in Figure II-6 for the same resins A and D systems. The highly crosslinked epoxypolybutadiene resin (resin D) relaxed to 50% of the initial stress and remained constant thereafter in contrast to the epichlorohydrin–bisphenol resin which relaxed to zero stress in 50 min.

b. Electrical Properties

The epoxypolybutadiene resin exhibits excellent electrical properties (207) as shown by absolute values for dielectric constants (K) and dissipation factor (D). More significantly, electrical performance shows good constancy with temperature. This is illustrated in Figures II-7 and II-8.

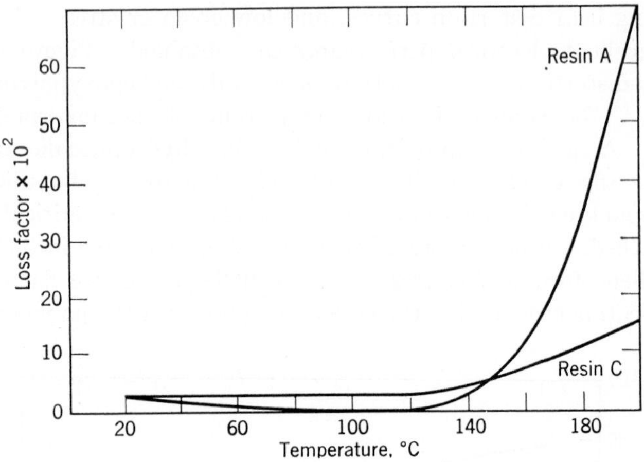

Fig. II-7. Dielectric loss factor at 50 cycles/sec. vs. temperature of epoxy resins.

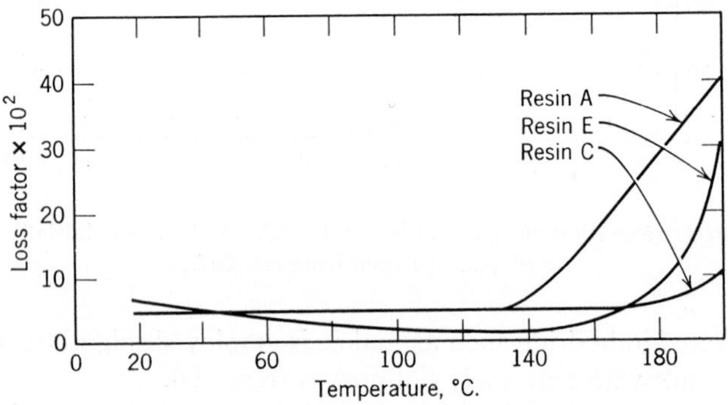

Fig. II-8. Dielectric loss factor at 10^4 cycles/sec. vs. temperature of epoxy resins.

5. Applications of Epoxidized Polymers

Epoxidized polymers of the type described in this chapter are generally applicable to the broad uses that have been developed for the older epoxy resins based on epichlorohydrin. These include electrical encapsulation, adhesives, surface coatings, tooling, flooring and road repair, molding compounds, reinforced plastics, stabilization of chlorinated polymers, and resin binders for propellants. In addition they lend themselves to a variety of novel applications based upon their different structure and final cured properties. Illustrative of these would be alloy laminates with

TABLE II-6. Properties of Unfilled Cured Epoxypolybutadienes[a]

		Cure	Flexural strength, psi	Flexural modulus, psi × 10^{-6}	Tensile strength, psi	Tensile modulus, psi × 10^{-6}	Tensile elongation, %	Hardness, Rockwell M	Heat deflection temp., °C.
Epoxidized polybutadiene resin[a]	100	4 hr. at 155°C.	17,000	0.40	9,000	0.42	3.5	112	98
Hexahydrophthalic anhydride	80								
Propylene glycol	8								
Epoxidized polybutadiene resin[a]	100	16 hr. at 90°C., 1 hr. at 120°C., 1 hr. at 130°C., 2 hr. at 150°C.	9,300	0.31	6,000	0.33	3.4	75	
BF_3 TEA	3								
Epoxidized polybutadiene resin[a]	100	2 hr. at 80°C., 18 hr. at 155°C.			282	.004	68	49[d]	
Dimer acid[b]	100								
2,5-Dimethyl-2,5-di-*tert*-butylperoxy)-hexane[c]	2								
Epoxidized polybutadiene resin[a]	100	3 hr. at 80°C., 3 hr. at 155°C.	16,200	0.36	6,800	0.66	—	83	94
Triethylenetetramine	24								
Resorcinol	2								
Epoxidized polybutadiene resin[a]	100	2 hr. at 90°C.; Post cure 3 hr. at 155°C.	10,100	0.34	4,000	0.10	—	—	214
Maleic anhydride	26								

[a] The epoxidized polybutadiene resin used was Oxiron 2000.
[b] Empol 1022, available from Emery Industries, Inc.
[c] Varox, available from R. T. Vanderbilt Co., Inc. Lupersol #101, available from Lucidol Div., Wallace & Tiernan, Inc.
[d] Shore A hardness.

TABLE II-7

Effects of the Addition of an Epoxidized Polybutadiene Resin on the Properties of Glass-Reinforced Polyester Laminates[a]

Polyester	Flexural strength, psi			Flexural modulus, psi × 10^{-6}			Edgewise compressive strength, psi		
	At room temperature	At 160°F.	At 300°F.	At room temperature	At 160°F.	At 300°F.	At room temperature	At 160°F.	At 300°F.
Polyester	71,700	60,400	12,300	2.98	3.00	1.57	30,000	23,100	8,400
20% Epoxypolybutadiene resin–80% polyester	89,800	77,400	21,200	3.61	3.41	2.13	61,700	43,400	13,700

[a] Glass type: 181 Style Fiber Glass Cloth, 136 Finish; cure cycles: 1 hr. at 240°F. and 2 hr. at 310°F.; pressure: 100 psi.

polyester resins, and modifications of rubber, both of which take advantage of the double bond structure of the polymers.

a. Surface Coatings

Epoxypolybutadienes show good film-forming properties and are generally characterized by excellent wetting of surfaces. Esterification with fatty acids produces esters which can be used as air-drying or baking resins. Baking with phenolic resins gives chemical-resistant coatings. Epoxypolybutadiene resins are reactive with nitrogen resins of the urea–formaldehyde, melamine–formaldehyde type on baking to provide good metal finishes.

Corrosion-resistant coatings that cure at ambient temperature have been developed based upon oxalic acid (212) in a two-component mix. A coating system based on epoxypolybutadiene and coal tar which will also cure at ambient temperature with chlorendic anhydride has been described (213).

Epoxypolybutadienes have been used in the formation of can coatings (214) and also can be used to crosslink and thus improve adhesion of vinyl resins containing carboxyl groups.

b. Reinforced Plastics

Epoxypolybutadienes find application in glass reinforced plastics for preparation of flat laminates and in filament winding (208). These systems generally employ anhydride curing agents. Epoxypolybutadienes can be coreacted with the typical unsaturated polyester resins.

Use of up to 20% of the epoxypolybutadiene with a polyester gives considerably improved physical properties (tensile and edgewise compression) and also improved resistance to high temperatures, to abrasion, and to chemicals as illustrated in Table II-7. These blends are applicable to flat laminates, filament winding, and premix molding.

Interesting premix molding compounds with excellent high temperature and electrical properties have been developed based upon epoxypolybutadiene cured with fumaric acid (215) as illustrated in Table II-8.

c. Modification of Rubber

The use of epoxypolybutadiene for modification of rubbers has been reported (209). Improved high temperature aging, tear strength, and oil resistance result.

TABLE II-8

Properties of a Typical Epoxidized Polybutadiene Premix Compound

Composition, parts by weight	
Epoxypolybutadiene resin[a]	100
Curing agent 325[b]	30
Styrene	10
Dicup T	1.5
Chopped glass fiber	60
Wollastonite P-1	140
Cab-O-Sil	7
Calcium stearate	1.2
Molded 2 min. at 350°F.	
Properties	
Heat distortion temperature, °C.	>300
Flexural strength, psi	
77°F.	17,300
160°F.	10,700
300°F.	7,600
Tensile strength, psi	8,600
Compressive strength, psi	26,000
Izod impact, ft.-lb./in.	1.3–1.6
Rockwell M hardness	108
Moisture absorption (48 hr. at 50°C.), %	0.30
Dielectric constant	
At 10^3 cycles	4.3
At 10^6 cycles	4.2
Dissipation factor	
At 10^3 cycles	0.010
At 10^6 cycles	0.007
Volume resistivity, ohm-cm.	2×10^{15}
Surface resistivity, ohm.	2×10^{15}

[a] An epoxidized polybutadiene

[b] A325 mesh fumaric acid (FMC Corp.)

d. Adhesives

Epoxypolybutadienes cured with polyamines or anhydrides show good adhesive properties to a variety of plastic and metallic substrates, and also show excellent adhesion to fiber glass with potential as a fiber finish (215).

F. HYDROGENATION

JOHN WICKLATZ

General Mills, Inc.

1. Introduction

Interest in hydrogenation of unsaturated polymers has never been extremely intense. On the other hand, publications on the subject have appeared in the literature in a relatively steady flow for almost a century. Of the early publications, perhaps the most significant historically are those of Harries (239,240) and Staudinger (241), who were interested in using hydrogenation to reveal structural characteristics of natural rubber. Harries claimed that his experiments supported an "aggregation" theory of the structure of rubber, while Staudinger maintained that hydrogenation tended to demonstrate that natural rubber molecules consist of units joined by normal covalent linkages. It appears, however, that the matter was not settled satisfactorily by hydrogenation experiments.

Natural rubber was the first unsaturated polymer subjected to conditions which might saturate double bonds with hydrogen. The earliest record of an attempt to do so is found in the work of Berthelot (242), who reacted natural rubber with hydriodic acid in a closed tube and severely degraded the polymer in the process. Products of this reaction included various high boiling paraffin hydrocarbons and hydrogen gas. The art in this field was subsequently advanced considerably in the early 1900's by the work of Hinrichsen (243), Harries (240), Pummerer (244,245), and others (246). Staudinger and his co-workers, however, appear to have been the most productive of the pioneers in this field (241,247–254). For the most part, reactions carried out by these early workers were accompanied by a considerable amount of chain scission. It was common, for example, to obtain obvious degradation products, such as oils, liquids, and even gases, as a result of hydrogenation. In a few cases elastic solids were obtained. Even these were formed under conditions which probably resulted in degradation of the base polymer.

In addition to that already cited, considerably more work has been done on the hydrogenation of natural rubber, balata, and gutta-percha. Much of the attention in this work was focused on the synthesis of lubricating oils, motor fuels, and products suitable for insulation and coatings. Cawley and King (255), for example, describe a hydrogenation-cracking process which converts natural rubber to motor fuel or to a mixture of hydrocarbons boiling over a wide range. Others have carried out work intended to accomplish a somewhat similar purpose (256–262).

More recently, attention has shifted largely to hydrogenation of synthetic unsaturated polymers. Generally speaking, it appears that there is more interest in nondestructive processes in connection with the hydrogenation of synthetic materials, as opposed to the greater emphasis on destructive hydrogenations in the early work on natural rubber, balata, and gutta-percha. However, work on destructive hydrogenation of synthetic materials has not been disregarded entirely. Ipatieff and Schaad (263), for example, have described the conversion of thermally polymerized butadiene to liquid products by hydrogenation in the presence of black nickel oxide catalyst. They reported that at a hydrogenation temperature of 100°C. no decomposition occurred, but that at 250°C. part of the rubbery polymer was converted to liquid products boiling over a wide range. A conclusion based on limited analytical work was that naphthenic hydrocarbons with one or two rings are produced when polybutadiene is destructively hydrogenated under the conditions described.

Destructive hydrogenations can obviously lead to numerous different distributions of products, depending on the selection of reaction conditions. In the case of nondestructive hydrogenation, products can also vary widely in physical characteristics, and these will depend on various factors, including the chemical composition of the base polymer. Copolymers of dienes and various vinyl monomers, for example, can provide a wide array of materials for use in hydrogenation studies. In this connection, Cupery (264) has described an interesting polymeric material obtained by hydrogenation of a butadiene–acrylonitrile copolymer with a mixture of palladium and nickel catalysts. The product in this case was a rubbery polymeric amine. Whether or not the double bonds of the polymer chain were saturated in the hydrogenation process is not discussed. Although numerous copolymers, of which the above is only one example, can yield hydrogenated products, only a relatively small number appear to have been hydrogenated. One of these is a butadiene–styrene copolymer reported by Jones, Moberly, and Reynolds (265). Copolymers of dienes with different vinyl monomers, such as acrylonitrile, ethyl acrylate, 2-methyl-5-vinylpyridine, and α-methylstyrene have been hydrogenated (266).

Polybutadiene has been studied more thoroughly in hydrogenation processes than any other synthetic unsaturated hydrocarbon polymer. In addition to the destructive hydrogenation of polybutadiene already mentioned (263), nondestructive hydrogenations of emulsion-polymerized polybutadiene (265), sodium-polymerized polybutadiene (267), and *cis*-1,4-polybutadiene (268–270) have been reported. Another stereoregular diene polymer, *cis*-1,4-polyisoprene, has also been hydrogenated, and the products described (271).

2. Hydrogenation Processes

In discussing methods for carrying out the hydrogenation of unsaturated polymers, a distinction will be drawn between destructive and nondestructive processes. Actually, this distinction is somewhat artificial, since the two processes differ principally in the severity of reaction conditions. A hydrogenation in which scission of carbon–carbon bonds occurs requires a higher reaction temperature than the process in which the carbon chain of the base polymer remains essentially intact. In addition to temperature, other factors such as the choice of a catalyst can also be important. Some chain degradation probably occurs in most hydrogenations that are essentially nondestructive, because even in this case a relatively high temperature will often be selected in order to take advantage of the higher rate of reaction and lower catalyst requirement characteristic of higher temperatures. Despite these considerations, it appears worthwhile to distinguish between hydrogenation processes in which extensive chain degradation occurs and those in which this is a relatively minor consideration because of the very obvious differences in physical characteristics of products from the two processes.

Since reaction temperature is a major factor in determining the nature of the product obtained by hydrogenation of an unsaturated polymer, it would be useful to know something about the temperature range in which major changes in product characteristics are apt to occur. Unfortunately, it is difficult to generalize on this point, because other factors must be considered as well. The previous history of the base polymer, for example, can be of considerable significance. Thus, emulsion-polymerized polybutadiene is likely to differ in this respect from a sodium-polymerized sample; two different batches of polybutadiene made by the same process may not behave in exactly the same manner, particularly if catalyst residues or remnants of other polymerization recipe ingredients are likely to remain dispersed in the polymer. This point is illustrated by the data of Jones, Moberly, and Reynolds (265), from which the conclusion is drawn that little, if any, polymer degradation occurs when emulsion-polymerized polybutadiene is hydrogenated at temperatures up to 260°C. with a nickel–kieselguhr catalyst. Subsequent work (266) with other samples of emulsion-polymerized polybutadiene, however, indicated that it was possible for a significant amount of degradation to occur at this temperature and with the same catalyst, as evidenced by a drastic change in inherent viscosity as well as tensile strength of the product. The extent of the change which these properties can undergo in the temperature range of 175–260°C. is shown in Table II-9.

TABLE II-9
Properties of Hydrogenated Polybutadienes Prepared at Various Temperatures[a]

Hydrogenation temperature, °C.	Properties of hydrogenated product		
	Residual unsaturation, %	Inherent viscosity	Tensile strength, psi
175	8.8	2.30	1820
205	8.4	1.34	1650
260	7.5	0.70	1130

[a] Taken from ref. 266.

In contrast to these results in which there was no evidence of the formation of liquid products even at the highest reaction temperature shown, Ipatieff and Schaad (263) showed that a significant amount of a thermally polymerized butadiene was converted to liquid products at 250°C.

a. Destructive Hydrogenation

A description of the apparatus and procedure used for destructive hydrogenation of both natural rubber and polybutadiene is given by Ipatieff and Schaad (263). They conducted these hydrogenations in an electrically heated rotating autoclave made of stainless steel. Equal weights of polymer to be hydrogenated and solvent were used in typical reactions along with an amount of hydrogenation catalyst equivalent to 10% of the weight of the polymer charged. Cyclohexane and *n*-pentane were mentioned as solvents. Hydrogen was charged to an initial pressure of 1400 psi at 25°C. Liquid products were obtained under these conditions from both natural rubber and polybutadiene after 4–12 hr. at 250°C.

Black nickel oxide was used as the catalyst in a destructive hydrogenation of polybutadiene by the process just outlined. The liquid product obtained from this reaction gave on distillation the fractions shown in Table II-10. Fractions 2 and 3 were identified as ethylcyclohexane. Fraction 6 was not identified positively, but its analysis corresponded to that of a naphthenic hydrocarbon with two rings.

TABLE II-10
Nickel-Catalyzed Destructive Hydrogenation of Polybutadiene[a]

Fraction no.	Boiling range at 750 mm., °C.	Volume of distillate, % of total charge
1	124–130	9.6
2	130–135	23.7
3	135–145	25.7
4	145–230	9.6
5	230–295	11.4
6	295–310	7.1
Bottoms	>310	11.9

[a] Taken from ref. 263.

A similar destructive hydrogenation process was used to produce liquid products from natural rubber. In this instance, however, a nickel–kieselguhr catalyst (272) was used instead of black nickel oxide. About 40–50% of the liquid product obtained boiled in the range of 97–300°C. at atmospheric pressure. Examination of the individual fractions indicated that they were naphthenic and polycyclic hydrocarbons, with *p*-methylisopropylcyclohexane being definitely identified as one of the components of the mixture.

A molybdenum catalyst has also been used to carry out the hydrogenation of natural rubber under cracking conditions (255). This particular catalyst was made by boiling to dryness an aqueous solution of ammonium molybdate to which had been added granular alumina gel. Drying was completed in an oven, and the dry material, which contained 25% ammonium molybdate, was then heated in air to convert the ammonium salt to molybdenum oxide.

The quantity of this molybdenum catalyst used in batch-type hydrogenations amounted to 20% of the natural rubber hydrogenated with an additional 5% of sulfur added. Hydrogenation was carried out in the absence of a solvent at temperatures ranging from 375 to 450° (temperature scale not specified; assumed to be °F.) and at an initial hydrogen pressure of 120 atm. At the lower temperature the product was mainly liquid, a relatively small amount of gas being formed. Gas formation became appreciable at the higher temperatures. In subsequent experiments in a continuous reaction system, a high boiling hydrocarbon oil was used as a solvent. Under these conditions there was less tendency to form gaseous products at higher reaction temperatures. Thus, at 450° conversion to liquid products was in excess of 96% as compared to only 79% in the solventless batch process.

b. Nondestructive Hydrogenation

Conditions for nondestructive hydrogenation of unsaturated polymers are not radically different from those used in the destructive processes described above. In general, however, nickel or noble metal catalysts and lower reaction temperature are preferred for the nondestructive process. With these catalysts it is possible to operate at reaction temperatures which are sufficiently low to avoid extensive degradation of the polymer chain. Copper chromite or molybdenum catalysts are not usually used. They are often sluggish in reactions involving unsaturated polymers at the required level of temperature for nondestructive hydrogenation and produce severely degraded products if the reaction temperature is increased to the point at which effective saturation of double bonds is achieved.

A simple and effective process for converting polymers and copolymers of butadiene to hydrogenated products under essentially nondestructive conditions involves use of a nickel–kieselguhr catalyst at a reaction temperature of 230°C. and at 500 psi hydrogen pressure measured at the operating temperature (266). Methylcyclohexane or decalin are suitable solvents. The amount of catalyst required will depend on the particular polymer to be hydrogenated and on the degree of saturation to be achieved. For a typical emulsion-polymerized polybutadiene, for example, the amount of catalyst may vary in the range of 5–10% of the polymer charged, depending on whether a product with a relatively low or a moderate degree of residual unsaturation is desired. Under these conditions the residual unsaturation level of polybutadiene, as determined by iodine monochloride (273), may be reduced from an initial value of approximately 95% to the range of 5–20% in 3–6 hr.

The method described above applies to batch reactions. A continuous reaction system based on essentially the same principles has also been described (265).

Sodium-polymerized polybutadiene as well as *cis*-1,4-polybutadiene and *cis*-1,4-polyisoprene have been hydrogenated in much the same fashion by Russian workers (267,271,274). They also used a nickel–kieselguhr catalyst, but in larger amounts ranging from about 12 to 300% of the polymer charged. Reaction temperatures were in the range of 60–240°C., and decalin was generally used as the reaction medium. It would appear from the results reported that unsaturated polymers obtained by solution polymerization of dienes are somewhat more readily hydrogenated than their emulsion-polymerized counterparts. There are no comparative data, however, to confirm this opinion.

If a sufficiently active catalyst is used, effective hydrogenation of polybutadiene can be achieved at atmospheric pressure and room temperature (275,276). Thus, palladium on nickel, palladium on calcium carbonate, platinum black, and a mixture of platinized charcoal and chloroplatinic acid were shown to be satisfactory catalysts under these very mild hydrogenation conditions. Palladium on calcium carbonate was reported to be particularly effective. It gave a product with a residual unsaturation of only 2% when it was used for hydrogenation of polybutadiene at atmospheric pressure and room temperature.

Since products of the nondestructive hydrogenation of high polymers provide extremely viscous solutions, product recovery is frequently complicated by problems of catalyst removal. Finely divided catalyst tends to remain suspended in these viscous solutions and to settle at extremely low rates. For this reason, various schemes have been devised for conveniently removing catalyst from the solutions. If a nickel catalyst has been used, it is possible to devise methods for magnetic separation of the catalyst particles. It is a relatively simple matter to accomplish this by passing the catalyst-containing polymer solution through a tube placed in a strong magnetic field. The method is even more effective if the column is packed with a magnetic substance, such as steel wool or iron particles. If this is done, the catalyst tends to be retained on the packing and much more efficient removal is achieved than is possible in an unpacked column. Details of this method are disclosed in the patent literature (277). Other methods which depend on the use of additives or special techniques of handling which cause agglomeration of the catalyst have also been described (278,279). An effective alternative to these methods is to remove the major portion of the catalyst by centrifuging at 500–1000 times the force of gravity. Filtration of the centrifuged solution through a precoated pressure filter is usually required to remove the last traces of catalyst. This method works quite well, but only if the viscosity of the solution is kept at a minimum during the operation. This can be done by diluting the solution of the product with solvent prior to centrifuging and by carrying out this operation as well as the filtration step at an elevated temperature.

Recovery of polymeric hydrogenated products from their catalyst-free solutions represents no serious problem in small-scale work. A standard laboratory procedure, such as precipitation of the polymer from solution by addition of a nonsolvent, works quite well. The product may also be isolated by evaporating the solvent and it has been found that a drum dryer is a satisfactory device for this purpose. For recovery of product on a larger scale, however, these methods are too unwieldy. Techniques which are more easily managed on a large scale have been described by Delap and Dietz (280,281).

Although the destructive and nondestructive hydrogenation processes differ mainly in the temperature at which the reaction is carried out, there can be no mistake about the radical difference in the nature of the products. It was shown previously that under conditions for destructive hydrogenation liquid and sometimes gaseous hydrocarbon products are obtained. Under the somewhat milder conditions employed in an essentially nondestructive reaction, it is possible to obtain thermoplastic polymers which are strong, tough, and flexible if a polydiene of high molecular weight is used as the starting material. In fact, some of the properties of hydrogenated emulsion-polymerized polybutadiene are similar to those of low density polyethylene. Typical properties of these materials are compared in Table II-11.

TABLE II-11

Comparison of Properties of Hydrogenated Polybutadiene with Low Density Polyethylene[a]

Property	Hydrogenated polybutadiene	Low density polyethylene
Tensile strength, psi	2350	1900
Elongation, %	750	600
Stiffness modulus, psi	15,000	20,000
Brittle point, °F.	<−100	>−100
Impact strength (Izod)	Does not break	Does not break
Refractive index	1.50	1.51

[a] Taken from ref. 265.

3. Factors Affecting Hydrogenation

a. Reaction Temperature

The effect of reaction temperature on physical characteristics of the hydrogenated product has already been discussed in some detail. Still another important consideration, however, is the influence of reaction temperature on the rate of saturation of double bonds in the polymer.

Data in Table II-12 show the effect of reaction temperature on the degree of hydrogenation of natural rubber and synthetic *cis*-1,4-polyisoprene. The difference in rate of reaction of the two materials has been attributed to a difference in molecular weight. The time of hydrogenation for experiments shown in Table II-12 was 150 min. and the hydrogenation pressure was 80–100 atm. Nickel–kieselguhr catalyst was used in rather large amounts; i.e., the ratio of rubber to catalyst was 1:2.

TABLE II-12
Effect of Reaction Temperature on Hydrogenation of Natural Rubber and Synthetic *cis*-1,4-Polyisoprene[a]

Hydrogenation temperature, °C.	Residual unsaturation of product, %	
	Natural rubber	Synthetic *cis*-1,4-polyisoprene
80	—	86.7
85	82.4	—
100	60.5	42.7
140	33.4	18.0

[a] Taken from ref. 271.

The rate of saturation of double bonds of a sample of polybutadiene prepared by emulsion polymerization at 5°C. has been studied in some detail over a temperature range of 175–260°C. (266). It was found in this study that, regardless of the reaction temperature, hydrogenation proceeds rapidly in the initial part of the reaction and slows down considerably in the latter stages. Under the conditions of these experiments, a significant change in rate of hydrogenation appears to occur after the first one to three hours of reaction. Thus, unsaturation of the base polymer was reduced from an initial value of 96% to 36, 13, and 6% at the end of 3 hr. at 175, 230, and 260°C., respectively. After an additional 3 hr. of reaction, however, at the same reaction temperatures, residual unsaturation levels had been reduced only slightly to 32, 11, and 4%.

More complete reaction rate data taken from the study discussed above are shown in Table II-13. In these experiments, all conditions except reaction temperature were kept constant. Nickel on kieselguhr was used as the catalyst; the reaction pressure was 500 psi.

The substantial change in hydrogenation rate with time is possibly due in some measure to accumulation of insoluble fractions of polymer on the surface of the catalyst. If this were an important factor, however, one would expect to achieve better results by incremental addition of catalyst

TABLE II-13
Effect of Reaction Temperature on Rate of Hydrogenation of Polybutadiene at 500 psi[a]

Reaction time at operating temperature, hr.	Residual unsaturation of product, %[b]		
	At 175°C.	At 230°C.	At 260°C.
0	96	96	96
1	41	19	12
2	38	15	8
3	36	13	6
4	34	12	5
6	32	11	4

[a] Taken from ref. 266.
[b] Values obtained by interpolation of reaction rate curves.

during the hydrogenation reaction. This would serve to reduce the average time of exposure of the catalyst to the reaction environment. Incremental addition, however, does not appear to improve results. This was shown in a series of tests (266) at 175°C. and at 260°C. at 500 psi pressure in which 0.1 g. of nickel–kieselguhr catalyst was used per gram of polymer charged in the first phase of the reaction. When hydrogenation ceased, a sample of product was withdrawn for analysis and additional catalyst was added to give a total of 0.27 g. catalyst per gram of polymer for the second hydrogenation step. In the third and fourth steps the total amount of catalyst was increased to 0.87 and 1.25 g. per gram of polymer. For comparison, hydrogenations of the same polymer were carried out under the same conditions, except that the total amount of catalyst used was added to the reaction mixture initially. Results, shown in Table II-14, indicate that

TABLE II-14
Effect of Addition of Catalyst in Increments[a]

Amount of catalyst, g./g. polymer	Residual unsaturation of product, %		
	Batch addition of catalyst at 150°C.	Increment addition of catalyst	
		At 150°C.	At 205°C.
0.1	70.4	90.2	88.3
0.27	46.3	69.8	46.7
0.87	31.2	48.5	26.9
1.25	14.7	32.0	12.8

[a] Taken from ref. 266.

hydrogenation is much more effective when the catalyst is all added initially rather than in increments.

Still another explanation for the decay in rate of hydrogenation is offered by Yakubchik and Gromova (275), who also observed a rapid decrease of reaction rate with time in a study of the hydrogenation of polybutadiene at atmospheric pressure and ambient temperature. They attributed the drop in rate to the inherently greater difficulty of hydrogenating double bonds in a partly hydrogenated rubber.

b. Reaction Pressure

Hydrogenation of unsaturated polymers is normally carried out at low to moderate pressure. When extremely active catalysts are used, it is even possible to hydrogenate polybutadiene to a low level of residual unsaturation at atmospheric pressure. Reaction rates, however, are low under these conditions. Most of the hydrogenations reported thus far have been carried out in the pressure range of 500–1000 psi. In this range, and even somewhat beyond it, reaction rate does not appear to be affected markedly by pressure, although there appears to be a moderate trend toward higher rates of reaction as the pressure is increased from 650–3000 psi. The magnitude of this effect on the hydrogenation of polybutadiene at 260°C. is shown in Table II-15.

TABLE II-15
Effect of Pressure on Hydrogenation of Polybutadiene with Nickel–Kieselguhr Catalyst at 260°C.[a]

Pressure, psi.	Residual unsaturation of product, %[b]
650	31
1000	28
1220	24
1350	20
1600	19
1950	19
3000	16

[a] Taken from ref. 266.
[b] After 3 hr. using 0.1 g. catalyst per gram of polymer.

c. Catalyst

Most of the catalysts generally used in hydrogenation reactions have been tried in connection with the hydrogenation of unsaturated polymers. These include platinum and palladium on various supports, numerous nickel catalysts, molybdenum sulfide as well as sulfides and oxides of other heavy metals of Group VI (282), cobalt and cobalt oxide (246), and copper chromite. Fuller's earth has also been claimed as a catalyst for the hydrogenation of natural and synthetic rubbers (283). All of these catalysts appear to be useful to some degree in destructive hydrogenation processes, but only platinum, palladium, and nickel catalysts seem to be really satisfactory for use in nondestructive processes. A comparison of results obtained in the hydrogenation of polybutadiene with various nickel catalysts is shown in Table II-16.

TABLE II-16
Hydrogenation of Polybutadiene with Nickel Catalysts[a]

Catalyst		Hydrogenation temperature, °C.	Residual unsaturation of product, %
Identity	Amount, g./g. polymer		
Nickel–kieselguhr	0.1	260	4
Nickel–copper–pumice	0.6	260	25
Unsupported nickel	0.1	260	80
Nickel–alumina	0.1	260	32
Raney nickel	0.1	260	41
Rufert nickel	0.25	205	39
Nickel–iron–kieselguhr	0.25	205	19

[a] Taken from ref. 266.

Using platinum and palladium as catalysts, Yakubchik and Gromova (275) were able to obtain the results given in Table II-17 at ambient temperature and atmospheric pressure.

As might be expected, the amount of catalyst used has a profound effect on the rate of hydrogenation and on the degree of hydrogenation. It has been shown (271), for example, that by using 0.5 g. of a nickel–kieselguhr

TABLE II-17
Hydrogenation of Polybutadiene with Platinum and Palladium Catalysts[a]

Catalyst	Residual unsaturation of product, %
Palladium on nickel	19.0
Palladium on calcium carbonate	2.0
Platinum black	85.2
Platinized charcoal + H_2PtCl_6	35.5

[a] Taken from ref. 275.

TABLE II-18
Effect of Catalyst Level on Hydrogenation of Polybutadiene[a]

Catalyst level, g./g. polymer	Hydrogenation temperature, °C.	Residual unsaturation of product, %
0.1	175	62
0.2	175	36
0.4	175	17
0.8	175	0.7
0.06	260	41
0.10	260	23
0.12	260	12
0.15	260	8

[a] Taken from ref. 266.

catalyst per gram of polymer, a product with a residual unsaturation of 52% is obtained when *cis*-1,4-polyisoprene is hydrogenated at 120°C. and 80–100 atm. of pressure. This is to be compared to an unsaturation level of 21.5% which is achieved at the same temperature and pressure when the amount of catalyst is increased to 2.0 g./g. of polymer. Essentially the same effect has been shown in greater detail for the hydrogenation of polybutadiene with nickel–kieselguhr catalyst at 500 psi pressure. These data are summarized in Table II-18.

Additional information showing the relationship between rate of hydrogenation of polybutadiene and the amount of nickel–kieselguhr catalyst used in the reaction is found in other publications (265).

The nickel–kieselguhr catalyst used successfully for hydrogenation of unsaturated polymers by Jones, Moberly, and Reynolds (265) and others, is generally available as nickel oxide deposited on a kieselguhr substrate. It is converted to an effective hydrogenation catalyst by reduction of the oxide to metallic nickel with hydrogen. This can be done simply by heating the powdered catalyst in a tube at 315–415°C. while a stream of oxygen-free hydrogen is passed through the tube. Optimum conditions for this activation step are best determined by trial on the batch of catalyst to be used; however, it has been reported that a particularly active catalyst was obtained after 4 hr. of reduction at 360°C. at a hydrogen space velocity of 35–100 vol./vol./hr. At somewhat higher activation temperatures the catalyst appears to begin sintering and its surface area declines. Provided the activation temperature is not sufficiently high to reduce the surface area of the catalyst significantly, its activity appears to be a function of the reduced nickel content. This relationship is shown in Table II-19, in which results at several reduced nickel/polymer ratios are shown.

TABLE II-19
Effect of Reduced Nickel Content of Catalyst on Hydrogenation of Polybutadiene at 175°C.[a]

Reduced nickel/ polymer ratio	Residual unsaturation of product, %
0.069	8.8
0.055	27.2
0.039	32.0

[a] Taken from ref. 266.

d. Polymer Composition

Rates of hydrogenation of unsaturated polymers and the ultimate degree of hydrogenation which can be achieved under a given set of conditions are very much dependent on the composition of the polymer. In general, synthetic polymeric hydrocarbons and natural rubber are quite readily hydrogenated. Gutta-percha is somewhat more difficult to hydrogenate. Copolymers derived from hydrocarbons appear to be less easily hydro-

TABLE II-20
Hydrogenation of Various Natural and Synthetic Polymers

Polymer	Unsaturation, %		Reference
	Unhydrogenated	Hydrogenated	
Emulsion polybutadiene	96	0.7–>60	265, 266
Sodium polybutadiene	95	1.4–27	267
Butadiene–styrene, 75/25	78	9.0	266
Butadiene–ethyl acrylate, 75/25	75	61	266
Butadiene–methylvinylpyridine, 90/10	No hydrogenation		266
Butadiene–acrylonitrile, 90/10	No hydrogenation		266
Butadiene–vinylidene chloride, 70/30	70	41[a]	266
Polymethylpentadiene	—	0.6–9.5	266
Methylpentadiene–α-methylstyrene, 98/2	—	13.5	266
Polydimethylbutadiene	80	47	266
Neoprene	Gelled		266
cis-1,4-Polybutadiene	—	6.5–70	274
cis-1,4-Polyisoprene	—	18–52	271
Natural rubber	—	5–60	266, 271

[a] Analysis obtained on small soluble fraction, product was mostly gel.

genated than homopolymers made from the corresponding diene monomers. It is difficult to say whether this is a reflection of an inherent difference in hydrogenation rate or simply a manifestation of the important part which the history of the polymer plays in the hydrogenation reaction.

In contrast to the hydrocarbon copolymers, those based, in part, on nitrogen-containing monomers hydrogenate very reluctantly, although hydrogenation of a butadiene–acrylonitrile copolymer to a polymeric amine has been reported (264). There is no indication in this report, however, that the double bonds of the copolymer were saturated in the process. In general, negative results have been reported for halogen-containing polymers which tend to form insoluble gels under hydrogenation conditions. Copolymers of dienes with acrylates are also somewhat difficult to hydrogenate, but it appears to be possible to achieve some degree of hydrogenation of the double bonds.

Various polymers which have been subjected to hydrogenation conditions are listed in Table II-20, together with the results accomplished.

4. Properties of Hydrogenated Products

Previous sections have dealt with gross differences in physical characteristics between products made under hydrogenation conditions which bring about severe degradation of the polymer chain and those which do not. Reaction temperature and catalyst were shown to be important in determining whether one or the other of these ends is achieved. Within the framework of each of these extreme cases, however, a number of additional factors influence the properties of the hydrogenated product. Not as much is known in this regard about processes which produce liquid products as is known about nondestructive hydrogenations. It has been shown, however, that in the hydrogenation cracking of natural rubber the reaction can be controlled to produce mainly motor fuel or a mixture of motor fuel and heavy oils. In this case, the nature of the product depends mainly on reaction temperature, as demonstrated by Cawley and King (255).

More detailed information on reaction variables and their effect on properties of the product has been reported for the nondestructive process. Of primary importance is the degree of hydrogenation, but reaction temperature and molecular weight of the base polymer are also of significance.

a. Degree of Hydrogenation

Hydrogenation of all of the double bonds of an unsaturated polymer is not easily accomplished. In fact, only one instance is reported in which this ultimate goal is approached. This was done by Jones, Moberly, and Reynolds (265) who indicated that one of the products prepared in the course of their work with polybutadiene had a residual unsaturation which was only 0.7% of that calculated for an unhydrogenated butadiene polymer. Others (266,275) have listed a few instances in which products with residual unsaturations of 0.5–2.0% were obtained. It is more common, however, to find reports of products in the residual unsaturation range of 5–20% or more. The question then arises as to how these materials differ in their physical characteristics.

Hydrogenation of *cis*-1,4-polybutadiene and *cis*-1,4-polyisoprene is accompanied by the development of crystallinity which increases with degree of hydrogenation. Thus, *cis*-1,4-polybutadiene is said to develop significant crystallinity after it has been hydrogenated to a residual unsaturation of 70%. The degree of crystallinity rises sharply with further increase in degree of hydrogenation. Development of crystallinity will, of course, have a marked affect on the properties of the hydrogenated product. Solubility characteristics, for example, are changed to the extent that hydrogenated stereoregular diene polymers are soluble only at elevated temperature, whereas the base polymer is soluble in the usual solvents at room temperature. At the same time, density increases and plasticity decreases with increasing degree of hydrogenation and the glass transition temperature is raised significantly as shown in Table II-21.

TABLE II-21

Effect of Degree of Hydrogenation on Glass Transition Temperature of Hydrogenated *cis*-1,4-Polybutadiene[a]

Residual unsaturation of product, %	Glass transition temperature, °C.
97.5	−117
63.2	−115
50.7	−116
35.2	−80
5.5	Not measured

[a] Taken from ref. 268.

For hydrogenated natural rubber and synthetic *cis*-1,4-polyisoprene, the glass transition temperature increases similarly as products become increasingly saturated. Hence, the glass transition for natural rubber at an unsaturation level of 87% is −74°C. and increases to −69°C. at 60% unsaturation For polyisoprene, T_g is −70°C. before hydrogenation (93%

unsaturation) and increases to −63°C. after hydrogenation to a residual unsaturation of 52% (271).

For sodium-polymerized polybutadiene, which consists largely of 1,2-units, increasingly lower glass transition temperatures and decreasing density values have been observed when residual unsaturation decreases from an initial value of 87.7 to 14.4%. Data which illustrate this point are shown in Table II-22.

TABLE II-22
Effect of Degree of Hydrogenation on Properties of Hydrogenated Sodium Polybutadiene[a]

Degree of unsaturation of product, %	Density, g./cc.	Glass transition temperature, °C.
87.7	0.897	−58
69.3	0.893	−59
48.0	0.884	−64
31.7	0.880	−66
21.3	0.877	−69
14.4	0.872	−69

[a] Taken from ref. 268.

Detailed information is not available, but it has been reported that no glassy state transition was found for hydrogenated emulsion polybutadienes of 7.2 and 21.3% unsaturation at temperatures as low as −160°C. (265).

In view of the basic changes occurring in the microstructure of a diene polymer as a consequence of hydrogenation, it is not surprising that very definite changes also occur in the stress-strain behavior. Thus, an increase in degree of hydrogenation serves also to increase the toughness of solid polymers. It has been shown, for example, that one sample of hydrogenated polybutadiene of 40% residual unsaturation had a tensile strength of 980 psi, but that the same polymer had a tensile strength of 2990 psi when the residual unsaturation was reduced to 7%. The ultimate elongation of the same polymer increased from 410% at the higher unsaturation level to 740% at the lower level (266).

Since hydrogenation of unsaturated polymers can be controlled to leave varying amounts of unsaturation in the molecule, it is possible to vulcanize these materials in much the same way that rubber is vulcanized. For hydrogenated polybutadiene, it has been shown that vulcanizates with excellent ozone resistance and low temperature properties can be obtained by vulcarization of products of 15–25% residual unsaturation (266). In general, vulcanized stocks have higher tensile strength, greater resistance to hydrocarbons, higher softening point, and lower elongation than the unvulcanized polymers.

As might be expected, the properties of vulcanized polymers are related to degree of unsaturation. Yakubchik and co-workers (268), however, have shown that this is a relatively complex relationship. They indicated that for hydrogenated sodium-polymerized polybutadienes, the tensile strength and elongation of vulcanizates pass through a minimum value when the hydrogenated polymers have a residual unsaturation of about 48%. The explanation presented is that the number of double bonds originally present in the base polymer has been reduced by approximately one-half. This level thus marks the point at which the polymer contains hydrogenated and unhydrogenated 1,2 and *trans*-1,4 units in comparable amounts, and represents the maximum degree of disorder that can be obtained. It is concluded, therefore, that chain irregularity has an unfavorable effect on properties of vulcanizates despite the fact that a crystallization phenomenon is not involved.

Further information on vulcanizates from hydrogenated diene polymers may be found in several other publications (265,266,268).

b. Reaction Temperature

For practical considerations, it is desirable to carry out the nondestructive hydrogenation of unsaturated polymers at as high a temperature as possible without adversely affecting the properties of the product. However, it is evident that if the process is to be operated on the fringe of the temperature region at which chain scission becomes a major factor, some degree of chain rupture will inevitably occur. Thus, although it has been shown that essentially no change occurs in solution viscosity when polybutadiene is hydrogenated at 260°C. (265), stronger and tougher products are obtained at somewhat lower reaction temperatures (see Table II-9). Optimum conditions for nondestructive hydrogenations will also depend on the composition of the base polymer and, as has already been shown, may also be affected by fortuitous circumstances, such as the presence of residual catalyst, emulsifying agents, or other materials that may be carried along from the polymerization reaction or from the handling of the polymer subsequent to polymerization (short-stopping, coagulation, drying). These points, although important, have never been investigated systematically to show their effect on the optimum temperature for nondestructive hydrogenation.

c. Molecular Weight

The well known relationship between molecular weight and mechanical properties applies generally to hydrogenated dienes. In the absence of a significant amount of chain scission, the higher molecular weight base polymers would be expected to yield hydrogenated products with superior mechanical properties. This point has not been studied exhaustively, but it has been shown that for a series of polybutadienes hydrogenated to the same level of unsaturation there is a definite trend toward higher tensile strength as the molecular weight of the base polymer increases. Data to support this conclusion are shown in Table II-23, in which melt viscosity (Mooney viscosity) of the unhydrogenated starting material is used as a relative measure of molecular weight.

TABLE II-23
Relationship Between Mooney Viscosity of Polybutadiene and Tensile Strength of Hydrogenated Product[a]

Mooney viscosity of unhydrogenated polybutadiene, ML-4	Tensile strength of hydrogenated product, psi
55	3000
35	2700
30	2500
19	2000

[a] Taken from ref. 266.

5. Microstructure of Hydrogenated Products

a. Stereoregular Polymers

Since the stereoregular diene polymers have a less complex structure than random polymers, changes which occur in their microstructure as a result of hydrogenation are relatively simple to evaluate. It was previously shown, for example, that some of the changes in physical properties which are observed when the degree of hydrogenation of *cis*-1,4-polybutadiene increases can be attributed to significant changes in crystallinity. This point has been investigated further by Tikhomirov et al. (269), who have related not only crystallinity, but spherulite structure and melting point as well to degree of hydrogenation of *cis*-1,4-polybutadiene. Table II-24 shows crystallinity values calculated from x-ray diffraction curves. As expected

TABLE II-24
Relationship Between Crystallinity and Degree of Hydrogenation of *cis*-1,4-Polybutadiene[a]

Residual unsaturation of product, %	Degree of crystallinity, %
70.5	20
54.1	35
48.0	35
28.5	40
19.0	45
10.0	50
6.5	60

[a] Taken from ref. 269.

from the increase in crystallinity, it was observed that melting points of the hydrogenated polymers also increased with degree of hydrogenation.

The same authors studied spherulite structure of the hydrogenated materials and found that at less than 50% unsaturation the polymers are capable of forming spherulites. At higher unsaturations, spherulites were not detected.

The infrared spectrum of hydrogenated natural rubber has been studied by Thompson and Torkington (284,285). The spectrum corresponded in many respects to that of a simple paraffin hydrocarbon with methyl branching.

b. Random Diene Polymers

Random diene polymers represent a somewhat more complex situation because they consist of a mixture of 1,2 and 1,4 units as well as *cis* and *trans* isomers. One of the first points of interest concerns the relative rates of hydrogenation of internal (1,4 units) and external (1,2 units) double bonds. From a study of the microstructure of hydrogenated sodium-polymerized polybutadiene, it has been shown that external double bonds appear to be hydrogenated much more rapidly than internal double bonds. The data in Table II-25 show the relationship between extent of hydrogenation and distribution of the two types of double bonds.

Emulsion-polymerized polybutadiene appears to behave in much the same way insofar as rate of hydrogenation of internal and external double bonds is concerned. This conclusion is based on a comparison of the infrared spectra of the base polymer and various hydrogenated products. The spectra show not only the change in distribution of types of double

TABLE II-25
Effect of Degree of Hydrogenation on the Microstructure of Hydrogenated Sodium Polybutadiene[a]

Degree of unsaturation of product, %	Composition of hydrogenated product	
	1,2 units, %	*trans*-1,4 units, %
87.7	68.7	19.5
48.0	36.4	12.4
31.7	20.8	11.0
21.3	13.2	8.6
14.4	5.5	7.4

[a] Taken from ref. 268.

bonds with increasing degrees of hydrogenation, but the development of isolated methyl and ethyl branching as well (265,266).

X-ray diffraction patterns for polybutadiene and hydrogenated polybutadiene have also been compared (265). Results indicate that the hydrogenated material appears to have about the same degree of ordering at room temperature as the unhydrogenated polymer has at Dry Ice temperature. However, only a very slight increase in the ordering of the hydrogenated polymer is observed when it is cooled to Dry Ice temperature. Lattice spacings calculated from x-ray diffraction patterns of the two materials at room temperature and at Dry Ice temperature are given in Table II-26.

TABLE II-26
Lattice Spacings for Hydrogenated and Unhydrogenated Polybutadienes[a]

	Lattice spacing, A.	
	Room temperature	Dry-Ice temperature
Polybutadiene, 95.3% unsaturation		
Diffuse ring	4.48	4.33
Sharp ring	—	3.93
Hydrogenated polybutadiene, 3.3% unsaturation		
Strong sharp ring	4.10	4.08
Weak sharp ring	3.93	3.91
Very weak ring	2.47	2.46

[a] Taken from ref. 265.

Permission to discuss hitherto unpublished information was granted by the Quartermaster Research and Engineering Command of the U. S. Army and by the Phillips Petroleum Company. Their cooperation is gratefully acknowledged.

G. REAGENTS WITH MULTIPLE BONDS*

J. Le Bras, R. Pautrat, and C. P. Pinazzi

Institut Français du Caoutchouc

For quite some time efforts have been made to modify chemically rubber hydrocarbons with the aim of obtaining products with new and unusual properties. These modifications have resulted first in substances which possess almost no elastic properties but which nevertheless have found numerous useful applications, such as chlorinated rubber, rubber hydrochloride, cyclized rubbers, etc. Then, especially after the synthetic rubbers appeared on the scene, attention was directed towards obtaining modifications which, while the high elasticity is unaffected, do lead to rubbers containing reactive groups capable of directly modifying certain properties or permitting new vulcanization systems to be employed which can affect the characteristics of the vulcanizates.

For the past few years, significant progress has been made in this direction not only in the case of natural rubber hydrocarbon (286–288) but also in the case of synthetic *cis*-1,4-polyisoprene and analogous diene polymers.

In this section we wish to describe those results which have been achieved in the field of chemical modifications of elastomers having to do principally with multiple bond reagents. However, some attention will be paid to the action of single bond compounds such as chlorine, hydrofluoric acid, and thiols, so as to provide a more complete picture of the reactivity of this type of diene polymer and of the mechanisms involved.

1. Relation between Structure and Elasticity

Materials which have the property of high elasticity are known to display three essential characteristics (289).

(*a*) They consist of long linear molecules with high internal flexibility. In the case of *cis*-1,4-polyisoprene, this flexibility is due to the free rotation of aliphatic single bonds. For a carbon–carbon bond located between two

* Translated from the French by M. A. Golub.

methylenes, the carbon atom in its rotation on its valence cone must surmount three potential barriers of 3 kcal. situated at 120° with respect to each other. If the single bond is placed in the neighborhood of a double bond, as in *cis*-1,4-polyisoprene, this potential barrier is reduced by half; that explains the exceptional flexibility of the *cis*-1,4-polyisoprene chain at ordinary temperature. By way of contrast, polymethylene, formed from C—C single bonds repeated a large number of times, does not have any rubbery properties.

(*b*) The interactions between the macromolecules must be weak and of the same order of magnitude as those which exist between the molecules of a nonassociated liquid. Thus, polyamides do not have elastic properties because of hydrogen bonds, but if these bonds are suppressed (by an *N*-methylation reaction), certain rubbery properties then show up.

(*c*) The property of high elasticity requires the establishment of widely separated chemical crosslinks between the macromolecules so as to form a network which limits molecular movements and viscous flow. This is what is obtained through vulcanization which permits a reversibility of the deformation process. The great ease of vulcanization of diene elastomers allows for the modification of the nature and density of three-dimensional networks which have a very marked effect on the mechanical properties.

The tendency of an elastomer to crystallize depends also on the form of its molecule. At ordinary temperature the irregularities in the natural rubber chain, resulting from the presence of *cis* double bonds and from the steric hindrance of the methyl groups, preclude the occurrence of the vitreous state above 8°C. in the absence of mechanical strains. On the other hand, at ordinary temperatures gutta-percha or balata hydrocarbon is oriented since it possesses chains which are more elongated than those of rubber, by virtue of their regular *trans* configuration; only at elevated temperatures are they elastomers. Poly(vinyl fluoride) has a regular structure with chains which are oriented in a parallel manner since the fluorine atom is small and does not greatly perturb the ordering of the system, whence a fibrous structure. In contrast, polyisobutylene and polyisoamylene are elastomers; the steric hindrance arising from the side groups leading to a state of matter where the disorder necessarily predominates.

Thus, it appears that in order to preserve the high elasticity of a rubbery substance, it is rather important that the chain have the features indicated above. Consequently, in seeking to modify a rubber by topochemical reactions, it is essential to avoid other reactions, inherent in the macromolecular nature of the chain, which might occur simultaneously (cyclization, chain scission, etc.) and which can cause such a severe structural disturbance that none of the initial elasticity features remains.

2. Reactions Altering the Polyisoprene Chain

The rubber hydrocarbon molecule consists of a sequence of 4000–6000 isoprenic (C_5H_8) units having a nearly all-*cis* configuration. Two recent papers indicate that the hydrocarbon *per se* must be regarded as a virtually 100% *cis* polymer (289a,289b). Most of the chemical processes considered for attaching functional groups onto the chain are accompanied by deformations of the skeleton caused by intramolecular or intermolecular reactions: cyclization, crosslinking or chain scission processes. Although there is some interest in these reactions (290,291), we will examine them only to the extent that they represent secondary processes which, as we have noted, should be avoided in order for the resulting products to retain the desired rubber elasticity.

When the rubber hydrocarbon is subjected to certain mechanical or thermal treatments in the presence of atmospheric oxygen, a significant decrease in the viscosity of the polymer solutions is observed. This phenomenon is generally regarded as a degradation which involves at once oxidation and isomerization processes distinct from a simple thermal depolymerization. Oxygen acts at very low concentrations according to an autoxidation reaction initiated by the formation of peroxides, the effects of which bear no relation to the amount of oxygen used. Degradation appears as homolytic ruptures of carbon–carbon and carbon–hydrogen bonds. The free radicals thus formed are stabilized in the presence of oxygen or other radical acceptors through their attachment onto the available active sites, resulting in a decrease in the molecular size. In the absence of oxygen, the free radicals combine with each other, and this explains why plasticization does not occur in an inert atmosphere. Maintenance of the chain dimensions thus implies an effective protection against atmospheric oxygen.

The crosslinking reactions are characterized by increased viscosity and even by insolubilization of the rubber in solution. The most characteristic example of this transformation is vulcanization by sulfur or by polyfunctional organic derivatives (quinones, imines, azo compounds, peroxides, etc.) which can form crosslinks between the rubber chains. A network of direct carbon–carbon bonds can likewise be obtained under the influence of radiations. Insofar as it is a secondary reaction, crosslinking perturbs the combinations induced by heat, radiations or radical catalysts. Insoluble substances are obtained which are very difficult to purify and use.

The cyclization of natural polyisoprenes (discussed more fully in Section B), which proceeds by an ionic mechanism, is characterized by an increase of density, index of refraction, and softening point, and especially by a loss of elasticity. This transformation results from the action of halides of amphoteric metals or of inorganic or organic acids. A particular case is that of the dehalogenation of rubber hydrochloride where the cyclization is accompanied by an isomerization of the residual double bonds. The mechanism of these reactions is not yet well understood. It could result from the addition of the cyclizing agent (Lewis acid) onto a double bond in polyisoprene. The carbocation thus formed would be stabilized by attacking the double bond of the adjacent isoprene unit to give a six-membered ring which is sterically most favorable. The cyclization process would then continue until eventually terminated by the release of a proton (H^+) from a methyl with the formation of a side vinylidene double bond. The deprotonation can also lead to tri- and tetra-substituted double bonds (291a, 291b). This mechanism is similar to that proposed for the ionic polymerization of olefins.

All these reactions altering the macromolecular skeleton are common to the majority of the diene polymers, but their importance evidently varies with the specific structure of the polymer considered.

3. Structure and Reactivity of Rubber

Natural polyisoprene can be considered as a chain of 2-methyl-2-butene units in the *cis* configuration (Fig. II-9). This macromolecule, theoretically a pure hydrocarbon, contains, in fact, 5–8% of nonrubber constituents; besides, it possesses certain "abnormal" chemical groups attached to the main chain (aldehydes, hydroperoxides) which would be responsible for anomalies observed in the behavior of this elastomer (292,293).

The chemical reactivity of polyisoprene resides in the ethylenic bond at carbons 2 and 3 and in the methylene groups at carbons 1 and 4. Depending upon the conditions employed and the reagents present, two types of reactions can be distinguished.

a. Radical Reactions

These reactions have been particularly studied by Farmer and coworkers (294). They are induced in a variety of ways: radical sources, thermal or mechanical energy, various kinds of radiation.

A large number of reactions of rubber proceed by means of free radicals. In the first place, halogenation reactions should be mentioned (cf. Section

A

B

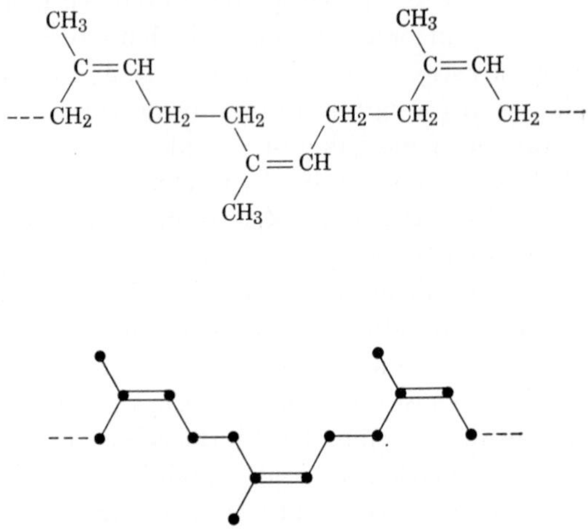

Fig. II-9. Structure of *cis*-1,4-polyisoprene: (*A*) chemical and (*B*) simplified representation.

D). In the presence of peroxides with chlorinating agents such as sulfur chloride (295) or phenyl iododichloride (296), Cl· radicals add readily onto the double bonds of polyisoprene. Halogenation by gaseous chlorine would involve, in the first place, substitution reactions at the methylene groups at carbons 1 and 4 (297,298). Bromination, although little studied up to the present time, could proceed by radical addition under certain conditions. On the other hand, substitutions become important in the presence of a source of Br· radicals such as *N*-bromosuccinimide. Recently, highly elastic brominated products have been obtained by subjecting a mixture of rubber and carbon tetrabromide to high energy radiation, or again by combining bromotrichloromethane with latex in the presence of a hydroperoxide (299). In this field the addition of hydrofluoric acid to polyisoprene (300) should also be mentioned. By working at low temperature, the secondary reactions which generally accompany this addition can be restricted. The products obtained, with 65–70% of their double bonds saturated with the elements of hydrogen fluoride, still retain a certain elasticity. These fluorinated polymers display remarkable heat resistance; after vulcanization, they possess good mechanical properties, high ozone resistance, limited swelling in aromatic hydrocarbons, and low gas permeability.

Sulfur dioxide has also been used to modify natural rubber by radical addition to the double bonds (301,302). This attachment is initiated by azo compounds, hydroperoxides, metallic nitrates or nitrites. For a low content of combined sulfur dioxide, the products have a rubbery aspect and swell in aromatic solvents. At higher levels of sulfur dioxide, they dissolve only in sulfuric and nitric acids.

Numerous workers have studied the attachment of thiols (RSH) onto rubber in the presence of radical donors (303,304), discussed previously in Section C. The resulting products have properties which vary with the nature of the thiol used but, in general, they are characterized by improved resistance towards oxygen and solvents, although their mechanical properties are quite poor. Their chief interest lies in their behavior at low temperatures. The reaction of thioacids (R–COSH) with rubber has also been studied (305,306); the resulting polymers show a significantly lower rate of crystallization. In this connection, attention should likewise be called to studies involving the addition of those mercaptans whose molecules contain chemical groups which are available for subsequent reactions. This is the case with ethyl thioglycolate ($C_2H_5O–CO–CH_2SH$), for example, which, after reacting with the polymer, allows it to be crosslinked with calcium hydroxide. The crosslinks which are formed in this way are due to ionic attractions and this explains their weakness.

In the field of thiol modification of polymeric dienes, certain chemical derivatives of polybutadiene have been prepared (307). These involve radical addition of low molecular weight alkyl mercaptans to polybutadiene which has been prepared mainly by emulsion techniques, the reaction being carried out in the absence of atmospheric oxygen. The resulting products are found to contain thioether side groups in higher or lower concentration depending upon the operating conditions. The "adduct rubbers" display different properties as a function of the density of the substituents and the residual unsaturation of the unchanged 2-butene units. It should be noted in particular that these products have a resistance to air and oxygen which is superior to that of chlorosulfonated polyethylene, and they also have low swelling in solvents. Their impermeability to gases is better than that of butyl rubber. These products are superior to natural rubber and to neoprene with regard to their behavior towards γ-rays (308). On the other hand, their mechanical properties on the whole are mediocre.

A particularly important aspect of the reactivity of rubber by the radical route is the production of graft polymers (cf. Chapter X-B). When vinyl monomers are polymerized in the presence of polyisoprene, a certain number of growing chains are attached to the substrate (309–311). Grafts of polyacrylonitrile, poly(methyl acrylate), and polystyrene, for example, can thus be obtained. The mechanism is assumed to be a chain transfer initiated by a peroxide capable of abstracting a hydrogen from the rubber backbone (312,313). The radicals thus formed intervene in the polymerization chain termination so that the grafted branches are somewhat shorter than the free homopolymer molecules. Among the products in this field which have been studied the most should be mentioned those resulting from the reaction of rubber with methyl methacrylate. Their properties are related to the number of grafted units; above 25% combined poly(methyl methacrylate) the products have markedly altered elastic properties. This is explained by the decrease in the mobility of the main chain which is restricted by the bulky side grafts. Moreover, the latter

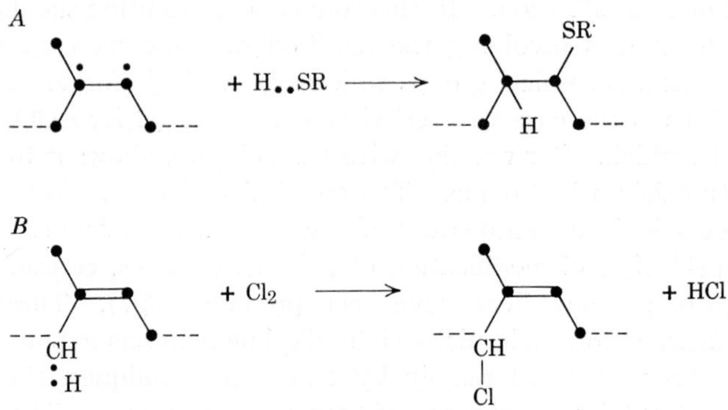

Fig. II-10. Radical additions to *cis*-polyisoprene: (*A*) Addition of a thiol to the double bond; (*B*) substituting addition to an α-methylene group.

complicate vulcanization by making the residue double bonds difficult to reach. Since the grafted chains no longer possess free chemical groups, these polymers are not very interesting from the point of view of reactivity.

It is also possible to create active radical sites on the polyisoprene chain by subjecting it to mechanical forces in the course of high energy shearing (314,315) as discussed in more detail in Chapter XIV. This process has made it possible to combine different macromolecules with rubber (316). The block high polymers obtained by mechanical action have a generally linear form and differ in their properties from rubbers with side grafts.

The reactions described in this part all depend on a radical mechanism. From an inspection of the structure of the repeating C_5H_8 unit, two methods for forming active sites can be distinguished. When the reaction occurs at the double bonds of rubber, the addition is directed generally in opposition to Markownikoff's rule (Kharasch effect); in the case of a thiol (R–SH), for example, the reaction will be as shown in Figure II-10*A*. The methylenes at carbons 1 and 4 can likewise take part by yielding a radical (H·) by homolytic scission which, in the case of chlorination, for example, gives a substitution addition (Fig. II-10*B*).

These radical processes are all generally accompanied by the secondary reactions described above, such as chain scission (in the presence of oxygen) and crosslinking.

b. Polar Additions

Certain reactions of the rubber hydrocarbon appear to proceed by a mechanism essentially different from that which has just been described. In contrast to the previous cases, there does not appear to be any intermediate formation of free radicals on the rubber chain or on the reagent. These reactions involve compounds whose basic characteristic is a tendency towards electrophilic additions, and they can be accounted for by the particular structure of the double bond in polyisoprene. The methyl group tends to make the ethylenic linkage richer in electrons and hence a nucleophilic center while the dissymmetry due to the methyl induces a partial polarization which directs the ionic addition in accordance with Markownikoff's rule (Fig. II-11).

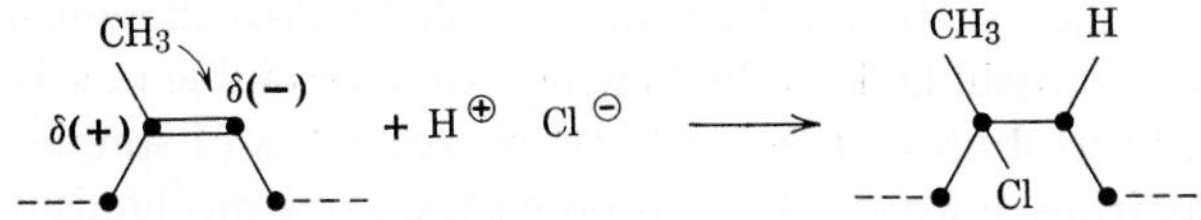

Fig. II-11. Ionic addition of HCl to the double bonds of polyisoprene.

This interpretation of the reactivity of the —C(CH_3)=CH— group is justified on the basis of known reactions. The formation of stable complexes with the Ag^+ ion in the nitrate or perchlorate form (317) may be mentioned; these addition compounds show a crystalline structure with x-rays.

In the area of halogenation and especially hydrohalogenation, certain workers have proposed ionic mechanisms. For this reason chlorination, under certain temperature and catalyst conditions, leads to the formation of Cl^- and Cl^+ ions which add to the double bond according to their respective polarities (318). The hydrochlorination would involve the addition of Cl^- and H^+ ions according to Markownikoff's rule (319).

Among the other ionic reactions of polyisoprene, it is appropriate to mention the action of hydrogen peroxide which reacts violently with the latex, in the presence of acids, to give polyhydroxylated products (320); the acids used induce secondary reactions of esterification and cyclization. A particularly interesting reaction is that of rubber with aldehydes which will be examined later.

In this field of ionic reactions it should be recalled that cyclization (321) generated by acid catalysts can be involved as a secondary reaction.

Thus, there are many reactions which can be applied to the rubber hydrocarbon and to analogous polymeric dienes. In the category of "chemical modification" reactions, as described previously, we will examine more particularly those which make use of C═C double bond (ethylenic) compounds or C═O compounds (aldehydes). The results obtained in this field have afforded certain data on the chemistry of ethylenic high polymers and have also made it possible to obtain new macromolecules.

4. Addition of Ethylenic Compounds to Rubber and Analogous Polymeric Dienes

Bacon and Farmer (322) had shown that it was possible, in the presence of benzoyl peroxide, to add maleic anhydride to the rubber hydrocarbon. These workers proposed two structures (Fig. II-12*A*, II-12*B*) corresponding to intra- and intermolecular reactions. Le Bras and Compagnon (309,310, 323) studied the reaction with some double-bonded monomers and likewise obtained crosslinked products which were insoluble in solvents.

Following the studies of Alder (324) on reactions of simple olefins with maleic anhydride, Farmer (325) proposed the same mechanism for rubber. The mechanism consists of a substituting addition of the anhydride on one of the adjacent methylenes of the isoprenic double bond. The initiation is due to benzoyl peroxide or, eventually, to heat. The aforementioned workers then proposed the structures given in Figures II-12*C* and II-12*D*.

Delalande (326), studying the reaction of *N*-methylmaleimide with rubber, showed the existence of a radical process which appears to have no effect on the double bonds of the chain.

A study of these reactions has been resumed by trying, with the help of techniques which can reduce to a minimum chain alterations, to determine the nature of the maleic anhydride additions to rubber. There are two cases to be considered depending on whether or not there are radical initiators present. The results obtained have led to a certain generalization of the reaction (327).

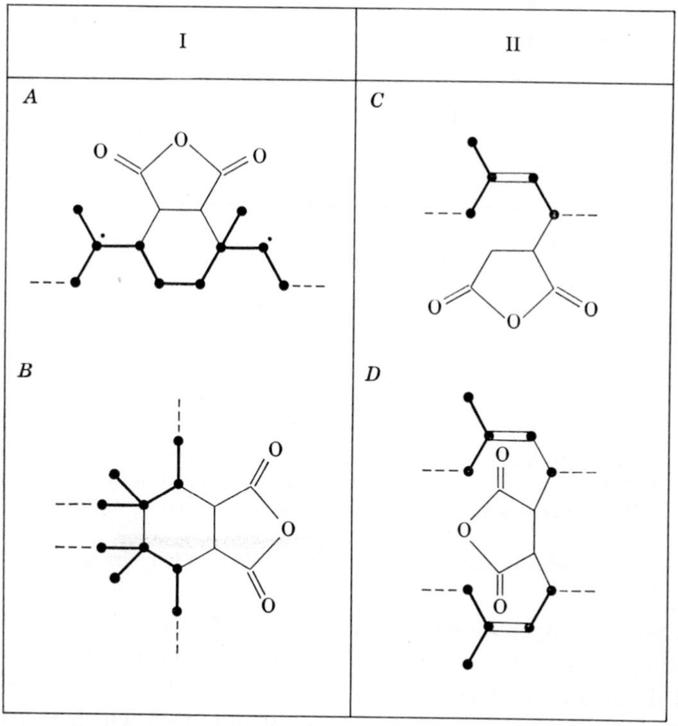

Fig. II-12. Addition of maleic anhydride to polyisoprene: (I) addition to double bonds by (*A*) intramolecular reaction and (*B*) intermolecular reaction; (II) addition to α-methylene groups by (*C*) intramolecular reaction and (*D*) intermolecular reaction.

a. Addition of Maleic Anhydride or N-*Methylmaleimide*

(1) Initiated Reactions

The addition initiated by benzoyl peroxide, as described by Farmer, did not preserve the linearity of the macromolecules and the solubility in solvents. In fact, to retain these properties it is necessary to protect the reagents very carefully from oxygen. By working in an aromatic solvent in the temperature range of 120–150°C., it has been possible to attach the anhydride or its imide with the help of benzoyl peroxide. Subsequently, other initiators were tried which did not cause very much crosslinking. This has made it possible to show the catalytic effects of the following types of substances: hydroperoxide, endoperoxide, azo compound, disulfide, and halogenated derivative of hydantoin. Table II-27 shows the effect of

TABLE II-27
Effect of Different Catalysts on the Radical Addition of Maleic Anhydride to Rubber Hydrocarbon

Catalyst[a]	Degree of addition n[b]	Gel formed, %[c]	Optimum reaction temperature, °C.
para-Menthane hydroperoxide	20	5	130
Benzoyl peroxide	19	23	130
Azobisisobutyronitrile (AIBN)	15	5	120
α-Terpinene endoperoxide (Ascaridol)	4	5	130
Dibenzothiazyl disulfide	4	10	150
Chlorobromodimethylhydantoin	3	8	130

[a] For $m = 0.5$, where m = molar ratio of maleic anhydride to C_5H_8 units before reaction.

[b] n = degree of addition of the reagent onto the polymer chain. It represents the average number of molecules of reagent attached to a segment of the chain consisting of 100 C_5H_8 units. This says nothing with regard to the distribution of the attached groups along the chain.

[c] Gel = amount of polymer insoluble in toluene at room temperature.

p-menthane hydroperoxide which is the most effective initiator used. It is interesting to note the activities of azobisisobutyronitrile and dibenzothiazyl disulfide, which confirm the radical character of the reaction and show that the peroxides are not the only initiators which can be used. Finally, it is worth remarking that the substances considered produce lower gel contents than those obtained with benzoyl peroxide. This indicates a less pronounced crosslinking of the macromolecules employed. Naturally, the optimal reaction temperature, within the limits specified above, depends on the nature of the catalyst and probably on its more or less marked ability to provide radicals at a given temperature.

The characteristic bands of the anhydride group can be detected by infrared spectroscopic examination of the products obtained (see Fig. II-14*B*). The unsaturation band and that of the *cis* structure are practically unchanged compared to the corresponding bands in the starting material. There is neither a decrease in the unsaturation nor isomerization of the double bonds.

(2) Uninitiated Reactions

More so than in the preceding cases, atmospheric oxygen must be very carefully eliminated from the medium. Under these conditions, maleic

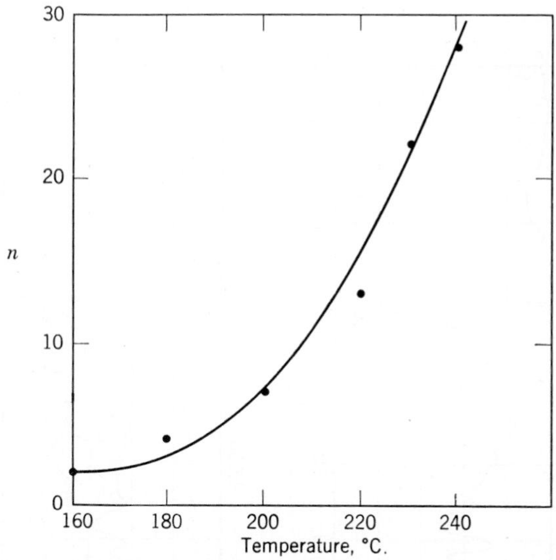

Fig. II-13. Addition of maleic anhydride (degree of addition = n) to *cis*-polyisoprene as a function of the temperature (time of reaction = 60 min.; m = 1).

anhydride begins to react with rubber at 160°C. in an aromatic solvent (328–330). At this temperature, the degree of addition is very low. It becomes appreciable only around 180°C. and then increases regularly with temperature reaching an optimum around 240°C. Above this temperature, decomposition phenomena enter into the picture to affect the process (Fig. II-13).

The addition of anhydrosuccinic residues onto the carbon chain is probably accompanied by a partial hydrolysis since a variable amount of succinic residues has been observed which in certain cases is very large. These residues are much more numerous in the thermal reaction than in the radical reaction. The unsaturation appears to be nearly intact, but particular bands show up in the infrared to indicate that a portion of the double bonds have been isomerized according to Figure II-15 (formation of vinylidene double bonds outside the main chain). These double bonds can not be detected at low degrees of maleic attachment, but are clearly evident beyond n = 8 (Fig. II-14*A*). The nuclear magnetic resonance spectrum confirms the existence of vinylidene double bonds.

It appears therefore that the products obtained by the so-called "thermal" reaction have a different structure from those resulting from the so-called "radical" reaction.

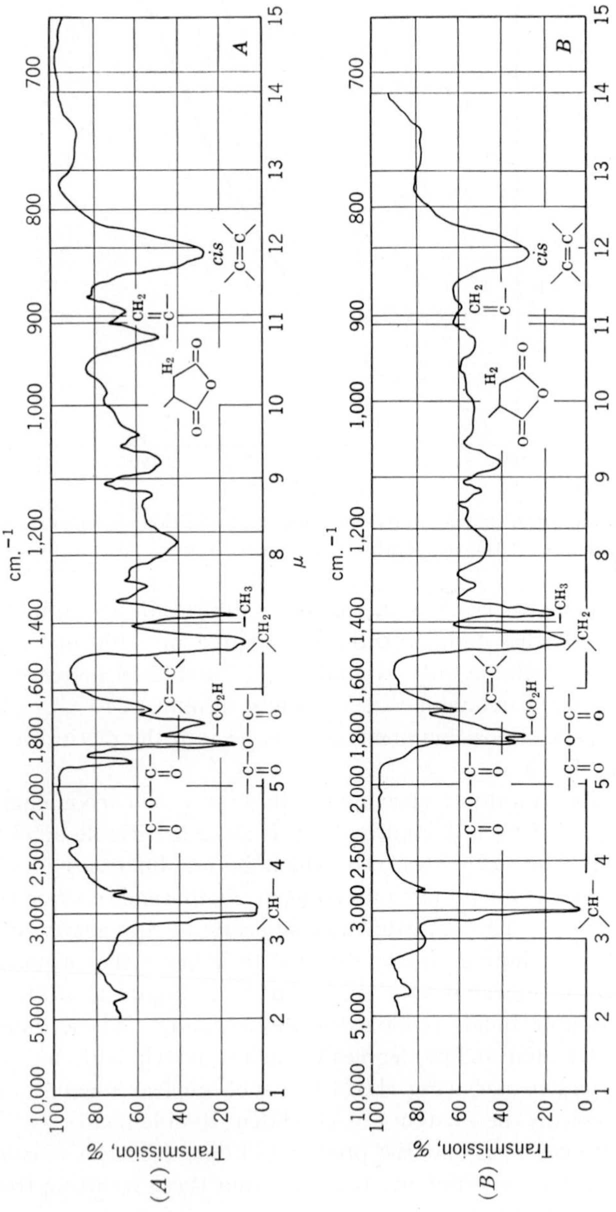

cm.⁻¹
Transmission, %
μ
cis
A
B
(A)
(B)

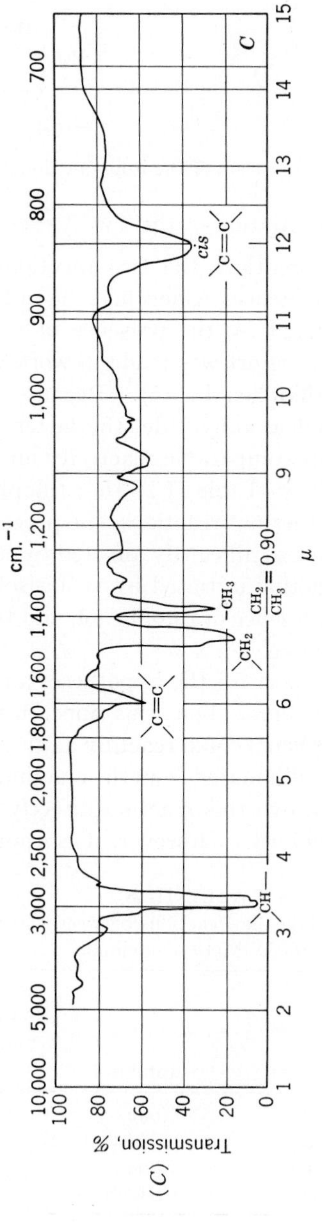

Fig. II-14. Infrared spectra of maleic anhydride-modified polyisoprenes: (*A*) uninitiated reaction; (*B*) initiated reaction; (*C*) polyisoprene control.

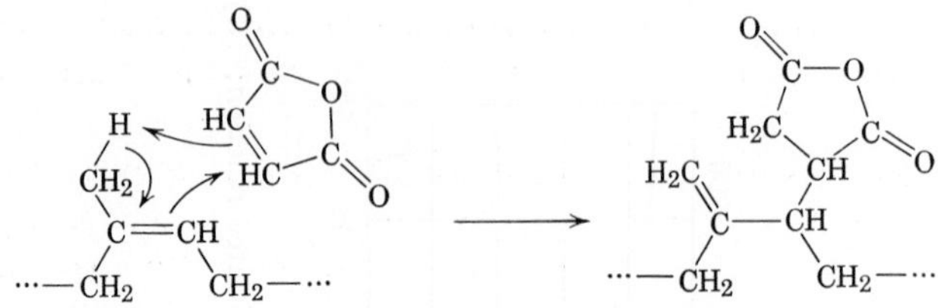

Fig. II-15. Transposition of the isoprenic double bond.

(3) Differentiation of the Two Reactions

In order further to differentiate the two reactions, it is desirable to examine some of the consequences which may be anticipated. Since the radical reactions are hindered by the presence of substances which can fix the radicals produced, an effort was made to work with a very effective radical acceptor, namely, thiophenol (315). Because this compound has a tendency to react with maleic anhydride, the latter was replaced by *N*-methylmaleimide which has comparable reactivity and degree of addition.

It is seen from the results in Table II-28 that thiophenol has practically no effect on the so-called thermal reaction: the process occurs despite the inhibitor and the yield is not significantly affected by its presence. On the other hand, the radical reaction initiated by azobisisobutyronitrile is considerably retarded by the presence of thiophenol, and the yield is reduced to one quarter of the initial value.

These results provide support for the hypotheses advanced, but it is not possible to be completely definite about this since, in the case of reactions carried out at 220°C., thiophenol could react by adding to the double bonds of polyisoprene and thus be eliminated from the reaction medium. It would appear difficult to try to prove this reaction directly in view of the very small amounts of thiol involved. However, it is appropriate to stress, in

TABLE II-28
Inhibiting Effect of Thiophenol on the Reactions between Natural *cis*-1,4-Polyisoprene and *N*-Methylmaleimide

Probable reaction	Initiator	Inhibitor	Reaction temperature, °C.	Degree of addition *n*
Radical	AIBN	None	130	24
	AIBN	C_6H_5SH	130	6
Thermal	None	None	220	9
	None	C_6H_5SH	220	10

justifying this approach, that the addition of thiophenol to polyisoprene requires experimental conditions (331) very different from those which have been used in these tests.

Previous workers assumed that the reaction involving the ethylenic compound took place according to a substituting addition process both for the initiated reactions and the other types. According to this theory, the addition of anhydrosuccinic residues is explained by the abstraction of a methylenic hydrogen atom from the chain, followed by the hooking up of the succinyl residue at the site of the migrating atom (Fig. II-12*C*). Farmer had advanced the hypothesis (294) that secondary reactions provoke a migration of the double bond from the carbon 2,3 position to the 3,4 position, the latter remaining in the chain. The presence of an initiator favoring the abstraction of a hydrogen atom probably can facilitate such a reaction. Therefore, it is impossible to neglect the hypothesis of a radical mechanism in the case of the reaction carried out at high temperature in the absence of catalyst. The assumed homolytic scission can result from the supply of thermal energy which replaces the effect of the catalyst.

On the basis of what has been stated previously, it is proposed that the process is one of addition of maleic anhydride to the double bonds according to a mechanism of the concerted electron transfer type (332). The latter has already been invoked for thermal reactions which show certain analogies to that described here, for example, combination of maleic anhydride with allylbenzene. This process applied to the *cis*-1,4-polyisoprenes amounts to granting the existence of vinylidene double bonds (Fig. II-15). The direction of electron displacement is determined by the inductive effect of the methyl group which tends to repel the electrons towards the extremity of the double bond. For the sake of convenience, this addition will be denoted as "thermal" in opposition to the "radical" addition.

To sum up, one must assume that there are two mechanisms possible for the combination carried out at high temperature and without catalyst: an addition according to Figure II-12*C* for which the elevation in temperature induces the appearance of active sites on the chain; and an addition according to Figure II-15 in which the supply of thermal energy induces the circular displacement of electrons, without the appearance of any radical sites.

b. Extension to Polymeric Dienes with Analogous Structures

The results obtained with rubber hydrocarbon have been applied to other polymeric dienes: gutta-percha hydrocarbon (*trans*-1,4-polyisoprene), *cis*-1,4-polybutadiene, and *cis*-1,4-polyisoprene. These materials react with maleic anhydride by radical and thermal reactions (Table II-29). In the case of the synthetic polymers, it is necessary to eliminate certain impurities which inhibit the addition of the anhydride. The gel contents are higher for the derivatives resulting from the synthetic products than for those obtained from natural rubber. Nevertheless, the solubility in solvents varies in the same way; thus, the solubility in ketones increases with the number of oxygenated groups attached to the chain. Infrared spectroscopy confirms that, in the case of high temperature reactions, the free acid rather than the anhydride is predominant. At lower temperatures and in the presence of catalysts, the maleic groups are almost completely in the form of the anhydride.

TABLE II-29
Reactions between Maleic Anhydride and Various Diene Polymers[a]

Diene polymer	Degree of addition, *n*	
	Radical reaction	Thermal reaction
cis-1,4-Polyisoprene (rubber)	14	9
cis-1,4-Polyisoprene (synthetic)	9	6
trans-1,4-Polyisoprene (gutta-percha)	7	8
cis-1,4-Polybutadiene (synthetic)	12	5

[a] Reaction conditions: radical reaction, $m = 1$, 2 hr. at 130°C., 3% AIBN (Azobisisobutyronitrile); thermal reaction, $m = 1$, 45 min. at 220°C.

c. Properties and Preparation of Maleic Rubbers

The chemical properties of the maleic rubbers have been studied. Amides, esters and urethanes have been prepared which correspond to the carboxyl or anhydride groups distributed along the chain. Bifunctional reagents, alcohols, amines, etc., as well as certain metal oxides, have led to characteristic crosslinking reactions.

The new materials produced were found to have different physical properties from those of the initial product. For example, their solubilities in hydrocarbon solvents are lower than those of rubber. Conversely, the solubility in oxygenated solvents (particularly in methyl ethyl ketone), although very low for rubber, is significant for the polyanhydrides produced.

All of the results described above pertain to modified rubbers which were obtained by reactions in solution. From the point of view of anticipating practical developments, it was essential to develop an easier reaction process; this has led to considering a solid-phase reaction (333,334). The removal of solvent alters the experimental conditions profoundly.

Mass reactions had already been examined in some studies (335). Le Bras and Compagnon had shown that a chemical combination between rubber and the anhydride could be accomplished by passing the rubber–reagent mixture between cold, tight rolls of a mill (310) and even by simple compression between the plates of a press (336,337). These reactions could be accounted for by the creation of radicals by mechanical forces (314); Tutorskii, Khrokhina, and Dogadkin discussed certain aspects of this reaction (338).

At relatively high temperatures the monomer could be attached to rubber in the presence of appropriate catalysts (310) or even in the absence of catalyst (339). Snyder and Paxton have applied this type of reaction to synthetic olefinic rubbers (340). They worked with a closed reactor or with an internal mill at temperatures between 150 and 240°C. in the presence of various polymerization inhibitors. These ingredients have the advantage of avoiding the crosslinking produced by the anhydride as well as those crosslinks which are apt to be formed at these temperatures in the elastomers under consideration. Green and Sverdrup (341,342) have reacted maleic anhydride and other olefins with reclaimed rubber. They utilized the simultaneous action of heat, strong mastication and reagent to obtain "carboxyl" reclaimed rubbers from vulcanized scrap. The products showed improved resistance to swelling in oils and hydrocarbon solvents as well as to aging when compared to the initial elastomer. The operation was carried out in a special plasticator (Reclaimator).

The proposed procedure (333) resembles that used by the latter authors, but the principle of the reactions is totally different for they are based on crude rubber and not on the loaded vulcanizates. Undegraded modified rubbers are thus obtained, the vulcanizates of which have excellent mechanical properties.

The incorporation of maleic anhydride in the rubber is carried out on an open mill at moderate temperature so as to avoid, in the first place, the crosslinking which develops when using mill rolls which are too cold and, in the second place, the sublimation of the anhydride which occurs above 52°C. To avoid crosslinking reactions at low temperature, small amounts of phenolic and amine antioxidants are also incorporated.

The reaction of addition to rubber involves heating the system at 200–250°C. in an internal mill-mixer of a very particular type, the polymer undergoing an intense and very effective mixing with only a very moderate degradation. The Buss mill-mixer appears to be a good instrument for

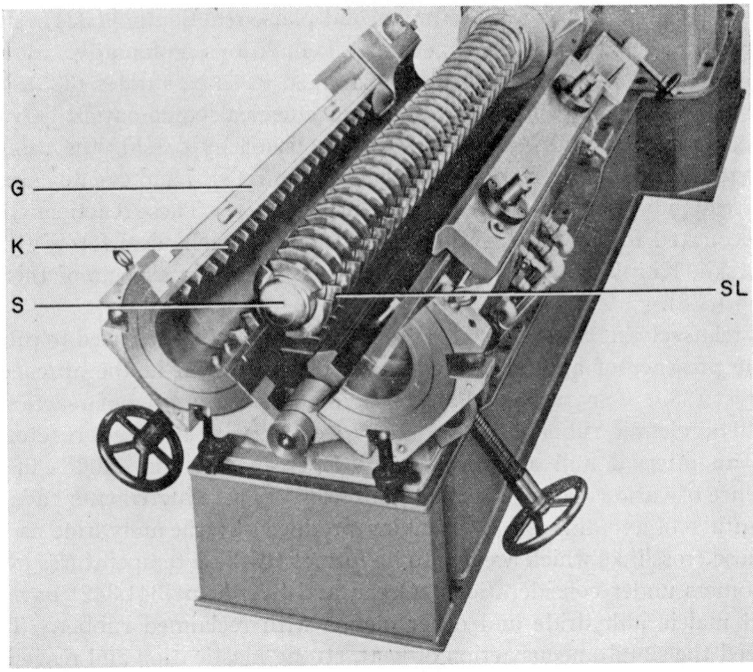

Fig. II-16. The Buss mill-mixer. G = jacketed chamber; K = teeth; S = worm screw; SL = blades.

carrying out this kind of chemical reaction on high polymers. This apparatus (Fig. II-16) consists principally of a chamber at the interior of which is a worm screw. There is a large number of blades spaced throughout the length of the screw while teeth are attached to the cylinder. The machine is characterized by combined movements of continuous rotation and alternating displacement along the axis of the screw in such a way that the teeth of the stator pass by the intervals of the blades of the screw. The material thus undergoes a very energetic mixing practically out of contact with the air. The diameters of the screw are variable, the inside diameter in the laboratory model being 46 mm. and that in the industrial models being 140 or 200 mm. Heating is obtained by circulating fluid, vapor, or oil in the body of the mixer using an appropriate system of regulation. The rubber-maleic anhydride mixture is heated in the Buss mill generally for 8–15 min. (Fig. II-17).

The reaction products containing 5–10% of combined anhydride can normally be vulcanized with sulfur, but they also have the characteristic of being able to yield noteworthy vulcanizates with oxides of bivalent metals, such as calcium, zinc, and especially magnesium. In addition to the mechanical properties which this type of crosslinking affords, it is characterized by a very long plateau of vulcanization which is of technical interest from the standpoint of vulcanizing thick sections. The mechanism of this vulcanization has not yet been clearly established. Nevertheless, it may be that if ionic bonds exist between the metal of the oxide and the carboxyl

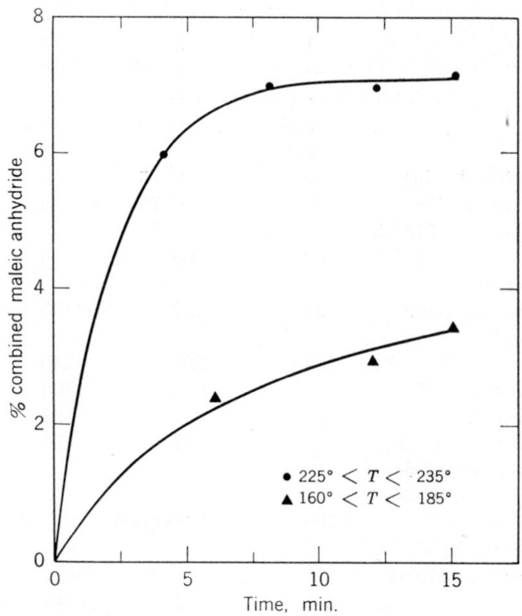

Fig. II-17. Solid-phase rubber–maleic anhydride reaction: anhydride combined as a function of the time (anhydride incorporated: 13%).

groups they only have a very limited importance, the strength of the network being attributable to homopolar bonds resulting from complex mechanisms (343). Table II-30 indicates some of the mechanical properties for vulcanizates of polysuccinic rubbers obtained with magnesium oxide.

Concerning reinforcement of these materials by carbon black, it may be seen from Table II-30 that it is sufficient to incorporate 30 parts, by weight, of reinforcing black in order to obtain properties which correspond, in the case of unmodified rubber, to those of a tire tread stock containing 50 parts of black.

TABLE II-30
Mechanical Properties of Rubber Vulcanizates Modified by Maleic Anhydride[a]

Compound parts/100 rubber	Gum vulcanizates		Loaded vulcanizates	
	Control	Maleic rubber	Control	Maleic rubber
Unmodified rubber	100	—	100	—
Modified rubber	—	100	—	100
ZnO	5	—	5	—
MgO	—	20	—	20
Stearic acid	1	1	2	2
Pine tar	—	—	5	5
HAF black	—	—	50	30
Sulfur	2.3	—	2.3	—
Santocure	0.8	—	0.8	—
Phenyl-β-naphthylamine	0.75	0.75	0.75	0.75
Aldol-α-naphthylamine	0.75	0.75	0.75	0.75
Time of vulcanization at 143°C., min.	30	60	30	60
Mechanical properties				
300% modulus, kg./cm.^{2}	20	120	130	170
Tensile strength, kg./cm.^{2}	250	225	240	240
Elongation at break, %	750	630	400	400
Shore hardness, A	38	57	63	72
Resistance to tear, kg./cm.	38	34	150	120
Resistance to repeated flexing (cut-growth test: 500% propagation)	2700	>2,000,000	500,000	>2,000,000
Loss of tensile strength (Geer oven; 1 month at 70°C.), %	50	2	45	<5

[a] Combined anhydride content: 8%; vulcanization by MgO.

The excellent resistance of these vulcanizates to repeated flexing should also be noted. The tests for resistance to accelerated aging have likewise given very interesting results.

d. Reactions of Other Ethylenic Compounds with Rubber

The hypothesis of the thermal reaction between maleic anhydride and *cis*-polyisoprene involves important consequences with regard to the choice of olefinic structures which can react. As shown previously, retention of chain linearity excludes grafting reactions which also involve ethylenic compounds. Now, the easier it is for these compounds to homo-

TABLE II-31
Influence of the Electronic Structure of the Double Bond on the Reactivity with *cis*-1,4-Polyisoprene

	Reactivity
Double bond rich in electrons	
Styrene	0
p-Aminostyrene	0
Allyl alcohol	0
Unactivated double bond	
Cyclohexene	0
1-Cyano-3-cyclohexene	0
Tetrahydrophthalic anhydride	Very slight
Indene	0
Pyrroline	0
Double bonds poor in electrons	
Maleic anhydride	+
N-Methylmaleimide	+
Chloromaleic anhydride	+
Fumaric acid	+
Maleic acid	+
γ-Crotonolactone	+
p-Benzoquinone[a]	+
Acrylonitrile	+
Itaconic anhydride	0
1-Cyclohexene-3-one	0
1-Cyano-1-cyclohexene	0
1-Cyano-1-cyclopentene	0
Fumaric dinitrile	0
Methyl vinyl ketone	0
1,4-Naphthoquinone	0
Vinylidene chloride	0

[a] A significant degree of crosslinking is observed in the case of *p*-benzoquinone.

polymerize, the more they are apt to produce grafting; thus, the most interesting compounds would be those which do not show this aptitude to a marked extent. The compounds will be limited particularly to those in which the two carbons on the double bond are substituted (344).

The thermal reactions are facilitated when the two compounds present have suitable electronic configurations about their double bonds. Substituents having an electronegative effect, which reduce the electron density of the double bond, favor this type of reaction. However, the possibility of an activation by groups having an inductive or positive electromeric effect cannot be excluded *a priori*. Different compounds have thus been tried in which the double bond has different electron densities. All these reagents are given in Table II-31, which includes olefinic compounds having nonactivated double bonds as well as those with double bonds either rich or poor in electrons. The possibility for reaction is indicated by a plus sign or zero, depending on whether there is addition or not.

It is clear from examination of Table II-31 that the compounds in which the double bond is not activated do not give any reaction, and even some of those compounds with activated double bonds do not react either. By using classical data pertaining to copolymerizable structures, other conditions have been revealed. To begin with, the reaction of two ethylenic substances depends on the electron density of the double bonds present (345,346). It is facilitated when these densities have opposite signs, that is, when one of the double bonds is rich and the other poor in electrons. Taking into account the structure of the isoprene units where the inductive effect of the methyl group leads to increased electron density at the extremity of the double bond, it can be appreciated that addition of monomers will be facilitated in the case of those compounds having a double bond with low electron density. This explains the absence of reactivity of monomers in the first two groups in Table II-31. If a hydrogen of the carbon–carbon double bond of maleic anhydride is replaced by a chlorine (chloromaleic anhydride) or by a methyl group (citraconic anhydride), the electronic effect of these substituents must lead to a reactive substance in the first case and a nonreactive substance in the second. This has been verified experimentally.

Nevertheless, making the double bonds poorer in electrons does not appear to be a sufficient condition for obtaining reaction. A factor of steric hindrance must still be introduced (347), and this is very important in the case of 1,4-naphthoquinone, for example. The absence of reactivity of the double bonds of cyclohexene is particularly noted. Thus, 1-cyclohexene-3-one and 1-cyano-1-cyclohexene do not combine with rubber and this could be attributed to the effect of the nonplanarity of these rings on the electronic structure of the double bond. On the other hand the explanation, in the light of present knowledge, for the nonreactivity of 1-cyano-1-cyclopentene, which is planar, must be attributed to the lack of the carbonyl group. Table II-32 shows the reactivities of the different monomers considered.

Among the monomers in which the double bond undergoes no interaction, it was logical in the first place to consider cyclohexene. However, it is practically impossible to demonstrate addition of such a reagent because its elemental formula does not differ sufficiently from that of polyisoprene and also because it lacks characteristic spectral bands for following the reaction

TABLE II-32
Reactivity of Ethylenic Monomers with *cis*-1,4-Polyisoprene as Indicated by Level of Attachment n[a]

Monomers	n Thermal reaction	n Radical reaction
Maleic anhydride	12	20
N-Methylmaleimide	12	22
Chloromaleic anhydride	10	—
γ-Crotonolactone	8	13
Fumaric acid	6	—
Maleic acid	5	6
p-Benzoquinone	8	—
Acrylonitrile	3	—
Tetrahydrophthalic anhydride	Very slight	

[a] Reaction conditions: $m = 1$; 45 min. at 220°C. for the thermal reaction; 2 hr. at 140°C. for the radical reaction, in the presence of *p*-menthane hydroperoxide.

under consideration. Thus, after inconclusive experiments on the evaluation of the properties of the polymer obtained, two substances were chosen for which addition could be readily detected. These compounds, tetrahydrophthalic anhydride and 1-cyano-3-cyclohexene, possess characteristic groups which are sufficiently far from the double bond to avoid any disturbing interaction.

From another standpoint, acrylonitrile was considered as a particular case because of its high tendency to homopolymerize. The experiments have been carried out between 40 and 220°C., with or without hydroquinone. In the presence of this inhibitor neither addition nor homopolymerization is observed. In the absence of hydroquinone, one can observe a zone of addition of the nitrile to polyisoprene between 115 and 130°C. Infrared spectroscopy reveals the characteristic band of the cyanide group (Fig. II-18).

It was necessary to determine whether the nitrile was attached as propionitrile, or as grafted chains, or was simply polyacrylonitrile within the rubber. The reaction conditions are not favorable for grafting (chain transfer) which requires, in principle, the presence of radical initiators. On the other hand, the idea that polyacrylonitrile is formed cannot be dismissed, but it appears unlikely for the following reasons: polymerization reactions involving the nitrile carried out in the presence of squalene (a substance whose chemical structure is very similar to that of polyisoprene) readily result in the formation of homopolymer, whereas with rubber under the same conditions there is no significant appearance of polyacrylonitrile.

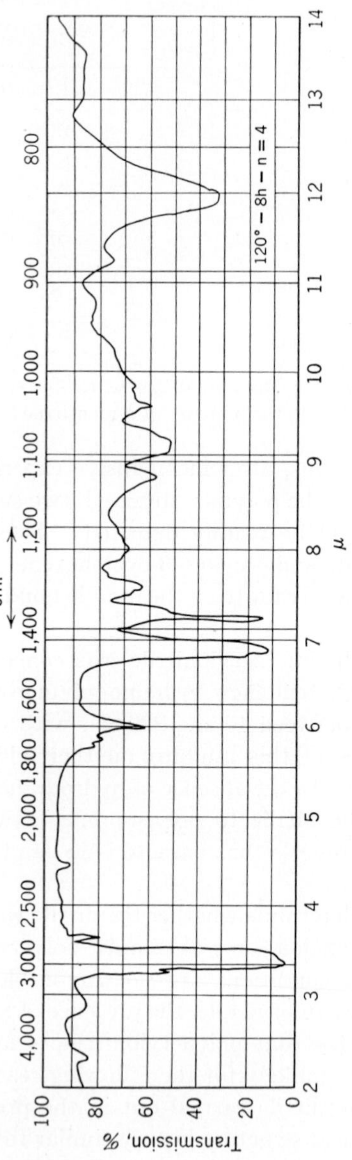

Fig. II-18. Infrared spectrum of acrylonitrile-modified natural rubber.

Moreover, this inhibitor effect in the case of rubber has already been noted (348). On the other hand, no change in nitrogen content is observed when the products obtained are subjected to an extraction with a solvent for polyacrylonitrile. For these reasons, it may be assumed that there is a reaction between rubber and acrylonitrile leading to the addition of propionitrile groups. The fact that hydroquinone completely inhibits this reaction is a strong indication for a radical mechanism catalyzed by heat.

The results obtained show the limits of the thermal reactions. They suggest the possibility of reactions with compounds having double bonds which are very poor in electrons, such as the class of π acids, particularly tetracyanoethylene (349). The possibility of ionic reactions with carbonyl reagents capable of reacting with the polyisoprene double bonds can also be visualized.

5. Reactions of Carbonyl Reagents with Rubber

The aldehyde group (HC═O) is an electrophilic reagent. The difference between the electronegativities of oxygen and carbon and the mobility of the π electrons combine to make the carbonyl group strongly polarized.

$$>\overset{\delta\oplus}{C}{=}\overset{\delta\ominus}{O}\ \text{(2.7–2.9 Debyes)}$$

This polarity is responsible for all the heterolytic reactions involving the carbonyl group. It is exceptionally high for a covalent bond which rarely exceeds 2 Debyes (C—Cl, 1.7 D.; C—H, 0.3 D.). Contrary to what is observed with ethylenic hydrocarbons, the direction of the polarizability of the $>C{=}O$ group is independent of the nature of the substituents attached to the carbon (350). As a general rule, the carbon atom will be the electrophilic center and the oxygen atom the nucleophilic center:

$$>\overset{\delta(+)}{C}\cdots\overset{\delta(-)}{O} + \overset{\delta(-)}{A}—\overset{\delta(+)}{B} \rightarrow —\underset{|}{\overset{A}{\overset{|}{C}}}—\bar{O}—B \qquad (53)$$

This is verified particularly in the Prins reaction (351,352), which provides a way to introduce into a molecule a methyl carrying a monovalent group (353). The aldehyde used is generally methanal which adds to hydrocarbons with double or triple bonds in the presence or absence of acid catalysts such as protonated acids, anhydrous metal chlorides or certain metal oxides. As shown in Figure II-19 and Table II-33, different struc-

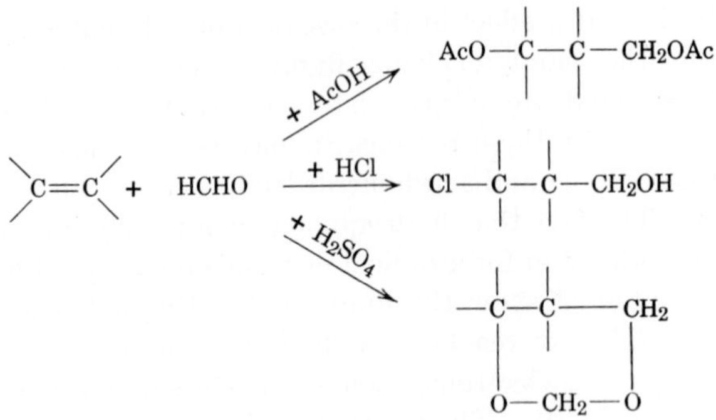

Fig. II-19. Structures obtained in the Prins reaction.

tures are obtained, depending upon the medium (354). A particularly interesting case is one in which the reaction is carried out in nonaqueous medium in the absence of protonated acids. The reaction then requires higher temperatures and especially an appropriate structure of the olefinic double bond which must be very rich in electrons (+*I* effect of methyl or phenyl groups). Under these conditions, structures are obtained having free alcohol groups, as shown in Table II-34.

TABLE II-33
Examples of Structures Obtained in the Prins Reaction in the Presence of Acid Catalysts

Reagents	Reaction media	Products obtained	Reference
Styrene + formaldehyde	AcOH	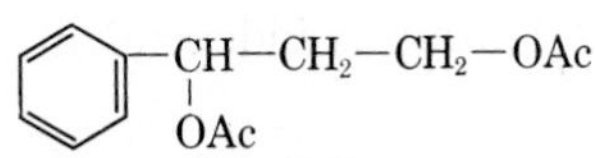 Diester of 1,3-glycol	355–359
Cyclohexene + formaldehyde	HCl	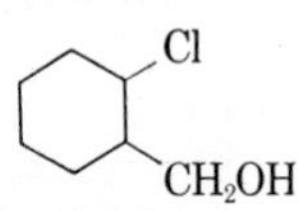 1-Hydroxymethyl-2-chloro-cyclohexane	360
Cyclohexene + formaldehyde	H_2SO_4, H_2O	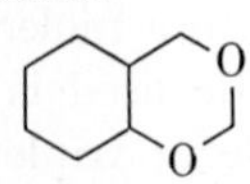 1,3-Dioxa decalin	360

TABLE II-34
Examples of Structures Obtained in the Prins Reaction in Nonaqueous Medium and in the Absence of Protonated Acids

Reagents	Experimental conditions	Products obtained	Reference
Propylene + formaldehyde	BF_3, 180°C.	$CH_3—CHOH—CH_2—CH_2OH$ 1,3-Butanediol	356–361
Methylenecyclohexane + formaldehyde	200°C.	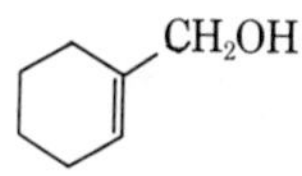 2-Hydroxymethyl-1-cyclohexene	362
β-Pinene + formaldehyde	170°C., 100 atm.	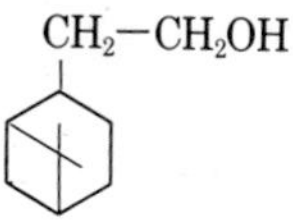 Homopinenol	363, 364

The mechanism of aldehyde addition to an olefin is depicted in Figure II-20. The essential step involves an attack on the olefin by the electrophilic center of the carbonyl. The resulting carbocation is stabilized through addition of an R^- residue present in the reaction medium or even through migration of a proton in the event that there is a hyperconjugation due to a methyl group adjacent to the double bond.

a. *Formaldehyde*

Various workers have studied the reaction of rubber with aldehydes, particularly formaldehyde. Kirchhof (365) first described a "formaldehyde rubber" obtained by treating a benzene solution of rubber with an aqueous solution of formaldehyde, in the presence of concentrated sulfuric acid; the resulting product is a yellow-gold powdery material. There are numerous patents pertaining to possible rubber derivatives obtained with certain aldehydes; they recommend reactions in solution, in dispersion, or in the solid phase.

(1) Reactions in Solution

The solvent used is generally carbon tetrachloride; the aldehyde is formaldehyde in aqueous solution (366) or its polymers (367,368). The reaction is carried out in the presence of organic or inorganic acids or an-

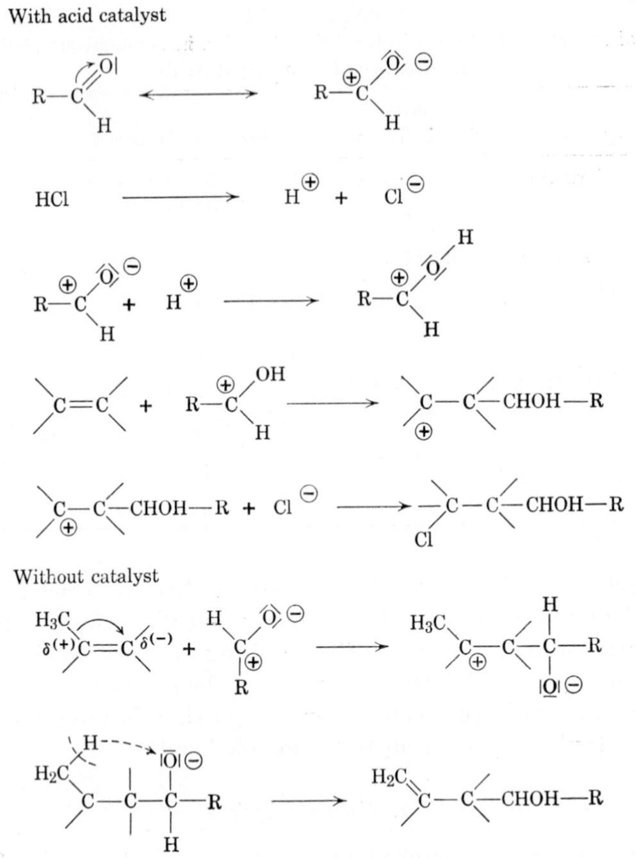

Fig. II-20. Addition of an aldehydic carbonyl group to a carbon–carbon double bond.

hydrous metal chlorides; gutta-percha and balata can also be used in the place of rubber (369). A catalyst of choice would be boron trifluoride in glacial acetic acid solution (370). The thermoplastic derivatives obtained are quite resistant to aromatic solvents, acids, and bases. That they can be partially crosslinked by means of diisocyanates (371) or polyamines (372) shows that some free alcohol groups exist.

(2) Reactions in Dispersion

Formaldehyde in aqueous solution is added to a stabilized latex in the presence of hydrochloric acid and a protective colloid (373). Some of the products obtained still show elastic properties and give vulcanizates having greatly improved resistance to swelling in solvents (374).

(3) Reactions in the Solid Phase

These consist of milling rubber together with a polymer of formaldehyde and inducing a reaction by heating the mixture in the presence of anhydrous metal chlorides (375). An important work in this field is that of Swift, who studied different catalytic systems and showed that the compounds obtained were partially crosslinked and contained few free OH groups (376).

To summarize, there is little information on the structure of rubber-formaldehyde derivatives. However, it appears that degradation and cyclization reactions occur simultaneously, and these alter significantly the chain structure without bringing about any really new chemical reactivity. In this connection, it is interesting to mention a patent (377) concerned with the modification, by means of formaldehyde, of butyl-type rubbers of low unsaturation. This process confers a certain reactivity as well as interesting properties on a polymer which has been noted for its relative chemical inertness.

From studies by Sekhar (292,293,378), the natural rubber macromolecule contains aldehyde groups at various places along the chain. According to Bonner (379), these groups would result from the oxidation of vinylidene CH_2 units formed in the course of biosynthesis. Sekhar thinks that the aldehyde groups are responsible for the spontaneous crosslinking of rubber on storage and also for the appearance of microgel in fresh latices, and that this crosslinking corresponds to the attack on a polyisoprene chain by a carbonyl group attached to a nearby chain.

The study of the reactions of diene polymers with aldehydes has been taken up again in line with the techniques described previously in order to obtain simple addition products. Among the results achieved, it is worthwhile to mention those concerned with the reaction of the rubber hydrocarbon with glyoxal (CHO–CHO) and chloral (Cl_3C–CHO). Because of their particular structures, these aldehydes are seen to be reagents of choice for electrophilic additions. Other structures are currently being investigated (380).

b. Glyoxal

These reactions can be carried out either in solution or in the solid phase (381,382).

(1) Reactions in Solution

Purified natural rubber which has been dried under deoxygenated nitrogen is reacted with anhydrous glyoxal prepared by a method similar to that described by Harries (383). The reagent is added to a 2% solution of natural rubber in xylene, followed by the catalyst, an aluminum chloride–sodium chloride eutectic. The optimum reaction temperature is 180°C. in the absence of catalyst and 120°C. in the presence of $AlCl_3$–NaCl. This eutectic, effective about 100°C., is considered to have a lower cyclizing tendency than pure aluminum chloride (381).

Figure II-21 shows the degrees of addition n obtained as a function of the initial molar ratio m. Above a degree of addition corresponding to $n = 11$, the products obtained show significant crosslinking and have the character of thermoplastic resins.

Stirring a solution of rubber and monomeric glyoxal for 48 hr. at room

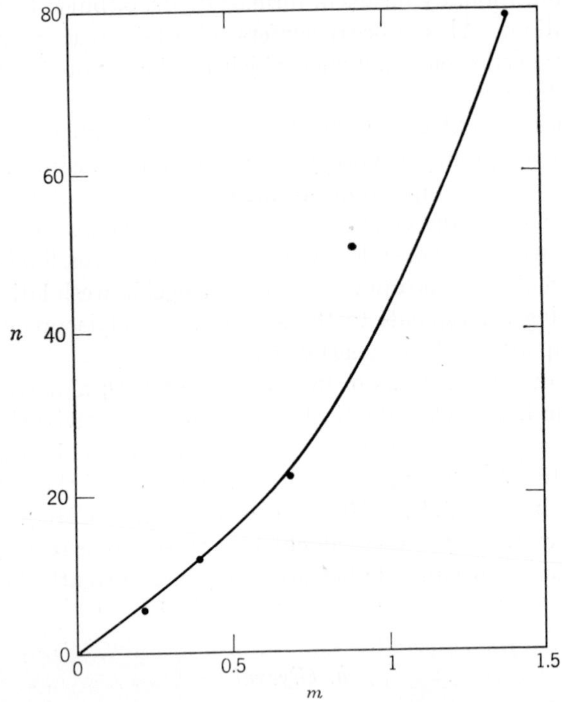

Fig. II-21. Rubber–glyoxal reaction. Influence of the initial molar ratio on the addition of glyoxal to the rubber hydrocarbon.

temperature results in a mixture of unchanged polyisoprene (up to 30% of the initial amount) and complex resinous products; these are insoluble even on boiling in aromatic and hydroxyl solvents and hence are very difficult to characterize.

(2) Reactions in the Solid Phase

Glyoxal may be obtained through thermal decomposition of its hydrated trimer according to eq. (54).

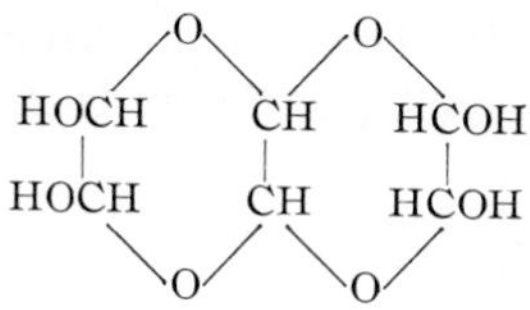

$$\rightarrow \ 3\ CHO—CHO + 2H_2O \qquad (54)$$

Polyglyoxal is introduced into the rubber by simple milling, and the mixture, on heating in a bomb or in a Buss mill, partially reacts above 175°C. to give, for example, the derivatives a and b indicated in Table II-35. These products can be crosslinked by being heated at 143°C. in a press in the presence of diamines or diisocyanates.

TABLE II-35
Results of Elementary Analysis on Products from the Solid-Phase Rubber–Glyoxal Reaction

Rubber	Treatment	Initial molar ratio m	Degree of addition n	Elemental composition C, %	H, %	O, %
Untreated rubber	—	—	0	86.71	12.76	0.29
Rubber–glyoxal(a)	Bomb; 60 min. at 180°C.	1	19	79.66	10.64	8.23
Rubber–glyoxal(b)	Buss; 8 min. at 220°C.	1	11	81.49	11.68	5.33

(3) Structure of the Products Obtained in Solution

Spectroscopic analysis reveals infrared absorption bands at 1080 (ethers), 1720 (carbonyls), and 3350 cm.$^{-1}$ (hydroxyls). The presence of these chemical groups can be confirmed by various characteristic reactions. The OH groups can be esterified or attacked by acrylonitrile in a cyanoethylation reaction. The carbonyl groups can be oxidized and then determined as —COOH groups. Oxidation makes it possible also to characterize —CHOH—CHO side chains; when treated with *tert*-butyl chromate, they give structures of the type —CO—COOH which decarboxylate on heating in hydrochloric acid.

From what has been indicated above, it may be assumed that glyoxal adds onto polyisoprene in the form of α-alcohol aldehyde side groups. By analogy to the attachment of phenylglyoxal to methylenecyclohexane (362), we may propose the reaction scheme given in Figure II-22*A*. The α-methylenic reactivity does not enable us, however, to dismiss the possibility that the attachment proceeds according to Figure II-22*B*.

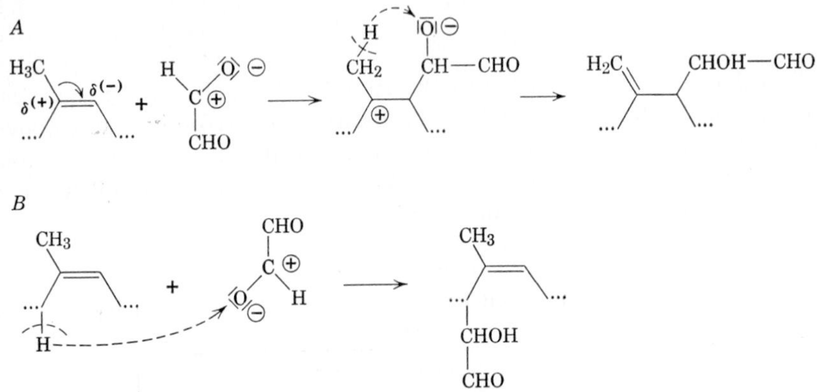

Fig. II-22. Addition of glyoxal to polyisoprene.

The glyoxal-modified products have a strong tendency to become insoluble spontaneously. This transformation occurs in a few days at ordinary temperature and seems to be due to the presence of —CHO side groups since a lasting stabilization is observed when the carbonyl groups are blocked by means of 2,4-dinitrophenylhydrazine.

c. *Chloral*

(1) Conditions and Mechanism

The results obtained with glyoxal have suggested an extension of this reaction to other aldehydes which are capable of giving more stable products. Chloral, for example, has a structure which, in principle, is favorably disposed to the combination sought. In fact, it may be noted that those aldehydes which react easily with olefins are readily accessible only in the form of hydrates, corresponding to the stabilization of the active form of the carbonyl group (eq. 55).

$$\left[\underset{\displaystyle H}{\overset{}{R{-}C{=}O}} \longleftrightarrow R{-}\underset{\displaystyle H}{\overset{\oplus}{C}}{-}\overline{\underline{O}}|^{\ominus}\right] + \overset{\oplus}{H}\ \overset{\ominus}{O}H \rightarrow R{-}C(OH)_2{-}H \qquad (55)$$

Addition reactions of chloral to simple olefins are known. There are two methods of attachment possible: (*a*) ionic addition (384) onto the ethylenic double bonds in the presence of metal chlorides according to the Prins re-

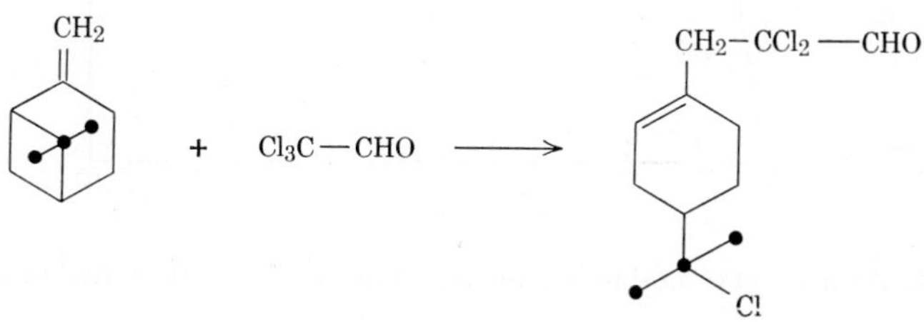

Fig. II-23. Radical addition of chloral to a vinylidene double bond.

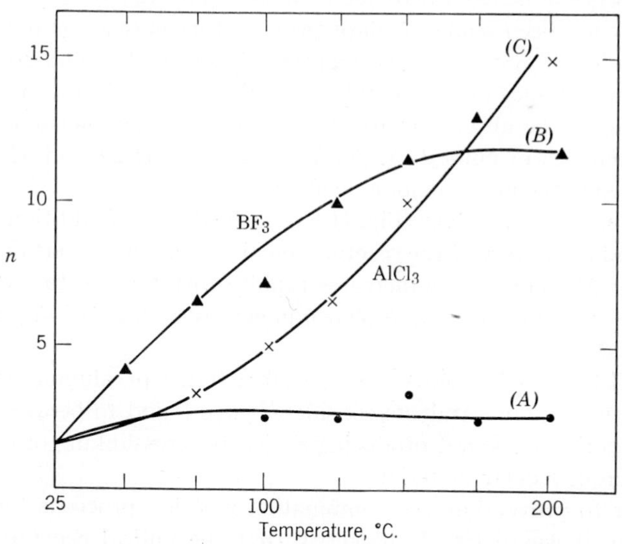

Fig. II-24. Addition of chloral to polyisoprene as a function of the temperature.

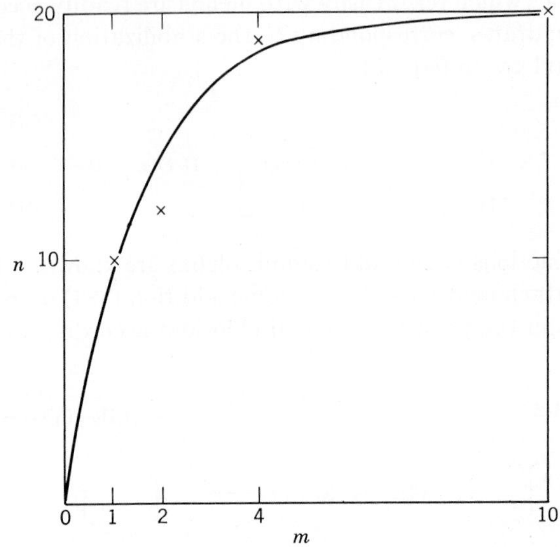

Fig. II-25. Addition of chloral to polyisoprene as a function of the initial molar ratio.

action; (*b*) radical attachment onto the terminal (vinylidene) double bonds in the presence of benzoyl peroxide (385,386) (Fig. II-23).

An effort has been made to adapt the ionic type of reaction to the rubber hydrocarbon (387,388). By working in solution with a nonaromatic solvent, in the presence of such catalysts as aluminum chloride or boron trifluoride and in the absence of oxygen, it has been possible to attach substantial amounts of chloral, as shown in Figures II-24 and II-25. The reagent used is the pure monomeric aldehyde.

In the absence of catalyst (Fig. II-24*A*), the degree of addition stays low ($n = 4$) and the nature of the reaction remains therefore uncertain. In the presence of $AlCl_3$ or BF_3, n increases rapidly with temperature and molar ratio of the reagents present, as shown in curves *B* and *C* of Fig. II-24 and in Fig. II-25.

Table II-36 clearly shows the special activity of aluminum chloride which, of the various catalysts considered, was found to be as efficient as boron trifluoride while not producing noticeable crosslinking or cyclization of the macromolecular material.

In order to prove that the combination reaction proceeds by an ionic mechanism, it was desirable to verify that the radical acceptors do not change significantly the course of the reaction; this is shown in Table II-37.

TABLE II-36
Influence of Catalyst on the Addition of Chloral to Polyisoprene

Catalyst (3%)	Degree of addition, *n*	Gel, %
$AlCl_3$	11	8
BF_3	11.5	17
$FeCl_3$	4	15
$SbCl_3$	3	12
$ZnCl_2$	1.5	25
$HgCl_2$	0	48

TABLE II-37
Influence of Free Radical Acceptors on the Addition of Chloral to Polyisoprene[a]

Radical acceptor (3%)	Degree of addition *n*
None (control)	11
Thiophenol	9
p-Benzoquinone	12
Nitrobenzene	14
Sodium diethyldithiocarbamate	11

[a] $AlCl_3$ (3%) as catalyst.

Furthermore, experiments which have been carried out in the presence of radical donors (peroxides, azo compounds, disulfides, etc.) with the use of ultraviolet radiation but in the absence of $AlCl_3$ gave no evidence for radical processes.

The addition of chloral to polyisoprene was also obtained when a mixture of rubber and chloral hydrate was heated in a bomb (180°C., 30 min.) in the absence of solvent. The degree of addition, as calculated from the chlorine content, was $n = 5.5$.

Other diene polymers have shown a definite reactivity towards chloral. The classical (96.5:3.5) copolymer of isobutylene and isoprene reacts by virtue of its isoprenic double bonds. The *cis*-1,4-polybutadiene, whose olefinic structure is not very favorable to ionic combination reactions, gives a degree of addition in which n is only 1.5. On the other hand, the same polymer gives a radical reaction with chloral ($n = 4$) when treated in the presence of benzoyl peroxide.

(2) Structure and Properties of Products

The compounds from chloral and polyisoprene contain hydroxyl groups having infrared bands at 3300–3500 cm.$^{-1}$ and also chlorine atoms which can be identified by 570, 620, 680, 730, and 1080 cm.$^{-1}$ bands; these absorptions can be attributed to —CHOH—CCl_3 side chains. In addition, the characteristic band of the *cis* configuration shows up in the spectra but with diminished intensity relative to that of the starting material. The enlargement of the 1640 cm.$^{-1}$ peak and the appearance of a band at 860 cm.$^{-1}$ indicate the presence of vinylidene double bonds.

The presence of —CHOH—CCl_3 side chains is confirmed by the chemical reactivity associated with these functional groups. The anticipated reactions occur readily, but they are limited by the formation of three-dimensional networks which lead to insoluble materials: thus a modified polyisoprene ($n = 15$) loses 60% of its chlorine content when heated at 130°C. in xylene solution in the presence of finely divided sodium; the remaining chlorine is difficult to remove because the radicals arising from the —CCl_3 groups produce intermolecular links. Phenyllithium shows effects analogous to those of sodium, but in addition it makes it possible to attach a certain number of phenyl residues. The presence of hydroxyl groups is further verified by the reaction with acetyl chloride. Bifunctional reagents, such as adipyl dichloride and hexamethylene diisocyanate, result in cross-linking.

In order to demonstrate that the alcohol functions of the side chains are α to the trichloromethyl residue, the degradation reaction with alcoholic potassium hydroxide (389), which removes chloroform from structures of the type R—CHOH—CCl_3, was used. The formation of chloroform was noted as well as, following degradation of the side chains, the formation of the —CHO and especially —COOH groups; these last groups resulted from oxidation.

If the attachment of —CHOH—CCl_3 side chains onto a certain number of C_5H_8 units, and the migration of double bonds in the units attacked, can thus be regarded as very likely, the possibility for partial cyclization of polyisoprene must also be considered since the role of the catalysts aluminum chloride or boron trifluoride in bringing about such a reaction is well known. In fact, in every case involving boron trifluoride, bands indicative of cyclization appear in the infrared at 770 and 1040 cm.$^{-1}$ (390). These bands are not present when aluminum chloride is used as catalyst. These spectroscopic data are supported by intrinsic viscosity measurements inasmuch as cyclization of the polymer chain causes a pronounced drop in viscosity (391). The products from the chloral–polyisoprene reaction ($n = 11$) were thus studied by comparing their intrinsic viscosities in the case of $AlCl_3$, $[\eta]_1$, and BF_3, $[\eta]_2$, with the viscosity of unmodified *cis*-1,4-polyisoprene, $[\eta]_3$, and that of a highly cyclized polyisoprene, $[\eta]_4$. The results obtained were: $[\eta]_1/[\eta]_2 = 0.87$; $[\eta]_2/[\eta]_3 = 0.50$; $[\eta]_4/[\eta]_3 = 0.40$.

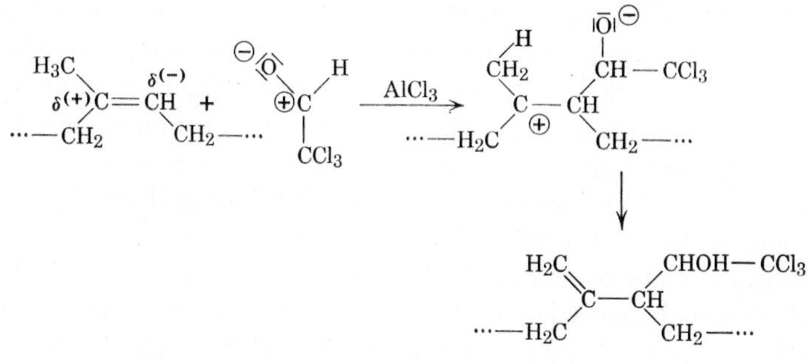

Fig. II-26. Addition of chloral to polyisoprene.

The indications from infrared spectroscopy are thus confirmed, and aluminum chloride appears to be the better catalyst.

The structure proposed for these substances corresponds to p $C_7H_9OCl_3$ units randomly distributed throughout a chain segment consisting of $(100 - p)$ isoprene units, as depicted by:

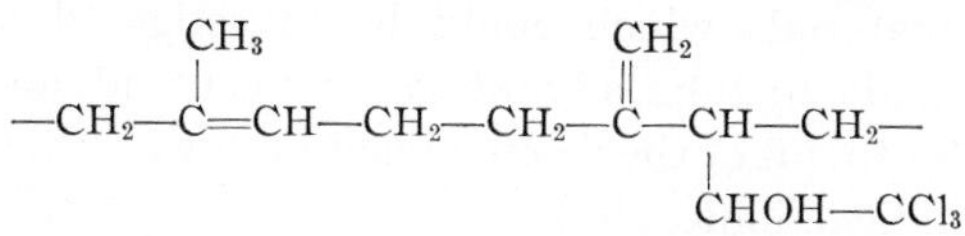

On the basis of what is known about the attachment of chloral to simple olefins, the reaction shown in Figure II-26 has been proposed.

In the case of the *cis*-1,4-polybutadienes where the double bonds have a different structure from that of the polyisoprene double bonds, another mechanism must be considered. This would involve, where chloral is used as a reagent, an addition of $\cdot CCl_2$–CHO residues, characterized by a band at 1780 cm.$^{-1}$ indicating the presence of carbonyl groups in the side chain and not of secondary alcohol groups.

6. Conclusions

The chemical study of the diene polymers is still fairly undeveloped and the earliest efforts have been concerned particularly with the rubber hydrocarbon. This naturally occurring material, which has been known for a long time, offers the chemist the advantage of having a very regular structure by virtue of its nearly all-1,4 repetition of isoprenic units having a *cis* configuration in excess of 98%.

For the last few years a number of synthetic diene polymers, in particular *cis*-1,4-polybutadiene and *cis*-1,4-polyisoprene, have offered the same advantages. Although the synthetic *cis*-polyisoprene shows many similarities to the corresponding natural polymer, it appears from studies carried out at the Rubber Research Institute of Malaya (292,293) that it shows some important differences as well. Thus, the presence of some aldehyde groups along the natural polyisoprene chain, and perhaps even some pyrophosphate groups, could undoubtedly account for the small differences in behavior manifested by the natural and synthetic products.

It is appropriate to stress the importance of certain chemical modifications of the polyisoprene structure and their consequences with regard to properties of the resulting materials. In fact, this approach appears to be particularly promising for adapting the physical, mechanical, and chemical properties of an elastomer to the requirements of new applications.

That significant results could be achieved in this field is partly due to the fact that two important features have characterized research work the past few years: (*a*) efforts have been made, wherever possible, to obtain a single reaction by slowing down or even eliminating side reactions involving the chain, such as cyclization, scission, crosslinking, etc., so as to obtain soluble and purifiable materials which could be investigated structurally; (*b*) attempts were made to take advantage of recent advances in structural chemistry in order to direct the desired reaction towards a very specific type of mechanism (radical, ionic, etc.).

At the fundamental level, there are still serious gaps in our knowledge and still important studies to be undertaken. Nevertheless, because of what has already been done, it is now possible to make inroads in this difficult and complex field with ideas and methods which are no longer strictly empirical as was formerly the case.

Among the best known gaps in our knowledge we may note that information on the average molecular weights is rather sketchy or even nonexistent. This is partly due to difficulties inherent in physicochemical determinations which are always delicate even under the best of circumstances and are often uncertain or impossible when the materials change rapidly in the course of time. The distribution of the attached groups along the molecular chain when the reaction is not complete is another important matter which is also almost unsolved at present.

There are quite a few other problems which remain to be solved before further progress can be made, but we will not mention them here. Despite these shortcomings, it should be stated that the outlook, on balance, is very favorable. Numerous applications of definite interest can emerge from these studies and, from a fundamental standpoint, a considerable effort has been made to depart from the empiricism which has prevailed heretofore. This effort is now bearing fruit. It remains to be hoped that such investigations, by being extended, will assist in providing a better understanding of the relationships which must exist between the structure of a macromolecule and the phenomenon of high elasticity.

References

A. Isomerization

1. Schildknecht, C. E., S. T. Gross, and A. O. Zoss, *Ind. Eng. Chem.*, **41**, 1998 (1949).
2. Grassie, N., *Chemistry of High Polymer Degradation Processes*, Butterworths, London, and Interscience, New York, 1956, pp. 315–319.
3. D'Ianni, J. D., F. J. Naples, J. W. Marsh, and J. L. Zarney, *Ind. Eng. Chem.*, **38**, 1171 (1946).
4. Gordon, M., *Ind. Eng. Chem.*, **43**, 386 (1951).
5. Gordon, M., *Proc. Roy. Soc. (London)*, **A204**, 569 (1951); *Chem. Abstr.*, **46**, 5877a (1952).
6. Ramakrishnan, C. S., S. Dasgupta, and N. V. C. Rao, *Makromol. Chem.*, **20**, 46 (1956).
7. Veersen, G. J. van, *Rec. Trav. Chim.*, **69**, 1365 (1950); *Rubber Chem. Technol.*, **24**, 957 (1951).
8. Wallenberger, F. T., *Monatsh.*, **93**, 74 (1962); *Chem. Abstr.*, **57**, 746a (1962).
8a. Lee, D. F., J. Scanlan, and W. F. Watson, *Proc. Roy. Soc. (London)*, **A273**, 345 (1963).
9. Golub, M. A., and J. Heller, *Can. J. Chem.*, **41**, 937 (1963).
9a. Golub, M. A., and J. Heller, *Tetrahedron Letters*, 2137 (1963).
10. Shelton, J. R., and L. H. Lee, *Rubber Chem. Technol.*, **31**, 415 (1958).
11. Topchiev, A. V., M. A. Geĭderikh, B. E. Davydov, V. A. Kargin, B. A. Krentsel, I. M. Kustanovich, and L. S. Polak, *Dokl. Akad. Nauk SSSR*, **128**, 312 (1959); *Chem. Ind. (London)*, **1960**, 184.
12. Geĭderikh, M. A., B. A. Davydov, B. A. Krentsel, I. M. Kustanovich, L. S. Polak, A. V. Topchiev, and R. M. Voĭtenko, *J. Polymer Sci.*, **54**, 621 (1961).
13. Burlant, W. J., and J. L. Parsons, *J. Polymer Sci.*, **22**, 249 (1956).
14. Grassie, N., and I. C. McNeill, *J. Polymer Sci.*, **27**, 207 (1958).
15. Linnig, F. J., and J. E. Stewart, *J. Res. Natl. Bur. Std.*, **60**, 9 (1958); *Rubber Chem. Technol.*, **31**, 719 (1958).
16. Shipman, J. J., and M. A. Golub, *J. Polymer Sci.*, **58**, 1063 (1962).
17. Bolland, J. L., *Quart. Rev. (London)*, **3**, 1 (1949).
18. Ross, J., A. I. Gebhart, and J. F. Gerecht, *J. Am. Chem. Soc.*, **71**, 282 (1949).
19. Privett, O. S., and E. C. Nickell, *Fette Seifen Anstrichmittel*, **61**, 842 (1959); *Chem. Abstr.*, **54**, 14731a (1960).
20. Bevilacqua, E. M., *Rubber Age (N.Y.)*, **80**, 271 (1956); *Rubber Chem. Technol.*, **30**, 667 (1957).
21. Bevilacqua, E. M., *J. Am. Chem. Soc.*, **79**, 2915 (1957).
22. Bevilacqua, E. M., *Science*, **126**, 396 (1957).
23. Bevilacqua, E. M., *J. Am. Chem. Soc.*, **81**, 5071 (1959).

24. For a typical infrared spectrum of oxidized natural rubber, see G. Salomon and A. Chr. van der Schee, *J. Polymer Sci.*, **14**, 181 (1954); or V. Kellö, A. Tkáč, and J. Hrivíková, *Chem. Listy.*, **49**, 1433 (1955); *Rubber Chem. Technol.*, **29**, 1245 (1956).
25. Golub, M. A., and J. J. Shipman, *Spectrochim. Acta*, **16**, 1165 (1960); *Chem. Abstr.*, **55**, 13056d (1961).
25a. Golub, M. A., and J. J. Shipman, *Spectrochim. Acta*, **20**, 701 (1964).
26. Evans, M. B., G. M. C. Higgins, and D. T. Turner, *J. Appl. Polymer Sci.*, **2**, 340 (1959).
27. Hayden, P., *Intern. J. Appl. Radiation Isotopes*, **8**, 65 (1960); *Chem. Abstr.*, **55**, 8909b (1961).
28. Golub, M. A., *J. Am. Chem. Soc.*, **82**, 5093 (1960).
29. Golub, M. A., unpublished results.
29a. Berger, M., and D. J. Buckley, *J. Polymer Sci.*, **A1**, 2945 (1963).
30. Sauer, M. C., Jr., and L. M. Dorfman, *J. Chem. Phys.*, **35**, 497 (1961); and references therein.
31. Salomon, G., and A. Chr. van der Schee, *J. Polymer Sci.*, **14**, 287 (1954).
32. Meyer, K. H., and C. Ferri, *Helv. Chim. Acta*, **19**, 694 (1936); *Rubber Chem. Technol.*, **9**, 570 (1936).
33. Ferri, C., *Helv. Chim. Acta*, **20**, 1393 (1937); *Rubber Chem. Technol.*, **11**, 350 (1938).
34. Scanlan, J., section B, chapt. II.
35. Zechmeister, L., *Chem. Rev.*, **34**, 267 (1944).
36. Golub, M. A., *J. Polymer Sci.*, **25**, 373 (1957).
37. Golub, M. A., U. S. Patent 2,878,175-6 (to B. F. Goodrich Co.), Mar. 17, 1959; *Chem. Abstr.*, **53**, 15622e (1959).
38. Trick, G. S., *J. Polymer Sci.*, **31**, 529 (1958).
39. Trick, G. S., *J. Polymer Sci.*, **41**, 213 (1959).
40. Steinmetz, H., and R. M. Noyes, *J. Am. Chem. Soc.*, **74**, 4141 (1952).
41. Sivertz, C., *J. Phys. Chem.*, **63**, 34 (1959).
42. Golub, M. A., *J. Am. Chem. Soc.*, **80**, 1794 (1958).
43. Golub, M. A., *J. Am. Chem. Soc.*, **81**, 54 (1959).
43a. Golub, M. A., *J. Phys. Chem.*, in press.
43b. Seely, G. R., *J. Am. Chem. Soc.*, **84**, 4404 (1962).
44. Olson, A. R., *Trans. Faraday Soc.*, **27**, 69 (1931); *Chem. Abstr.*, **25**, 2353 (1931).
45. Crombie, L., *Quart. Rev. (London)*, **6**, 101 (1952).
46. Kailan, A., *Z. Physik. Chem. (Leipzig)*, **87**, 333 (1914); *Chem. Abstr.*, **8**, 2104 (1914).
47. Höjendahl, K., *J. Phys. Chem.*, **28**, 758 (1924).
48. Charlesby, A., *Radiation Res.*, **2**, 96 (1955); *Chem. Abstr.*, **49**, 8711e (1955).
49. Kraus, G., paper presented before the German Chemical Society, Plastics and Rubber Division, Bad Nauheim, May, 1960.
50. Bishop, W. A., *J. Polymer Sci.*, **55**, 827 (1961).
50a. Ceselli, C. A., T. Garlanda, M. Camia, and G. Manza, *Chim. Ind. (Milan)*, **44**, 1203 (1962); *Chem. Abstr.*, **58**, 9307e (1963).
51. Bateman, L., R. W. Glazebrook, and C. G. Moore, *J. Chem. Soc.*, **1958**, 2846.
52. Bateman, L., R. W. Glazebrook, and C. G. Moore, *J. Appl. Polymer Sci.*, **1**, 257 (1959).

53. Bateman, L., and C. G. Moore, in *Organic Sulfur Compounds*, N. Kharasch, ed., Vol. 1, Pergamon Press, New York, 1961.
54. Ermakova, I. I., B. A. Dolgoplosk, and E. N. Kropacheva, *Dokl. Akad. Nauk SSSR*, **141**, 1363 (1961); *Chem. Abstr.*, **56**, 12717f (1962).
55. Cunneen, J. I., and F. W. Shipley, *J. Polymer Sci.*, **36**, 77 (1959).
56. Cunneen, J. I., W. P. Fletcher, F. W. Shipley, and R. I. Wood, *Trans. Inst. Rubber Ind.*, **34**, 260 (1958); *Chem. Abstr.*, **53**, 9711d (1959).
57. Cunneen, J. I., and W. F. Watson, *J. Polymer Sci.*, **38**, 521 (1959).
58. Cunneen, J. I., and W. F. Watson, *J. Polymer Sci.*, **38**, 533 (1959).
59. Cunneen, J. I., G. M. C. Higgins, and W. F. Watson, *J. Polymer Sci.*, **40**, 1 (1959).
60. Cunneen, J. I., P. McL. Swift, and W. F. Watson, *Trans. Inst. Rubber Ind.*, **36**, 17 (1960); *Chem. Abstr.*, **54**, 12631e (1960).
61. Cunneen, J. I., *Proc. Intern. Rubber Conf. Preprints Papers, Washington, D. C.*, 1959, p. 514; *Rubber Chem. Technol.*, **33**, 445 (1960).
62. Cook, R. E., F. S. Dainton, and K. J. Ivin, *J. Polymer Sci.*, **26**, 351 (1957).
63. Golub, M. A., *J. Polymer Sci.*, **36**, 523 (1959).
64. Fitzpatrick, J. D., and M. Orchin, *J. Am. Chem. Soc.*, **79**, 4765 (1957).
65. Fitzpatrick, J. D., and M. Orchin, *J. Org. Chem.*, **22**, 1177 (1957).
66. Dolgoplosk, B. A., E. N. Kropacheva, and K. V. Nelson, *Dokl. Akad. Nauk SSSR*, **123**, 685 (1958); *Rubber Chem. Technol.*, **32**, 1036 (1959).
67. Boldyreva, I. I., B. A. Dolgoplosk, E. N. Kropacheva, and K. V. Nelson, *Dokl. Akad. Nauk SSSR*, **131**, 830 (1960); *Rubber Chem. Technol.*, **33**, 985 (1960).
67a. Danon, J., and M. A. Golub, *Can. J. Chem.*, in press.
67b. Golub, M. A., and J. Danon, to be published.

B. Cyclization

68. Dawson, T. R., and P. Schidrowitz in *Chemistry and Technology of Rubber*, C. C. Davis and J. T. Blake, eds., Reinhold, New York, 1937, p. 656.
69. Fisher, H. L., *Ind. Eng. Chem.*, **19**, 1325 (1927).
70. Gordon, M., British Patent 634,879 (to Dunlop Rubber Co. Ltd.), Aug. 23, 1947.
71. Veersen, G. J. van, U. S. Patent 2,555,068 (to Rubber-Stichting), May 29, 1951; *Chem. Abstr.*, **45**, 10658a (1951).
72. Bruson, H. A., L. B. Sebrell, and W. C. Calvert, *Ind. Eng. Chem.*, **19**, 1033 (1927).
73. D'Ianni, J. D., F. J. Naples, J. W. Marsh, and J. L. Zarney, *Ind. Eng. Chem.*, **38**, 1171 (1946).
74. Staudinger, H., and W. Widmer, *Helv. Chim. Acta*, **9**, 529 (1926); *Chem. Abstr.*, **20**, 3587 (1926).
75. Staudinger, H., and E. Geiger, *Helv. Chim. Acta*, **9**, 549 (1926); *Chem. Abstr.*, **20**, 3588 (1926).
76. Bloomfield, G. F., *J. Chem. Soc.*, **1943**, 289.
77. Gordon, M., *Ind. Eng. Chem.*, **43**, 386 (1951).
78. Gordon, M., *Proc. Roy. Soc. (London)*, **A204**, 569 (1951); *Chem. Abstr.*, **46**, 5877a (1952); *Rubber Chem. Technol.*, **24**, 924 (1951).
79. Flory, P. J., *J. Am. Chem. Soc.*, **61**, 1518 (1939).
80. Fisher, H. L., and E. M. McColm, *Ind. Eng. Chem.*, **19**, 1328 (1927).
81. Veersen, G. J. van, *Rec. Trav. Chim.*, **69**, 1365 (1950); *Rubber Chem. Technol.*, **24**, 957 (1951).

82. Rao, N. V. C., *Makromol. Chem.*, **16,** 198 (1955).
83. Lee, D., J. Scanlan, and W. F. Watson, *Proc. Roy. Soc.* (*London*), **A273,** 345 (1963).
84. Barnard, D., *J. Chem. Soc.*, **1957,** 4547.
84a. Golub, M. A., and J. Heller, *Can. J. Chem.*, **41,** 937 (1963).
84b. Wallenberger, F. T., *Monatsh. Chem.*, **93,** 74 (1962).

C. Addition of Thiols

85. Posner, J., *Chem. Ber.*, **38,** 646 (1905).
86. Walling, C., *Free Radicals in Solution*, Wiley, New York, 1957, pp. 313–326.
87. Pryor, W. A., *Mechanisms of Sulfur Reactions*, McGraw-Hill, New York, 1962.
88. Brindell, G. D., and S. J. Cristol, in *Organic Sulfur Compounds*, N. Kharasch, ed., Vol. 1, Pergamon Press, New York, 1961, p. 121.
89. Cunneen, J. I., G. M. C. Higgins, and W. F. Watson, *J. Polymer Sci.*, **40,** 1 (1959).
90. Cunneen, J. I., *Proc. Intern. Rubber Conf. Preprints Papers*, Washington, D. C., 1959, p. 514; *Rubber Chem. Technol.*, **33,** 445 (1960).
91. Pallen, R. H., and C. Sivertz, *Can. J. Chem.*, **35,** 723 (1957).
92. Pierson, R. M., W. E. Gibbs, G. E. Meyer, F. J. Naples, W. M. Saltman, R. W. Schrock, L. B. Tewksbury, and G. S. Trick, *Rubber Plastics Age*, **38,** 592–599 and 708–721 (1957). Shortened versions of this paper also appeared in *Rubber World*, **136,** 529–536 and 695–701 (1957), and *Rubber Chem. Technol.*, **31,** 213 (1958).
93. Cunneen, J. I., C. G. Moore, and B. R. Shephard, *J. Appl. Polymer Sci.*, **3,** 11 (1960).
94. Marvel, C. S., K. G. Clarke, H. K. Inskip, W. K. Taft, and B. G. Labbe, *Ind. Eng. Chem.*, **45,** 2090 (1953).
95. Selker, M. L., and A. R. Kemp, *Ind. Eng. Chem.*, **36,** 16 (1944).
96. Bovey, F. A., I. M. Kolthoff, A. I. Medalia, and E. J. Meehan, *Emulsion Polymerization*, High Polymer Series, Vol. IX, Interscience, New York, 1955.
97. Kharasch, M. S., W. Nudenberg, and F. Kawahara, *J. Org. Chem.*, **20,** 1550 (1955).
98. Fryling, C. F., U. S. Patent 2,543,844 (to Phillips Petroleum Co.), Mar. 6, 1951; *Chem. Abstr.*, **45,** 4960f (1951).
99. Kolthoff, I. M., and W. E. Harris, *J. Polymer Sci.*, **2,** 49 (1947).
100. Krause, A. H., *Rubber Age* (*N. Y.*), **75,** 217 (1954).
101. Serniuk, G. E., F. W. Banes, and M. W. Swaney, *J. Am. Chem. Soc.*, **70,** 1804 (1948).
102. Swaney, M. W., and F. W. Banes, U. S. Patent 2,556,856 (to Standard Oil Development Co.), June 12, 1951; *Chem. Abstr.*, **45,** 8801f (1951).
103. Kharasch, M. S., W. Nudenberg, and G. J. Mantell, *J. Org. Chem.*, **16,** 524 (1951).
104. Oswald, A. A., *J. Org. Chem.*, **26,** 842 (1961).
105. Grassie, N., *Chemistry of High Polymer Degradation Processes*, Butterworths, London and Interscience, New York, 1956.
106. Foxley, G. H., *Proc. Inst. Rubber Ind.*, **8,** 63 (1961); *Rubber Chem. Technol.*, **34,** 1212 (1961).
107. Harrington, R., *Rubber Age* (*N. Y.*), **85,** 963 (1959).
108. Meyer, G. E., F. J. Naples, and H. M. Rice, *Rubber World*, **140,** 435 (1959).
109. Holmberg, B., *Chem. Ber.*, **65,** 1349 (1932); *Rubber Chem. Technol.*, **6,** 71 (1933).

110. Holmberg, B., *Arkiv. Kemi*, **23B,** No. 6, 1 (1946); *Rubber Chem. Technol.*, **20,** 978 (1947).
111. Cunneen, J. I., *India Rubber J.*, **114,** 543 (1948); *Chem. Abstr.*, **42,** 7081d (1948).
112. Cunneen, J. I., *J. Chem. Soc.*, **1947,** 36.
113. Cunneen, J. I., *J. Appl. Chem. (London)*, **2,** 353 (1952).
114. Serniuk, G. E., U. S. Patent 2,589,151 (to Standard Oil Development Co.), Mar. 11, 1952; *Chem. Abstr.*, **46,** 5355f (1952).
115. Brown, H. P., U. S. Patent 2,662,874 (to B. F. Goodrich Co.), Dec. 15, 1953; *Chem. Abstr.*, **48,** 4247b (1954).
116. Brown, H. P., *Rubber Chem. Technol.*, **30,** 1347 (1957).
117. Golub, M. A., *J. Polymer Sci.*, **25,** 373 (1957); *Rubber Chem. Technol.*, **30,** 1142 (1957).
118. Ritter, F. J., *Rubber Chem. Technol.*, **33,** 1 (1960).
119. Neal, A. M., *India Rubber World*, **104,** No. 3, 39 (1941); *Chem. Abstr.*, **35,** 7755b (1941).
120. E. I. duPont deNemours & Co., French Patent 816,453, Aug. 6, 1937; *Chem. Abstr.*, **32,** 1978[4] (1938).
121. E. I. duPont deNemours & Co., British Patent 490,292, Aug. 11, 1938; *Chem. Abstr.*, **33,** 1171[1] (1939).
122. Garvey, B. S., U. S. Patent 2,193,624 (to B. F. Goodrich Co.), Mar. 12, 1940; *Chem. Abstr.*, **34,** 5316[1] (1940).
123. Hastings, J. D., *J. Rubber Research Inst. Malaya Commun.*, **9,** 101 (1939); *Chem. Abstr.*, **34,** 2640[8] (1940).
124. Kheraskova, E. P., and A. P. Gamayunova, *Kolloidn. Zh.*, **12,** 146 (1950); *Rubber Chem. Technol.*, **24,** 161 (1951).
125. Montu, M., *Rev. Gen. Caoutchouc*, **29,** 506 (1952); *Rubber Chem. Technol.*, **26,** 143 (1953).
126. Watson, W. F., *Makromol. Chem.*, **34,** 240 (1959).
127. Angier, D. J., R. J. Ceresa, and W. F. Watson, *Chem. Ind. (London)*, **1958,** 593.

D. Halogenation

128. Marchionna, F., *Latex and Rubber Derivatives and Their Industrial Application*, Vol. III, Rubber Age, New York, 1937, p. 1313.
129. Clark, G. C., *Rubber Age (N.Y.)*, **38,** 139 (1935); *Chem. Abstr.*, **30,** 898[6] (1936).
130. Tinsley, J. S., *Colloid Chem.*, **6,** 1118 (1946); *Chem. Abstr.*, **40,** 2672[3] (1946).
131. Staudinger, H., and H. Staudinger, *J. Prakt. Chem.*, **162,** 148 (1943); *Rubber Chem. Technol.*, **17,** 15 (1944).
132. Bloomfield, G. F., *J. Chem. Soc.*, **1943,** 289; *Rubber Chem. Technol.*, **17,** 1 (1944).
133. Bloomfield, G. F., *J. Chem. Soc.*, **1944,** 114; *Rubber Chem. Technol.*, **17,** 759 (1944).
134. Kraus, G., and W. B. Reynolds, *J. Am. Chem. Soc.*, **72,** 5621 (1950).
135. Ramakrishnan, C. S., D. Raghunath, and J. B. Pande, *Trans. Inst. Rubber Ind.*, **29,** 190 (1953); *Rubber Chem. Technol.*, **26,** 902 (1953).
136. Ramakrishnan, C. S., D. Raghunath, and J. B. Pande, *Trans. Inst. Rubber Ind.*, **30,** 129 (1954); *Rubber Chem. Technol.*, **28,** 598 (1955).
137. Troussier, M., *Rev. Gen. Caoutchouc*, **32,** 229 (1955); *Rubber Chem. Technol.*, **29,** 302 (1956).

137a. van Amerongen, G. J., C. Koningsberger, and G. Salomon, *J. Polymer Sci.*, **5,** 639 (1950).
138. Canterino, P. J., *Ind. Eng. Chem.*, **49,** 712 (1957).
139. Blömer, A., German Patent 728,640 (to I. G. Farbenindustrie A.-G.), Oct. 29, 1942; *Chem. Abstr.*, **38,** 430[2] (1944).
140. Lichty, J. G., U. S. Patent 2,560,869 (to Wingfoot Corp.), July 17, 1951; *Chem. Abstr.*, **45,** 9299h (1951).
141. Blömer, A., and W. Becker, U. S. Patent 2,222,345 (to I. G. Farbenindustrie A.-G.), Nov. 19, 1940; *Chem. Abstr.*, **35,** 2019[2] (1941).
142. Reid, R. J., U. S. Patent 2,537,630 (to Firestone Tire & Rubber Co.), Jan. 9, 1951; *Chem. Abstr.*, **45,** 3653a (1951).
143. Blömer, A., and E. Konrad (vested in Alien Property Custodian), U. S. Patent 2,301,926, Nov. 17, 1942; *Chem. Abstr.*, **37,** 2219[5] (1943).
144. Canterino, P. J., and J. N. Baptist, U. S. Patent 2,831,839 (to Phillips Petroleum Co.), Apr. 22, 1958; *Chem. Abstr.*, **52,** 14217i (1958).
145. Canterino, P. J., U. S. Patent 2,943,988 (to Phillips Petroleum Co.), July 5, 1960; *Chem. Abstr.*, **54,** 21829e (1960).
146. Polson, A. E., in *Encyclopedia of Chemical Technology,* R. E. Kirk and D. F. Othmer, eds, Vol. 11, 1st ed., Interscience, New York, 1953, pp. 704, 705, 709.
147. Newton, E. P., British Patent 576,744 (to Hercules Powder Co.), Apr. 17, 1946; *Chem. Abstr.*, **42,** 3613d (1948).
148. de Decker, H. C. J., H. A. W. Nijveld, and G. Schuur, *Rev. Gén. Caoutchouc,* **31,** 43 (1954); *Chem. Abstr.*, **48,** 7329b (1954).
149. van Amerongen, G. J., *Ind. Eng. Chem.*, **43,** 2535 (1951).
150. Salomon, G., G. J. van Amerongen, G. J. van Veersen, G. Schuur, and H. C. J. de Decker, *Ind. Eng. Chem.*, **43,** 315 (1951).
151. Hercules Chemical Company, *Parlon-Properties and Uses,* March 1963.
152. D'Ianni, J. D., F. J. Naples, J. W. Marsh, and J. L. Zarney, *Ind. Eng. Chem.*, **38,** 1171 (1946).
153. Calvert, W. C., U. S. Patent 1,989,632 (to Wingfoot Corp.), Jan. 29, 1935; *Chem. Abstr.*, **29,** 2028 (1935).

E. Epoxidation

154. Swern, D., *Chem. Rev.*, **45,** 1 (1949).
155. Gordon, J., *Hydrocarbon Process Petrol. Refiner,* **41,** 141, 185 (1962).
156. Wallace, J. G., in *Encyclopedia of Chemical Technology,* R. E. Kirk and D. F. Othmer, eds., 2nd Suppl., 1st ed., Interscience, New York, 1960, pp. 325–46.
157. Greenspan, F. P., *Ind. Eng. Chem.*, **50,** 861 (1958).
158. Aries, R. S., H. Schneider, and K. Gerzon, in *Encyclopedia of Chemical Technology,* R. E. Kirk and D. F. Othmer, eds., Vol. 5, 1st ed., Interscience, New York, 1950, pp. 906–25.
159. Weitz, E., and A. Scheffer, *Chem. Ber.*, **54B,** 2327 (1921).
160. Adams, R., and W. Herz, *J. Am. Chem. Soc.*, **71,** 2551 (1949).
161. Payne, G. B., *J. Am. Chem. Soc.*, **81,** 4901 (1959).
162. Skinner, J. R., and C. H. Wilcoxen, U. S. Patent 2,938,040 (to Shell Oil Co.), May 24, 1960; *Chem. Abstr.*, **55,** 2675f (1961).
163. Payne, G. B., *J. Am. Chem. Soc.*, **80,** 6461 (1958).

164. Milas, N. A., P. F. Kurz, and W. P. Anslow, *J. Am. Chem. Soc.*, **59,** 543 (1937).
165. Milas, N. A., and S. Sussman, *J. Am. Chem. Soc.*, **59,** 2345 (1937).
166. Carlson, G. J., J. R. Skinner, C. W. Smith, and C. H. Wilcoxen, Jr., U. S. Patent 2,833,787 (to Shell Development Co.), May 6, 1958.
167. Smith, C. W., and G. B. Payne, U. S. Patent 2,786,854 (to Shell Development Co.), Mar. 26, 1957; *Chem. Abstr.*, **51,** 14791c (1957).
168. N. V. de Bataafsche Petroleum Maatschappji, British Patent 754,359, Aug. 8, 1956; *Chem. Abstr.*, **51,** 10583i (1957).
169. Gable, C. M., U. S. Patent 2,870,171 (to Shell Development Co.), Jan. 20, 1959; *Chem. Abstr.*, **53,** 10250i (1959).
170. Prileschajew, N., *Chem. Ber.*, **42,** 4811 (1909).
171. Greenspan, F. P., and R. J. Gall, *Ind. Eng. Chem.*, **45,** 2722 (1953).
172. Lidov, R. E., H. Bluestone, S. B. Soloway, and C. W. Kearns, "Agricultural Control Chemicals" (*Advan. Chem., Ser.*, **1,** 175 (1950)), American Chemical Society, Washington, D. C.
173. Oliveto, A. P., and E. B. Hershberg, U. S. Patent 2,677,695 (to Schering Corp.), May 4, 1954; *Chem. Abstr.*, **49,** 4734e (1955).
174. Gall, R. J., J. J. Rizzo, and H. M. Castrantas, *Mod. Plastics*, **37** (7), 137 (1960).
175. Anon., *Chem. Week*, **78** (3), 90 (1956).
176. Greenspan, F. P., C. W. Johnston, and M. H. Reich, *Mod. Plastics*, **37,** (2), 142, (1959).
177. Swern, D., *J. Am. Chem. Soc.*, **69,** 1692 (1947).
178. Chakravorty, P. N., and R. H. Levin, *J. Am. Chem. Soc.*, **64,** 2317 (1942).
179. Kolthoff, I. M., T. S. Lee, and M. A. Mairs, *J. Polymer Sci.*, **2,** 199 (1947).
180. Smit, W. C., *Rec. Trav. Chim.*, **49,** 691 (1930).
181. Greenspan, F. P., *J. Am. Chem. Soc.*, **68,** 907 (1946).
182. FMC Corp., Inorganic Chemicals Division, Bulletin No. 4 "Peracetic Acid 40%."
183. Easton, B. K., *Mod. Textiles Mag.*, **35** (4), 66 (1954).
184. Greenspan, F. P., and D. G. MacKellar, *Food Technol.*, **5** (3), 95 (1951); *Chem. Abstr.*, **45,** 4371h (1951).
185. Findley, T. W., D. Swern, and J. T. Scanlan, *J. Am. Chem. Soc.*, **67,** 412 (1945).
186. Greenspan, F. P., U. S. Patent 2,490,800 (to Buffalo Electro-Chemical Co.), Dec. 13, 1949; *Chem. Abstr.*, **44,** 2013c (1950).
187. Phillips, B., F. C. Frostick, Jr., and P. S. Starcher, *J. Am. Chem. Soc.*, **79,** 5982 (1957).
188. Phillips, B., F. C. Frostick, Jr., and P. S. Starcher, U. S. Patent 2,804,473 (to Union Carbide Corp.), Aug. 27, 1957; *Chem. Abstr.*, **52,** 2051h (1958).
189. Frostick, Jr., F. C., and B. Phillips, U. S. Patent 2,716,123 (to Union Carbide Co.), Aug. 23, 1955; *Chem. Abstr.*, **50,** 7852f (1956).
190. Phillips, B., and P. S. Starcher, U. S. Patent 2,745,847 (to Union Carbide Corp.), May 15, 1956; *Chem. Abstr.*, **51,** 1259g (1957).
191. Phillips, B., and P. S. Starcher, U. S. Patent 2,785,185 (to Union Carbide Corp.), Mar. 12, 1957; *Chem. Abstr.*, **51,** 6685a (1957).
192. Union Carbide Corp., British Patent 735,974, Aug. 31, 1955; *Chem. Abstr.*, **50,** 8730c (1956).
193. Bludworth, J. E., U. S. Patent 2,314,385 (to Celanese Corp. of America), Mar. 23, 1943; *Chem. Abstr.*, **37,** 5081a (1943).

194. Celanese Corp. of America, British Patent 892,631, Mar. 28, 1962; *Chem. Abstr.* **57,** 13621e (1962).
195. Celanese Corp. of America, British Patent 892,632, Mar. 28, 1962; *Chem. Abstr.*, **57,** 14943g (1962).
196. Niederhauser, W. D., and J. E. Koroly, U. S. Patent 2,485,160 (to Rohm & Haas Co.), Oct. 18, 1949; *Chem. Abstr.*, **44,** 7346b (1950).
197. Gall, R. J., and F. P. Greenspan. *Ind. Eng. Chem.*, **47,** 147 (1955).
198. Greenspan, F. P., and R. J. Gall, U. S. Patent 2,801,253 (to FMC Corp.), July 30, 1957; *Chem. Abstr.*, **51,** 14296d (1957).
199. FMC Corp., British Patent 739,609, Nov. 2, 1955; *Chem. Abstr.*, **50,** 9765i (1956).
200. Greenspan, F. P., and R. J. Gall, U. S. Patent 2,919,283 (to Food Machinery and Chemical Corp.), Dec. 29, 1959; *Chem. Abstr.*, **54,** 7189a (1960).
201. Chadwick, A. F., D. O. Barlow, A. A. D'Addieco, and J. G. Wallace, *J. Am. Oil Chemists' Soc.*, **35,** 355 (1958); *Chem. Abstr.*, **52,** 15095g (1958).
202. Latourette, H. K., H. M. Castrantas, R. J. Gall, and L. H. Dierdorff, *J. Am. Oil Chemists' Soc.*, **37,** 559 (1960); *Chem. Abstr.*, **55,** 2148b (1961).
203. N. V. de Bataafsche Petroleum Maatschappji, British Patent 794,373, Apr. 30, 1958; *Chem. Abstr.*, **53,** 3065a (1959).
204. Rowland, S. P., and R. G. White, U. S. Patent 2,836,605 (to Rohm & Haas Co.), May 27, 1958; *Chem. Abstr.*, **52,** 19248g (1958).
205. Rohm & Haas Co., British Patent 790,063, Feb. 5, 1958; *Chem. Abstr.*, **52,** 14218f (1958).
206. Hercules Powder Co., British Patent 892,361, Mar. 28, 1962; *Chem. Abstr.*, **57,** 4877h (1962).
207. Johnston, C. W., and F. P. Greenspan. *Mod. Plastics,* **38** (8), 135 (1961).
208. Cullen, C. G., and C. W. Johnston, Proceedings of 17th Annual Technical & Management Conference, The Society of the Plastics Industry, Inc., Chicago, Illinois, February 6–8, 1962.
209. Reich, M. H., and C. F. Ferraro, paper presented at Meeting of the Division of Rubber Chemistry of The American Chemical Society, Cleveland, Ohio, Oct. 17–19, 1962.
210. Durbetaki, A. J., and C. Miles, paper presented at the 145th Meeting of the American Chemical Society, New York, N. Y., Sept. 8–13, 1963.
211. FMC Corp., Plastics Department, Technical Bulletin No. 3, "Organic Acid and Anhydride Curing Possibilities with Oxiron Epoxy Resins."
212. Hopper, T. R., F. Lister, and C. G. Cullen, U. S. Patent applied for.
213. Hopper, T. R., paper presented at the 19th Annual National Association of Corrosion Engineers Conference, New York City, N. Y. March 12, 1963.
214. *U. S. Federal Register*, **27,** 2445, 1963.
215. FMC Corp., Plastics Department, Technical Bulletin No. 5, "Oxiron Resin in Premix Molding."
216. Clark, H. A., and E. P. Plueddemann, *Mod. Plastics*, **40** (10), 133 (1963).
217. Böeseken, J., and C. J. A. Hanegraaff, *Rec. Trav. Chim.*, **61,** 69 (1942); *Chem. Abstr.*, **37,** 5012[8] (1943).
218. Böeseken, J., and J. Stuurman, *Koninkl. Ned. Akad. Wetenschap. Proc.*, **39,** 2 (1936); *Chem. Abstr.*, **30,** 3304[5] (1936).
219. Böeseken, J., and J. Stuurman, *Rec. Trav. Chim.*, **55,** 925 (1936).
220. Stuurman, J., *Koninkl. Ned. Akad. Wetenschap. Proc.*, **38,** 450 (1935); *Chem. Abstr.*, **29,** 4657[8] (1935).

221. Heinanen, P., *Ann. Acad. Sci. Fennicae,* **A59** (13), 3 (1943); *Chem. Abstr.*, **41,** 2307f (1947).
222. Böeseken, J., W. C. Smit, and Gaster, *Koninkl. Ned. Akad. Wetenschap. Proc.*, **32,** 377 (1929); *Chem. Abstr.*, **23,** 4192 (1929).
223. Smit, W. C., *Rec. Trav. Chim.*, **49,** 686 (1930); *Chem. Abstr.*, **24,** 4261 (1930).
224. Greenspan, F. P., and R. E. Light, Jr., U. S. Patent 2,829,135 (to FMC Corp.), Apr. 1, 1958; *Chem. Abstr.*, **52,** 11470g (1958).
225. Phoenix Gummiwerke A.-G., German Patent 1,111,399 (by R. Meyer), July 20, 1961; *Chem. Abstr.*, **56,** 3613g (1962).
226. Greenspan, F. P., and R. E. Light, Jr., U. S. Patent 2,829,130 (to FMC Corp.), Apr. 1, 1958); *Chem. Abstr.*, **52,** 11470e (1958).
227. George, D. K., and L. Gunkel, U. S. Patent applied for.
228. FMC Corp., British Patent 787,293, Dec. 4, 1957; *Chem. Abstr.*, **52,** 7767i (1958).
229. Greenspan, F. P., and R. E. Light, Jr., U. S. Patent 2,833,747 (to FMC Corp.), May 6, 1958; *Chem. Abstr.*, **52,** 17800d (1958).
230. CIBA, Ltd., British Patent 885,872, Dec. 28, 1961, *Chem. Abstr.*, **56,** 12800e (1962).
231. Tocker, S., U. S. Patent 3,043,818 (to E. I. duPont de Nemours & Co.), July 10, 1962; *Chem. Abstr.*, **57,** 12738a (1962).
232. Rees, R. W., U. S. Patent 3,050,507 (to Shawinigan Chemicals, Ltd.), Aug. 21, 1962; *Chem. Abstr.*, **57,** 16885i (1962).
233. Greenspan, F. P., and R. E. Light, Jr., unpublished work.
234. Greenspan, F. P., and R. E. Light, Jr., Canadian Patent 560,690, July 20, 1958.
235. Greenspan, F. P., and A. E. Pepe, U. S. Patent 2,826,556 (to FMC Corp.), Mar. 11, 1958; *Chem. Abstr.*, **52,** 9665a (1958).
236. Greenspan, F. P., and R. E. Light, Jr., U. S. Patent 2,851,441 (to FMC Corp.), Sept. 9, 1958; *Chem. Abstr.*, **53,** 1834b (1959).
237. Greenspan, F. P., and R. E. Light, Jr., U. S. Patent 2,921,921 (to FMC Corp.), Jan. 19, 1960; *Chem. Abstr.*, **54,** 8148g (1960).
238. Wheelock, C. E., and B. Franzus, U. S. Patent 2,876,214 (to Phillips Petroleum Co.), Mar. 3, 1959; *Chem. Abstr.*, **53,** 10841d (1959).

F. Hydrogenation

239. Harries, C. D., *Untersuchungen über die naturlichen und künstlichen Kautschukarten,* Julius Springer, Berlin, 1919, p. 48.
240. Harries, C. D., *Chem. Ber.*, **56,** 1048 (1923); *Chem. Abstr.*, **17,** 2806 (1923).
241. Staudinger, H., and J. Fritschi, *Helv. Chim. Acta,* **5,** 785 (1922); *Chem. Abstr.*, **17,** 2974 (1923).
242. Berthelot, P. E. M., *Bull. Soc. Chim. France,* **11,** 33 (1869).
243. Hinrichsen, F. W., and R. Kempf, *Chem. Ber.*, **45,** 2106 (1912); *Chem. Abstr.*, **6,** 2924 (1912).
244. Pummerer, R., and P. A. Burkard, *Chem. Ber.*, **55,** 3458 (1922); *Chem. Abstr.*, **17,** 898 (1923).
245. Pummerer, R., and A. Koch, *Ann. Chem.*, **438,** 294 (1924); *Chem. Abstr.*, **18,** 3737 (1924).
246. Geiger, E., *Gummi-Ztg.*, **40,** 2143 (1926); *Chem. Abstr.*, **20,** 3165 (1926).
247. Staudinger, H., and J. K. Senior, *Helv. Chim. Acta,* **13,** 1321 (1930); *Chem. Abstr.* **25,** 3518 (1931).

248. Staudinger, H., *Helv. Chim. Acta*, **13**, 1324 (1930); *Chem. Abstr.*, **25**, 3518 (1931).
249. Staudinger, H., E. Geiger, E. Huber, W. Schaal, and A. Schwalbach, *Helv. Chim. Acta*, **13**, 1334 (1930); *Chem. Abstr.*, **25**, 3518 (1931).
250. Staudinger, H., and R. Nodzu, *Helv. Chim. Acta*, **13**, 1350 (1930); *Chem. Abstr.*, **25**, 3519 (1931).
251. Staudinger, H., and W. Schaal, *Helv. Chim. Acta*, **13**, 1355 (1930); *Chem. Abstr.*, **25**, 3519 (1931).
252. Staudinger, H., and W. Feisst, *Helv. Chim. Acta*, **13**, 1361 (1930); *Chem. Abstr.*, **25**, 3519 (1931).
253. Staudinger, H., M. Brunner, and E. Geiger, *Helv. Chim. Acta*, **13**, 1368 (1930); *Chem. Abstr.*, **25**, 3519 (1931).
254. Staudinger, H., and G. V. Schulz, *Chem. Ber.*, **68**, 2320 (1935); *Chem. Abstr.*, **30**, 4380[1] (1936).
255. Cawley, C. M., and J. G. King, *J. Soc. Chem. Ind.*, **54**, 117 (1935); *Rubber Chem. Technol.*, **8**, 360 (1935); *Chem. Abstr.*, **29**, 4625[7] (1935).
256. Flint, R. B., U. S. Patent 2,046,257 (to E. I. duPont de Nemours & Co.), June 30, 1936; *Chem. Abstr.*, **30**, 5833[9] (1936).
257. Pier, M., F. Christmann, and E. Donath, U. S. Patent 2,093,096 (to Standard-I.G. Co.), Sept. 14, 1937; *Chem. Abstr.*, **31**, 6551[5] (1937).
258. Hugel, G. L., British Patent 491,850, Sept. 9, 1938; *Chem. Abstr.*, **33**, 1541[3] (1939).
259. Tanaka, Y., and R. Kobayashi, *Nippon Gomu Kyokaishi*, **15**, 487 (1942); *Chem. Abstr.*, **43**, 3648g (1949).
260. British Rubber Producers Research Association, British Patent 577,472 (by K. C. Roberts, and J. Wilson), May 20, 1946; *Chem. Abstr.*, **42**, 6152h (1948).
261. Dazeley, G. H., D. Gall, and C. C. Hall, *J. Inst. Petrol.*, **34**, 647 (1948); *Chem. Abstr.*, **43**, 2418f (1949).
262. Nakahara, E., S. Orihata, and Y. Koga, Japanese Patent 175,814 (to Oriental Fuel Industrial Co.), Mar. 11, 1948; *Chem. Abstr.*, **44**, 10311h (1950).
263. Ipatieff, V. N., and R. E. Schaad, *Ind. Eng. Chem.*, **32**, 762 (1940).
264. Cupery, M. E., U. S. 2,526,639 (to E. I. duPont de Nemours & Co.), Oct. 24, 1950; *Chem. Abstr.*, **45**, 1384a (1951).
265. Jones, R. V., C. W. Moberly, and W. B. Reynolds, *Ind. Eng. Chem.*, **45**, 1117 (1953).
266. Unpublished Report, Phillips Petroleum Company to Quartermaster Research and Engineering Command, U. S. Army, Contract DA44-109-qm 357, 1953.
267. Yakubchik, A. I., B. I. Tikhomirov, and L. N. Mikhailova, *Zh. Prikl. Khim.*, **34**, 652 (1961); *Chem. Abstr.*, **55**, 18252a (1961).
268. Yakubchik, A. I., V. N. Reikh, B. I. Tikhomirov, and A. V. Pavlikova, *Zh. Prikl. Khim.*, **34**, 2501 (1961); *J. Appl. Chem.*, **34**, 2368 (1961).
269. Tikhomirov, B. I., A. I. Yakubchik, and I. A. Klopotova, *Vysokomolekul. Soedin.*, **4**, 25 (1962); *Chem. Abstr.*, **56**, 15649a (1962).
270. Tikhomirov, B. I., A. I. Yakubchik, and I. A. Klopotova, *Vysokomolekul. Soedin.*, **3**, 486 (1961); *Chem. Abstr.*, **56**, 570i (1962).
271. Yakubchik, A. I., B. I. Tikhomirov, and V. S. Sumilov, *Vestn. Leningr. Univ.*, **16**, *No. 22, Ser. Fiz. i Khim.*, No. 4, 135 (1961); *Rubber Chem. Technol.*, **35**, 1063 (1962).
272. Ipatieff, V. N., and B. B. Corson. *Ind. Eng. Chem.*, **30**, 1039 (1938).

273. Lee, T. S., I. M. Kolthoff, and M. A. Mairs, *J. Polymer Sci.*, **3**, 66 (1948).
274. Yakubchik, A. I., B. I. Tikhomirov, and I. A. Klopotova, *Zh. Prikl. Khim.*, **34**, 942 (1961); *Chem. Abstr.*, **55**, 23309c (1961).
275. Yakubchik, A. I., and G. N. Gromova, *Zh. Obshch. Khim.*, **26**, 1381 (1956); *Chem. Abstr.*, **50**, 15115a (1956).
276. Yakubchik, A. I., and G. N. Gromova, *Zh. Obshch. Khim.*, **26**, 1626 (1956); *Chem. Abstr.*, **51**, 1637d (1957).
277. Jones, R. V., and C. W. Moberly, U. S. Patent 2,786,047 (to Phillips Petroleum Co.), March 19, 1957; *Chem. Abstr.*, **51**, 9202f (1957).
278. Cines, M. R., and B. B. Buchanan, U. S. Patent 2,845,406 (to Phillips Petroleum Co.), July 29, 1958; *Chem. Abstr.*, **52**, 21206i (1958).
279. Wicklatz, J. E., and K. R. Mills, U. S. Patent 2,964,506 (to Phillips Petroleum Co.), Dec. 13, 1960; *Chem. Abstr.*, **55**, 10960h (1961).
280. Delap, J. A., and R. E. Dietz, U. S. Patent 2,965,585 (to Phillips Petroleum Co.), Dec. 20, 1960; *Chem. Abstr.*, **55**, 8913g (1961).
281. Dietz, R. E., U. S. Patent 2,905,658 (to Phillips Petroleum Co.), Sept. 22, 1959; *Chem. Abstr.*, **54**, 15988c (1960).
282. Dunkel, M., and W. Breuers, German Patent 598,060 (to I. G. Farbenindustrie), June 5, 1934; *Chem. Abstr.*, **28**, 5714[7] (1934).
283. Marks, E. M., U. S. Patent 2,109,495 (to Atlantic Refining Co.), Mar. 1, 1938; *Chem. Abstr.*, **32**, 3203[2] (1938).
284. Thompson, H. W., and P. Torkington, *Trans. Faraday Soc.*, **41**, 246 (1945).
285. Thompson, H. W., and P. Torkington, *Proc. Roy. Soc. (London)*, **A184**, 3 (1945); *Chem. Abstr.*, **40**, 276[8] (1946).

G. Reagents with Multiple Bonds

286. Pinazzi, C., R. Chéritat, and R. Pautrat, *Rev. Gén. Caoutchouc*, **39**, 1951 (1962).
287. Le Bras, J., *Kautschuk u. Gummi*, **15**, WT407 (1962).
288. Le Bras, J., *Rev. Gén. Caoutchouc*, **40**, 1501 (1963).
289. Natta, G., *Quelques aspects généraux de la science des macromolécules*, C. N. R. S., Strasbourg, 1954, p. 69.
289a. Fraga, D. W., *J. Polymer Sci.*, **41**, 522 (1959).
289b. Golub, M. A., S. A. Fugua, and N. S. Bhacca, *J. Am. Chem. Soc.*, **84**, 4981 (1962).
290. Le Bras, J., and A. Delalande, *Les dérivés chimiques du caoutchouc naturel*, Dunod, Paris, 1950.
291. Bloomfield, G. F., in *The Applied Science of Rubber*, W. J. S. Naunton, ed., E. Arnold, London, 1961, pp. 72–150.
291a. Golub, M. A., and J. Heller, *Can. J. Chem.*, **41**, 937 (1963).
291b. Lee, D. F., J. Scanlan, and W. F. Watson, *Proc. Roy. Soc. (London)*, **A273**, 345 (1963).
292. Sekhar, B. C., *Proc. Nat. Rubber Res. Conf. Kuala Lumpur, 1960*, Rubber Research Institute of Malaya, Kuala Lumpur, Malaya, p. 512.
293. Sekhar, B. C., *J. Polymer Sci.*, **48**, 133 (1960).
294. Farmer, E. H., *J. Soc. Chem. Ind.*, **66**, 86 (1947).
295. van Amerongen, G. J., and C. Koningsberger, *J. Polymer Sci.*, **6**, 653 (1950).
296. Ramakrishnan, C. S., D. Raghunath, and J. B. Pande, *Trans. Inst. Rubber Ind.*, **30**, 129 (1954); *Rubber Chem. Technol.*, **28**, 598 (1955).

297. Bloomfield, G. F., *J. Chem. Soc.*, **1943**, 249.
298. Kraus, G., and W. B. Reynolds, *J. Am. Chem. Soc.*, **72**, 5621 (1950).
299. Cockbain, E. G., T. D. Pendle, and D. T. Turner, *Chem. Ind. (London)*, **1960**, 318.
300. Tom, D. H. E., *J. Polymer Sci.*, **20**, 381 (1956).
301. van Amerongen, G. J., *J. Polymer Sci.*, **6**, 633 (1951).
302. Farmer, E. H., in *Advances in Colloid Science*, H. Mark and G. S. Whitby, eds., Vol. II, Interscience, New York, 1946, p. 299.
303. Cunneen, J. I., *J. Chem. Soc.*, **1947**, 36.
304. Holmberg, B., *Chem. Ber.*, **65B**, 1349 (1932); *Rubber Chem. Technol.*, **6**, 71 (1933).
305. Cunneen, J. I., *J. Chem. Soc.*, **1947**, 134.
306. Ritter, F. J., Thesis, Delft, 1956; [A condensation of this thesis is published in *Rubber Chem. Technol.*, **33**, 1–41 (1960)].
307. Pierson, R. M., W. E. Gibbs, G. E. Meyer, F. J. Naples, W. M. Saltman, R. W. Schrock, L. B. Tewksbury, and G. S. Trick, *Rubber Plastics Age*, **38**, 592, 708 (1957). Shortened version of this paper also appeared in *Rubber World*, **136**, 529–536 and 695–701 (1957), and *Rubber Chem. Technol.*, **31**, 213 (1958).
308. Meyer, G. E., F. J. Naples, and H. M. Rice, *Rubber World*, **140**, 435 (1959).
309. Compagnon, P., and J. Le Bras, *Compt. Rend.*, **212**, 616 (1941); *Chem. Abstr.*, **38**, 1905[6] (1944).
310. Le Bras, J., and P. Compagnon, *Bull. Soc. Chim. France*, **11**, 553 (1944); *Rubber Chem. Technol.*, **20**, 938 (1947).
311. Bloomfield, G. F., F. M. Merrett, J. F. Popham, and P. M. Swift, in *Proceedings of the 3rd Rubber Technology Conference, London, 1954*, T. H. Messenger, ed., Institution of the Rubber Industry, London, p. 185.
312. Bateman, L. C., *Ind. Eng. Chem.*, **49**, 704 (1957).
313. Kobryner, W., and A. Banderet, *Rev. Gén. Caoutchouc*, **34**, 1017 (1957); *Chem. Abstr.*, **53**, 9710c (1959).
314. Pike, M., and W. F. Watson, *J. Polymer Sci.*, **9**, 229 (1952).
315. Watson, W. F., *Trans. Inst. Rubber Ind.*, **29**, 32 (1953); *Rubber Chem. Technol.*, **26**, 377 (1953).
316. Angier, D. J., and W. F. Watson, *J. Polymer Sci.*, **20**, 235 (1956).
317. Salomon, G., and C. Koningsberger, *J. Polymer Sci.*, **2**, 522 (1947).
318. Salomon, G., G. J. van Amerongen, G. J. van Veersen, G. Schuur, and H. C. J. de Decker, *Ind. Eng. Chem.*, **43**, 315 (1951).
319. Veersen, C. J. van, in *Proceedings of the 2nd, Rubber Technology Conference, 1948*, T. R. Dawson, ed., Institution of the Rubber Industry, London, 1949, p. 87.
320. Bloomfield, G. F., and E. H. Farmer, *J. Soc. Chem. Ind.*, **53**, 121T (1934); *Chem. Abstr.*, **28**, 4626[9] (1934).
321. Veersen, C. J. van, *Rec. Trav. Chim.*, **69**, 175 (1950); *Chem. Abstr.*, **44**, 6183e (1950); *Rubber Chem. Technol.*, **24**, 169 (1951).
322. Bacon, R. G., and E. H. Farmer, in *Proceedings of the 1st Rubber Technology Conference, 1938*, T. R. Dawson and J. R. Scott, eds., Institution of the Rubber Industry, 1938, p. 256; *Rubber Chem. Technol.*, **12**, 200 (1939).
323. Le Bras, J., *Rev. Gén. Caoutchouc*, **19**, 43 (1942); *Chem. Abstr.*, **38**, 2844[2] (1944).
324. Alder, K., F. Pascher, and A. Schmitz, *Chem. Ber.*, **76B**, 27 (1943).
325. Farmer, E. H., *Trans. Faraday Soc.*, **38**, 340 (1942); *Rubber Chem. Technol.*, **15**, 765 (1942); **16**, 769 (1948).
326. Delalande, A., *Compt. Rend.*, **224**, 1511 (1947); *Rubber Chem. Technol.*, **21**, 344 (1948).

327. Pinazzi, C., J. C. Danjard, and R. Pautrat, *Bull. Soc. Chim. France,* **1961,** 2433; *Rubber Chem. Technol.,* **36,** 282 (1963).
328. Le Bras, J., C. Pinazzi, and G. Milbert, *Compt. Rend.,* **246,** 1214 (1958); *Chem. Abstr.,* **52,** 11454g (1958).
329. Le Bras, J., C. Pinazzi, and G. Milbert, *Rev. Gén. Caoutchouc,* **36,** 215 (1959); *Chem. Abstr.,* **55,** 25311a (1961).
330. Milbert, G., Thesis, Paris (1959).
331. Cunneen, J. I., *J. Chem. Soc.,* **1947,** 26.
332. Mathieu, J., J. Valls, and P. Apreleff, *Bull. Soc. Chim. France,* **1957,** 1509; *Chem. Abstr.,* **52,** 12744i (1958).
333. Pinazzi, C., R. Pautrat, and J. C. Danjard, *Rev. Gén. Caoutchouc,* **37,** 663 (1960); *Chem. Abstr.,* **55,** 22888d (1961).
334. Pinazzi, C., J. C. Danjard, and R. Pautrat, Ref. 292, p. 551.
335. Le Bras, J., *Rev. Gén. Caoutchouc,* **34,** 131 (1957); *Chem. Abstr.,* **52,** 5869h (1958).
336. Le Bras, J., P. Compagnon, and A. Delalande, *Compt. Rend.,* **241,** 61 (1955); *Chem. Abstr.,* **50,** 597a (1956).
337. Le Bras, J., P. Compagnon, and A. Delalande, *Rev. Gén. Caoutchouc,* **33,** 148 (1956), *Chem. Abstr.,* **50,** 7493a (1956).
338. Tutorskii, I. A., L. S. Khrokhina, and B. A. Dogadkin, *Kauchuk i Rezina,* **19,** No. 5, 3 (1960); *Chem. Abstr.,* **55,** 18155d (1961).
339. Rubber-Stichting, French Patent 913,434, Sept. 10, 1946.
340. United States Rubber Co., French Patent 1,095,954 (by R. H. Snyder and H. M. Paxton), 1959; German Patent 1,066,024, Sept. 24, 1959; *Chem. Abstr.,* **55,** 14958h (1961).
341. Green, J., and E. F. Sverdrup, *Ind. Eng. Chem.,* **48,** 2138 (1956).
342. Green, J., and E. F. Sverdrup, *Rev. Gén. Caoutchouc,* **34,** 25 (1957); *Chem. Abstr.,* **52,** 5870d (1958).
343. Chéritat, R., unpublished work.
344. Alfrey, T., J. J. Bohrer, and H. Mark, *Copolymerization,* High Polymer Series, Vol. VIII, Interscience, New York, 1946.
345. Price, C. C., *Reaction at the Carbon-Carbon Double Bond,* Interscience, New York, 1946.
346. Alfrey, T., and C. C. Price, *J. Polymer Sci.,* **2,** 101 (1947).
347. Price, C. C., *J. Polymer Sci.,* **1,** 83 (1946).
348. Compagnon, P., and A. Delalande, *Rev. Gén. Caoutchouc,* **20,** 133 (1943); *Rubber Chem. Technol.,* **20,** 689 (1947).
349. Pinazzi, C., and R. Pautrat, unpublished work.
350. Tchoubar, B., *Les mécanismes électroniques en chimie organique,* Dunod, Paris, 1960.
351. Prins, H. J., *Chem. Weekblad,* **14,** 932 (1917); *Chem. Abstr.,* **12,** 1437 (1918).
352. Prins, H. J., *Chem. Weekblad,* **16,** 1510 (1919); *Chem. Abstr.,* **14,** 1119 (1920).
353. Mathieu, J., and A. Allais, *Cahiers de synthèse organique,* Vol. I, Masson, Paris, 1957, p. 46.
354. Robert, H., *Chim. Mod.,* **5,** 187 (1960).
355. Beets, M. G. J., *Rev. Trav. Chim.,* **70,** 20 (1951); *Chem. Abstr.,* **45,** 9502c (1951).
356. Baker, J. W., *J. Chem. Soc.,* **1944,** 296.
357. Baker, J. W., *J. Chem. Soc.,* **1948,** 89.
358. Baker, J. W., *J. Chem. Soc.,* **1949,** 770.
359. Fourneau, M. E., G. Benoit, and R. Firmenich, *Bull. Soc. Chim. France* [4], **47,** 858 (1930); *Chem. Abstr.,* **24,** 5740 (1930).

360. Nenitzescu, C. D., and V. Przemetzky, *Chem. Ber.*, **74,** 676 (1941).
361. Mikeska, L. A., and E. Arundale, U. S. Patent 2,449,001 (to Standard Oil Development Co.), Sept. 7, 1948; *Chem. Abstr.*, **43,** 673c (1949).
362. Arnold, R. T., and J. F. Dowdall, *J. Am. Chem. Soc.*, **70,** 2590 (1948).
363. Bain, J. P., *J. Am. Chem. Soc.*, **68,** 638 (1946).
364. Okloff, C., *Arch. Pharm.*, **287,** 266 (1954).
365. Kirchhof, F., *Chem.-Ztg.*, **47,** 513 (1923); *Chem. Abstr.*, **17,** 3112 (1923).
366. McGavack, J., U. S. Patent 1,640,363 (to The Revere Rubber Co.), Aug. 30, 1927; *Chem. Abstr.*, **21,** 3490 (1927).
367. Dunlop Rubber Co., Ltd., British Patent 348,303 (by D. F. Twiss and F. A. Jones), Mar. 24, 1930; *Chem. Abstr.*, **27,** 447 (1933).
368. Dunlop Rubber Co. Ltd., French Patent 709,816, Jan. 13, 1931; *Chem. Abstr.*, **26,** 1156 (1932).
369. Dunlop Rubber Co. Ltd. (D. F. Twiss and F. A. Jones), British Patent 371,339, Jan. 13, 1931; *Chem. Abstr.*, **27,** 3096 (1933).
370. Dunlop Rubber Co. Ltd., British Patent 523,734 (by D. F. Twiss and F. A. Jones), July 22, 1940; *Chem. Abstr.*, **35,** 6484[2] (1941).
371. Latham, G. H., U. S. Patent 2,417,424 (to E. I. du Pont de Nemours & Co.), Mar. 18, 1947; British Patent 574,901, Jan. 25, 1946; *Chem. Abstr.*, **41,** 3994h (1947).
372. Smith, A. H., and C. L. Shreiner, U. S. Patent 1,881,142 (to Rubber Service Laboratories Co.), Oct. 4, 1932; *Chem. Abstr.*, **27,** 631 (1933).
373. Hirano, S., and R. Oda, *J. Soc. Chem. Ind. Japan*, **47,** 833 (1944); *Chem. Abstr.*, **42,** 7082b (1948).
374. I. G. Farbenindustrie A.-G., British Patent 486,878, June 10, 1938; *Chem. Abstr.*, **32,** 9560[1] (1938).
375. Twiss, D. F., and F. A. Jones, U. S. Patent 1,915,808 (to Dunlop Rubber Co. Ltd.), June 27, 1933; *Chem. Abstr.*, **27,** 4717 (1933).
376. Swift, P. M., unpublished work.
377. Esso Research & Engineering Co., French Patent 1,259,093, March 13, 1961.
378. Sekhar, B. C., in *Proceedings of the 5th Rubber Technology Conference, London, 1962*, T. H. Messenger, ed., Institution of the Rubber Industry, 1962, p. 460.
379. Bonner, J., Ref. 292, p. 515.
380. Pinazzi, C., R. Pautrat, and R. Chéritat, *Makromol. Chem.*, **70,** 260 (1964).
381. Pinazzi, C., and R. Pautrat, *Compt. Rend.*, **254,** 1997 (1962); *Chem. Abstr.*, **56,** 15647e (1962).
382. Pinazzi, C., and R. Pautrat, *Rev. Gén. Caoutchouc*, **39,** 799 (1962).
383. Harries, C., *Chem. Ber.*, **37,** 2708 (1904); *Bull. Soc. Chim. Paris* [3], 434 (1905).
384. Colonge, J., and A. Perrot, *Bull. Soc. Chim. France*, **1957,** 204; *Chem. Abstr.*, **51,** 10417h (1957).
385. Vilkes, M., *Compt. Rend.*, **238,** 1598 (1954); *Chem. Abstr.*, **49,** 7527i (1955).
386. Kharasch, M. S., W. H. Urry, and B. M. Kuderna, *J. Org. Chem.*, **14,** 248 (1949).
387. Pinazzi, C., R. Pautrat, and R. Chéritat, *Compt. Rend.*, **256,** 2390 (1963).
388. Pinazzi, C., R. Pautrat, and R. Chéritat, *Compt. Rend.*, **256,** 2607 (1963).
389. Colonge, J., and A. Perrot, *Bull. Soc. Chim. France*, **1957,** 658; *Chem. Abstr.*, **51,** 12851h (1957).
390. Salomon, G., and A. C. van der Schee, *J. Polymer Sci.*, **14,** 181 (1954).
391. D'Ianni, J. D., F. J. Naples, J. W. Marsh, and J. L. Zarney, *Ind. Eng. Chem.*, **38,** 1171 (1946).

Chapter III

REACTIONS OF SATURATED POLYMERIC HYDROCARBONS

GIFFIN D. JONES

Dow Chemical Co.

A. POLYOLEFIN SUBSTITUTION

1. General Considerations

The making of derivatives of polymers has reached the stage where procedures are available for nearly every kind of reaction and the problems are more the defining of objectives, evaluating of structural variations, and achieving of more practical processes in the few cases which may be worthwhile commercially. In reviewing the literature one looks for both theoretical and practical considerations. Unfortunately it is necessary to intermingle these in order to take up papers one at a time. It is tempting to pursue the subsequent reactions of the functional groups introduced, and to a limited extent this has been done in this review. While outside the scope of the review, the similar chemistry of polymers of polar monomers has contributed greatly to the interpretation of the derivatives of the hydrocarbon polymers. The review begins with some general considerations but it is characteristic of polymers that specific information is essential, and a selection of such information follows the general section.

a. Physical Factors

Physical phenomena are as important as chemical in practical processes for substitution in polymers. The use of dilute solutions in solvents is usually not practical, and, because drastic changes in solubility usually accompany substitution, one can rarely preserve solubility throughout the process. Permeability is a factor in substitution of solid polymers. With

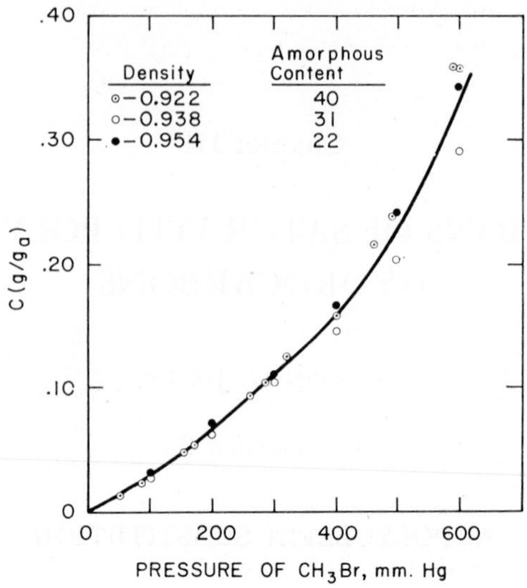

Fig. III-1. Sorption isotherms for polyethylenes and methyl bromide at 0°C. (based on amorphous content only). (Taken from ref. 1.)

crystalline polymers impermeability can be correlated with crystallinity, and if crystallinity decreases during substitution, permeability increases. A number of graft copolymers of polyethylene showed no great changes in crystallinity or in permeability to gases but increased permeability to organic vapors at higher pressures where swelling becomes appreciable (cf. Fig. III-1) (1,2). Solubility is a sensitive measure of crystallinity. Even poly(vinyl chloride), in which crystallinity is very low, becomes more soluble at room temperature after chlorination which presumably destroys the regularity and hence the crystallinity. There are at least two mechanisms of permeation. Small molecules which are poor solvents exhibit Fickean diffusion. Larger molecules diffuse by a solution process. The better the solvent power of the diffusing species the faster the permeation by the solution mechanism. The diffusion constant increases with increased swelling. Diffusion of a good solvent into a crosslinked glassy polymer is particularly likely to set up a sharp concentration boundary. The significance in regard to polymer substitution in the solid phase is that to achieve a uniform partial substitution it is necessary that the rate of reaction be slower than the rate of permeation.

Chemical phenomena of importance in substitution of polymers concerns both the propensity for the desired reaction and for side reactions. Perhaps the most striking side reactions of hydrocarbon polymers are crosslinking and scission, the latter reaction implying substitution on the polymer backbone. Practically all useful replacements of aliphatic hydrogen are chain reactions with a free radical mechanism, but some few appear to be ionic, and these, for reason of the small amount of subject matter, are dealt with here lest they be lost. An example of direct metalation in the side chain, which may be the only known example of proton replacement, is cited in the section of aromatic substitution for reasons of practical similarity.

b. Ionic Processes

Some substitution reactions of aliphatic hydrocarbons are hydride transfer reactions brought about by Friedel-Crafts catalysts. The branching of polypropylene, which appears to occur in the polymerization of propylene with aluminum bromide activated with hydrogen bromide, is an example (eq. 1). Fontana (3–5) showed that an atactic polypropylene of molecular weight up to a million, but low viscosity, was obtained by polymerization of propylene at Dry Ice temperatures and contact times rather long (30 min.) for cationic polymerization. Presumably, the mechanism is similar to that proposed by Schmerling (6) for alkylation.

$$CH_3CH{=}CH_2 + HAlBr_4 \rightarrow CH_3\overset{+}{C}HCH_3$$

$$\underset{\text{Dead polymer}}{-CH_2CH_2CH_2-} + CH_3\overset{+}{C}HCH_3 \rightleftharpoons -CH_2\overset{+}{C}HCH_2- + CH_3CH_2CH_3$$

$$\xrightarrow{CH_3CH{=}CH_2} \begin{array}{c} -CH_2CHCH_2- \\ | \\ CH_2\underset{+}{C}HCH_3 \end{array} \qquad (1)$$

Polymer with growing branch

Scission is a probable side reaction if the process is conducted at higher temperatures, as in acid-catalyzed cracking. Thus, Grignard reported in 1924 that *n*-octane with anhydrous aluminum chloride at 120–150°C. gives butane and polymeric olefins.

Sulfonation of polyethylene with chlorosulfonic acid may be a hydride abstraction mechanism, and perhaps iodination is also. A free radical chain reaction with iodine is not possible at moderate temperatures.

Isotactic polypropylene has been deuterated with nickel–kieselguhr catalyst at 150°C. in cyclohexane (7). It was expected that racemization would occur, but the product was even higher in density and stiffness than the starting material. It seems likely that a heterogeneous reaction requiring adsorption and desorption would affect only segments of the polymer chain; however, the authors of this paper questioned the basic concept of a stereoregular structure.

c. Free Radical Processes

Most processes for aliphatic substitution of hydrocarbons are of the free radical chain reaction type. Crosslinking and scission are very important side reactions in free radical substitution of hydrocarbon polymers. Crosslinking predominates with polyethylene, ethylene–propylene copolymers (other than those far on the propylene side), polymers of terminal olefins higher than propylene (other than isobutylene) and polystyrene. Scission usually predominates with polypropylene, polyisobutylene, and poly-α-methylstyrene, although it is possible to introduce some gel fraction. The efficiency of crosslinking is said to be high if the extractable fraction is small even though the gel fraction swells highly. The degree of crosslinking is high if the gel fraction swells little (when swelled in a good solvent at a temperature at which it is not crystalline). It is possible, and commercially practiced in the case of butyl rubber, to introduce functionality such as unsaturation and halogen in order to make crosslinking efficient. Under conditions of vacuum pyrolysis polyisobutylene undergoes depolymerization, but on heating with peroxides at atmospheric pressure the polymer

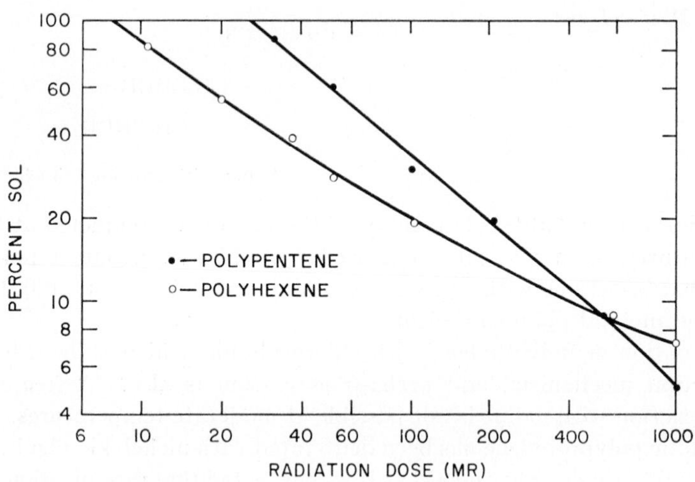

Fig. III-2. Variation of gel fraction with radiation dose. (Taken from ref. 9.)

undergoes scission. Thus, heating for 1 hr. at 140°C. with 1.5 wt.-% dicumyl peroxide reduced M_n by a factor of 40 with no detectable monomer formation (8).

As shown in Figure III-2 and Table III-1 (9), poly-1-hexene and poly-1-pentene undergo crosslinking under irradiation, but the crosslinking is accompanied by sufficient branching and/or scission that there is a decrease in intrinsic viscosity at low dose. Figure III-3 shows the crosslinking of polyethylene to require a somewhat lower dose (10). Within the range of the comparison the crosslinking is not sensitive to dose rate (11). The higher olefin polymers developed *trans*-vinylene unsaturation fragments and may have lost side chain fragments, inasmuch as butyl- and amyl-branched polymethylene lost butane and pentane under high energy irradiation (12).

TABLE III-1
Intrinsic Viscosities of Polypentene and Polyhexene[a]

Dose, (Mrep)	[η], dl./g.[b]	
	Polypentene	Polyhexene
0	1.68	2.01
1	1.08	1.69
2	0.95	1.40
5	0.80	1.43
6		1.55
10	0.76	
15	0.84	

[a] Taken from ref. 9.
[b] In benzene, 25°C.

The presence of oxygen not only reduces crosslinking, it promotes scission (eq. 2). It was suggested that oxygen reacts with secondary electrons to form hydrogen peroxide (10). In the free radical substitution processes oxygen effects are sometimes detectable, often overshadowed, sometimes essential.

$$R\cdot - \begin{cases} \xrightarrow{O_2} RO_2\cdot \xrightarrow{RH} R\cdot + ROOH \rightarrow RO\cdot + \cdot OH \xrightarrow{\text{Scission}} R'CHO + R\cdot'' \\ \xrightarrow{X_2} RX + X\cdot \end{cases} \qquad (2)$$

Electron spin measurements help to identify the more stable radicals derived from the polyolefins. In the case of polyethylene, ionizing irradia-

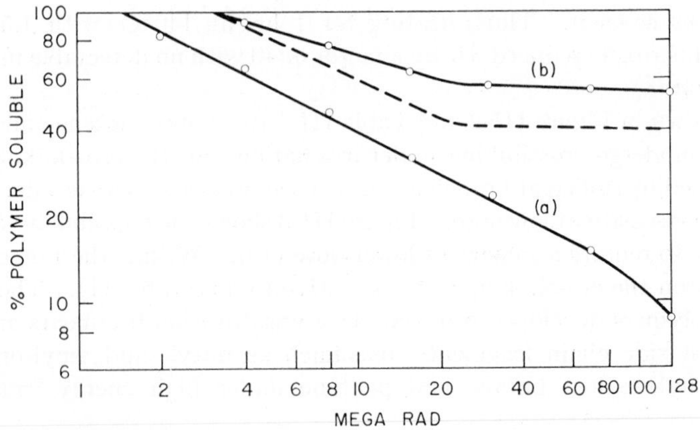

Fig. III-3. Relationship between per cent polymer rendered insoluble and dose for 18 μ thick polyethylene films irradiated with 2 M.e.v. electrons: (O) experimental values for irradiation (*a*) *in vacuo* and (*b*) in air; (- -) theoretical curve where there is one main chain break for every crosslink, assuming the crosslinking efficiency to be the same as *in vacuo*. (Taken from ref. 10.)

tion at liquid nitrogen temperature produces a six-line spectrum as expected. In the case of polypropylene the behavior is more complicated. Irradiation of isotactic polypropylene at liquid nitrogen temperature produces a four-line spectrum which rearranges at higher temperatures to a nine-line spectrum (measured at liquid nitrogen temperature). A surprising discovery is that atactic polypropylene does not form the secondary spectrum (13,14). The rate of decay of the primary spectrum of atactic polypropylene is faster than that from isotactic (14) and it may be that mobility restriction due to crystallinity is necessary to retain enough total radical content that the secondary spectrum can be seen.

If the primary spectrum is that of structure I or II (formed by abstracting primary or secondary hydrogen, which are statistically favored) one might have expected the secondary spectrum to be an eight-line spectrum of structure III resulting from a hydrogen shift without scission. That it

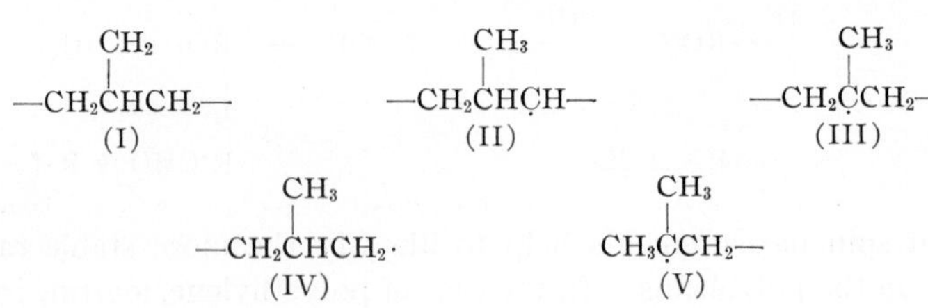

is a nine-line spectrum suggested that scission might have occurred in the first step to give IV as the primary and V as the secondary radical. That this is not the case has been shown by Loy (14) with isotactic poly-1,1-dideuteropropene. The primary spectrum was still a four-line spectrum such as would be explained by structure I (but not II or IV in the case of the deuterated derivative). After heating of the irradiated deuterated derivative there remained a four-line spectrum, as would be expected with structure III (deuterated). The concentration of radicals had been greatly reduced by heating to 30°C. for 15 min. It appears that the so-called secondary spectrum is present in, and obscured by, the primary spectrum.

In the case of polyisobutylene, a doublet is observed above −100°C.,

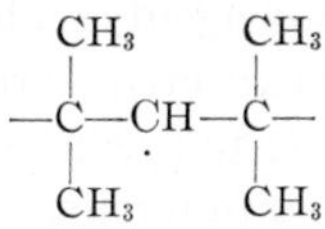

whereas attack on a methyl which might have been expected did not occur or did not give a long-lived radical. At −150°C., the doublet appears as a singlet due to dipolar broadening.

In the case of poly-1-butene or poly-1-pentene the loss of a side chain would leave the backbone intact and with vinylene unsaturation. The primary spectrum from isotactic poly-1-butene is less resolvable than that from polypropylene but is either a four- or six-line spectrum, and the secondary spectrum is a doublet which may be present initially and masked by the primary spectrum (all observed at liquid nitrogen temperature, (14). Speculatively, one might ascribe the doublet with polybutylene to formation of methane.

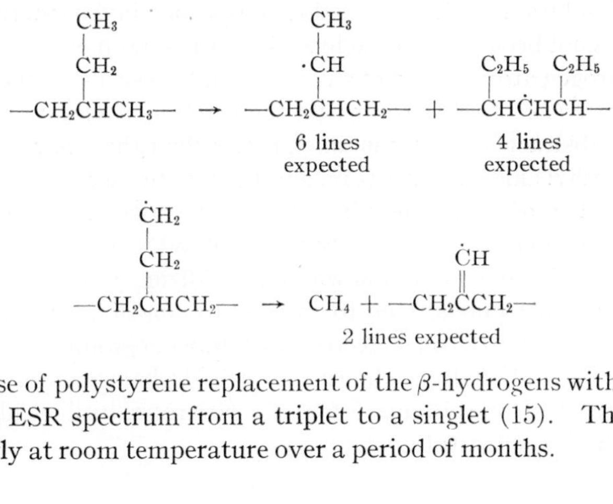

(3)

In the case of polystyrene replacement of the β-hydrogens with deuterium reduces the ESR spectrum from a triplet to a singlet (15). The spectrum decays slowly at room temperature over a period of months.

Ionizing irradiation is perhaps too energy-rich to produce the same radical as chlorination. Chlorination however, makes the ESR spectrum vague. Evidently, the surviving radicals are on carbons bearing chlorine and the quadrupole moment of chlorine broadens the spin signal. Only a broad line is obtained from irradiated poly(vinyl chloride).

The degree to which crosslinking and scission occur in the preparation of a polymer derivative depends not only on the stability of the radical but also on the reactivity of the reagent. One would expect bromine to react more rapidly than chlorine with a polymer radical (and also the bromine concentration is likely to be higher); therefore one would expect less crosslinking and scission during bromination than during chlorination. The more discriminating halogenation agents such as *tert*-butyl hypochlorite and *N*-bromosuccinimide might be expected to react more slowly with the carbon radical, but the outcome is unpredictable because the initial attack on the polymer may be somewhat different.

$$\left.\begin{array}{c}(CH_3)_3CO\cdot \\ \downarrow \\ (CH_3)_2CO + CH_3\cdot\end{array}\right\} \xrightarrow{RH} R\cdot \xrightarrow{(CH_3)_3COCl} RCl + (CH_3)_3CO\cdot \qquad (4)$$

Bromine has a greater selectivity than does chlorine for abstraction of tertiary hydrogen (16) and also for abstraction of hydrogen from carbon bearing a group such as phenyl, which is capable of a resonance contribution to the transition state. Russell (17–19) discovered that solvents such as carbon disulfide and aromatic compounds make chlorine atoms more selective in the same sense. It was known that aliphatic hydrogens can, to a degree, be chlorinated preferentially in the presence of aromatic hydrogens (20) and, as an example, there can be cited the chlorination of polyethylene in biphenyl solution (21). The halogenation of vinylaromatic polymers, however, has not been directed exclusively to the side chain.

Only hydrogen atoms abstract chlorine readily (except from CCl_4, $CClF_3$, etc.). Szwarc (22,23) points out that the reaction of methyl radicals with methane to abstract hydrogen is much faster than the abstraction of chlorine from methyl chloride by methyl and the difference cannot be explained by considerations of bond strength. It is not surprising, therefore, that free radical substitution reactions of poly(vinyl chloride) do not involve chlorine abstraction. Moreover it is known that oxidizing radicals (those which tend to form stable anions) tend to abstract hydrogen from a carbon which does not bear halogen or other electron withdrawing group. The formation of unsaturation and of allylic chlorine by dehydrohalogenation complicates the structure which one obtains, especially with reagents like chlorine which can add as well as substitute.

In chlorinated poly(vinyl chloride) (having Cl/C = 1) only 25% of the methylenes remain unchlorinated (infrared evidence) (24). A comparison of the chlorination rates of poly(vinyl chloride) and polyethylene shows that the latter chlorinates faster initially but that the rate falls off with increasing substitution.

d. *Fluorination*

The direct fluorination of aliphatic hydrocarbons leads to complicated mixtures of products because of the low selectivity (cf. Table III-2) characteristic of a high energy reactant, because of the disruptive heat of reaction, and because monofluorinated products are subject to acid-catalyzed decomposition.

TABLE III-2A
Comparison of Selectivity of Halogen Atoms for Gas-Phase Hydrogen Abstraction from Alkanes at 300°K.[a]

	Relative selectivities		
Halogen	CH_3	CH_2	CH
F·	1	1.2	1.4
Cl·	1	3.9	5.1
Br·	1	82	1600

[a] Taken from ref. 25.

TABLE III-2B
Comparison of Selectivity of Halogen Atoms in Halogenation of *n*-Butyl Fluoride in Gas Phase[a]

		Relative selectivities at each position			
Halogen	Temp., °C.	FCH_2	CH_2	CH_2	CH_3
F·	20	0.3	0.8	1.0	1
Cl·	35	0.8	1.6	3.7	1
Br·	146	10	9	82	1

[a] Taken from ref. 26.

It has not been proven that a free radical chain reaction exists in fluorination as in chlorination and bromination. The fact that the F—F bond energy is so much less than that of chlorine as shown in Table III-3 has been taken to indicate that not only is a chain reaction possible, but that thermal dissociation is a likely initiation process (27). In the gas-phase fluorina-

TABLE III-3
Approximate Heats of Reaction for ΔH Aliphatic Hydrocarbons[a]

$$X\cdot + RH \rightarrow XH + R\cdot \quad (1)$$

$$R\cdot + X_2 \rightarrow RX + X\cdot \quad (2)$$

Halogen (X)	ΔH_1, kcal./mole	ΔH_2, kcal./mole	E_1, kcal./mole
F	−34.0	−68.0	0.2–0.3
Cl	−3.0	−23.0	0.5–1.0
Br	+12.5	−23.0	14

[a] Taken from ref. 27.

tion of methane, Hadley and Bigelow obtained C_2F_6 and C_3F_8 as well as CF_4 and proposed a free radical mechanism (28). In the fluorination of benzene, addition as well as substitution occurs. The mechanism of addition of chlorine to benzene (and toluene) is promoted by light and high energy radiation and is usually considered to be a free radical chain reaction with a high halogen concentration. Fluorination does not seem to be conducted with ultraviolet or high energy radiation. Halogen exchange between carbon tetrachloride and inorganic fluorides is claimed to be promoted by γ-ray treatment but elemental fluorine was not used (29).

Fluorine monochloride acts as a chlorinating agent rather than a fluorinating agent. Inasmuch as hydrogen fluoride has a higher free energy of formation than hydrogen chloride and also because the polarity of fluorine monochloride must have some effect in the transition state of reaction with an alkyl radical, one cannot base a comparison of the reactivity of fluorine and chlorine on the reactivity of fluorine monochloride. Furthermore, if any hydrogen chloride were formed it would be oxidized to chlorine by the fluorine monochloride.

Iodine monofluoride has been added to fluorinated olefins and the conclusion drawn that it is a polar process (30).

$$F_3CCF{=}CF_2 + IF \rightarrow F_3CCFICF_3 \quad (5)$$

$$ClCF{=}CF_2 + IF \rightarrow ClCFICF_3\ (45\%) + ClCF_2CF_2I\ (55\%) \quad (6)$$

$$CF_2{=}CH_2 + IF \rightarrow CF_3CH_2I \quad (7)$$

Bockemüller (31) called attention to the fact that the heat of fluorination is far in excess of the carbon–carbon bond strength. The use of less energetic fluorinating agents is beneficial in reducing cleavage. Silver difluoride, introduced by Cady (32), and cobaltic fluoride, introduced by Fowler (33), are still too potent for fluorination of hydrocarbons in the liquid phase. Manganese trifluoride and cerium tetrafluoride have been used for fluorinating oils (34).

Iodobenzene difluoride gives fluorine addition to 1,1-diphenylpropene with rearrangement; therefore, it is likely an ionic process (35).

$$(C_6H_5)_2C{=}CHCH_3 + C_6H_5IF_2 \rightarrow C_6H_5CF_2\underset{}{\overset{CH_3}{\overset{|}{C}}}HC_6H_5 + C_6H_5I \qquad (8)$$

Although over half the heat evolved in fluorination is due to the stability of the hydrogen fluoride, the addition of two fluorines to a double bond is as exothermic as the substitution reaction. It would be desirable, therefore, to be able to fluorinate with a reagent which is less energy-rich than fluorine and does not give hydrogen fluoride as a by-product, but gives instead a more unstable species (eq. 9) (where QH is energy-rich). Few of the known

$$RH + FQ \rightarrow RF + QH \qquad (9)$$

fluorinating agents seem to meet these peculiar requirements. Nitrogen fluorine compounds may do so, but sulfur fluorine compounds are less likely. It is considered unlikely that SHF_5 could exist (36), and SF_6 is a fluorinating agent only under highly activating conditions. In the case of SF_4, fluorination involves oxygen rather than hydrogen replacement (37).

Sulfur chloride pentafluoride is a chlorinating agent under polar and free radical conditions.

$$CH_3CH{=}CH_2 + SF_5Cl \xrightarrow[\text{or 90°C. in autoclave}]{\text{UV}} CH_3CHClCH_2SF_5 \qquad (10)$$

$$C_6H_6 + SF_5Cl \xrightarrow[\text{Fr–Cr cat.}]{} C_6H_5Cl + SF_4 + HF \qquad (11)$$

Oxygen-fluorine compounds are very energy-rich and form stable by-products. They evolve oxygen from aqueous alkali.

Electrofluorination, while perhaps providing a way of reducing the energy problem, is less applicable to polymers. It is interesting that, unlike the Simons process wherein perfluoro compounds are produced, electrofluorination in organic solvents with a platinum electrode can be caused to give monofluorides (38). Thus butyric acid was monofluorinated and the ratio of products ($\alpha{:}\beta{:}\gamma = 1{:}2{:}2$) was suggestive of a free radical mechanism. In electrofluorination hydrogen is produced, and the voltage is kept low enough not to generate fluorine. Water is excluded.

2. Halogenation of Polyethylene

a. Fluorination

The fluorination of polyethylene can be carried out in the dark by exposure of sheet or powder to fluorine diluted with nitrogen and up to 10%

fluorine introduced slowly without destroying the polymer (39,40). Penetration is only a few mils in depth and produces an altered surface (less heat-sealable) (41). Complete fluorination over a several day period of a 3 mil film on a 100 mesh phosphor bronze gauze has been reported (42). Fluorination with cupric and mercuric fluoride in hydrofluoric acid was carried to 20% fluorine in 50 hr. at 110°C. (43).

Like fluorination, nitration of paraffinic hydrocarbons is too energy-rich a process for the preparation of derivatives of intact polyolefins.

b. Chlorination

It is possible to chlorinate polyethylene in the dark at a temperature of 150°C without deliberately adding an initiator The initiator is probably residual peroxide under these conditions. In chlorination below 100°C. it is stated that oxygen must be removed for controlled chlorination. While a trace of oxygen may be catalytic, the presence of larger quantities has an

TABLE III-4
Chlorinated Polyethylene[a]

Chlorine, wt.-%	Brittle point, °C.	Softening point, °C.	Description
2		82	
8		69	
25		<20	Rubbery
40		≈20	Soft, sluggish
45	−20	30	Leathery
54	+20	52	Rigid
60	+40	67	Brittle

[a] Taken from ref. 48.

inhibiting and degrading effect (44). Residual titanium chloride seems to be catalytic if present (45). Photochlorination with visible light is promoted by the presence of a trace of oxygen which can be converted to carbonyl compounds (44). Ultraviolet light beyond 2500 A. promotes crosslinking. It is not clear why this should be the case if chlorine is available. Fawcett, who obtained a basic patent on chlorinated polyethylene, found an azo catalyst to be effective in boiling carbon tetrachloride and only a slow rate without added catalyst (46). It is reported that the presence of a chain transfer agent such as chloroform reduces the tendency to crosslink and this effect suggests a surprising selectivity, perhaps, of peroxy radicals derived from the polymer and oxygen (47).

The effect of chlorination on polyethylene is, as shown in Table III-4 and Figure III-4, a reduction in crystallinity and then at higher levels an increase in stiffness. The effect of bromination is similar. At 55% bromine content the polymer is noncrystalline and rubbery (46). When crystallinity has been eliminated (and the precise degree of substitution at which this occurs is a measure of the randomness of substitution) the polymer becomes soluble at room temperature and further substitution can be

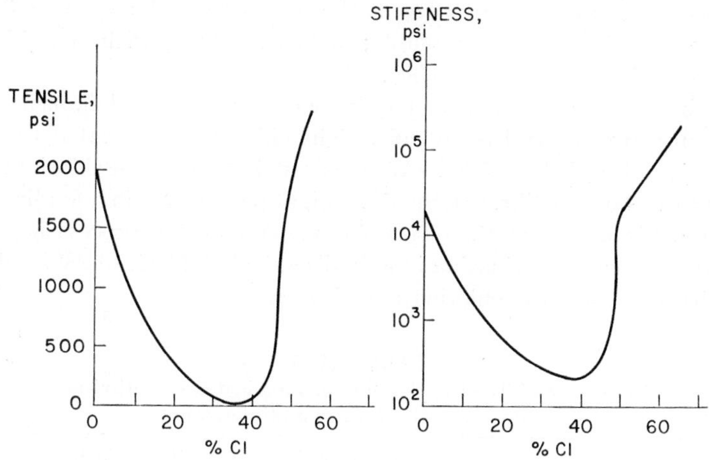

Fig. III-4. Stiffness and tensile strength of chlorinated polyethylene. (Taken from ref. 49.)

carried out in homogeneous solution under mild temperature conditions. In the case of noncrystalline ethylene–propylene copolymers, chlorination can be carried out completely homogeneously even at low temperatures (50).

Heterogeneous processes of chlorination which depend on a fine state of subdivision for uniform chlorination have the problem of agglomeration. The softening which results as the crystallinity is reduced increases the tendency to agglomerate. If chlorination is carried out at 65°C. in aqueous suspension the tendency to agglomerate is worse at about 40% chlorine. After this conversion the temperature may be raised to 75°C. to drive the conversion higher. The saturation of the water with hydrogen chloride or the addition of calcium chloride is reported to reduce agglomeration (51). If a slurry in an organic solvent is chlorinated, the conversion at which the polymer begins to dissolve is a stage of high agglomeration tendency. For example, in carbon tetrachloride the temperature may be kept below 45°C. until chlorination reaches 40% chlorine and below 65°C. until it reaches 60%. For further chlorination it must be raised to 90°C. If a high molecular weight polyethylene is used, the solids content must be kept to a few per cent or the mass becomes a gel (52).

The finely divided polymer required for slurry chlorination may be made by cooling a solution below the point of precipitation (44) or obtained directly in polymerization. A slurry process in liquid chlorine has been described. As chlorination proceeds the polymer dissolves. At −35°C., polymer with 65% chlorine is soluble; at 28°C., polymer with 54% chlorine, and perhaps less, is soluble (53,54).

Chlorination in a fluidized bed requires care to prevent inflammation (21) and temperature control is difficult. The chlorine is preheated to 90°C. and the jacket cooled at 85°C. With external illumination chlorination is carried to 45–50% in 4 hr. (21,55–57). Light penetration in a fluidized bed is presumably no better than in a slurry. A two-step process is recommended, involving chlorination in a fluidized bed at 43°C. to 28% chlorine and subsequent solution chlorination with peroxide.

TABLE III-5
Comparison of Thermal Stability of Chlorinated Polyethylene (60% Cl) with Poly(vinyl Chloride)[a]

	HCl evolved, mg./g. at 165°C. in 1/2 hr. periods				
	1	2	3	4	Total
Poly(vinyl chloride)[b]	1.3	0.8	0.6	0.5	3.2
Chlorinated polyethylene	0.7	1.2	1.0	1.0	3.9

[a] Taken from ref. 58.
[b] With 20 parts dibutyl sebacate plasticizer, no stabilizer added.

The collecting, washing, and drying of a polymer is always a problem. Drying requires either that the polymer be melted or if it is dried as a solid that it be kept in a finely divided condition. In this case a surface treatment may be needed to prevent agglomeration.

The stability of chlorinated polyethylene with respect to loss of hydrogen chloride is somewhat worse than that of poly(vinyl chloride) (Table III-5), but the same stabilizers are effective. One patent recommends washing with oxalic acid to remove contamination by iron (51).

3. Halogenation of Other Aliphatic Polymers

a. Halogenation of Polypropylene and Polyisobutylene

The chlorination of polypropylene is usually accompanied by severe degradation. For example, chlorination at 60°C. to a chlorine content of 40% was reported to have dropped the molecular weight from 24,000 to 3,000 (59). The use of titanium tetrachloride as a chlorination catalyst was reported to give a less brittle product. This could conceivably be a hydride transfer mechanism (45). By mixing a fine powder of polypropylene with a large amount of salt, chlorination was carried out in the dark (as shown in Table III-6) with perhaps less degradation (60). The crystalline polymer

TABLE III-6
Chlorination of Isotactic Polypropylene Mixed with Sodium Chloride at 100°C.[a]

Time, hr.	Chlorine, %	$[\eta]$[b]	Softening point, °C.
0	0	2.25	163–163
1.25	5	1.99	146–148
2	6.7	2.02	148–150
3	8.8	2.07	148–150
5	12.6	2.02	148–150
7	14.7	1.95	147–149
12	21.6	1.77	145–147
12 (at 105°C.)	25.8	1.38	161–163

[a] Taken from ref. 60.
[b] Measured at 135°C. with no heat stabilizer, in dl./g.

was much slower to chlorinate than the noncrystalline, and inasmuch as there was not much loss in crystallinity the chlorination was probably nonrandom and limited to amorphous areas. The viscosity decrease is probably due to both branching and scission.

The overall chlorination rate does not reflect the somewhat more replaceable tertiary hydrogen as might be expected with a chain reaction. The use of more selective chlorinating agents might give a high proportion of tertiary halogen but no assurance of overcoming the degradation problem. Bromine substitution is more selective for tertiary hydrogen and it was found that brominated polypropylene was unstable, undergoing dehydrohalogenation at room temperature. Bromination of atactic polypropylene in carbon tetrachloride solution was slow in the dark at 60°C. (about 0.5%/

hr.) with no added catalyst. When a suspension of isotactic polypropylene in carbon tetrachloride was brominated under ultraviolet light the product was discolored and partly crosslinked.

The chlorination of polyisobutylene also produces severe degradation, but not the halogenation of butyl rubber as used to aid vulcanization and limited to about the amount calculated to be equivalent to the unsaturation (61). It is recommended that chlorination of butyl be carried out below −20°C. and limited to 2% to minimize degradation. Hypochlorite and *N*-chloro compounds can be used as alternates for chlorine in this process. Properties of vulcanizates made with chlorinated butyls are given in Table III-7. The bromination of butyl in the presence of chlorine gave a higher degree of bromination (62). Although the amount of bromine introduced is not in excess of that predicted for addition to the unsaturation, this catalytic action of chlorine seems more reconcilable with a free radical substitution. It is noteworthy that even with 3% bromine content, brominated butyl is still nearly half as unsaturated as the sample before bromination (63,64).

TABLE III-7
Properties of Vulcanizates Made with Chlorinated Butyl[a]

Cl, %	300% Modulus, psi	Tensile strength, psi	Elongation, %
1.10	1050	3100	600
1.25	1075	3550	650
1.30	1300	3175	600
1.50	2100	2725	410
1.96	850	2575	600

[a] Taken from ref. 61.

b. *Chlorination of Poly(vinyl Chloride)*

The chlorination of poly(vinyl chloride) is practiced commercially to produce a polymer of higher second-order transition temperature. It is claimed (65) that by photochlorination in aqueous suspension in the presence of chloroform at mild temperatures (55°C.) and with enough chlorine flow and a porous resin it is possible to reach a conversion to dichloride of 90 mole-% with only 2.6 mole-% of 1,1-dichloro units. The ratio of 1,1-dichloro to 1-chloro structure was determined from the ratio of infrared absorption intensity at 9.50 μ to that at 7.47 μ. Some dehydrohalogenation evidently occurred, because the 1,1-dichloro structure rose to 7.3 mole-%

and fell again during the progressive chlorination. Evidently addition of chlorine is not a favored reaction under the conditions, or possibly the loss occurred after the chlorination.

Photochlorination of dry poly(vinyl chloride) is described (66).

4. Chlorosulfonation

Chlorosulfonation is believed to have in common with chlorination the step of hydrogen abstraction by chlorine atoms, and it is accompanied by chlorination. The presence of pyridine is reported (67) to favor chlorosulfonation, even though the amount of pyridine is less than stoichiometric and this amount must be largely complexed with the sulfuryl chloride and hydrogen chloride. It is conceivable that the sulfonyl radical, which is the assumed intermediate in chlorosulfonation, may be stabilized by complexing with pyridine, pyridinium ion, or the pyridine complex of sulfuryl chloride.

$$RH + Cl\cdot \xrightarrow{-HCl} R\cdot \begin{cases} \xrightleftharpoons{SO_2} RSO_2\cdot \xrightarrow{Cl_2} RSO_2Cl + Cl\cdot \\ \xrightarrow[Cl_2]{} RCl + Cl\cdot \end{cases} \qquad (12)$$

The effect is reminiscent of—but apparently unrelated to—the role of pyridine in controlling the configuration in the reaction of thionyl chloride with alcohols (68).

The proportion of chlorosulfonation to chlorination can be raised by increasing the ratio of sulfur dioxide to chlorine or lowering the temperature, as shown in Table III-8. Apparently the use of preformed sulfuryl chloride gives no advantage, at least for reactions carried out in solution.

TABLE III-8
Photochlorosulfonation of Polyethylene in a Fluidized Bed[a]

Jacket temperature, °C.	Gas flow, l./hr.		Product, wt.-%	
	SO_2	Cl_2	S	Cl
50	50	50	3.2	18.0
60	60	30	5.85	12.5

[a] Taken from refs. 69–71.

Chlorosulfonation is a chain reaction and peroxides, as well as light, have been used to initiate it.

The effect of pyridine is illustrated by an example in which polyethylene was photochlorosulfonated with sulfuryl chloride in refluxing carbon tetrachloride. With the incorporation of 44–47% chlorine the sulfur content was 0.56% without pyridine and 2.6% with pyridine (72).

The isolation of the product is described in a process in which a 7% solution of chlorosulfonated polyethylene in carbon tetrachloride is injected into a steam nozzle to form a 1% slurry in water at 95°C., the solvent being steam-distilled. It was necessary to add 0.001% gelatin to the suspension to prevent agglomeration during filtering and drying (73).

Hypalon, a commercially available vulcanizable chlorosulfonated polyethylene, contains 26–29% chlorine and 1.3–1.7% sulfur, according to publications (74,75). A higher sulfur content would result in overcure. The chlorine, other than that in sulfonyl chloride groups, is presumably desired for the self extinguishing effect and resistance to certain solvents, but primarily to eliminate crystallinity which would stiffen the rubber. A higher chlorine content would also stiffen the rubber and raise the brittle point which is below −50°C. with the preferred composition. It is true that both chloro and sulfonyl chloride groups may be involved in vulcanization depending on the choice of vulcanizing agent.

A chemical analysis of chlorosulfonated polyethylene was attempted with progressively more drastic amine treatment and by dehalogenation with potassium iodide and with zinc. So many possibilities exist that the interpretation is complicated. The chlorosulfonated polyethylene was made from high pressure polyethylene by use of chlorine in carbon tetrachloride solution with a free radical catalyst and contained 31% chlorine and 1.2% sulfur. The results indicated that 2.7% of the total chlorine was primary, 89.8% secondary, 3.5% tertiary, and 4% sulfonyl chloride (76).

Chlorine in the β-position relative to sulfonyl chloride groups (estimated 0.5% of total chlorine) underwent dehydrohalogenation upon amine treatment as shown by the development of an infrared absorption band at 225 mμ. About 3% of the total chlorine could be removed with potassium iodide and 17.7% with zinc dust in dioxane, but these are not very clear-cut reactions. The amination test is only slightly more definite and is complicated by such effects as allylic structures produced during amination and the effect of amination upon reactivity of neighboring chlorine.

Vulcanization with metallic oxides, such as litharge or zinc oxide, depends upon the presence of acid, in this case sulfonyl groups. Water accelerates the cure, presumably by promoting hydrolysis of the sulfonyl chloride groups (77). Screening tests of the reactivity of chlorosulfonated polyethylene with a variety of reagents are summarized by Busse and Billmeyer

(78). The commercial product containing 27.5% chlorine and 1.5% sulfur was used in 15% solution in tetralin. Most polyfunctional amines caused rapid gelation at room temperature but melamine and hexamethylenetetramine were sluggish, presumably because they are not soluble in tetralin. The prior reaction with a monofunctional amine eliminates the possibility of subsequently forming a permanent crosslink with a diamine (proof that sulfonyl chloride group is involved). Reaction with urea is slow; subsequent heating evolves gas. Sodium sulfide reacts to form a gel on prolonged heating at 100°C. Again, these reagents are not soluble in tetralin. The reagents of Table III-9 all caused gelation eventually but showed differences in rate.

TABLE III-9
Screening Tests for Reaction at 100°C. for 5 Hr. with Chlorosulfonated Polyethylene in Tetralin[a]

Reagent	Result
Zinc diethyldithiocarbamate	Medium strength gel
Zinc dibutyldithiocarbamate	Little change in viscosity
Lead dimethyldithiocarbamate	Very strong gel
Tetramethylthiuram monosulfide	Moderate increase in viscosity
Tetramethylthiuram disulfide	Little change in viscosity
2-Mercaptoimidazoline	Medium strength gel
2-Mercaptobenzothiazole 2-Benzothiazyl disulfide 2-Mercaptothiazoline	Little change in viscosity

[a] Taken from ref. 78.

When chlorosulfonated polyethylene is heated as a solid or in solution to temperatures near 150°C. without stabilizers (or to lower temperatures when catalysts are present), sulfur dioxide and a small amount of hydrogen chloride are given off. Infrared studies showed that all of the sulfonyl chloride groups had been removed from chlorosulfonated polyethylene in tetralin solution by heating for 2 hr. at 175°C. At 175°C. some reagents still cause crosslinking of the preheated polymer, e.g., ethylenediamine, 2-mercaptoimidazoline, and iron carbonyl. It was proposed that these react with active chlorine atoms on the chain. Some reagents react more readily with the preheated polymer, namely sulfur monochloride or sulfuric acid. It was proposed that these react with unsaturation produced by preheating.

After treatment with a monofunctional amine under mild conditions the polymer can still be crosslinked by dithiocarbamates, thiourea, or sodium polysulfide, but the reaction with sulfur monochloride is inhibited. Perhaps the first three react as nucleophiles with active chlorine atoms on the chain and the latter by a homolytic reaction inhibited by excess amine. Pretreatment with pyridine promoted the activity of thiourea, sodium polysulfide, and also metal oxides.

Chlorinated polyethylene can be vulcanized with sulfur and diphenylguanidine or thiuram disulfide (79).

Polypropylene has been chlorosulfonated to the extent of 6% chlorine and 1.4% sulfur without embrittlement. Treatment with litharge and a disulfide gave a vulcanizate with 500% ultimate elongation and 1400 psi tensile strength whereas tensile strengths of 5000 psi can be obtained with chlorosulfonated polyethylene. The polypropylene was of molecular weight 40,000 and, although partially crystalline, was soluble in carbon tetrachloride at 55°C.; the reaction was carried out at this temperature (67). The presence of the sulfur dioxide is said to result in less degradation for a given degree of chlorination. This effect could be produced if the equilibrium lies on the right and only the carbon radical undergoes scission.

$$R\cdot + SO_2 \rightleftharpoons RSO_2\cdot \qquad (13)$$

From a polypropylene of lower molecular weight (13,500) a product was obtained with 4.6% chlorine and 1.3% sulfur which upon vulcanization was nearly as strong (1240 psi tensile, 500% ultimate elongation). Pyridine was used as the catalyst, and the reaction was carried out with light with the use of sulfuryl chloride in carbon tetrachloride at 53°C. In another experiment the same polypropylene was chlorosulfonated further (10.2% chlorine, 2.7% sulfur) and the vulcanizate was stronger (1700 psi tensile strength, 450% ultimate elongation). If the chlorine content is taken to 30% the product is hard and softens above 100°C.

Ethylene–propylene elastomers have been chlorosulfonated to permit vulcanization (80).

5. Other Chain Reactions Involving Halogen

a. Chlorocarbonylation

Other chain reactions involving halogen as the carrier are known. Kharasch, Kane, and Brown (81,82) showed that oxalyl chloride and phosgene could be used to introduce the chloroformyl group into cyclohexane and, much more slowly, into acyclic hydrocarbons. They demonstrated that the reaction is a chain reaction which is retarded by toluene.

$$RH + Cl\cdot \rightarrow R\cdot + HCl \qquad (14)$$

$$\mathrm{R\cdot + Cl\overset{O}{\overset{\|}{C}}\overset{O}{\overset{\|}{C}}Cl \rightarrow RCOCl + \cdot COCl \rightarrow CO + Cl\cdot} \qquad (15)$$

Apparently, the benzyl radical is nearly incapable of this unusual radical displacement reaction. It was attempted to conduct the reaction with polyethylene; however, the product contained chlorine but no oxygen (72). Evidently, the acyclic radical tends to abstract chlorine rather than causing displacement.

b. Phosphorylation

Phosphorus trichloride and oxygen react at room temperature with hydrocarbons to introduce the phosphonyl chloride group (83). The reaction is a free radical chain reaction, although the fact that it is promoted by free radical catalysts is somewhat obscured by the competitive autoxidation reaction (84).

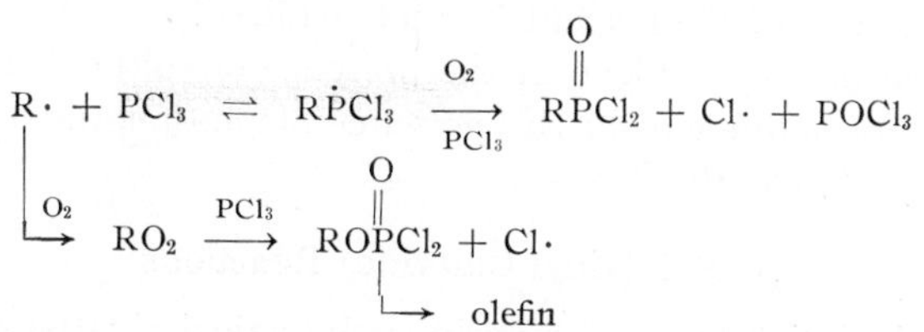

(16)

The application of this reaction to high molecular weight polyethylene required a temperature of 55°C. or higher to obtain solubility in the phosphorus trichloride. The rate was dependent on oxygen supply and not very sensitive to temperature in the 50–70°C. range. Peroxides were somewhat catalytic but introduced side reactions; a number of powerful inhibitors were found: iodine, tetramethylthiuram disulfide, sulfur, copper resinate, octyl mercaptan, and phosphorus pentachloride. The reaction was promoted by the addition of olefins or the presence of unsaturation in the polymer. The polymers with higher degree of chlorophosphonation, e.g., 7% phosphorus, were no longer soluble in hot hydrocarbons but were soluble in hot quinoline. The hydrolyzed derivative could be cured with litharge. The chlorophosphonated polymers could be esterified. The diethyl ester having a phosphorus content of 5.9% was of low crystallinity. It was tranasprent and tough (1700 psi tensile strength and 400% extensibility). At 11.5% phosphorus the diethyl ester was soft, tacky, and partly soluble in ethanol (85). A phosphorylated polyethylene was hydrolyzed to a polymer almost completely soluble in water and containing 15.5% phosphorus (86).

With several other polymers, namely, polystyrene, poly(methyl methacrylate), and polyisobutylene, the reaction produced degradation without much substitution. In the case of ethylene–propylene copolymer, the reaction has been used as a method of imparting vulcanizability with lead oxide (87). Litharge was used as the reinforcing filler as well as curing agent. Rubbery properties were optimum with about 1% combined phosphorus. The reaction was carried out in phosphorus trichloride solution or with an unspecified inert diluent.

The analogous reaction with phenyldichlorophosphine has been applied to polyethylene and polypropylene (88). Schroeder and Sopchak (85) found the reactions of polyethylene with phenyldichlorophosphine and with diphenylchlorophosphine in the presence of oxygen to be slower than chlorophosphonation with phosphorous trichloride and oxygen. The reaction with phenyldichlorophosphine was promoted by light. The reaction with diphenylchlorophosphine was carried out in benzene to obtain solubility and most of the reagent became oxidized.

Chlorination of polyethylene in the presence of sulfur dichloride introduced a trace of sulfur and in the presence of phosphorus oxychloride, a trace of phosphorous (89).

6. Poly(vinyl Chloride) Reactions

The technological success of preparing polymeric derivatives from chloromethylated aromatic polymers has not been duplicated with poly(vinyl chloride) and chlorinated aliphatic polymers. Reactions are incomplete and complicated but do go to some extent. Thus, ethanedithiol was reported to react appreciably with chlorinated polyethylene (89). It was stated that chlorinated polyethylene, like poly(vinyl chloride), can be caused to react with thiosorbitol (90). Aniline could be caused to alkylate but piperidine gave dehydrohalogenation (91). Hexamethylenediamine gave a crosslinked yellow product with a neutral equivalent of 410 (92). Benzidine seems to react with the chlorines of chlorosulfonated polyethylene, in addition to reacting with sulfonyl groups (90).

It is not easy to predict whether poly(vinyl chloride) should be more readily substituted than chlorinated polyethylene (because of the greater possibility of allylic chloride) or merely more readily dehydrohalogenated. In any case it may be of interest to note that weak base anion exchange membranes have been made from poly(vinyl chloride) at the National Chemical Laboratory, Teddington, England (Table III-10) (93). The reaction rate was higher with a more concentrated ethylenediamine but the membrane could not then be preserved intact. In attempting to make a

TABLE III-10
Membranes Made by Reaction of Poly(vinyl Chloride) Film with Ethylenediamine (75% in Water) at 100°C.[a]

Reaction time, hr.	Resistance in 0.1N H_2SO_4, ohm/cm.^{2}	Nitrogen content, %
1	2300	1.15
2	535	2.06
3	73	3.05
4	38	3.85
5	31	3.95

[a] Taken from ref. 93.

strong base resin by reaction of poly(vinyl chloride) with hexamethylenediamine and subsequent methylation it was observed that the strong base capacity was rapidly lost at high pH.

7. Oxidation of Polyolefins

The oxidation of polyethylene in the dark at 120°C. was studied by Grafmüller and Huseman (94), both in solution and as a powder. Oxidation in solution was accompanied by scission; both the viscosity and osmotic molecular weight decreased. In xylene the intrinsic viscosity (measured at 120°C. in decalin) decreased from 2.4 to 0.6 dl./g. while an 0.96% oxygen content was developed, and in *o*-dichlorobenzene the viscosity dropped to 0.3 while 1.87% oxygen content was developed (161 hr.). With powdered polymer, oxidation was faster (5.10% oxygen content in 100 hr.), and after this conversion gel formation began. Some volatile by-products were formed. The oxygen content was found to be 10% hydroxyl and 20% carbonyl, and the crosslinks were proved to be ester links. The crosslinked polymer could be solubilized by hydrolysis or reduction with lithium aluminum hydride. The C=O and COC absorption bands disappeared with reduction, and the reduced polymer contained 1% hydroxyl as determined by chlorine analysis after reaction with chlorophenylisocyanate. Evidently the few ester links that were present in the polymer which was oxidized in solution were of an intramolecular nature, for there was little change in viscosity on reducing this polymer. When powder was pretreated with sodium methoxide there was no crosslinking on oxidation but only scission. The presence of acids, organic or inorganic, promoted crosslinking. In oxidation in *o*-dichlorobenzene the presence of acetic anhydride promoted scission; the presence of benzoyl peroxide did like-

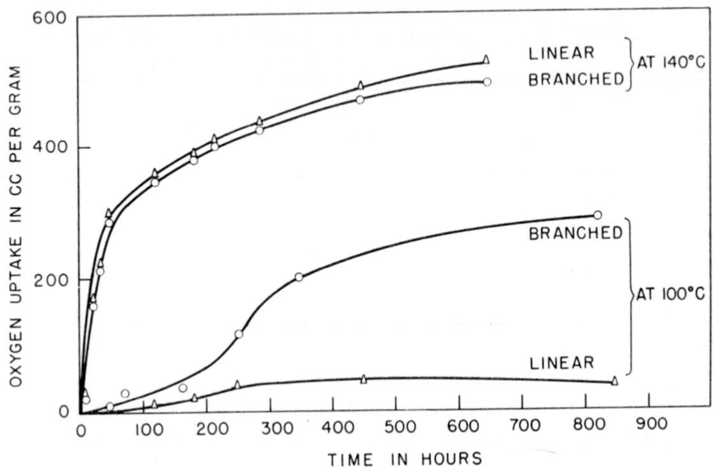

Fig. III-5. Oxygen uptake with linear and branched polyethylene. (Taken from ref. 96.)

wise, but azobisisobutyronitrile had no effect on viscosity. In *p*-xylene, benzoyl peroxide had no effect on viscosity. Evidently benzoate radicals attack *p*-xylene and in the absence of *p*-xylene attacked polymer so fast at 120°C. that the oxygen supply was inadequate to control crosslinking.

Polypropylene as 13 mil sheet consumed oxygen at 130°C. at the rate of 0.05 mmoles/base mole/min. with the formation of carbonyl groups. In view of the susceptibility of polypropylene to breakdown one would expect severe breakdown (95).

The oxidation of polyethylene proceeds faster with polymer of lower crystallinity (96) and the crystallinity is not lost by oxidation at 100°C. (97). The difference is not due to greater reactivity at the branch point. Thus in Figure III-5 the difference in rate vanishes above the melting point. Except for a shorter induction period isotactic polypropylene does not oxidize at 100°C. much faster or to a greater degree than branched polyethylene, which it resembled in content of amorphous polymer. Atactic polypropylene takes up twice as much oxygen as isotactic polypropylene before the rate levels off at 100°C. Poly-4-methyl-1-pentene and poly-3-methyl-1-butene take up more oxygen than can be explained unless the crystalline regions are accessible to oxygen in these polymers (97). As much as 400 cc. oxygen/g. is eventually absorbed at 100°C. The material balance of polymeric versus nonpolymeric products was not reported. A comparison of oxidation and chlorination of polyethylene at 80°C. was made (98), and it was pointed out that chlorination is more dependent on surface condition, perhaps because oxidation alters the surface by crosslinking whereas chlorination proceeds along paths opened up during substitution. Initially the rate of permeation of chlorine in polyethylene is fast relative to reaction at 60–80°C. As substitution increases, the rate of diffusion falls due to filling of free volume despite reduced crystallinity. The reaction does not stop, like oxidation, with consumption of amorphous areas but continues to completion. Oxidation of polyethylene at elevated temperatures (120°C.) becomes diffusion-controlled at a thickness between 10 mil and 1/4 in.

8. Reaction of Polyethylene with Sulfur

The reaction of sulfur with polyethylene occurs in the temperature range 200–250°C. As shown in Figure III-6, the combination of sulfur with the polymer (curve *3*) is accompanied by the evolution of hydrogen sulfide (curve *1*) and formation of unsaturation (curve *5*) and by crosslinking (curves *2* and *4*). Crosslinking occurs before much sulfur has been combined. This is not unexpected, in view of the fact that polyethylene and ethylene–propylene copolymers can be vulcanized by heating with peroxide and sulfur. The ratio of combined sulfur to sulfur charged to the reaction mixture is 31–37%, and there is only a slight drop in combined sulfur on continued heating after all of the free sulfur is consumed. The rates of combination of sulfur and evolution of hydrogen sulfide are shown in Figures III-7 and III-8, respectively, as a function of temperature and amount of

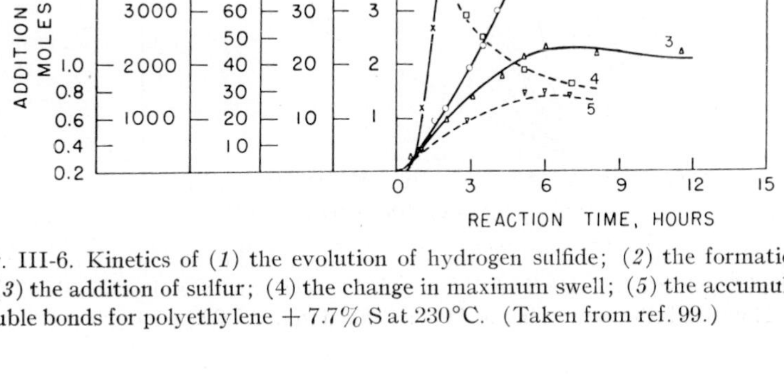

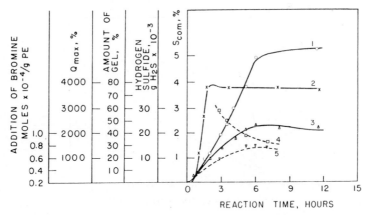

Fig. III-6. Kinetics of (*1*) the evolution of hydrogen sulfide; (*2*) the formation of gel; (*3*) the addition of sulfur; (4) the change in maximum swell; (*5*) the accumulation of double bonds for polyethylene + 7.7% S at 230°C. (Taken from ref. 99.)

sulfur charged to the reaction mixture. The final amount of combined sulfur does not seem to depend on temperature in the range of 230–320°C. but the rate is actually slower at 320°C. (99).

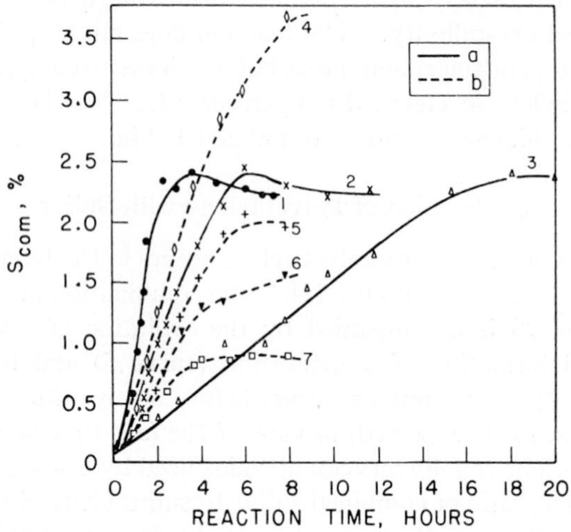

Fig. III-7. Kinetics of the addition of sulfur as a function of (*a*) reaction temperature and of (*b*) the total sulfur content (based on polymer) of the mixture: (*1*) 7.7% S, 240°C.; (*2*) 7.7% S, 230°C.; (*3*) 7.7% S, 320°C.; (*4*) 10.0% S, 230°C.; (*5*) 6.58% S, 230°C.; (*6*) 3.98% S, 230°C.; (*7*) 2.35% S, 230°C. (Taken from ref. 99.)

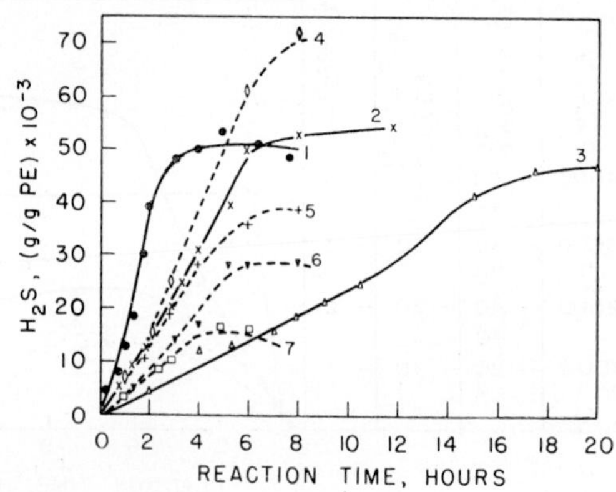

Fig. III-8. Kinetics of the evolution of hydrogen sulfide during the interaction of sulfur with polyethylene as a function of reaction temperature and of initial sulfur content. Notation is the same as in Fig. III-7. (Taken from ref. 99.)

B. SIDE CHAIN SUBSTITUTION OF POLYVINYLAROMATICS

Metz and Mesrobian (100) advanced the hypothesis of steric inhibition of resonance to explain the low rate of autoxidation of polystyrene compared to propylated polystyrene. Thus, it is assumed that in polystyrene the tertiary position is not activated because the phenyl group is sluggish in assuming the coplanar position required to stabilize the radical. Whether this is true or whether the tertiary hydrogen is merely inaccessible, the same effect applies to halogenation. The fact that the spin signal of irradiated polystyrene is a three-line rather than a five-line signal suggests that the substituted benzyl radical is not simultaneously coplanar with both β-carbons.

1. Oxidation

Polystyrene itself was not easily converted to a peroxide by autoxidation except after alkylation with propylene (100). The alkylation was carried out in nitrobenzene with aluminum chloride and isopropyl chloride at 40–45°C. for 5.5 hr. Based on evolved hydrogen chloride, the alkylation could be carried quite far with excess isopropyl chloride, but a product with 34% alkylation was used for autoxidation in cumene at 80°C. with benzoyl peroxide. After 8.5 hr. a peroxide value of 2.37 hydroperoxide groups per 100 monomer units was found in precipitated polymer. Autoxidation could not be carried out in chlorobenzene. A commercial alkylated polystyrene containing nonyl groups was much less reactive than the propylated polystyrene. The intrinsic viscosity in benzene dropped from 0.58 to 0.55 on alkylation and to 0.48 on oxidation. The polymeric peroxide was used for graft polymerization.

A similar procedure was employed with the polymer of *p*-isopropylstyrene (101).

2. Halogenation

The chlorination of polystyrene in the side chain does not seem to be a very useful way to prepare a soluble derivative. It is accompanied by nuclear chlorination and dehydrochlorination as tertiary chlorine is poorly replaceable, except with solvolysis which is difficult because of the incompatibility of polystyrene with hydroxylic solvents. The chlorination of polyvinyltoluene is more useful, because chlorination can be directed to the methyl group to a sufficient degree to give a water-soluble polymer on amination with trimethylamine. Based on the selectivities determined (102) for the chlorination of cumene and toluene with *tert*-butyl hypochlorite, which has a selectivity similar to that of chlorine, one can calculate that the chlorination of isopropyltoluene to a monochloro derivative should go 68.5% on the methyl, 24.7% on the α-position of the isopropyl group, and 6.8% on the β-position. In the case of polyvinyltoluene the α-position of the polymer chain, as pointed out by Mesrobian, does not have the full resonance stabilization of cumene and the β-position is more reactive because it is secondary. Dichlorination would be appreciable at the average chlorine content corresponding to monochlorination and the favored structure would have the chlorines remote from each other. Nuclear chlorination can be considerably suppressed by complexing metal ions, for example with phosphoric acid, to prevent catalysis; but with trialkyl benzenes metal catalysis is probably not required for nuclear chlorination or at least not for bromination of mesitylene (103,104).

It is possible to crosslink polystyrene by side chain chlorination and subsequent treatment with a Friedel-Crafts catalyst (105,106) or by merely chlorinating the solid polymer to give mixed nuclear and side chain substitution (107).

Bromination of polystyrene with *N*-bromosuccinimide and benzoyl peroxide at room temperature in carbon tetrachloride was carried to 61% conversion in 4 hr. with considerable degradation. Dehydrobromination with sodium butoxide was accompanied by an increase in solution viscosity. Some bromine remained, and subsequent grafting with vinyl acetate may have involved chain transfer with this residual bromine if it was not all aromatic. The graft was soluble when prepared under some conditions and could be saponified (108).

C. NUCLEAR SUBSTITUTION OF POLYVINYLAROMATICS

1. Chloromethylation

The preparation of ion exchange resins from styrene–divinylbenzene copolymers by sulfonation and by chloromethylation and amination has been reviewed by the author and others (109). Because chloromethyl ether is a good solvent for vinyl aromatic polymers and rapidly swells crosslinked copolymers of vinyl aromatics it has been used generally for chloromethylation. The reaction produces methanol which tends to deactivate the Friedel-Crafts catalyst and the reaction slows down with increasing conversion. Chloromethylation is accompanied by crosslinking, and the preparation of a soluble chloromethylated polystyrene (110) is favored by the use of a high ratio of chloromethyl ether to polystyrene, a low molecular weight polystyrene and (apparently from Figure III-9) a

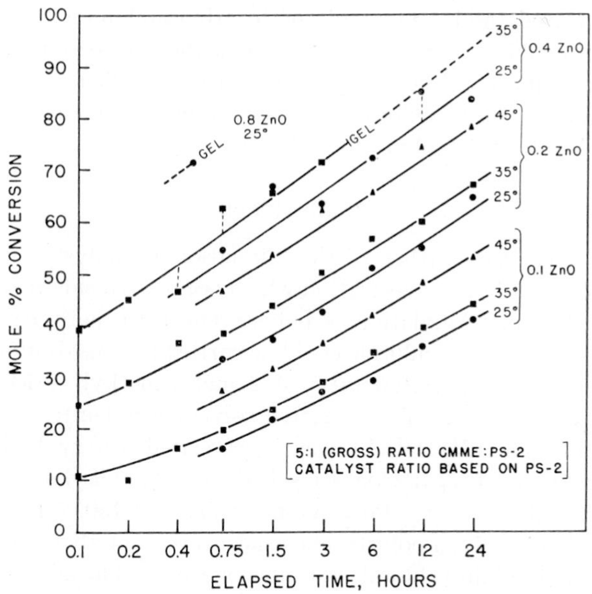

Fig. III-9. Effect of mole ratio of zinc oxide to aromatic rings in the chloromethylation of low molecular weight polystyrene (M_w = 26,000). (Taken from ref. 111.)

low catalyst concentration. Some catalysts such as aluminum chloride are more prone to cause crosslinking than zinc chloride (or zinc oxide which is converted to zinc chloride). The reactions of chloromethylation and alkylation are consecutive and competitive.

$$CH_3OCH_2Cl + RC_6H_5 \rightarrow RC_6H_4CH_2Cl + CH_3OH \quad (17)$$

$$RC_6H_4CH_2Cl + RC_6H_5 \rightarrow (RC_6H_4)_2CH_2 + HCl \quad (18)$$

The chloromethylation of styrene–divinylbenzene copolymer can also be conducted with formaldehyde and methanol with aluminum chloride as the catalyst and ethylene dichloride as a swelling agent (112). Chloromethylation with formaldehyde and hydrogen chloride involves the synthesis of dichloromethyl ether *in situ*.

Vinylnaphthalene–divinylbenzene copolymer was chloromethylated once on the average per naphthalene ring. With very high content of divinylbenzene the styrene–divinylbenzene copolymer was incompletely chloromethylated with respect to all the benzene rings present (113).

Grafts of styrene on other polymers have been used for substitution reactions. For example, a graft of 28% styrene on poly(vinyl chloride) was chloromethylated and aminated with trimethylamine. The chloromethylation could be carried out on film without destroying the film by diluting the chloromethyl ether with petroleum ether. The anion exchange membrane had a chloride transport number of 0.85–0.90 and resistance in 0.1N salt of 3–5 ohm/cm.$^{-2}$ (114).

2. Alkylation

Mention was made earlier of the alkylation of polystyrene with isopropyl chloride and of the alkylation which occurs as a side reaction during chloromethylation. Alkylation of polystyrene with methyl undecylenate at 85°C. with aluminum chloride could be carried to a maximum conversion of 50%, even with an initial ratio of 2 moles methyl undecylenate per mole polystyrene (115). The preferred solvent was 1-nitropropane (116). The effect of molecular weight was investigated. Very high molecular weight polystyrene ($\bar{M}_v$ 3,200,000) gelled at 35% alkylation even when alkylated at high dilution. Polystyrene of $\bar{M}_v$ = 1,150,000 gelled at 45% alkylation. Normally, a polystyrene concentration of about 10% was used and a mole of aluminum chloride per mole of ester. The alkylated polymer was saponified in propanol more rapidly than in ethanol, and the polysoap precipitated more completely, but still as a viscous mass. Methyl oleate was reacted with polystyrene to the extent of 38% alkylation and the product saponified to a polysoap. Polystyrene was alkylated with undecylenyl acetate, and after saponification the polyalcohol converted to the acid sulfate. The degree of alkylation was estimated from carbonyl absorption in the infrared. The polysoaps did not dissolve in water to give clear solutions but after dissolving in methanol could be diluted with water to give clear solutions.

3. Amine Derivatives of Chloromethylated Polystyrene

At complete conversion, chloromethylated polystyrene is essentially equivalent to poly(vinylbenzyl chloride) which has been made from the monomer. Copolymers of vinylbenzyl chloride with styrene and vinyltoluene resemble partially chloromethylated polystyrene. By amination of such copolymers with trimethylamine and driving the reaction to completion at 60°C., it has been found that 25 mole-% of quaternary ammonium groups is sufficient for water solubility (117). Previous work (110) had indicated a slightly higher value with chloromethylated polystyrene, but the amination was not quite complete. In the range of 15–25 mole-% conversion the quaternary polymers will not dissolve in water but dissolve in aqueous acetone or aqueous alcohol, and these solutions can be diluted with water without causing precipitation.

Crosslinked membranes have been made by the amination of films of chloromethylated polystyrene in mixtures of trimethylamine and diethylenetriamine (110). Oil-soluble nucleophilic amines give most satisfactory results in amination. It is sometimes desirable to dissolve the amine and chloromethylated polystyrene in dioxane and to add water progressively as amination proceeds in order to maintain a homogeneous reaction.

4. Sulfonium Derivative of Chloromethylated Styrene Polymers

The reactive chlorine of chloromethylated styrene polymers can be displaced by sulfides, which do not have too bulky alkyl groups, to prepare hydrophilic sulfonium derivatives. The reaction is not as rapid as quaternization with tertiary amines and the products are not as stable; therefore the reaction may reach a steady state short of complete conversion. The reaction is reversible, but the sulfonium group is subject to reactions other than displacement by chloride ion. The preparation of sulfonium derivatives has been studied both with chloromethylated styrene–divinylbenzene copolymers (118,119) and with soluble chloromethylated polystyrene (120).

The stability of sulfonium ion exchange resins made from dimethyl sulfide and chloromethylated styrene–divinylbenzene copolymer was studied under a variety of conditions by Berger (119), as shown in Figure III-10. Strong base causes rapid hydrolysis to the substituted benzyl alcohol with some formation of the substituted benzyl methyl thioether. The sulfur content does not go to zero.

$$^{-}OH + RC_6H_4CH_2S^{+}(CH_3)_2 \longrightarrow \begin{cases} RC_6H_4CH_2OH + (CH_3)_2S \\ RC_6H_4CH_2SCH_3 + CH_3OH \end{cases} \qquad (19)$$

Likewise, the chloride form of the resin loses all ion exchange capacity on heating at 87°C. for 8 hr. but retains half of the sulfur content. In strong acid (4*N* sulfuric or hydrochloric) hydrolysis is apparently reversible.

The decomposition of a sulfonium ion is favored at low ionic strength (121).

It was recognized by Hatch (122) that the relative instability of benzylsulfonium compounds with respect to replacement of the sulfonium group by nucleophilic reagents provided advantage in the preparation of derivatives of chloromethylated vinylaromatic polymers. The formation of these derivatives by the reaction of sulfide with the chloromethylated polymer,

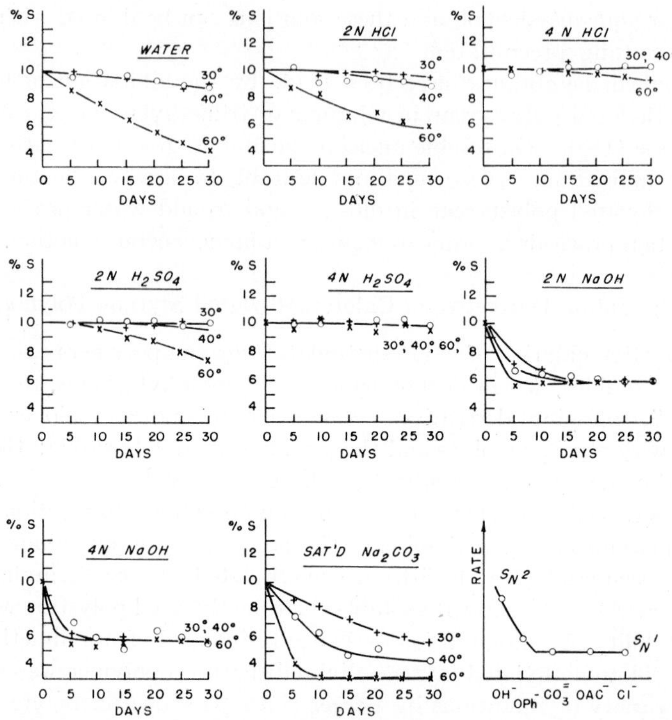

Fig. III-10. Stability of sulfonium ion exchange resins: (+) 30°C.; (O) 40°C.; (×) 60°C. (Taken from ref. 119.)

while not as rapid as amination and limited by reason of instability of the product to moderate temperatures, nevertheless proceeds to the extent of 60–80% conversion in a few hours at 50°C. with the more nucleophilic sulfides such as dimethyl sulfide, diethyl sulfide, or methyl 2-hydroxyethyl sulfide. The reaction is reversible but other decomposition reactions may occur also such as hydrolysis or displacement of the group R.

$$ArCH_2Cl + R_2S \rightleftharpoons ArCH_2\overset{+}{S}R_2 + Cl^- \qquad (20)$$

One application of the reaction is the use of the sulfonium derivative as an intermediate in the preparation of chelating ion exchange resins. For example, by reaction with disodium imino diacetate the sulfonium group is displaced by the amino group. The advantage over direct reaction of the amino acid salt with chloromethylated styrene–divinylbenzene copolymer is that the intermediate is hydrophilic and can be readily penetrated by the amino acid salt. The sulfonium compound in this process can be made with dimethyl sulfide which readily dissolves in the chloromethylated copolymer. The reaction can be carried out in two steps or in one with the dimethyl sulfide acting as a catalyst.

$$ArCH_2Cl + (CH_3)_2S \rightleftharpoons ArCH_2\overset{+}{S}(CH_3)_2\overset{-}{Cl} \xrightarrow{HN(CH_2CO_2Na)_2} (CH_3)_2S + ArCH_2N(CH_2CO_2Na)_2 \quad (21)$$

Similarly sodium mercaptosuccinate reacts as a mercaptide with the sulfonium resin to form the substituted benzyl thiosuccinate. Reaction of the sulfonium resin with sodium sulfite readily forms the sulfonate. Conversions are high but accompanied by some hydrolysis. There is an increase in rate when the nucleophile is an anion because of the attractive electrostatic effect.

$$ArCH_2\overset{+}{S}R_2 + {}^{-}S\underset{\displaystyle CH_2CO_2^-}{\underset{|}{C}}HCO_2^- \rightarrow ArCH_2S\underset{\displaystyle CH_2CO_2^-}{\underset{|}{C}}HCO_2^- + R_2S \quad (22)$$

It is important to remove all of the dimethyl sulfide in order to prepare a nonodorous product; this can be accomplished moderately well with a final treatment with a stronger nucleophile, such as ammonia (122).

Water-soluble or water-dispersible sulfonium polymers have been used to produce coatings which become water-insoluble on drying and especially when heated. In this case it is preferred to use a derivative of a high boiling sulfide, such as thiodiglycol, in order to minimize odor (123).

Sulfonium polymers of a similar nature have been used to improve the dimensional stability of wool felt (124).

5. Thiol Derivative

A crosslinked polythiol was prepared by the reaction of potassium xanthogenate with chloromethylated styrene–divinylbenzene copolymers. Polymercaptostyrene had been prepared earlier by polymerization of vinylphenylthiol acetate (125,126).

6. Acylation

The acylation of polystyrene involves the exposure of the polymer to stoichiometric amounts of catalyst, and consequently more side reactions. Acetylation has been carried out (127,128) with acetyl chloride in carbon disulfide under reflux or in carbon tetrachloride. The conversion was high but the effect on molecular weight was not reported. Many subsequent reactions were carried out, including the preparation of the oxime, the condensation with benzaldehyde and side chain bromination. The condensation with benzaldehyde was carried out in excess benzaldehyde with sulfuric acid as the catalyst. The products were sensitive to strong acid on drying but remained soluble if neutralized. Attempts to carry out the condensation with basic catalyst gave a crosslinked product. The soluble products could be photo-insolubilized with ultraviolet light. Absorption is strong at 3080 A., yet the polymer does not absorb in the visible, at least when first prepared. Partial isomerization of *trans* to *cis* structure accompanied the crosslinking (129).

7. Sulfonation

The sulfonation of polyvinylaromatics is usually accompanied by crosslinking. Evidence that this crosslinking is due to sulfone formation is provided by comparison of sulfur analyses with sulfonic acid content. A detectable excess of the former over the latter is seen only in cases in which sulfone formation was encouraged by the use of chlorosulfonic acid and a Friedel-Crafts catalyst. The same reaction is assumed responsible for the lower degree of crosslinking usually observed as microgel or if still lower as an abnormal dependence of viscosity upon polymer concentration and sensitivity of viscosity to salt concentration. Ordinarily the crosslink is not hydrolyzable, although the susceptibility of microgel in concentrated solution to alteration by agitation may create the illusion of hydrolytic instability. In some cases there evidently is formed a sulfonic anhydride crosslink which is hydrolyzable. Roth (130,131) detected this effect when sulfonating with sulfur trioxide which was not entirely monomeric.

Sulfone formation presumably is a reaction of the protonated arylsulfonic acid (eq. 23). The effect of Lewis base solvents in reducing sulfone forma-

$$\begin{array}{c} ArSO_3H + H_2SO_4 \rightleftharpoons ArSO_2\overset{+}{O}H_2 + HSO_4^- \\ \downarrow ArH \\ ArSO_2Ar + H_2O \end{array} \quad (23)$$

tion would not be explicable in terms of competition with polystyrene for an intermediate if the mechanism of sulfone formation were the same as the mechanism of sulfonation. It seems likely, therefore, that sulfone formation, but not sulfonation, involves as a rate-determining step the formation of a very reactive intermediate which is swept up by the Lewis base. Such a condition would be met if sulfone formation involves a sulfonyl cation, and

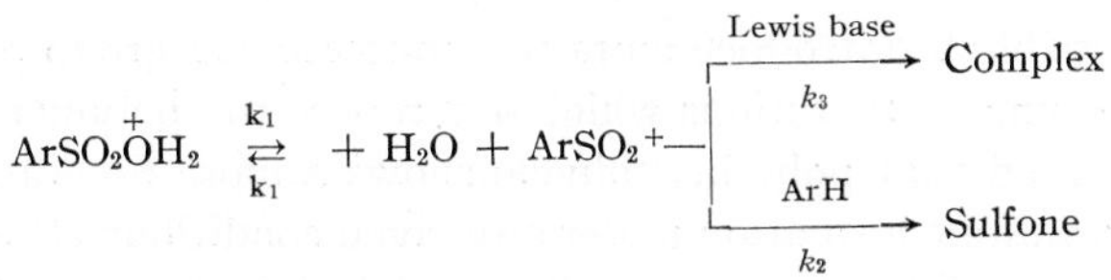

$$k_3 > k_2 \gg k_1 \qquad (24)$$

sulfonation involves no such cation (eq. 24). An example of this performance of a Lewis base is given by the report that carboxylic acids are antisulfone agents (132). Tertiary phosphoramides are reported to be especially effective in preventing sulfone formation (133). Sulfonation is accompanied by precipitation even in this type of solvent; thus the effect cannot be ascribed to homogeneous kinetics.

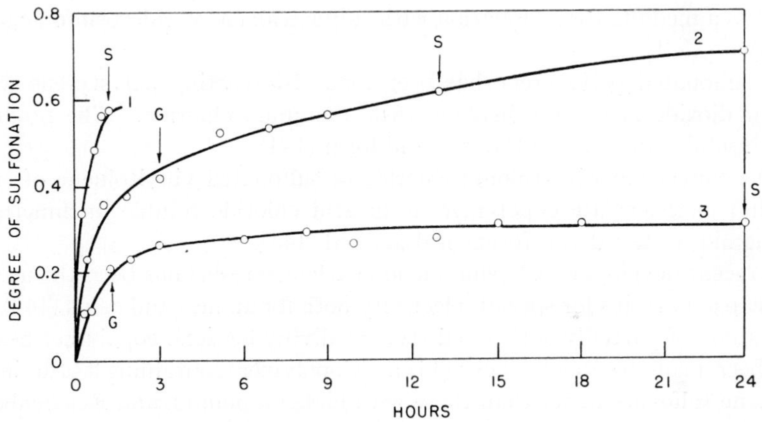

Fig. III-11. Progress of sulfonation as a function of temperature and ratio of polystyrene to sulfur trioxide: (*1*) $C_8H_8:SO_3$ = 1.0, 50°C.; (*2*) $C_8H_8:SO_3$ = 1.0, 20°C.; (*3*) $C_8H_8:SO_3$ = 0.375, 20°C. G denotes time of gelation, S denotes onset of syneresis. (Taken from ref. 134.)

Partial sulfonation in the presence of ethers gives a water-soluble product above 50% conversion and a product soluble in aqueous organic solvents above 25% sulfonation (134,135) (cf. Fig. III-11). The dioxane–sulfur trioxide complex is used in a chlorinated hydrocarbon and the partially sulfonated polymer gels or precipitates at a fairly low conversion (136,137). A similar precipitation occurred with bis(2-chloroethyl) ether as the sole solvent and sulfur trioxide as the sulfonating agent (138). Ketones, too, have been used to complxe the sulfur trioxide for sulfonation of polystyrene in halogenated solvents (139).

It is not possible to introduce more than one sulfonic group per benzene ring without going to conditions which decompose the polymer (140). It has been observed that polyvinyltoluene shows a more favorable ratio of sulfonation to sulfone formation under any given conditions (130,131).

Sulfonation of solid polymer in a fluidized bed with sulfur trioxide or chlorosulfonic acid gives a crosslinked sulfonate with high thickening power (141).

Sulfonation in halogenated solvents with sulfur trioxide is initially homogeneous in the oil phase but, inasmuch as the sulfonated polymer precipitates at an early stage and carries with it sulfur trioxide and sulfuric acid, the reaction is completed with a swollen solid slurried in the organic solvent (142).

Liquid sulfur dioxide is a swelling agent for polystyrene and has been used as a medium for sulfonation with sulfur trioxide or chlorosulfonic acid (143).

A sulfonated polystyrene has been made by reacting polystyrene with sulfur dioxide in carbon disulfide with aluminum chloride. The product was insoluble in water in the free acid form (144).

The conversion with thionyl chloride of sulfonated vinyltoluene of or a methyl methacrylate copolymer to an acid chloride soluble in dimethylformamide or tetrahydrofurane is described (145).

A recent development in sulfonic ion exchange resins has been the use of low capacity resins for special selectivity both for amines and acids (146).

A study of partially sulfonated styrene–divinylbenzene copolymer beads has been made by Reichenberg (147). Copolymers containing less divinylbenzene sulfonate faster than those with higher amounts, and Reichenberg found that the difference lies in chemical rate, not diffusion. By sulfonation in the presence of nitrobenzene he could make partially sulfonated polymers with a random distribution of sulfonic groups. Partially sulfonated polymer can be made also by desulfonation. For example, one quarter of the sulfonic groups can be removed by heating a fully sulfonated highly crosslinked resin for 24 hr. at 165°C. in 36% hydrochloric acid. The more highly crosslinked polymer desulfonates faster than the less highly crosslinked. Varying the degree of sulfonation, Reichenberg found that the selectivity of the resins for potassium versus sodium at half loading could be correlated with the water uptake per sulfonic group for a variety of degrees of crosslinking.

The low capacity resin prefers hydrogen possibly because of π-bonding with benzene rings but this effect was not duplicated at a high degree of sulfonation by increased crosslinking. Hydrogen is normally favored more at high loadings of other cations, apparently because it can lose water of hydration more readily and occupy a small space.

8. Nitration

Polystyrene was nitrated in 1845 by boiling with fuming nitric acid (148). A product containing up to 11% nitrogen (calculated for the mononitro derivative, 9.4%; for the dinitro derivative, 14.4%) is obtainable by this method (149). Zenftman (150,151) found that polystyrene could be converted to the dinitro derivative by using nitric acid–sulfuric acid mixtures capable of dissolving the polymer. The influence of time and

TABLE III-11
Influence of Temperature and Time on the Viscosity of Nitropolystyrene[a]

Nitration conditions[b]			
Temp., °C.	Time, hr.	N, %	η_{sp}/c[c]
			1.87
20	2	13.2	0.90
	4	13.4	0.76
	5	13.6	0.71
30	1	13.1	0.69
	3	13.7	0.59
	4	14.1	0.52
40	1	13.3	0.53
	2	13.8	0.50
	4	14.3	0.48
50	1	13.7	0.39
	2	14.2	0.36
	3	14.4	0.34

[a] Taken from ref. 150.
[b] In nitric–sulfuric mixture with 72.7% nitric acid.
[c] Measured in cyclohexanone.

temperature on reaction is shown in Table III-11. The mononitro derivative was found to be soluble in 90% nitric acid or ethylene dinitrate and swelled by cyclopentanone or nitrobenzene. At 11.7% nitrogen the derivative was soluble in the latter two solvents and gelatinized by cyclohexanone. At 12.4% nitrogen it was soluble in cyclohexanone. Even the dinitro derivative was merely swelled by acetone. It was soluble in dimethyl formamide. If the polystyrene used was of higher molecular weight the viscosity of the nitropolystyrene was slightly higher (e.g., η_{sp}/c = 1.07 from polystyrene of $\eta_{sp}/c = 4.80$) but degradation was severe. Further data on degradation during nitration are available (152).

Nitration is an example of a reaction in which the polymer dissolves with increasing substitution. The rate is dependent on the physical form. The amount of nitration mixture used is high (10–15 parts per part of polystyrene) in order to permit agitation.

It is interesting that nitrated isotactic polystyrene can be crystallized, even with higher than monosubstitution (153). References were cited showing that *ortho* substituents actually increase the crystallization rate. The polystyrene which was nitrated had a reduced specific viscosity of 2.4 as measured in α-chloronaphthalene at 135°C. The nitrate polymer (average of 1.6 nitro groups per benzene ring) had a reduced specific viscosity of 0.80 as measured in dimethyl sulfoxide at 25°C.

The nitration of poly-*p*-fluorostyrene and subsequent displacement of fluorine with *unsym*-diphenylhydrazine has been reported. The product was oxidized to a stable radical (154).

9. Amino Aromatic Polymers

One of the main reasons for interest in nitration of polystyrene is for the reactivity of the polyaminostyrene which can be prepared by reduction. Reduction of polymers is not usually done catalytically, but in this case it is possible (155). Bachman and co-workers (149) found ammoniacal sodium hydrosulfite to be the best reducing agent. After three days of heating the product was soluble in dilute acid. It was then diazotized and coupled with phenols and amines to give dyes which are very insoluble in all solvents. Kenyon, Minsk, and Waugh reduced a nitrated styrene-maleic anhydride copolymer to an amphoteric polymer and produced azo dyes therefrom (156).

Polyaminostyrene has been converted to a crosslinked isocyanate derivative (157,158). Upon heating with water the evolution of carbon dioxide is only half of the calculated amount but no free amino groups were found in the product; it is believed that urea crosslinks are formed initially, in addition to isocyanate groups, by the phosgene reaction and that the isocyanate groups are converted to urea groups by water treatment.

The nitration and reduction of vinylaromatic polymers offer several routes to electron exchange resins. One route involved diazotization of polyaminostyrene and coupling with hydroquinone (159) and with ferrocene, the latter reacting to low conversion. Another route involves the nitration of polyvinylphenol (160).

Styrene–divinylbenzene copolymer has been nitrated, reduced, diazotized, and treated with potassium xanthogenate and a crosslinked polymercaptostyrene obtained (161).

10. Phenolic Aromatic Polymers

Phenolic aromatic polymers could be made either by the Sandmeyer reaction or by the oxidation of metalated polymers but have usually been made from monomer. For greater hydrophilic properties these polymers have been sulfonated. There was an elevation of oxidation potential in the case of sulfonated polymeric hydroquinone (in the absence of salts) which indicated complexing of the ceric ion which was used to oxidize the resin (162).

Caustic fusion of sulfonated polymers is too drastic a reaction to be very successful for making phenolic polymers.

11. Metalation

Like the chloromethyl and amino derivatives of polystyrene, the metal derivatives have spawned a family of second generation derivatives by Grignard-like reactions. A variety of methods of metallation has been applied. Direct replacement of hydrogen has not been very successful, perhaps because the product is soluble at low conversion whereas in the direct metalation of benzene (with amyl sodium) the insolubility of the product favors the reaction. Morton and Taylor (163) made a potassium derivative by stirring a benzene solution of polystyrene with potassium metal and sodium oxide for 15 hr. at 80°C. The color became chocolate-brown, and after carbonation there was recovered in 36% yield a polymer soluble in aqueous alkali and having a neutral equivalent of 178. The carboxyl was judged to be in the side chain.

Braun (164,165) started with polyiodostyrene which he prepared by iodination of polystyrene in nitrobenzene with iodine and iodic acid. After 30 hr. at 90°C. the iodine content approached that of a monoiodo derivative. There was a drop in viscosity, but this is largely due to altered solubility because the polystyrene regenerated after metalation showed a much less marked decrease as can be seen from the data in Table III-12. Braun reported the following α-values for the polyhalostyrenes in toluene ($[\eta] = KP^{\alpha}$): polystyrene, 0.71 (in benzene); *p*-chloro, 0.575; *p*-bromo, 0.53; and *p*-iodo, 0.50. The iodopolystyrene was pale yellow, but a benzene solntion turned rose-colored after a few days with exposure to light.

TABLE III-12
Viscosity in Benzene (20°C.) of Iodinated and Regenerated Polystyrene[a]

[η] of initial polystyrene, dl,/g.	[η] of iodinated polystyrene, dl./g.	[η] of regenerated polystyrene, dl./g.
1.19	0.35	0.85
0.243	0.086	0.202
0.198	0.074	0.174
0.145	0.064	0.141
0.165	0.081	0.168

[a] Taken from ref. 164.

The reaction of butyllithium with the polyiodostyrene was carried out at room temperature by adding the latter to the former in order to avoid a crosslinking reaction. The iodo polymer and the lithio derivative had the *para* structure.

Polylithiostyrene was converted to a poly-*p*-mercaptostyrene of degree of substitution 0.67 by reaction in benzene solution with sulfur at room temperature in the absence of oxygen. It was soluble in 2*N* sodium hydroxide, and even after disulfide crosslinking with air, iodine, or hydrogen peroxide it could be solubilized in sodium hydroxide by equilibration with thioglycolic acid. Precipitation occurred on reduction of pH to 8.0 (161).

The polydisulfide was used as an electron exchange resin to oxidize hydrazobenzene in alcohol solution to azobenzene but many hours were required for the reaction.

Polylithiostyrene has been used to make an aromatic ketone and an aromatic tertiary alcohol and these converted to polymeric radicals by ketyl formation from the former and from the latter by reduction of the triaryl chloride with zinc (154).

The isomers of bromostyrene were polymerized and lithiated by the maintaining of butyllithium in relatively high concentration in tetrahydrofuran–hydrocarbon solutions at −35°C. in order to avoid crosslinking by the Wurtz-Fittig reaction. In the case of poly-*o*-bromostyrene this crosslinking reaction did not occur, and the reaction of the *ortho* lithiated polymer with trialkyltin chloride was less complicated (166).

Polystyrene has been mercurated. In the first work the reaction was carried out in boiling acetic acid to the degree of substitution 0.5–0.6 and with some oxidation. Mercuration in nitrobenzene with mercury diisobutyrate was carried to a degree of substitution 0.96 in 20 hr. at 100°C. The polymer was a pale yellow powder insoluble in cold nitrobenzene. A soluble polystyrene could be regenerated from it. The replacement reaction with bromine was carried out (167).

Poly-α-vinylthiophene was lithiated, mercurated, and thalliated. Mercuration was more rapid than with polystyrene and was conducted in a few minutes in hot benzene. Thalliation was conducted with thallium triisobutyrate and with equal rapidity. The monosubstituted polymers precipitated (168).

Polyvinylfurane was metalated in the α-position.

12. Halogenation

Nuclear halogenation of polyvinylaromatic proceeds readily in the dark without the intentional addition of Friedel-Crafts catalysts but, as observed earlier, the importance of traces of iron can be shown by the retarding effect of phosphoric acid. Polystyrene has been chlorinated in liquid chlorine solution at atmospheric pressure (169) and in a variety of solvents.

Usually some side chain halogenation occurs, and a tendency to crosslink has been observed despite the usual degradation caused by Friedel-Crafts catalysts (170). Evidently some free radical reaction may occur either because of incidental illumination or residual peroxide or oxygen.

Bachman (149) used the chlorination of polystyrene and subsequent depolymerization as a route to dichlorostyrene, chiefly the 3,4-isomer.

References

1. Myers, A. W., C. E. Rogers, V. Stannett, and M. Szwarc, *Mod. Plastics*, **34**, No. 9, 157 (1957); *Chem. Abstr.*, **51**, 18691a (1957).
2. Rogers, C. E., V. Stannett, and M. Szwarc, *J. Polymer Sci.*, **45**, 61 (1960).
3. Fontana, C. M., and G. A. Kidder, *J. Am. Chem. Soc.*, **70**, 3745 (1948).
4. Fontana, C. M., G. A. Kidder, and R. J. Herold, *Ind. Eng. Chem.*, **44**, 1688 (1952).
5. Fontana, C. M., R. J. Herold, E. J. Kinney, and R. C. Miller, *Ind. Eng. Chem.*, **44**, 2955 (1952).
6. Schmerling, L., and J. P. West, *J. Am. Chem. Soc.*, **74**, 3592 (1952).
7. Case, L. C., and J. D. Atlas, *J. Polymer Sci.*, **45**, 435 (1960).
8. Thomas, D. K., *Trans. Faraday Soc.*, **57**, 511 (1961); *Chem. Abstr.*, **55**, 22887d (1961).
9. Cooper, G. D., and A. R. Gilbert, *J. Polymer Sci.*, **38**, 275 (1959).
10. Alexander, P., and D. Toms, *J. Polymer Sci.*, **22**, 343 (1956).
11. Atchison, G. J., *J. Polymer Sci.*, **35**, 557 (1959).

12. Harlen, F., W. Simpson, F. B. Waddington, J. D. Waldron, and A. C. Baskett, *J. Polymer Sci.*, **18,** 589 (1955).
13. Buch, T., Ph.D. Thesis, Northwestern University, 1960; *Dissertation Abstr.*, **22,** 88 (1961).
14. Loy, B. R., *J. Polymer Sci.*, **A1,** 2251 (1963).
15. Florin, R. E., L. A. Wall, and D. W. Brown, paper presented at the 140th Meeting of American Chemical Society, Chicago, Ill., Sept. 3–8, 1961.
16. Roberts, J. D., and G. R. Coraor, *J. Am. Chem. Soc.*, **74,** 3586 (1952).
17. Russell, G. A., *J. Am. Chem. Soc.*, **80,** 4987 (1958).
18. Russell, G. A., *J. Am. Chem. Soc.*, **80,** 4997 (1958).
19. Russell, G. A., *J. Am. Chem. Soc.*, **80,** 5002 (1958).
20. Brown, H. C., and G. A. Russell, *J. Am. Chem. Soc.*, **74,** 3995 (1952).
21. Klug, H., U. S. Patent 2,959,562, Nov. 8, 1960 and German Patent 1,042,894, Nov. 6, 1958 (to Farbwerke Hoechst A. G.); *Chem. Abstr.*, **55,** 2193d (1961).
22. Evans, F. W., and M. Szwarc, *Trans. Faraday Soc.*, **57,** 1905 (1961); *Chem. Abstr.*, **57,** 107b (1962).
23. Fox, R. J., F. W. Evans, and M. Szwarc, *Trans. Faraday Soc.*, **57,** 1915 (1961); *Chem. Abstr.*, **57,** 107d (1962).
24. Louis, D., Thesis, Tech. University Aachen, 1957.
25. Anson, P. C., P. S. Fredericks, and J. M. Tedder, *J. Chem. Soc.*, **1959,** 918.
26. Fredericks, P. S., and J. M. Tedder, *J. Chem. Soc.*, **1960,** 144.
27. Tedder, J. M., in *Advances in Fluorine Chemistry,* M. Stacey, J. C. Tatlow, and A. G. Sharpe, eds., Vol. II, Butterworths, London, 1961, p. 104.
28. Hadley, E. H., and L. A. Bigelow, *J. Am. Chem. Soc.*, **62,** 3302 (1940).
29. Zimin, A. V., S. V. Churmanteev, and A. D. Verina, *Trudy Pervogo Vsesoyuz Soveshchaniya po Radiatsion Khim. Akad. Nauk SSSR Otdel. Khim. Nauk Moscow,* **1957,** 221–223; *Chem. Abstr.*, **53,** 12019d (1959).
30. Chambers, R. D., W. K. R. Musgrave, and J. Savory, *Proc. Chem. Soc.*, **1961,** 113.
31. Bockemüller, W., *Ann. Chem.*, **506,** 20 (1933); *Chem. Abstr.*, **28,** 1184 (1934).
32. Cady, G. H., A. V. Grosse, E. J. Barber, L. L. Burger, and Z. D. Sheldon, *Ind. Eng. Chem.*, **39,** 291 (1947).
33. Fowler, R. D., W. B. Burford III, J. M. Hamilton, Jr., R. G. Sweet, C. E. Weber, J. S. Kasper, and I. Litant, *Ind. Eng. Chem.*, **39,** 292 (1947).
34. Haszeldine, R. N., and A. G. Sharpe, *Fluorine and Its Compounds,* Methuen, London, and Wiley, New York, 1951.
35. Bornstein, J., *Chem. Ind. (London),* **1959,** 1193.
36. Roberts, H. L., *Quart. Rev. (London),* **15,** 30 (1961).
37. Hasek, W. R., W. C. Smith, and V. A. Engelhardt, *J. Am. Chem. Soc.*, **82,** 543 (1960).
38. Schmidt, H., and H. D. Schmidt, *J. Prakt. Chem.* [4], **2,** 250 (1955).
39. Kropa, E. L., U. S. Patent 2,497,046 (to American Cyanamid Co.), Feb. 7, 1950; *Chem. Abstr.*, **44,** 4721c (1950).
40. Joffre, S. P., U. S. Patent 2,811,468 (to Shulton Inc.), Oct. 29, 1957; *Chem. Abstr.*, **52,** 2453g (1958).
41. Pinsky, J., A. Adakonis, and A. R. Nielson, *Mod. Packaging,* **33** (6), 130 (1960); *Chem. Abstr.*, **54,** 11554g (1960).
42. Imperial Chemical Industries, Ltd., British Patent 710,523 (by A. J. Rudge), June 16, 1954; *Chem. Abstr.*, **49,** 2778c (1955).

43. Dynamit Nobel A. G., German Patent 1,086,891 (by I. Vogt and W. Krings), Aug. 11, 1960; *Chem. Abstr.*, **55,** 18186h (1961).
44. Myles, J. R., and P. J. Garner, U. S. Patent 2,422,919 (to Imperial Chemical Industries, Ltd.), June 24, 1947; *Chem. Abstr.*, **41,** 6274a (1947).
45. Baxter, W. N., U. S. Patent 2,849,431 (to E. I. du Pont de Nemours & Co.), Aug. 26, 1958; *Chem. Abstr.*, **52,** 21244e (1958).
46. Fawcett, E. W., U. S. Patent 2,183,556 (to Imperial Chemical Industries, Ltd.), Dec. 19, 1939; *Chem. Abstr.*, **34,** 2500^3 (1940).
47. Becker, W., and O. Bayer, U. S. Patent 2,748,105 (to Farbenfabriken Bayer A. G.), May 29, 1956; *Chem. Abstr.*, **50,** 11055f (1956).
48. Oakes, W. G., and R. B. Richards, *Trans. Faraday Soc.*, **42A,** 197 (1946); *Chem. Abstr.*, **43,** 6019g (1949).
49. Brooks, R. E., D. E. Strain, and A. McAlevy, *Rubber World,* **127,** 791 (1953).
50. Tinsley, J. S., U. S. Patent 2,926,159 (to Hercules Powder Co.), Feb. 23, 1960; *Chem. Abstr.*, **54,** 13735h (1960).
51. Taylor, R. S., U. S. Patent 2,592,763 (to E. I. du Pont de Nemours & Co.), Apr. 20, 1952; *Chem. Abstr.*, **46,** 11772f (1952).
52. Babayan, V. K., U. S. Patent 2,481,188 (to Pierce Laboratories, Inc.), Sept. 6, 1949; *Chem. Abstr.*, **44,** 2543h (1950).
53. Ludlow, J. L., Canadian Patent 471,037 (to E. I. du Pont de Nemours & Co.), Jan. 23, 1951.
54. E. I. du Pont de Nemours & Co., British Patent 623,705, May 20, 1949.
55. Noeske, H., U. S. Patent 2,890,213 (to Ruhrchemie A. G.), June 9, 1959; *Chem. Abstr.*, **53,** 15645e (1959).
56. Ruhrchemie A. G., German Application R14643, Nov. 8, 1956.
57. Ruhrchemie A. G., British Patent 799,952, Aug. 13, 1958; *Chem. Abstr.*, **53,** 2691d (1959).
58. Anderson, A. W., and S. C. Overbaugh, U. S. Patent 2,541,492 (to E. I. du Pont de Nemours & Co.), Feb. 13, 1951; *Chem. Abstr.*, **45,** 4091h (1951).
59. Montecatini S. p. A., Belgian Patent 540,361, Feb. 6, 1956; British Patent 811,-848, Apr. 15, 1959; *Chem. Abstr.*, **53,** 23100f (1959).
60. Kambara, S., and T. Ohshika, *Kogyo Kagaku Zasshi,* **62,** 1781 (1959); *Chem. Abstr.*, **57,** 13959i (1962).
61. Morrissey, R. T., and M. R. Frederick, Canadian Patent 538,730 (to B. F. Goodrich Co.), Mar. 26, 1957.
62. Cottle, D. L., L. S. Minckler, Jr., and T. Lemiszka, U. S. Patent 2,962,482 (to Esso Research and Engineering Co.), Nov. 29, 1960; *Chem. Abstr.*, **55,** 6008d (1961).
63. Baldwin, F. P., and S. B. Robison, U. S. Patent 2,955,103 (to Esso Research and Engineering Co.), Oct. 4, 1960.
64. Esso Research and Engineering Co., British Patent 835,639, May 25, 1960; *Chem. Abstr.*, **54,** 20278b (1960).
65. Dannis, M. L., and F. L. Ramp, U. S. Patent 2,996,489 (to B. F. Goodrich Co.), Aug. 15, 1961; *Chem. Abstr.*, **55,** 27983h (1961).
66. Seidel, F., W. Singer, H. Springer, and H. Heinrich, German Patent 1,110,873 (to VEB Farbenfabrik Wolfen), July 13, 1961; *Chem. Abstr.*, **55,** 26544e (1961).
67. Montecatini S.p.A., British Patent 811,848, Apr. 15, 1959; *Chem. Abstr.*, **53,** 23100f (1959).

68. Kenyon, J., H. Phillips, and F. M. H. Taylor, *J. Chem. Soc.*, **1931,** 382.
69. Ruhrchemie A. G., British Patent 815,234, June 24, 1959; *Chem. Abstr.*, **54,** 14790c (1960).
70. Ruhrchemie A. G. (by H. Noeske and O. Roelen) German Patent 970,578, Oct. 2, 1958.
71. Noeske, H., and O. Roelen, U. S. Patent 2,889,259, June 2, 1959, and British Patent 815,234, June 24, 1959 (to Ruhrchemie A. G.); *Chem. Abstr.*, **54,** 14790c (1960).
72. McAlevy, A., U. S. Patent 2,405,971 (to E. I. du Pont de Nemours & Co.), Aug. 20, 1946; *Chem. Abstr.*, **40,** 7702[6] (1946).
73. Ludlow, J. L., Canadian Patent 530,791 (to E. I. du Pont de Nemours & Co.), Sept. 25, 1956.
74. Warner, R. R., *Rubber Age* (*N. Y.*), **71,** 205 (1952).
75. Brooks, R. E., D. E. Strain, and A. McAlevy, *Rubber World*, **127,** 791 (1953).
76. Nersasian, A., and D. E. Anderson, *J. Appl. Polymer Sci.*, **4,** 74 (1960).
77. Rodman, E. A., U. S. Patent 2,630,425 (to E. I. du Pont de Nemours & Co.), Mar. 3, 1953; *Chem. Abstr.*, **47,** 5713i (1953).
78. Busse, W. F., and F. W. Billmeyer, Jr., *J. Polymer Sci.*, **12,** 599 (1954).
79. Scott, S. L., U. S. Patent 2,416,069 (to E. I. du Pont de Nemours & Co.), Feb. 18, 1947; *Chem. Abstr.*, **41,** 2931a (1947).
80. Natta, G., G. Mazzanti, and M. Bruzzone, Italian Patent 563,508 (to Montecatini S.p.A.), Apr. 24, 1956.
81. Kharasch, M. S., and H. C. Brown, *J. Am. Chem. Soc.*, **64,** 329 (1942).
82. Kharasch, M. S., S. S. Kane, and H. C. Brown, *J. Am. Chem. Soc.*, **64,** 1621 (1942).
83. Clayton, J. O., and W. L. Jensen, *J. Am. Chem. Soc.*, **70,** 3880 (1948).
84. Mayo, F. R., and L. J. Durham, paper presented at 140th meeting of American Chemical Society, Chicago, Ill., Sept. 3–8, 1961.
85. Schroeder, J. P., and W. P. Sopchak, *J. Polymer Sci.*, **47,** 417 (1960).
86. Schroeder, J. P., and E. C. Leonard, U. S. Patent 3,008,939, Nov. 14, 1961, and British Patent 849,059, Sept. 21, 1960 (to Union Carbide Corp.); *Chem. Abstr.*, **55,** 6902f (1961).
87. Leonard, E. C., Jr., W. E. Loeb, J. H. Mason, and W. L. Wheelwright, *J. Appl. Polymer Sci.*, **5,** 157 (1961).
88. Yolles, S., U. S. Patent 2,829,137 (to E. I. du Pont de Nemours & Co.), Apr. 1, 1958; *Chem. Abstr.*, **52,** 13606b (1958).
89. McAlevy, A., D. E. Strain, and F. S. Chance, Jr., U. S. Patents 2,416,060–1 (to E. I. du Pont de Nemours & Co.), Feb. 18, 1947; *Chem. Abstr.*, **41,** 2938e (1947).
90. Dorough, G. L., U. S. Patent 2,432,296 (to E. I. du Pont de Nemours & Co.), Dec. 9, 1947; *Chem. Abstr.*, **42,** 5296a (1948).
91. Fawcett, E. W., U. S. Patent 2,261,757 (to Imperial Chemical Industries, Ltd.), Nov. 4, 1941; *Chem. Abstr.*, **36,** 1118[2] (1942).
92. Hardy, V. R., U. S. Patent 2,304,637 (to E. I. du Pont de Nemours & Co.), Dec. 8, 1942; *Chem. Abstr.*, **37,** 2858[2] (1943).
93. Report of the National Chemical Laboratory, Teddington, England, 1958, p. 41.
94. Grafmüller, F., and F. Husemann, *Makromol. Chem.*, **40,** 161, 172 (1960).
95. Russell, C. A., and J. V. Pascale, paper presented at 140th meeting of American Chemical Society, Chicago, Ill., Sept. 3–8, 1961.

96. Hawkins, W. L., W. Matreyek, and F. H. Winslow, *J. Polymer Sci.*, **41**, 1 (1959).
97. Winslow, F. H., and W. Matreyek, paper presented at 141st Meeting of American Chemical Society, Washington, D. C., Mar. 21–29, 1962.
98. Keller, A., W. Matreyek, and F. H. Winslow, *J. Polymer Sci.*, to be published.
99. Dogadkin, B. A., and A. A. Dontsov, *Dokl. Akad. Nauk. SSSR*, **138**, 1349 (1961); *Chem. Abstr.*, **55**, 25723i (1961).
100. Metz, D. J., and R. B. Mesrobian, *J. Polymer Sci.*, **16**, 345 (1955).
101. Chinai, S. N., J. D. Matlack, A. L. Resnick, and R. A. Guzzi, U. S. Dept. of Commerce, Office Techn. Serv., P. B. Report 161,047, 1959.
102. Walling, C., and W. Thaler, *J. Am. Chem. Soc.*, **83**, 3877 (1961).
103. Keefer, R. M., J. H. Blake, III, and L. J. Andrews, *J. Am. Chem. Soc.*, **76**, 3062 (1954).
104. Josephson, R., R. M. Keefer, and L. J. Andrews, *J. Am. Chem. Soc.*, **83**, 2128 (1961).
105. Bevington, J. C., and R. G. W. Norrish, *J. Chem. Soc.*, **1948**, 771.
106. Bevington, J. C., and R. G. W. Norrish, *J. Chem. Soc.*, **1949**, 482.
107. Eichhorn, J., L. C. Rubens, C. E. Fahlgren, and G. J. Pomranky, U. S. Patent 3,009,906 (to Dow Chemical Co.), Nov. 21, 1961; *Chem. Abstr.*, **56**, 4963f (1962).
108. Saigusa, T., and R. Oda, *Bull. Inst. Chem. Research, Kyoto Univ.*, **33**, 126 (1955); *Chem. Abstr.*, **50**, 1357 (1956).
109. Jones, G. D., in *Styrene*, R. H. Boundy and R. F. Boyer, eds., Reinhold, New York, 1952, p. 674.
110. Jones, G. D., *Ind. Eng. Chem.*, **44**, 2686 (1952).
111. Raley, C. F., Dow Chemical Co., unpublished work.
112. Seifert, H., U. S. Patent 3,008,927, Nov. 14, 1961; and German Patent 1,058,737, June 4, 1959 (to Farbenfabriken Bayer A. G.); *Chem. Abstr.*, **55**, 7919d (1951).
113. Trostyanskaya, E. B., S. B. Makarova, and A. S. Tevlina, *Khim. Prom.*, **1959**, 577; *Chem. Abstr.*, **55**, 1063b (1961).
114. Report of the National Chemical Laboratory, Teddington, England, 1959.
115. Medalia, A. I., H. H. Freedman, and S. Sinha, *J. Polymer Sci.*, **40**, 15 (1959).
116. Monsanto Chemical Co., British Patent 668,290 (by J. M. Butler), Mar. 12, 1952.
117. Jones, G. D., and S. J. Goetz, *J. Polymer Sci.*, **25**, 201 (1957).
118. Hwa, J. C. H., U. S. Patent 2,895,925 (to Rohm and Haas Co.), July 21, 1959; *Chem. Abstr.*, **54**, 12428g (1960).
119. Berger, K., *J. Prakt. Chem.* [4], **12**, 152 (1961); *Chem. Abstr.*, **55**, 15984h (1961).
120. Hatch, M. J., paper presented at 138th Meeting of American Chemical Society, New York, N. Y., Sept. 11–16, 1960.
121. Swain, C. G., and L. E. Kaiser, *J. Am. Chem. Soc.*, **80**, 4089 (1958).
122. Mattano, L. A., and M. J. Hatch, U. S. Patent 2,977,328 (to Dow Chemical Co), Mar. 28, 1961; *Chem. Abstr.*, **55**, 14756h (1961).
123. Hatch, M. J., "High Polymer Conference," Society for Coatings Technology, Los Angeles, Sept. 15, 1961.
124. Lloyd, W. G., and T. Alfrey, Jr., U. S. Patent 3,022,199 (to Dow Chemical Co.). Feb. 20, 1962; *Chem. Abstr.*, **57**, 6176h (1962).
125. Gregor, H. P., D. Dolar, and G. K. Hoeschele, *J. Am. Chem. Soc.*, **77**, 3675 (1953).
126. Overberger, C. G., and A. Lebovits, *J. Am. Chem. Soc.*, **78**, 4792 (1956).
127. Kenyon, W. O., and G. P. Waugh, *J. Polymer Sci.*, **32**, 83 (1958).
128. Unruh, C. C., *J. Appl. Polymer Sci.*, **2**, 358 (1959).

129. Unruh, C. C., *J. Polymer Sci.*, **45,** 325 (1960).
130. Roth, H. H., *Ind. Eng. Chem.*, **46,** 2435 (1954).
131. Roth, H. H., *Ind. Eng. Chem.*, **49,** 1820 (1957).
132. Rueggeberg, W. H. C., T. W. Sauls, and S. L. Norwood, *J. Org. Chem.*, **20,** 455 (1955).
133. Turbak, A. F., *Ind. Eng. Chem., Prod. Res. Develop.*, **1,** 275 (1962).
134. Signer, R., A. Demagistri, and C. Muller, *Makromol. Chem.*, **18/19,** 139 (1956).
135. Signer, R., and A. Demagistri, *J. Chim. Phys.*, **47,** 704 (1950); *Chem. Abstr.*, **45,** 4483 (1951).
136. Baer, M., U. S. Patent 2,533,211 (to Monsanto Chemical Co.), Dec. 12, 1950; *Chem. Abstr.*, **45,** 3651h (1951).
137. Signer, R., U. S. Patent 2,604,456, July 22, 1952; *Chem. Abstr.*, **46,** 9891c (1952).
138. Baer, M., U. S. Patent 2,533,210 (to Monsanto Chemical Co.), Dec. 12, 1950; *Chem. Abstr.*, **45,** 3651g (1951).
139. Blaser, B., M. Rugenstein, and G. Tischbirek, U. S. Patent 2,764,576 (to Henkel & Cie G.m.b.H.), Sept. 25, 1956; *Chem. Abstr.*, **51,** 6218d (1957).
140. Unpublished work, Dow Chemical Co.
141. Eichhorn, J., and J. M. Steinmetz, U. S. Patent 2,945,842 (to Dow Chemical Co.), July 19, 1960; *Chem. Abstr.*, **54,** 23426c (1960).
142. Teot, A. S., U. S. Patent 2,763,634 (to Dow Chemical Co.), Sept. 18, 1956; *Chem. Abstr.*, **51,** 6218b (1957).
143. Eichhorn, J., U. S. Patent 2,877,213 (to Dow Chemical Co.), Mar. 10, 1959; *Chem. Abstr.*, **53,** 11884a (1959).
144. Allen, C. F. H., and L. M. Minsk, U. S. Patent 2,735,841 (to Eastman Kodak Co.), Feb. 21, 1956; *Chem. Abstr.*, **50,** 8250e (1956).
145. Teot, A. S., U. S. Patent 2,867,611 (to Dow Chemical Co.), Jan. 6, 1959; *Chem. Abstr.*, **53,** 6685d (1959).
146. Sargent, R. N., and D. L. Graham, *Ind. Eng. Chem. Process Design Develop.*, **1,** 56 (1962).
147. Reports of the National Chemical Laboratory, Teddington, England, 1958, p. 36.
148. Blyth, J., and A. W. Hofman, *Ann. Chem.*, **53,** 316 (1845).
149. Bachman, G. B., H. Hellman, K. R. Robinson, R. W. Finholt, E. J. Kahlar, L. J. Filar, L. V. Heisey, L. L. Lewis, and D. D. Micucci, *J. Org. Chem.*, **12,** 108 (1947).
150. Zenftman, H., *J. Chem. Soc.*, **1950,** 982.
151. Zenftman, H., and A. McLean, and Imperial Chemical Industries, Ltd., British Patent 616,453, Jan. 21, 1949; *Chem. Abstr.*, **43,** 5040f (1949).
152. Pujo, A. M., J. Boileau, and F. M. Lang, *Mém. Poudres*, **35,** 41 (1953); *Chem. Abstr.*, **50,** 4848c (1956).
153. Matlack, A. S., and D. S. Breslow, *J. Polymer Sci.*, **45,** 265 (1960).
154. Braun, D., and I. Loflund, *Makromol. Chem.*, **53,** 219 (1962).
155. Hanford, W. E., U. S. Patent 2,396,786 (to E. I. du Pont de Nemours & Co.), Mar. 19, 1946; *Chem. Abstr.*, **40,** 3630[1] (1946).
156. Kenyon, W. O., L. M. Minsk, and G. P. Waugh, U. S. Patent 2,274,551 (to Eastman Kodak Co.), Feb. 24, 1942; *Chem. Abstr.*, **36,** 4043[4] (1942).
157. Brandenberger, H., *J. Polymer Sci.*, **20,** 215 (1956).
158. Manecke, G., and S. Singer, *Makromol. Chem.*, **37,** 119 (1960).
159. Rao, M. L. B., B. Mukerjee, and S. R. Palit, *Chem. Ind. (London)*, **1961,** 145.
160. Report of National Chemical Laboratory, Teddington, England (1960), p. 20, 7.

161. Braun, D., *Chimia (Switz.)*, **14,** 24 (1960); *Chem. Abstr.*, **54,** 24490i (1960).
162. Luttinger, L., and H. G. Cassidy, *J. Polymer Sci.*, **22,** 271 (1956).
163. Morton, A. A., and L. D. Taylor, *J. Org. Chem.*, **24,** 1167 (1959).
164. Braun, D., *Makromol. Chem.*, **30,** 85 (1959).
165. Braun, D., *Makromol. Chem.*, **44–46,** 269 (1961).
166. Leavitt, F. C., and L. U. Matternas, *J. Polymer Sci.*, **45,** 249 (1960).
167. Smirnov, R. N., *Dokl. Akad. Nauk. SSSR*, **119,** 508 (1958).
168. Glushkova, V. P., E. D. Delinskaya, and K. A. Kocheshkor, *Dokl. Akad. Nauk. SSSR*, **129,** 109 (1959); *Chem. Abstr.*, **54,** 7224i (1960).
169. Kaganoff, S. D., British Patent 606,400 (to Standard Telephones and Cables, Ltd.), Aug. 12, 1948; *Chem. Abstr.*, **43,** 1608c (1949).
170. Ushakov, S. N., and P. A. Matuzov, *J. Appl. Chem., USSR (English Transl.)*, **17,** 538 (1944); *Chem. Abstr.*, **39,** 3969[6] (1945).

Chapter IV

ADDITION POLYMERS WITH REACTIVE TERMINALS

R. H. Gobran

Thiokol Chemical Corporation

A. GENERAL INTRODUCTION

Polymers containing one or more reactive groups per chain are of great interest, mainly because they provide the means for further reactions to give modified polymers with controlled properties. In general, the best known examples of these polymers are prepared by condensation polymerization such as the polyesters which are extensively used in the urethane field. Recently, interest has been growing in addition-type polymers with reactive endgroups for various applications.

Depending on the nature of the reactive groups available in a polymer, it can undergo step-wise coupling reactions or free radical chain reactions. Thus, similar or dissimilar polymers containing hydroxyl, carboxyl, or isocyanate groups can be coupled with appropriate di- or trifunctional reagents to high molecular weight products, either linearly extended or crosslinked. On the other hand, polymers containing peroxide, hydroperoxide, or perester groups can react with unsaturated monomers to give graft copolymers under appropriate conditions (1,2).

Condensation-type polymerizations give polymers with reactive terminals and the type of such terminals can be controlled by adjusting the ratio of components used. For example, polyesters can be prepared with two hydroxyl terminals, two carboxyl terminals, or one hydroxyl and one carboxyl terminal (on the average) by varying the ratio of glycol to diacid used.

Addition type polymers with randomly located reactive groups can be easily prepared by copolymerization with the appropriate comonomers. Thus, it is possible, for example, to introduce carboxyl groups into polystyrene by copolymerizing styrene and acrylic acid by use of a free radical initiator. However, the preparation of addition polymers with terminal reactive groups requires different techniques and can only be accomplished with certain monomers.

Chain extension and crosslinking of polymers containing reactive groups can be accomplished irrespective of whether the reactive groups in the polymer are random or terminal. However, the final properties resulting from the two systems are quite different since polymers with random reactive groups lead to structures with a large number of chain ends as compared to polymers with terminal functional groups. It has been demonstrated by Flory (3), in the case of rubber vulcanizates, that only the principal chains contribute to general elastic properties whereas chain ends or inactive branches are detrimental to strength. Thus, to obtain the optimum properties by reacting the functional groups present on a polymer, it is necessary to have such groups at the chain ends of the polymer, rather than randomly distributed along the chain.

This chapter will deal exclusively with the principles involved in the polymerization of unsaturated monomers to give polymers with two reactive terminals. Polymerizations of such monomers are generally classified as free radical, ionic, or coordination polymerizations, depending on the nature of the propagating reactive center. Of these three types, the free radical and ionic polymerization mechanisms can be used to produce polymers with reactive terminals.

B. TERMINALLY REACTIVE POLYMERS PREPARED BY FREE RADICAL MECHANISM

1. Introduction

The polymerization of unsaturated monomers by free radical initiators has been extensively studied and the mechanism of polymerization is fairly well established. However, since different authors use different definitions for expressing the rate constants of initiation and termination, it is necessary to set up the kinetic scheme used in this chapter.

In the simple case where polymerization is carried out in bulk (no solvent), and in which the initiator is soluble in the monomer to give a homogeneous system, the free radical polymerization proceeds according to the following kinetic steps.

Initiator decomposition:

$$\text{Initiator} \xrightarrow{k_d} 2\text{R}. \qquad (1)$$

Initiation step:

$$R^{\cdot} + M \rightarrow RM_1^{\cdot} \quad (2)$$

Propagation step:

$$RM_1^{\cdot} + M \xrightarrow{k_p} RM_2^{\cdot} \quad (3)$$

$$RM_x^{\cdot} + M \xrightarrow{k_p} RM_{x+1}^{\cdot} \quad (4)$$

Termination step:
(a) Combination:

$$RM_x^{\cdot} + RM_y^{\cdot} \xrightarrow{k_{tc}} RM_{x+y}R \quad (5)$$

(b) Disproportionation:

$$RM_x^{\cdot} + RM_y^{\cdot} \xrightarrow{k_{td}} RM_x + RM_y \quad (6)$$

According to this simplified mechanism, the initiator decomposes thermally to give two free radicals according to eq. (1). Depending on the efficiency of the initiator, a fraction or all of the radicals formed in the decomposition step react with the monomer molecules present to produce growing polymer chains as represented by the initiation step, (eq. 2). The growing chain radical continues to add monomers in the propagation steps, represented by eqs. (3) and (4). In absence of chain transfer reactions, consumption of the chain radicals takes place either by combination or disproportionation, according to eqs. (5) and (6).

Applying the standard kinetic treatment (4), the rates of initiation, propagation, and termination can be represented by the following expressions:

$$R_i = 2fk_d[\mathrm{I}] = 2k_i[\mathrm{I}] \quad (7)$$

$$R_p = k_p[\mathrm{M.}][\mathrm{M}] \quad (8)$$

$$R_t = 2k_t[\mathrm{M.}]^2 \quad (9)$$

In eq. (7), [I] represents the initiator concentration, k_d its rate of thermal decomposition, and f its efficiency; k_i, the initiation rate constant, equals fk_d and is equal to k_d if the initiator has 100% efficiency in starting polymer chains ($f = 1$).

In eqs. (8) and (9), [M.] represents the concentration of all chain radicals, [M] the monomer concentration, k_p the propagation rate constant, whereas k_t represents the termination rate constant which is the summation of combination (k_{tc}) and disproportionation (k_{td}). Under steady-state conditions, the rate of initiation (R_i) equals rate of termination (R_t). Thus, from eqs. (7) and (9)

$$[M.] = (k_i/k_t)^{1/2}[I]^{1/2} \quad (10)$$

An examination of the kinetic scheme presented shows that one polymer terminal is provided by the initiator in the initiation step, whereas the second polymer terminal may be an initiator fragment or not, depending on whether termination takes place by combination or disproportionation, respectively.

Thus, the first step in preparing a polymer with reactive terminals is to choose an initiator containing reactive groups so arranged that every free radical produced contains one such group. The second requirement is that termination takes place by combination rather than disproportionation and that transfer reactions to monomer, solvent, etc., are negligible.

Some of the initiators that can be used for obtaining polymers with reactive terminals are presented, followed by a discussion of the mechanism of termination in free radical polymerizations.

2. Initiators with Functional Terminals

a. Hydroxyl Terminals

(1) Hydrogen Peroxide

Hydrogen peroxide is the simplest initiator used to prepare polymers with reactive terminals. It is generally used with a reducing agent, such as ferrous ion, in the so-called redox systems (5) in which hydroxyl radicals are produced by an electron transfer process represented by eq. (11). In the

$$H_2O_2 + Fe^{+2} \rightarrow HO. + {}^{-}OH + Fe^{+3} \quad (11)$$

presence of an unsaturated monomer, the hydroxyl radical produced will initiate polymerization, giving rise to a growing polymer chain with a hydroxyl endgroup, as represented by eqs. (12) and (13). Assuming termina-

$$HO^{\cdot} + CH_2{=}\underset{\displaystyle X}{\underset{|}{CH}} \rightarrow HOCH_2{-}\underset{\displaystyle X}{\underset{|}{CH}}. \quad (12)$$

$$HOCH_2\underset{\displaystyle X}{\underset{|}{CH}}. + n\ CH_2{=}\underset{\displaystyle X}{\underset{|}{CH}} \rightarrow HO(CH_2\underset{\displaystyle X}{\underset{|}{CH}})_nCH_2\underset{\displaystyle X}{\underset{|}{CH}} \quad (13)$$

tion by combination of two growing chains, the resulting polymer contains one hydroxyl group on each terminal.

Evans (6) used hydrogen peroxide for the polymerization of styrene monomer and concluded that termination takes place by combination based on the presence of two hydroxyl groups per polymer chain. Seligman (7) described a method for preparing hydroxyl-terminated polychloroprene using a $FeSO_4$–H_2O_2 emulsion recipe.

(2) δ,δ′-Azobis(δ-cyano-*n*-pentanol)

This initiator can be prepared from acetopropanol (8), by reaction with hydrazine and sodium cyanide followed by oxidation with bromine. It was used by Bamford, Jenkins, and Johnston (9) and by Bamford, Jenkins, and Wayne (8) for the preparation of hydroxyl-terminated polyacrylonitrile and polystyrene, respectively. The initiator, being of the azo type, under-

$$HOCH_2CH_2CH_2\overset{\displaystyle CH_3}{\underset{\displaystyle CN}{C}}—N{=}N—\overset{\displaystyle CH_3}{\underset{\displaystyle CN}{C}}—CH_2CH_2CH_2OH \rightarrow 2HOCH_2CH_2CH_2—\overset{\displaystyle CH_3}{\underset{\displaystyle CN}{C}}\cdot + N_2 \quad (14)$$

goes first-order decomposition (eq. 14), is not susceptible to induced decomposition or transfer reactions, and has the same rate in different solvents. The solvents generally used with this initiator are ethylene carbonate and dimethylformamide which are known to have low chain transfer constants.

b. Carboxyl Terminals

(1) γ,γ′-Azobis(γ-cyano-*n*-valeric acid)

This initiator is prepared from levulinic acid (10,11) and has the advantages of other azo initiators. It has been extensively used to introduce carboxyl terminals in polymers (eq. 15) and, particularly, to determine the

$$HOOCCH_2—CH_2—\overset{\displaystyle CH_3}{\underset{\displaystyle CN}{C}}—N{=}N—\overset{\displaystyle CH_3}{\underset{\displaystyle CN}{C}}—CH_2—CH_2COOH \rightarrow$$

$$2HOOC—CH_2—CH_2—\overset{\displaystyle CH_3}{\underset{\displaystyle CN}{C}}\cdot + N_2 \quad (15)$$

mode of termination during the free radical polymerization of various monomers. Thus, it was used to prepare carboxyl-terminated polystyrene (12,13), polyacrylonitrile (9), polychloroprene (7), polyisoprene, and polybutadiene (14). The rate of thermal decomposition of this initiator in water at 80°C. is reported to be 5.38×10^{-3} min.$^{-1}$, and the activation energy is $E_a = 34.0$ kcal./mole (15).

(2) Organic Acid Peroxides

An example of these peroxides is succinic acid peroxide,

$$HOOC(CH_2)_2—\overset{\overset{\displaystyle O}{\|}}{C}—O—O—\overset{\overset{\displaystyle O}{\|}}{C}—(CH_2)_2COOH \rightarrow$$

$$2HOOC(CH_2)_2—\overset{\overset{\displaystyle O}{\|}}{C}—O\cdot \rightarrow 2HOOC(CH_2)_2^{\cdot} + 2CO_2 \quad (16)$$

which is prepared from succinic anhydride and hydrogen peroxide. The thermal decomposition of succinic acid peroxide in acetone was studied by Doehnert and Mageli (16), who reported a first-order rate constant of 0.101, 0.436, and 1.57 hr.$^{-1}$ at 70, 85, and 100°C., respectively. Succinic acid peroxide undergoes thermal decomposition to give $HOOC(CH_2)_2—CO—O\cdot$ or $HOOC(CH_2)_2^{\cdot}$ radicals in a manner similar to the decomposition of benzoyl peroxide. Either of the initiator fragments can initiate polymerization of unsaturated monomers giving rise to carboxyl terminated polymers.

(3) Potassium Permanganate–Oxalic Acid

Palit and co-workers (17) reported that reactions involving the oxidation of organic acids, such as $KMnO_4$–oxalic acid or $KMnO_4$–tartaric acid in nitrogen atmosphere, can be used to initiate polymerization of unsaturated monomers in aqueous medium and introduce carboxyl endgroups. It is assumed, in such cases, that either $\cdot COO^-$ or $\cdot COOH$ radicals are formed and that these initiate polymerization. This technique was reported to introduce carboxyl endgroups in poly(methyl methacrylate) (18). It is to be expected, however, that the resulting poly(methyl methacrylate) would have only one carboxyl terminal, whereas polystyrene prepared in a similar manner would have two carboxyl terminals. This is due to the fact that termination is predominantly by disproportionation in the case of methyl methacrylate and by combination in the case of styrene.

Palit and Konar (18) also reported that oxalic acid alone can initiate the aqueous polymerization of methyl methacrylate in presence of ultraviolet light, sunlight, or even diffused light and that the resulting polymer contains carboxyl groups. However, quantitative data showing the number of carboxyl groups per chain were not given.

(4) Cyclohexanone Peroxide–Ferrous Salts

The peroxide formed from cyclohexanone and hydrogen peroxide has been shown (19) to have the structure I.

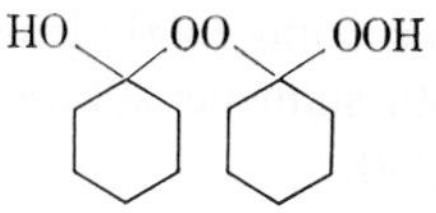

(I)

Kharasch and Nudenberg (20) have shown that in presence of an aqueous solution of ferrous sulfate, cyclohexanone peroxide polymerizes butadiene to give long chain α,ω-dicarboxylic acids. The authors postulated that free radical II is first formed, and is converted to free radical III which adds to butadiene, followed by dimerization to give the dicarboxylic acids.

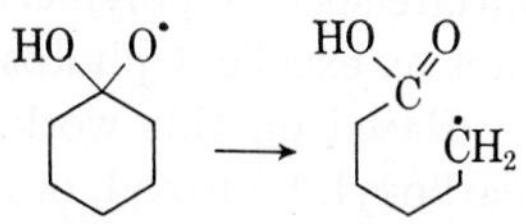

(II) (III)

Adjusting the ratio of butadiene to cyclohexanone peroxide should thus yield carboxyl-terminated polybutadienes with varying molecular weights.

(5) Potassium Persulfate: Special Cases

Using persulfates with radioactive sulfur, S^{35}, as initiators for the polymerization of tetrafluoroethylene, Berry and Peterson (21) showed that the polymer does not contain any sulfur from the initiator. Later, Bro and Sperati (22) identified carboxyl groups as the terminals for polytetrafluoroethylene initiated with persulfate. This can be explained if the sulfate ion radicals initiate the polymerization, producing fluoroalkyl sulfuric acid esters, which would be rapidly hydrolyzed (eqs. 17–18). Alternatively

$$S_2O_8^{-2} \rightarrow 2SO_4^{\overline{\cdot}} \tag{17}$$

$$SO_4^{\overline{\cdot}} + n(CF_2{=}CF_2) \rightarrow {}^{\ominus}O_3SO(CF_2{-}CF_2\!\!\rightarrow\!\!)_n \xrightarrow{H_2O} HO(CF_2CF_2\!\!\rightarrow\!\!)_n \tag{18}$$

the sulfate ion radical may be first hydrolyzed to give hydroxyl radicals which could initiate the polymerization (eqs. 19–20). In either case, the

$$SO_4^{\overline{\cdot}} + H_2O \rightarrow HSO_4 + HO^{\cdot} \tag{19}$$

$$HO^{\cdot} + n(CF_2{=}CF_2\!\!\rightarrow\!\!) \rightarrow HO(CF_2CF_2\!\!\rightarrow\!\!)_n \tag{20}$$

resulting difluorocarbinol endgroups would hydrolyze rapidly to carboxyl groups

$$HO(CF_2CF_2)_n \xrightarrow{H_2O} HOOC—CF_2(CF_2CF_2)_{n-1} + 2HF \quad (21)$$

In a similar manner, chlorotrifluoroethylene monomer was polymerized in suspension by use of potassium persulfate as initiator to produce carboxyl-terminated polymer (23).

c. General

(1) Organic Polysulfides

Organic polysulfides of the general formula RS_xR, where $x = 2–4$ and where R is phenyl, tolyl, benzyl, or benzoyl, have been studied as initiators for free radical polymerization by Otsu (24). The author found that, while these compounds do not initiate styrene polymerization in the temperature range of 60–120°C., they act as excellent photosensitizers with the exception of dibenzyl disulfide. Based on this work, it is very likely that, if these compounds contain carboxyl, hydroxyl, or amine groups, they can be used for the introduction of such functional groups in various monomers.

Pierson, Constanza, and Weinstein (25) in a study of bis-type structures as modifiers found that disulfides, particularly aryl disulfides, can be used as modifiers to incorporate desired endgroups in polystyrene. Bis(4-carboxyphenyl) disulfide and bis(4-carboxymethylphenyl) disulfide were used to introduce carboxyl endgroups, whereas bis(2- or 4-aminophenyl) disulfide and bis(2-aminophenyl) disulfide were used to incorporate amine groups in polystyrene. Bis(2- or 4-hydroxymethylphenyl) disulfide gives hydroxyl terminals.

Constanza et al. (26), used similar modifiers for the emulsion polymerization of butadiene, but did not obtain quantitative data to show the presence of two reactive terminals per primary polymer molecule.

Xanthogen disulfides, $[ROC(S)S]_2$, were also used as modifiers (27) during the polymerization of styrene and butadiene to give the corresponding polymeric xanthate esters. On hydrolysis, these products are reported to give polymers with mercaptan terminals.

3. Termination in Free Radical Polymerization

Use of one of the free radical initiators just described, for the polymerization of an unsaturated monomer introduces a functional terminal at one end of its growing chain. Assuming that transfer reactions are negligible, and depending on whether termination takes place by combination (eq. 5) or disproportionation (eq. 6), the second terminal of the polymer may be a functional group derived from the initiator or a dead terminal, respectively. For the purpose of this discussion, termination of a growing chain by reaction with primary radicals (28,29) is considered termination by combination, since both methods give two initiator fragments per polymer molecule. The relative importance of combination and disproportionation varies from one monomer to another, just as has been found for small radicals. In some instances, attempts were made to deduce the mechanism of termination during the polymerization of a monomer by comparing it to a simple molecule of similar structure. A detailed discussion of this subject is given by Burnett (30). For example, α-cyanoisopropyl radicals, obtained by the decomposition of azobisisobutyronitrile, were used as a model for growing methacrylonitrile chains. The fact that α-cyanoisopropyl radicals were found by Bickel and Waters (31) to yield tetramethylsuccinonitrile was used as evidence that termination in methacrylonitrile polymerization takes place by combination. Kharasch, McBay, and Urry (32) studied the decomposition of acetyl peroxide in several alkyl benzenes and have obtained bibenzyl derivatives, indicating coupling of radicals rather than disproportionation. Mayo, Gregg, and Matheson (33) used this model as an indication for termination by combination in the polymerization of styrene.

However, conclusions drawn from the use of simple model radicals could not be completely relied upon for predicting the nature of termination in radical polymerizations. The effect of neighboring groups, cage effects, and diffusion effects may cause deviations in the reactivity of polymer radicals as compared to model radicals. Thus, while it has been possible to approximate statistically (34) and thermodynamically (35) the extent of combination and disproportionation for simple radicals, no such calculations could be made for polymerizations.

The nature of termination in radical polymerizations can be derived by investigations of the polymer itself by using one of the methods described in the following section.

4. Determination of the Termination Mechanism in Radical Polymerizations

a. Kinetic Method

The kinetic chain length ν or the average number of monomer molecules reacting with an initiator radical is defined by the ratio of the rate of propagation R_p to the rate of initiation R_i. Since the rate of initiation R_i is equal to the rate of termination R_t under steady-state conditions, the kinetic chain length can be represented by the following relationships:

$$\text{Kinetic chain length } \nu = \frac{\text{Rate of propagation}}{\text{Rate of termination}} = \frac{R_p}{R_t} \quad (22)$$

Substituting the values for R_p and R_t from eqs. (8), (9), and (10) yields

$$\nu = k_p[\text{M}]/2k_i^{1/2}k_t^{1/2}[\text{I}]^{1/2} \quad (23)$$

The average degree of polymerization, $\bar{P}_n$ or the average number of monomers per molecule can be related to the kinetic chain length if chain transfer reactions are negligible. Thus, if termination takes place only by combination of two growing chains (eq. 5), the average number of monomers constituting a polymer molecule is twice the kinetic chain length; $\bar{P}_n = 2\nu$; if disproportionation is the exclusive mode of termination (eq. 6), however, the average degree of polymerization is equal to the kinetic chain length; $\bar{P}_n = \nu$. In cases where the termination mechanism takes place by both combination and disproportionation of growing chains, the average degree of polymerization has an intermediate value between one and two kinetic chain lengths. If y represents the fraction of the termination that takes place by combination, i.e.,

$$y = k_{tc}/k_t = k_{tc}/(k_{tc} + k_{td}) \quad (24)$$

where

$$k_t = k_{tc} + k_{td}$$

a general expression relating the average degree of polymerization to the kinetic chain length can be represented by:

$$\bar{P}_n = 2\nu/(2 - y) \quad (25)$$

Hence, by substituting eq. (23) in eq. (25) and obtaining reciprocals,

$$\frac{1}{\bar{P}_n} = (2 - y)k_i^{1/2}k_t^{1/2}[\text{I}]^{1/2}/k_p[\text{M}] \quad (26)$$

Thus, a plot of the reciprocal average degree of polymerization, $(1/\bar{P}_n)$ versus the square root of the initiator concentration $[\text{I}]^{1/2}$ gives a straight line whose slope is $(2 - y)k_i^{1/2}(k_t^{1/2}/k_p)/[\text{M}]$. From the value of the slope it is possible to calculate y, or the fraction of the termination reactions occurring by combination, provided that k_i and $(k_t^{1/2}/k_p)$ for the monomer are known from separate measurements. If termination takes place exclusively by combination, $y = 1$, whereas, if disproportionation predominates, $y = 0$ on the basis of eq. (24).

The kinetic method was used by Mayo, Gregg, and Matheson (33) and by Baysal and Tobolsky (36) either in the form described here or in a slightly modified manner to determine the mechanism of termination during the free radical polymerization of styrene. Recently, Bamford, Jenkins, and Johnston (9) employed this technique to show that the termination during acrylonitrile polymerization takes place by combination. Applying this method, it is important to note that loss of low molecular weight polymer during isolation by fractionation affects the results. When using values of the termination rate constant, k_t, or the ratio $k_t^{1/2}/k_p$ reported in the literature, the definition of the termination rate used to obtain these values must be borne in mind. Some authors write the termination rate as $2k_t[M^{\cdot}]^2$, as is done in this chapter, while others write it as $k_t[M^{\cdot}]^2$.

b. Endgroup Methods

These methods are based on the fact that in absence of transfer reactions a polymer molecule contains one or two initiator fragments, depending on whether termination takes place by disproportionation or combination. Thus, determination of the average number of initiator fragments per polymer molecule gives a direct method of ascertaining the mechanism of termination. This method requires accurate determinations of the number of initiator fragments attached to polymer chains and the number-average molecular weight of the polymer. The number-average molecular weight can be determined by osmometry for high molecular weights or by ebulliometry, cryoscopy, or vapor pressure methods if the molecular weight is low. It is important that unreacted initiator or its decomposition products are carefully and thoroughly removed from the polymer by repeated washings and precipitation. Loss of low molecular weight fractions during polymer isolation and purification does not affect this method.

Endgroup analysis can be accomplished by either of two methods: by use of labeled initiators or by use of initiators with functional groups.

(1) Use of Labeled Initiators

This method involves the use of initiator molecules labeled with radioactive tracers and determination of the radioactivity of the resulting polymers. Thus, potassium persulfate with radioactive sulfur was used by Smith (37) to show that termination in the emulsion polymerization of styrene takes place by combination. Bevington, Melville, and Taylor (38,39) used α,α'-azobisisobutyronitrile labeled with C^{14} as initiator to show that polystyrene radicals combine at 25°C. and 60°C. whereas with poly(methyl methacrylate) radicals disproportionation is more predominant, particularly at high temperatures. Bailey and Jenkins (40) used the same method to show that the mechanism of termination in the polymerization of acrylonitrile in dimethylformamide at 60°C. takes place by combination.

(2) Use of Initiators with Functional Groups

Initiators that have been used successfully for this purpose include hydrogen peroxide (6) and azo-type initiators with functional groups. The concentration of functional groups in polymers resulting from the use of such initiators can be determined by wet analytical methods or by infrared analysis. These analytical techniques can only be relied upon for low molecular weight polymers to allow for a relatively high concentration of functional endgroups. This method was used to show that termination in polystyrene (13), polybutadiene, and polyisoprene takes place by combination (14).

While endgroup analysis is the most direct method of assessing the mechanism of termination, it is essential that certain conditions are satisfied. These conditions were discussed by Bevington, Melville, and Taylor (38), namely: (*a*) the composition of the initiator fragment that starts the chain growth must be known; (*b*) initiation by thermal or photochemical mechanisms must be negligible; (*c*) dehydrogenation of the monomer by initiator radicals must not be significant; (*d*) if radioactive materials are used, their radiations must not produce free radicals from the monomer or solvent; (*e*) transfer reactions must be negligible, otherwise polymer radicals may terminate by mechanisms other than combination or disproportionation of two growing chains.

c. Coupling Method

This method was discussed by Bamford and Jenkins (12) and involves the use of the azo initiators with functional groups described before. These functional groups become incorporated into the polymer as terminals which can be linked together by means of suitable difunctional reagents. Determination of the molecular weight of the polymer before and after coupling gives an indication of the mechanism of termination. Thus, an increase in the molecular weight of the polymer, after coupling, by a factor of 2 indicates disproportionation, whereas an increase by a factor substantially greater than 2 indicates that combination predominates. Bamford and Jenkins (12) used this method to prove that termination for polystyrene takes place by combination, whereas termination for methyl methacrylate, methyl acrylate, and vinyl acetate takes place by disproportionation. Later, Bamford, Jenkins, and Johnston (9) used the same procedure to show that termination in the polymerization of acrylonitrile takes place by combination. The initiators used for these studies are γ,γ'-azobis(γ-cyanovaleric acid) and δ,δ'-azobis(δ-cyano-*n*-pentanol) which produce carboxyl- and hydroxyl-terminated polymers, respectively. The carboxyl terminals were converted to acid chloride groups by reaction with thionyl chloride, and then coupling was carried out by reaction with one equivalent of 1,10-decamethylenediol. Polymers with hydroxyl terminals were coupled with adipoyl chloride.

Bamford, Jenkins, and Wayne (8) used the coupling technique to prepare alternating block copolymers of polystyrene–polyacrylonitrile by reacting carboxyl-terminated polystyrene with hydroxyl-terminated polyacrylonitrile. For the preparation of random block copolymers, the initial polymers may contain the same type of reactive terminals which are coupled with appropriate difunctional reagents.

d. Retardation Method

This method was developed by Bonsalle, Valentine, and Melville (41) and is carried out by studying the effect of added retarders upon the rate of polymerization and upon the number-average molecular weight of the product. If a retarder molecule reacts with a polymer radical and thus prevents it from further reaction with monomer or another polymer radical, this mode of termination is equivalent to disproportionation as far as the molecular weight is concerned. The resulting polymer will have one initiator fragment per chain. Thus, in the case of monomers that terminate by disproportionation, addition of a retarder to reduce the rate of polymerization by a certain factor should result in the molecular weight being reduced by the same factor, if the rate of initiation is kept constant. In the case of monomers that normally terminate by combination, the reduction in molecular weight should be twice as much. By comparing the rates and molecular weights for retarded and unretarded polymerization, it would be possible to determine the predominant mode of termination. In this method, it is essential that the retarder reduces the rate of polymerization by stopping the growing polymer radical and not by acting directly on the initiator to reduce the rate of initiation. Using *p*-benzoquinone as the retarder, Bonsalle, Valentine, and Melville (41) were able to establish that disproportionation is the predominating mechanism of termination for methyl methacrylate polymerizations.

5. Mode of Termination of Various Monomers

The predominant mode of termination of a number of monomers is listed in Table IV-1 together with the method of determination used. If a monomer terminates by combination, then it is possible to prepare its polymer with two functional endgroups by using one of the initiators discussed in a previous section.

TABLE IV-1

Monomer	Method[a]	Predominant termination mechanism[b]	References
Styrene	1	C	33, 36
	2a	C	1, 38, 42
	2b	C	6, 13
	3	C	12
Acrylonitrile	1	C	9
	2a	C	40
	3	C	9
Methyl acrylate	3	D	12
Methyl methacrylate	2a	D	38, 39, 43
	3	D	12
	4	D	41
Vinyl acetate	2a	D	42
	3	D	12
Vinyl chloride	2a	D and C	44
	2a	Transfer	45
Tetrafluoroethylene	2a	C	21
Chlorotrifluoroethylene	2	C	23
Butadiene	2b	C	73
	3	C	73
Isoprene	2b	C	73
	3	C	73
Chloroprene	3	C	7
Acrylamide	1	D	46

[a] Method 1: kinetic method; method 2a: labeled initiators; method 2b: functional initiators; method 3: coupling method; method 4: retardation method.
[b] C = combination; D = disproportionation.

C. TERMINALLY REACTIVE POLYMERS PREPARED BY IONIC MECHANISM

1. Introduction

In the ionic polymerization of unsaturated monomers, the propagating active center is either a carbonium ion or a carbanion, depending on whether a cationic or an anionic initiator is used. Cationic initiators include Lewis acids, such as BF_3, $AlCl_3$, $AlBr_3$, $TiCl_4$, and $SnCl_4$, usually with complexing cocatalysts. The monomers that can be polymerized cationically usually contain electron donating substituents attached to the vinyl double bond, such as isobutylene, α-methylstyrene, and vinyl alkyl ethers. Anionic initiators include alkali metals, metal alkyls or aryls, metal amides, alkoxides, or hydroxides, and the monomers that can be polymerized anionically generally have electron-withdrawing groups or unsaturated substituents to stabilize the negative charge of the resulting anion, e.g., acrylonitrile, methacrylates, and dienes.

The charged active end of an ionically growing polymer is usually associated with an oppositely charged counterion. In the case of cationic polymerizations the initiation and propagation steps proceed as shown in eqs. (27) and (28):

$$H^{\oplus}X^{\ominus} + CH_2{=}\underset{R_2}{\overset{R_1}{C}} \rightarrow H{-}CH_2{-}\underset{R_2}{\overset{R_1}{C}}{}^{\oplus}X^{\ominus} \quad (27)$$

$$H{-}CH_2{-}\underset{R_2}{\overset{R_1}{C}}{}^{\oplus}X^{\ominus} + CH_2{=}\underset{R_2}{\overset{R_1}{C}} \rightarrow H{-}CH_2{-}\underset{R_2}{\overset{R_1}{C}}{-}CH_2{-}\underset{R_2}{\overset{R_1}{C}}{}^{\oplus}X^{\ominus} \quad (28)$$

where $X^{\ominus}$ represents the negative counterion accompanying the growing cation.

In the case of anionic polymerizations, the initiation step may occur according to two different mechanisms, as will be discussed later, but the propagation step proceeds as shown in eq. (29). Here $M^{\oplus}$ represents the

$$-CH_2{-}\underset{R_4}{\overset{R_3}{C}}{}^{\ominus}M^{\oplus} + CH_2{=}\underset{R_4}{\overset{R_3}{C}} \rightarrow -CH_2{-}\underset{R_4}{\overset{R_3}{C}}{-}CH_2{-}\underset{R_4}{\overset{R_3}{C}}{}^{\ominus}M^{\oplus} \quad (29)$$

positive counterion accompanying the growing carbanion. While the terminal in eq. (29) is represented as ionic in nature, in cases where Li metal is involved it is considered to be covalent, such as one finds in butyllithium.

While in free radical polymerizations the most important termination step involves the bimolecular reaction of two terminal radicals by combination or disproportionation, such reactions do not take place in ionic polymerizations. In cationic polymerizations the charged terminal of a polymer and its counterion may recombine, forming a stable covalent bond and thus terminating the growing chain. If this happens rapidly enough, the polymer growth will be prevented and the net result would be the addition of the initiator across the double bonds of the monomer. To prevent this from taking place, the interaction of the opposite ions must be reduced by use of solvating agents which stabilize the counterions long enough to allow the polymer to grow. Termination of a growing carbonium ion generally takes place as the counterion abstracts a proton from a CH_2 group adjacent to the carbonium ion followed by formation of a terminal double bond. This is represented in eq. (30) for the termination

$$-CH_2-\overset{\overset{CH_3}{|}}{\underset{\underset{CH_3}{|}}{C}}{}^{\oplus}X^{\ominus} \rightarrow -CH=\overset{\overset{CH_3}{|}}{\underset{\underset{CH_3}{|}}{C}} + H^{\oplus}X^{\ominus} \tag{30}$$

of a growing polyisobutylene chain. As it can be seen from the mechanism of cationic polymerizations, the two terminals are different, and there is no possibility that a polymer with two reactive terminals can be formed.

The situation is quite different in anionic polymerizations, since many such polymerizations do not exhibit any termination reactions. Thus, by using initiators such as alkali metals it is possible to obtain reactive terminals on both ends of a polymer chain which can be converted to useful functional groups. It is essential for the success of such reactions that extreme care be taken to remove traces of reactive impurities such as water, carbon dioxide, and oxygen, which can alter the mechanism of polymerization. The details of anionic polymerizations leading to polymers with functional terminals will be discussed later.

Termination in anionic systems may take place by other mechanisms which are discussed in detail in two recent articles by Szwarc (47) and Mulvaney, Overberger, and Schiller (48). In a manner similar to the termination of cationic polymerizations by the loss of a proton, a chain with a growing anion may terminate by losing a hydride ion with the formation of a terminal double bond and metal hydride. However, such a step is energetically unfavorable especially when the ions are well solvated by a solvent such as tetrahydrofuran. Except in cases involving C-Al bonds, loss of a hydride ion by the terminal carbanion is unlikely to contribute to the termination in anionic polymerizations. Another possibility is the isomerization of the reactive carbanion to a less reactive ion incapable of propagation. Examples of this type of termination have been suggested for poly(methyl methacrylate) (49,50).

Termination in anionic polymerizations can also take place by chain transfer to monomer as found for the anionic polymerization of acrylonitrile with quaternary ammonium hydroxides (51) or by proton transfer from solvent as suggested for the polymerization of styrene in liquid ammonia (52,53).

2. Anionic Polymers with "Living" Terminals

For the preparation of polymers with functional endgroups by anionic initiators, it is necessary first to prepare polymers with two "living" terminals which can then be reacted with suitable reagents to produce specific endgroups. The absence of termination in anionic polymerizations allows for the preparation of such polymers, provided the initiators used are such that two carbanions are present per chain. As indicated earlier, it is necessary to remove from the system all traces of impurities that can react prematurely with the growing terminals. The initiators used to polymerize unsaturated monomers and provide living terminals include alkali metals, sodium naphthalene or sodium biphenyl, and dimetal alkyls.

a. Alkali Metal Initiators

The use of alkali metals as initiators for polymerizations has been known for many years, long before the mechanism or even the concept of high polymers had been established. Synthetic rubbers based on sodium polymerized butadiene were produced in Germany and Russia in the nineteen-twenties. The details of the mechanism of alkali-metal initiated polymerizations of dienes are discussed by Mulvaney, Overberger, and Schiller (48) and are beyond the scope of this chapter. The accepted mechanism for the bulk polymerization of butadiene was suggested by Ziegler (54) and by Abkin and Medvedev (55) to proceed according to eqs. (31) and (32), the nature of the termination step not being postulated.

$$CH_2{=}CH{-}CH{=}CH_2 + 2Na \rightarrow \overset{\oplus}{Na}\overset{\ominus}{C}H_2{-}CH{=}CH{-}\overset{\ominus}{C}H_2\overset{\oplus}{Na} \tag{31}$$

$$\overset{\oplus}{Na}\overset{\ominus}{C}H_2{-}CH{=}CH{-}\overset{\ominus}{C}H_2\overset{\oplus}{Na} + (n{-}1)\,CH_2{=}CH{-}CH{=}CH_2 \rightarrow \overset{\oplus}{Na}\,\overset{\ominus}{[}CH_2{-}CH{=}CH{-}CH_2]_n\overset{\ominus}{}\overset{\oplus}{Na} \tag{32}$$

In the presence of toluene as a solvent, Robertson and Marion (56) postulated a termination step involving the transfer of a proton from the solvent (eq. 33):

$$\sim\!CH_2\!-\!CH\!=\!CH\!-\!\overset{\ominus}{C}H_2\overset{\oplus}{Na} + C_6H_5CH_3 \rightarrow \sim\!CH_2\!-\!CH\!=\!CH\!-\!CH_3 + C_6H_5\overset{\ominus}{C}H_2\overset{\oplus}{Na} \quad (33)$$

While it was not realized at the time, the diene polymers prepared long ago using alkali metals as initiators are in fact what we are calling, today, living polymers. The interest in alkali metal polymerized dienes has been recently revived since the discovery that, by using lithium as an initiator in bulk or in hydrocarbon solvents, polymers of high degree of stereospecificity can be obtained. Thus, polyisoprene with 90% or more *cis*-1,4 structure can be obtained by polymerizing isoprene in bulk or in hydrocarbon solvents with lithium as initiator. Polybutadienes with high 1,4 content can also be produced in a similar manner. The other alkali metals were found to give polyisoprenes or polybutadienes having high 3,4 or 1,2 content. The microstructure of diene polymers prepared with lithium initiation is very dependent on the nature of the solvent used. In polar solvents, the 1,4 stereospecificity is generally lost.

b. Ion Radical Initiators: Use of Sodium Naphthalene or Sodium Biphenyl

In 1939, a patent issued to Scott (57) described the use of sodium in various aromatic hydrocarbons as initiator for conjugated hydrocarbon monomers such as styrene, butadiene, and cyclopentadiene. The mechanism of such polymerizations was not known at the time. The initiators used, e.g., sodium naphthalene or sodium biphenyl, have been shown to be actually ion-radicals (58) which react with the monomer by electron transfer giving a monomer ion-radical. The resulting ion-radical dimerizes to a difunctional carbanion that can grow on both ends by further addition of monomer. The mechanism initially proposed by Szwarc (59,60) for the polymerization of styrene in tetrahydrofuran by use of sodium naphthalene as initiator can be represented by eqs. (34)-(37).

Initiation:

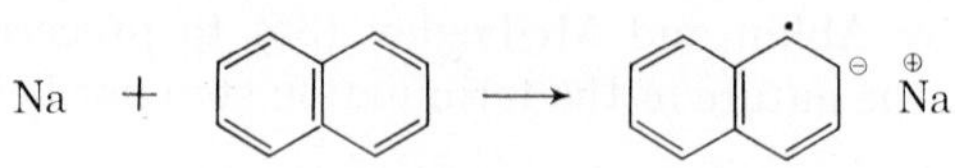

(34)

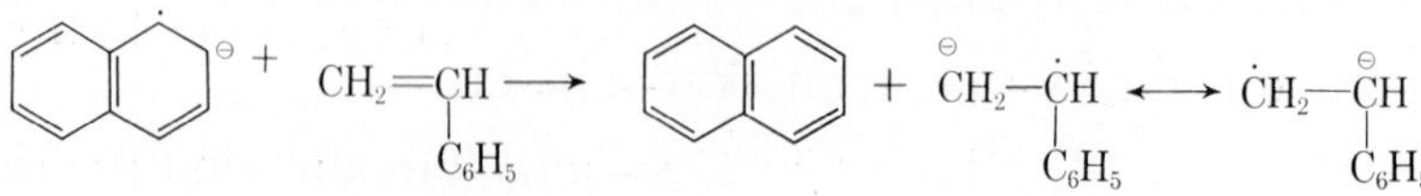

(35)

$$2\,\underset{\displaystyle C_6H_5}{CH_2\text{—}\overset{\ominus}{CH}} \rightarrow \underset{\displaystyle C_6H_5}{\overset{\ominus}{CH}}\text{—}CH_2\text{—}CH_2\text{—}\underset{\displaystyle C_6H_5}{\overset{\ominus}{CH}} \qquad (36)$$

Propagation:

$$\overset{\oplus}{Na}\underset{\displaystyle C_6H_5}{\overset{\ominus}{CH}}\text{—}CH_2\text{—}CH_2\text{—}\underset{\displaystyle C_6H_5}{\overset{\ominus}{CH}}\overset{\oplus}{Na} + 2n\,CH_2\text{=}\underset{\displaystyle C_6H_5}{CH} \rightarrow$$

$$\overset{\oplus}{Na}\text{(}\underset{\displaystyle C_6H_5}{\overset{\ominus}{CH}}\text{—}CH_2\text{)}_n\underset{\displaystyle C_6H_5}{CH}\text{—}CH_2\text{—}CH_2\text{—}\underset{\displaystyle C_6H_5}{CH}\text{—}(CH_2\text{—}\underset{\displaystyle C_6H_5}{\overset{\ominus}{CH}}\text{)}_n\overset{\oplus}{Na} \qquad (37)$$

Using conductivity measurements, Worsfold and Bywater (61) showed that in the case of "living" polystyrene polymerized with sodium naphthalene in tetrahydrofuran, the active chain ends are primarily ion pairs with sodium gegenion. The equilibrium constant for dissociation was determined to be 1.5×10^{-7}. In this type of polymerization, termination does not occur; rather, the monomer adds to the carbanion ends until it is all depleted, provided that impurities such as water, carbon dioxide, and oxygen are scrupulously eliminated.

Based on the above mechanism, if the initiation takes place very fast as compared to the propagation, the polymer chains grow to the same length, i.e., are monodisperse; and the number-average degree of polymerization ($\overline{DP}_n$) can be given by:

$$\overline{DP}_n = m/n \qquad (38)$$

where m is the number of monomer molecules and n the number of growing chains which is half the initiator concentration in the above case (59,60). With sodium naphthalene or the sodium salt of α-methylstyrene tetramer as the initiator, polystyrene with very narrow molecular weight distribution was prepared (62,63).

Polybutadiene and polyisoprene were also prepared by Szwarc and coworkers (64) by the same technique. Methyl methacrylate (60,65,66) similarly gives a "living" polymer, but extra care has to be taken in purifying the monomer and eliminating traces of impurities.

c. *Use of Organometallic Initiators*

The anionic polymerization of unsaturated monomers using organometallic initiators is another example of "living" polymers in which no termination takes place. It is difficult to distinguish between anionic polymerizations in which alkali metals or organometallics are used as initiators, since the reaction product of an alkali metal with an unsaturated monomer can be considered as an organometallic compound. The main difference, however, lies in the fact that when an organometallic compound is used as an initiator the polymerization system is homogeneous, whereas alkali metals give heterogeneous systems at least initially.

The mechanism of polymerization, with organometallics as initiators, can be represented by the polymerization of butadiene with butyllithium or ethyllithium as initiator in ether (54) as shown in eqs. (39) and (40).

$$\text{BuLi} + \text{CH}_2\text{=CH—CH=CH}_2 \rightarrow \text{Bu—CH}_2\text{—CH=CH—CH}_2\text{Li} \quad (39)$$

$$\text{Bu—CH}_2\text{—CH=CH—CH}_2\text{Li} + n\,\text{CH}_2\text{=CH—CH=CH}_2 \rightarrow \text{Bu(CH}_2\text{—CH=CH—CH}_2)_{n+1}\text{Li} \quad (40)$$

Similar initiators include lithium benzyl, potassium phenyl isopropyl, and triphenyl methyl sodium. Such systems provide only one living terminal per chain and in order to produce polymers with two terminal functional groups, it is necessary to use a dilithium alkyl which would add to the unsaturated monomer on both ends and thus allow chain growth to proceed at both terminals. Dilithium alkyls are generally prepared by reacting lithium dispersion with the corresponding dihalide in the presence of a hydrocarbon solvent (67). The use of dilithium alkyls as initiators has only been reported in the patent literature. Pentamethylene dilithium (68), for example, was used to polymerize butadiene (68a), isoprene (68b), and to copolymerize butadiene or isoprene with styrene (68c). Polymers prepared by using these initiators must have a carbanion at each terminal that is capable of further reaction. Recently, Uraneck, Hsieh, and Buck (69) reported on the use of bis(alkali metallorgano) compounds as initiators for the preparation of low molecular weight butadiene polymers in solution. The resulting polymers with alkali metal terminals were reacted with carbon dioxide and then acidified to yield carboxyl-terminated polybutadiene.

3. Reactions of "Living" Terminals

Polymers prepared according to an anionic mechanism and having "living" terminals can be reacted in a number of different ways to give various structures. In the presence of reagents with active hydrogen, e.g., H_2O, alcohols, acids, or phenols, termination takes place giving a dead terminal which is of no further interest. However, certain carbanion terminals can be used to prepare block copolymers. Thus, ethylene oxide (70–72) or methyl methacrylate (71,73) monomer can be added to a growing polystyryl anion to form the corresponding block copolymers, but the reverse reaction does not take place. On the other hand, styrene and butadiene (or isoprene) can form block copolymers of any desired composition by adding butadiene (or isoprene) monomer to living polystyrene or styrene monomer to living butadiene (or isoprene) polymer (71,74).

In general, when the difference in electronegativity of two carbanions is large, a block copolymer can be prepared by adding the monomer with the weaker base ion to the living polymer of the other monomer with the strong base ion terminal. The reciprocal initiation of such two monomers is not possible. If, however, the electronegativity difference between the two carbanions is very small or absent, the reciprocal initiation of the two species to form block copolymers and, indeed, the formation of random copolymers is possible.

Another type of reaction that can be performed with living carbanions is a coupling reaction by use of difunctional reagents such as $COCl_2$, $SOCl_2$, PBr_3, alkyl dihalides, or esters of dicarboxylic acids. With such reagents it is possible to couple living polymers of similar or dissimilar backbones (75). For illustration, eq. (41) represents the coupling of two different polymers by use of an alkyl dihalide as the reagent:

$$\sim\!\sim AAAA^{\ominus} + ClRCl + {}^{\ominus}BBBB\sim\!\sim \rightarrow \sim\!\sim AAAA{-}R{-}BBBB\sim\!\sim + 2Cl^{\ominus} \quad (41)$$

The third type of reaction, which concerns us the most in this chapter, is one in which the living terminals of a polymer are converted into functional groups which are stable and can be used at any later time for chain extension and crosslinking purposes. Examples of such reactions are given in the following section.

4. Conversion of "Living" Terminals into Functional Endgroups

a. Hydroxyl Endgroups

The living terminals of a polymer prepared according to the methods described previously can be converted into hydroxyl endgroups by reacting the terminals with ethylene oxide. Richards and Szwarc (72) described a method for preparing hydroxyl-terminated polystyrene by first polymerizing styrene in tetrahydrofuran with the use of sodium salt of α-methylstyrene tetramer as initiator and then terminating the growth by addition of traces of ethylene oxide as shown in eq. (42). This results in a marked

$$\sim\!\sim CH_2{-}\underset{\displaystyle C_6H_5}{\underset{|}{\overset{\ominus}{C}H}}\ \overset{\oplus}{Na} + \underset{\displaystyle O}{CH_2{-}CH_2} \rightarrow \sim\!\sim CH_2{-}\underset{\displaystyle C_6H_5}{\underset{|}{CH}}{-}CH_2{-}CH_2\overset{\ominus}{O}\ \overset{\oplus}{Na} \quad (42)$$

increase in the viscosity of the solution due to association of the alcoholate terminals. On exposure to moisture, water hydrolyzes the alcoholate terminals to hydroxyl endgroups and NaOH (eq. 43) resulting in a breakdown of the association and a sharp drop in solution viscosity.

$$\sim\!CH_2\!-\!\underset{\displaystyle C_6H_5}{\underset{|}{CH}}\!-\!CH_2\!-\!CH_2\overset{\ominus}{O}\ \overset{\oplus}{Na} \xrightarrow{H_2O} \sim\!CH_2\!-\!\underset{\displaystyle C_6H_5}{\underset{|}{CH}}\!-\!CH_2\!-\!CH_2OH + NaOH \quad (43)$$

The presence of two hydroxyl groups per chain was confirmed by active hydrogen analysis by means of the Zerewitinov technique and calculation of the molecular weight from intrinsic viscosity determinations. A similar technique (76,77) was described for the preparation of low molecular weight hydroxyl terminated polybutadiene and polyisoprene by first preparing lithium terminated polymers (using lithium naphthalene or lithium in presence of tetrahydrofuran as solvent) and then reacting with ethylene oxide.

b. Carboxyl Endgroups

If the living terminals of the above described polymers are reacted with carbon dioxide followed by hydrolysis, carboxyl endgroups result (70), as shown in eq. (44). In a similar manner, polyisoprene and polybutadiene

$$\sim\!CH_2\!-\!\underset{\displaystyle C_6H_5}{\underset{|}{\overset{\ominus}{CH}}}\ \overset{\oplus}{Na} \xrightarrow[H_2O]{CO_2} \sim\!CH_2\!-\!\underset{\displaystyle C_6H_5}{\underset{|}{CH}}\!-\!COOH + NaOH \quad (44)$$

with carboxyl terminals were prepared (77,69).

Rempp and Loucheux (78) obtained carboxyl terminated polystyrene by reacting the carbanion ends with succinic or phthalic anhydride as shown in eq. (45):

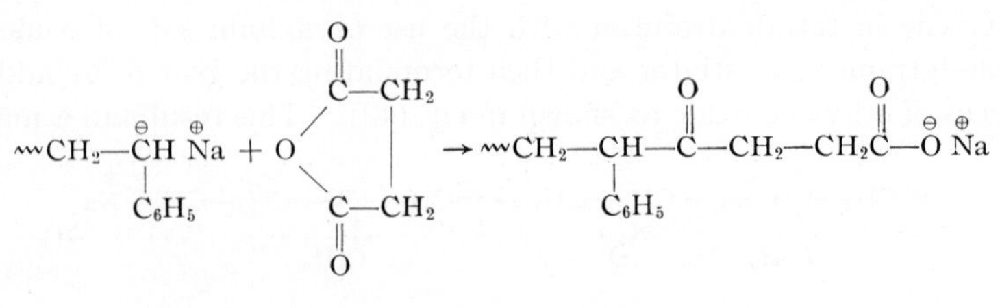
(45)

c. Terminal Double Bonds

When the carbanion terminals of polystyrene were reacted with allyl chloride or allyl bromide, Rempp and Loucheux (78) obtained terminal double bonds (eq. 46):

$$\sim\!\sim CH_2{-}\overset{\ominus}{C}H(C_6H_5)\ \overset{\oplus}{Na} + ClCH_2{-}CH{=}CH_2 \rightarrow \sim\!\sim CH_2{-}CH(C_6H_5){-}CH_2{-}CH{=}CH_2 + NaCl \quad (46)$$

d. Amine Endgroups

The conversion of living carbanion terminals into primary amine groups by reaction with amine containing reagents presents a problem in that a proton from the amine group itself can react with the carbanion, giving a dead terminal. To overcome this tendency, Loucheux, Meyer, and Rempp (79) used reagents containing an ester group in addition to a primary amine group. In this case, the ester group reacts with the carbanion preferentially leaving the amine group intact. Thus, by reacting living polystyrene with *p*-aminoethyl benzoate, an amine-terminated polystyrene was obtained as represented in eq. (47):

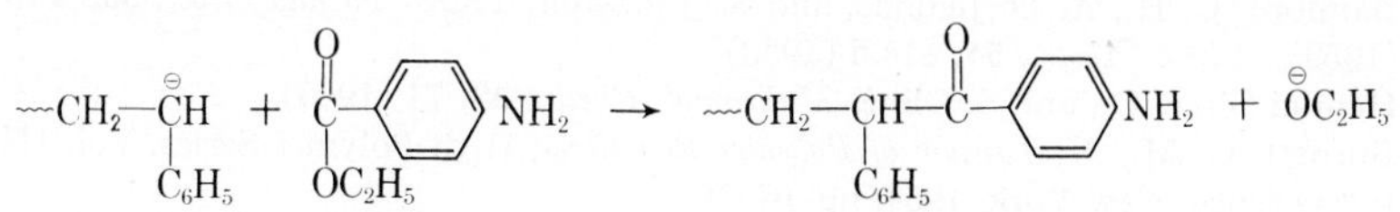

(47)

References

1. Smets, G., and R. Hart, *Fortschr. Hochpolymer. Forsch.*, **2,** 173 (1960).
2. Smets, G., A. Poot, and G. L. Duncan, *J. Polymer Sci.*, **54,** 65 (1961).
3. Flory, P. J., *Ind. Eng. Chem.*, **38,** 417 (1946).
4. Flory, P. J., *Principles of Polymer Chemistry*, Cornell University Press, Ithaca, New York, 1953, chap. IV.
5. Baxendale, J. H., M. G. Evans, and G. S. Park, *Trans. Faraday Soc.*, **42,** 155 (1946); *Chem. Abstr.*, **41,** 640c (1947).
6. Evans, M. G., *J. Chem. Soc.*, **1947,** 266.
7. Seligman, K. L., U. S. Patent 2,877,212 (to E. I. du Pont de Nemours & Co.), Mar. 10, 1959; *Chem. Abstr.*, **53,** 12730g (1959).
8. Bamford, C. H., A. D. Jenkins, and R. P. Wayne, *Trans. Faraday Soc.*, **56,** 932 (1960); *Chem. Abstr.*, **54,** 21837e (1960).
9. Bamford, C. H., A. D. Jenkins, and R. Johnston, *Trans. Faraday Soc.*, **55,** 179 (1959); *Chem. Abstr.*, **54,** 957g (1960).

10. Haines, R. M., and W. A. Waters, *J. Chem. Soc.*, **1955,** 4256.
11. Robertson, J. A., U. S. Patent 2,520,338 (to E. I. du Pont de Nemours & Co.), Aug. 29, 1950; *Chem. Abstr.*, **45,** 1386d (1951).
12. Bamford, C. H., and A. D. Jenkins, *Nature*, **176,** 78 (1955).
13. Misra, G. S., R. C. Rastogi, and V. P. Gupta, *Makromol. Chem.*, **50,** 72 (1961).
14. Thiokol Chemical Corp., unpublished work.
15. Lewis, F. M., and M. S. Matheson, *J. Am. Chem. Soc.*, **71,** 747 (1949).
16. Doehnert, D. F., and O. L. Mageli, paper presented at 13th Annual Meeting of the Reinforced Plastics Division, Chicago, Ill.; preliminary copy published in the Society of the Plastics Industry, Inc., Section 1-B, page 1 (1958).
17. Palit, S. R., B. N. Mukherjee and R. S. Konar, *J. Polymer Sci.*, **50,** 45 (1961).
18. Palit, S. R., and R. S. Konar, *J. Polymer Sci.*, **57,** 609 (1962).
19. Criegee, R., W. Schnorrenberg, and J. Becke, *Ann. Chem.*, **565,** 7 (1949); *Chem. Abstr.*, **44,** 1916g (1950).
20. Kharasch, M. S., and W. Nudenberg, *J. Org. Chem.*, **19,** 1921 (1954).
21. Berry, K. L., and J. H. Peterson, *J. Am. Chem. Soc.*, **73,** 5195 (1951).
22. Bro, M. I., and C. A. Sperati, *J. Polymer Sci.*, **38,** 289 (1959).
23. Muramatsu, H., M. Iwasaki, and R. Kojima, *Kogyo Kagaku Zasshi*, **64,** 1096 (1961); *Chem. Abstr.*, **57,** 4859b (1962).
24. Otsu, T., *J. Polymer Sci.*, **21,** 559 (1956).
25. Pierson, R. M., A. J. Constanza, and A. H. Weinstein, *J. Polymer Sci.*, **17,** 221 (1955).
26. Constanza, A. J., R. J. Coleman, R. M. Pierson, C. S. Marvel, and C. King, *J. Polymer Sci.*, **17,** 319 (1955).
27. Byrd, N. R., U. S. Patent, 3,047,544 (to Goodyear Tire and Rubber Co.), July 31, 1962; *Chem. Abstr.*, **58,** 1616h (1963).
28. Bamford, C. H., A. D. Jenkins, and R. Johnston, *Trans. Faraday Soc.*, **55,** 1451 (1959); *Chem. Abstr.*, **54,** 8143i (1960).
29. Henrici-Olivé, G., and S. Olivé, *Makromol. Chem.*, **37,** 71 (1960).
30. Burnett, G. M., *Mechanism of Polymer Reactions*, High Polymer Series, Vol. III, Interscience, New York, 1954, pp. 67–76.
31. Bickel, A. F., and W. A. Waters, *J. Chem. Soc.*, **1950,** 1764.
32. Kharasch, M. S., H. C. McBay, and W. H. Urry, *J. Org. Chem.*, **10,** 401 (1945).
33. Mayo, F. R., R. A. Gregg, and M. S. Matheson, *J. Am. Chem. Soc.*, **73,** 1691 (1951).
34. Ausloos, P., and E. W. R. Steacie, *Can. J. Chem.*, **33,** 1062 (1955).
35. Bevington, J. C., *Trans. Faraday Soc.*, **48,** 1045 (1952); *Chem. Abstr.*, **47,** 5223f (1953).
36. Baysal, B., and A. V. Tobolsky, *J. Polymer Sci.*, **8,** 529 (1952).
37. Smith, W. V., *J. Am. Chem. Soc.*, **71,** 4077 (1949).
38. Bevington, J. C., H. W. Melville, and R. P. Taylor, *J. Polymer Sci.*, **12,** 449 (1954).
39. Bevington, J. C., H. W. Melville, and R. P. Taylor, *J. Polymer Sci.*, **14,** 463 (1954).
40. Bailey, B. E., and A. D. Jenkins, *Trans. Faraday Soc.*, **56,** 903 (1960); *Chem. Abstr.*, **54,** 21844b (1960).
41. Bonsalle, E. P., L. Valentine, and H. W. Melville, *Trans. Faraday Soc.*, **49,** 686 (1953); *Chem. Abstr.*, **48,** 399i (1954).
42. Funt, B. L., and W. Pasika, *Can. J. Chem.*, **38,** 1865 (1960).

43. Allen, P. W., G. Ayrey, F. M. Merrett, and C. G. Moore, *J. Polymer Sci.*, **22**, 549 (1956).
44. Danusso, F., G. Pajar, and D. Sianesi, *Chim. Ind. (Milan)*, **41**, 1170 (1959); *Chem. Abstr.*, **55**, 20499c (1961).
45. Razuvaev, G. A., G. G. Petukhov, and V. A. Dodonov, *Vysokomolekul. Soedin.*, **3**, 1549 (1961); *Resins, Rubbers, Plastics*, **1962**, pp. 1081–1082; *Chem. Abstr.*, **56**, 10377f (1962).
46. Cavell, E. A. S., *Makromol. Chem.*, **54**, 70 (1962).
47. Szwarc, M., *Fortschr. Hochpolymer. Forsch.*, **2**, 275 (1960).
48. Mulvaney, J. E., C. G. Overberger, and A. M. Schiller, *Fortschr. Hochpolymer. Forsch.*, **3**, 106 (1961).
49. Goode, W. E., W. H. Snyder, and R. C. Fettes, *J. Polymer Sci.*, **42**, 367 (1960).
50. Schreiber, H., *Makromol. Chem.*, **36**, 86 (1960).
51. Zilkha, A., B. Feit, and M. Frankel, *J. Polymer Sci.*, **49**, 231 (1961).
52. Overberger, C. G., E. M. Pearce, and N. Mayes, *J. Polymer Sci.*, **31**, 217 (1958).
52a. Overberger, C. G., E. M. Pearce, and N. Mayes, *J. Polymer Sci.*, **34**, 109 (1959).
53. Wooding, N. S., and W. C. E. Higginson, *J. Chem. Soc.*, **1952**, 1178.
54. Ziegler, K., L. Jakob, H. Wollthan, and A. Wenz, *Ann. Chem.*, **511**, 64 (1934); *Chem. Abstr.*, **28**, 5431[6] (1934).
55. Abkin, A., and S. Medvedev, *Trans. Faraday Soc.*, **32**, 286 (1936); *Chem. Abstr.*, **30**, 2472[5] (1936).
56. Robertson, R. E., and L. Marion, *Can. J. Res.*, **26B**, 657 (1948).
57. Scott, N. D., U. S. Patent 2,181,771 (to E. I. du Pont de Nemours & Co.), Nov. 28, 1939, *Chem. Abstr.*, **34**, 2104[5] (1940).
58. Paul, D. E., D. Lipkin, and S. I. Weissman, *J. Am. Chem. Soc.*, **78**, 116 (1956).
59. Szwarc, M., *Nature*, **178**, 1168 (1956).
60. Szwarc, M., M. Levy, and R. Milkovich, *J. Am. Chem. Soc.*, **78**, 2656 (1956).
61. Worsfold, D. J., and S. Bywater, *J. Chem. Soc.*, **1960**, 5234.
62. McCormick, H. W., *J. Polymer Sci.*, **36**, 341 (1959).
63. Waack, R., A. Rembaum, J. D. Coombes, and M. Szwarc, *J. Am. Chem. Soc.*, **79**, 2026 (1957).
64. Brody, H., M. Ladacki, R. Milkovich, and M. Szwarc, *J. Polymer Sci.*, **25**, 221 (1957).
65. Glusker, D. L., E. Stiles, and B. Yoncoskie, paper presented at the 135th Meeting of the American Chemical Society, Boston, Mass., Apr. 5–10, 1959.
66. Graham, R. K., D. L. Dunkelberger, and E. S. Cohn, *J. Polymer Sci.*, **42**, 501 (1960).
67. Eberly, K. C., U. S. Patent 2,947,793 (to Firestone Tire and Rubber Co.), Aug. 2, 1960; *Chem. Abstr.*, **55**, 382g (1961).
68. Gaylord, N. G., and H. F. Mark, *Linear and Stereoregular Addition Polymers*, Polymer Reviews Series, Vol. II, Interscience, New York, 1959.
68a. Ref. 68, Table XII-15, p. 398–399, No. 11.
68b. Ref. 68, Table XII-16, p. 400–401, Nos. 30–32.
68c. Ref. 68, Table XII-17, p. 406–407, Nos. 7, 15, 16.
69. Uranek, C. A., H. L. Hsieh, and O. G. Buck, *J. Polymer Sci.*, **46**, 535 (1960).
70. Brody, H., D. H. Richards, and M. Szwarc, *Chem. Ind. (London)*, **45**, 1473 (1958).
71. Franta, E., and P. Rempp, *Compt. Rend.*, **254**, 674 (1962); *Chem. Abstr.*, **56**, 14466d (1962).

72. Richards, D. H., and M. Szwarc, *Trans. Faraday Soc.*, **55,** 1644 (1959); *Chem. Abstr.*, **54,** 9350g (1960).
73. Szwarc, M., and A. Rembaum, *J. Polymer Sci.*, **22,** 189 (1956).
74. Schlick, S., and M. Levy, *J. Phys. Chem.*, **64,** 883 (1960).
75. Finaz, G., Y. Gallot, J. Parrod, and P. Rempp, *J. Polymer Sci.*, **58,** 1363 (1962).
76. Goldberg, E. J., U. S. Patent 3,055,952 (to E. I. du Pont de Nemours & Co.), Sept. 25, 1962; *Chem. Abstr.*, **58,** 645f (1963).
77. Schoenberg, E., *J. Polymer Sci.*, **49,** S9 (1961).
78. Rempp, P., and M. H. Loucheux, *Bull. Soc. Chim. France*, **1958,** 1497; *Chem. Abstr.*, **53,** 16026e (1959).
79. Loucheux, M. H., G. Meyer, and P. Rempp, *Compt. Rend.*, **252,** 2552 (1961); *Chem. Abstr.*, **55,** 20489f (1961).

Chapter V

REACTIONS OF CELLULOSE

Kyle Ward, Jr., and A. J. Morak

The Institute of Paper Chemistry

A. INTRODUCTION

The structure of the β-1,4-glucan, cellulose, has already been discussed in Chapter I-C. The chain is linear and there is no evidence of either cross-linking or branching. Many volumes have been devoted to the subject of its properties and reactions. Much valuable information can be found in the ten volumes of Worden (436,437) and the two of Faust (111), but more recent works, Heuser (177), Wise and Jahn (432), and Ott (295) are more up to date. Heuser (177) and Spurlin (378) have given good general reviews of cellulose reactivity.

In its reactions, cellulose is usually attacked in one or several of three ways. First, in hydrolysis and some other degradations, the glycosidic linkage is attacked. Second, the very reactive hydroxyls may be oxidized or substituted in various ways. Third, the C–H bond or other low-energy bonds may be broken, which probably occurs in many degradations and in the initiation of graft polymerization.

Before going on to discuss specific reactions, it should be pointed out that the fine structure of the cellulose is usually of great importance in determining the course of the reaction and the properties of the products. Where the reactions occur in dilute solution, they take place randomly along the molecular chain, but this type of reaction is not the most common. In fibrous reactions there is usually a rapidly reacting accessible region of low lateral order and a much less reactive region of high order. Particularly in reactions of the hydroxyl groups, the properties of the reaction products will depend on the extent of the reaction as well as on the distribution of the reaction sites and both of these factors are governed in large part by the fine structure. There are a number of reviews of the reactivity of cellulose (177,378,401a).

There may be up to 10,000 or more hydroxyl groups per cellulose molecule. In certain processes used to modify textile or paper fibers only a few of these need react to produce a considerable change in the properties. If the reaction is more extensive, so that appreciable numbers of reacted and unchanged hydroxyls occur simultaneously, we have yet another type of product, while a completely reacted cellulose, virtually free of hydroxyl groups, is different from either. All of these types will be discussed in this chapter.

The literature is too vast to cite all references. The authors have tried to use those articles, frequently reviews, which will give the reader the most information, and in most cases the older papers are not directly cited.

B. DEGRADATIVE REACTIONS

1. Hydrolysis

The hydrolysis of polymers in general is discussed in Chapter VIII-A. Some excellent reviews of cellulose hydrolysis are available (208,309), notably that of McBurney (245), who has discussed the kinetics and the differences between reaction in solution and in the fibrous state (see Chapter I-C).

The glycoside linkage is stable to alkalies, but sensitive to acids. Cellulose dissolves in concentrated mineral acids, (70% H_2SO_4, 40% HCl, or 85% H_3PO_4) at 0–10°C., a process involving oxonium compound formation and esterification (39,45,102,198,293), as well as hydrolysis and reversion, or condensation of the lower sugars. To obtain the end-product, glucose, the solution can be diluted and heated (177a,279a). By interrupting the hydrolysis before completion, various oligosaccharides of the cellobiose series and mixtures of partly hydrolyzed glucans with degrees of polymerization intermediate between the oligosaccharides and cellulose can be isolated (431,440).

Most investigators (208,245,271,309,369) accept the conclusion of Freudenberg (119,120) that the glycoside linkages in native cellulose are alike, but several have interpreted the data as indicating the presence of a few bonds which are more easily broken (181,189,237,298,353–355). However, many structural changes, conversion of a hydroxyl to carbonyl or carboxyl (311) or the opening of the pyrane ring (202), facilitate glycoside cleavage (374), and these are so easily introduced during purification of the cellulose that the idea of a strictly uniform native cellulose seems entirely compatible with the evidence. In this connection it has been pointed out that regeneration without chemical change can introduce acid sensitivity (276a).

The hydrolysis of fibrous cellulose does indeed proceed more rapidly at first than later, but the explanation advanced in Chapter I-C is the usual one. Although the glycoside linkages are alike, the molecular arrangement of a cellulose fiber is varied. In regions of relatively poor order, the easily accessible material is readily attacked (61,90,286,288,389). If the reaction is stopped at this point, the product is weak, with increased reducing power and lower solution viscosity, all indications of lower degree of polymerization. It is a mixture of polymer-homologous "hydrocelluloses" with a high degree of order, and subsequent hydrolysis is much slower. This phenomenon of a rapidly reacting accessible region and a slowly reacting ordered region is frequently observed for cellulose reactions in the fibrous state (89,316), as has been stated earlier. While the loss of weight continues slowly in extended hydrolyses, especially with regenerated cellulose, the degree of polymerization reaches what Battista (16) calls the "leveling-off degree of polymerization" corresponding to the isolation of "crystallites."

Aqueous acids are good swelling agents, and the chain ends produced from scission in the accessible regions have some mobility. This promotes "recrystallization" and the production of higher order than originally existed in these regions (197,253). It has been pointed out that this effect needs to be considered in interpreting the results of the commonly used acid hydrolysis methods of measuring order (16,186,303,335,369). These methods involve plotting of the rate curves of hydrolysis under strictly specified conditions and extrapolation of the final linear portion back to zero time or simply measurement of weight loss after a specified time for comparative values. Boiling HCl, 2.5–6N (16,303), has commonly been used for the hydrolysis.

Hydrolysis of cellulose can be used as a source of glucose and indirectly of alcohol or of yeast. This is not important in normal times in countries with sufficient reservoirs of starch or sugar, but much research has been carried on all over the world and there are important industrial installations in some countries. The technical processes of wood hydrolysis were reviewed by Stamm and Harris (384), while special monographs on current Japanese (234) and Russian (151,368) practice exist.

2. Oxidation

Oxidation of polymers in general is treated in another chapter but the special case of the oxidation of cellulose is a very complicated process; however, there are good reviews (245,272,273,309,411). Oxidative attack occurs (or at least begins) almost exclusively at the hydroxyl groups, but there are two secondary (numbers 2 and 3) hydroxyls and one primary (number 6) hydroxyl on each glucose unit, as well as an extra secondary hydroxyl at the nonreducing end of the molecule and a hemiacetal hydroxyl at the reducing end. For a degree of polymerization n, therefore, there would be $3n + 2$ hydroxyls. If n is 1000 (it is higher than this for native cellulose), this is 3002 hydroxyls. If we consider only conversion of the hydroxyl to carbonyl and assume random attack, there would be 2^{3002} possibilities, an astronomical figure.

Attack is usually not completely random and the situation is further complicated by two other factors. First, other products besides simple carbonyl functions are formed, and different oxidants (or even the same oxidant under different conditions) will attack the glucose unit in different ways; complete specificity of an oxidizing agent is practically never achieved. Second, there are frequently secondary transformations; in particular, there is usually chain breakdown (388).

In spite of this, we know a surprising amount about the oxidation of cellulose, both the nature of the products and the kinetics. Most kinetic studies cover degradation during oxidation and this has been well discussed by McBurney (245). The general principles already discussed for hydrolytic degradation apply here, but the kinetics and products of the primary nondegrading oxidation processes cannot be generalized in any simple manner, and one must treat various oxidants separately. When this is done, we find that although complete specificity is extremely rare, there are oxidants which under carefully controlled conditions yield predominantly one product.

There are for instance, a few reagents, like hypoiodite (29) and acidified chlorite solutions (3a), which have little or no action on the alcoholic hydroxyl groups, but which will oxidize the terminal reducing group to a carboxyl. The pyranose ring is opened, and a gluconic acid residue formed or the lactone thereof. These oxidations are sufficiently specific that they have been used for quantitative measurement of endgroups or of aldehyde groups in cellulose. In the first, a suspension of cellulose buffered at pH 10.6 is treated with $0.05N$ iodine in 4% aqueous potassium iodide at 10°C. (265a). In the second, cellulose is treated with a $0.4M$ solution of sodium chlorite acidified with acetic acid to pH 2.5 (338a).

Another case of relative specificity is the action of nitrogen oxides, dinitrogen tetroxide in particular (344,371,438). Here the initial reaction occurs predominantly, although not exclusively, with the primary alcohol groups. The oxidized product contains mainly carboxyl groups, although reducing groups (247,269,283) and nitrogenous ester groups (381) are also present. Such esters, in fact, are probably the first intermediates in the oxidation (109,246). The oxidant may be in the gas phase (246) or dissolved, for instance in carbon tetrachloride (438), and the reaction takes place at room temperature.

The periodate ion is another relatively specific oxidant (170). This reagent attacks the 2,3-glycol, breaking the ring with the formation of two aldehyde groups (203). The aldehyde groups may hydrate (337) or form acetals (167) or hemiacetals (167,284); the reaction product usually contains carboxyl groups as well. By carrying out the reaction with aqueous sodium metaperiodate at room temperature, secondary reactions can be hindered (88). By means of various subsequent treatments, the aldehyde groups can be reduced to alcohols or oxidized to acids and by a combination (periodate followed by nitrogen oxides) to a derivative containing tricarboxylic acids as units (202).

In the oxidation discussed, secondary reactions usually occur before the primary reaction is complete (88). Reaction is random along the chain, except for the marked influence of accessibility (the periodate oxidation is the basis for a suggested measure of accessibility (145)). This randomness of reaction is still more evident with the less specific oxidizing agents.

The reaction of cellulose with hypochlorite (or with the chlorine–water system in general) has been much studied (56,57,104,108), for these are common bleaching agents, and the deleterious effects of overbleaching are attributable to oxidation. The effect of pH, an effect by no means limited to chlorine oxidations (95), is, speaking broadly, to produce "reducing oxycelluloses" (with a preponderance of carbonyl groups) on the acid side and "acidic oxycelluloses" (with a preponderance of carboxyl groups) on the alkaline side (28). Epstein and Lewin (108), who have recently studied this reaction over the pH range 5–10 found as high as 3.5 aldehyde and 5 ketone groups per carboxyl in the pH 5 oxycellulose, but only 0.16 carbonyl, all aldehyde, at pH 10. Chain scission and oxidation occur simultaneously and at similar rates. These rates are highest at pH 6–8, which is in harmony with the well-known fact that degradation often occurs in bleaching done near the neutral point. The authors propose a free radical mechanism involving a hydroxyl radical and a hypothetical hydroperoxide of chlorine monoxide.

Potassium permanganate has been suggested as specific for the reducing endgroup (180), but it has not been found suitable for this purpose (188, 274). In the usual oxidation of fibrous cellulose with aqueous permanganate at room temperature, the nature of the product changes with pH in a manner similar to hypochlorite oxidations (95). The oxidation is much more deep-seated and uniform if carried out on a solution of cellulose in cuprammonium hydroxide solution, and glucuronic acid can be isolated from the product (217).

Chromic acid (an acidified solution of potassium dichromate) (57,89) or chromium trioxide (dissolved in a mixture of acetic acid and acetic anhydride (141,270) react with cellulose at room temperature to produce a reducing-type oxycellulose containing both aldehyde and ketone groups, but the reaction is much less specific than that of periodic acid. The chromium trioxide reaction rate is the basis of a method for determining accessibility (142), the slow reaction being extrapolated back to zero time to measure the nonaccessible fraction. *tertiary*-Butyl chromate in benzene reacts slowly with cellulose (336) at room temperature in the presence of acetic acid and acetic anhydride and more rapidly at 65–70°C. The main reaction is oxidation of the 6-carbon to the aldehyde, but there is also some carboxyl formation.

Hydrogen and sodium peroxides are used widely in bleaching (17,99,416); it is obvious, therefore, that the action of peroxide on cellulose can be kept to very low levels (345,388). Still, under strongly alkaline conditions, peroxide oxidizes cellulose in a very complex manner (166,201), producing ring scission and a variety of functional groups, including esters and lactones. Ozone also acts on wet cellulose in a complex manner (95a).

Cellulose is normally stable to oxygen; that is, the action of atmospheric oxygen is very, very slow at room temperature. However, at elevated temperatures, under strongly alkaline conditions, or in the presence of catalysts the reaction is accelerated, producing carbonyl and carboxyl groups and chain scission.

Major (256) concludes, from a review of previous work and from his own experiments, that "thermal" damage to cellulose at 170°C. is largely oxidative in the presence of air. The action is not specific, involving the formation of several types of carbonyl and carboxyl, as well as chain scission and occurs primarily in the less ordered regions. The chain scission eventually slows down and a leveling-off degree of polymerization is reached.

One example of the susceptibility of cellulose to oxidation by oxygen in the presence of bases is found in the behavior of solutions of cellulose in the strongly alkaline cuprammonium hydroxide solutions (345,353). In the presence of air, degradation is rapid. Since copper–amine solutions are used for the measurement of chain length in cellulose, the exclusion of air is a necessary precaution in the preparation and use of such solutions (149,335).

The most important case, however, of the effect of alkali on the oxidation of cellulose with oxygen is the so-called "aging" or autoxidation of alkali cellulose. This controlled oxidation is an important step in the manufacture of viscose rayon (84,177,227,430). It is carried out by impregnating a purified cellulose with 16–18% sodium hydroxide, pressing (or centrifuging) out the excess liquor, shredding, and letting stand in air for a day or two at 25–30°C. The removal of excess liquor is necessary (420a); in fact, the rate of aging varies with the degree of pressing (430). Oxygen is absorbed, carbon dioxide is produced, carboxyl groups are introduced into the cellulose, and there is a marked decrease in molecular weight. A free radical mechanism, analogous to that for air autoxidation of hydrocarbons and aldehydes, has been proposed for the reaction (106,107,245).

Of the several examples of catalysts affecting air oxidation, one of the most interesting is the accelerated decomposition of cellulosic fabrics containing reduced vat dyes (40). The effect of this redox system is consistent with a free radical mechanism. Catalysts, such as iron and manganese, can also be used during the aging of alkali cellulose. Manganese is particularly interesting, as results vary with the method of adding the metal salt (296). If the pulp is impregnated with manganous sulfate before steeping, the reaction is retarded (84); if the manganous sulfate is added to the liquor, the reaction is accelerated (13).

Other oxidations of cellulose are also susceptible to catalysis. For instance, the hypochlorite oxidation can be catalyzed by chromium salts (57) or by the presence of a reduced vat dye (282). The catalysis of this system has been very well reviewed by Purves (309).

Examples have been given where oxidation may be either a desirable or an undesirable factor in the industrial utilization of cellulose, and the list could be greatly extended. In many cases very slight oxidations occurring during the isolation and purification of cellulosic raw materials have considerable effect on the subsequent processing and properties of the products.

For instance, the carbonyl and carboxyl groups introduced by oxidation produce inductive effects which promote cleavage of the glycoside linkages (311). Particularly troublesome is the alkaline instability of "reducing oxycelluloses" (67,272,275,299,309,311). This is a special case of the alkaline degradation of β-carbonyl ethers and has been well discussed by McBurney (245). This phenomenon is responsible for many of the bad effects of overbleaching cellulosic textiles and pulp, as has been reviewed by Meller (270a). In oxidized cotton (83a) this is evidenced in partial solubility and loss of fiber strength. In wood pulps the α-cellulose content is lowered, a matter of concern with dissolving pulps (275a). The use of viscosity in copper solvents, either for control purposes in industrial processes or for molecular weight determinations, is also affected (41a,84a, 86, 87).

The phenomenon of color reversion in bleached cellulosic materials is complicated, but at least part of the yellowing with time appears to be related to carbonyl content (28,138,377). This is observed with textiles, pulp, and paper.

The carboxyl content is responsible for most of the ion-exchange properties of oxidized cellulose (90a). However, it is not as much a promoter of subsequent degradation as the carbonyl group; in fact, conversion of carbonyl to carboxyl will improve the alkali stability of oxidized celluloses.

Treatment with chlorous acid (acidified solutions of sodium chlorite) will prevent alkali damage in periodate-oxidized cotton (315a,338a), as will treatment with ethereal solutions of diazomethane (315a,316a). On the other hand, diazomethane, but not chlorous acid, has a similar effect on hypochlorite-oxidized cotton. Perhaps this is because of the non-oxidizable ketone groups in the latter. Recently the stabilizing effect of sodium borohydride (139,214,312,418,420), especially on color reversion, has been intensively studied. This is potentially very useful, as the reduction of carbonyl so produced, introduces hydroxyl and no foreign group like carboxyl.

3. Nonoxidative Alkaline Degradation

Even in cellulose unmodified by oxidation, there is a reducing endgroup, so that a reaction similar to the alkalinebreakdown of oxidized cellulose may occur here also, although elevated temperatures are necessary (67,118, 272). The mechanism corresponds to that involved in forming glucoisosaccharinic acid from glucose except that a cellulosate ion is split off instead of a hydroxyl ion. This produces another chain with a reducing endgroup, and the process repeats itself progressively to shorten the chain, the so-called "peeling" reaction.

Other transformations occur besides the main reaction (249). One of these, the "stopping" reaction, corresponds to a glucometasaccharinic acid conversion of the terminal glucose unit, and this does not involve scission of the chain. It is this competing reaction that prevents the peeling reaction from completely degrading the cellulose, for the new molecule does not contain a reducing endgroup. The stopping reaction is faster in lime-water than in sodium hydroxide, and therefore chain degradation does not proceed so far in the presence of calcium hydroxide (250).

4. Other Types of Degradation

Closely related to acidic hydrolysis is enzymolysis, or hydrolysis by enzymes, which is of tremendous practical importance because this is the mechanism of most microbiological degradation of cellulose. There are many reviews (69,132,133,196,314,375,376), and there is great scientific activity in the field, as might be expected since it is important for such varied groups as the biologist, the food processor, and the wood, paper, and textile producer (and consumer) (131).

Alcoholysis is the breakdown of cellulose by alcohols in the presence of an acid catalyst, usually hydrogen chloride. The products of alcoholysis differ from those of hydrolysis in that the resulting carbohydrate fragments are nonreducing alkyl glycosides. The reaction is faster than hydrolysis and can be followed at room temperature. The initial process may involve hydrolysis, water being formed from the alcohol and the acid (417), but the medium is essentially nonswelling and recrystallization does not occur. It has therefore been suggested as a measure of order in the cellulose fiber (232) instead of hydrolysis. Methanolysis of cellulose acetate at 125°C. has been used to produce methyl glucosides and is almost quantitative (177a,199a).

If cellulose is treated with acetic anhydride and relatively large amounts of sulfuric acid at low temperature and allowed to stand, chain scission occurs in addition to acetylation (114). If the concentrations and temperature are so chosen, insoluble cellobiose octaacetate will crystallize out (293), but the acetolysis reaction can be interrupted to obtain acetates of the β-1,4 series of oligosaccharides (93,433) as well as of higher homologues (20). Large amounts of glucose pentaacetate are also formed, of course (293,427). Acetolysis has been used to prepare the β-1,4-oligosaccharides and their derivatives (93,434).

The wood distillation industry is not within the scope of this chapter, but the pyrolysis of cellulose should be mentioned (255). Even if oxygen is rigorously excluded, cellulose breaks down on heating (256). That levoglucosan is produced by dry distillation in vacuum has been known for a long time (304), and the formation has been very thoroughly studied recently (150). Levoglucosan is probably an intermediate in heat degradation at atmospheric pressure. Thermal degradation of polymers in general is discussed in Chapter VIII-B.

Other forms of energy besides thermal energy can break the cellulose chain, even mechanical action (176,387) like ball-milling (see also Chapter XIV). Damage to cellulosic textiles or paper by visible or ultraviolet irradiation has been observed for a long time and there are many reviews (3,329). Recently the effect of high energy radiations has been widely studied (31,32,195). In all these cases, it is doubtful if specific types of bonds are broken exclusively, but low energy bonds would be expected to be more easily and predominantly broken. Radicals so formed can participate in secondary reactions. The most obvious gross result is the degradation of the molecule, but crosslinking may also occur. (A general discussion of radiation cleavage is given in Chapter VIII-C.)

C. SUBSTITUTION REACTIONS

1. Esters

The hydroxyls of cellulose can be esterified like any other hydroxy groups. The commonest method is the simplest; reaction with the acid or the anhydride in the presence of an acid catalyst, usually sulfuric (177). Less frequently other catalysts, like perchloric acid (235b, 235c), perchlorates (235a), or zinc chloride (120a) are used. Many acids do not esterify readily, and other methods can be used to promote esterifications. Cellulose reacts with acyl chlorides or anhydrides in the presence of pyridine or another base (387a); this will frequently minimize concomitant hydrolytic degradation. There are also certain anhydrides which do not themselves esterify cellulose but which will "impel" esterification by other acids; such anhydrides are chloroacetic (55) and trifluoroacetic anhydride (380). Esterifications also proceed more readily in the presence of more polar media like dimethylformamide (31a). Ketene will acetylate cellulose, if the latter is properly activated (161), and substituted ketenes have also been used (90b). Finally, there is the special case of cellulose xanthation, to be discussed in more detail later.

An extremely large number of esters has been prepared, and there are many reviews (44,177). The chapters of Barsha (11) and of Malm and Hiatt (260) in Ott's *Cellulose and Cellulose Derivatives* are excellent. Malm has also published a briefer review more recently (257). Esterification, frequently to a very slight extent, as a means of imparting water repellency to textiles forms one section of the review of this field by Schuyten and co-workers (358). Cyrot's 1959 list of cellulose derivatives (74), also slanted toward textile conversions, lists esters of 129 acids. All of these cannot be discussed, but certain important esterifications should be handled individually.

a. Inorganic Acids

Nitration of cellulose, as the formation of the nitrate ester is commonly called, was the first substitution reaction applied to cellulose. It produces cellulose nitrate which was, for a long time, the most important cellulose derivative. Industrially, this is prepared by reaction with a mixture of nitric and sulfuric acids at ordinary temperatures for about $^1/_2$ hr. The active agent is the nitronium ion (225), which penetrates even the crystalline regions of the cellulose so rapidly that there is little effect of accessibility. The composition of the ester is determined by an equilibrium with the composition of the nitrating liquor (21,22). There will be some unsubstituted hydroxyls and some esterified with sulfuric acid (71) as well as with nitric acid (22). There is, then, for the large cellulose molecule, a tremendous number of theoretically possible cellulose nitrates. In the usual nitration, the sulfate groups are eliminated or nearly so by prolonged heating with dilute nitric acid or water, and the substitution of the hydroxyls by nitrate groups along the chain seems to be random, so that, in general, the nitrates can be distinguished simply by their nitrogen contents.

During the industrial nitration of cellulose there is a certain amount of degradation, largely due to the sulfuric acid catalyst. This is not necessarily undesirable; in fact, in some cases either the cellulose or the nitrate must be additionally degraded so that the viscosity may be controlled, since for many purposes, low viscosity is necessary. The pulp may be degraded by mercerization followed by hydrolyzing in boiling 1% sulfuric acid (357). The cellulose nitrate is degraded by heating with water for 25 min. at a pressure in excess of 100 psi (279).

Often, however, one wishes to nitrate cellulose without degradation. In the laboratory, for instance, in the determination of molecular weights by the nitrate viscosity method (3,73,266,267), two procedures are frequently used to obtain practically complete nitration with minimal degradation. In one, the nitrating acid is produced by dissolving phosphorus pentoxide in 90% nitric acid (3,73). In the other, it is produced by adding acetic anhydride to 90% nitric acid (19a,23,73,164a,409). While nitrations with the use of phosphorus pentoxide can be carried out at 20°C., it is better to operate at 0°C. or less in the case of the acetic anhydride mixture on account of explosive by-products.

Various nitrogen oxides have also been used experimentally for the nitration of cellulose. Nitrogen pentoxide (75,76,412), in the vapor phase or in chloroform solution, is a good nitrating agent and can be added to nitric acid instead of sulfuric acid or phosphorus pentoxide for nitrating cellulose

(334). Nitrogen trioxide added to nitric acid causes increased nitration of cellulose and also increased degradation (334). This is also true of dinitrogen tetroxide and nitric acid (305,334,371). (It has already been pointed out that the ester is probably formed first in the oxidation of cellulose with this oxide.) The use of an anhydrous mixture of dinitrogen tetroxide and hydrogen fluoride has recently been shown to produce successful nitration in the temperature range from -10°C. to $+12$°C. (53).

The solubilities and other properties vary with the nitrogen content and therefore so do the uses. The useful range of substitution runs from about 11% nitrogen or a little less, up to 13.5% or a little higher. The theoretical nitrogen content of the completely nitrated product (three nitrate groups per glucose unit) is 14.14%. Highly nitrated products are used in explosives, those of lower nitrogen content in plastics, lacquers, and adhesives (11).

Esterification with sulfuric acid is one of the reactions occurring during nitration of cellulose (71), as has already been mentioned. The simple sulfate esters are also known, and methods for producing them, as well as mixed cellulose esters of acetic and sulfuric acid, have been reviewed by Barsha (11). The simplest method, discovered in 1819 (39), is solution in concentrated sulfuric acid and reprecipitation in water (45). The partially hydrolyzed residue from treatment with 50% sulfuric acid also contains some half-esters of sulfuric acid and has ion-exchange properties. (Esters with sulfuric acids are usually of this type.) Fibrous cellulose sulfates can be made by treating cellulose with a mixture of sulfuric acid with an aliphatic alcohol at low temperatures (115,258). Dry cellulose will also react with sulfur trioxide vapor (406) or with sulfur trioxide in carbon disulfide (406a) at 0°C. to give a trisulfate. Degradation can be reduced by the use of pyridine as a medium and pyrosulfuric acid (328) or chlorosulfonic acid (137, 406a) as the reagent. Liquid sulfur dioxide at -20°C. has also been recommended in the presence of sulfuric acid, sulfur trioxide, or chlorosulfonic acid (9). An unusual method for obtaining esters with low degrees of substitution consists of impregnating cellulose with an aqueous solution of urea sulfamate and heating (400a). The conversion results in the introduction of the ammonium salt of the half-ester of sulfuric acid.

Esterification with phosphoric acid can also be carried out in various ways. Phosphoric acid with another mineral acid catalyst (sulfuric acid) (193), with dinitrogen tetroxide (109), or with phosphorus oxychloride (192) gives cellulose phosphate of low degree of substitution (D.S.), as do phosphorus oxychloride and pyridine (324,325). Small amounts of phosphorus can be introduced, as the ammonium salt of a cellulose ester of phosphoric acid, to flameproof cellulose by impregnation with urea phosphate and curing 20 min. at 140°C. (66). Substituted phosphoric acids yield substituted phosphates with similar treatments (79,80,348). The phosphate ester usually formed is an acid ester (325), as is also true of sulfate, and the product is therefore a polyelectrolyte with ion-exchange properties of some interest (169,198,215,301a). Phosphites and phosphinates can be produced by transesterification with alkyl phosphite esters with the use of sodium as a catalyst (301b).

Champetier (44) gives references to the perchlorate, the nitrosilicate, the nitrite, and the ester of hydrogen chloride. The first three of these have not been well characterized, but chlorocellulose, produced by the action of thionyl chloride upon a suspension of cellulose in toluene and pyridine, has been studied a little more thoroughly (35,42). 6-Chloroglucose has been isolated from the hydrolyzate of this substance (35).

b. Organic Acids

There are too many cellulose esters of organic acids for full treatment, especially when one considers the numerous mixed esters and the ether-esters. One cannot even describe all the simple esters fully. Malm has recently reviewed the general subject of cellulose esterification with carboxylic acids (257).

Cellulose formylation (44,260) is not typical of the aliphatic series, for the formates are not stable. Formylation occurs with formic acid alone or with various catalysts.

Cellulose acetylation is, however, a good prototype. The various cellulose acetates and mixed esters are produced in great quantity for plastics, sheeting, films, and rayon.

Accessibility plays an important role during the acetylation of cellulose (285,386,413) (see Chapter I-C). As a result, acetyl content alone is not a sufficient criterion for distinguishing the various acetates; one must also know the location of the acetyl groups which depends upon the method of preparation. There are three important commercial products; the triacetate (primary acetate), the acetone-soluble, secondary acetate, and the fibrous acetate (acetylated textiles). The simple expression "cellulose acetate" usually refers to the most common, secondary acetate.

The primary acetate is the first stage of the usual commercial solution process (262). This is essentially an esterification with acetic anhydride and sulfuric acid catalyst, although in the laboratory many other catalysts may be used (264), as well as impelling agents (55,380). There is usually a pretreatment with acetic acid to activate the cellulose. Glacial acetic acid is less effective, but more economical because water consumes anhydride later. Catalyst may be present, but will cause degradation and reduction of viscosity. The entire process can be conveniently carried out in a heavy-duty mixer to ensure uniformity of the thick suspension and later of the viscous solution.

After the pretreatment, acetic anhydride is added and additional catalyst, if necessary. The reaction must be kept cool during the first stages at least, but the temperature may later be allowed to rise (the reaction is exothermic). Primary hydroxyls react first. The sulfuric acid esterifies more rapidly than the acetic anhydride and in the intermediate stages may be quantitatively bound to the cellulose. When esterification is complete, a clear solution is formed of a completely esterified acetate sulfate of high sulfate content. If the reaction is allowed to continue, transesterification of the sulfate groups produces the triacetate (262,263,396).

The secondary acetate is produced from the solution of the fully esterified material while it still has the sulfate ester groups present. Water is added, usually as dilute acetic acid and sometimes containing more catalyst. The resulting hydrolysis removes most of the sulfate groups. The amount of acetyl groups split off and the extent of chain degradation will depend upon the conditions of hydrolysis. Deacetylation is promoted by excess amounts of water, which retards reacetylation. Residual sulfuric acid ester may be removed with boiling water. There are various modifications of the process, a commercial variant being the use of methylene chloride (184,191) as a solvent during the acetylation. There are several types of secondary cellulose acetate in commercial use, usually with a D.S. of 2–2.5. Hydrolysis can be continued in the presence of more water to give a water-soluble product of D.S. 0.5–1.0 (113a).

Acetylation can also be carried out in the presence of a nonsolvent for cellulose acetate, such as benzene. In this case, the acetylated product retains its fibrous form. Even in the absence of a nonsolvent diluent, acetylation with perchloric acid catalyst can be interrupted before completion to give a fibrous acetate with only partial substitution (6). With the nonsolvent, sulfoacetic acid, sulfuric acid, and other catalysts (339–341), or the impelling agent, trifluoroacetic anhydride (164), may also be used. A fibrous triacetate has been produced with the use of amyl acetate (41c) or isopropyl acetate (254a) as a diluent.

The product obtained by direct acetylation of one-third the hydroxyls is quite different from the product produced by deacetylation of the primary acetate (41b). This should not be too surprising, as the distribution of the substituents and the molecular arrangement of the two products are both different. Direct acetylation substitutes the accessible groups and does not break the hydrogen bonds that join molecules in the ordered regions, so that a block copolymer is produced. The deacetylated product is made from a uniformly dispersed triacetate in which groups are equally accessible, so that the acetyl groups are randomly distributed along the chain, although there may be a preponderance of secondary hydroxyls remaining acetylated.

The fibrous acetylation of cotton produces products of high heat stability and resistance to microorganisms (6,148,339). Vapor-phase acetylation has also been studied (46,223,339), and a partly acetylated rayon is so manufactured (395). Direct acetylation to a very low degree of substitution actually increases the moisture sorption of cellulosic pulps (2), probably due to opening up the fine structure. As acetylation proceeds, the affinity for water drops. Paper sheets with good properties can be made from more highly acetylated fibers, but acetone must be used instead of water for forming them (30).

Cellulose propionate and cellulose butyrate may be prepared similarly to the acetate. They are not as important commercially as the mixed esters acetate–propionate or acetate–butyrate, produced by incorporation of propionic or butyric acid into the acetylation bath (260).

Malm and his co-workers have prepared the whole series of cellulose esters from acetate to stearate (55) by reaction of the free acid at 60–65°C. in the presence of an impelling agent (chloroacetic anhydride) and a catalyst (magnesium perchlorate). In addition to this general method, there is another which may be used, the action of acid chlorides in the presence of a base, especially pyridine (160,261) or quinoline (308). Cruz-Lagrange and co-workers, using cotton fabric, have prepared fibrous partial esters of acetic, butyric, capric, and stearic acids, as well as some of their unsaturated analogues (72), using trifluoroacetic anhydride and benzene with the corresponding acid at room temperature.

Esterification with aliphatic acids has been discussed first because this is the typical reaction. An equally important esterification industrially is xanthation (227), however, which is the basis of the viscose rayon and cellophane industries. There are several chemical changes involved in this process. The first of these is the formation and aging of alkali cellulose, already discussed as one of the oxidative processes. Sodium hydroxide is used industrially, but other alkalies have been used in laboratory studies (1,14,179a).

In the esterification proper, carbon disulfide reacts with the alkali cellulose to form the sodium salt of cellulose xanthate:

$$\text{Cell—O}^- + CS_2 \rightarrow \text{Cell—O—}\overset{\overset{\displaystyle S}{\|}}{C}\text{—S}^-$$

It is an oversimplification to write only this reaction, for the system O_2–NaOH–H_2O–CS_2–cellulose is a complicated one and many other reactions occur (227,419). These reactions result in the production of sodium carbonate, sodium sulfide, and sodium trithiocarbonate. The latter is responsible for the yellow color from which the name "xanthate" is derived. All three salts can be formed from aqueous alkali and carbon disulfide, but the detailed mechanism of their formation and of other reactions during the viscose process is still the subject of investigation (419).

There are various recent modifications of the conventional processes of alkali cellulose preparation and aging, xanthation, and xanthate solution. They are followed by a ripening step. The chemical change occurring here is the reverse of xanthation, cellulose being regenerated from the sodium cellulose xanthate. With time, the disappearance of carbon disulfide by reaction with alkali favors the equilibrium shift to produce cellulose (419). This results in changes in the degree of hydration and of aggregation and thus in the viscosity. If ripening is prolonged, the system will coagulate. In practice, the cellulose is regenerated short of this point by spinning into an acid bath, usually sulfuric acid containing salts such as sodium and zinc sulfates. Bivalent salts can form insoluble cellulose xanthate salts from the residual cellulose xanthate which are somewhat less unstable. Sisson has summarized the effect of spinning conditions on the structure and properties of the regenerated cellulose (374a).

Although a trixanthate of cellulose can be prepared by the reaction of carbon disulfide on a molecular solution of cellulose in aqueous tetraalkylammonium hydroxides (238c), the degree of substitution reached in commercial xanthation is usually much lower, about 0.5, probably due to the fact that the reaction is with cellulose fibers swollen, but not dissolved. Thoroughly satisfactory methods for determining the distribution of the xanthate groups do not exist (309a), but the best evidence available seems to indicate that in well ripened viscose, most of the xanthate groups are on primary hydroxyls (394b,430a), although during the earlier stages the percentage of primary hydroxyls substituted is lower. This is compatible with the idea that the secondary hydroxyls react faster and that the secondary xanthates are split off faster during ripening.

Sodium cellulose thiocarbonate can be formed analogously to the xanthate by using carbon oxysulfide instead of carbon disulfide in this reaction (7,173), and sodium cellulose carbonate has also been mentioned (332), while the methyl esters of these ester-acids can be formed by reaction of alkali cellulose with the chlorides of monomethyl thiocarbonate (332) and monomethyl carbonate (179).

Aromatic acids, like benzoic and substituted benzoic acids, will esterify cellulose under the influence of impelling agents (55,380). The acid chloride may also be used with alkali cellulose or pyridine (294). Esterification with other cyclic acids can be similarly achieved. Furoic (230) esters of high substitution have been made with furoyl chloride and pyridine. A fibrous coumarilate of very low degree of substitution has been prepared with benzene, trifluoroacetic anhydride, and coumarilic acid (163).

Like the aliphatic acids, unsaturated acids may also esterify cellulose with a mineral acid as catalyst, provided the tendency to polymerize is not too great. Thus, crotonic acid with methylene chloride and perchloric acid gives cellulose tricrotonate (105). Acrylic acids and substituted acrylic acids esterify only to very low degree of substitution by this method and not very much more if trifluoroacetic anhydride is used as an impelling agent (163), but mixed esters can be produced by the action of methacrylic anhydride on cellulose acetate in acetone in the presence of sodium carbonate or by successive esterifications (24). Unsaturated acids of higher molecular weight, like cinnamic (55,117), undecylenic (134), or oleic acids (163), can react by the impeller reaction or by using the acid chloride and pyridine. The highly unsaturated sorbate can be prepared with trifluoroacetic anhydride (163).

Esterification of cellulose with acids containing additional functional groups sometimes requires less usual techniques. A special case is that of dibasic acids. In this case there are theoretically two possible monoesters, which may be equivalent for symmetrical acids, and one diester of the acid. The diester is usually formed less easily. The simplest reaction is with the half-esters of the dibasic acids, which, of course, forms a derivative of the simple monoester. Frank and Caro used alkyl oxalyl chlorides in the presence of pyridine (116). The half-esters will also react with cellulose in the presence of chloroacetic anhydrides and magnesium perchlorate catalyst to form, for instance, cellulose alkyl succinates and cellulose alkyl phthalates (259). Half-esters of cellulose containing one free carboxyl group can be prepared by reaction of the anhydride in the presence of an organic base (259,356). Dibasic esters in which both carboxyl groups are esterified to produce crosslinked cellulose molecules of low degree of substitution have been formed by reaction of cotton with the dibasic acid chloride in dimethylformamide (268). Adipic, sebacic, succinic, terephthalic, hexahydroterephthalic, and glycol biscarboxymethyl ether chlorides were used.

Esterification of cellulose with halogen-substituted acids of higher molecular weight proceeds normally (54,333), but the haloacetic acids esterify cellulose with difficulty (12), although they will esterify secondary cellulose acetate. Such mixed esters may also be formed by halogenation of cellulose acetates (190). Halogen can also be introduced into unsaturated cellulose esters by simple addition (105). A somewhat similar situation occurs with other substituted acetic acids, although partial esterification to a very low degree is produced with trifluoroacetic anhydride as an impelling agent (163) or, in the case of amino acids, by reaction with the halide and pyridine in dimethylformamide (333). The perfluoroacids react similarly (18).

A special case occurs in the production of cellulose acetoacetate by reaction of cotton with diketene and a sulfuric acid or sodium acetate catalyst (194). Cellulose can also be made to react with ketene in an inert solvent with a perchloric acid catalyst (161) if first preswollen with water and solvent-exchanged. Substituted diketenes are used to size paper by producing superficial esterification (90b).

Somewhat related to the ketene reaction is the production of urethanes which are esters of carbamic acid. Various substituted urethanes have been produced by the action of the corresponding isocyanates on cellulose in the presence of pyridine (100,162). Thiourethanes may be produced by the action of amines on aqueous slurries of zinc cellulose xanthate (4,5).

Sulfonic acids do not esterify cellulose directly, but esterification with sulfonyl chlorides is relatively easy (25,174,224,435). The toluenesulfonate, basis of the so-called "immunized" yarn which is used for special dyeing effects on cotton, has been well investigated (25,174), but the methanesulfonate (224,435) and many others (220) have also been prepared. Toluenesulfonyl chloride esterifies the primary groups preferentially, although not exclusively (70,178,185). The cellulose esters of sulfonic acids react with many nucleophiles to replace the ester group (224). For instance, ammonia or amines give nitrogenous derivatives (220,435), while halide ions substitute halogen for the primary sulfonate (70,178,185,300). For this reason. if the original esterification in pyridine is prolonged, the final product will contain nitrogen and chlorine as well as sulfur (174), the former by reaction of the sulfonic acid ester with pyridine and the second from the chloride ion formed in the original esterification. Phenyl ethers can be produced by heating cellulose toluenesulfonate 4 hrs. at 100°C. with sodium phenolate (332). Anhydride derivatives of cellulose have also been reported from the reaction of cellulose toluenesulfonate with sodium in pyridine (78).

Finally, there are some cases where the esterification is the result of more complex transformations. Although the nature of the reaction is still under discussion (291), there is evidence that cellulose cyanate is produced by heating cellulose impregnated with urea or biuret (364). Another unusual case is the production of cellulose anthranilate by reaction of cellulose with isatoic anhydride in the presence of alkali or potassium acetate (322).

2. Ethers

The etherification of cellulose can be brought about in several ways (15,343). Most common is the reaction of alkali cellulose with an alkyl ester, especially a halide, to form a salt and the cellulose ether. Other methods include the addition of ethylene oxide and its derivatives and the addition of activated olefins. Less common is the reaction of cellulose with pyridinium salts or other quaternary nitrogen salts to form the free base and the cellulose ether. In the special case of methylation, diazomethane can be used.

As in the case of the esters, not only the nature of the substituent, but also the degree of substitution of cellulose ethers and the distribution of the substituents determine the properties and thereby the uses of the products (212). Products of low substitution may be important, very much so in the textile field (101,113,143,144), and increasingly so in the paper industry (165,278,281,306,397,422,424), to modify the properties of cellulosic fibers and their aggregates. Cellulose esters of low substitution can also be used for various industrial purposes, but the ethers have the advantage of much greater stability to hydrolysis. Very high substitutions are difficult to achieve, but this is largely a matter of accessibility and can sometimes be overcome, at least in the case of methylation (316). Mixed ethers containing more than one substituent are readily formed (160) and are of some importance (212,213).

Methylation is the simplest example of etherification. Methylcellulose is prepared industrially by the action of methyl chloride on alkali cellulose (203a). The commercial product is only partly etherified (D.S. 1.5–2.0) and is soluble in cold water. These solutions gel or precipitate on heating. The insolubility in hot water is apparently due to thermal breakdown of the hydration complex and consequent molecular aggregation. At substitutions below 1, the product is soluble in cold alkali, but not in water;

at substitutions above 2.5, it is insoluble in aqueous media, but soluble in chlorinated or other polar organic solvents. When the methylation is carried out homogeneously in quaternary ammonium bases so as to get uniform substitution (32a), water and alkali solubility are reached at much lower degrees of substitution. A similar effect is obtained by methylation of sodium or thallium cupricellulose (407a).

The most common methylating agent used in the laboratory has been dimethyl sulfate. Anyone wishing to become familiar with the investigations of this reaction should read one or more of the several reviews (15,177, 203a,343). As carried out by Timell (402), various types of cellulose were suspended in an emulsion of 35% aqueous sodium hydroxide in toluene and treated with dimethyl sulfate at 30°C. It is difficult to reach high degrees of substitution in this way; in most investigations repeated remethylations have been necessary, and the importance of reaction conditions has become increasingly evident. By carrying out a single methylation at −20 to −30°C. in trimethylbenzylammonium hydroxide solution, a methoxyl content of 43.5% has been obtained (208a) (theory for the trimethyl ether 45.6%). A similar result (42.8% methoxyl) has been obtained with aqueous 45% sodium hydroxide if the contact is improved by grinding the cellulose and making use of vigorous (1700 rpm) stirring (316).

Several other agents for introducing the methyl group are available. Methyl iodide has been used for raising the methyl content of partially methylated cellulose in the presence of sodium hydroxide (177), and Traube has methylated thallium cupricellulose in the presence of thallium hydroxide (407a). Methyl toluenesulfonate can be used, suitably with 15.5*N* NaOH at 100°C. with good stirring at 1700 rpm (426). Diazomethane in ether will also methylate cellulose (290), but water is necessary and the degree of methylation increases with the amount of water (167,317).

Ethylation proceeds similarly, and ethyl chloride is used commercially with alkali cellulose (242a). At low degrees of substitution, (about 1), ethyl cellulose is water soluble (211), but the reaction is generally carried to the stage of solubility in organic solvents, which is around D.S. = 2.2–2.8. It too can be prepared in the laboratory with other ethylating agents, such as diethyl sulfate (32a) or ethyl toluenesulfonate (426). The chlorides (or other etherifying agents) of the higher alcohols do not react so readily. This is due to the heterogeneous nature of the reaction and the necessity for the etherifying agent to diffuse through an aqueous alkali phase (242a). Propyl, butyl, and amyl ethers have been prepared, however (160,343), by the action of alkyl chlorides on alkali cellulose. Better results can be obtained by reaction of the alkyl bromide on alkali cellulose or cellulose dissolved in a quaternary base. Even branched-chain halides react under these conditions (401b).

Benzylation is not commercial in the United States, but benzyl cellulose is manufactured elsewhere by reaction of cellulose with alkali and benzyl chloride (277). Lorand has discussed the effect of morphology of the fiber and of the polyphase system on this reaction (243). Other aralkyl groups have also been used. For instance, *p*-chlorobenzyl chloride reacts with alkali cellulose, but not *o*-chlorobenzyl chloride (290a). The reaction of triphenyl methyl chloride (172) with cellulose when agitated with pyridine at 100–120°C. substitutes the primary groups more rapidly than the secondary and has been used to differentiate them, although some secondary hydroxyls react also (185). Benzhydryl chloride or bromide react similarly with cellulose (385), but 2,6-lutidine gives much better results than pyridine.

Carboxymethylation is one of several etherifications which introduce a reactive functional group into the cellulose derivative. The commercial product (37,159) is in the form of a water-soluble sodium salt of D.S. slightly less than 1, although more highly substituted products can be formed (38,52,254). It is prepared by the reaction of alkali cellulose and chloroacetic acid or sodium chloroacetate. The use of alcohols (higher than ethyl) (228) or other organic liquids as reaction media is also possible. The reaction proceeds at room temperature. Carboxyethylcellulose may be similarly prepared (52).

Textile (81,144) or pulp (422) fibers can be very slightly carboxymethylated so as to promote affinity for water without reaching the stage of solubility. In textile treatments, the cellulose is first swollen with aqueous chloroacetic acid and then treated with alkali; with pulp the medium is alcoholic. The presence of the new functional group improves the affinity for basic dyes and the resistance to soiling of cotton and is acid enough to exchange cations (81,301a) and to catalyze other chemical reactions, such as resinifications (81). In the salt form, it improves the bonding of paper pulps (424). It also undergoes many of the usual reactions of the carboxyl group. By carboxymethylating cotton to a higher degree of substitution, soluble yarns can be produced (81a).

More strongly acid groups than the carboxyl group can be introduced as ethers into the cellulose molecule, but these have been of interest mainly as textile modifications and as ion-exchange materials. It has been stated that sodium chloromethylsulfonate does not react with alkali cellulose (343), but Porath reports the formation of a sulfomethylcellulose in this way (306a). Sulfoethylcellulose can be similarly prepared by using a haloethylsulfonate (306a,403). It can also be prepared with ethionic acid (or its anhydride, carbyl sulfate) (94) or with vinyl sulfonic acid salts (153). It is also possible to introduce a phosphoric acid group by reaction of alkali cellulose with the disodium salt of chloromethylphosphonate (97,182).

The introduction of amine-substituted ether groups into the cellulose (280,318) or the cellulose acetate (129a) molecule produces a material with reactive basic groups. Interest has centered on compounds of low nitrogen content, largely to obtain dyeing effects (319) or ion-exchange properties (158,205,276,367). Etherification is generally achieved by impregnating cellulosic fibers, yarns, or fabrics with alkali and with an amine containing a reactive functional group and then heating at about 100°C. Aminoethylcellulose (156) has received the most attention. It can be prepared by means of either β-chloroethylamine or β-aminoethylsulfuric acid. Dimethylaminoethylcellulose has also been prepared both with the chloride (205) and with the sulfato derivative (318). Other chlorides which have been used for this reaction (205) are 2-chloroethyldiethylamine (301a), 2-chloroethyldiisopropylamine, 2-chloroethyldibutylamine, and 3-chloro-2-aminopropane. Other sulfuric acids used with success were 1,3-diamino-2-sulfatopropane sulfate monohydrate, sulfatoethylethylenediamine hydrochloride, 3-sulfatopropylamine, and monopotassium (disulfatoethyl)amine monohydrate. The last of these produced crosslinking as evidenced by the insolubility in cuprammonium hydroxide solution (318). Less reactive were 1-sulfato-2-diethylaminopropane, 2-sulfatoethyl-*o*-toluidine, and 2-sulfatoethylaniline, while 2-aminoethylphosphoric acid and 2-bromoethylsuccinimide did not react at all. A more complicated reaction is that of alkali cellulose with triethanolamine and epichlorohydrin to give a nitrogenous ether (301a). The reaction of cellulose with ethyleneimine (280) has been reported to give aminoethylcellulose (276), but others have interpreted the product to be a graft polymer (65) or simply a homopolymer of the ethylenimine (96a).

Cyanoethylation of cellulose results from the action of acrylonitrile and alkali on cellulose (26,27,33,60,62,83,297,307). It has been of particular interest as a chemical modification for textiles, but can also be produced by treating viscose solutions with acrylonitrile (248). This is an example of the Michael reaction, and the behavior of other activated olefins has been determined (124). Of these, acrylamide (34) reacts readily (34,124), while *N*,*N*′-methylenebisacrylamide, fumaronitrile, methyl acrylate, crotonaldehyde, acrylic acid, maleic acid, and itaconic acid react slightly. The cyanoethyl ether is not as stable as most ethers to hydrolysis due to the effect of the nitrile, and under alkaline conditions it may be cleaved (83) or converted to a carboxyethyl ether group, probably with intermediate conversion to the amide (248). This is the same amide group produced by reaction of cellulose with acrylamide. Acrylonitrile, and other similar compounds, can also form graft polymers with cellulose, but this is a different reaction, which is discussed later in this chapter.

Hydroxyethylation of cellulose can be achieved by reaction of alkali cellulose with halohydrins (350), but preferably with ethylene oxide (310,350). Like carboxymethylation, this reaction increases the affinity for water, but the product is nonionic, and the affinity less dependent on pH. The commercial product may be either alkali-soluble or water-soluble. The functional group introduced is a hydroxyl like the one replaced. The effect on water sorption and on solubility seems to depend on the increased accessibility, due to steric effects (as in methylation, only more so) (343). This is further increased by the increased tendency of the hydroxyethyl group (primary and more accessible) to react further during hydroxyethylation, forming a condensation graft polymer although the side chains are very short (280a). Partially hydroxyethylated cellulose is also more reactive to other reactions than unsubstituted cellulose (70a,350).

Like other etherification reactions, hydroxyethylation to very low degrees of substitution is useful for modifying the properties of textile and pulp fibers. Hydroxyethylated pulps produce papers with better bonding and strength characteristics (165,424). These have only a partial solubility in alkali (140). A number of epoxides react under alkaline conditions to modify the properties of cotton (252). Only a few of these will react with acid catalysts and to a lesser extent (251).

Cellulose ethers of phenol (332) and of substituted phenols can be produced also. Cellulose *p*-toluenesulfonate reacts with sodium phenolate to introduce the phenyl groups, but the chlorine of 1-chloro-2,4-dinitrobenzene is active enough for direct etherification with alkali cellulose.

The reaction of cellulose with β-propiolactone has two possible pathways. One leads to an ether with a free carboxyl group and the other to an ester with a free hydroxyl group. Both reactions occur (82), although one investigator finds that the ester predominates (144). In either case the substituent may react further to form a condensation-type graft polymer. The reaction may be carried out in hot organic solvents (refluxing xylene) or with alkali cellulose in the presence of water (82). Carboxyethyl cellulose of low degree of substitution can be produced by alkaline saponification of the ester linkages in the initial product.

The reaction of cellulose with quaternary halides to form ethers gives derivatives of low substitution and has been of interest largely in introducing small amounts of hydrophobic groups to impart water repellency (358). That stearoamidomethylpyridinium chloride actually forms small amounts of stearoamidomethyl ethers when so used has been shown by a study of the products (359).

Various unsaturated ethers of cellulose have been studied. Allyl cellulose can be prepared from allyl halides and alkali cellulose (342,401a). Similarly, cellulose will react with chloropinene in aqueous alkali to give a myrtenyl ether (244) or with dichlorobutene refluxing in an aromatic solvent to give chlorocrotyl ethers (200). Vinyl ethers can also be prepared. If cellulose treated with 20–40% potassium hydroxide is autoclaved several hours with acetylene at 130–175°C., a fibrous ether with a degree of substitution of about 0.5 and an alkali-soluble resin are produced (373). If the reaction is carried out in dioxane, soluble ethers of D.S. 1.3–2.3 are formed (372). Unsaturated ethers of cellulose readily undergo the anticipated reactions of olefins.

The preceding discussion has dealt with the preparation and properties of the simple ethers of cellulose. Polyfunctional etherifying agents result in crosslinking, the subject of the next section. Before we leave the simple ethers, a word on the distribution of substituent groups is in order.

Since, in general, the etherification reaction is essentially irreversible, the distribution of substituents between the three types of hydroxyls reflects the relative reactivities of these hydroxyls and has therefore been widely studied by those interested in the reactivity of cellulose. The volume of work has been summarized in recent good reviews (70a,309a,378). Representing K_3, the rate of reaction of the hydroxyl at C_3, as 1, Croon (70a) has presented the results shown in Table V-1 for the relative rates of the three hydroxyls, K_2, K_3, and K_6. There are several methods for determining the position substituted, but the most direct method is to hydrolyze the sample in question and separate, usually chromatographically, the individual possible substituted glucoses (eight, in the simple case). The usually higher

TABLE V-1[a]

Reagent	K_2	K_3	K_6
Methyl sulfate	3.5	1	2
Methyl chloride	5	1	2
Diazomethane	1.2	1	1.5
Ethyl chloride	4.5	1	2
Ethylene oxide	3	1	10
Chloroacetic acid	2	1	2.5

[a] Taken from ref. 70a.

reactivity at C_2 is consistent with the higher acidity of this hydroxyl, and the resulting greater ionization (etherification is generally an S_{N_2} reaction) (238a). The formation of an ion at one hydroxyl will tend to restrict ionization of the neighboring hydroxyl. Steric effects, on the other hand, favor the reactivity at C_6 and it will be seen that K_6 is also high, especially during hydroxyethylation. Additional evidence that this is steric is Croon's finding that the reactivity of the new hydroxyl group (on the hydroxyethyl substituent) is 20 times K_3. Croon's results confirm the views of Spurlin (378) and Timell (401a) that the laws of probability govern the reaction. Diffusion into the less accessible regions is slower, and the rates of reaction there are correspondingly lower, but the ratios of the rates are constant. This is true in most etherifications where the cellulose is in the swollen alkaline condition. The relative rates are not greatly changed when the reaction occurs in solution, but Croon has found (70a) that for the reaction with ethereal diazomethane, the rates of all three hydroxyls are nearly alike. Some investigators have found that sodium cellulosates react similarly to alkali cellulose (238a,331a), but others (363) have found differing effects.

Substitution of a secondary hydroxyl will affect the reactivity of the other. Methylation causes a great increase in the reactivity of the neighboring unsubstituted hydroxyl (70a,238a), which is to be expected because methylation removes the field effect of the first cellulosate ion upon the other hydroxyl. On the other hand, carboxymethylation of either secondary hydroxyl reduces the reactivity of the other (70a), due both to field and to steric effects.

3. Crosslinking

Crosslinking in general will be discussed in Chapter IX and will be treated here only lightly to complete the chemical classification of the reactions of cellulose. By crosslinking of cellulose is meant the linking of two cellulose molecules, usually through the hydroxyl groups, by means of a difunctional agent (crosslinking of cellulose derivatives with reactive groups will not be described here). Crosslinking stabilizes cellulose dimensionally to changes in humidity, and dimensional stability is of interest to the wood (146,426a), paper (59), and textile (127) industries. In the textile industry, many types of finishes (36,63,96,301,401,425,441) depend on this action, especially those imparting wrinkle and crease resistance (64,127,130,292,323, 404). Because of the relative stability of the ethers to acid and alkali, etherification has been emphasized, but esterification has also been studied (268). Crosslinking by means of hydrogen bonding, which may occur on thorough drying or heating (321), is not included in this discussion, which is limited to covalent bonds.

Only a few hydroxyls need to crosslink to produce marked changes in characteristics (130). There is continuing investigation of the number, length, and location of crosslinkages required and the effect on the useful properties (68,122,123,130,221,321,398,401,404,408).

The reaction of cellulose with formaldehyde (98,265,330) is one of the simplest which might give a crosslink. If cellulose is steeped in aqueous formaldehyde, some of the latter is sorbed, probably as a methylolcellulose without crosslinking (110,331). This reaction is readily reversible. The linkage is not stable, but it may react with a second molecule of cellulose (292) so as to produce a formal, a dioxymethylene bridge; there are both chemical (421) and infrared (391) data to indicate that this occurs under the proper conditions, which usually include high acidity and elevated temperatures (153a,394). Crosslinking does indeed occur with boric acid and cellulose heated with formaldehyde vapor (391,421), but it has been pointed out that boric acid forms complexes and is not so weak an acid in the presence of cellulose or formaldehyde (287). Usually the vapor-phase reaction has been catalyzed with stronger acids (59,155) or salts like zinc chloride (59,383). The dioxymethylene bridge can also be produced under anhydrous conditions (147,346), as in acetone or sulfuric acid or by adding formaldehyde to an acetylation bath (the acetates can be saponified with retention of the crosslink). However, the usual procedure is to treat the cellulose with an aqueous solution of formaldehyde and catalyst and cure at elevated temperature (221,265,330). This produces the usual dry crease resistance; wet crease resistance is imparted by using a strong catalyst in aqueous formaldehyde solutions and omitting the cure (48,50,157,265,320, 321).

Other aldehydes behave similarly to formaldehyde, but most investigators have been particularly interested in the dialdehydes. Glyoxal will creaseproof cellulosic textiles (302), but the theoretical types of reaction are more numerous. Hemiacetals can be formed with the hydroxyls and either or both of the aldehydes may participate (168). It has been shown that simple immersion in aqueous glyoxal with a catalyst forms the hemiacetal (168) and the crosslinked dihemiacetal (110). The curing of this system at elevated temperature gives a product containing hemiacetals and both mono- and diacetals (168). There is a difference of opinion, however, as to whether the crosslinkages so formed are entirely of the three-atom type like formaldehyde (187,394) or whether there may be crosslinkages involving both aldehyde groups (126). Other aldehydes reacting like glyoxal are glutaraldehyde (168,187) and α-hydroxyadipaldehyde (187).

Schenck (346) showed several decades ago that simple formals would react with cellulose to form a dioxymethylene bridge. It is probable, therefore, that the more complicated acetals now being promoted as finishing agents (199,235) react similarly by transacetalization of the alkyl group for the cellulose molecule.

Use is also made of formaldehyde to form reactive derivatives containing difunctional chloromethyl, hydroxymethyl, alkoxymethyl, acyloxymethyl, quaternary methyl halide, or Mannich base groups, of which the first are the most and the last the least reactive. In each group, one finds considerable difference in reactivity among the members (127). These are resin-forming compounds, and there is still much work continuing to gather evidence that crosslinking by reaction with the cellulose actually occurs. In the case of dimethylolurea, it has been shown that ammonium chloride catalyst produces crosslinking (390,393), but that sodium carbonate seems to cause only resinification (390). Most of the studies with dimethylolethyleneurea and related compounds (121,122,423) indicate crosslinking.

Practically all the common types of etherification have been tried as a basis for crosslinking, providing only that the agent is difunctional. Considerable work has been done with dihalides (240), diepoxy compounds (19,129,239,251,352,392,401), diaziridinyl groups (49,210), diisocyanates (100,233), difunctional quaternary ammonium salts (313,398), and activated divinyl compounds, especially divinyl sulfone (349) and its derivatives (400). Di-β-hydroxyethyl sulfones also react (399). Tetraalkyl titanates will also react to form crosslinked titanium esters of cellulose (154). Certain reactive dyes (see Chapter XV) are also polyfunctional and may crosslink (92,103). Finally, one should mention the direct crosslinking of cellulose derivatives in aqueous solution by high energy radiation (238), Tovey's review of wrinkle resistance gives an exhaustive list of crosslinking agents (404).

4. Miscellaneous Derivatives

There are a number of other reactions involving the hydroxyl groups of cellulose which do not fall into the above classifications. Some of them can be mentioned briefly.

At least one group, the reactions introducing metals in one way or another, contains some extremely important examples (289). At the head of the list from the standpoint of simplicity and usefulness stand the alkali celluloses. The term is usually not applied to a simple chemical compound, but to the complex mixture produced by treating cellulose with an aqueous base. With sodium hydroxide most of the base is present as a swelling complex both in the crystalline and noncrystalline regions, but the chemical reactions, such as etherification, are indicative of the presence of cellulosate ions also. X-ray diffraction studies show that alkali has actually penetrated and distorted the crystal lattice, but does not disrupt the crystalline regions sufficiently for solution to occur.

Cellulosates without excess alkali have been prepared by reaction of cellulose with sodium in liquid ammonia (347) or by interchange of cellulose with metal alcoholates (363). The interchange of cellulose with thallous ethylate in various solvents (10) has been shown to be strongly influenced by fine structure, reaction being limited to those regions which are accessible to the particular solvent used. If a monosodium cellulosate is prepared by reaction of cellulose with sodium hydroxide in butanol, distilling off water as formed, the 2-hydroxyl is, to some extent, the most reactive (238a), but the reaction is not specific, as believed at first (394a).

Another interesting set of reactions involving metals consists of those forming coordination complexes with metal salts or oxides. The most important ones are those which are soluble in the medium, and they include cuprammonium–cellulose (175,183,209,315), cupriethylenediamine–cellulose (183,209,405,407), similar complexes (207) with cadmium, nickel, cobalt, and zinc, and the different type of complex with sodium ferric tartrate (207). As a rule, cellulose dissolves only as a derivative or a complex (379,382), in other words, after reaction of some sort, but the exact nature of the reactions involved in dissolving cellulose in solutions of these metal complexes is still not cleared up.

It is generally accepted that the cellulose in copper solutions is combined with copper, probably as an alcoholate, to form an anion and that the solution also contains cationic copper–amine complexes. Addition of aqueous sodium hydroxide to such a solution precipitates a sodium–copper–cellulose (290b). This is probably the sodium salt of the copper–cellulose anion. The reason for insolubility is not clear, although Reeves (315) points out reasons for suspecting crosslinking. It may also be that the solutions obtained by adding cobalt metal to cellulose solutions in copper–ethylenediamine are cobalt salts of the same anion, for Traube (407b) claims there is no cobalt in the anion, but Jayme's cobalt solutions certainly contain cobalt as the only metal (206).

However, the solutions based on sodium ferric tartrate are of a different type. Jayme (207) has found sodium salts of two different anionic ferritartrate complexes which will render cellulose soluble in solutions containing excess sodium hydroxide and proposed that solution is due to disruption of the crystal lattice of cellulose by the hydrated ferritartrate complex to the point that molecular separation and solution occur in the sodium hydroxide. This he considers analogous to the effect of sodium zincate, sodium beryllate, and sodium stannate in making cellulose, especially somewhat degraded or oxidized cellulose, more soluble in alkali (85,226, 264a). Still another solvent involving zinc is zinc chloride, important in the manufacture of vulcanized fiber; it has been proposed that this forms an oxonium compound with the glycosidic oxygen (222).

To return briefly to the question of the swelling and solubility of cellulose in alkalies, it should be noted that certain strong organic bases will dissolve cellulose (32a,238c). The quaternary ammonium bases are the most thoroughly studied, but phosphonium, arsenonium, sulfonium, and selenonium hydroxides behave similarly, provided only that the molecular volume of the hydrated cation is large enough (238b) to effect dispersion of the crystal lattice.

The action of amines does not always produce solubility. The simpler and less basic amines simply swell cellulose, but in many cases this produces changes in the crystallinity and fine structure, both before and after removal of the amine (91,242,365,366,410).

The silicon derivatives of cellulose are analogous to the ethers, are usually of low degree of substitution, and have been considered mainly in connection with textile or paper finishing. While complex resinifications occur, true reaction with the cellulose has also been verified (359,360).

As already mentioned, there are also reactive dyes (103,428,442), complex colored substances which react with cellulose, usually to form an ester or ether linkage. Since these are being discussed separately in Chapter XV, they will be omitted from the present discussion.

D. GRAFT POLYMERS

Since the general reaction of graft polymerization is discussed elsewhere (Chapter X-B), this discussion will be limited to the use of cellulose as a substrate for vinyl graft polymerization. This is quite a different matter from the condensation graft polymers produced by the reaction of cellulose with ethylene oxide, β-propiolactone, or possibly ethylenimine. The vinyl, or addition type of grafting, is usually initiated by a free radical produced in any of several ways (361). The cellulose molecule can be ruptured mechanically, for instance, as by grinding, and, if cellulose derivatives are masticated in the presence of vinyl monomers, grafts are produced (43). The energy for rupture can also be produced by irradiation—high energy irradiation, like γ-rays (8,229,338,414), and even such low energy irradiation as ultraviolet in the presence of certain photo-tendering dyestuffs, especially the sodium salt of anthraquinone-2,7-disulfonic acid (135,136). Ozone (219,414) and peroxide initiators (236) have also been used to promote grafting on cellulose and so have a variety of redox systems (41): ferrous ions and hydrogen peroxide (327), potassium persulfate (166a), and the ceric ion system (8,216,361), especially ceric nitrate (77). Graft polymers can also be produced by reactions with the side chains of cellulose derivatives (112), e.g., by chain transfer to mercaptoethyl side chains (51), but this is not a case of the cellulose chain itself reacting, and, in general, the reactions of cellulose derivatives have not been treated in this chapter.

Many different monomers have been grafted to cellulose. Acrylonitrile forms grafts very easily by most methods (8,41,43,77,135), and acrylamide is also very reactive (218). Acrylates and methacrylates are fairly easy to graft (43,135,216), but vinyl acetate (135) and vinylidene chloride (216) have been found to be much less so. Grafting is reported with methylvinylpyridine (236) and other vinylpyridines (41). Styrene grafts have been formed by mastication (43), by γ-irradiation (229), by ozone initiation (219), and by some redox systems (41), but it grafts poorly or not at all with cellulose when initiated by ultraviolet irradiation (135) or ceric ion (361). Poor results in graft polymerizations of cellulose initiated by the ceric ion have been attributed to insolubility of the monomer in water (216).

The nature of the bond at the graft is largely a matter of speculation; it has been observed, however, that the infrared spectra indicate a decrease of hydroxyl band intensities for cellulose graft polymers initiated by γ-irradiation or by ceric ion (8). There is considerable variation in the initiation mechanisms and in the properties of the products among the different types of grafting, but this is outside the scope of this discussion.

References

1. Adamek, E. G., and C. B. Purves, *Can. J. Chem.*, **35**, 960 (1957).
2. Aiken, W. H., *Ind. Eng. Chem.*, **35**, 1206 (1943).
3. Alexander, W. J., and R. L. Mitchell, *Anal. Chem.*, **21**, 1497 (1949).

3a. Alfredsson, B., W. Czerwinsky, and O. Samuelson, *Svensk Papperstid.*, **64**, 812 (1961); *Chem. Abstr.*, **56**, 7546h (1962).

4. Allewelt, A. L., *Ind. Eng. Chem.*, **49**, 71 (1957).
5. Allewelt, A. L., and W. R. Watt, *Ind. Eng. Chem.*, **49**, 68 (1957).
6. Anderson, E. V., and A. S. Cooper, Jr., *Ind. Eng. Chem.*, **51**, 608 (1959).
7. Andrews, D. A., F. G. Hortubise, and H. Krässig, *Can. J. Chem.*, **38**, 1381 (1960).
8. Arthur, J. C., Jr., and R. J. Demint, *Textile Res. J.*, **30**, 505 (1960); **31**, 988 (1961).
9. Asami, R., and N. Tokura, *Kogyo Kagaku Zasshi*, **62**, 1593, A97 (1959); *Abstr. Bull., Inst. Paper Chem.*, **31**, 947 (1961); *Chem. Abstr.*, **57**, 15391d (1962).

10. Assaf, A. G., R. H. Haas, and C. B. Purves, *J. Am. Chem. Soc.*, **66,** 59, 66 (1944).
11. Barsha, J., in *Cellulose and Cellulose Derivatives*, E. Ott, H. M. Spurlin, and M. W. Grafflin, eds., High Polymer Series, Vol. V, Part II, 2nd ed., Interscience, New York, 1954, chap. IXB.
12. Barnett, W. L., *J. Soc. Chem. Ind. (London)*, **40,** 253T (1921); *Chem. Abstr.*, **16,** 341 (1922).
13. Bartell, F. E., and H. Cowling, *Ind. Eng. Chem.*, **34,** 607 (1942).
14. Bartunek, R., *Holzforschung*, **16** (1), 17 (March, 1962); *Chem. Abstr.*, **57,** 2465g (1962).
15. Bass, S. L., A. J. Barry, and A. E. Young, "Cellulose Ethers" in *Cellulose and Cellulose Derivatives*, E. Ott, ed., High Polymer Series, Vol. V, 1st ed., Interscience, New York, 1943, chap. VIIIE.
16. Battista, O. A., *Ind. Eng. Chem.*, **42,** 502 (1950).
17. Beeman, L. A., and J. S. Reichert, "Peroxides in Pulp Bleaching Processes," in *Bleaching of Pulp*, TAPPI Monograph 10, TAPPI, New York, 1953.
18. Benerito, R. R., R. J. Berni, and T. F. Fagley, *Textile Res. J.*, **30,** 393 (1960).
19. Benerito, R. R., B. G. Webre, and J. B. McKelvey, *Textile Res. J.*, **31,** 757 (1961).
19a. Bennett, C. F., and T. E. Timell, *Svensk Papperstid.*, **58,** 281 (1955); *Chem. Abstr.*, **50,** 2973i (1956).
20. Bergmann, M., and H. Machemer, *Ber.*, **63,** 316 (1930).
21. Berl, E., and E. Berkenfeld, *Z. Angew. Chem.*, **41,** 130 (1928); *Chem. Abstr.*, **22,** 3044 (1928).
22. Berl, E., and O. Hefter, *Cellulosechemie*, **14,** 65 (1933); *Chem. Abstr.*, **27,** 5183 (1933).
23. Berl, E., and W. Smith, Jr., *Ber.*, **41,** 1837 (1908).
24. Berlin, A. A., and T. A. Makarova, *Zh. Obshch. Khim.*, **21,** 1267 (1951); *Chem. Abstr.*, **46,** 1996c (1952).
25. Bernoulli, A. L., and H. Stauffer, *Helv. Chim. Acta*, **23,** 627 (1940); *Chem. Abstr.*, **34,** 6811[6] (1940).
26. Bikales, N. M., A. H. Gruber, and L. Rapoport, *Ind. Eng. Chem.*, **50,** 87 (1958).
27. Bikales, N. M., and L. Rapoport, *Textile Res. J.*, **28,** 737 (1958).
28. Birtwell, C., D. A. Clibbens, and B. P. Ridge, *J. Textile Inst.*, **16,** T13 (1925); *Chem. Abstr.*, **19,** 1350 (1926).
29. Blair, M. G., and R. E. Reeves, *J. Am. Chem. Soc.*, **74,** 2622 (1952).
30. Bletzinger, J. C., *Ind. Eng. Chem.*, **35,** 474 (1943).
31. Blouin, F. A., J. C. Arthur, Jr., R. S. Orr, and V. J. Ott, *Textile Res. J.*, **31,** 597 (1961).
31a. Blume, R. C., and F. H. Swezey, *Tappi*, **37,** 481 (1954).
32. Bobeth, W., A. Heger, and A. Weihs, *Faserforsch. Textiltech.*, **12,** 381, 423 (1961); *Chem. Abstr.*, **56,** 4981f, 7529a (1962).
32a. Bock, L. H., *Ind. Eng. Chem.*, **29,** 985 (1937).
33a. Bock, L. H., and A. L. Houk, U. S. Patents 2,332,048; 2,332,049 (to Rohm and Haas Co.), Oct. 19, 1943; *Chem. Abstr.*, **38,** 1640 (1944).
33b. Bock, L. H., and A. L. Houk, U. S. Patent 2,349,797 (to Rohm and Haas Co.), May 30, 1944; *Chem. Abstr.*, **39,** 1291[1] (1945).
34. Bock, L. H., and A. L. Houk, U. S. Patent 2,338,681 (to Rohm and Haas Co.), Jan. 4, 1944; *Chem. Abstr.*, **38,** 3855[8] (1944).
35. Boehm, R. L., *J. Org. Chem.*, **23,** 1716 (1958).

36. Borghetty, H. C., *Textile World*, **108** (4), 89 (1958).
37. Bouttemy, M., *Chim. Ind.* (*Paris*), **84**, 891 (1960); *Chem. Abstr.*, **55**, 7831h (1961).
38. Bouttemy, M., *Bull. Soc. Chim. France*, **1960**, 1750; *Chem. Abstr.*, **56**, 11856b (1961).
39. Braconnot, H., *Ann. chim. et phys.* [2], **12**, 185 (1819).
40. Brear, J., and H. A. Turner, *J. Soc. Dyers Colourists*, **61**, 273 (1945); *Chem. Abstr.*, **40**, 739[3] (1946).
41. Bridgeford, D. J., *Ind. Eng. Chem. Prod. Res. Develop.*, **1**, 45 (1962).
41a. Brownsett, T., and G. F. Davidson, *J. Textile Inst.*, **32**, T25 (1941).
41b. Buras, E. M., Jr., A. S. Cooper, E. J. Keating, and C. F. Goldthwait, *Am. Dyestuff Reptr.*, **43**, P203 (1954); *Chem. Abstr.*, **48**, 7307b (1954).
41c. Buras, E. M., Jr., S. R. Hobart, C. Hamalainen, and A. S. Cooper, Jr., *Textile Res. J.*, **27**, 214 (1957).
42. Carré, P., and P. Mauclère, *Bull. Soc. Chim. France*, **49**, 1150 (1931); *Chem. Abstr.*, **25**, 5891 (1931).
43. Ceresa, R. J., *Polymer*, **2**, 213 (1961).
44. Champetier, G., *Dérivés cellulosiques*, 2nd ed., Dunod, Paris, 1953.
45. Champetier, G., and J. Bonnet, *Bull. Soc. Chim. France* [5], **10**, 585 (1943); *Chem. Abstr.*, **38**, 4127[6] (1944).
46. Champetier, G., and M. Foëx, *Bull. Soc. Chim. France*, **9**, 711 (1942); *Chem. Abstr.*, **38**, 3125[3] (1944).
47. Champetier, G., G. Montegudet, and J. Petit, *Compt. Rend.*, **240**, 1896 (1955); *Chem. Abstr.*, **49**, 13643f (1955).
48. Chance, L. H., E. K. Leonard, and W. A. Reeves, *Textile Res. J.*, **32**, 481 (1962).
49. Chance, L. H., R. M. Perkins, and W. A. Reeves, *Textile Res. J.*, **30**, 305, 918 (1960).
50. Chance, L. H., R. M. Perkins, and W. A. Reeves, *Textile Res. J.*, **31**, 71, 366 (1961).
51. Chaudhuri, D. K. R., and J. J. Hermans, *J. Polymer Sci.*, **48**, 159 (1960); **51**, 373, 381 (1961).
52. Chowdhury, J. K., *Biochem. Z.*, **148**, 76 (1924); *Chem. Abstr.*, **19**, 640 (1925).
53. Clark, I. T., and M. A. Millett, *Tappi*, **44**, 144 (1961).
54. Clarke, H. T., and C. J. Malm, U. S. Patent 1,698,049 (to Eastman Kodak Co.), Jan. 8, 1929; *Chem. Abstr.*, **23**, 1267 (1929).
55. Clarke, H. T., and C. J. Malm, U. S. Patent 1,880,808 (to Eastman Kodak Co.), Oct. 4, 1932; *Chem. Abstr.*, **27**, 600 (1933).
56. Clibbens, D. A., and A. H. Little, *J. Textile Inst.*, **37**, T219 (1946).
57. Clibbens, D. A., and B. P. Ridge, *J. Textile Inst.*, **18**, T135 (1927); *Chem. Abstr.*, **21**, 2192 (1927).
59. Cohen, W. E., A. J. Stamm, and D. J. Fahey, *Tappi*, **42**, 934 (1959).
60. Compton, J., W. H. Martin, B. H. Word, Jr., and D. D. Thompson, *Textile Inds.*, **117**, 138A, 188 (1953); *Chem. Abstr.*, **47**, 12820h (1953).
61. Conrad, C. C., and A. G. Scroggie, *Ind. Eng. Chem.*, **37**, 592 (1945).
62. Conrad, C. M., D. J. Stanonis, P. Harbrink, and J. J. Creely, *Textile Res. J.*, **30**, 339 (1960).
63. Cooke, T. F., *Textile Res. J.*, **24**, 197 (1954).
64. Cooke, T. F., J. H. Dusenbury, R. H. Kienle, and E. E. Lineken, *Textile Res. J.*, **24**, 1015 (1954).

65. Cooper, W., and R. K. Smith, *Makromol. Chem.*, **40,** 148 (1960).
66. Coppick, S., and W. P. Hall, in *Flameproofing Textile Fabrics,* R. W. Little, ed., Reinhold, New York, 1947, p. 179.
67. Corbett, W. M., in *Recent Advances in the Chemistry of Cellulose and Starch,* J. Honeyman, ed., Interscience, New York, 1959, p. 106.
68. Corbett, W. M., and J. E. McKay, *J. Soc. Dyers Colourists,* **77,** 543 (1961); *Textil-Rundschau,* **16,** 511 (1961); *Chem. Abstr.,* **56,** 7544i (1962).
69. Cowling, E. B., U. S. Forest Products Laboratory, Report 2116, U. S. Forest Prod. Lab., Madison, Wis., 1958.
70. Cramer, F. B., and C. B. Purves, *J. Am. Chem. Soc.,* **61,** 3458 (1939).
70a. Croon, I., *Svensk Papperstid.,* **63,** 247 (1960); *Chem. Abstr.,* **54,** 15925h (1960).
71. Cross, C. F., E. J. Bevan, and R. L. Jenks, *Ber.,* **34,** 2496 (1901).
72. Cruz-Lagrange, M. D., C. Hamalainen, and A. S. Cooper, Jr., *Am. Dyestuff Reptr.,* **51,** 428 (1962).
73. Cyrot, J., *Bull. Inst. Textile France,* **No. 77,** 27 (1958); *Chem. Abstr.,* **53,** 7584d (1959).
74. Cyrot, J., *Bull. Inst. Textile France* **No. 85,** 29 (1959); *Chem. Abstr.,* **54,** 13648c (1960).
75. Dalmon, R., *Compt. Rend.,* **201,** 1123 (1935); *Chem. Abstr.,* **30,** 854[5] (1936).
76. Dalmon, R., J. Chédin, and L. Brissaud, *Compt. Rend.,* **201,** 664 (1935); *Chem. Abstr.,* **30,** 282[9] (1936).
77. Daniel, J. H., Jr., S. T. Moore, and N. R. Segro, *Tappi,* **45,** 53 (1962).
78. Danilov, S. N., and A. A. Lopatenok, *Zh. Obshch. Khim.,* **28,** 3189 (1958); *Chem. Abstr.,* **53,** 10743[6] (1959).
79. Daul, G. C., and J. D. Reid, U. S. Patent 2,592,544 (to the U. S. Secy. of Agriculture), Apr. 15, 1952; *Chem. Abstr.,* **46,** 7768d (1952).
80. Daul, G. C., and J. D. Reid, U. S. Patent 2,610,953 (to the U. S. Secy. of Agriculture), Sept. 16, 1952; *Chem. Abstr.,* **47,** 1389g (1953).
81. Daul, G. C., R. M. Reinhardt, and J. D. Reid, *Textile Res. J.,* **22,** 787 (1952).
81a. Daul, G. C., R. M. Reinhardt, and J. D. Reid, *Textile Res. J.,* **23,** 719 (1953).
82. Daul, G. C., R. M. Reinhardt, and J. D. Reid, *Textile Res. J.,* **24,** 738, 744 (1954); **25,** 330 (1955).
83. Daul, G. C., R. M. Reinhardt, and J. D. Reid, *Textile Res. J.,* **25,** 246 (1955).
83a. Davidson, G. F., *J. Soc. Dyers Colourists,* **56,** 58 (1940); *Chem. Abstr.,* **34,** 3075[7] (1940).
84. Davidson, G. F., *J. Textile Inst.,* **23,** T95 (1932).
84a. Davidson, G. F., *J. Textile Inst.,* **25,** T174 (1934).
85. Davidson, G. F., *J. Textile Inst.,* **28,** T27 (1937).
86. Davidson, G. F., *J. Textile Inst.,* **29,** T195 (1938).
87. Davidson, G. F., *J. Textile Inst.,* **31,** T81 (1940).
88. Davidson, G. F., *J. Textile Inst.,* **32,** T109 (1941).
89. Davidson, G. F., *J. Textile Inst.,* **32,** T132 (1941).
90. Davidson, G. F., *J. Textile Inst.,* **34,** T87 (1943).
90a. Davidson, G. F., and T. P. Nevell, *J. Textile Inst.,* **39,** T59 (1948).
90b. Davis, J. W., W. H. Roberson, and C. A. Weisgerber, *Tappi,* **39,** 21 (1956).
91. Davis, W. E., A. J. Barry, F. C. Peterson, and A. J. King, *J. Am. Chem. Soc.,* **65,** 1294 (1943).

92. Dawson, T. L., A. S. Fern, and C. Preston, *J. Soc. Dyers Colourists*, **76**, 210 (1960); *Chem. Abstr.*, **54**, 14695g (1960).
93. Dickey, E. E., and M. L. Wolfrom, *J. Am. Chem. Soc.*, **71**, 825 (1949).
94. Dickey, J. B., and J. G. McNally, U. S. Patent 2,422,000 (to Eastman Kodak Co.), June 10, 1947; *Chem. Abstr.*, **41**, 5306b (1947).
95. Dorée, C., and A. C. Healey, *J. Soc. Dyers Colourists*, **49**, 290 (1933); *Chem. Abstr.*, **27**, 5964 (1933).
95a. Dorée, C., and A. C. Healey, *J. Textile Inst.*, **29**, T27 (1938).
96. Drake, G. L., Jr., and J. D. Guthrie, *Textile Res. J.*, **29**, 155 (1959).
96a. Drake, G. L., Jr., W. A. Reeves, and J. D. Guthrie, *Textile Res. J.*, **23**, 639 (1953).
97. Drake, G. L., Jr., W. A. Reeves, and J. D. Guthrie, *Textile Res. J.*, **29**, 270 (1959).
98. Dusenbury, J. H., E. Pacsu, E. P. Teulings, and W. Lobunez, *J. Appl. Polymer Sci.*, **5**, 704 (1961).
99. Easton, B. K., *Am. Dyestuff Reptr.*, **51**, 499 (1962).
100. Eckert, P., and E. Herr, *Jentgen's Kunstseide u Zellwolle*, **25**, 204 (1947); *Chem. Abstr.*, **43**, 1563d (1949).
101. Einsele, U., *Melliand Textilber.*, **41**, 721 (1960); *Chem. Abstr.*, **54**, 18967g (1960).
102. af Ekenstam, A., *Ueber die Cellulose-Lösungen in Mineralsäuren*, Bloms, Lund, 1936.
103. Elöd, E., and Y. Nakahara, *Melliand Textilber.*, **41**, 567 (1960); *Chem. Abstr.*, **54**, 16838d (1960).
104. Elöd, E., and F. Vogel, *Melliand Textilber.*, **18**, 64 (1937); *Chem Abstr.*, **31**, 6891^4 (1937).
105. Engelmann, H., and F. Exner, *Makromol. Chem.*, **23**, 233 (1957).
106. Entwistle, D., E. H. Cole, and N. S. Wooding, *Textile Res. J.*, **19**, 527 (1949).
107. Entwistle, D., E. H. Cole, and N. S. Wooding, *Textile Res. J.*, **19**, 609 (1949).
108. Epstein, J. A., and M. Lewin, *Textil-Rundschau*, **16**, 494 (1961); *Chem. Abstr.*, **56**, 3670c (1962).
109. Ermolenko, I. N., and F. N. Kaputsky, *J. Polymer Sci.*, **53**, 141 (1961).
110. Farrow, B., W. J. Roff, and S. C. Simmens, *J. Textile Inst.*, **49**, T516 (1958).
111. Faust, O., ed., *Celluloseverbindungen*, Springer, Berlin, 1935, 2 vols.
112. Fetscher, C. A., U. S. Patent 2,789,030 (to Cluett, Peabody and Co.), April 16, 1957; *Chem. Abstr.*, **51**, 10085d (1957).
113. Fisher, C. H., and F. S. Perkerson, *Textile Res. J.*, **28**, 769 (1958).
113a. Fordyce, C. R., U. S. Patent 2,129,052 (to Eastman Kodak Co.), Sept. 6, 1938; *Chem. Abstr.*, **32**, 8777^8 (1938).
114. Franchimont, A. P. N., *Ber.*, **12**, 1938 (1879).
115. Frank, G., U. S. Patent 2,559,914, July 10, 1951; *Chem. Abstr.*, **45**, 8770g (1951).
116. von Frank, G., and W. Caro, *Ber.*, **63**, 1532 (1930).
117. von Frank, G., and H. Mendrzyk, *Ber.*, **63**, 875 (1930).
118. Franzon, O., and O. Samuelson, *Svensk Papperstid.*, **60**, 872 (1957); *Chem. Abstr.*, **52**, 9587h (1958).
119. Freudenberg, K., and G. Blomqvist, *Ber.*, **68**, 2070 (1935).
120. Freudenberg, K., W. Kuhn, W. Dürr, F. Bolz, and G. Steinbrunn, *Ber.*, **63**, 1510 (1930).
120a. Frey, W., and E. Elöd, *Ber.*, **64**, 2556 (1931).
121. Frick, J. G., Jr., B. A. Kottes, and J. D. Reid, *Am. Dyestuff Reptr.*, **48** (13), 23 (June 29, 1959).

122. Frick, J. G., Jr., B. A. Kottes, and J. D. Reid, *Textile Res. J.*, **29,** 314 (1959).
123. Frick, J. G., Jr., A. G. Pierce, Jr., and V. W. Tripp, *Textile Res. J.*, **32,** 425 (1962).
124. Frick, J. W., W. A. Reeves, and J. D. Guthrie, *Textile Res. J.*, **27,** 92, 294 (1957).
126. Fujimura, T., and S. Okamoto, *J. Polymer Sci.*, **51,** 173, 182 (1961).
127. Gagliardi, D. D., and F. B. Shippee, *Textile Res. J.*, **31,** 316 (1961).
128. Gagnon, P. E., B. T. Newbold, and J. Thomas, *Tappi,* **44,** 749 (1961).
129. Galligan, J., A. M. Sookne, J. T. Adams, Jr., H. Guest, and G. H. Lourigan *Textile Res. J.*, **30,** 208 (1960).
129a. Gardner, T. S., *J. Polymer Sci.*, **1,** 121, 289 (1946).
130. Gardon, J. L., and R. Steele, *Textile Res. J.*, **31,** 160 (1961).
131. Gascoigne, J. A., *Chem. Ind. (London)*, **1961,** 693.
132. Gascoigne, J. A., *J. Soc. Dyers Colourists,* **77,** 53 (1961); *Chem. Abstr.*, **55,** 10876h (1961).
133. Gascoigne, J. A., and M. M. Gascoigne, *Biological Degradation of Cellulose,* Butterworths, London, 1960.
134. Gault, H., and M. Urban, *Compt. Rend.*, **179,** 333 (1924); *Chem. Abstr.*, **18,** 3714 (1924).
135. Geacintov, N., V. Stannett, and E. W. Abrahamson, *Makromol. Chem.*, **36,** 52 (1959).
136. Geacintov, N., V. Stannett, E. W. Abrahamson, and J. J. Hermans, *J. Appl. Polymer Sci.*, **3,** 54 (1960).
137. Gebauer-Fülnegg, E., W. H. Stevens, and O. Dingler, *Ber.*, **61,** 2000 (1928).
138. Giertz, H. W., *Svensk Papperstid.*, **48,** 317 (1945); *Chem. Abstr.*, **39,** 3927[8] (1945).
139. Giertz, H. W., and J. McPherson, *Svensk Papperstid.*, **59,** 93 (1956); *Chem. Abstr.*, **51,** 17162i (1957).
140. Gillespie, R. H., M. Mueller, H. Swenson, and K. Ward, Jr., *Tappi,* **44,** 662 (1961).
141. Gladding, E. K., and C. B. Purves, *Tech. Assoc. Papers,* **26,** 119 (1943); *Paper Trade J.*, **116** (14), 26 (April 8, 1943).
142. Glegg, R. E., *Textile Res. J.*, **21,** 143 (1951).
143. Goheen, G. E., *Tappi,* **41,** 737 (1958).
144. Gokal, N., and J. K. Skelly, *J. Soc. Dyers Colourists,* **75,** 486 (1959); *Chem. Abstr.*, **54,** 2749f (1960)
145. Goldfinger, G., H. Mark, and S. Siggia, *Ind. Eng. Chem.*, **35,** 1083 (1943).
146. Goldstein, I. S., W. A. Dreher, E. B. Jeroski, J. F. Nielson, W. J. Oberley, and J. W. Weaver, *Ind. Eng. Chem.*, **51,** 1313 (1959).
147. Goldthwait, C. F., *Textile Res. J.*, **21,** 55 (1951).
148. Goldthwait, C. F., E. M. Buras, Jr., and A. S. Cooper, *Textile Res. J.*, **21,** 831 (1951).
149. Golova, O. P., and V. I. Ivanov, *Bull. Acad. Sci. (USSR), Classe sci. chim.*, **1945,** 279; *Chem. Abstr.*, **40,** 1653 (1946).
150. Golova, O. P., R. G. Krylova, and I. I. Nikolaeva, *Vysokomolekul. Soedin.*, **1,** 1295, 1305 (1959); *J. Polymer Sci.*, **43,** 282 (1960).
151. Gorokhov, G. I., and I. V. Korsokov, *Gidrolizn. i Lesokhim. Prom.*, **13** (5), 26 (1960); *Abstr. Bull. Inst. Paper Chem.*, **32,** 502 (1961).
152. Grangaard, D. H., E. K. Gladding, and C. B. Purves, *Tech. Assoc. Papers,* **25,** 385 (1942); *Paper Trade J.*, **115** (7), 41 (August 13, 1942).
153. Grassie, V. R., U. S. Patent 2,580,352 (to Hercules Powder Co.), Dec. 25, 1951; *Chem. Abstr.*, **46,** 2802b (1952).

153a. Gruntfest, I. J., and D. D. Gagliardi, *Textile Res. J.*, **18,** 643 (1948).
154. Gulledge, H. C., U. S. Patent 2,980,490 (to E. I. du Pont de Nemours and Co.), Apr. 18, 1961; *Chem. Abstr.*, **55,** 24043d (1961).
155. Guthrie, J. D., *Am. Dyestuff Reptr.*, **51,** 507 (1962).
156. Guthrie, J. D., *Textile Res. J.*, **17,** 625 (1947).
157. Guthrie, J. D., *Textile Res. J.*, **29,** 834 (1959).
158. Guthrie, J. D., and A. L. Bullock, *Ind. Eng. Chem.*, **52,** 935 (1960).
159. Hader, R. N., W. F. Waldeck, and F. W. Smith, *Ind. Eng. Chem.*, **44,** 2803 (1952).
160. Hagedorn, M., and P. Möller, *Cellulosechemie*, **12,** 29 (1931); *Chem. Abstr.*, **25,** 5982 (1931).
161. Hamalainen, C., and J. D. Reid, *Ind. Eng. Chem.*, **41,** 1018 (1949).
162. Hamalainen, C., J. D. Reid, and W. N. Berard, *Am. Dyestuff Reptr.*, **43,** 453 (1954); *Chem. Abstr.*, **48,** 14221h (1954).
163. Hamalainen, C., R. H. Wade, and E. M. Buras, Jr., *Textile Res. J.*, **27,** 168 (1957).
164. Hamalainen, C., R. H. Wade, and M. D. Cruz, *Textile Res. J.*, **29,** 821 (1959).
164a. Harland, W. G., *J. Textile Inst.*, **45,** T678 (1954).
165. Harpham, J. A., A. R. Reid, and H. W. Turner, *Tappi*, **41,** 758 (1958).
166. Haskins, J. F., and M. S. Hogsed, *J. Org. Chem.*, **15,** 1264 (1950).
166a. Haydel, C. H., H. J. Janssen, J. F. Seal, H. L. E. Vix, and E. A. Gastrock, *Textile Res. J.*, **27,** 975 (1927).
167. Head, F. S. H., *J. Textile Inst.*, **43,** T1 (1952).
168. Head, F. S. H., *J. Textile Inst.*, **49,** T345 (1958).
169. Head, A. J., N. F. Kember, R. P. Miller, and R. A. Wells, *J. Chem. Soc.*, **1958,** 3418.
170. Heidt, L. J., E. K. Gladding, and C. B. Purves, *Tech. Assoc. Papers*, **28,** 178 (1945); *Paper Trade J.*, **121** (9), 35 (August 30, 1945).
171. Helberger, J. H., G. Manecke, and R. Heyden, *Ann. Chem.*, **565,** 22 (1949); *Chem. Abstr.*, **44,** 1892a (1950).
172. Helferich, B., and H. Koester, *Ber.*, **57,** 587 (1924).
173. Hess, K., and H. Grotjahn, *Z. Elektrochem.*, **56,** 58 (1952); *Chem. Abstr.*, **46,** 6379d (1952).
174. Hess, K., and N. Ljubitsch, *Ann. Chem.*, **507,** 62 (1933).
175. Hess, K., and E. Messmer, *Ber.*, **54,** 834 (1921); **56,** 587 (1923); *Kolloid-Z.*, **36,** 260 (1925).
176. Hess, K., and E. Steurer, *Z. Physik. Chem. (Leipzig)*, **193,** 234 (1944); *Chem. Abstr.*, **40,** 6939^5 (1946).
177. Heuser, E., *Chemistry of Cellulose*, Wiley, New York, 1944.
177a. Heuser, E., and S. S. Aiyar, *Z. Angew. Chem.*, **37,** 27 (1924); *Chem. Abstr.*, **18,** 2246 (1924).
178. Heuser, E., M. Heath, and W. H. Shockley, *J. Am. Chem. Soc.*, **72,** 670 (1950).
179. Heuser, E., and F. Schneider, *Ber.*, **57,** 1389 (1924).
179a. Heuser, E., and M. Schuster, *Cellulosechemie*, **7,** 17 (1926); *Chem. Abstr.*, **20,** 2077 (1926).
180. Hiller, L. A., Jr., and E. Pacsu, *Textile Res. J.*, **16,** 318 (1946).
181. Hiller, L. A., Jr., and E. Pacsu, *Textile Res. J.*, **16,** 490 (1946).
182. Hobart, S. R., G. L. Drake, Jr., and J. D. Guthrie, *Textile Res. J.*, **29,** 884 (1959).
183. Hoelkeskamp, F., *Papier*, **16,** 102 (1962); *Chem. Abstr.*, **57,** 1123i (1962).
184. Hofmann, R., U. S. Patent 2,126,190 (to Hercules Powder Co.), Aug. 9, 1938; *Chem. Abstr.*, **32,** 7723^9 (1938).

185. Honeyman, J., *J. Chem. Soc.*, **1947,** 168.
186. Howsmon, J. A., *Textile Res. J.*, **19,** 152 (1949).
187. Hurwitz, M. D., and L. E. Conlon, *Textile Res. J.*, **28,** 257 (1958).
188. Husemann, E., and U. Consbruch, *Makromol. Chem.*, **5,** 179 (1950).
189. Husemann, E., and E. Springler, *Makromol. Chem.*, **24,** 79 (1957).
190. I. G. Farbenindustrie A.-G., British Patent 306,132, Feb. 17, 1928; *Chem. Abstr.*, **23,** 5040 (1929).
191. I. G. Farbenindustrie A.-G., British Patent 337,366, July 25, 1929; *Chem. Abstr.*, **25,** 2288 (1931).
192. I. G. Farbenindustrie A.-G., German Patent 547,812, March 29, 1932; *Chem. Abstr.*, **26,** 3667 (1932).
193. I. G. Farbenindustrie A.-G., German Patent 556,590, August 17, 1932; *Chem. Abstr.*, **27,** 413 (1933).
194. Iida, H., N. Kuwabara, and K. Konishi, *Tokyo Kogyo Shikensho Hokoku*, **54,** 182 (June, 1959); *Abstr. Bull. Inst. Paper Chem.*, **30,** 313 (1959).
195. Imamura, R., and H. Mizukami, *J. Soc. Textile Cellulose Ind. Japan*, **15,** 931 (1959); *J. Soc. Dyers Colourists*, **76,** 250 (1960).
196. Imschenezki [Imshenetskii], A. A., *Mikrobiologie der Cellulose*, Akademie-Verlag, Berlin, 1959 (a German translation of the Russian, originally published in Moscow in 1953).
197. Ingersoll, H. G., *J. Appl. Phys.*, **17,** 924 (1946).
198. Iritani, H., *Yakugaku Kenkyu*, **29,** 101 (1957); **30,** 601 (1958); *Chem. Abstr.*, **53,** 5668f, 20789h (1959).
199. Irvine, J. B., and B. H. Kress, *Textile Res. J.*, **28,** 148 (1958).
199a. Irvine, J. C., and E. L. Hirst, *J. Chem. Soc.*, **121,** 1585 (1922).
200. Isagulyants, V. I., and T. A. Azizyan, *Dokl. Akad. Nauk Arm. SSR*, **27,** 75 (1958); *Chem. Abstr.*, **53,** 7036 (1959).
201. Ivanov, V. I., E. D. Stakheeva-Kaverzneva, and Z. I. Kuznetsova, *Bull. Acad. Sci. USSR, Div. Chem. Sci. (English Transl.)*, **1953,** 341; *Faserforsch. Textiltech.*, **4,** 172 (1953); *Chem. Abstr.*, **48,** 10335, 13211 (1954).
202. Ivanov, V. I., N. Ya. Lenshina, and V. S. Ivanova, *J. Polymer Sci.*, **53,** 93 (1961).
203. Jackson, E. L., and C. S. Hudson, *J. Am. Chem. Soc.*, **59,** 2049 (1937); **60,** 989 (1938).
203a. Jahn, E. C., in *Wood Chemistry*, L. E. Wise and E. C. Jahn, eds., 2nd ed., Vol. 1, Reinhold, New York, 1952, pp. 350–368.
205. Jakubovic, A. O., and B. N. Brook, *Polymer*, **2,** 18 (1961).
206. Jayme, G., *Papier*, **5,** 244 (1951); *Chem. Abstr.*, **45,** 9267a (1951).
207. Jayme, G., *Tappi*, **44,** 299 (1961).
208. Jörgensen, L., *Studies on the Partial Hydrolysis of Cellulose*, Moestue, Oslo, 1950.
208a. Johnston, G. G., *J. Am. Chem. Soc.*, **63,** 1043 (1941).
209. Jolley, L. J., *J. Textile Inst.*, **30,** T4, T22 (1939).
210. Jones, F. B., H. G. Hammon, R. I. Leininger, and R. G. Heiligman, *Textile Res. J.*, **31,** 57 (1961).
211. Jullander, I., *Acta Chem. Scand.*, **9,** 1291 (1955); *Chem. Abstr.*, **50,** 8201d (1956).
212. Jullander, I., *Chim. Ind. (Paris)*, **71,** 288 (1954); *Chem. Abstr.*, **48,** 6689a (1954).
213. Jullander, I., *Ind. Eng. Chem.*, **49,** 364 (1957).
214. Jullander, I., and K. Brune, *Svensk Papperstid.*, **62,** 728 (1959).
215. Jurgens, J. F., J. D. Reid, and J. D. Guthrie, *Textile Res. J.*, **18,** 42 (1948).

216. Kaizerman, S., G. Mino, and L. F. Meinhold, *Textile Res. J.*, **32,** 136 (1962).
217. Kalb, L., and F. von Falkenhausen, *Ber.*, **60,** 2514 (1927).
218. Kamogawa, H., and T. Sekiya, *Textile Res. J.*, **31,** 585 (1961).
219. Kargin, V. A., Kh. U. Usmanov, and B. I. Aikhodzhaev, *Vysokomolekul. Soedin.*, **1,** 149 (1959); *Chem. Abstr.*, **53,** 18476 (1959).
220. Karrer, P., and W. Wehrli, *Z. Angew. Chem.*, **39,** 1509 (1926); *Chem. Abstr.*, **21,** 1015 (1927).
221. Kärrholm, E. M., *Textile Res. J.*, **25,** 756 (1955).
222. Kasbekar, G. S., *Current Sci. (India)*, **9,** 411 (1940); *Chem. Abstr.*, **35,** 1220[9] (1941).
223. Kido, I., and K. Suzuki, *Sen-i Gakkaishi*, **15,** 447 (1959); *Chem. Abstr.*, **53,** 16533 (1959).
224. Klein, E., and J. E. Snowden, *Ind. Eng. Chem.*, **50,** 80 (1958).
225. Klein, R., and M. Mentser, *J. Am. Chem. Soc.*, **73,** 5888 (1951).
226. Kleinert, T. N., O. Dioszegi, and R. M. Dlouhy, *Svensk Papperstid.*, **62,** 834 (1959); *Chem. Abstr.*, **54,** 8074e (1960).
227. Kline, E., in *Cellulose and Cellulose Derivatives*, E. Ott, H. M. Spurlin, and M. W. Grafflin, eds., High Polymer Series, Vol. V, Part II, 2nd ed., Interscience, New York, 1954, Chap. IXF.
228. Klug, E. D., and J. Tinsley, U. S. Patent 2,517,577 (to Hercules Powder Co.), Aug. 8, 1950; *Chem. Abstr.*, **44,** 10318i (1950).
229. Kobayashi, Y., *J. Polymer Sci.*, **51,** 359, 368 (1961).
230. Kobe, K. A., and R. E. Montonna, *J. Am. Chem. Soc.*, **53,** 1889 (1931).
232. Korol'kov, I. I., V. I. Sharkov, and E. N. Garmanova, *Zh. Prikl. Khim.*, **30,** 586 (1957); *Chem. Abstr.*, **51,** 14258 (1957).
233. Krässig, H., *Makromol. Chem.*, **10,** 1 (1953).
234. Kratzl, K., *Holzforsch. Holzverwert.*, **13,** 11 (1961).
235. Kress, B. H., *Am. Dyestuff Reptr.*, **48** (4), 33 (Feb. 23, 1959).
235a. Krüger, D., and W. Roman, *Angew. Chem.*, **47,** 58 (1934); *Chem. Abstr.*, **28,** 2521[9] (1934).
235b. Krüger, D., and E. Tschirsch, *Ber.*, **64,** 1874 (1931).
235c. Krüger, D., and E. Tschirsch, *Melliand Textilber.*, **13,** 541 (1932).
236. Kryazhev, Yu. G., and Z. A. Rogovin, *Vysokomolekul. Soedin.*, **3,** 1847 (1961); *Chem. Abstr.*, **56,** 14505 (1962).
237. La Diega, G. N., *Chim. Ind. (Milan)*, **41,** 539 (1959); *Chem. Abstr.*, **54,** 1332 (1960).
238. Leavitt, F. C., *J. Polymer Sci.*, **45,** 536 (1960); **51,** 349, 357 (1961).
238a. Lenz, R. W., *J. Am. Chem. Soc.*, **82,** 182 (1960).
238b. Lieser, T., and R. Ebert, *Ann. Chem.*, **528,** 276 (1937).
238c. Lieser, T., and E. Leckzyck, *Ann. Chem.*, **522,** 56 (1936).
239. Lindner, K., *Melliand Textilber.*, **41,** 82 (1960).
240. Lobunez, W., and J. H. Dusenbury, *J. Appl. Polymer Sci.*, **5,** 686 (1961).
241. Locke, E. G., and E. Garnum, *Forest Prod. J.*, **11,** 380 (1961).
242. Loeb, L., and L. Segal, *J. Polymer Sci.*, **15,** 343 (1955).
242a. Lorand, E. J., *Ind. Eng. Chem.*, **31,** 891 (1939).
243. Lorand, E. J., and E. A. Georgi, *J. Am. Chem. Soc.*, **59,** 1166 (1937).
244. Lyubimova, E. N., *Tr. Lenigr. Lesotekhn. Akad*, **No. 91,** 135 (1960); *Chem. Abstr.*, **55,** 25243 (1961).

245. McBurney, L. F., in *Cellulose and Cellulose Derivatives*, E. Ott, H. M. Spurlin and M. W. Grafflin, eds., High Polymer Series, Vol. V, Part I, 2nd ed., Interscience, New York, 1954, Chap. IIIC.
246. McGee, P. A., W. F. Fowler, Jr., E. W. Taylor, C. C. Unruh, and W. O. Kenyon, *J. Am. Chem. Soc.*, **69,** 355 (1947).
247. McGee, P. A., W. F. Fowler, Jr., C. C. Unruh, and W. O. Kenyon, *J. Am. Chem. Soc.*, **70,** 2700 (1948).
248. MacGregor, J. H., *J. Soc. Dyers Colourists*, **67,** 66 (1951); *Chem. Abstr.*, **45,** 4047h (1951).
249. Machell, G., and G. N. Richards, *J. Chem. Soc.*, **1960,** 1924, 1932, 1938.
250. Machell, G., and G. N. Richards, *Tappi*, **41,** 12 (1958).
251. McKelvey, J. B., B. G. Webre, and R. R. Benerito, *Am. Dyestuff Reptr.*, **49,** 804 (1960).
252. McKelvey, J. B., B. G. Webre, and E. Klein, *Textile Res. J.*, **29,** 918 (1959).
253. McKeown, J. J., and W. I. Lyness, *J. Polymer Sci.*, **47,** 9 (1960).
254. McLaughlin, R. R., and J. H. E. Herbst, *Can. J. Research*, **28B,** 731 (1950).
254a. McMillan, O. J., Jr., K. M. Decossas, A. S. Cooper, Jr., C. Hamalainen, A. L. Murphy, and E. F. Pollard, *Am. Dyestuff Reptr.*, **49,** No. 23, 51 (1960).
255. Madorsky, S. L., V. E. Hart, and S. Straus, *J. Res. Natl. Bur. Std.*, **56,** 343 (1956).
256. Major, W. D., *Tappi*, **41,** 530 (1958).
257. Malm, C. J., *Svensk Kem. Tidskr.*, **73,** 523 (1961).
258. Malm, C. J., and C. L. Crane, U. S. Patent 2,539,451 (to Eastman Kodak Co.), Jan. 30, 1951; *Chem. Abstr.*, **45,** 4453e (1951).
259. Malm, C. J., and C. R. Fordyce, *Ind. Eng. Chem.*, **32,** 405 (1940).
260. Malm, C. J., and G. D. Hiatt, in *Cellulose and Cellulose Derivatives*, E. Ott, H. M. Spurlin, and M. W. Grafflin, eds., High Polymer Series, Vol. V, Part II, 2nd ed., Interscience, New York, 1954, Chap. IXC.
261. Malm, C. J., J. W. Mench, D. L. Kendall, and G. D. Hiatt, *Ind. Eng. Chem.*, **43,** 684 (1951).
262. Malm, C. J., and L. J. Tanghe, *Ind. Eng. Chem.*, **47,** 995 (1955).
263. Malm, C. J., L. J. Tanghe, and B. C. Laird, *Ind. Eng. Chem.*, **38,** 77 (1946).
264. Malm, C. J., L. J. Tanghe, and J. T. Schmitt, *Ind. Eng. Chem.*, **53,** 363 (1961).
264a. Mantell, C. L., *Textile Res. J.*, **16,** 481 (1946).
265. Marsh, J. T., *J. Soc. Dyers Colourists*, **75,** 244 (1959); *Chem. Abstr.*, **53,** 13599f (1959).
265a. Martin, A. R., L. Smith, R. L. Whistler, and M. Harris, *J. Res. Natl. Bur. Std.*, **27,** 449 (1941).
266. Marx-Figini, M., *Makromol. Chem.*, **50,** 196 (1961).
267. Marz-Figini, M., *Papier*, **13,** 572 (1959); *Chem. Abstr.*, **54,** 10314h (1960).
268. Matschat, K., *Textil-Rundschau*, **16,** 580 (1961); *Chem. Abstr.*, **56,** 3671a (1962).
269. Maurer, K., and G. Reiff, *Makromol. Chem.*, **1,** 27 (1943).
270. Meesook, B., and C. B. Purves, *Tech. Assoc. Papers*, **29,** 508 (1946); *Paper Trade J.*, **123,** (18), 35 (Oct. 31, 1946).
270a. Meller, A., *Australian Pulp Paper Ind. Tech. Assoc. Proc.*, **9,** 192 (1955); *Chem. Abstr.*, **51,** 701e (1957).
271. Meller, A., *Holzforschung*, **9,** 149 (1955); *Chem. Abstr.*, **50,** 1299f (1956).
272. Meller, A., *Holzforschung*, **14,** 78, 129 (1960); *Chem. Abstr.*, **54,** 25787h (1960).
273. Meller, A., *Rev. Pure Appl. Chem.*, **6,** 40 (1956); *Chem. Abstr.*, **50,** 10397h (1956).

274. Meller, A., *Tappi*, **33**, 11 (1950).
275. Meller, A., *Tappi*, **34**, 171 (1951); **35**, 72 (1952).
275a. Meller, A., *Tappi*, **38**, 682 (1955); **39**, 722 (1956).
276. Micheel, F., and W. Schminke, *Chem. Ber.*, **91**, 984 (1958).
276a. Michie, R. I. C., A. Sharples, and A. A. Walter, *J. Polymer Sci.*, **51**, 85 (1961).
277. Mienes, K., *Celluloseester und Celluloseäther*, Chem.-tech. Verlag Dr. Bodenbender, Berlin-Steglitz, 1934.
278. Miller, H. F., and R. G. Flowers, U. S. Patent 2,535,690 (to General Electric Co.), Dec. 26, 1950; *Chem. Abstr.*, **45**, 3533f (1951).
279. Milliken, M. G., *Ind. Eng. Chem.*, **22**, 326 (1930).
279a. Monier-Williams, G. W., *J. Chem. Soc.*, **119**, 803 (1921).
280. Montegudet, G., *Peintures Pigments Vernis*, **34**, 204, 271, 311 (1958); *Chem. Abstr.*, **52**, 21067 (1958).
280a. Morgan, P. W., *Ind. Eng. Chem. Anal. Ed.*, **18**, 500 (1946).
281. Morton, J. L., and N. M. Bikales, *Tappi*, **42**, 855 (1959).
282. Nabar, G. M., F. Scholefield, and H. A. Turner, *J. Soc. Dyers Colourists*, **53**, 5 (1937); *Chem. Abstr.*, **31**, 1622[5] (1937).
283. Nevell, T. P., *J. Textile Inst.*, **42**, T91 (1951).
284. Nevell, T. P., and S. H. Zeronian, *J. Textile Inst.*, **53**, T90 (1962).
285. Nevell, T. P., and S. H. Zeronian, *Polymer*, **3**, 187 (1962).
286. Nickerson, R. F., *Ind. Eng. Chem.*, **33**, 1022 (1941).
287. Nickerson, R. F., *Textile Res. J.*, **22**, 554 (1952).
288. Nickerson, R. F., and J. A. Habrle, *Ind. Eng. Chem.*, **37**, 1115 (1945); **38**, 299 (1946).
289. Nicoll, W. D., N. L. Cox, and R. F. Conaway, in *Cellulose and Cellulose Derivatives*, E. Ott, H. M. Spurlin and M. W. Grafflin, eds., High Polymer Series, Vol. V, Part II, 2nd ed., Interscience, New York, 1954, Chap. IXD.
290. Nierenstein, M., *Ber.*, **58**, 2615 (1925).
290a. Niethammer, H., and W. König, *Cellulosechemie*, **10**, 201 (1929); *Chem. Abstr.*, **24**, 3641 (1930).
290b. Normann, W., *Chemiker-Ztg.*, **30**, 584 (1906); *Chem. Abstr.*, **1**, 486 (1907).
291. Nuessle, A. C., *Textile Res. J.*, **31**, 990 (1961).
292. O'Brien, S. J., and W. J. van Loo, Jr., *Textile Res. J.*, **31**, 276, 340 (1961).
293. Ost, H., *Ann. Chem.*, **398**, 313 (1913).
294. Ost, H., and F. Klein, *Z. Angew. Chem.*, **26**, 437 (1913); *Chem. Abstr.*, **7**, 3661 (1913).
295. Ott, E., H. M. Spurlin, and M. W. Grafflin, eds., *Cellulose and Cellulose Derivatives*, High Polymer Series, Vol. V, Parts I, II, III, 2nd ed., Interscience, New York, 1954.
296. Oye, R., K. Sugiyama, T. Mizuno, and E. Nokihara, *Kami-pa Gikyoshi*, **14**, 593 (1960); *Abstr. Bull. Inst. Paper Chem.*, **31**, 623 (1961).
297. Pacetti, S., and G. Prati, *Ann. Chim. (Rome)*, **48**, 1070 (1958); *Chem. Abstr.*, **53**, 11844 (1959).
298. Pacsu, E., *Fortschr. Chem. Org. Naturstoffe*, **5**, 128 (1948).
299. Pacsu, E., *Textile Res. J.*, **15**, 354 (1945).
300. Pacsu, E., and R. F. Schwenker, Jr., *Textile Res. J.*, **27**, 173 (1957).
301. Perkerson, F. S., W. A. Reeves, and V. W. Tripp, *Textile Res. J.*, **30**, 944 (1960).
301a. Peterson, E. A., and H. A. Sober, *J. Am. Chem. Soc.*, **78**, 751 (1956).

301b. Petro, K. A., and E. E. Nifant'ev, U. S. S. R. Patent 136,347, Mar. 14, 1961; *Abstr. Bull. Inst. Paper Chem.*, **32**, 1337 (1962).
302. Pfeffer, E. C., Jr., and J. Epelberg, U. S. Patent 2,436,076 (to Cluett, Peabody and Co.), Feb. 17, 1948; *Chem. Abstr.*, **42**, 3190h (1948).
303. Philipp, H. J., M. L. Nelson, and H. M. Ziifle, *Textile Res. J.*, **17**, 585 (1947).
304. Pictet, A., and J. Sarasin, *Helv. Chim. Acta*, **1**, 87 (1918); *Chem. Abstr.*, **12**, 2187 (1918).
305. Pinck, L. A., *Ind. Eng. Chem.*, **22**, 1241 (1930).
306. Plunguian, M., *Assoc. Tech. Ind. Papetiere Bull.*, No. 4, 277 (1961).
306a. Porath, J., *Arkiv Kemi*, **11**, No. 11, 97 (Nov., 1957).
307. Prati, G., and S. Pacetti, *Ann. Chim. (Rome)*, **48**, 428, 437 (1958); *Chem. Abstr.*, **52**, 19117i, 19118f (1958).
308. Pringsheim, H., E. Lorand, and K. Ward, Jr., *Cellulosechemie*, **13**, 119 (1932); *Chem. Abstr.*, **26**, 6123 (1932).
309. Purves, C. B., Ref. 432, Chap. 7.
309a. Purves, C. B., *Chem. Can.*, **12**, No. 12, 25 (Dec., 1960).
310. Quinchon, J., *Compt. Rend.*, **247**, 1006 (1958); *Chem. Abstr.*, **53**, 4725d (1959).
311. Rånby, B. G., *J. Polymer Sci.*, **53**, 131 (1961).
312. Rapson, W. H., and K. A. Hakim, *Pulp Paper Mag.*, **58**, No. 8, 151 (1957); *Chem. Abstr.*, **52**, 3338a (1958).
313. Rath, H., and U. Einsele, *Melliand Textilber.*, **40**, 526 (1959); *Chem. Abstr.*, **53**, 16531c (1959).
314. Reese, E. T., *Appl. Microbiol.*, **4**, 39 (1956); *Chem. Abstr.*, **50**, 5059i (1956).
315. Reeves, R. E., in *Advances in Carbohydrate Chemistry*, W. W. Pigman and M. L. Wolfrom eds., Vol. VI, Academic Press, New York, 1951, p. 107.
315a. Reeves, R. E., *Ind. Eng. Chem.*, **35**, 1281 (1943).
316. Reeves, R. E., B. J. Barrett, and L. W. Mazzeno, Jr., *J. Am. Chem. Soc.*, **74**, 4491 (1952).
316a. Reeves, R. E., and F. F. Darby, Jr., *Textile Res. J.*, **20**, 172 (1950).
316b. Reeves, R. E., and J. R. Jung, Jr., *Textile Res. J.*, **21**, 22 (1951).
317. Reeves, R. E., and H. J. Thompson, *Contrib. Boyce Thompson Inst.*, **11**, 55 (1940); *Chem. Abstr.*, **34**, 3923[4] (1940).
318. Reeves, W. A., and J. D. Guthrie, *Textile Res. J.*, **23**, 522 (1953).
319. Reeves, W. A., O. J. McMillan, Jr., and J. D. Guthrie, *Textile Res. J.*, **23**, 527 (1953).
320. Reeves, W. A., R. M. Perkins, and L. H. Chance, *Am. Dyestuff Reptr.*, **49**, 639 (1960).
321. Reeves, W. A., R. M. Perkins, and L. H. Chance, *Textile Res. J.*, **30**, 179 (1960).
322. Reeves, W. A., and R. H. Wade, U. S. Patent 2,926,063 (to U. S. Secy. of Agriculture), Feb. 23, 1960; *Chem. Abstr.*, **54**, 11502a (1960).
322a. Reid, J. D., and G. C. Daul, *Textile Res. J.*, **17**, 554 (1947); **18**, 551 (1948).
323. Reid, J. D., J. G. Frick, Jr., R. M. Reinhardt, and R. L. Arceneaux, *Am. Dyestuff Reptr.*, **48** (3), 81 (Feb. 9, 1959).
324. Reid, J. D., and L. W. Mazzeno, Jr., *Ind. Eng. Chem.*, **41**, 2828 (1949).
325. Reid, J. D., L. W. Mazzeno, and E. M. Buras, Jr., *Ind. Eng. Chem.*, **41**, 2831 (1949).
326. Reinhardt, R. M., J. D. Reid, and G. C. Daul, *Textile Res. J.*, **26**, 1 (1956).
327. Richards, G. N., *J. Appl. Polymer Sci.*, **5**, 539 (1961).

328. Rigby, G. W., U. S. Patent 2,025,073 (to E. I. du Pont de Nemours and Co.). Dec. 24, 1935; *Chem. Abstr.*, **30,** 1232^4 (1936).
329. Robinson, H. M., and W. A. Reeves, *Am. Dyestuff Reptr.*, **50,** 1 (1961).
330. Roff, W. J., *J. Textile Inst.*, **49,** T646 (1958).
331. Roff, W. J., *J. Textile Inst.*, **50,** T353 (1959).
331a. Rogovin, Z., and V. Derevitskaya, *Faserforsch. Textiltech.*, **8,** 61 (1957); *Chem. Abstr.*, **51,** 9146a (1957).
332. Rogovin, Z. A., *J. Polymer Sci.*, **30,** 537 (1958).
333. Rogovin, Z. A., V. A. Derevitskaya, S. Tun [T. Sun], C. Weĭ-gan [W. Chiang], and S. Gal'braikh, *J. Polymer Sci.*, **53,** 117 (1961).
334. Rogovin, Z., and K. Tikhonow, *Cellulosechemie,* **16,** 11 (1935); *Chem. Abstr.*, **29,** 4169^5 (1935).
335. Roseveare, W. E., *Ind. Eng. Chem.*, **44,** 168 (1952).
336. Roth, C. B., U. S. Patent 2,758,111 (to Hercules Powder Co.), Aug. 7, 1956; *Chem. Abstr.*, **51,** 713g (1957).
337. Rowen, J. W., F. H. Forziati, and R. E. Reeves, *J. Am. Chem. Soc.*, **73,** 4484 (1951).
338. Rutherford, H. A., A. A. Armstrong, Jr., L. H. Kiser, and R. D. Kirby, *Textile Res. J.*, **30,** 546 (1960).
338a. Rutherford, H. A., F. W. Minor, A. R. Martin, and M. Harris, *J. Res. Natl. Bur. Std.*, **29,** 131 (1942).
339. Sakurada, I., and Y. Sakaguchi, *Sen-i Gakkaishi,* **13,** 13, 67, 194, 199, 297, 301, 365, 367 (1957); *Chem. Abstr.*, **51,** 15116h, 18585b (1957); **52,** 7707c (1958).
340. Sakurada, I., Y. Sakaguchi, and K. Nagai, *Sen-i Gakkaishi,* **13,** 292 (1957); *Chem. Abstr.*, **51,** 18585e (1957).
341. Sakurada, I., Y. Sakaguchi, and H. Yamaguchi, *Sen-i Gakkaishi,* **13,** 431 (1957); *Abstr. Bull. Inst. Paper Chem.*, **28,** 486 (1957).
342. Sakurada, I., *Z. Angew. Chem.*, **42,** 549 (1929); *Chem. Abstr.*, **23,** 3572 (1929).
343. Savage, A. B., A. E. Young, and A. T. Maasberg, Ref. 295, Chap. IXE.
344. Schaarschmidt, A., *Z. Angew. Chem.*, **42,** 618 (1929).
345. Scheller, E., *Melliand Textilber.*, **16,** 787 (1935); *Chem. Abstr.*, **30,** 3225^9 (1936).
346. Schenck, M., *Helv. Chim. Acta,* **14,** 520 (1931); **15,** 1088 (1932).
347. Scherer, P. C., Jr., and R. E. Hussey, *J. Am. Chem. Soc.*, **53,** 2344 (1931).
348. Schiffner, R., and G. Lange, *Faserforsch. Texiltech.*, **9,** 417 (1958); *Chem. Abstr.*, **54,** 11489a (1960).
349. Schoene, D. L., and V. S. Chambers, U. S. Patent 2,524,399 (to U. S. Rubber Co.), Oct. 3, 1950; *Chem. Abstr.*, **45,** 1780d (1951).
350. Schorger, A. W., and M. J. Shoemaker, *Ind. Eng. Chem.*, **29,** 114 (1937).
351. Schroeder, C. W., U. S. Patent 2,826,514 (to Shell Development Co.), Mar. 11, 1958; *Chem. Abstr.*, **52,** 9621e (1958).
352. Schroeder, C. W., and F. E. Condo, *Textile Res. J.*, **27,** 135 (1957).
353. Schulz, G. V., *Chem. Ber.*, **80,** 335 (1947).
354. Schulz, G. V., *J. Polymer Sci.*, **3,** 365 (1948).
355. Schulz, G. V., E. Husemann, and H. J. Löhmann, *Z. physik. Chem.* (*Leipzig*), **B52,** 23 (1942); *Chem. Abstr.*, **37,** 5862^2 (1943).
356. Schulze, F., U. S. Patent 2,069,974 (to E. I. du Pont de Nemours and Co.), Feb. 9, 1937; *Chem. Abstr.*, **31,** 2430^4 (1937).
357. Schur, M. O., and B. G. Hoos, *Ind. Eng. Chem.*, **29,** 26 (1937).

358. Schuyten, H. A., J. D. Reid, J. W. Weaver, and J. G. Frick, Jr., *Textile Res. J.*, **18**, 396, 490 (1948).
359. Schuyten, H. A., J. W. Weaver, J. G. Frick, Jr., and J. D. Reid, *Textile Res. J.*, **22**, 424 (1952).
360. Schuyten, H. A., J. W. Weaver, J. D. Reid, and J. F. Jurgens, *J. Am. Chem. Soc.*, **70**, 1919 (1948).
361. Schwab, E., V. Stannett, and J. J. Hermans, *Tappi*, **44**, 251 (1961).
362. Schwab, E., V. Stannett, D. H. Rakowitz, and J. K. Magrane, *Tappi*, **45**, 390 (1962).
363. Schwenker, R. F., Jr., T. Kinoshita, K. Beurling, and E. Pacsu, *J. Polymer Sci.*, **51**, 185, 197 (1961).
364. Segal, L., and F. V. Eggerton, *Textile Res. J.*, **31**, 460, 991 (1961).
365. Segal, L., and L. Loeb, *J. Polymer Sci.*, **42**, 341, 351 (1960).
366. Segal, L., L. Loeb, and J. J. Creely, *J. Polymer Sci.*, **13**, 193 (1954).
367. Semenza, G., *Helv. Chim. Acta*, **43**, 1057 (1960); *Chem. Abstr.*, **55**, 406g (1961).
368. Sharkov, V. I., ed., *Tekhnologiya gidroliznogo i sul'fitno-spirtovogo proizvodstva*, Goslesbumizdat, Moscow, 1959.
369. Sharples, A., *Chem. Ind.* (London), **1953**, 870; *J. Polymer Sci.*, **13**, 393; **14**, 95 (1954).
371. Shorygin, P. P., and E. V. Khait, *Zh. Obshch. Khim.*, **7**, 188 (1937); *Chem. Abstr.*, **31**, 4810 (1937).
372. Shostakovskiĭ, M. F., En. N. Prilezhaeva, and L. V. Tsymbal, *Zh. Obshch. Khim.*, **26**, 739 (1956); *Chem. Abstr.*, **50**, 14564 (1956).
373. Shtitevskii, V. V., N. A. Oblonskaya, and N. I. Nikitin, *Zh. Prikl. Khim.*, **24**, 1045 (1951); *Chem. Abstr.*, **46**, 4221 (1952).
374. Sihtola, H., *Makromol. Chem.*, **35**, 250 (1960).
374a. Sisson, W. A., *Textile Res. J.*, **30**, 153 (1960).
375. Siu, R. G. H., *Microbial Decomposition of Cellulose*, Reinhold, New York, 1951.
376. Siu, R. G. H., and E. T. Reese, *Botan. Rev.*, **19**, 377 (1953); *Chem. Abstr.*, **47**, 9418d (1953).
377. Spinner, I. H., *Tappi*, **45**, 495 (1962).
378. Spurlin, H. M., Ref. 295, chap. IXA.
379. Spurlin, H. M., in *Cellulose and Cellulose Derivatives*, E. Ott, H. M. Spurlin, and M. W. Grafflin, eds., High Polymer Series, Vol. V, Part III, 2nd ed., Interscience, New York, 1954, Chap. XA.
380. Stacey, M., E. J. Bourne, J. C. Tatlow, and J. M. Tedder, *Nature*, **164**, 705 (1949).
381. Stakheeva-Kaverzneva, E. D., and A. S. Salova, *Izv. Akad. Nauk. SSSR Otd. Khim. Nauk*, **1959**, 2033; *Chem. Abstr.*, **54**, 10314 (1960).
382. Stamm, A. J., Ref. 432, Chap. 8.
383. Stamm, A. J., *Tappi*, **42**, 39, 44 (1959).
384. Stamm, A. J., and E. E. Harris, *Chemical Processing of Wood*, Chemical Publishing Co., New York, 1953.
385. Stanonis, D. J., and W. D. King, *Textile Res. J.*, **30**, 802 (1960).
386. Staudinger, H., and W. Döhle, *J. Prakt. Chem.*, **161**, 219 (1943); *Chem. Abstr.*, **37**, 5233[1] (1943).
387. Staudinger, H., and E. Dreher, *Ber.*, **69**, 1091 (1936).
387a. Staudinger, H., and H. Eilers, *Ber.*, **68**, 1611 (1935).

388. Staudinger, H., and J. Jurisch, *Papier-Fabr.*, **35,** 462 (1937); *Chem. Abstr.*, **32,** 2342^8 (1938).
389. Staudinger, H., and M. Sorkin, *Ber.*, **70,** 1565 (1937).
390. Steele, R., *J. Appl. Polymer Sci.*, **4,** 45 (1960).
391. Steele, R., *Textile Res. J.*, **25,** 545 (1955).
392. Steele, R., *Textile Res. J.*, **31,** 257 (1961).
393. Steele, R., and L. E. Giddings, Jr., *Ind. Eng. Chem.*, **48,** 110 (1956).
394. Steiger, F. H., S. Y. Wang, and M. D. Hurwitz, *Textile Res. J.*, **31,** 327 (1961).
394a. Sugihara, J. M., and M. L. Wolfrom, *J. Am. Chem. Soc.*, **71,** 3509 (1949).
394b. Swan, E. P., and C. B. Purves, *Can. J. Chem.*, **35,** 1522 (1957).
395. Takagi, T., and J. B. Goldberg, *Mod. Textiles Mag.*, **41** (4), 49 (April, 1960).
396. Takahashi, S., *Sen-i Gakkaishi,* **17,** 125 (1961); *Chem. Abstr.*, **55,** 10877 (1961).
397. Talwar, K. K., *Tappi,* **41,** 207 (1958).
398. Tesoro, G. C., *Textile Res. J.*, **30,** 192 (1960).
399. Tesoro, G. C., *Textile Res. J.*, **32,** 189 (1962).
400. Tesoro, G. C., P. Linden, and S. B. Sello, *Textile Res. J.*, **31,** 283 (1961).
400a. Thomas, J. C., U. S. Patent 2,511,229 (to E. I. du Pont de Nemours and Co.), June 13, 1950; *Chem. Abstr.*, **44,** 8657c (1950).
401. Thomas, W. B., U. S. Patent 2,829,072 (to Bates Mfg. Co.), Apr. 1, 1958; *Chem. Abstr.*, **52,** 15084h (1958).
401a. Timell, T., *Studies on Cellulose Reactions,* Esselte, Stockholm, 1950.
401b. Timell, T., *Svensk Kem. Tidskr.*, **61,** 49 (1949); *Chem. Abstr.*, **43,** 5942g (1949).
402. Timell, T., *Svensk Papperstid.*, **51,** 52, 199, 509 (1948); *Svensk Kem. Tidskr.*, **62,** 49 (1950); *Chem. Abstr.*, **42,** 8466f (1948); **43,** 396d, 2770h (1949).
403. Timell, T., *Svensk Papperstid.*, **51,** 254 (1948); *Chem. Abstr.*, **43,** 396f (1949).
404. Tovey, H., *Textile Res. J.*, **31,** 185 (1961).
405. Traube, W., *Ber.*, **54,** 3220 (1921); **55,** 1899 (1922); **56,** 268 (1923).
406. Traube, W., B. Blaser, and C. Grunert, *Ber.*, **61,** 754 (1928).
406a. Traube, W., B. Blaser, and E. Lindemann, *Ber.*, **65,** 603 (1932).
407. Traube, W., G. Glaubitt, and V. Schenck, *Ber.*, **63,** 2083 (1930).
407a. Traube, W., R. Piwonka, and A. Funk, *Ber.*, **69,** 1483 (1936).
407b. Traube, W., and V. Schenck-Thiekötter, *Cellulosechemie,* **12,** 301 (1931); *Chem. Abstr.*, **26,** 4710 (1932).
408. Tripp, V. W., A. T. Moore, and M. L. Rollins, *Textile Res. J.*, **31,** 295 (1961).
409. Trogus, C., *Ber.*, **64,** 405 (1931).
410. Trogus, C., and K. Hess, *Z. Physik. Chem. (Leipzig)*, **B14,** 387 (1931); *Chem. Abstr.*, **26,** 591 (1932).
411. Unruh, C. C., and W. O. Kenyon, *Textile Res. J.*, **16,** 1 (1946).
412. Urbański, T., and Z. Janiszewski, *Roczniki Chem.*, **17,** 349 (1937); *Chem. Abstr.*, **31,** 8927 (1937).
413. Urquhart, A. R., *Textile Res. J.*, **28,** 159 (1958).
414. Usmanov, Kh. U., B. I. Aĭkhodzhaev, and U. Azizov, *J. Polymer Sci.*, **53,** 87 (1961).
416. Valko, E. I., in *Cotton,* K. Ward, Jr., ed., Interscience, New York, 1955, p. 190.
417. Valley, R. B., *Textile Res. J.*, **25,** 930 (1955).
418. Varshney, M. C., and P. Luner, *Tappi,* **44,** 285 (1961).
419. Vermaas, D., *Chem. Weekblad,* **54,** 33 (1958); *Chem. Abstr.*, **52,** 8564 (1958).
420. Virkola, N. E., and O. Lehtikoski, *Paperi Puu,* **42,** 559, 564 (1960).

420a. Waentig, P., *Kolloid-Z.*, **41,** 152 (1927); *Chem. Abstr.*, **22,** 1039 (1928).
421. Wagner, R. E., and E. Pacsu, *Textile Res. J.*, **22,** 12 (1952).
422. Walecka, J. A., *Tappi,* **39,** 458 (1956).
423. Walter, H. C., J. K. Buxbaum, and L. Q. Green, *Textile Res. J.*, **27,** 146 (1957).
424. Ward, K., Jr., *Tappi,* **43,** 54 (1961).
425. Wayland, R. L., Jr., *Textile Res. J.*, **29,** 170 (1959).
426. Weaver, J. W., C. A. Mackenzie, and D. A. Shirley, *Ind. Eng. Chem.*, **46,** 1490 (1954).
426a. Weaver, J. W., J. F. Nielson, and I. S. Goldstein, *Forest Prod. J.*, **10,** 306 (1960); *Chem. Abstr.*, **54,** 21753b (1960).
427. Webber, C. S., C. J. Staud, and H. LeB. Gray, *J. Am. Chem. Soc.*, **52,** 1542 (1930).
428. Wegmann, J., *Textil-Rundschau,* **13,** 323 (1958).
430. Weltzien, W., and G. zum Tobel, *Ber.*, **60,** 2024 (1927).
430a. Willard, J. J., and E. Pacsu, *J. Am. Chem. Soc.*, **82,** 4350 (1960).
431. Willstätter, R., and L. Zechmeister, *Ber.*, **46,** 2401 (1913); **62,** 722 (1929).
432. Wise, L. E., and E. C. Jahn, eds., *Wood Chemistry,* 2nd ed., Reinhold, New York, 1952, 2 vols.
433. Wolfrom, M. L., J. C. Dacons, and D. L. Fields, *Tappi,* **39,** 803 (1956).
434. Wolfrom, M. L., and D. L. Fields, *Tappi,* **40,** 335 (1957); **41,** 204 (1958).
435. Wolfrom, M. L., J. C. Sowden, and E. A. Metcalf, *J. Am. Chem. Soc.*, **63,** 1688 (1941).
436. Worden, E. C., *Technology of Cellulose Esters,* Eschenbach, Easton, Pa., 1921, 5 vols.
437. Worden, E. C., *Technology of Cellulose Ethers,* Worden Laboratory and Library, Milburn, New Jersey, 1933, 5 vols.
438. Yackel, E. C., and W. O. Kenyon, *J. Am. Chem. Soc.*, **64,** 121 (1942).
440. Zechmeister, L., and G. Tóth, *Ber.*, **64,** 854 (1931).
441. Ziifle, H. M., R. J. Berni, and R. R. Benerito, *Textile Res. J.*, **31,** 349 (1961).
442. Zollinger, H., *Angew. Chem.*, **73,** 125 (1961).

Chapter VI

REACTIONS OF PROTEINS

R. E. Whitfield and W. L. Wasley

Western Utilization Research and Development Division,
U. S. Department of Agriculture

A. INTRODUCTION

1. General

The proteins compose one of the largest and most widely diversified groups of natural macromolecules. These polymers are the products of living organisms, both plant and animal, and are of paramount importance for the life processes and sustenance. Two main classes are the globular and fibrous proteins. Globular proteins are water-soluble, fairly labile chemically, and exist as spheroid particles, a characteristic which provides the basis for the class name. This group of proteins is extremely versatile in their biological functions and is intimately involved with the vital life processes. They function as enzymes, hormones, antibodies and toxins, and other essential constituents of multiplying cells.

Fibrous proteins, on the other hand, are primarily insoluble and serve to protect the living organism from its hostile environment. These proteins form fibers which are utilized to build quite stable structures to support the organs. This class includes silk, wool, skins and hides, horns, hooves, hair, and feathers. The individual proteins are not visibly crystalline.

Probably thousands of proteins go into the makeup and functioning of a single living cell. This multitude of proteins within a cell perform thousands of acts in an exact sequence that constitutes the "life" of the cell. The mechanism by which this very complex activity is accomplished is not understood and will likely remain essentially unknown for a long time. Each protein is adapted apparently to its specific task by a unique combination of side groups, size, folding, and shape.

By a variety of experimental methods, protein molecules have been shown to exist in an enormous range of sizes, shapes, and chemical constitution. They range in molecular weight from as low as 1000 to as high as one billion or more. Most known proteins are stereospecific polymers in which each asymmetric carbon atom of the main chain has an identical absolute configuration. In the diversity of reactive groups, their biological function, and the multitude of biochemical and chemical reactions they undergo, these substances are unsurpassed by any other group of polymers. In addition to their participation in the basic life processes, the proteins have wide industrial uses as food, fiber, plastics, adhesives, paints, and a host of other uses too numerous to itemize here.

2. Multiplicity of Residues: Sequences

Elementary analysis reveals most simple proteins to contain carbon, hydrogen, oxygen, and nitrogen as major constituents, with varying amounts of iodine, phosphorus, and sulfur in some instances. Many proteins occur combined with lipids, carbohydrates, nucleic acids, and other organic materials; these are referred to as *conjugated* proteins and will not be considered in the present treatment which is restricted to the *simple* proteins.

Since its first proposal by Hofmeister and Fischer (1,2) independently, the peptide theory of the primary structure of proteins has received extensive experimental confirmation and is accepted as the true covalent structure of the main chain of proteins and polypeptides, no facts having been found incompatible with it. According to this theory, the α-amino acids are linked through condensation of the carboxyl group of one acid with the α-amino group of another to form peptide bonds. The macromolecules so formed may be represented by the general formula I:

$$\mathrm{H}\left(\mathrm{-NH{-}\overset{\displaystyle R}{\overset{|}{C}}H{-}\underset{\underset{\displaystyle O}{\|}}{C}-}\right)_x\mathrm{OH}$$

(I)

Hydrolysis of a protein results in cleavage of the polypeptide chain into its constituent α-amino acids. Although some thirty amino acids have been identified, twenty of these form the main building blocks of most proteins (Table VI-1). These amino acids differ from one another primarily in the nature of the side groups R. Four general classes of R groups are known (*1*) nonpolar, such as glycine, alanine, and proline; (*2*) anionic, typified by the

TABLE VI-1
Structure of R Groups in the Common Amino Acids of Proteins[a]

Amino acid	R group
Glycine	—H
Alanine	—CH_3
Valine	—$CH(CH_3)_2$
Leucine	—$CH_2CH(CH_3)_2$
Isoleucine	—$CH(CH_3)CH_2CH_3$
Serine	—CH_2OH
Threonine	—$CHOH(CH_3)$
Tyrosine	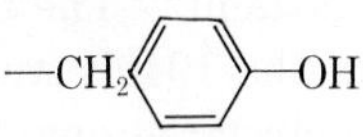
Phenylalanine	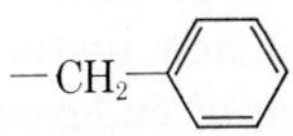
Tryptophan	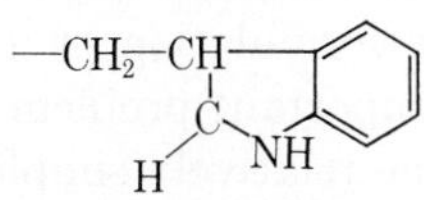
Aspartic acid	—CH_2COOH
Asparagine	—CH_2CONH_2
Glutamic acid	—CH_2CH_2COOH
Glutamine	—$CH_2CH_2CONH_2$
Lysine	—$CH_2(CH_2)_3NH_2$
Arginine	—$CH_2(CH_2)_2NHC(NH_2){=}NH$
Histidine	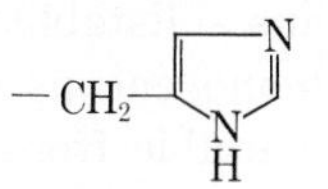
Cysteine	—CH_2SH
Cystine	—$CH_2SSCH_2CH(NH_2)COOH$
Methionine	—$CH_2CH_2SCH_3$
Proline	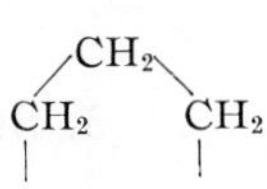
Hydroxyproline	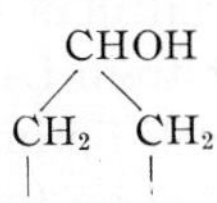

[a] R in NH_2—CHR—COOH.

carboxyl groups of aspartic and glutamic acids; (*3*) cationic, as represented by lysine and arginine; (*4*) polar nonionic, such as serine, threonine, and hydroxyproline. Tristram (3) has summarized the available data on amino acid composition of proteins.

Within the last decade, significant strides have been made in further elucidation of the exact structure of several proteins. Although hydrolysis of proteins and subsequent analysis of the hydrolyzate had, prior to that, given information on the relative number and kinds of amino acids, it had provided no knowledge of the distribution of these along the polypeptide chain of the protein. The methods of analysis and of separation of amino acids prior to the 1940's were extremely tedious, time consuming, and required relatively large quantities of materials. During the 1940's the advent of significant new methods of analysis and separation of amino acids, and determination of endgroups in proteins and small polypeptides, made possible the formulation of a strategy and methodology for tackling the extremely important problem of unraveling the specific sequence of amino acids in some relatively simple proteins. The first great landmark in this area of activity was the elucidation by Sanger and co-workers (4) of the amino acid sequence of the insulin molecule. Since that first magnificent achievement of what had for a long time appeared to be beyond the realm of possibility, the complete amino acid sequence of several proteins has been elucidated. Knowledge of sequence has important consequences and applications in the study of the chemical reactions of the side chains and main chains of proteins. Establishing that the macromolecules of a specific protein are of homogeneous molecular weight and contain a sequence of amino acids, invariable from macromolecule to macromolecule, has been one of the most important achievements in the history of protein chemistry. Among the proteins whose amino acid sequence has been elucidated are insulin (4), cytochrome C (5–7), tobacco mosaic virus protein (8–10), ribonuclease (11–13), the α- and β- chains of human hemoglobin (14,15), whale myoglobin (16–18), corticotropin (19–21), glucagon (22), and the sequence of several smaller polypeptides and partial sequence of larger proteins (23).

3. Structure of Proteins

One of the most fruitful of recent concepts of protein structure was first advanced by Linderstrøm-Lang (24). This formulation viewed protein structure at three levels: primary, secondary, and tertiary. The primary structure is represented by the covalently bonded sequence of amino acids in the polypeptide chains of the protein (i.e., the covalent structure); secondary structure relates to the patterns of conformational order of the individual polypeptide chains, stabilized in general by hydrogen bonds; the tertiary structure refers to the more involved folds and twists characteristic of the structure of a particular protein in the native state, as imposed by disulfide crosslinks and various other interchain interactions—the packing of the macromolecules among themselves. This particular view of protein structure has been widely adopted by protein chemists and is useful for discussion of the chemical reactivity of a protein as influenced by its structure. Reaction conditions may have a marked influence on the secondary or tertiary structure of a protein and thereby indirectly exert a marked influence on accessibility of groups and rates of reactions, as a consequence of the conformational changes of the protein molecule induced by the changes in environment.

Protein structure is a subject in its own right and is far too extensive for treatment here. The reader is referred to several good reviews of this subject (25–32), which in turn will provide leads to the extensive literature pertinent thereto.

4. Chemical Reactions

The chemical modification of proteins has been pursued for a multitude of purposes. These include: (*1*) to change the biological activity or physical properties of the native proteins to make them more suitable for medicinal or industrial use, (*2*) to ascertain the details of structure responsible for the biological activity of proteins, particularly the reactive sites, (*3*) to prepare derivatives for use in comparative studies of physical or biological properties, (*4*) to assist in elucidation of the primary structure of the protein. In most of these chemical modification studies the investigator has been faced with the challenge (not too different in principle from the challenges in many of the other activities in his daily life, i.e., of getting that which he desires without having to sacrifice something he would prefer to keep) of eliminating or suppressing the unwanted characteristics of the parent macromolecules without eliminating or reducing the desirable ones. With industrial proteins, this has been particularly the case. Most studies related to biological activity and structure have used reagents and modification under rather mild conditions, with great emphasis on achieving a highly specific reaction of a particular group with as little change in the physical structure and properties of the protein as possible. This has been an ideal seldom attained in practice. Modification of the industrial proteins, on the other hand, has been less concerned with specificity and mild conditions, the objective being more that of getting extensive reaction to build in as many new properties as possible.

In the present treatment, neither of these approaches will be favored. Instead, an effort will be made to illustrate the great diversity of chemical reactions characteristic of proteins, and to focus the emphasis on mechanisms involved in certain of these reactions.

Most research on the chemical reactions of proteins has suffered to a degree due to the reactions *per se* being of secondary interest to the investigator. The reactions have been carried out to ascertain reactive sites in biologically active polymers, to convert industrial proteins into materials of greater commercial utility, to ascertain the gross structure, primary structure or analytical composition of the protein, and rarely, if ever, to elucidate in detail the chemistry inherent in the reactions involved. As a consequence, one finds a paucity of thorough studies of proteins from the standpoint of basic organic chemistry in spite of the wide range of reactions in which they participate. This area of research on proteins is a very fertile field for attack by the investigator who has great courage, unremitting patience, and creative ingenuity and who is dedicated to meticulous detail and has unshakable faith in the ultimate possibility of unravelling the detailed order and reactivity of seemingly highly disordered and intractable natural polymers. With the marked strides in elucidation of amino-acid sequence of many proteins and of the secondary and tertiary structures of these substances, the organic chemist now has available materials which can serve as useful models for the study of specific chemical or biological modifications, the mechanism of the pertinent reactions, and varied other aspects of structure and reactivity. Within the present decade, great strides are already under way based on the use of these materials as model substances.

The present treatment takes the approach of the organic polymer chemist. The proteins are viewed as polymers with a diversity of reactive groups in the side chain, with reactive crosslinks, and with highly reactive (under certain conditions) main chain units. The reactions to be discussed are classified primarily on the basis of these three categories: (*1*) reactions of the side chains, (*2*) main chain reactions, (*3*) reactions of crosslinks (really a special case of side chain reactions).

This is not intended primarily as a review of the subject. Examples have been selected as illustrative of the particular reaction involved, and no effort or claim is made to these being exhaustive. Some care has been taken, however, to select what to the authors appeared to be among the better examples for the specific reactions. In particular, attention has been focused on examples in which there is fairly unambiguous evidence for the reaction under discussion and, also, to the nature of that evidence (at least in a general sense). We apologize to those investigators whose work has not been cited, and which might have afforded an equally good account of the reaction. To have cited all examples would have made the treatment burdensomely long without really adding significantly to the principle or reaction being stressed. The authors' main contribution consists in the particular selection and organization of material herein presented; in focusing attention on probable mechanisms involved in certain reactions; in reporting a particular approach developed by themselves for assessment of steric factors in main chain reactions; in bringing up to date various aspects of graft polymer formation in proteins; and in giving a brief coverage of some interesting aspects of the effects of radiant energy on these natural polymers.

B. REACTIONS OF SIDE CHAIN FUNCTIONAL GROUPS

There are several approaches for classification of the side chain reactions in proteins. One approach is to catalogue all known reactions for a particular functional group. After doing this for each group in the protein, all reactions of that protein will be covered. Another method catalogues by type of reaction, such as alkylation, acylation, esterification. This, as well as the first, has been a commonly used system in reviews of chemical reactions of proteins. A third approach is to classify the reactions, insofar as possible, on the basis of mechanistic type, such as nucleophilic displacement reactions, electrophilic displacements, elimination reactions, and various others. Each approach has merit. However, the last mentioned is particularly appealing to the authors and has been adopted for this section of the reactions of proteins.

The mechanistic classification provides a logical basis for discussion of the relative reactivities of groups and will perhaps bring a different perspective to current thought on chemical reactions of proteins and the relative reactivities of groups within a single protein. This approach is not, however, without its limitations. In the first place, there is a paucity of data on mechanism studies on proteins *per se*. One is forced, consequently, into classification by analogy with reactions of known simple compounds rather than on the basis of actual data obtained from reactions of the proteins. In the second place, reactions are not always clearly one type or another, but often are of a mixed character mechanistically. Fully aware of these limitations, an attempt has been made nonetheless to group the reactions of side chain groups of proteins into mechanistic categories, and we ask the indulgence of the reader who may be a specialist in mechanisms, if certain of the reactions are not unambiguously of the mechanistic class in which they are herein placed, but have been placed in that particular class for our discussion. An element of arbitrariness is almost unavoidable. Occam's weapon (33) has been used within the limits of our judgment.

Discussion of protein reactions on the basis of their probable mechanistic character will perhaps make clear, and even emphasize, that the reactivity derives from centers of nucleophilic or electrophilic character, rather than from reactive hydrogen, as has so often been the view of many previous review articles. This is not meant to suggest that a readily transferable hydrogen is not important in the sequence of events occurring during the reactions. Rather, that when such transfer occurs, it may be merely incidental to the main events from which the reaction receives its driving force.

1. Nucleophilic Substitution Reactions

a. General

A list of the nucleophiles present in proteins is given in Table VI-2. Some proteins, such as silk, may contain as few as three or four of these; others, such as the keratins, may contain all.

It is convenient to discuss the inherent relative reactivities of these groups in terms of an equation suggested by Swain et al. (34) for nucleophilic displacements on carbon

$$\log k/k^0 = sn + s'e \tag{1}$$

This equation assumes that nucleophilic displacements involve both nucleophilic and electrophilic attack; n is a measure of the *nucleophilicity* of the nucleophilic reagent; s, the sensitivity of the reactant to changes in nucleophilicity; e, the *electrophilicity* of the electrophilic reagent; s', the sensitivity toward changes in electrophilicity; k, the rate constant for a given nucleophilic and electrophilic reagent; and k^0, the rate constant for a standard nucleophilic reagent and standard electrophilic reagent whose n and s- values are, respectively, zero. For nonsolvolytic displacements in water, eq. (1) simplifies to

$$\log k/k^0 = sn \tag{1a}$$

In Table VI-3 a list of values of n for a variety of nucleophiles is given; in Table VI-4, a list of s values for some typical reactions. Other things be-

TABLE VI-2
Nucleophiles in Proteins

Nucleophile	Structure	Occurrence in proteins
Carboxyl	$—COOH, —COO^-$	Glutamic acid Aspartic acid Chain ends
Phenol	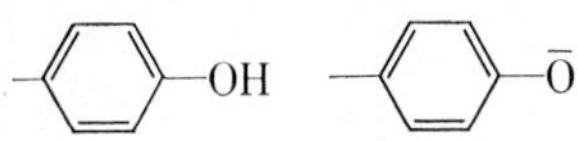	Tyrosine
Amino	$—NH_2$	Lysine Chain ends
Imidazole	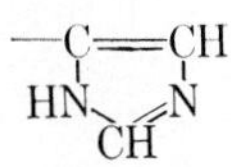	Histidine
Guanidyl		Arginine
Indole	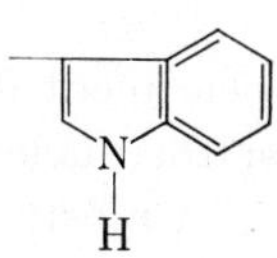	Tryptophan
Amide	$—CONH_2$	Glutamine Asparagine
Aliphatic hydroxyl	$—OH, —O^-$	Serine Threonine
Sulfhydryl	$—SH, —S^-$	Cysteine
Disulfide	—S—S—	Cystine
Thioether	$—SCH_3$	Methionine

TABLE VI-3
Nucleophilic Constants *n* of Various Nucleophilic Reagents[a]

Reagent	*n*
ClO_3^-, ClO_4^-, BrO_3^-, IO_3^-	0
H_2O	0.00
p-$CH_3C_6H_4SO_3^-$	1.0
NO_3^-	1.03
Picrate anion	1.9
F^-	2.0
$SO_4^{=}$	2.5
CH_3COO^-	2.72
Cl^-	3.04
C_5H_5N	3.6
HCO_3^-	3.8
$HPO_4^{=}$	3.8
Br^-	3.89
N_3^-	4.00
$(NH_2)_2CS$	4.1
OH^-	4.20
$C_6H_5NH_2$	4.49
SCN^-	4.77
I^-	5.04
CN^-	5.1
SH^-	5.1
$SO_3^{=}$	5.1
$S_2O_3^{=}$	6.36
$HPSO_3^{=}$	6.6

[a] Taken from ref. 35.

ing equal, the rate of a nucleophilic displacement involving these groups will be proportional to the value of *n* for the nucleophile involved, being faster for reactants with higher value of *n*. Unfortunately, *n* values are not available for each of the nucleophiles in proteins, listed in Table VI-2. However, close analogues may be found in Table VI-3, and hence a fair guess may be made of the relative reactivities of these various groups in a particular displacement reaction from estimated *n* values. When variations from the expected order of reactivity arises, they may be due to steric hindrance, limited accessibility, local environment effects (neighboring groups, or breaking of hydrogen bonds in the vicinity of the reaction site). Therefore, in a sense, a finding of an abnormal order gives information suggestive of one or more of these factors. In some cases, diffusion of the reagent to the reaction site may be rate controlling, and all nucleophiles will demonstrate essentially equivalent reactivity.

TABLE VI-4
Relative Susceptibilities *s* of Various Reactants to Changes in Nucleophilicity of Attacking Reagent[a]

Reactant	*s*
$C_2H_5OSO_2C_6H_4CH_3$-*p*	0.66
$C_6H_5CH_2Cl$	0.87
β-Propiolactone[b]	0.77
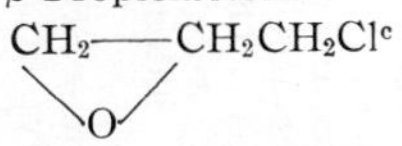	0.93
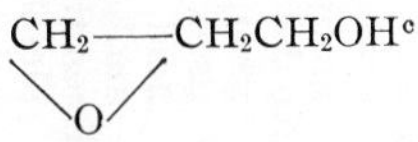	1.00
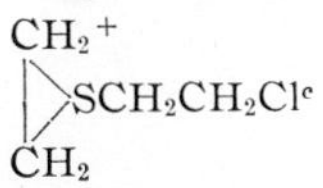	0.95
CH_3Br	1.00
$C_6H_5SO_2Cl$	1.25
C_6H_5COCl	1.43

[a] Taken from ref. 35.
[b] Refers to nucleophilic attack on the α-carbon atom.
[c] Refers to ring-opening attack.

In considerations of the relative reactivity of several RY reagents with a single nucleophile, the nature of the displaced group, Y, is quite important, as is the nature of the R group to which Y is attached. Some of the more common groups, in order of their increasing ease of displacement from aliphatic carbon, are:

(Hardest displaced)

$$R_2N < OR < NR_3^+ < OSO_3^- < F^- < SMe_2^+ \sim OH_2^+ < Cl^- < NO_3^- < Br^- < I^- < OSO_2R < -N{\equiv}N^+$$

(Easiest displaced)

This list is subject to variations and inversions in specific instances but holds fairly well for most reactions in aqueous solutions.

b. Alkylation

Among the oldest and most widely studied of displacement reactions are those involving the displacement of halogens from carbons (36,37). As a group, these are also among the more important reactions which have been used for the chemical modification of proteins. The reaction results in the

TABLE VI-5
Alkylation of Proteins with Organic Halides

Reagent	Protein	Reaction conditions	Reaction sites	Comments
$BrCH_2COOH$	Ribonuclease (38)	pH 7.0	Histidine	Reacts specifically. Generally applicable to soluble proteins. No degradation of protein
	Bovine serum albumin (39)	pH 9.0, 16–24 hr. 35°C.	—NH_2, tyrosine, imidazole	
ICH_2COOH	Ribonuclease, lysozyme (40) protein first reduced.	pH 8.2, 2 hr. room temp., 10-fold excess reagent	—SH	Specificity for —SH alkylation under the conditions was shown by several methods
	Ribonuclease (41)	pH 2.8–10, 40°C.	Histidine (pH 5.5–6) Amino (pH 8.5–10) S of methionine (pH 2.8)	Study of inactivation of ribonuclease by reaction with the reagent. Interest in determining the reactive site
	Egg albumin (42)	pH 7.3, 25°C., 1–6 hr.	—SH	Faster reaction with —SH followed by slower one with amino groups, and possibly others
	Keratins (reduced) (44,45,47)	pH 7.4, 25°C., 2 hr.	—SH	No detectable reaction with amino groups. Other reagents also used were α-bromopropionic acid, iodoacetamide, iodoethanol
	Tobacco mosaic virus (TMV) (46)	pH 8, 37–55°C., 1–10 hr.	—SH	Even the —SH did not react completely; other groups may have reacted to lesser degree

ICH_2CONH_2	Papain (48)	Alkaline pH, 0–25°C.	—SH	Reaction fairly specific for —SH under conditions
	Serum albumin, insulin (45,49,50), TMV (46) Egg albumin (43,49)	pH 7.5–8.5, 25–40°C., 1–3 days	—SH, —NH_2, perhaps others	Fairly good evidence that this reagent may react with several groups of protein, other than —SH
ICH_2COOCH_3	Ribonuclease (41) Wool	pH 5–6 pH 8.5–10 pH 2.8	Histidine Amino Methionine	Study of the nature of the amino acid residues involved in inactivation of the enzyme
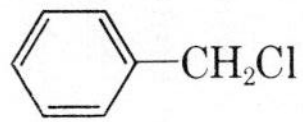	Wool (51)	100°C., 2 hr., various alcohols used to assist penetration of wool	Not determined	Benzylated wool shows increased alkali solubility, increased breaking strength, elongation, and supercontraction. Decreased acid solubility and hygroscopicity
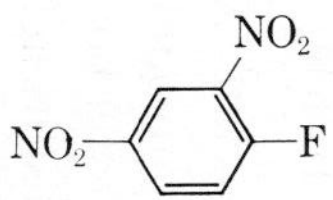	Many proteins (52,53)	Slightly alkaline, H_2O–alcohol solvent, 25–50°C.	Amino, tyrosine, —SH, imidazole	A very useful reagent for *N*-terminal endgroup detn. Extensive literature on use of this reagent in sequence work
CH_3I, CH_3Br, CH_3Cl	Variety (50,54)	Slightly alkaline pH, room temp., variety of condition	Carboxyl, amino, phenolic, hydroxyl, sulfhydryl	Useful reagents for extensive methylation of variety of groups. Not very specific
$ClCH_2CH_2$—S—CH_2CH_2Cl	Variety (55)	pH 5.5–6 room temp.	Carboxyl	No evidence for reaction with amino groups in most cases

alkylation of any or all of the nucleophiles present in the protein, depending on the availability of the groups, reaction conditions, and quantity of reagent used. Table VI-5 lists several aliphatic and aromatic halides which have been reacted with proteins, typical reaction conditions, possible site of reaction, and utility of the reaction for research and industrial purposes. Among the halides the iodides are generally most reactive, followed by bromides (almost same reactivity as iodides), chlorides, and fluorides, respectively. This order may be reversed, however, in certain aromatic compounds, since the reactivity of RY depends on the nature of R as well as on Y.

An elegant demonstration of the utility of knowledge of amino acid sequence in helping to pinpoint the location of a single reacting residue has been reported on ribonuclease (38,41). Reaction of this enzyme with bromoacetic acid results in introduction of a single carboxymethyl group, with loss in activity of the enzyme. By a variety of techniques, it was demonstrated fairly conclusively that a single histidine residue in the enzyme had been alkylated. Ribonuclease, however, contains four histidine units. By use of labeled bromoacetic acid and subsequent oxidation and cleavage of the alkylated enzyme into four large peptides, and separation of these by electrophoresis and chromatography, the peptide containing the labeled $—CH_2COOH$ was identified. The single histidine which had been alkylated was located nearest the *C*-terminal end of the protein chain. This is an excellent example of the type of results obtainable by use of enzymes of known sequence as model substances, in conjunction with tagged reagents, and the better methods of separation and identification of peptides.

c. *Acylation*

Acylation by means of nucleophilic displacement reactions is closely related to alkylation. The most commonly used reagents are acid halides, anhydrides, and azides, the halide ion, carboxylate ion, and azide ion being displaced, respectively

$$\mathrm{R{-}\underset{\underset{O}{\|}}{C}{-}Y + X{-}\Big|_{\text{Protein}} \rightarrow R{-}\underset{\underset{O}{\|}}{C}{-}X{-}\Big|_{\text{Protein}} + Y} \qquad (2)$$

where Y = halide, azide, carboxylate, X = nucleophile of protein. When the nucleophile is an amino group, amide bonds are formed; when a hydroxyl, ester bonds; thiol, a thioester bond. Some typical reagents, reaction conditions, proteins used, and results achieved are given in Table VI-6.

TABLE VI-6
Acylation of Proteins with Various Reagents

Reagent	Protein	Reaction conditions	Reaction sites	Comments
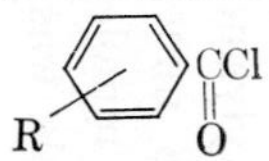 CH_3COCl	Keratins, eggwhite (50,54,56) Gluten, casein, zein, peanut protein, collagen (57)	Anhydrous 0–125°C.	Most basic groups, hydroxyl, carboxyl	R = H, halogen, alkyl. Extensive reactions; not very selective
RCOCl	Egg albumin, zein, soybean, peanut, cottonseed, gluten, casein (58,59)	Slurry of the protein in aqueous alkali. pH 7–12, 0–25°C., 1 hr. or more	Amino, hydroxyl, carboxyl, tyrosine, and others	R = variety of long-chain aliphatics. The modified proteins have reduced affinity for water
$(RCO)_2O$	Collagen and many others (50,54,56,57)	Aqueous or anhydrous, pH 7–8, 0–25°C., 30 min. or longer	Amino, hydroxyl, tyrosine, and possibly other basic groups	R = phenyl, substituted phenyl, short-chain, and long-chain aliphatics
$CH_3CONHCH_2CH_2$-$SC(=O)CH_3$	Albumin (60)	pH 10, room temp., several days	Amino and possibly others	This reagent is readily soluble in H_2O, stable in dilute acids and alkalis. Believed to be fairly specific for amino groups

Acetylation reactions have been studied extensively. Acetic anhydride has been useful for selective reaction with amino groups of several proteins when used in cold sodium acetate-buffered solutions, pH 7–8, employing only limited quantities of the anhydride (50,61). The technique employed seems quite useful. To 1 g. of protein, dissolved or suspended in 20 ml. of half to fully saturated sodium acetate solution and cooled in an ice bath is added with stirring in several portions and over about 1 hr. a total of 1.2 ml. of acetic anhydride. After the odor of reagent has disappeared, the protein derivative is isolated without loss by dialysis. The amino nitrogen is in the range of 5–40% of the original value for most proteins. The Folin color value is 80–90% of that of the original for various proteins, and 90–100% of that obtained after exposing the protein for 10 min. at pH 11. Analyses for acetyl introduced indicate amounts equal to losses in amino nitrogen.

Typical results obtained with bovine serum albumin, egg albumin, and insulin are given in Table VI-7. It is pointed out that this selectivity may not hold for other proteins and other conditions.

TABLE VI-7
Effect of Acetic Anhydride on Reactive Groups of Proteins

Protein	Original amino groups, g.-moles/10^4 g.	Loss in amino groups, g.-moles/10^4 g.	Acetyl introduced, g.-moles/10^4 g.
Bovine serum albumin	8.5	7.9	8.5
Egg albumin	4.7	4.0	4.7
Insulin	5.0	4.5	4.5

In searching for ways to *N*-acetylate or *O*-acetylate collagen, Green et al. (62) found the above method to be selective for *N*-acetylation. To obtain both *N*-acetylation and *O*-acetylation, the collagen was reacted with cold acetic anhydride and an equal amount of acetic acid using 6 : 1 ratio of the anhydride to collagen and 8 days reaction time. The results are summarized in Table VI-8.

In the aqueous system, complete acetylation of the lysine and hydroxylysine (0.38 mmole/g. collagen, sum of these residues in collagen) occurs with no acetylation of serine, threonine, hydroxylysine, hydroxyproline, or tyrosine (for these amino acid residues, 1.68 mmole/g.). With acetic anhydride in acetic acid a maximum of 1.76 mmole acetyl per gram of collagen was introduced. Of this, 1.33 mmole was alkali-labile (easily

TABLE VI-8
Acetylation of Collagen with Acetic Anhydride

Conditions	Acetyl, mmoles/g. collagen		Amino N, (Van Slyke) mmole/g.
	O-acetyl	*N*-acetyl	
Sodium acetate (pH 8)			
First acetylation	0	0.24	0.12
Second acetylation	0	0.36	0.01
Third acetylation	0	0.38	0.00
Fourth acetylation	0	0.38	0.00
Acetic anhydride–acetic acid	1.33	0.40	0.00

removed by 0.05*N* NaOH) and hence probably present as esters of hydroxyl groups of the collagen; 0.40 mmole was not alkali-labile (slightly in excess of 0.38 mmole of lysine and hydroxylysine per gram of collagen). Even more complete acetylation of collagen was achieved by Bose and Joseph (66) by suspending 5 g. collagen in 50 ml. ethyl acetate, 3 ml. of 90% formic acid, and 30 ml. of acetic anhydride at room temperature for 7 days. By this method the *O*-acetyl introduced was 2.1 mmoles/g. collagen. In a related procedure, use of thiocyanic acid instead of formic acid resulted in fairly exclusive *O*-acetylation with practically no *N*-acetylation. Use of acetylpyridinium chloride in toluene, 75°C., 2 hr., resulted in *N*-alkylation with relatively little *O*-acetylation. Comparative results of various procedures are summarized in Table VI-9.

These results on the acetylation of collagen are illustrative of the effects of conditions on extent of acetylation and the site of reaction. Wool has been acetylated with acetic anhydride in glacial acetic acid containing sulfuric acid monohydrate and dimethylaniline, 60 min. at 58°C. (63); 90% of the amino groups in the wool were blocked.

TABLE VI-9
Acetylation of Collagen with Several Reagents

Method of acetylation	Amino N, mmole/g. collagen	*N*-Acetyl, mmole/g. collagen	*O*-Acetyl, mmole/g. collagen
Untreated collagen	0.37	0	0
Acetic anhydride in ethyl acetate	0.00	0.39	1.71
Acetic anhydride in presence of HCNS	0.35	0.02	0.78
Acetylpyridinium chloride	0	0.39	0.17

Reaction of protein nucleophiles with acid chlorides is illustrated by the work of Gordon, Brown, and Jackson (58) employing an aqueous slurry of the protein, pH 12, to which is added the acid chloride in dry ether, and reaction allowed to proceed for 1 hr. Typically, about 20% acyl could be introduced by this procedure. The acid chlorides included acetyl, butyryl, caproyl, caprylyl, pelargonyl, capryl, lauroyl, myristoyl, palmitoyl, oleoyl, stearoyl, succinyl, adipoyl, sebacoyl. Palmitoyl chloride was also reacted with egg albumin, zein, soybean protein, peanut protein, cottonseed protein, and wheat gluten. Evidence for reaction included a nonextractible gain in weight, decrease in total nitrogen, large decrease in amino nitrogen, negative Millon test for tyrosine, selective hydrolysis of *N*-acyl and *O*-acyl groups, and significant decrease in affinity of the modified protein for water.

d. Esterification

In view of the variety of mechanisms by which esterification may occur (64), this reaction cannot be classified unambiguously under nucleophilic displacements or addition to unsaturated systems. Nonetheless, for present purposes it is being included under nucleophilic displacement reactions. Esterification is achieved by displacement of OH by an OR, by the attack of OR on the carbonyl of the carboxylic acid, eq. (3),

$$RO^- + R'COOH \rightarrow R'COOR + OH^- \qquad (3)$$

or in some instances by nucleophilic attack by —COO⁻ on suitable reagents, such as epoxides, mustards, or other active halogen-containing compounds, and by dimethyl sulfate, as shown in eq. (4),

$$RCOO^- + X{-}R \rightarrow RCOOR + X \qquad (4)$$

where X = epoxide, halogen, $O_2SO_2R_1$, N_2. The OH groups in proteins (located in serine, threonine, tyrosine, hydroxylysine, and hydroxyproline) may act as the nucleophile in reactions with carboxylic acids as indicated above, R being the protein.

A preferred method for selective and fairly quantitative esterification of carboxyl groups in proteins was introduced by Fraenkel-Conrat and Olcott (65). The dry protein is suspended in a 100-fold quantity of alcohol made 0.02–0.10*N* with concentrated HCl, and reacted at 0–25°C. for one to several days. Larger primary alcohols react more slowly and less quantitatively. The reactivity with poly(glutamic acid) and various alcohols illustrates these observations (Table VI-10). The applicability and selectivity with a variety of proteins are shown in Table VI-11. The stability of the peptide and amide bonds of the proteins under the esterification conditions was demonstrated by osmotic pressure measurements on poly(glutamic acid) and its methyl ester. The esterification caused no breakdown in the polypeptide, which is more labile toward acids than most peptide bonds in proteins. The stability of the peptide and amide bonds in acidic alcohol is further illustrated by no increase in the number of free amino groups or loss of amide groups during the esterification. At elevated temperatures, however, amounts of methoxyl introduced into several proteins were in excess of their original carboxyl content, and the products contained more free amino groups and fewer amide groups than the parent proteins, an indication of occurrence of methanolysis under these more drastic conditions. Although the preferred conditions apparently have little effect on

TABLE VI-10
Esterification of Poly(glutamic Acid) at 22–24°C.

Alcohol	Catalyst	Extent of esterification, %		
		4 hr.	1 day	6 days
Methanol	0.05*N* HCl	64	97	—
	0.2*N* HCl	84	—	—
Ethanol	0.05*N* HCl	—	54	83
n-Propanol	"	—	—	50
Isopropanol	"	—	0	4
Benzyl alcohol	"	—	—	6
Propylene glycol	"	—	40	76

TABLE VI-11
Acid-Catalyzed Esterification of Proteins with Methanol at 22–24°C.

Protein	Groups per 10^4 g. protein		Groups in methylated proteins, % of those in original protein	
	Original carboxyl	Introduced methoxyl	Phenol + Indole	Amino
β-Lactoglobulin	13.7	13.6	101	98
Serum albumin (bovine)	10.8	10.3	94	—
Casein	16.0	10.0	98	104
Egg albumin	9.5	9.0	100	88
Insulin	8.0	8.4	100	96
Lactogenic hormone	8.8	7.9	100	—
Hoof powder	6.6	6.2	—	97
Lysozyme	—	4.2	97	100
Gluten	3.6	3.6	—	—
Silk fibroin	2.4	2.3	101	—
Gliadin	3.9	2.1	—	—

the primary structure of the protein, the secondary and tertiary structures might be considerably altered.

Displacement reactions in which the carboxyl groups of the protein act as a nucleophile to give esterification are illustrated by reaction with 1,2-epoxides under conditions favoring esterification (66). The *S*-mustards (67), diazomethyl acetate, and diazoacetamide have also been employed (68,69). The 1,2-epoxides are not selective even under most favorable conditions. There is considerable reaction with free amino groups, tyrosine, indole, and thiol groups. Windmueller, Ackerman, and Engel

TABLE VI-12
Acid-Catalyzed Esterification of Wool[a]

Alcohol	Proportion of hydroxyl groups esterified, %	Acid combining power of esterified wool, meq./100 g.
Methanol	67	28
Ethanol	56	36
n-Propanol	54	38
Isopropanol	15	70
n-Butanol	39	50
Isobutanol	21	65
sec-Butanol	15	70
n-Amyl alcohol	21	65
Ethylene glycol	51	40
Glycerol	46	44
Pentane-1,5-diol	21	65
Benzyl alcohol	12	72
Cetyl alcohol (dissolved in xylene)	12	72

[a] Anhydrous alcohol in presence of 0.1*N* HCl; 6 hr., 100°C. or boiling point of alcohol, if lower.

have also presented evidence (70) for reaction with the nitrogen atoms of imidazole ring in histidine and the sulfur atom of methionine, to give hydroxyethylation of these groups. Although diazomethane is very non-selective in its reactions with proteins, diazomethyl acetate, and diazo-acetamide appear to be fairly selective under some conditions.

The first fairly unambiguous demonstration of reaction of carboxyl of protein (collagen) with a mustard reagent was given by Goodlad (67) employing S^{35}-labeled reagent and determination of ester by hydroxamic acid, along with studies on suitable model compounds.

The number of —COOH groups in wool accessible to acid-catalyzed esterification with alcohols decreases with increasing size of the alcohol, as shown in Table VI-12 (71). Hydrolysis of the peptide bonds was not serious under the anhydrous conditions, although considerable hydrolysis of these occurred during esterification in presence of small amounts of water. It was further demonstrated that variation in maximum esterification with different alcohols was not due to different equilibrium constants, but rather to steric factors in the wool and accessibility to the reagents. All esters hydrolyzed at the same rate to regenerate the original carboxyl groups.

e. Sulfation and Phosphorylation

Reaction of proteins with concentrated sulfuric acid has been shown to involve the hydroxyl and thiol groups, yielding sulfate esters and thiosulfates, respectively (72). In general, the reaction consisted of mixing proteins with concentrated sulfuric acid below 0°C., allowing the acid mixture to warm to room temperature, the reaction periods being relatively short. Characterization of the product by analysis for total sulfur, sulfate sulfur, total nitrogen, amino nitrogen, functional group analysis, and studies with model compounds indicated fairly selective reaction with the OH and SH groups of the protein. Sulfuric acid is known to react with alcohols to form alkyl acid sulfates (73) and was shown to react with cysteine (72) to yield *S*-cysteinyl sulfonate. Sulfonation of the benzene nucleus of tyrosine competes with sulfation of the phenolic hydroxyl, becoming the predominating reaction under more drastic conditions. The amount of sulfate sulfur introduced into a variety of proteins and synthetic polyamides and polypeptides corresponded rather closely with hydroxyamino acids of the proteins as shown in Table VI-13.

Sulfated proteins contained amino nitrogen in amounts equal to or slightly higher than that of the original protein. Failure of protamine sulfate, rich in guanidyl groups, to react demonstrates the inactivity of these groups toward sulfuric acid. The small amounts of sulfate bound by gliadin, gluten, and polyglutamine rich in amide nitrogen, demonstrates the nonparticipation of this group. The low sulfate in reacted polyglycine, nylon, poly(glutamic acid), and polyglutamine demonstrate inactivity of the peptide bond. The stability of the peptide bond to cold concentrated sulfuric acid had been demonstrated earlier by Uchino (74), with silk fibroin kept in contact with this reagent at 7–8°C. for up to 12 days, with no measurable hydrolysis as measured by amino nitrogen determinations; evidence of hydrolysis beyond the twelfth day was obtained, however. Tryptophan and phenylalanine bound measurably more total sulfur than sulfate sulfur (traces), indicating nuclear substitution as with tyrosine.

Sulfation by means of chlorosulfonic acid is not selective, however, as demonstrated by Ferrel, Olcott, and Fraenkel-Conrat (75). The proteins were reacted at 70–80°C. for 2.5 hr. with chlorosulfonic acid and

TABLE VI-13
Reaction of Concentrated Sulfuric Acid with Proteins

Protein	Sulfate sulfur, %	Nitrogen, %	Sulfate sulfur introduced, g.-mole	Hydroxyamino acid content of unreacted material, g.-mole
Sericin	7.7	9.8	37.7	37.1
γ-Globulin	45	11.5	17.3	16.8
Gelatin	3.9	12.5	15.2	14.2
Keratin (chicken feathers)	4.4	11.2	18.0	14.0
Silk fibroin	4.1	12.8	16.9	12.8
Wool (keratin)	4.0	12.3	15.0	12.0
Fibrin	3.5	13.1	12.6	10.5
Isinglass	3.7	13.8	13.7	10.2
Egg albumin	3.7	12.4	13.6	10.0
Cattle hoof	3.6	12.9	13.1	9.6
Casein	2.7	11.5	10.5	9.4
Zein	2.7	13.2	9.7	7.4
β-Lactoglobulin	2.4	12.9	8.6	6.3
Insulin	2.2	12.4	7.9	6.1
Glutenin	2.6	12.2	9.3	6.1
Wheat gluten	2.4	13.7	7.5	5.6
Gramicidin	1.3	10.4	5.9	4.8
Gliadin	2.3	14.6	7.9	4.6
Protamine sulfate	1.9	—	6.4	4.3
Poly(glutamic acid)	0.4	7.6	1.6	0.5
Polyglutamine	0.2	18.5	0.7	—
Nylon	0.2	10.4	0.5	—
Polyglycine	0.2	—	0.5	—

excess pyridine. This resulted in the introduction of much larger amounts of covalently bound sulfate sulfur (up to 10%) than with cold concentrated sulfuric acid. Under these conditions, part or all of the aliphatic and phenolic hydroxyl, thiol, primary amide, amino, guanidyl, and indole groups were converted to sulfates or sulfamates. In most instances, there was good correlation between the sum of these groups and the amount of

TABLE VI-14
Comparison of Reactive Groups[a] with Sulfate Sulfur Bound by Various Proteins and Model Substances on Reaction with Chlorosulfonic Acid

Protein	(1) β-Hydroxy	(2) Indole	(3) Phenol	(4) Total basic	(5) Amide	(6) Sum of (1)–(5)	Sulfate and sulfamate sulfur bound
Sericin	37.1	0.3	3.0	5.4	10.4	56.2	53.2
Polyglutamine	0	0	0	1.1	55	56.1	28.4
Wheat gluten	5.6	0.3	2.1	5.3	20.6	33.0	42.2
Protamine sulfate	4.3	0	0	40.0	0	44.3	23.6
Gliadin	4.6	0.3	1.8	4.7	30.0	41.4	34.7
Egg albumin	9.2	0.5	2.4	8.8	7.8	28.7	29.8
Chicken feathers	13.2	0	1.9	4.5	7.4	27.0	26.8
Wool	12.3	0	3.5	8.2	10.4	34.4	26.2
Silk fibroin	13.3	0.3	5.9	1.3	2.9	23.7	23.7
Gelatin	14.2	0	0.6	6.0	2.9	23.7	20.6
Globin	5.2	0.6	2.0	13.4	4.5	25.7	20.2
Isinglass	10.2	0	0.4	9.3	3.0	22.9	20.2
β-Lactoglobulin	6.3	1.0	2.4	11.6	7.1	28.4	19.3
Gramicidin	4.8	19.6	0	0	0	24.4	18.1
Polymethyl polyglutamate	0	0	0	1.4	0	1.4	2.7
Polyglutamic acid	0	0	0	1.9	0	1.9	2.2
Nylon	0	0	0	0.6	0	0.6	0.9

[a] Equivalents per 10^4 g. of protein or other substance.

sulfur introduced (Table VI-14). The imidazole and carboxyl groups and the peptide linkages did not participate in the reaction.

Phosphorylation of proteins has received considerable attention in recent years. Reaction of proteins with phosphoric acid–phosphorus pentoxide at room temperature for 3 days results in formation of esters of ortho phosphoric and metaphosphoric acid and the hydroxyl groups of the serine, threonine, hydroxyproline residues, and possibly part of the phenolic hydroxyl groups. No other functional group appeared to participate in the stable fixation of phosphate by this method (75).

f. Guanidylation

This is a reaction in which the α-amino groups of the lysine residues in proteins are converted to guanidyl groups, by reaction with *O*-methylisourea or *S*-methylisourea. The reaction is probably a nucleophilic displacement of $—OCH_3$ or $—SCH_3$ from *O*-methylisourea or *S*-methylisourea by the amino group of the protein, as shown in eq. (5). α-Amino groups do not react appreciably, if at all. The reaction was first studied with amino acids (76,77) and peptides (77); selectivity for ε-amino groups

$$\underset{\text{Protein}}{|\text{—}NH_2} + \begin{matrix} NH_2 \\ H\text{—}N \end{matrix}\!\!>\!C\text{—}OCH_3\,(SCH_3) \rightarrow \underset{\text{Protein}}{|\text{—}NH\text{—}C}\!\!<\!\begin{matrix} NH_2 \\ NH \end{matrix} + CH_3OH\,(SCH_3) \qquad (5)$$

and lack of reactivity with α-amino groups were indicated. Hughes, Saroff, and Carney (78) first studied *O*-methylisourea as a protein reagent. At pH 10.5, 0°C., and 3 days reaction time, 54–57 of the 68 amino groups in serum albumin were converted to guanidyl groups. The decrease in Van Slyke amino nitrogen was equivalent to the decrease of moles of reagent in the solution, as determined analytically. Evidence was presented for reactivity of ε-amino groups and nonparticipation of α-amino groups. Essentially quantitative conversion of ε-amino groups to guanidyl groups has been observed in reactions with serum albumin, casein, hemoglobin, lysozyme and ovalbumin (79), chymotrypsinogen (80), ribonuclease (81,82), growth hormone (somatotropin), lactogenic hormone (prolactin), lysozyme (82), and insulin (83). In all of these instances, the reactions were carried out at 0–5°C., pH 10.5, and 3–5 days reaction time. Under similar conditions, however, complete reaction of ε-amino was not obtained with thyroglobulin, gelatin, insulin, and β-corticotropin (82), tobacco mosaic virus protein (84), or fibrinogen (85). Chervenka and Wilcox made the first very thorough study of this reaction as part of a series of papers on chemical derivatives of chymotrypsinogen (80). Characterization of crystalline derivatives obtained by reaction of this protein with *O*-methylisourea for 4 days at 5°C. and pH 10.3 showed that the 13 lysine residues had been converted to homoarginine with little or no reaction of the one α-amino group. The specificity of the reaction for the ε-amino groups of the lysine residues was confirmed in several ways. There was quantitative correspondence between amount of reagent reacted and decrease in amino groups (Van Slyke). The results of Van Slyke analyses on completely guanidylated product agreed with both the quantity of homoarginine which appeared and of the amount of lysine which disappeared during the reaction as shown by amino acid analysis on the product. *N*-Terminal amino group analysis by the 1-fluoro-2,4-dinitrobenzene (FDNB) method gave the same result on both the unreacted chymotrypsinogen and the completely guanidinated derivative, providing conclusive evidence that this α-amino group did not enter into the guanidylation reaction. This conclusion was further confirmed by reaction of the completely guanidylated derivative with carbon disulfide; this derivative took up and released 0.9 mole CS_2/mole protein in a manner analogous to unreacted chymotrypsinogen. It had been shown in previous work (80) that the α-amino group of this protein reacts selectively with CS_2, the ϵ-amino groups showing no reaction with this reagent.

The reaction with insulin has been studied quite thoroughly by Evans and Saroff (83). A crystalline derivative was obtained after 7 days reaction at pH 10 and 5°C. in which the ϵ-amino group of the single lysine residue of the protein had been converted to the guanidyl group. However, the reaction in this instance was not specific for the ϵ-amino; under the conditions used one half of the α-amino of *N*-terminal glycine and one-tenth of the α-amino of *N*-terminal phenylalanine also reacted. The extent of participation of *N*-terminal α-amino groups was ascertained by FDNB analyses, and total analyses for amino acids in the hydrolyzate of the derivative. No lysine was detectable in this hydrolyzate, and homoarginine was detected in amounts equal to 90–100% of the original lysine. Sedimentation values changed only slightly from those of the native insulin. In contrast to these results, Klee and Richards reported that insulin could not be completely guanidylated under any of the conditions studied (81). These investigators also reported a quite thorough study of reaction with ribonuclease. Specific guanidylation of the 10 ϵ-amino groups of lysine residue in this protein was achieved by reaction with *O*-methylisourea at 2°C. and pH 10.5 for 4 days. The rates of reaction were followed at pH values from 8.5 to 11; the rate increased with pH, particularly above pH 10. Analysis of the rate curves suggested that 9 of the 10 lysine residues were available for reaction, but that the tenth residue reacted only after prolonged times. Interestingly, nine guanidyl groups could be introduced without affecting the biological activity of the protein; but when 10 guanidyl groups had been introduced, there was a complete loss in activity. The derivative was characterized by complete amino acid analysis and by appropriate functional group analysis, and comparison with similar analysis on the native protein.

Geschwind and Li (82) made a detailed study of reaction with a growth hormone (somatotropin), lactogenic hormone (prolactin) and lysozyme, and less detailed study on insulin, α-corticotropin, and ribonuclease. Conditions were similar to those employed by previous investigators. In the detailed study, derivatives were characterized by amino nitrogen analyses, determination of arginine, homoarginine, and lysine in the acid hydrolyzates, and by FDNB reactions followed by determination of amount of free ε-dinitrophenyl present following acid hydrolysis. The reaction was essentially quantitative for ε-amino groups with little or no participation by α-amino. In contrast, only three of the four lysines in α-corticotropin reacted. Reaction with tobacco mosaic virus protein was studied by Ramachandran (84). Under the conditions found by others to be quantitative for ε-amino for several proteins, no reaction was observed with the two lysine residues of TMV protein (even when 1000-fold excess of *O*-methyl-isourea was used). If the protein was denatured by heat or urea prior to reaction, one of the two lysines became available for reaction. As in previous studies, thorough characterization of the product was made by the appropriate techniques.

Maekawa and Liener (86) reacted *S*-methyl glucosylisothiourea (SMG) with trypsin (0°C., 3 days, pH 8.4) to obtain a derivative in which the ε-amino groups of three lysine residues and the imidazole ring of three histidine residues had reacted. Reaction with the imidazole ring had been demonstrated previously in a study of the reaction with histidine at the 2- and 4-positions of the imidazole ring. Characterization of the trypsin derivative consisted of analysis for free amino groups and protein bound glucose, reaction with FDNB followed by hydrolysis and analysis for dinitrophenyl derivatives. Reaction of SMG with amino acids (87) and proteins (88) had been reported earlier, the results on proteins indicating that the amount of SMG combining was proportional to the lysine contents of these materials.

S-Methylisothiourea has been used by several investigators, though it is less reactive than the *O*-methylisourea. Using the *S*-methylisothiourea, Schutte (89) guanidylated several amino acids and peptides and proteins in 3.5% aqueous NH_4OH solution at room temperature. After 3 days, only 20–30% of the free amino groups of lactalbumin and casein had reacted (measured by decrease in amino groups), but 85–90% had reacted after 3 weeks. Roche and co-workers (79) found it necessary to use a higher temperature with the *S*-methyl compound than required with the *O*-methylisourea to obtain equivalent reaction.

2. Electrophilic Substitution Reactions

a. Halogenation

The best understood of these reactions is electrophilic substitution in aromatic systems. With proteins, the reaction with iodine has been most widely investigated. The peptide residues which react most readily and cleanly include tyrosine, phenylalanine, histidine, and tryptophan.

Although all halogens have been reacted with proteins of one type or another, the iodination reaction has been most widely studied. In reactions with proteins, iodine may in principle enter into three main types: (*a*) substitution reactions, mainly electrophilic, in which half of the iodine is consumed in substitution and the other half appears as HI, (*b*) addition reactions in which all the iodine appears in the product as organic iodide, and (*c*) oxidation reactions (such as the conversion of —SH to disulfide) in which all iodine appears as inorganic iodide in the product. The addition reactions have not been observed with proteins. Oxidation reactions are well known, but will be discussed under disulfide crosslinks. Several reviews have treated various aspects of the iodination reaction and contain extensive references to the literature (50,90–92). Examples selected for the present discussion are for purposes of illustration of the types of reactions and of the general scope, selectivity, and utility.

Proteins have been iodinated for numerous reasons: to impart thyroactivity; to ascertain active centers in hormones and enzymes; to modify antigenicity; to modify the protein by incorporation of heavy atoms in known positions for use in x-ray structure studies; to ascertain side chain interactions; to assist in amino acid analysis and endgroup determination.

The extent of iodination is dependent on the structure of the protein, the temperature, the pH, and the nature and concentration of the reagent.

In neutral or alkaline medium, the available tyrosine groups in several proteins react readily and specifically to yield the 3,5-diiodotyrosine. That substitution was selective in these cases was shown by detailed analyses on the products with serum albumin (93), zein (94), pepsin (95), lactogenic hormone (96), insulin (97), and wool (98). This specificity does not occur in the reactions with hemoglobin (99) and a number of other proteins (100), in which substitution or oxidation of imidazole groups occurs even in neutral and acid medium.

In general, at low reagent concentration and at neutral or alkaline pH, substitution in the tyrosine groups is the predominant reaction, with oxidation being less important.

Native proteins usually react with iodine more slowly than does free tyrosine; in contrast, denatured proteins react more readily than does the free tyrosine (93,101). In acidic solutions and at high iodide concentration, oxidation reactions, particularly that of the sulfhydryl groups, appear to be specific. Iodine in acid medium has a high oxidation potential, which decreases with increasing pH. Competition between oxidation and substitution as a function of pH can be understood in terms of this variation in oxidation potential and the nature of the iodine species in solution.

In a rather thorough study of the iodination of human serum albumin, Hughes and Straessle (102) used a number of analytical and physical methods to characterize the reaction with iodine, its specificity under different conditions, and the nature of the products obtained. Selective oxidation of sulfhydryl groups was achieved initially with only negligible substitution reaction occurring concomitantly. Following this, up to 70% of the tyrosine residues could be diiodinated prior to other substitution reactions competing. Complete iodination of the tyrosine residues was realized only at the expense of extensive substitution of the histidine residues (presumably). Maximum iodine was introduced into the protein by using high pH and 150 moles iodine/mole protein; 64 iodine atoms per molecule of the protein resulted. However, extensive oxidative destruction of tryptophan occurred when large excess of iodine was used at pH 10.3.

That this particular sequence of reactions is not general for all proteins was shown by Fraenkel-Conrat (100) using lysozyme. In this protein, the single histidine residue reacts under conditions that result in reaction with only half the tyrosine. This observation doubtless reflects an effect of structure on availability and reactivity of the respective groups in this protein, and difficulties encountered in extrapolation of results from one protein to another. The rate of iodination of free amino acid histidine has been reported to be 30–100 times slower than that of tyrosine (103), suggesting that histidine in proteins might react in presence of excess iodine and longer reaction times. This suggests that the observations on iodination of lysozyme were a consequence of the protein structure, rather than differences in inherent reactivity of the histidine and tyrosine residues in this protein.

In iodination reactions which are selective for tyrosine residues, the bound iodine may appear as monoiodotyrosine, diiodotyrosine, or thyroxine. The nature of the reaction by which thyroxine is obtained is still somewhat obscure.

Interest in iodination reactions has been stimulated by the isolation and identification of the naturally occurring iodoproteins, thyroglobulin, gorgonin, and spongin. Thyroglobulins are found in vertebrate thyroid glands. Iodination of inert proteins constitutes a unique way of conferring biological activity on several of these.

b. Nitration

The nitration of proteins under mild condition results primarily in introduction of a nitro group into the aromatic residues of the polymer.

Under more severe conditions, oxidation reactions resulting in partial or complete destruction of various residues become increasingly more important. The present discussion is limited to electrophilic substitutions which have been demonstrated fairly conclusively in reactions of nitric acid with proteins and related model compounds.

The nitration of aromatic nuclei has played a very important role in the development of the general theory of aromatic substitution, orientation effects, and mechanisms of electrophilic aromatic substitution in general. Excellent summaries of this work have appeared (36,64). The preponderance of evidence indicates that the active species in nitration with nitric acid and related substances is the nitronium ion, NO_2^+.

Tyrosine, whether as the free amino acid or incorporated in proteins, reacts readily with concentrated nitric acid to yield 3-nitrotyrosine (104). The dinitro derivative is not obtained under these conditions. Reaction with a mixture of concentrated nitric acid and sulfuric acid, on the other hand, results in smooth formation of 3,5-dinitrotyrosine (104). 3-Nitrotyrosine was identified among the hydrolysis products of nitrated fibroin, as determined by structure proof and comparison with authentic sample. No evidence of a dinitrotyrosine was obtained, however (105,106); this observation on nitrated silk fibroin was later confirmed by Lieben (107) and shown to obtain with a number of other proteins, including casein, lactalbumin, serum globulin, serum albumin, edestin, and keratin. Analyses of the nitrated proteins for nitro groups, tyrosine, and tryptophan indicated mononitration equivalent to the tyrosine content of these proteins. That nitration is not limited to the tyrosine residues was shown by Bauer and Strauss (99), in reaction of serum albumin, serum globulin, and ovalbumin with nitric acid at room temperature. The extent of mononitration was shown to equal the sum of the tyrosine and tryptophan, nitration of the tryptophan occurring in the indole group. It was later demonstrated by Roche and Mourgue (108,109) that guanidino groups may also be nitrated in reactions of salmine, edestin, and thymohistone with fuming nitric acid in sulfuric acid. The products isolated did not give a positive Sakaguchi reaction (characteristic of monosubstituted guanidines). Analysis of the hydrolysis products from nitrated edestin indicated 9.25% nitroarginine and 14.7% unreacted arginine. Many years earlier, Kossel and Weiss (110) had already shown that guanidyl groups in protamines and proteins react with nitric acid in sulfuric acid at 0°C. The nitro arginine was isolated from the hydrolysis products of the nitrated proteins and identified.

All of the tyrosine in wool was mononitrated by reaction with 1*N* nitric acid for 24 hr. at 70°C., with little or no oxidation of the cystine (111). The nitrated wool showed new x-ray reflections at 40 and 83 A., which suggested that tyrosine repeats in the crystalline regions at these distances.

Rabbit fur keratin was nitrated with 1–5*M* nitric acid at 20–40°C. (112,113). Under these conditions the tyrosine was mononitrated, tryptophan was completely destroyed, but cystine was not attacked. The reaction was characterized by product analysis for cystine, tyrosine, tryptophan, and 3-nitrotyrosine. The acid hydrolyzate of the nitrated protein, studied by chromatography, contained no tryptophan, no tyrosine, no 3,5-dinitrotyrosine, but contained 3-nitrotyrosine equivalent to the tyrosine present in the parent protein.

Tetranitromethane has been reported as a nitrating agent for proteins (114,115), although the nature of the reaction is not very well understood and the nitrated proteins were not very thoroughly characterized. It was presumed that the nitro groups were introduced into the tyrosine residues.

c. Diazotization and Coupling

Two types of reactions are discussed. The first class involves the coupling of a diazonium salt with protein; the second, coupling of diazotized proteins with small molecules, such as phenols or amines. The products obtained by either procedure are similar, although obtained by somewhat different chemical reactions.

The active species in diazo coupling reactions is the electrophilic substituting agent, $R{-}N_2^+$, as indicated fairly conclusively by kinetic studies (116–118) and earlier by aromatic orientation theory. The chemistry of the related reactions of nitrosation, diazotization and deamination has been reviewed recently (119) and appears to consist of the sequence of reactions shown in eq. (6).

$$RNH_2 \rightarrow RNHNO \rightarrow RN{=}NOH \rightarrow RN{=}N^+ \rightarrow R^+ + N_2 \rightarrow \text{Deaminated products} \quad (6)$$

For the first class reactions with proteins, an amine (usually an aromatic amine) is diazotized by reaction with nitrous acid to yield the diazonium salt RN_2X, which is subsequently coupled with the protein by electrophilic substitution. The advantages of this approach are the mild reaction conditions required for the coupling reaction (0–25°C., pH 7–9, fast reaction), and the variety of diazo compounds which can be prepared separately and then used for coupling to the protein. Hundreds of azo proteins have been prepared in this manner; the greatest interest being in the field of

TABLE VI-15

Amino Acid or Protein Groups Reacting with Diazonium Compounds[a]

Group	Number of diazonium groups accepted (literature data)[b]															λ_{max} for product, mμ (Refs. 123–129, 143)
	Refs. 130, 131	Ref. 132	Ref. 133	Refs. 134, 135	Refs. 136–138	Ref. 139	Ref. 140	Ref. 141	Ref. 142	Refs. 116, 128	Ref. 143	Ref. 129	Refs. 125–127	Ref. 123	Summary	
Imidazole	2									1 or 2			1		1 or 2	380(1), 490(2)[c]
Phenolic	2									1 or 2			1		1 or 2	325(1), 480(2)[c]
Indolyl			+		+		1					1			1	270
α-Amino																
Glycine		2	+				2				+	2	2		2	363
Other			+				*				+	+	2		+*	
ε-Amino							2						2	2	2	363
Imino			+	+	+	+								1	1	317
Guanidino							3		+		+			+	3	356
Sulfhydryl						+	1								1	
Aliphatic OH								+							+	

[a] Taken from ref. 123.

[b] Plus (+) denotes reactive group; asterisk (*) indicates deamination.

[c] Figures in parentheses are number of diazonium groups per imidazole or phenolic.

immunology. This material has been described in detail in the prior literature and will not be discussed further here (120–122).

The diversity of the reactions of diazo compounds with amino acids and protein is illustrated in Table VI-15, taken from a recent article by Higgins and Harrington (123). The great utility of absorption spectra in identification of the site and extent of reaction was also illustrated and reviewed by these same authors. The reaction of ε-amino, guanidino, and imino groups with diazonium compounds is supported by spectroscopic data. At appropriate concentration, serum albumin, fibrinogen, casein, pepsin, gelatin, and fibroin can form bis-derivatives from about two thirds of their phenolic and imidazole groups. Differences in the rate of reaction of various groups in the protein molecule require that for proper investigation of the azoproteins by spectroscopic means a range of relative concentrations of protein to diazonium salt should be used.

Another approach to the study of the diazo coupling reaction is illustrated in this work of Howard and Wild (140), who employed diazotized *p*-arsanilic acid for reactions with several proteins. The coupled proteins were analyzed very carefully for total nitrogen and for arsenic. From the known amino acid composition of the proteins and the amount of combined arsenic in the derivatives, an indication of the groups involved can be ascertained. These indications can be further confirmed by auxiliary reaction with model compounds, and analyses on the protein derivatives for the groups believed to be involved in the reaction. The variation of the extent of coupling with pH is shown by the data of Table VI-16 for the reaction of *p*-arsanilic acid with casein. Data from the reaction of *p*-arsanilic acid with several proteins are summarized in Table VI-17.

The homogeneity of the protein derivatives was ascertained by electrophoresis. No reaction occurred with peptide bonds or with primary

TABLE VI-16

Variation of Arsenic/Nitrogen in Azo Casein from Coupling with *p*-Arsanilic Acid

pH	*p*-Arsanilic acid, g./g. casein	Analysis of Product: As, %	N, %	As/N
7.5	1	7.1	11.6	0.612
9.3	1	8.9	11.1	0.802
9.1	2	9.5	11.6	0.819
9.8	1	10.2	12.3	0.848
9.8	2	11.1	11.7	0.949
11.5	1	4.6	11.8	0.390

TABLE VI-17
Arsenic/Nitrogen Ratios of Protein Derivatives Obtained by Reaction with Diazotized *p*-Arsanilic Acid at pH 9.8

Protein	*p*-Arsanilic acid, g./g. protein	Analysis of derivative			Theoretical values As/N[a]		
		As, %	N, %	As/N	1	2	3
Casein	4	11.5	11.7	0.983	0.939	0.837	0.440
	3	11.7	11.9	0.983			
	2	11.1	11.7	0.949			
	1	10.2	12.3	0.848			
Ovalbumin	4	10.8	11.8	0.915	0.883	0.721	0.300
	3	11.1	12.0	0.925			
	2	10.1	12.0	0.855			
Edestin	6	12.1	12.1	1.000	1.034	0.678	0.289
	4	12.1	12.2	0.992			
	3	11.6	12.4	0.936			
	2	11.2	12.3	0.911			
Bovine plasma albumin	4	12.7	11.6	1.095	1.088	0.968	0.424
	3	12.7	11.6	1.095			
	2	11.0	12.1	0.975			
	1	9.6	12.4	0.774			

[a] Column 1: Values assuming that 2 moles of diazo react with 1 mole phenolic, imidazole, α-amino of terminal glycine, and ε-amino groups; 3 moles of diazo with 1 mole guanidino; 1 mole diazo with indoyl and —SH; assuming deamination of α-amino groups of terminal groups other than glycine. Column 2: Same as Column 1, except 1 mole diazo compound assumed to react with 1 mole guanidino. Column 3: Values assuming 2 moles of diazo compound react with 1 mole of phenolic and imidazole groups, no other groups reacting.

amide groups. Extreme care was taken to purify the azo proteins before analyses.

Both the spectral and chemical evidence demonstrate the high reactivity of diazo compounds toward several of the functional groups of proteins. However, a degree of selectivity may be obtained through use of limited amounts of diazo compound.

The coupling reaction has been used extensively in chemical modification of proteins. It occurs readily at neutral or slightly alkaline pH and low temperature. Its utility for the introduction of a variety of simple to complex structures into protein molecules is based primarily on the simplicity of reaction and ease with which it can be performed: these factors have encouraged its wide use. Examples of variations in R of R—C_6H_4—N_2^+ in compounds which have been coupled with proteins include aliphatic or aromatic acids, ethers, and alcohols, anionic radicals, morphine or strychnine, amino acids, polypeptides, cholesterol, aspirin, quinine, thyronine, optically active sugars, histamine, androstanediol, adrenalin, and type-specific polysaccharides of some of the pneumococci capsules (144).

The second group of reactions include those in which the protein is diazotized and then coupled with suitable agents. This diazotization is accomplished by means of nitrous acid. As indicated previously, nitrous acid reacts with several groups of protein; deamination of the free amino group being the most rapid. With more extended periods, the tyrosine groups become diazotized by a multistep reaction. The first step of this sequence of reactions involves formation of an *O*-nitrosotyrosine, probably by an electrophilic substitution reaction. The *O*-nitroso derivative is not very stable, being converted quite readily to the diazo compound by reaction with nitric oxide. This reaction has been studied in most detail by Philpot and Small (145). The sequence of reaction may be represented as in eq. (7). In the presence of cupric ion, the nitroso compound is

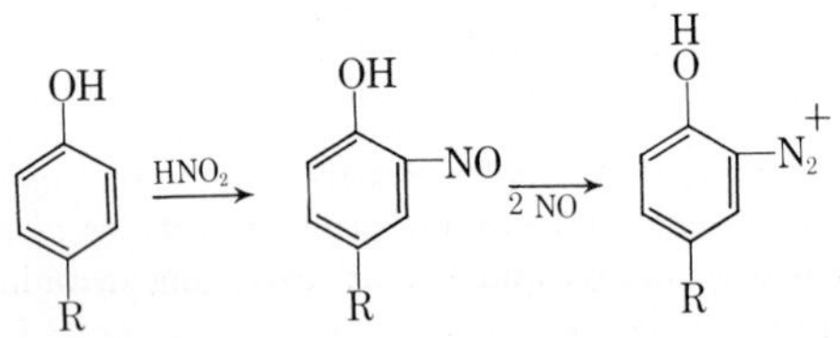

(7)

trapped as the metal chelate, and no diazo grouping is formed. The reaction is pictured in eq. (8). The diazo compound shows the reactions

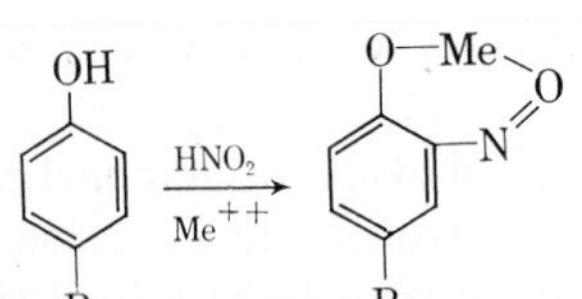

(8)

given in eq. (9). It may also be coupled with a variety of compounds normally employed in coupling reactions. The general course of these reactions was first demonstrated with free tyrosine and simple phenols (145) and subsequently shown to be similar for tyrosine bound to a protein (pepsin). The rates of formation of the metal chelate in presence of Cu^{++}

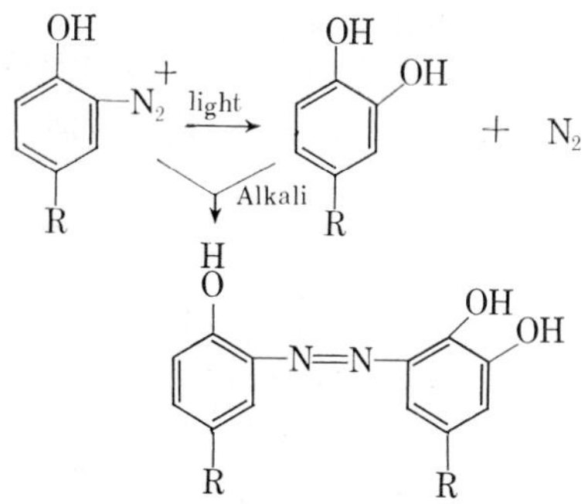

(9)

and of diazo compound in absence of Cu^{++} were shown to be identical, and strongly suggest that the nitroso compound is the intermediate in the diazotization reaction. Tryptophan reacted about 20 times as fast as tyrosine. The tyrosine in pepsin reacted at essentially the same rate as that of free tyrosine, although only about half the tyrosine in the protein was available for reaction. The protein derivative was homogenous in ultracentrifuge tests and had approximately the same sedimentation constant as pepsin. More recently, Leveau and co-workers (146,147) have reported work on this reaction involving wool. The reaction resulted in decreased solubility of the wool in alkali and urea-bisulfite, criteria often used to indicate increased crosslinking in the wool. In the presence of Cu^{++}, however, the alkali solubility is increased. This would indicate the crosslinking reaction to have been blocked by formation of metal chelates. The presence or absence of Cu^{++}, on the other hand, has no effect on the urea-bisulfite solubility of the derivative, decreased solubility being noted in both instances. The authors interpret this as indication that nitrosation in the presence of Cu^{++} does not merely eliminate tyrosine interactions but instead substitutes metal linkages which are more or less stable in alkaline medium but more so in urea. In earlier work on reaction of nitrous acid with silk (148), insolubilization resulted unless Cu^{++} was present in the reaction medium; this indicates the occurrence of the crosslinking reaction also.

That the reaction with nitrous acid with wool is quite complicated was shown by complete amino acid analysis on the derivative obtained by reaction with 0.125*M* sodium nitrite, 0.25*M* sodium acetate at pH 4.0 for 24 hr. at 38°C. (147). The analyses showed that all amino acids of the wool were more or less altered by the treatment; lysine, phenylalanine, and tyrosine being particularly affected. Cystine was only slightly affected (Table VI-18).

TABLE VI-18
Composition of Merino 115 Wool and Nitrosated Merino 115 Wool

Amino acid	Amino acids, %	
	Untreated	Treated
Alanine	4.58	3.77
Arginine	9.79	9.37
Aspartic acid	7.19	6.57
Cystine	11.34	10.18
Cysteine	0.14	0.05
Cysteic acid	0.60	1.21
Glutamic acid	15.22	13.33
Glycine	5.59	5.55
Histidine	1.07	1.09
Isoleucine	3.20	2.89
Leucine	9.06	7.83
Lysine	3.92	0.91
Phenylalanine	3.51	1.77
Proline	7.93	6.49
Serine	10.79	9.58
Threonine	6.39	5.59
Tyrosine	6.34	0.94
Valine	5.62	5.39
Total	112.28	92.51

d. Sulfonation

Although sulfonation of simple aromatic compounds has been very widely studied, the reaction has not been extensively investigated with proteins. This is undoubtedly due to the relatively high reactivity of most sulfonating agents, and the consequent nonspecificity. The wide reactivity of chlorosulfonic acid, for example, has been indicated in the section on sulfation. The sulfonation of aromatic and related compound consists in electrophilic attack of the sulfonating agent on the aromatic nucleus. Although the reaction has not been employed very widely with proteins, in a few instances fairly convincing evidence has been obtained for its occurrence.

In the studies on the reaction of concentrated sulfuric acid with proteins, it was found that sulfation of hydroxyl groups occurred fairly readily and under some conditions was quite specific (72). However, in some cases with both tyrosine and proteins it was noted that with longer exposure times and higher temperatures, sulfonation becomes much more competitive with sulfation. In the case of sulfonation, the sulfur becomes irreversibly bound to the protein. This behavior parallels that observed in the reaction of phenols with sulfuric acid (73). Reaction of tyrosine under conditions normally used for proteins (cold concentrated sulfuric acid for about 30 min.) resulted in the formation of 25% sulfate ester and 63% sulfonate, as determined by total sulfur and sulfate sulfur analyses. The sulfate sulfur was readily hydrolyzed with sulfuric acid at room temperature (72). Evidence for the sulfonation of the tyrosine in proteins was obtained by estimation of the tyrosine content in the product before and after hydrolysis. Reaction of egg albumin, β-lactoglobulin, insulin, and silk fibroin with concentrated sulfuric acid at room temperature for increasing lengths of time resulted in a gradual reduction in the tyrosine content of the protein. After one week at 23°C., the tyrosine in silk fibroin was about 85% sulfonated.

3. Addition of Unsaturated Systems

The diversity of functional groups in proteins and the large number of unsaturated molecules available for reaction with these groups make addition to unsaturated systems one of the more important types of reactions of proteins. The unsaturated molecules include olefinic compounds, ketenes, isocyanates, isothiocyanates, aldehydes, ketones, carbon suboxide, and carbon disulfide. These reactions have been used widely for the chemical modification of proteins of biological and medical interests, in protein structure work involving endgroup and sequence studies, and for the modification of proteins of industrial interest, such as wool, collagen, casein, gelatin, and silk.

These reactions will be discussed by reference to the individual type of unsaturated compound.

a. Ketene

A decade or more ago ketene was one of the most widely used reagents for modification of proteins. It was widely studied for protein group specificity and ranked close to nitrous acid and formaldehyde in extent of use for modification of serum proteins, antigens, and antibodies. More recently, however, its use has been greatly curtailed due to its very high reactivity, and consequently its nonspecificity in most cases, its toxicity, and its relative inconvenience as a reagent compared with other acetylating agents, such as acetic anhydride (54).

Reaction of ketene with —NH_2, —SH, and OH may be viewed as addition to the C=C bond of CH_2=C=O, or to C=O to form an enol which rearranges to the acetyl group. In any instance, the first step of the addition likely involves nucleophilic attack on the carbon of the carbonyl group resulting in displacement of an electron pair from the C=C or the C=O double bond to the terminal C or O atom, respectively, followed by addition of hydrogen to the carbanion or oxyanion so produced, and ketonization of the enol so formed. The overall reaction is illustrated by eq. (10).

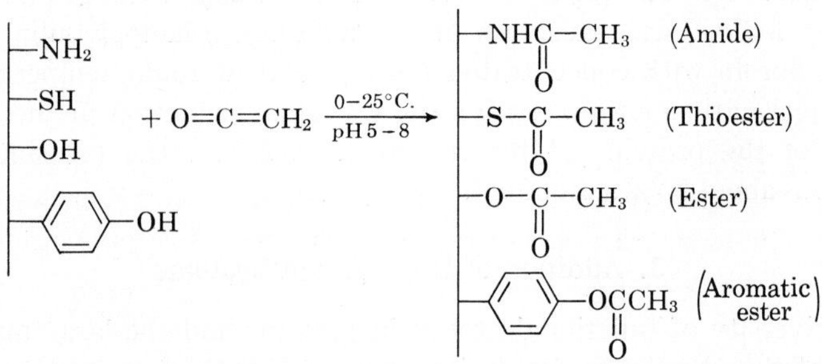

(10)

The order of reactivity of these groups appears in general to parallel their nucleophilicity, although exceptions are known. Amide and guanidyl groups react very slowly, if at all. Since the thioester and the ester bonds are more readily hydrolyzed than the amide, *N*-acetylation can be achieved by first acetylating all the groups and then subjecting the product to a mild hydrolysis (50).

b. Carbonyl Bonds

The isolated carbonyl group is noted in organic chemistry for the great diversity of its reactions. This group occurs most commonly in aldehydes and ketones. It has not been found in proteins, although reaction with reagents containing the function, particularly formaldehyde, are among the oldest in modification of proteins. The carbonyl function has been postulated as an intermediate in many protein degradations.

The majority of reactions of a carbonyl group involve addition to the function to yield stable compounds, or addition followed by elimination to yield a modified or related carbonyl function. In all of these reactions, the initial step is thought to involve nucleophilic attack on the carbon of the carbonyl (which may or may not be assisted by prior electrophilic combination at the oxygen atom, enhancing electron deficiency at the carbon atom of the carbonyl function). It is not surprising, therefore, that most of the nucleophiles found in proteins react with the carbonyl group.

As a reagent for proteins, formaldehyde is perhaps the oldest and most widely used. Its use in the formal titration of amine acids and peptides, based on the classical studies of Sorensen, is familiar to most protein chemists (149). It has been used widely as a tanning agent for collagen and other fibrous proteins, rendering these proteins more inert to biological attack, or attack by acid or alkaline solutions. It has been very important to the immunologist through its use in converting the toxins of diphtheria and tetanus into the relatively inert toxoids which, though far less dangerous than the unmodified bacterial poisons, still possess the ability to evoke specific antitoxins on injection into man or animals.

Formaldehyde reacts with most of the nucleophiles found in proteins. In view of the diversity of these groups and the range of their nucleophilicity, the rates of reaction with formaldehyde vary widely. Many of the reactions are reversible; others are essentially irreversible. Some occur readily at room temperature; others require elevated temperatures. The understanding of the reaction was rather nebulous until relatively recently. The most thorough and critical review of the formidable literature on this reaction has been given by French and Edsall (150). The present account includes selected examples from the review illustrative of the chemistry involved.

In contrast to many earlier views on the reaction, it is now known to be highly nonspecific. The conflicting interpretations in earlier publications have been discussed, and the possible reactions have been elucidated in a series of studies by Fraenkel-Conrat and co-workers (151,155). These workers (151) showed that at pH 3–7 and 70°C., reaction occurs with the primary amino and the primary amide groups of proteins, but only to a minor extent with the phenolic groups or the peptide bonds of the main chain. These conclusions were confirmed with protein derivatives, synthetic polypeptides, and simple model substances containing a maximal or minimal number of reactive groups. Polyglutamide, prepared from poly(glutamic acid), bound more formaldehyde, as much as 88 formaldehyde per 100 amide residues, than any of the proteins studied. Poly(glutamic acid), polyglycine, and poly(hexamethylene adipamide), on the other hand, bound less than one formaldehyde per 100 monomer residues, demonstrating that the carboxyl and peptide or secondary amide groups do not react to an appreciable extent. Proteins modified by reaction with phenylisocyanate or by deamination prior to the reaction showed a greatly reduced affinity for the formaldehyde. Reaction was characterized by analysis for total combined formaldehyde, free amino groups (Van Slyke), total basic groups, and primary amide. Reaction at pH

3.5 and 70°C. for 4 days resulted in products with maximum amounts of bound formaldehyde; 50% of the final amount of formaldehyde was bound within 8 hr., and 90% within 24 hr. Polyglutamine bound 47 formaldehyde per 10^4 g. at pH 3.4 and 31 formaldehyde at pH 6.7. In contrast, basic groups have a higher affinity with increasing pH. Thus, the ratio of amide to basic groups can greatly alter the effect of pH on amount of formaldehyde bound by various proteins. The reactivity of guanidyl groups was demonstrated (156) in neutral and acid solutions at 70°C. by the reaction of protamine sulfate (rich in guanidyl groups), as well as simple substituted guanidine salts (methylguanidine sulfate), and arginine hydrochloride, all of which bind up to 2 formaldehyde per guanidine group; free guanidine combines with 3 molecules. At room temperature the reaction is slower and proceeds to a lesser extent. The formylated derivatives are much less reactive with nitrous acid than are the unmodified substances. With protamine at concentrations in excess of 3%, insoluble products result; at 1–3%, pH 6.7, soluble products with increased molecular weight (measured by osmotic pressure) are formed. These results suggest subsequent reaction of bound methylol groups to give crosslinking. A more detailed account of this reaction has been reported (153–155).

Gramicidin, which contains no polar groups other than indole (40% of residues are tryptophan) and aliphatic hydroxyl, was used as a model system (152) to study reaction of tryptophan residues with formaldehyde. Simple indoles were used to confirm the results with gramicidin, and the conclusions were tested on proteins rich in tryptophan. Gramicidin combines rapidly in alkaline solution an amount of formaldehyde equivalent to its tryptophan. In acid solution the reaction occurs only at a high temperature and higher concentrations of formaldehyde. The formaldehyde probably combines as methylol groups on the nitrogen of the indole rings. Group analyses on the starting materials and the derivatives gave adequate demonstration of the location and extent of the reaction. Sulfhydryl also adds readily to formaldehyde in excess to yield *S*-methylol derivatives which are labile toward reversal or further secondary reactions involving the methylene group (157).

In summary, the most rapid reaction occurring at neutrality or in alkaline solution at low temperatures is almost instantaneous addition of the free amino group to the formaldehyde to yield *N*-methylol derivatives; at higher concentration, dimethylol compounds may be formed (eq. 11). These reactions are easily reversible. In acid or alkaline solution and at higher temperatures, guanidyl and primary amide groups and the indole

$$\Big|\!-NH_2 \overset{CH_2O}{\rightleftharpoons} \Big|\!-NHCH_2OH \overset{CH_2O}{\rightleftharpoons} \Big|\!-N\begin{matrix} \diagup CH_2OH \\ \diagdown CH_2OH \end{matrix} \qquad (11)$$

rings add readily and much less reversibly to formaldehyde. The addition of the primary amide is catalyzed by acid, and that of the indole and guanidyl groups to a lesser degree (eq. 12).

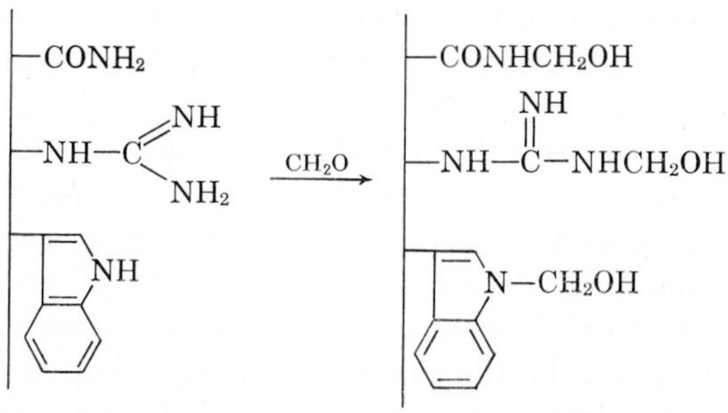

(12)

The methylol derivatives show a tendency to undergo further reaction to yield crosslinked products (153–155). These reactions are discussed further in the section concerned with crosslinking.

This secondary reaction may also be used to prepare protein derivatives of the type shown in eq. (13) (153–155). It may be also applied to make the

$$\Big|\!-NCH_2OH \rightarrow \left[\,\Big|\!-NCH_2{}^{+}\right] \xrightarrow{RNH_2} \Big|\!-N-CH_2-\overset{\displaystyle R}{\overset{|}{N}H} \qquad (13)$$

reaction of formaldehyde more specific and therefore of greater utility in modification particularly those related to biological function and activity.

Reaction with other aldehydes has been studied only to a limited extent. Ross and Stanley (158) found that acetaldehyde, propionaldehyde, and butyraldehyde reacted with tobacco mosaic virus qualitatively in the same manner as formaldehyde. Each aldehyde caused a simultaneous decrease in virus activity in groups that react with ninhydrin and in groups that react with Folin's phenol reagent. Reactivation could be achieved in each case, although generally to a lesser degree than with the formaldehyde derivative. Furfural insolubilized part of the protein, although the soluble portion was essentially inactive and showed less color with ninhydrin and Folin's reagent than did the original active virus protein. Benzaldehyde also reacted to a limited extent.

Several chemical derivatives of gramicidin have been prepared with the use of aldehydes (159) under conditions which were optimum for reaction with formaldehyde. The reaction occurred primarily with the indole groups of the protein. The aldehydes included formaldehyde, acetaldehyde, glyoxal, glyoxalic acid, benzaldehydes, and glucose. Evidence of reaction consisted of detailed analysis for the groups involved.

Involvement of aldehydes in the so-called "browning" reaction of proteins has been shown by Mohammad, Fraenkel-Conrat, and Olcott (160). Treatment of proteins, protein derivatives, and model substances with glucose (160) and acetaldehyde (160) results in browning, the rate being proportional to the temperature and pH. Acetaldehyde reacts about 35 times as fast as glucose under comparable conditions. The reaction involves primarily the free amino groups, and to a much lesser extent the guanidyl groups. Amide groups do not participate. These observations were confirmed in reaction with amino acids, simple amines, and poly(glutamic acid) derivatives, and by detailed chemical analysis for changes in number of functional groups in the protein. Blocking of the free amino groups in the protein by acetylation or conversion to guanidyl groups, resulted in derivatives with little or no affinity for acetaldehyde; the browning reaction was blocked. Further confirmation of reaction was demonstrated on wool (160) which reacted slowly with acetaldehyde in a few hours at room temperature, slightly less rapidly with aldol, much less rapidly with propionaldehyde. Wool acetylated to varying extents showed progressively less reaction with formaldehyde as the degree of acetylation increased.

c. Olefinic Compounds

The reaction of maleimides with sulfhydryl groups in simple compounds is extremely rapid, requiring as little as 1–2 min. to reach complete reaction (161). Application of this reaction to reduced wool has been reported by Moore and Lundgren (162), using *N*-phenylmaleimide, *m*-phenylenedimaleimide, and *m*-phenylenedimaleimide. Reduced wool was shaken with a suspension of the maleimide at pH 8.0, room temperature, until the test for sulfhydryl was negative, as measured by nitroprusside in 8*M* guanidine hydrochloride. The maleimide combined only with —SH groups under these conditions. The reaction product of the maleimides and sulfhydryl was identified in hydrolyzates of the modified wool by paper chromatography, as the 2-amino-2-carboxyethyl-succinic acid, the inside bonds of both the mono- and the dimaleimides having been destroyed during hydrolysis of the protein. The chromatogram gave no evidence of reaction of the maleimides with any of the other functional groups of the protein. The sulfhydryl groups of bovine plasma albumin also react with these same maleimides (163).

Although maleimides were commonly believed to be specific for thiol groups in proteins, Kovacic and Hein (164) demonstrated that gelatin, which contains no —SH groups, is converted readily into a gel by *N,N*-ethylenedimaleimide in hot aqueous solution; in the absence of the dimaleimide, or in presence of the monofunctional *N*-phenylmaleimide no gel was formed. The reaction was believed to involve the free amino groups of lysine, arginine, and histidine. Although confirmatory evidence was not given that these amino groups in gelatin were involved, reaction of maleimides with polyethyleneimine and other synthetic polymers containing only free amino groups was demonstrated; this constitutes indirect confirmatory evidence.

Schöberl (165) reacted *N*-*p*-phenetyl maleimide with reduced wool in 50% methanol at pH 5.1 for 1 hr. at room temperature and with dimethyl maleate or poly(diglycol dimaleate) for reaction times of 3–6 hr.

Vinyl sulfones and divinyl sulfones react readily at room temperature with sulfhydryl groups of reduced wool (165,166) and of urease (165) in aqueous solution at pH 8.7. Earlier, reaction of sulfhydryl groups in urease had been reported (167). The possibility of reaction of other functional groups of the proteins with these reagents was not examined, although it is known that reaction with hydroxyl or amine does occur though at slower rates (168,169).

Acrylonitrile reacts with wool (169–171), soluble keratin derivatives derived from wool (172,173), α-lactalbumin and β-lactalbumin (174), casein, gelatin, glue, gluten, soybean protein, and zein (175). Reaction occurs readily in aqueous and organic solution, in the vapor phase, and under a variety of conditions. When sulfhydryl groups are available, these react most rapidly, the double bond of the acrylonitrile (172–174) being selective and quantitative in certain instances (174), but involving reaction with amino groups in others (173). Cyanoethylated derivatives of the proteins are obtained. Although the reaction with acrylonitrile is fastest with sulfhydryl groups, other groups of the proteins are most certainly amenable to cyanoethylation (170,171,173,175). Acrylonitrile is known to react readily with hydroxyl, amino, active methylene, and other functional groups in a large variety of compounds (175). Although used to only a minor extent thus far in chemical reactions of proteins, acrylonitrile will be studied undoubtedly in much greater detail in the future, possibly providing selectivity in its reactions with certain proteins under controlled conditions. Proteins react with a variety of unsaturated aldehydes. Wool and reduced wool react with acrolein, α-methylacrolein, crotonaldehyde, and cinnamaldehyde (169). Of these aldehydes, acrolein reacts most readily, combining with the free sulfhydryl groups and under alkaline conditions with the free amino groups. Reduced wool, for example, was markedly more reactive than the unreduced protein. Evidence of reaction included gains in weight, determination of thiol, disulfide sulfur, and aldehyde groups, comparative reaction with acetylated wool (in which a number of the reaction sites had been blocked by acetylation prior to reacting with the unsaturated aldehyde), and modification of several physical properties of the wool. Acetylated wool showed a greatly reduced affinity for the aldehydes, compared with unacetylated wool.

d. Isocyanates and Isothiocyanates

The reactions of amines, alcohols, thiols, and related compounds with isocyanates are well known in organic chemistry. The reaction probably involves as a first step the nucleophilic addition of the reagent to the carbon atom of the isocyanate group followed by addition of hydrogen to the oxygen or nitrogen. When present in macromolecules these same functional groups maintain their reactivity toward isocyanates. The reaction with proteins is depicted in eq. (14).

$$\left|\begin{array}{l} -SH \\ -NH_2 \\ -OH \end{array}\right. + O{=}C{=}N{-}R \xrightarrow[\text{pH 7–8}]{0\text{–}25^\circ\text{C.}} \left|\begin{array}{l} -S-\overset{O}{\overset{\|}{C}}-NH-R \\ -NH-\overset{O}{\overset{\|}{C}}-NH-R \\ -O-\overset{O}{\overset{\|}{C}}-NH-R \end{array}\right. \qquad (14)$$

Phenyl isocyanate reacts readily with many proteins at pH 8 and 0°C. For a long time it was believed to react selectively with the amino groups of the proteins. This belief developed largely from the studies of Wormall and co-workers (176,177) on the reaction of serum globulins, casein, gelatin, and insulin with phenyl isocyanate and *p*-bromophenyl isocyanate. From bromine and amino nitrogen analysis of the derivatives and the known amino nitrogen contents of the unreacted proteins, a one to one correspondence between bromine introduced and decrease in amino nitrogen was noted, although the quantitative aspects of the analyses were questionable. Subsequent studies on urease (178), tobacco virus (179) protein, and egg albumin (180), however, have demonstrated that sulf-

TABLE VI-19
Reaction of Phenyl Isocyanate with Acid and Basic Groups of Proteins[a]

Protein	Acid groups[c]		Basic groups[c]	
	Untreated	Treated	Untreated	Treated
Egg albumin	13.5	0.4	8.8	0.0
Gliadin	4.3	2.7	4.7	1.1
Gluten	6.7	2.2	4.3	0.5
Cattle hoof keratin	10.4	1.6	8.8	1.0
Silk fibroin[b]	8.4	1.3	1.3	0.0
Casein	15.6	0.7	7.4	0.7
Insulin	17.5	2.3	9.4	0.0

[a] Two days reaction, 70°C.; protein:phenyl isocyanate:pyridine, 1:1:2.5.
[b] *o*-Chlorophenyl isocyanate used in this example.
[c] Equivalent per 10^4 g. of protein.

hydryl groups and possibly the OH of tyrosine also react under similar conditions.

The reaction has also been useful for introduction of heterocyclic groups into proteins (181,182). Under anhydrous conditions and higher temperature using pyridine as solvent, phenyl isocyanate reacts with all protein groups containing active hydrogen, but does not react with the peptide bonds (183). Typical results obtained with a variety of proteins are given in Table VI-19.

The derivatives were characterized by weight increases on extracted samples, chlorine analysis on samples treated with *o*-chlorophenyl isocyanate, decrease in hydrophilic properties, extensive protein group analyses to estimate the degree of substitution of specific polar groups, binding of dyes to measure total basic and acidic groups, and suitable reactions on selected model compounds to confirm reactivity with specified functional groups of the proteins. Reaction was demonstrated to have occurred with the basic groups (amino, guanidino, and imidazole), the acidic groups (thiol, phenolic, and carboxyl), the primary amide, and probably part of the aliphatic hydroxyl.

Farnsworth (184) employed this method for reaction of phenyl isocyanate with wool, after experiencing difficulty in obtaining reaction in aqueous media. Under anhydrous conditions with pyridine as solvent, increases in weight up to 45% could be obtained. If all side chain groups capable of reacting with phenyl isocyanate had reacted, the maximum weight increase of 50% would have been realized. The weight increases obtained indicated fairly complete reaction of the groups. Amino, carboxyl, and thiol groups all react and probably phenolic, amide, guanidyl, and glyoxaline groups also. The rate of reaction increased greatly with increasing temperature, but at the expense of some degradation of the protein. The fiber diameter was measurably increased by hot pyridine, and this was believed to improve the accessibility of the reactive groups to the isocyanate. Acetylated wool had a greatly reduced affinity for the isocyanate, indicating that the acetyl groups were probably located at some sites at which the isocyanate would have reacted.

Moore (185) reacted α-naphthyl, phenyl, octadecyl, and ethyl isocyanates with wool in pyridine at 97°C. and higher temperatures. The modified wool had improved resistance to chemical attack by hot acid, alkali, and oxidizing or reducing agents. Uptakes of 3–40% were realized. It was assumed that the same groups were involved as had been indicated by Fraenkel-Conrat (183) and by Farnsworth (184). The modification of wool by tolylene and hexamethylene diisocyanates was subsequently studied by Moore and O'Connell (186), employing similar conditions, for reaction. Weight increases of 1–8% were realized with toluene diisocyanate, 4–19% with hexamethylene diisocyanate. These diisocyanates required longer reaction time than for the monofunctional isocyanates. More recently Koenig (187) has reported that hot dimethyl sulfoxide is superior to pyridine as a solvent for reaction of monoisocyanates with wool. The reaction is very rapid; with 3 ml. dimethyl sulfoxide, 2 ml. phenyl isocyanate and 1.2 g. of dry wool, uptakes of isocyanate equal to 30% of the weight of the wool were realized in 10 min. at 105°C. A variety of aromatic and aliphatic isocyanates react under these conditions, with uptakes of up to 60% in some instances. The hot dimethyl sulfoxide solvent is believed to swell the wool fiber appreciably, making possible penetration of the isocyanate to the reactive sites; little or no reaction occurs in the absence of the solvent. The isocyanates included phenyl, *o*-tolyl, *m*-tolyl, *p*-tolyl, *o*-methoxyphenyl, *p*-methoxyphenyl, 1-naphthyl, 2-biphenylyl, *n*-butyl, *n*-octadecyl, and carbethoxymethyl. The mechanical properties of the modified wool were significantly altered; greatly improved resistance to acid, alkali, and oxidizing media was noted with the modified materials.

The reaction of phenyl isothiocyanate with amino groups in proteins is fairly analogous to the reaction with isocyanates. Phenyl isothiocyanate has been found useful for determination of amino endgroups in proteins and sequence of amino acid residues in polypeptides and proteins by stepwise degradation from the amino end of the molecule. The method is based on the reactivity of the phenyl isothiocyanate in pyridine with the terminal amino group to yield a phenylthiocarbamyl peptide (PTC). The PTC rearranges readily on heating with anhydrous hydrogen chloride in nitromethane to yield the phenylthiohydantoin of the *N*-terminal residue of the starting protein. On heating, the phenylthiohydantoin is cleaved by alkali to give the free amino acid which may be identified by paper chromatography. Modifications of the technique and a study of its general applicability and utility have been described by Fraenkel-Conrat (188).

e. Carbon Suboxide

Carbon suboxide is a gas with reactivity comparable to that of ketene. Its preparation and chemical properties have been reviewed (189). In general each molecule reacts with a functional group of the protein and one molecule of water, yielding half-amides or half-esters of malonic acid. The reaction is illustrated in eq. (15). Under anhydrous conditions, it

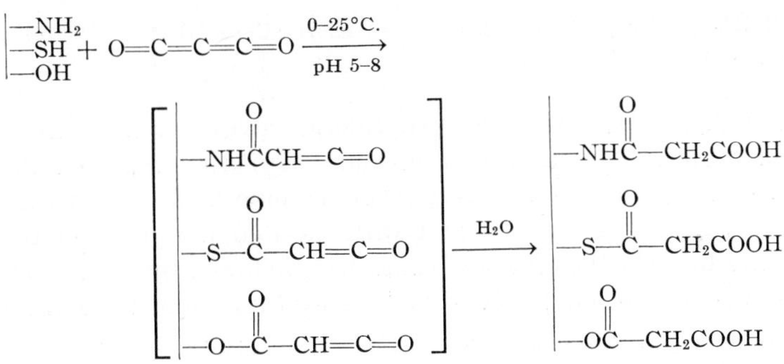

(15)

may act as a difunctional reagent, reacting with two groups of the protein as shown in eq. (16) for amino groups. Model experiments with amino

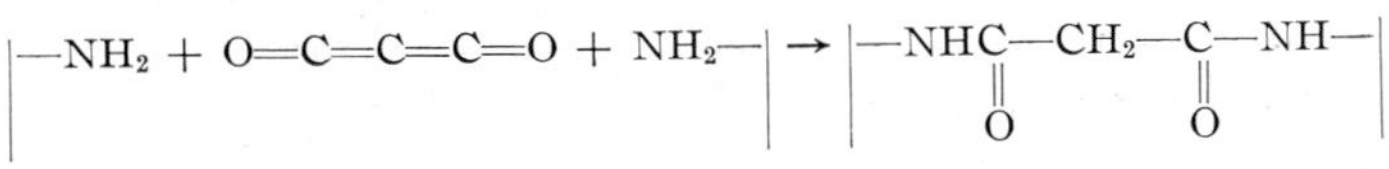

(16)

acids indicate that carbon suboxide does not react with guanidyl, imidazole, and aliphatic hydroxyl groups (190). The order of reactivity in proteins is —SH, —NH_2, and phenolic OH. In proteins containing no sulfhydryl groups, selectivity for amino groups can be achieved by malonylation followed by mild alkaline hydrolysis, which hydrolyzes the labile phenolic ester groups (191). The derivatives have considerably lower isoelectric points than the original proteins, since for each molecule of carbon suboxide reacted, one free carboxyl group is introduced. Reaction with horse serum albumin at pH 7.5 yielded a derivative in which the number of malonyl residues introduced corresponded very closely to the decrease in amino nitrogen, as determined by the Van Slyke procedure (192); decrease in amino nitrogen was also found in malonylated egg albumin and chymotrypsin. With serum albumin, better than 90% of the amino groups and 60–80% of the tyrosine hydroxyls were malonylated (193); pepsin was similarly malonylated at pH 5.3 (191). Fraenkel-Conrat (194) found that in reacting with egg albumin at pH 5–6, the sulfhydryl groups react faster than the tyrosine hydroxyl or the free amino groups. Due to the general inconvenience and its lack of specificity, carbon suboxide has not been widely used for chemical modification of proteins.

f. Carbon Disulfide

Primary and secondary amines react readily with carbon disulfide to give *N*-alkylated dithiocarbamic acids and their amine salts (eq. 17). Treat-

$$RNH_2 + CS_2 \rightarrow RNH\underset{\underset{S}{\|}}{C}{-}SH \xrightarrow{RNH_2} RNH{-}\underset{\underset{S}{\|}}{C}{-}S\ NH_3R \qquad (17)$$

ment of $RNHC(S){-}SNH_3R$ with mercuric chloride gives mercuric sulfide and an isothiocyanate. Cook, Heilbron, and Levy (195) reported the first example of a rather unusual reaction of α-amino acid amides with carbon disulfide, involving reaction first with the α-amino group of the amide of glycine to yield the dithiocarbamic acid, followed by cyclization and elimination of ammonia (eq. 18). Levy applied the method to stepwise

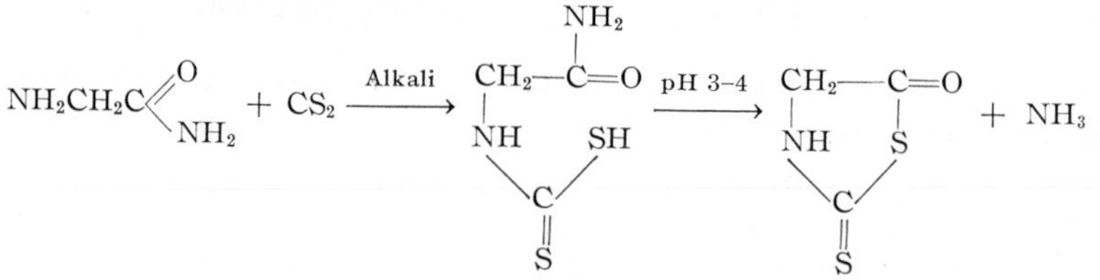

(18)

cleavage of several simple (196) peptides and suggested the possibility of it being a useful technique for the determination of *N*-terminal groups (197), and for the stepwise degradation of a polypeptide chain.

However, Leonis (198) had shown earlier that carbon disulfide reacts not only with the α-amino groups of α-amino acids, but also with the ε-amino, imino, and thiol groups, although at different rates. It reacts about ten times more rapidly with α-amino groups than with ε-amino groups. Under mild conditions of temperature and pH, the free imino group of proline and hydroxyproline, the sulfhydryl, α-amino, and ε-amino groups of free amino acids react quantitatively. No other groups were reactive. Corticotropin (199) from pituitary gland of sheep reacts readily. These amino groups react about six times more rapidly than either the ε-amino group of lysine or tha ε-amino groups of several proteins so far studied.

The reaction of chymotrypsin (80) with carbon disulfide results in conversion of amino groups to dithiocarbamates, the number and type of amino group involved depending on reaction conditions. Chymotrypsinogen contains 14 free amino groups (13 ε-amino groups and one α-amino group) (80). At pH 10.3 and 5°C., reaction was not complete in 6 days. At higher concentrations of protein, only 10 or 11 of the theoretical 14 groups had reacted after 7 days. At pH 7.5 and 25°C., only 3.2 groups had reacted after 31 hr. In other experiments with chymotrypsinogen, insulin and β-lactoglobulin, at pH 7.5 to 7.9, ε-amino groups reacted slowly, but appreciably. At pH 6.9, substitution of only one amino group could be achieved, which was demonstrated to be the α-amino group. Conversion of the 13 ε-amino groups of chymotrypsinogen to guanidino groups by reaction with *O*-methylisourea and reaction of the guanidinated chymotrypsinogen with carbon disulfide at pH 7.3 for 1 day at 25°C. gave a derivative containing one dithiocarbamate group per mole of protein. Treatment of the dithiocarbamate derivatives at pH 3.0 reverses the reaction with elimination of carbon disulfide to give the original protein. By sedimentation analysis, the monodithiocarbamate derivative was shown to be homogeneous and monomeric at pH 8.7. The derivatives were characterized by direct analysis for dithiocarbamic acid groups by two methods.

The early expectation for utility of this reaction in endgroup analysis and stepwise degradation has not been realized. Reversal of the reaction on acidification competes too severely with cyclization and elimination of the 2-thiothiazolid-5-one, the reversal being almost quantitative in case of several proteins studied.

C. MAIN CHAIN REACTIONS

1. Reactions of Endgroups

The determination of endgroups has been a very useful technique in the characterization of macromolecules. Knowledge of the number of chain ends and of their composition has been helpful in assessing the validity of various theories of polymer science and in gaining an insight into the mechanisms of the formation of macromolecules from their constituent monomers and of the degradation of large molecules into smaller subunits under the influence of hostile environments (heat, light, high energy radiation, and reactive chemicals). Endgroup determination in proteins has provided the fundamental toehold, when used in conjunction with various degradative reactions, which has made possible the elucidation of the covalent structure (amino acid sequence) of several protein molecules.

Endgroups in proteins are usually contained in the terminal amino acids of the polypeptide chains. The terminal α-amino acid may be linked to the polypeptide chain through its carboxyl group, leaving the amino group free; these are referred to as *N*-terminal. When the terminal α-amino acid is attached to the main chain through its amino group, leaving the carboxyl group free, it is called *C*-terminal. Consequently, the chemistry of endgroups in most proteins relates to free amino or carboxyl groups. Reactions characteristic of these groups have been discussed previously in several sections on reactions of side chain groups. The present discussion will be limited to reagents and reactions which have been found most useful in protein endgroup studies.

a. α-Amino Endgroups

(1) 1-Fluoro-2,4-dinitrobenzene (FDNB)

One of the great landmarks in protein chemistry was the introduction by Sanger (52,200) of this reagent for the identification and estimation of free amino groups of proteins and peptides. The reaction consists of a nucleophilic displacement of fluoride from the FDNB by the amino group of the protein to yield a dinitrophenyl (DNP) derivative. The reaction is carried out under conditions which preserve the integrity of peptide bonds. Subsequent hydrolysis of the DNP-protein or DNP-peptide yields free amino acids and DNP derivatives of *N*-terminal amino acids. The DNP derivatives are bright yellow compounds which can be extracted with suitable organic solvents, fractionated chromatographically and determined colorimetrically. The reactions are shown in eq. (19).

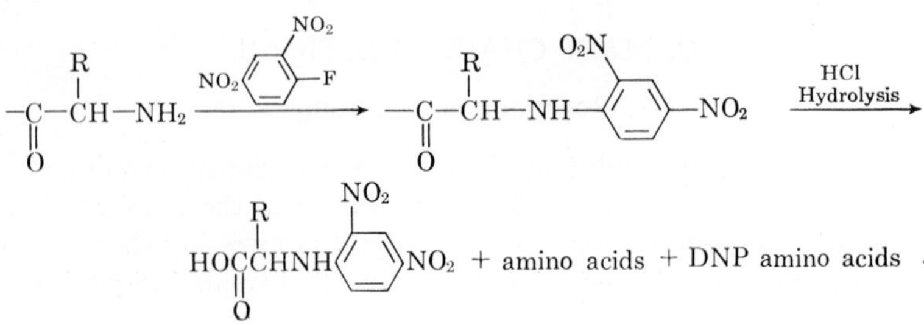

(19)

Detailed procedures, application, and the status of this reaction in amino acid sequence studies have been reported (188,201–204).

(2) Phenyl Isothiocyanates

The use of phenyl isothiocyanate (PTC) as an endgroup reagent was introduced by Edman (205). The phenyl thiocarbamate formed as a primary product rearranges under acid conditions to a phenylthiohydantoin of the *N*-terminal amino acid and a polypeptide chain shortened by one amino acid, as shown in eqs. (20) and (21). In principle, the process

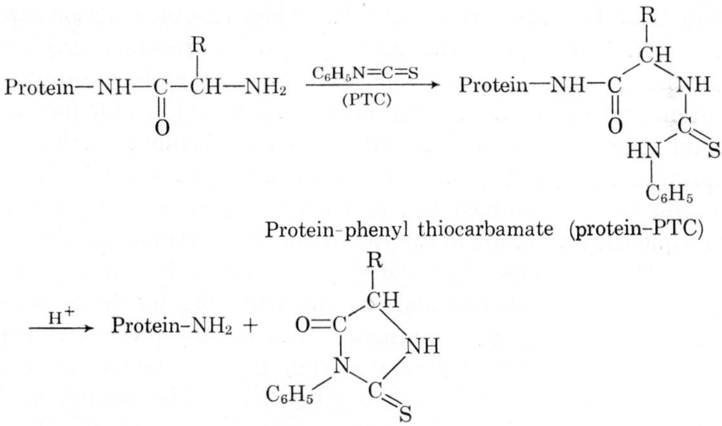

Protein-phenyl thiocarbamate (protein-PTC)

Phenylthiohydantoin (PTH)

(20)

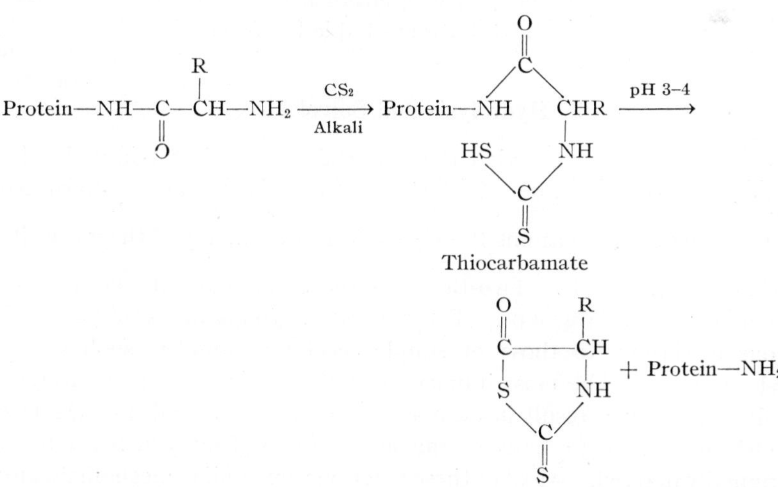

Thiocarbamate

2-Thiothiazolid-5-one

(21)

could be repeated, thereby lending itself to the stepwise determination of the sequence of amino acids in small peptides or proteins. It has not been widely used, however.

b. Carboxyl Endgroups

Although several chemical methods for *C*-terminal amino acids have been studied (206), none have been sufficiently satisfactory to be widely adopted. The most generally used method is not a chemical one but is based on the enzymatic reaction with carboxypeptidase, which attacks only those peptides with a free —COOH. Since enzyme reactions are not included in this discussion the carboxypeptidase reaction will not be described here, beyond pointing out that it is not without problems of sufficient magnitude to have warranted a continued search for reliable and broad spectrum chemical methods. Three chemical methods have been shown to be at least of limited value, such as providing confirmatory evidence for results obtained by the carboxypeptidase method, and for peptide sequence elucidation in the vicinity of the *C*-terminus of the protein molecule. These include hydrazinolysis, esterification and reduction of the ester to an amino alcohol, and reaction with inorganic thiocyanate.

The hydrazinolysis method consists of heating the protein or peptide with anhydrous hydrazine, whereby all but the *C*-terminal amino acids are converted into hydrazides which may be separated by suitable methods from the free amino acids which were originally *C*-terminal. The free amino acids are then identified by conventional procedures (204,207–209), such as reaction with FDNB to give identifiable DNP derivatives.

2. Hydrolysis and Solvolysis

All evidence supports the view that the main chain of protein molecules consists of peptide groups —CONHR— (secondary amide) alternated with asymmetric carbon atoms $\mathrm{R{-}\overset{|}{\underset{|}{C}}{-}H}$ derived from any of the naturally occurring α-amino acids. Two-thirds of the main chain atoms are contained in the peptide groups. These peptide groups are susceptible to reactions analogous to those of simple secondary amides, such as *N*-methylacetamide. The most important of these reactions are hydrolysis and solvolysis, which result in cleavage of the peptide bond into the free —COOH and —NH_2 (in case of aqueous reactions) from which the bond was originally derived. Most of these reactions are similar mechanistically and involve nucleophilic attack on the carbon atom (sp^2 configuration) of the peptide carbonyl to form a tetrahedral (sp^3) species which subsequently disproportionates to either the starting materials or the products (35,64). This is illustrated for the general case by the following sequence shown in eq. (22) (analogous to esterification and saponification), where: AY may be H_2O, OH^-, ROH, RO^-, RSH, RS^-, RNH_2, or RNH^-. The

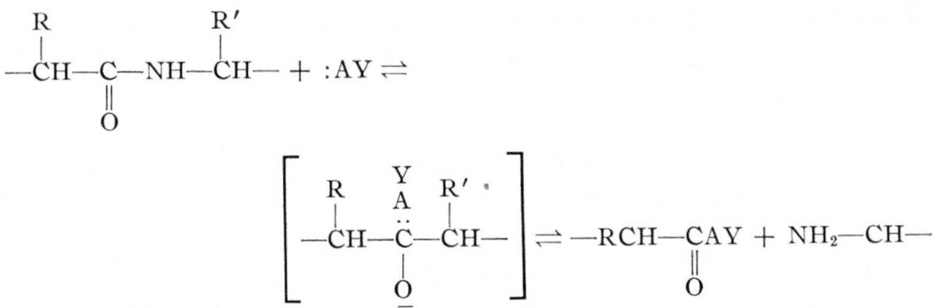
(22)

rate of addition of the nucleophile (particularly for solvolysis) can be increased greatly by acid catalysis, in which case the peptide carbonyl is activated by addition of the acid to its oxygen (or nitrogen) atom prior to attack by the nucleophile, i.e., with H^+.

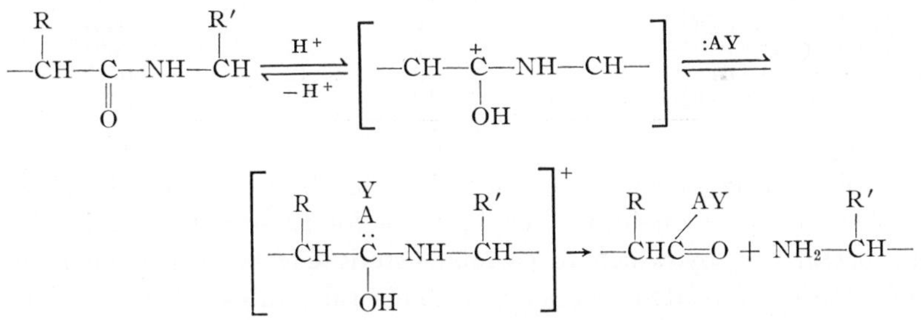
(23)

The many factors which influence the rate of cleavage of the peptide bond of a protein can be understood in terms of this mechanism. These factors include steric ones, the nature of the nucleophile attacking, the nature of the acid in acid-catalyzed reactions, the charge of the tetrahedral intermediate (neutral, negative, or positive), the nature of the departing group in the final step, and the main chain conformation in the vicinity of the reaction site (helical, hydrogen-bonded, random coil, etc.), *cis* or *trans* geometry about the peptide bond. The steric and electrical effects are for the most part in the expected direction, as will become apparent in the ensuing discussion.

a. Steric Effects

Steric effects have been shown to be fairly parallel for acid or base hydrolysis of esters, esterifications of the corresponding acids, and for hydrolysis of amides. Therefore, in the absence of extensive data for the hydrolysis of amides, the steric effects on esterification and saponification reactions can provide a useful guide for assessment of the probable magnitude of similar effects in the hydrolysis of peptide bonds. Esterification rates for a series of acids with increasing steric hindrance are given in Table VI-20 (210).

TABLE VI-20
Effects of Steric Hindrance on the Rate of Esterification of Various Acids by Methanol at 40°C.

Acid	Atoms in position six			Relative Rate
	C	H	Total	
CH_3COOH	0	0	0	1.0
$CH_3CH_2CH_2COOH$	0	3	3	0.51
$(CH_3)_3CCOOH$	0	0	0	0.037
$(CH_3)_3CCH_2COOH$	0	9	9	0.023
$(CH_3)_3C\underset{CH_3}{\underset{\mid}{C}}HCOOH$	0	9	9	0.00062
$(CH_3)_3CC(CH_3)_2COOH$	0	9	9	0.00013
$(CH_3CH_2)_3CCOOH$	0	9	9	0.00016
$(i\text{-}C_3H_7)_2CHCOOH$	0	12	12	$<10^{-4}$
$(CH_3)_3CH(C_2H_5)COOH$	0	12	12	$<10^{-4}$

An empirical rule known as the Rule of Six has been advanced by Newman (211) to give a qualitative explanation for these data. It is also a very useful rule by which to correlate steric effects in a given reaction of a series of related compounds. This rule states: "In reactions involving addition to an unsaturated function containing a double bond, the greater the number of atoms in the six position the greater will be the steric effect." The number of atoms in the 6 position is called the six number (*sn*). The numbering system for the coiled structure for amides is shown in II: This rule also correlates well with quantitative rate data

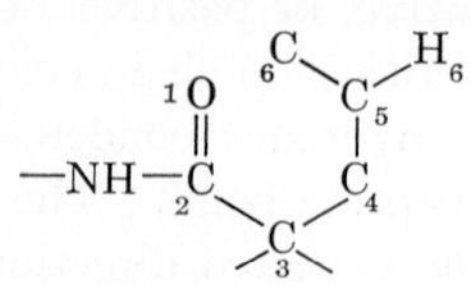

(II)

on the hydrolysis of simple dipeptides (212) and on polypeptides (213). It is shown in Table VI-21 (214) that peptides with *sn* of zero hydrolyze fastest; those with *sn* of 3, at intermediate rates; and those with *sn* of 6, slowest. The same observation is shown in Table VI-22 for the polypeptides. The range in relative rates covers a factor of about 100.

TABLE VI-21

Correlation of the Rule of Six with Rates of Hydrolysis of Dipeptides[a]

Dipeptide	Atoms or groups in position 6[b]		Relative rates of hydrolysis	
	No. and kinds	Total	Acid	Base
Gly.Gly	None	0	1	1
Ala.Gly	None	0	0.62	0.24
Gly.Ala	3H	3	0.62	0.21
Gly.Leu	2H, 1 i-C_3H_7	3	0.40	0.061
Gly.Try	2H, 1 indole	3	0.35	—
Gly.Val	1H, 2 CH_3	3	0.31	0.049
Leu.Gly	1H, 2 CH_3	3	0.23	0.048
Leu.Leu	3H, 2CH_3, 1 i-C_3H_7	6	0.048	0
Leu.Try	3H, 2CH_3, 1 indole	6	0.041	—
Val.Gly	6H	6	0.015	0

[a] Taken from refs. 212, 214.

[b] Excluding O of C═O and OH in carboxyl group of main chain, common to all the compounds. This is true for all six number (*sn*) values discussed herein.

TABLE VI-22

Correlation of Rule of Six with Rates of Acid Hydrolysis of Polypeptides

Polypeptide	Six number *sn*	Relative rate[a]
Polyglycine	0	500
Poly-DL-alanine	3	100
Poly-DL-α-aminobutyric acid	6	22
Poly-DL-phenylalanine	5	13
Poly-DL-norleucine	6	20
Poly-DL-leucine	6	17
Poly-DL-isoleucine	9	5

[a] Poly-DL-alanine = 100; relative rates of hydrolysis in 4*M* dichloroacetic acid.

The marked stability of valyl peptides has been known for a long time. The valyl group exerts a much stronger influence when attached to the carbonyl side of a peptide bond than when bonded to the NH side; in the former position it contributes 6 to the *sn* of the peptide bond compared with

3 in the latter position. The valyl.valyl peptide bond is exceptionally stable, with a *sn* of 9, being isolated from gramicidin in 5–6% yield after 6 hr. in boiling 16% HCl, and 1.5% yield after 24 hr. under the same conditions (215).

The application of the Rule of Six for assessment of steric hindrance about a peptide bond in polypeptides or proteins has been reported (214). The *sn* values for peptide bonds are obtained by using the counting system shown in III.

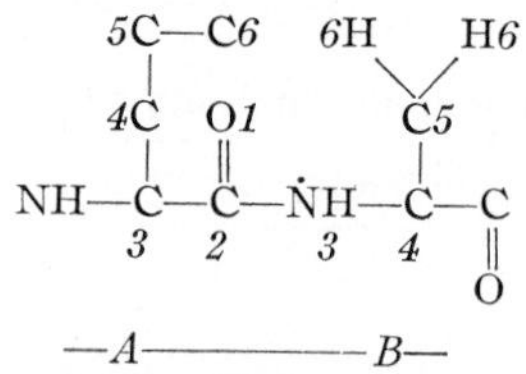

(III)

The six numbers *sn* have been calculated (Table VI-23) for the peptide bonds between A and B of all possible —A—B— peptide sequences of the commonly occurring α-amino acids in which the R groups of the A and B contain no heteroatoms, i.e., only H or hydrocarbon. These may be useful in predicting the relative stabilities of these peptide bonds in proteins and related substances to hydrolysis, hydrazinolysis, alcoholysis, and related reactions centered at the peptide bond. Particularly so since for this group of α-amino acids, steric factors are probably more important than other factors, there being no heteroatoms in the side chain to provide neighboring group participation in main chain cleavages.

TABLE VI-23
Number of Atoms in Six Position for Dipeptide Sequences —A—B—
(No Heteroatoms in Side Chains)[a]

	B							
A	Ala	Gly	Isoleu	Leu	Phe	Pro	Sar	Val
Ala	3	0	3	3	3	6	0	3
Gly	3	0	3	3	3	6	0	3
Isoleu	9	6	9	9	9	12	6	9
Leu	6	3	6	6	6	9	3	6
Phe	5	2	5	5	5	8	2	5
Pro	9	6	9	9	9	12	6	9
Sar	6	3	6	6	6	9	3	6
Val	9	6	9	9	9	12	6	9

[a] See text for numbering system, formula III.

Other peptide units contain heteroatoms in the side chain. The presence of —OH, —COOH, —SH, —SO_3H, and C═C at position 6 (less so at position 5) is known to accelerate the rate of cleavage of peptide bonds flanked by these groups. The ability of heteroatoms to assist in such cleavage may be greatly influenced by steric factors. As will be seen in Table VI-24, some —A—B— peptides contain A groups with heteroatoms and the B units without. A similar set of *sn* could be derived for —A—B— peptide bonds in which B contains a heteroatom and A does not (or in which both A and B contain heteroatoms). The extent of neighboring group participation may be less for a given —A—B— unit when the *sn* is larger. It has been noted by Elliott that not all serine and threonine peptide bonds are equally reactive in hydrolysis of various

TABLE VI-24
Six Numbers *sn* for Dipeptide Sequences —A—B— Containing Heteroatom for Neighboring Group Participation[a]

	B							
A	Ala	Gly	Isoleu	Leu	Phe	Pro	Sar	Val
Asp	$^{2}5$	$^{2}2$	$^{2}5$	$^{2}5$	$^{0}5$	$^{2}8$	$^{2}2$	$^{2}5$
Thr	$^{0}7$	$^{0}4$	$^{0}7$	$^{0}7$	$^{0}7$	$^{0}10$	$^{0}4$	$^{0}7$
Ser	$^{0}4$	$^{0}1$	$^{0}4$	$^{0}4$	$^{0}4$	$^{0}7$	$^{0}1$	$^{0}4$
Cysteine	$^{0}4$	$^{0}1$	$^{0}4$	$^{0}4$	$^{0}4$	$^{0}7$	$^{0}1$	$^{0}4$
Cysteic acid	$^{3}6$	$^{3}3$	$^{3}6$	$^{3}6$	$^{3}6$	$^{3}9$	$^{3}3$	$^{3}6$

[a] The heteroatom is located in the A group, position 6; no heteroatoms in B. The superscript number to the left of the *sn* value for each A—B pair represents the number of heteroatoms in position 6. Those with zero values have a heteroatom in position 5 in the A location. See formula III.

proteins (216), and that threonine does not appear to be as amenable to *N* to *O* peptidyl shift as is serine.

The contributions of specific amino acid R groups to the *sn* of a peptide bond when present in either the A or the B group contiguous to the peptide bond are given in Table VI-25 along with the number of heteroatoms in position 6 for either location. These *sn* are particularly useful when considering steric factors about peptide bonds in modified proteins, derivatives, and related compounds. Finally, a complete list of *sn* for all possible combinations of peptides, —A—B—, for the more commonly known natural α-amino acids is given in Table VI-26. Although one can always calculate the *sn* for a given peptide, lists such as those of Tables VI-23–VI-26 are convenient and facilitate comparisons. For proteins of known amino acid sequence, for example, a listing of the *sn* for each peptide bond along the sequence gives a steric topography, so to speak, for the molecule.

It should be stressed that the *sn* are intended to give only a qualitative evaluation of the extent of steric hindrance. Their use is best applied in reactions in which the intermediate is of a tetrahedral configuration. Molecular models can give a more lucid picture of the steric condition and should be used when possible for confirmatory purposes. The actual

TABLE VI-25
Contribution to Peptide Six Numbers *sn* by Various Amino Acids when Located in Either the A or B Position of an —A—B— Peptide Sequence

	Number of atoms in position 6		Number of heteroatoms in position 6	
Amino acid	A	B	A	B
Alanine	0	3	0	0
Arginine	3	3	0	0
Aspartic acid	2	3	2	0
Glutamic acid	3	3	0	0
Glycine	0	0	0	0
Histidine	2	3	1	0
Isoleucine	6	3	0	0
Leucine	3	3	0	0
Lysine	3	3	0	0
Methionine	3	3	1	0
Phenylalanine	2	3	0	0
Proline	6	6	0	0
Serine	1	3	0	1
Threonine	4	3	0	1
Tryptophan	2	3	1	0
Tyrosine	2	3	0	0
Valine	6	3	0	0
Cysteine	1	3	0	1
Cystine	1	3	1	1
Cysteic acid	3	3	3	1

size of the atom in position 6 is also important, though this is not considered in the qualitative treatment. Examination of the molecular models for specific compounds will make it quite clear why larger *sn* tend to give greater steric hindrance. With greater number of atoms in position 6, it becomes increasingly difficult to remove a blocking group from the reaction path, since rotation of a given blocking group out of the path merely results in the rotation of a new blocking group into the path.

TABLE VI-26

Six Numbers *sn* for Various —A—B— Peptide Sequences in Proteins and Polypeptides[a]

A	B																		
	Ala	Arg	Asp	Glu	Gly	His	Isoleu	Leu	Lys	Met	Phe	Pro	Ser	Thr	Tyr	Try	Val	Cys	Cysteine
Ala	3	3	3	3	0	3	3	3	3	3	3	6	3	3	3	3	3	3	3
Arg	6	6	6	6	3	6	6	6	6	6	6	9	6	6	6	6	6	6	6
Asp	5	5	5	5	2	5	5	5	5	5	5	8	5	5	5	5	5	5	5
Glu	6	6	6	6	3	6	6	6	6	6	6	9	6	6	6	6	6	6	6
Gly	3	3	3	3	0	3	3	3	3	3	3	6	3	3	3	3	3	3	3
His	5	5	5	5	2	3	5	5	5	5	5	8	5	5	5	5	5	5	5
Isoleu	9	9	9	9	6	9	9	9	9	9	9	12	9	9	9	9	9	9	9
Leu	6	6	6	6	3	6	6	6	6	6	6	9	6	6	6	6	6	6	6
Lys	6	6	6	6	3	6	6	6	6	6	6	9	6	6	6	6	6	6	6
Met	6	6	6	6	3	6	6	6	6	6	6	9	6	6	6	6	6	6	6
Phe	5	5	5	5	2	5	5	5	5	5	5	8	5	5	5	5	5	5	5
Pro	9	9	9	9	6	9	9	9	9	9	9	12	9	9	9	9	9	9	9
Ser	4	4	4	4	1	4	4	4	4	4	4	7	4	4	4	4	4	4	4
Thr	7	7	7	7	4	7	7	7	7	7	7	10	7	7	7	7	7	7	7
Tyr	5	5	5	5	2	5	5	5	5	5	5	8	5	5	5	5	5	5	5
Try	5	5	5	5	2	5	5	5	5	5	5	8	5	5	5	5	5	5	5
Val	9	9	9	9	6	9	9	9	9	9	9	12	9	9	9	9	9	9	9
Cys	4	4	4	4	1	4	4	4	4	4	4	7	4	4	4	4	4	4	4
Cysteine	4	4	4	4	1	4	4	4	4	4	4	7	4	4	4	4	4	4	4

[a] For numbering system, see formula III in text.

With *sn* of 9, 12, and higher it becomes rather difficult to obtain a molecular conformation with no groups blocking the reaction site.

It should be pointed out that *sn* are also useful for assessment of the magnitude of steric factors on main chain conformations of polypeptides and proteins, the tendency of these materials to crystallize, and the tendency for hydrophobic bond formation, since these factors, too, have an indirect effect on rates of chemical reactions at specific bonds. For example, it is known that certain α-amino acids tend to not form α-helix conformations; others form α-helix, β-, or random coil conformations. Blout (217) has given a good account of this work, and the correlation of six numbers of peptide bonds with main chain conformational preferences has been reported (214).

b. Electrical Effects and Neighboring Group Participation

The effect of polar groups on relative rates of alkaline hydrolysis of esters is illustrated in the following data (64): The K/K_{MeOAc} ratios for CH_3-COOMe, $ClCH_2COOMe$, and $Cl_2CHCOOMe$ are 1.0, 761, and 16,000, respectively. For the most part, the side chain polar groups of proteins are fairly far removed from the peptide bond and the inductive effect will not be very prominent. However, in chemically modified proteins in which polar groups are introduced at the α-carbon atom, this effect could become important.

The presence of a positive charge in the vicinity of the peptide bond, such as exists with free α-amino groups, ϵ-amino, imidazole, indole, and guanidyl of proteins or peptides in acid solution, results in a decreased rate of hydrolysis of the peptide bond. In these cases the reaction intermediate will have a doubly positive charge (IV) which is not energetically

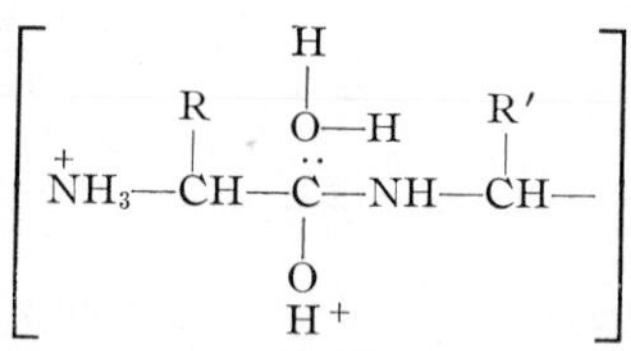

(IV)

favorable. The result is stabilization of the peptide bonds in the vicinity of the positively charged groups. α-Amino groups will be most effective in this respect; this results in the peptide bond of an *N*-terminal residue being relatively stable to acid. This is perhaps the reason for the accumulation of dipeptides in the hydrolysis of proteins, illustrated in Table

TABLE VI-27
Hydrolysis of Silk Fibroin by Concentrated HCl, 40°C.[a]

Time, hr.	Average peptide length
0.5	29.5
1.5	9.6
3.0	5.7
6.0	4.0
10.0	3.0
17.2	2.3
24.0	2.3
33.0	2.2
42.7	2.05
48.0	2.06
96.0	1.95

[a] Taken from ref. 218.

VI-27 for the hydrolysis of silk fibroin by concentrated HCl at 40°C. (218). The rate of production of amino nitrogen was rapid during the initial hours but leveled out as the peptide chain length approached 2.0. The production of free amino groups continued at a slow steady rate. After 40 hr. of hydrolysis, the fibroin hydrolyzate contained approximately 25% free amino groups and 75% peptides. For alkaline hydrolysis, the free —COOH groups will be present as the carboxylate ion. This, too, will tend to stabilize the peptide bond in its general vicinity since the reaction intermediate in this case (V) will have a doubly negative charge.

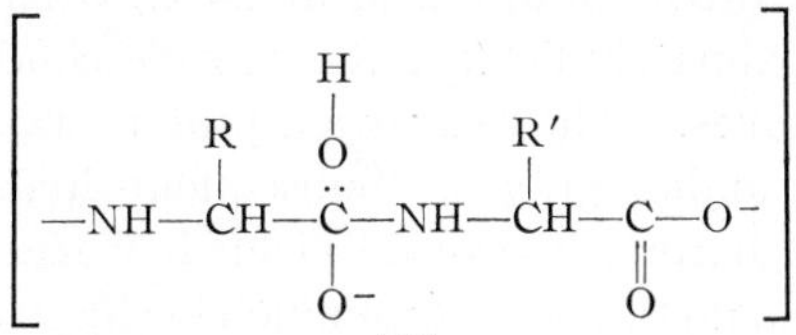

(V)

3. Peptidyl Shift: Nitrogen to Oxygen

The ready cleavage of peptide bonds of serine and threonine has been known for a long time. As early as 1907, Fischer and Abderhalden (219) demonstrated the partial hydrolysis of silk by concentrated sulfuric or hydrochloric acid at 16–36°C. and several days exposure. Further work on silk over the next 25 years (220) established the lability of the *N*-acetylserine peptides toward dilute acid and suggested that the ready cleavage of serine peptide linkages was a consequence of neighboring participation of the —OH of the serine, resulting in an $N \rightarrow O$ acyl shift as shown in eq. (24). This rearrangement results in the formation of an ester bond

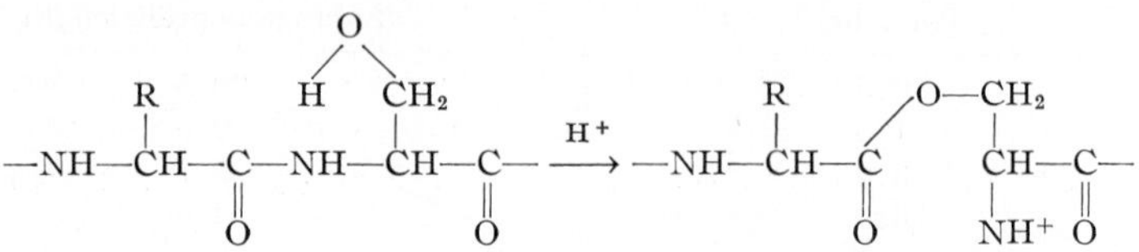 (24)

in the main chain of the polymer in place of the original amide bond. Ester bonds are known to hydrolyze much more rapidly than amide bonds, and thus the ready cleavage of peptides adjacent to serine and threonine seemed plausible on the basis of the peptidyl shift hypothesis for the proteins and its known counterpart with model dipeptides and hydroxyamides. This rearrangement has been shown to occur in silk (216,221–223), lysozyme (224,227), gliadin (225), wheat gluten (226), glycylserine, glycylthreonine, insulin, ribonuclease, glucagon, serum albumin (227), wool keratin (228,229), rabbit fur keratin (113), and polyserine (230).

Desnuelle and co-workers (221,222) showed that serine and threonine are much more readily liberated from peptide bonds during acid hydrolysis than are other amino acids of silk. The cleavage of the protein at the serine and threonine became more selective at higher acid concentrations and lower temperatures. Of all the free groups present in proteins, only the hydroxyls were found to exercise an appreciable labilization of peptide bonds in their vicinity. Elliott (223,224) found that treatment of silk fibroin with concentrated sulfuric acid at 25°C. resulted in *N* to *O* rearrangement of approximately 60% of the peptide bonds linked to nitrogen atoms of serine residues. The rearranged protein was acetylated to block the newly formed amino groups. Subsequent hydrolysis of the ester links by cold dilute barium hydroxide yielded *N*-acetyl peptides. About 60% of the serine and no threonine (not much in silk) were shown by FDNB analysis to be *N*-terminal. Similar results have been reported by other workers for gliadin (225) and wheat gluten (226) under similar conditions of acid treatment and employing FDNB endgroup analyses. With gliadin a maximum rearrangement of 60–70% of the theoretical was achieved by treatment with anhydrous sulfuric acid at 0°C. for 35 hr. No rearrangement at threonine residues was detected. In an alternate scheme for degradation, nitrous acid deamination of the free amino groups of the rearranged protein and amino acid analysis of the deaminated product revealed a loss in serine content of the protein.

Bock and Thakur (227) employed hydroxylamine to cleave the ester bonds of rearranged proteins. The proteins were treated with anhydrous acid, the acid removed with ether, and the ester bonds cleaved at pH 7.3 by 2*N* salt-free hydroxylamine. The stoichiometry and specificity of the cleavage were determined by (*1*) colorimetric determination of the hydroxamic acid formed, (*2*) periodate determination of serine groups exposed, (*3*) FDNB determination of *N*-terminal endgroups produced, and (*4*) chromatography of cleavage products. The method was tested on glycylserine, glycylthreonine, insulin, ribonuclease, glucagon, serum albumin, and lysozyme.

The *N* to *O* acyl rearrangement has also been observed in the carbonizing of wool (228,229) (a method involving treatment of wool with H_2SO_4 to remove cellulosic impurities) and in the carrotting of rabbit fur (113) to make it more prone to felting. The evidence for rearrangement and main chain cleavage consisted of endgroup determinations, significant increase in the number of serine and threonine endgroups, reversal of the rearrangement under suitable conditions, and a weakening of the strength of the wool fibers.

Fasman (230) has provided the most direct and unambiguous demonstration of the $N \rightarrow O$ rearrangement in a polypeptide. Using poly-DL-serine (MW about 5000), it was shown that 70% of the amide bonds rearranged to ester bonds on treatment with concentrated sulfuric acid at room temperature for 3 days. The remaining 30% of the free hydroxyls were converted to the *O*-acid sulfate, determined by total sulfur analysis of the product. Infrared spectra of the parent poly-DL-serine, the rearranged product, and suitable model compounds gave direct evidence for

TABLE VI-28
Infrared Spectra of Poly-DL-serine before and after H_2SO_4 Treatment and of Model Compounds[a]

Compound	Absorption, cm.$^{-1}$
Poly-DL-serine (before H_2SO_4)[b]	1655, 1545, 1520, 1400, 1245, 1065
Poly-DL-serine (after H_2SO_4)[b]	1740, 1700, 1610, 1545, 1520, 1440, 1200, 1040
DL-Serine acid sulfate[c]	1755, 1600, 1520, 1215, 1060, 1005
DL-Serine methyl ester HCl[c]	1745, 1595, 1505, 1450, 1390, 1200, 1005

[a] Taken from ref. 230.
[b] KBr disks.
[c] Cast films from H_2O.

the presence of ester bonds in the product. The data are shown in Table VI-28. The spectra show the appearance of an ester band at 1740 cm.$^{-1}$, a decrease in the amide II frequency at 1545 cm.$^{-1}$, strong NH_3^+ frequencies at 1610 and 1520 cm.$^{-1}$ due to ammonium salt of sulfuric acid, and sulfate absorption at 1440 and 1040 cm.$^{-1}$. By means of the hydroxamic acid test for esters, 70% of the original amide bonds was shown to have rearranged to ester. The reaction scheme of eq. (25) depicts the course of the transformation.

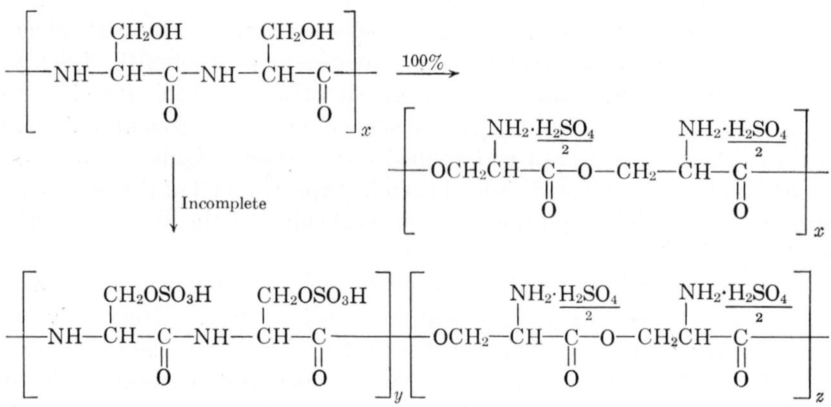

(25)

4. Selective Main Chain Cleavages

The strategy employed in the determination of the sequence of amino acids in proteins has made extensive use of enzymatic degradations and the matching of overlapping sequences of the smaller polypeptides isolated and characterized from such degradations. There remains, however, a great need for selective and quantitative chemical methods for cleavage of the main chain of proteins. Quite recently several chemical methods have been discovered which cleave peptide bonds next to the amino acids methionine, tryptophan, histidine, and tyrosine. Many of these chemical cleavages are highly specific and occur at points in the protein molecule inaccessible to enzymes. These chemical methods should prove useful in the specific cleavage of one, two, or three peptide bonds of a protein molecule–preferably adjacent to an amino acid which occurs only one to three times in the primary sequence of the protein.

Recently, Witkop (231) and Thompson (204) have reviewed the status of research on preferential and selective cleavage and modification of

TABLE VI-29
Survey of Principles and Reactions Employed in the Preferential or Selective Cleavage of Peptide Bonds

Amino acid	Functional group	Cleaving agent	Type of cleavage	Yield, %
Serine, threonine	β-Hydroxyl	Strong acids (H_2SO_4, H_2F_2, etc.)	$N \rightarrow O$ Acyl shift	60 (impractical for many proteins)
	DFP-Serine	1. DFP 2. H_2O, 100°C.	Special β-Elimination	30–80
Aspartic (asparagine)	β-Carboxyl	HOAc, pH 2–3, 115°C. or 0.03*N* HCl, 105°C.	Preferential hydrolysis	45–85 70–90
Glutamic (glutamine)	γ-Carboxyl	HCl in HOAc	Preferential (?) hydrolysis	—
Tyrosine	γ,δ-Double bond of phenol	NBS,[a] NBA[b]	Selective displacement	60–80 (models) 20–30 (proteins)
Tryptophan	γ,δ-Double bond of indole	NBS, NBA, HIO_4, etc.	Selective displacement	60–90 (models) 10–40 (proteins)
Histidine	γ,δ-Double bond of imidazole	NBS, NBA	Selective displacement	15–35
Methionine	γ-*S*-Methyl	ICH_2CONH_2, BrCN	Selective displacement	60–90 (models and proteins)
Cysteine (cystine)	β-Mercapto	1. CH_2Br in HOAc or FDNB at pH 6 2. H_2O, 100°C., 2 hr.	Selective β-elimination and pref. hydrolysis	80–90
δ-Hydroxylysine	δ-Hydroxyl	Lactonizing agents	δ-Lactone formation	Not tested
Proline	Tertiary amide	Na in NH_3	Preferential amide cleavage	So far not tested
Hydroxyproline	Tertiary amide	Na in NH_3	Preferential amide cleavage	—
	γ-Hydroxyl	Solvolytic agents	Displacement of O-Ts γ-Lactone formation	—

[a] *N*-Bromosuccinimide.
[b] *N*-Bromoacetamide.

proteins. For a more detailed account of the past, present, and projected research activity in this field, the reader is referred to these articles. Table VI-29 taken from Witkop's review summarizes the principles and reactions employed in preferential and selective cleavage of peptide bonds.

Preferential cleavage refers to competitive or hydrolytic reactions, primarily nucleophilic in character, and usually involves intramolecular (i.e., neighboring group) assistance. Examples of these have already been discussed.

Selective cleavage, on the other hand, also makes use of intramolecular assistance, but makes use of electrophilic agents or groups in contrast to the nucleophilic types in preferential cleavages. Several examples, discussed briefly later, will illustrate the principle of selective cleavage.

A number of criteria are summarized by Witkop as essential for a useful selective peptide cleavage, suitable for use on sensitive proteins (enzymes, etc.) without concomitant side effects or denaturation: (*1*) the reagent must be highly selective; (*2*) the reaction should be a fast one; (*3*) addition of the reagent to the reactive site should yield a highly unstable intermediate; (*4*) the instability of the intermediate should make for a rapid, concerted, 1,5-intramolecular displacement reaction by only one peptide group, namely the *C*-peptide group; (*5*) the resulting iminolactone should break down immediately into a *C*-terminal lactone fragment and a new *NH*$_2$-terminal; (*6*) the entire sequence of reactions must occur rapidly in aqueous buffer solutions at neutral or slightly acidic pH and at room temperature.

A few typical examples will illustrate that these criteria are met almost in full by several fairly simple reagents.

a. Tryptophan Peptides

This cleavage may be brought about by either *N*-bromosuccinimide (NBS) or bromine and is illustrated in eq. (26) with indole-3-propionyl

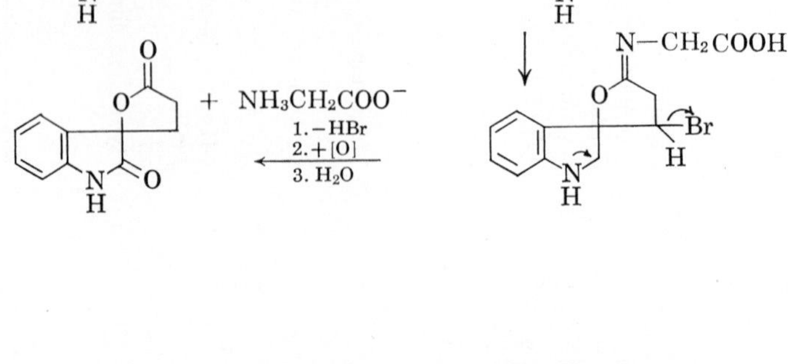

(26)

peptides. The lactonization reaction may be viewed as a concerted intramolecular displacement by the carbonyl of the peptide on the initially formed, highly labile bromonium intermediate to yield a labile iminolactone which hydrolyzes easily to the lactone and the respective amino acids. The reaction is almost instantaneous at room temperature. *N*-Bromoacetamide reacts similarly, though more slowly.

b. Tyrosine Peptides

The selective cleavage of tyrosine peptides is shown in eq. (27).

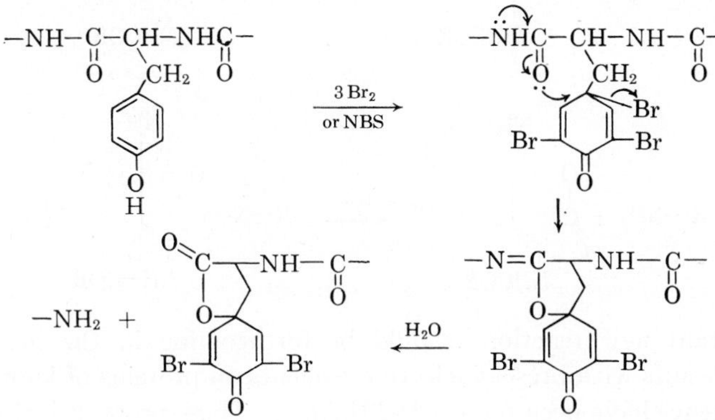

(27)

c. Methionine Peptides

The cleavage of methionine peptides is illustrated in eq. (28). In place of iodoacetamide, one may employ methyl iodide, iodoacetic acid, ethyl

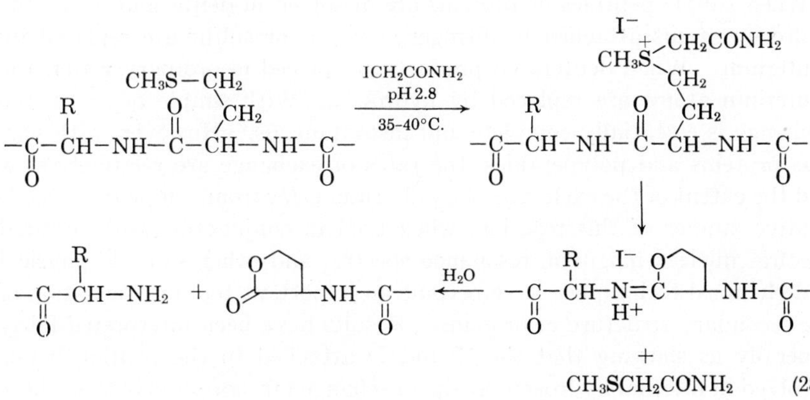

(28)

bromoacetate, diethyl bromomalonate, 2,4-dinitrofluorobenzene, or cyanogen bromide. Cyanogen bromide is a preferred reagent among these.

d. Histidine Peptides

Selective cleavage of histidine peptides illustrated in eq. (29).

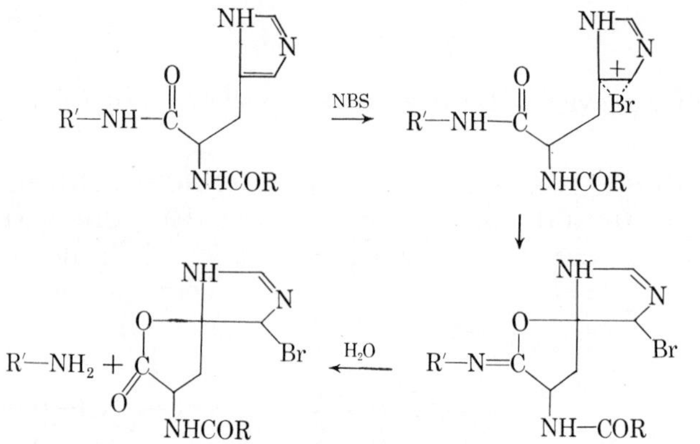

(29)

Important new reactions should be forthcoming in the near future. Specific results with present selective reagents on proteins of known amino acid sequence have been reported (204,231). These proteins include TMV protein, gramicidin A, ribonuclease, human hemoglobin A, cytochrome C, trypsin and trypsinogen, and zymogen.

5. Hydrogen–Deuterium Exchange

When simple peptides or proteins are dissolved in deuterium oxide, the hydrogen atoms attached to nitrogen, oxygen, or sulfur are replaced by deuterium. When deuterated products are placed in ordinary water, the deuterium atoms are replaced by hydrogen. With simple peptides, the exchange is essentially complete and instantaneous. However, with various proteins and polypeptides, the rates of exchange are relatively slow and the extent of the exchange at equilibrium is far from complete. Quantitative studies of this reaction, when used in conjunction with infrared spectra, nuclear magnetic resonance spectra, and other suitable physical and chemical techniques, have become an important tool in elucidation of the secondary structure ot proteins. Results have been interpreted fairly generally as showing that the H and D attached to the peptide bonds involved in internal hydrogen bonding exchange far more slowly than those fully exposed to the solvent or present in side chain groups. Other hydrogens, however, may exchange slowly when shielded by hydrophobic regions or when present in peptide bonds which have a high degree of steric hindrance. Several reviews relating to this technique have appeared (25b,27,28,232–236).

Linderstrøm-Lang (232,233) was among the first to attribute the reduced rate of hydrogen exchange to structural organization in protein molecules, particularly hydrogens of the peptide linkage. Earlier work by Blout (237) on polypeptides had, however, provided a background for this suggestion. Infrared spectra obtained by Haggis (238) support the view that the slowly exchanging hydrogen atoms are, indeed, those of the peptide bond rather than of side chain groups. Although it is generally considered that hydrogens which exchange almost instantaneously (within about 30 sec.) at near 0°C. in dilute solutions are free hydrogens and that those which exchange more slowly under these conditions are involved in hydrogen bonds, Scheraga (27) emphasizes very strongly that this interpretation is an assumption—reasonable but as yet not completely proven. Scheraga points out the possibility that shielded or inaccessible hydrogens may occur "buried" in hydrophobic regions. In addition, as discussed in an earlier section, exchange may be greatly retarded by steric hindrance about certain peptide bonds (214), although no direct experimental evidence has been obtained as yet to support this view.

Further, Wishnia and Saunders (239) have demonstrated recently by means of nuclear magnetic resonance spectra of ribonuclease and guanidinated ribonuclease in D_2O at pD between 2.8 and 4.5 that whereas ribonuclease showed slow exchange of 24 $\pm$ 5 protons the guanidinated ribonuclease contained 54 $\pm$ 7 hydrogens exchanging at a comparable rate. When both proteins were heated to 72°C. exchange of all NH protons was noted. It was suggested that the very slowly exchanging protons are attached to the guanidinium groups of both proteins. Wishnia and Saunders agree with Linderstrøm-Lang that the exchange of NH hydrogens of proteins with deuterium can yield valuable information about protein structure. However, they warn that analysis of the experimental data must be circumspect and, in particular, the interpretation that slowly exchanging hydrogens are located in the main chain linkages cannot be assumed.

Ribonuclease has been widely used as a model protein for the study of H and D exchange reactions, since its complete amino acid sequence, secondary structure, and tertiary structure have been elucidated in fair detail (25b,27,28,232–239). Typically, this protein has been shown to

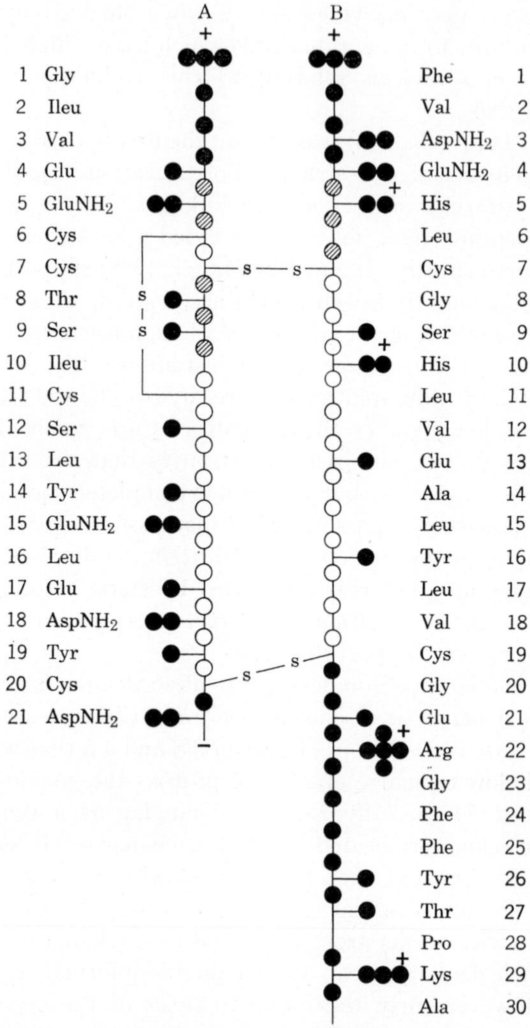

Fig. VI–1. Exchangeable hydrogen atoms in the monomer of pig insulin. Each circle corresponds to an exchangeable hydrogen atom. Number in backbone = 48; number in side chains and endgroups = 43; (●) Instantaneously exchangeable = 61; (⊘) rapidly exchangeable = 7; (O) more slowly exchangeable = 23. (Taken from ref. 27.)

possess a distribution of OH and NH protons with widely differing exchange rates, both distributions and rates having a marked dependence on pH, temperature, and other conditions. In Figure VI-1 is shown the structural information provided by exchange reactions.

Fraser and MacRae (240) have reported a quantitative study of hydrogen and deuterium exchange reactions in keratins by means of infrared spectra. About 30% of the hydrogens of peptide linkages had not reacted after 50 hr. at 30°C.; in fact, there was no evidence of further exchange between 50 and 1000 hr. Interestingly, elevation of pD or temperature caused additional exchange. Evidence is presented to support the interpretation that the unreactive peptide linkages occur in the organized regions of the keratin (i.e., the microfibrils) and that complete exchange of side chain replaceable hydrogens occurs. However, if the native conformation of the keratin is destroyed by stretching or supercontraction, complete exchange of all hydrogens is observed (240c). Neither cleavage of disulfide bonds nor treatment with CH_3COOD, which reduces appreciably the crystallinity of the protein, effects complete exchange of all hydrogens. The slowly exchanging hydrogens of the α-keratins are believed to be present in the α-helical conformations in the crystalline areas of the fiber. In contrast to α-keratin, when collagen was reacted with D_2O there was complete and rapid exchange of all hydrogens. This was in agreement with the known structure of hydrated collagen which is appreciably stabilized by side chain interactions and which contains a very low amount of intrahelical hydrogen bonds.

D. CROSSLINK REACTIONS

1. General

This discussion will be restricted to crosslinks which are covalent bonds and will not include those due to secondary forces such as hydrogen bonds, Van der Waals forces, or electrostatic forces.

The main crosslink found in native proteins is due to the —CH_2—S—S—CH_2— bridge derived from cystine. In addition, several new crosslinks have been introduced into various industrial proteins to confer new and improved properties. In principle, many of the reactions used to build new crosslinks are related to those discussed previously as side chain reactions. The main difference is found in the use of difunctional or polyfunctional rather than monofunctional reagents. When reactive groups of contiguous chains are suitably located, they react with opposite ends of the bifunctional reagent to yield synthetic crosslinks in the protein. Intramolecular crosslinking may sometimes compete with the intermolecular reaction; also, one group of a difunctional reagent may react with solvent molecules or other species in the medium and only one group with the protein. This later reaction results in the formation of a new side chain and reduces the crosslinking efficiency of the desired reaction. In special cases, end-to-end linking occurs also. These competitive side reactions will occur to varying extents.

The presence of crosslinks in proteins confers characteristic properties such as insolubility, less susceptibility to swelling in polar solvents, and relatively high wet strength. With small biologically active proteins, such as insulin and ribonuclease, the disulfide crosslinks appear essential to maintenance of biological activity, not by direct participation but through stabilization of that conformation of the protein molecule essential for the biological activity. Modification of the disulfide crosslinks of wool, and introduction of new crosslinks, often imparts interesting new properties to this protein. These new properties may include increased tensile strength, reduced felting tendency, increased stability to various degradative chemical media (such as alkalis, acids, and oxidizing or reducing agents), improved resistance to moths, greater resistance to wear, and dyeing resistance. With collagen, the tanning reaction which is essential for conversion of the raw product to commercially useful products has been shown to involve crosslinking. Since collagen does not contain cysteine or cystine, crosslinking during tanning must involve other groups—perhaps amino and hydroxyl and possibly others. The present treatment will deal primarily with crosslinking of the above mentioned classes of protein. Wool, typical of keratins, has been studied in detail and provides some excellent examples of both disulfide and synthetic crosslinks.

2. Experimental Methods

One of the main problems inherent in all studies on crosslinks in proteins is that of demonstration of their actual existence, their abundance, and distribution within the network structure. This problem also occurs in the field of macromolecular chemistry in general, in such products as vulcanized rubber, modified cellulosics, regenerated protein fibers, and various plastics. Since the interpretation of results of various crosslink reactions in proteins will be discussed in terms of methods employed to demonstrate the existence of the crosslinks, a brief discussion of several of those methods will be given first. Several of these methods have been particularly useful in studies on wool.

a. Solubility

Changes in solubility of the protein following reaction may provide indirect evidence of changes in the extent of crosslinking. With wool, four media have been widely used for this purpose: alkali, acid, peracetic acid, and urea-bisulfite. One of the most widely used is the alkali solubility, introduced by Harris and Smith (241). Wool is immersed in 0.1*N* NaOH at 65°C. for 1 hr. and the loss in weight measured. The method is quite sensitive in detecting the introduction of new alkali-stable crosslinks and for measuring damage to wool. Since one of the most pronounced effects of introduction of several types of synthetic crosslinks is improvement in alkali stability, data on alkali solubility may be rather informative. Zahn and Würz (242) introduced an acid solubility test. The wool is exposed to 4*M* hydrochloric acid for 1 hr. at 65°C. and the loss in weight measured. An oxidizing solvent was suggested by Alexander (243) and co-workers. Wool is immersed in 2% peracetic acid for 25 hr. at room temperature and subsequently treated with 0.3% aqueous ammonia. The peracetic acid oxidizes the —S—S— to —SO_3H groups; up to 90% of untreated wool is soluble in weak alkali following the treatment. The introduction of synthetic crosslinks stable to oxidation results in a significant decrease in the solubility produced by treatment with peracetic acid. Another solubility test of fairly recent vintage employs urea-bisulfite (244), a reducing agent. The sample is immersed in a solution of 3% sodium metabisulfite and 50% urea at 65°C. for 1 hr. at pH 7.0, and the loss in weight is determined.

Obviously, each of these solubility tests is somewhat arbitrary (as to temperature, time, etc.) and it is difficult to attach too quantitative an interpretation (on a molecular basis) to the changes in solubility observed. However, when used in conjunction with other methods, and when interpreted with due caution, they can provide useful information on changes in crosslinking.

b. Supercontraction

When placed in certain liquids, wool fiber decreases in length; this phenomenon is called supercontraction (245). Reagents which destroy the disulfide crosslinks in wool produce this effect. For example, the reducing agent, sodium bisulfite (246) (one of the first employed for studying supercontraction) or the oxidizing agent, peracetic acid (243), are effective in producing supercontraction. When the disulfide bonds of wool are broken, the wool becomes quite rubberlike in character, and there is a simultaneous decrease in the fiber length. The introduction of synthetic crosslinks stable to oxidizing or reducing agents prevents this supercontraction. However, certain hydrogen bond-breaking agents, such as phenol or formamide (247) which have no effect on the disulfide bonds, also produce supercontraction to varying degrees. Hence, although the method is quite sensitive, it must be interpreted with caution and used in conjunction with other tests. A typical test procedure follows (248): Single fibers are exposed to 5% $NaHSO_3$ at 97°C. for 1 hr., and length changes produced are measured.

c. Properties of Single Fibers

Speakman (249) pioneered the development of the use of single fiber properties for detecting changes in the fibers after chemical and physical treatments. When a wool fiber is stretched rapidly in water at 25°C. the stress-strain curve is reproducible for extension of 30% or less; the fiber must be removed from tension immediately, however, and permitted to relax several hours before being stressed again. From the area under the stress-strain curve up to 30% extension, the work required for stretching is determined. Following a period for relaxation, the same fibers are given a specified chemical (i.e., crosslinking reaction) or physical treatment and the work required to stretch to 30% is measured again. The per cent change in this value (based on the value for the untreated fibers) is used to assess chemical and physical alteration in the fibers. In some cases, new crosslinks have been detected by this method. The method should be used with other confirmatory tests; interpretation at a molecular level of the basis for changes in single fiber properties is somewhat dubious, at best.

d. Chemical Analysis

Chemical analysis is particularly useful for estimation of changes in amount of disulfide in protein fibers, it being fairly unambiguously established that the disulfide bond is present as a crosslink between two polypeptide chains.

e. Chemical Degradation

For the organic chemist, the most convincing proof that crosslinking has occurred in a reaction, or is present in a given macromolecule, is the isolation and unambiguous identification of the crosslinks from the hydrolyzate of a protein. Zahn (250) has outlined the requirements for success in this direction: (*a*) the crosslink and the amino acid pair from contiguous polypeptide chains must not be destroyed during complete hydrolysis of the peptide bonds of the protein; (*b*) it must be possible to detect them in the presence of the large excess of other amino acids in the hydrolyzate; and (*c*) they must be readily separated from these free amino acids.

The use of known synthetic bridged amino acid pairs is quite essential and helpful in this type of work. The various methods of chromatography (gas, paper, etc.) are also indispensable, along with the conventional techniques of organic chemistry for identification of unknowns, such as elemental analysis and determination of physical properties.

f. Swelling Behavior

The theory of swelling in network polymers has been covered by Flory (251). Suitable swelling experiments may provide information on the degree of crosslinking and the distribution of crosslinking in a network polymer.

g. Solution Properties

By means of changes in solution viscosity, sedimentation characteristics of the solute macromolecule in an ultracentrifuge, or other suitable physical methods for ascertaining the molecular weight of the protein in solution, a crosslinking reaction may be followed by quenching at various stages and determining the molecular weight of the reaction products for the respective extents of reaction.

The greater the number of these methods which yield positive indication for crosslinking and changes in extent of crosslinking in suitable chemical modifications, the better the evidence therefore. Even under the best circumstances, it is not easy to prove that a crosslink has formed or was present in a protein. Only through a combination of independent physical and chemical methods, used in conjunction with meticulous control experiments, can a fairly unambiguous answer be achieved.

3. Disulfide Crosslinks

The disulfide crosslink in proteins is derived from the constituent diamino acid, cystine:

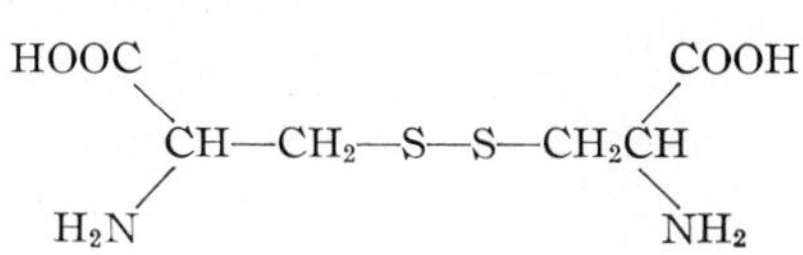

The evidence for its existence in protein is quite extensive and has been summarized in part by Alexander and Hudson (252). Briefly, it consists in: (*a*) the isolation of cystine from hydrolyzates of proteins (3), (*b*) demonstration that of the possible ways in which the cystine might be incorporated into a protein molecule (structures VI–XII), form VI is confirmed most substantially, chemically, and is most consistent with the preponderance of the data (252); (*c*) the demonstration of reactions, by the native proteins, characteristic of the —S—S— bond; and (*d*) changes in mechanical behavior of the proteins (particularly wool fibers) with changes in the cystine content, parallel to what one would predict with changes in extent of crosslinking.

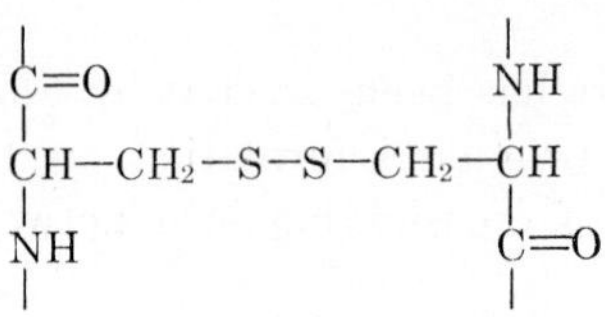
(VI)

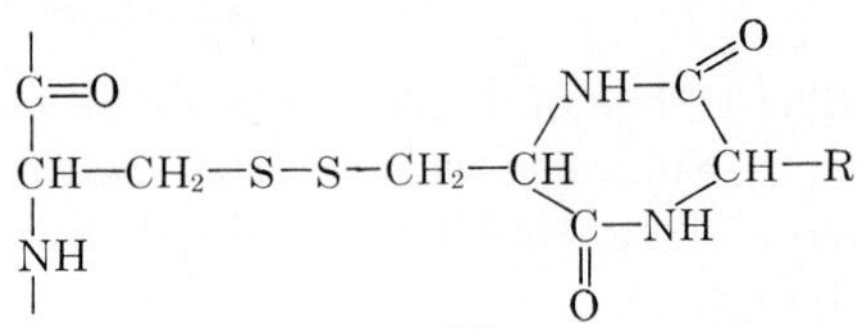
(X)

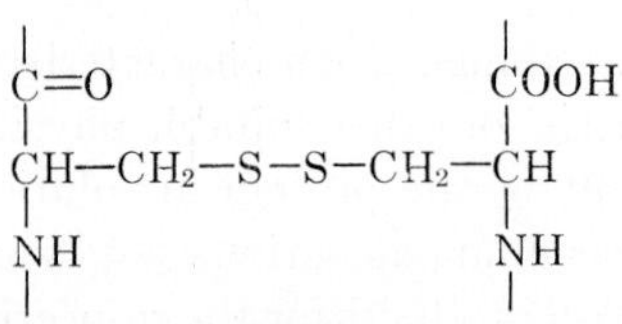
(VII)

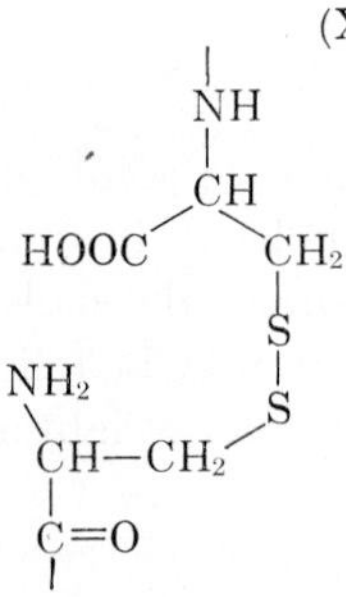
(XI)

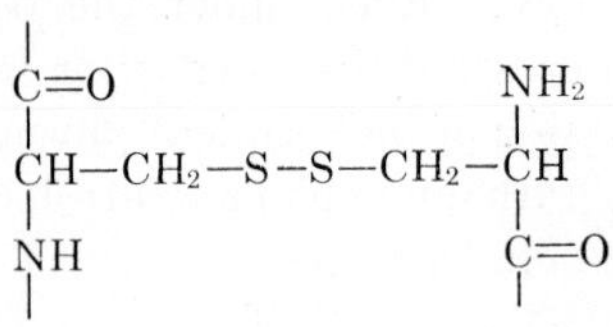
(VIII)

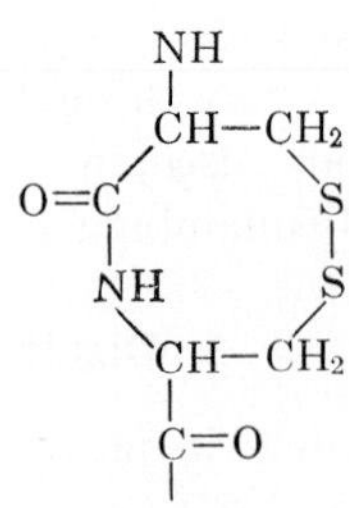
(XII)

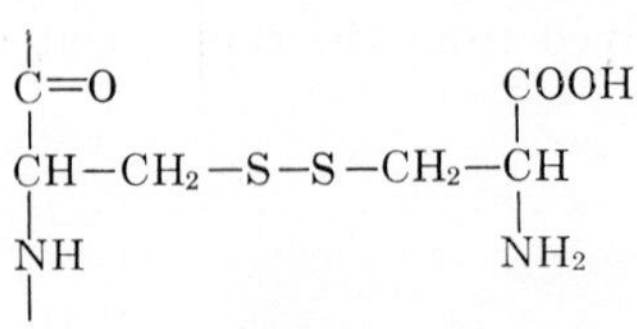
(IX)

There are several reviews of the chemistry of disulfide bonds in proteins (252,253) and organic molecules of other types (254–258). Kharasch (254,257) and Pryor (256) have been quite active in studies on mechanisms and their reviews classify many of the —S—S— reactions on a mechanistic basis. Current interest in the cleavage and formation of —S—S— bonds in natural polymers has several aspects (255); (*a*) the electronic theory and stereochemistry of the —S—S bond; (*b*) the relationship between biological activity and macromolecular conformation, and the role of —S—S— in stabilization of the active conformation; (*c*) the role of —S—S— in denaturation, coagulation, and other conformational changes in protein molecules; (*d*) the permanent setting and supercontraction of keratin fibers (hair and wool); (*e*) the role of —S—S— in studies of the primary covalent structure (amino acid sequence) of proteins.

Reactions of the —S—S— bond will be discussed in two general categories: cleavage reactions, and the formation of the —S—S— bond from —SH.

a. Cleavage Reactions

These may be classed into three general groups, mechanistically (254, 256,257): (*a*) homolytic substitutions (*SH*), (*b*) electrophilic substitution (*SE*) and (*c*) nucleophilic substitution (*SN*). Each of these substitutions may be unimolecular or bimolecular. The substitution is viewed as taking place on the sulfur atom. A schematic representation of each of these is given in eqs. (30)–(35).

Homolytic substitution

Unimolecular (SH_1);

$$\text{—S—S—} \xrightarrow[\text{light}]{\text{Heat or}} \text{—S} + \cdot\text{S—} \tag{30}$$

Bimolecular (SH_2)

$$\text{—S—S—} \xrightarrow{\text{X}\cdot} \text{—SX} + \cdot\text{S—} \tag{31}$$

Electrophilic substitution

Unimolecular (SE_1)

$$\text{—S—S—} \rightarrow \text{—}\ddot{\underset{\cdot\cdot}{\text{S}}}^{+} + :\ddot{\underset{\cdot\cdot}{\text{S}}}^{-}\text{—} \tag{32}$$

Bimolecular (SE_2)

$$\text{—S—S—} \xrightarrow{-\ddot{\underset{\cdot\cdot}{\text{X}}}} \text{—SX} + {}^{+}\ddot{\underset{\cdot\cdot}{\text{S}}}\text{—} \tag{33}$$

Nucleophilic substitution
Unimolecular (SN_1)

$$-S-S- \rightarrow -\overset{-}{\underset{..}{\ddot{S}}}: + \overset{+}{\underset{..}{\ddot{S}}}- \qquad (34)$$

Bimolecular (SN_2)

$$-S-S- \xrightarrow{-\ddot{\underset{..}{X}}:} -SX + :\overset{-}{\underset{..}{\ddot{S}}}- \qquad (35)$$

Typical reagents for these substitution reactions are summarized in Table VI-30. From this great diversity of mechanisms by which a —S—S— bond may undergo reaction, its reactivity and the great variety of reagents with which it reacts may, perhaps, be understood. No further discussion of mechanism will be made here. For further details, the references should be consulted.

TABLE VI-30
Substitution Reactions on Sulfur Atoms of Disulfide Bonds

Substitution reaction	Reagents
SH_1	Heat, light, and high energy radiation
SH_2	Alkyl˙, Aryl˙, Nascent hydrogen, RS˙, $R(S)_x$˙, etc.
SE_1	Ionizing media and/or radiant energy
SE_2	Acids, sulfonyl halides, carbonium ions, acyl carbonium ions, halogens, peracids, hydrogen peroxide, ozone, oxygen
SN_1	Ionizing media and radiant energy
SN_2	Water, hydroxide, sulfide ion, polysulfide ion, sulfites, thiosulfates, cyanides, sulfinates, amines, triphenylphosphine, $(RO)_3P$ (R = alkyl), $(RO)_2OP$, AlH_4^-, carbanions

Not all reagents of Table VI-30 have been useful for reactions of —S—S— in proteins. Many are not selective in their reaction with —S—S— but also react with other groups in the protein. Only a few of these, those which have been most widely applied in protein chemistry, will be discussed here.

(1) Oxidizing Agents

Peracids. Performic and peracetic acids are among the preferred reagents. The advantages of the peracids are their good solubility, ease of removal of excess reagent, their conversion of the —S—S to —SO_3H groups, which may facilitate electrophoretic separation of the peptides, reasonable selectivity for reaction with the disulfide bond, and irreversibility. The reaction is shown in eq. (36).

$$R{-}S{-}S{-}R' \xrightarrow[H_2O]{RCO_3H} RSO_3H + R'SO_3H \qquad (36)$$

In dilute aqueous solutions all the disulfide bonds of wool were readily accessible and were oxidized completely (63). The time of reaction required depends on the fiber diameter, concentration of the peracid, and the temperature. Typical results are given in Table VI-31. During the reaction with the peracid, none of the wool went into solution. However, on subsequent extensive hydrolysis, the wool became soluble. After

TABLE VI-31
Reaction of Wool with Aqueous Peracetic Acid at 22°C.

	Cystine reacted, %	
Time, min.	1.6% CH_3CO_3H	30% CH_3CO_3H
1	—	29.7
5	19.8	38.6
30	46.3	—
60	71.1	81.8
120	75.0	100.0
240	77.0	—
1440	92.0	—

TABLE VI-32
State of Sulfur in Wool after Reaction with 0.25*N* Peracetic Acid at 22°C.[a]

Time of reaction, min.	Total sulfur, %	Cystine sulfur, %[b]	Cysteic acid sulfur, %
0	3.5	2.66	—
5	3.60	2.10	0.5
30	3.50	1.44	1.2
60	3.46	0.66	2.0
1500	3.56	0.27	2.3

[a] Taken from ref. 259.
[b] Determined after hydrolysis in 15% HCl, 125°C., 5 hr.

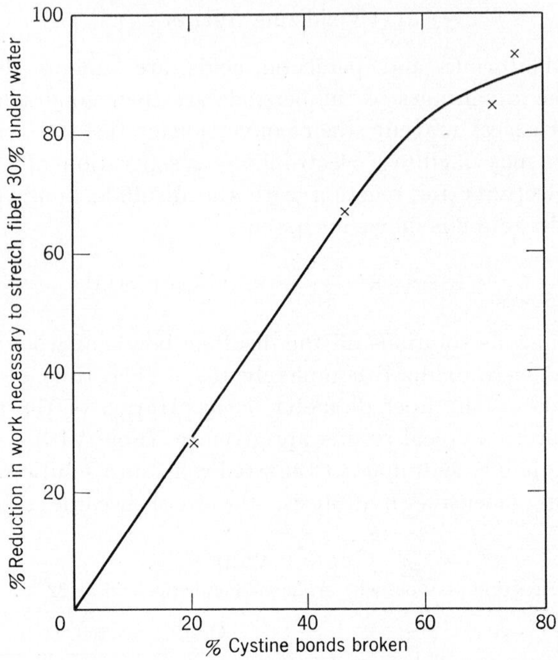

Fig. VI-2. Relationship between wet strength of wool fibers and the number of disulfide bonds. (Taken from ref. 259.)

hydrolysis, all the cystine oxidized by the peracetic acid could be determined as cysteic acid (259) and there was no loss in total sulfur during the reaction (Table VI-32).

Experiments with model peptides under similar conditions showed that there was no main chain degradation due to oxidative or hydrolytic attack on peptide bonds (260). Higher peracids also react with the disulfide bond in wool (261). When tested with performic acid, dissolved in anhydrous formic acid (262), the disulfide bond of wool was oxidized to —SO_3H. However, a large amount of the wool dissolved during the reaction, probably due to acid hydrolysis. Subsequent work has indicated, however, that performic acid is the preferred reagent for conversion of the disulfide bond to two cysteic acid (263). There was no peptide bond hydrolysis during reaction with proteins, nor any evidence of racemization. However, methionine is oxidized quantitatively to the sulfone, and tryptophan is destroyed, thus imposing some restrictions on use of the reagent in specified cases.

The deterioration of the wet strength of the wool fiber when the disulfide crosslinks are destroyed is shown in Figure VI-2. The dry strength, however, is not so dependent on disulfide crosslink content of the fibers This loss in wet strength is characteristic of the results obtained when crosslinks are destroyed by any of the chemical methods.

Hydrogen Peroxide. An extensive study of the reaction of hydrogen peroxide on wool has been reported by Smith and Harris (264), who found that all the cystine could be oxidized. The reaction yields a variety of sulfur-containing products, however, including sulfuric acid, the disulfoxide of —S—S—, and cysteic acid. The rate of reaction is dependent on the temperature, concentration of hydrogen peroxide, pH of the medium, and the presence of trace metals such as copper or nickel. With increasing extent of reaction of the disulfide bond, there was a gradual increase in alkali solubility of the modified protein. Simultaneous attack on the peptide bond occurs, as was shown by Elöd, Nowotny, and Zahn (265); both silk (which contains no disulfide, or other crosslinks) and wool were completely dissolved by 3% H_2O_2 in 3 days at 60°C. No high molecular weight peptides could be isolated from the reaction.

Halogens. The reaction of the halogens with wool has been studied extensively. A summary of the results has been reported (251). Consden, Gordon, and Martin (266) showed that cysteic acid is produced when wool disulfide bonds react with bromine and chlorine in acid solution. Reaction is not restricted to the disulfide bond, however, since it has been shown that at pH 2 chlorine reacts rapidly with most amino acids, but more slowly at pH 10 (267). The rate of reaction with the disulfide bond is fast enough however, to give a measure of selectivity. With stoichiometric proportions of chlorine or hypochlorite at any pH, cystine in certain peptides was converted quantitatively to the corresponding combined cysteic acids (260). In other cases, the reaction was not quantitative (268); with excess of reagent, quantities of chlorine were consumed far in excess of the amount required for conversion of —S—S— to —SO_3H. The reaction of bromine with disulfide bonds is similar to that with chlorine, though a bit more selective since the bromine is not as strong an oxidizing agent.

Iodine, on the other hand, does not oxidize the disulfide bond of wool. Even after prolonged exposure of wool to cold aqueous solutions of iodine in potassium iodide (269), there was no change in the cystine content. Reaction does occur at other groups in the wool (such as tyrosine, histidine, and cysteine).

(2) Reducing Agents

In general, the reducing agents are much more specific for the disulfide bond than are the oxidizing agents. Typical reagents include thioglycolic acid (or its ammonium salt), mercaptoethanol, sodium bisulfite, sodium cyanide, and sodium borohydride.

Thiols. Thioglycolic acid and mercaptoethanol are the more commonly used thiol compounds. The reaction is reversible, and therefore it is difficult to obtain complete reduction of the disulfide even with large excess of the reagents. The extent of reduction is markedly dependent on pH, and may be greatly increased in some cases by the presence of hydrogen bond-breaking agents such as urea or detergents. The effect of pH (Fig. VI-3) and of concentration of thioglycolate (Fig. VI-4) on the extent of reduction of cystine bonds in wool has been reported by Harris and co-workers (270). The reaction is faster and goes more nearly to completion with an alkaline medium and in presence of large excess of reagent. Due to the reversibility of the reaction it is seldom possible to achieve complete reduction of all disulfide bonds in one treatment. Repeated treatments are required to obtain reduction of more than 60% of the disulfide in wool; up to 90% reduction is achieved eventually. Reduction with thiols requires several hours to reach equilibrium. The

$$\text{Protein—S—S—Protein}' \xrightarrow{\text{RSH}} \text{Protein-SH} + \text{Protein}'\text{—SH} + \text{R—S—S—R} \quad (37)$$

reaction is shown in eq. (37). The thiol groups in the reduced protein are sensitive to reoxidation, either by extended exposure to air or by treat-

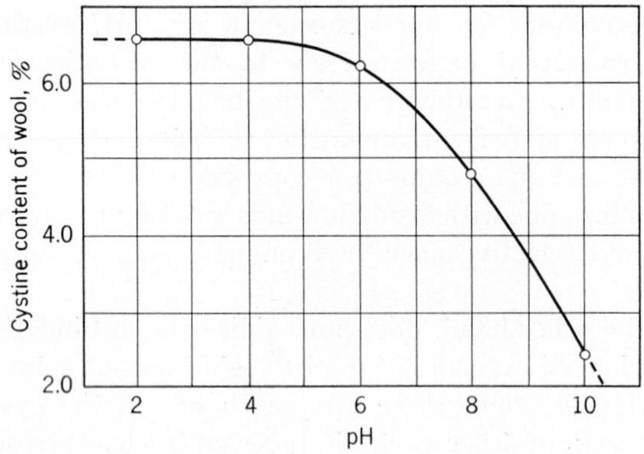

Fig. VI-3. Cystine content of wool after reduction at various pH values for 20 hr. at 35°C. with 0.2M thioglycolate solution. (Taken from ref. 270.)

ment with mild oxidizing agents. This reversible process is the basis for the permanent wave formulation used on hair and for permanent creases and flat setting in wool garments. The reversibility of the reaction has also been demonstrated by mechanical properties. The wet strength of fibers, which had been decreased to one-tenth their original value by reduction, was restored to essentially the original value by subsequent oxidation (271).

As distinguished from several other reducing agents, the thiols tend to give complete conversion to —SH groups, two —SH being obtained for each —S—S—. Many other reducing agents give only one —SH, along with one other sulfur containing group. Disulfide interchange reactions frequently occur in this reaction, which produces complications in protein structure determinations.

Bisulfite Compounds. Although the splitting of disulfide bonds by aqueous sulfite solutions is a highly selective equilibrium process, the point of equilibrium and the rate of reaction varies widely with different disulfides (272,273). The reaction yields one thiol group and one *S*-sulfocysteine group per —S—S— bond as illustrated in eq. (38). The

$$\text{Protein—S—S—Protein} \xrightleftharpoons{Na_2SO_3} \text{Protein—SH} + NaO_3\text{—S—S—Protein} \qquad (38)$$

equilibrium constants are lower for disulfides containing negatively charged groups than for positively charged or neutral molecules. Kinetic studies have shown that the rate of reaction with HSO_3^- is negligible compared with that of $SO_3^=$. At above pH 9, the reaction is a simple, reversible bimolecular nucleophilic attack by $SO_3^=$ on —S—S—. At below pH 9, the mechanism of reaction is much more complex. In the presence of Cu^{++}, complete conversion of disulfide to $—SSO_3^-$ is achieved (253,274), as shown in eqs. (39) and (40).

$$|\text{—S—S—}| + 2Cu^{++} + 2SO_3^= \rightarrow |\text{—S—}\underset{Cu^+}{\bar{SO_3}}\ \underset{Cu^+}{\bar{O_3}S}\text{—S—}| \qquad (39)$$

$$RSH + 2Cu^{++} + SO_3^= \rightarrow RSSO_3^- + 2Cu^+ + H^+ \qquad (40)$$

The decrease in strength of wool fibers after reduction by sulfite solution, pH 3.6–11, has been measured by Stoves (275). As expected, the destruction of the disulfide crosslink results in a marked reduction in fiber wet strength.

Cyanides. Cyanide ion reacts with —S—S— in the manner shown in eq. (41). Since cyanide solutions are strongly alkaline, degradative reactions complicate the utility of this reagent. Extensive cleavage of

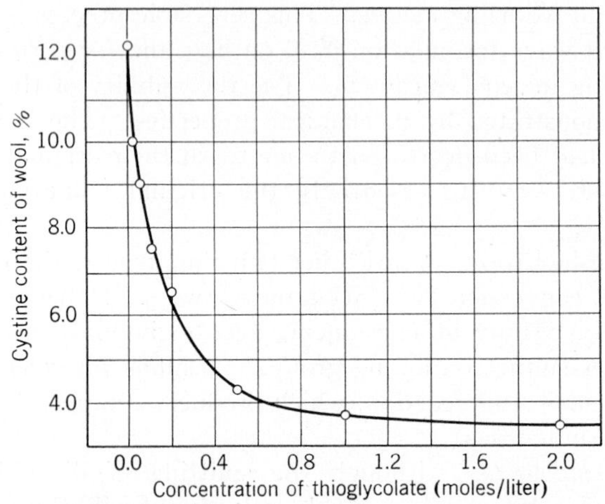

Fig. VI-4. Cystine content of wool after reduction with thioglycolate solutions of various concentrations for 20 hr. at pH 4.5 and 35°C. (Taken from ref. 270.)

peptide bonds and disulfide bonds and destruction of the thiocyanate may occur in the alkaline medium. By continually oxidizing the cysteine formed back to cystine, it is sometimes possible to convert all the sulfur of cystine to thiocyanate (276).

$$\text{R—S—S—R} \xrightarrow{\text{CN}^-} \text{RSCN} + \bar{\text{S}}\text{—R} \qquad (41)$$

Boiling of wool with dilute aqueous solutions of cyanide for 30 min. or treatment for 16 hr. at 66°C. resulted in almost quantitative conversion of the disulfide to lanthionine (277). This, however, was believed to be a consequence of subsequent reactions of the products from the primary reaction. This is a useful reaction for conversion of —S—S— to —S—, a more stable crosslink. A fairly thorough review is available (253).

Borohydrides. Quantitative reduction of the disulfide bonds of ribonuclease, trypsinogen, lysozyme, and β-lactoglobulin has been realized with sodium borohydride in 8*M* urea at 41°C. and pH near 10 (278). At pH 8.5 quantitative reduction is more difficult. Since the reduction introduces no new sulfur atoms into the protein, it has certain advantages over thiols. Also, subsequent alkylation to stabilize the —SH of the protein can be achieved without use of a large excess of alkylating agent, with which the borohydride does not react. The disulfide bonds of wool have also been completely reduced with sodium borohydride (279), and alkylated with iodoacetic acid as evidenced by cystine analysis of

5 μmole/g. wool, compared with 470 for normal wool. Peptide bond cleavage and racemization reactions may occur simultaneously, thus limiting the utility of the borohydrides in certain applications (263).

(3) Hydrolytic Cleavages

The exact mechanism of the cleavage of —S—S— by water or hydroxide ion is not known but is believed to involve the initial steps shown in eq. (42). Studies of the hydrolytic attack on disulfide bonds in proteins (252,253) have been reviewed.

$$R—S—S—R + H_2O \rightarrow R—SOH + HS—R \tag{42}$$

Zahn found that in boiling water the total sulfur content of wool decreased during a period of 8 days (280). There was no change in total nitrogen (Table VI-33) or in acid uptake, although wool substance and

TABLE VI-33
Changes in Wool Protein Produced by Boiling Water

Time of treatment, days	Wool dissolved, %	Total N in residual wool, %	Total sulfur, %	Cystine content, %	Acid uptake, meq./g.
0	0	16.5	3.65	10.6	0.92
0.5	1.0	16.4	3.44	9.4	—
1	4.0	16.0	3.33	8.6	0.89
2	7.3	16.5	3.11	7.5	0.86
4	10.7	16.5	3.07	6.9	0.87
8	37.2	16.6	2.66	4.6	0.89

total cystine decreased. These results indicate that the reaction with boiling water took place with the disulfide bond of the wool. Since the initial products of hydrolysis are unstable compounds, subsequent reaction of these with other solvent molecules, or other reactive groups in the protein molecule, complicates interpretation of the results and limits the utility of the method for cleavage of disulfide bonds. Peptide bond cleavage, racemization, and related reactions are usually competitive with the desired reaction.

One of the most interesting and more thoroughly understood of the subsequent reactions of the initially formed unstable intermediates in hydrolysis of disulfide in wool is the formation of lanthionine. The accumulated evidence for the mechanism of this transformation has been surveyed (252,253), and is believed to involve a β-elimination followed by addition of —SH to the double bond so derived, yielding a thioether crosslink in place of the original disulfide. This is not, however, a unique pathway. Other mechanisms for lanthione formation are believed to prevail in reactions of wool with cyanate ion, and in compounds in which β-elimination is precluded by the absence of hydrogen atoms on the β-carbon but in which lanthionine has been shown to be formed (252,253). The formation of lanthione crosslinks in wool confers increased stability of this protein to hydrolysis, oxidative and reductive reagents, resistance to supercontraction, etc.

b. Disulfide Bond Formation

(1) From Cysteine

The formation of disulfide bonds in proteins usually occurs by oxidation of sulfhydryl groups within the molecule. The general reaction is as shown in eq. (43). Oxidizing agents which have been most useful for

$$|\text{—SH}\quad \text{HS—}| \xrightarrow{[\text{O}]} |\text{—S—S—}| + H_2O \qquad (43)$$

this conversion with proteins include ferricyanide, porphyrindin, iodosobenzoate, iodine, and phosphotungstate, which react quantitatively under appropriate conditions. Various aspects of these reactions will be found in several reviews (54,252,253). The reactions have been useful for the quantitative determination of —SH groups. Use of these reagents for formation of disulfide crosslinks in protein requires, of course, the presence of two —SH in the fairly contiguous positions of adjacent polypeptide chains. The reactions proceed under fairly mild conditions. Some difficulty may arise in stopping the oxidation at the —S—S— stage with further reaction to sulfoxides, sulfur, and sulfuric acids taking place if conditions are favorable. Ferricyanide, for example, is specific at pH 6.8, but reacts with phenol and indole at higher pH. The reaction occurs as given in eq. (44). Iodosobenzoate is specific at pH 7 and is a satisfactory reagent for the conversion (eq. 45). Porphyrindin, though a rapidly

$$2[\text{Fe(CN)}_6]^{-3} + 2\text{RSH} \rightarrow \underset{\text{Prussian blue}}{2[\text{Fe(CN)}_6]^{-4}} + \text{RSSR} + 2\text{H}^+ \qquad (44)$$

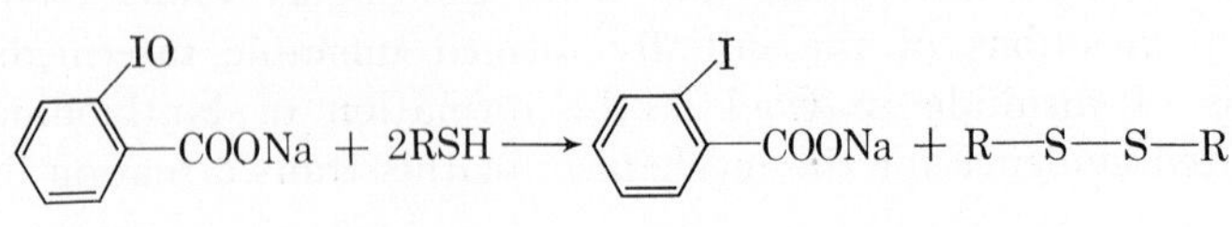

(45)

reacting and quantitative reagent, is expensive and unstable. The reactions occurring with the thiol are shown in eq. (46). Iodine reacts at

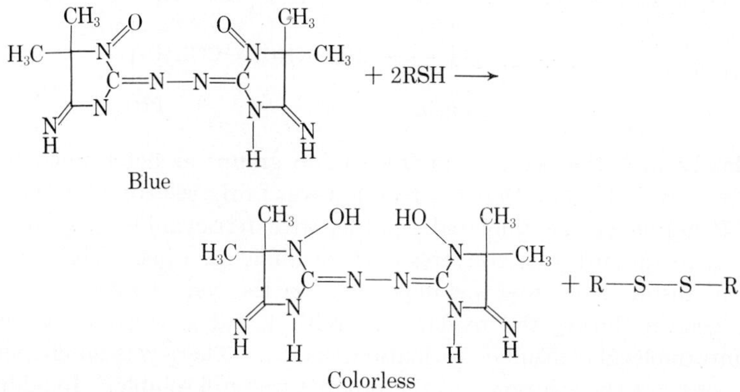

(46)

pH 7 in 5–30 min. in dilute aqueous solutions containing high concentration of iodide ions (eq. 47). Hydrogen peroxide, potassium bromate,

$$RSH + I_2 \rightarrow R{-}S{-}S{-}R + 2HI \qquad (47)$$

and related mild oxidizing agents have been used for bringing about this transformation in hair protein in commercially useful processes such as permanent waving. The hair is first treated with a suitable agent to reduce the disulfide bonds to —SH, a curl is imparted to the reduced hair, following which oxidizing agent is applied to destroy excess reagent from the first step and to reform the —S—S— bonds.

(2) From Synthetically Introduced Thiol

Disulfide bonds in proteins may also be introduced by incorporation into the protein of a thiol-containing reagent, and subsequent oxidation of the modified protein with any of the reagents discussed above. In this instance, the disulfide bond will not, of course, be present as disulfide of cystine. These reactions are valuable for introduction of —SH and —S—S— into sulfur-free proteins.

One of the better methods for introduction of —SH into proteins uses thiolactones as the thiolating agent (281). *N*-Acetylhomocysteine thiolactone, for example, in the presence of silver reacts rapidly with the amino groups of proteins at pH 7.5 and room temperature, according to the scheme shown in eq. (48). Thiolation of gelatin to varying extents gave the results shown in Table VI-34. The amount of —SH introduced

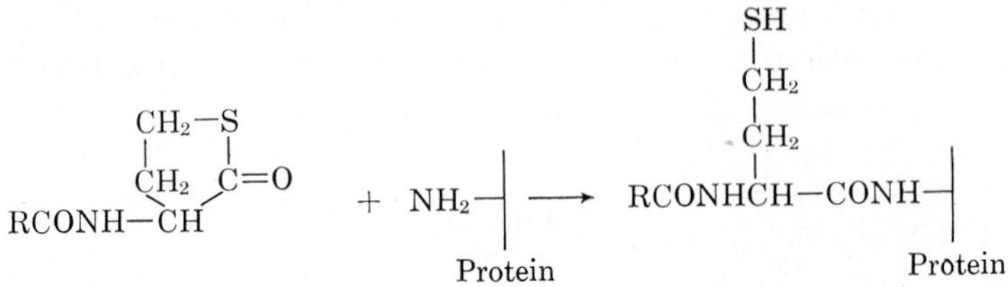

(48)

agreed closely with the decrease in free amino groups as determined by formol titration, indicating that the reaction was fairly selective for those groups. Reaction of the thiolated gelatins with ferricyanide in neutral solutions gave quantitative conversion to disulfide gelatins. The character of the disulfide gelatins was dependent on the concentration of the thiolated gelatin during the oxidation. With a 0.2% solution of the protein, intramolecular disulfide formation ensued. There was no change in the viscosity of the solution and the product was still soluble. In addition, results obtained from sedimentation with the ultracentrifuge showed no significant difference between the molecular weight of the parent gelatin, the same gelatin modified by 30 —SH groups per 10^5 g., and the disulfide gelatin obtained from this by oxidation with ferricyanide. The intramolecular disulfide gelatins show a marked reduction in tendency to form gels.

TABLE VI-34
Thiolation of Gelatin

Reagent, moles/$-NH_2$ group	NH_2 Groups/10^5 g.			$-SH$ formed, groups/10^5 g.[a]
	Initial	Final	Blocked	
1	32.5	22.3	10.2	10.7
2	36.1	19.8	16.3	16.7
3	32.5	12.3	20.2	20.3
4	36.1	11.6	24.5	22.5
10	36.1	6.4	29.7	29.5

[a] Method described in ref. 405.

In contrast, when solutions of thiolated gelatins (at concentrations of protein of 5% or more) with 17 or more —SH groups per 10^5 g. are oxidized with slightly less than a theoretical amount of ferricyanide, a clear, colorless, rigid gel forms almost instantly. These gels are insoluble in concentrated solutions of urea and guanidine chloride and do not melt even at 100°C. They are, however, "melted" by treatment with a thiol.

4. New Crosslinks in Proteins

Although the disulfide crosslink is the main naturally occurring one in proteins, its great reactivity and relative instability have prompted studies to build more stable crosslinks into proteins. Two general approaches have been used. The first consists in conversion of the disulfide bond itself into a more stable derivative in which the two sulfurs are separated by relatively inactive groups. This general scheme is shown in eq. (49).

$$\text{R—S—S—R} \rightarrow \text{RSH} + \text{HSR} \xrightarrow{\text{Y—X—Y}} \text{R—S—X—S—R} + 2\text{HY} \quad (49)$$

Preferably X will be an inert residue. This group of reactions will be referred to as disulfide expansions. The second group of reactions does not involve sulfur chemistry. In these, synthetic crosslinks devoid of sulfur are introduced by reaction of a polyfunctional reagent with the reactive groups of contiguous polypeptide chains. In special cases, the crosslink may be formed by reaction of two contiguous functional groups of the protein itself, no exterior reagent being required.

a. Disulfide Expansion

This type of reaction has been extremely popular in studies of the chemical modification of wool (252). Typically, the —S—S— of wool is reduced to —SH groups and these are then reacted with a host of difunctional organic molecules. In examples selected for inclusion herein, it will be assumed that the wool is in the reduced state when subjected to the reactions being discussed.

This method was pioneered and studied extensively by Harris and coworkers (270,282), although the general idea had been advanced earlier by Speakman (283), who had suggested the reduction of wool with thiols and rebuilding the bonds with alkyl dihalides. Results of some typical experiments by the Harris group are shown in Table VI-35.

Wool modified in this fashion is greatly improved in its resistance to degradation by alkalis, acids, and oxidizing or reducing agents. The fibers do not supercontract in bisulfite, since the expanded crosslink is not susceptible to attack by this reagent. Interestingly, the wool with stabilized crosslinks is much less susceptible to attack by moths, carpet beetles, and enzymes. By use of a reducing agent such as hydrosulfite or sulfoxylate which does not react with the alkylating compound, the wool may be reduced and alkylated in a single step (284), thereby making it a commercially feasible process.

TABLE VI-35
Disulfide Expansion Reactions of Wool Fibers[a]

Treatment (reduced wool + dihalide)	Reduction in work for 30% extension in H_2O, %	Dry breaking strength, g.	Alkali solubility, %
Untreated wool	1.0	1310	10.5
Reduced wool	35.0	1170	75.0
CH_3I	33.0	1190	33.0
C_2H_5Br	30.0	1250	18.3
$ClCH_2COOH$	33.0	1240	75.0
CH_2I_2	6.0	1380	5.2
$(CH_2)_2Br_2$	8.0	1420	6.6
$(CH_2)_3Br_2$	10.0	1460	5.3
$(CH_2)_4Br_2$	12.0	1380	7.0
H_2O_2	3.0	1310	12.5

[a] Taken from ref. 270.

Although the combined changes in chemical and physical properties of these disulfide expanded crosslinked proteins strongly suggested that new and stable crosslinks had, indeed, been built into the protein, the most convincing proof eventually came from the organic chemical approach (250). The bridged polymethylenebiscysteines, —S—$(CH_2)_n$—S—, produced by reaction of reduced wool with $Br(CH_2)_nBr$ (n = 1–6) were isolated from the hydrolyzate (6N HCl) of the modified protein. The bisthioethers so obtained were characterized by elemental analysis, melting points, and R_f values in chromatograms and comparison of these values with the known synthetic bisthioethers. Kirst (285) has also studied the alkylation of reduced wool with a large variety of dihalides.

Sulfhydryl groups add readily to active carbon-carbon double bonds. Suitable diolefinic reagents may be used in the formation of expanded disulfide crosslinks. Moore and Lundgren (162) employed dimaleimides for modification of wool. Typical results are shown in Table VI-36. The wool was reduced with mercaptoethanol, thoroughly rinsed with water and immediately transferred to a suspension of the maleimide in 0.1M sodium borate buffer (pH 8.0) containing 0.2% of wetting agent (eq. 50). The closed container was shaken at room temperature until the nitroprusside test (for —SH groups) was negative. Wool modified with the dimaleimides does not supercontract in bisulfite, has markedly reduced solubility in alkali, acid, and oxidizing media (peracetic acid–NH_3). The 30% index was increased, indicating a rebuilding of the strength loss imparted to the wool by reduction. In contrast, the mono-

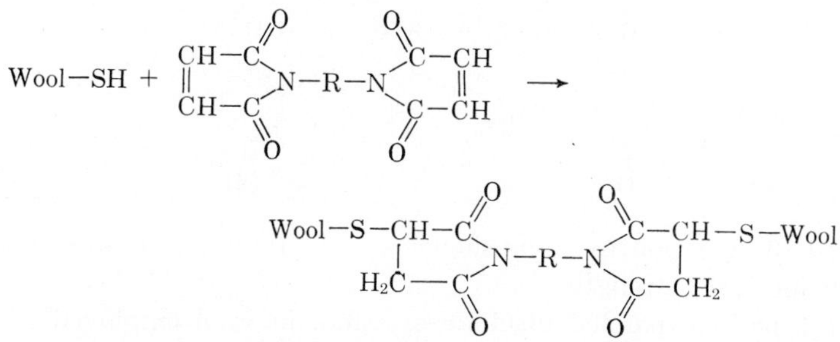

(50)

maleimide gave none of these beneficial results. Cystine analysis indicated that only a fraction of the —SH had added to the maleimides, the remaining amounts having been reoxidized by air to the disulfide. More direct evidence was obtained by identification (paper chromatography) of the expected 2-amino-2-carboxyethylmercaptosuccinic acid in the hydrolyzate of the modified wool. Unfortunately, the maleimides are not stable to hydrolysis and the mono- and dimaleimides yield the same acid. The results demonstrate, however, that the expected addition of —SH to the maleimide double bond had occurred, with no evidence of reaction with other functional groups.

TABLE VI-36
Modification of Wool with Mono- and Dimaleimides

Tests	Treatment			
	N-Phenyl-maleimide	*m*-Phenylene-dimaleimide	*o*-Phenylene-dimaleimide	Buffer alone
Uptake, %	8.4	5.5	4.3	0
30% Index[a]	0.81	0.88	0.88	0.77
Cystine content, %	5.7	6.5	7.5	11.4
Supercontraction, %	22	0.3	0.8	28
Alkali solubility, %	24.4	6.9	7.6	25.3
Acid solubility, %	12.8	6.4	7.0	13.0
Peracetic acid–NH_3 sol., %	73	44	56	89

[a] The 30% index of the reduced wool was initially 0.67 in all cases.

Moore and Ward (163) studied reaction of the maleimides with a soluble protein, bovine serum albumin, and demonstrated that reaction with the dimaleimide resulted in a gradual increase in molecular weight (determined by ultracentrifugation) of the protein.

Schöberl has used divinyl sulfone to achieve comparable results with wool (165). Benzoquinone was studied by Speakman and Peill (286),

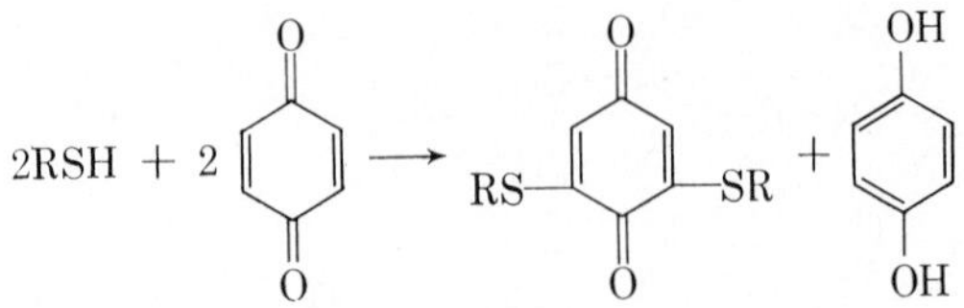 (51)

who viewed the reaction to be as shown in eq. (51). The treated fibers had greatly increased strength.

Another type of expanded disulfide crosslink in wool employed polymethylene dithiosulfates (165) $HO_3S—S—(CH_2)_n—S—SO_3H$, where n = 2,3,4). The reaction is as shown in eq. (52). Interestingly, although the

$$2\text{Wool—SH} + \text{NaO}_3\text{S—S—(CH}_2)_n\text{—S—SO}_3\text{Na} \rightarrow \text{Wool—S|S—(CH}_2)_n\text{—S|S—Wool} + 2\text{NaHSO}_3 \quad (52)$$

original disulfide bond is expanded, the product contains more disulfide bonds than the initial protein.

b. Crosslinks Containing No Sulfur

(1) Formaldehyde

The reaction of formaldehyde with proteins has been considered in some detail in a previous section and will be considered at much greater length here. The essential chemistry involved has been elucidated by Fraenkel-Conrat and coworkers as already cited. Crosslinking of two primary amino groups by formaldehyde does not occur; instead, the crosslink is formed between nitrogens of amides, guanidyl, and imidazole groups.

Fraenkel-Conrat and Mecham (155) provided some of the first solid evidence for crosslinking of proteins by formaldehyde. Intermolecular crosslinking was demonstrated by increased molecular weights of the treated proteins, as determined by osmotic pressure measurements (Table VI-37). Aqueous solutions of serum albumin were allowed to react with the formaldehyde at room temperature for 10–15 days. Similar results were obtained on reaction of formaldehyde with egg albumin. With the concentrated protein solutions, crosslinking was achieved even at low formaldehyde concentrations at both pH 3.5 and 7.5. At low protein concentrations (1%) the extent of increase in molecular weight was marginal, indicating only limited crosslinking. Perhaps in the dilute solutions (protein) intramolecular reaction predominates; at higher concentrations, intermolecular. This is however, speculative.

TABLE VI-37
Molecular Weights of Soluble Preparations of Formaldehyde-Treated Serum Albumin

Protein, % (aqueous soln.)	CH_2O concentration, %	Final pH	Final molecular weight	M.W. Final / M.W. Initial
10	4.4	3.5	330,000	8
10	5	3.5	262,000	6.5
10	1	3.5	78,000	2
10	0.4	3.8	95,000	2.3
5	10	3.5	80,000	2
1	5	3.5	61,000	1.5
1	0.5	3.5	53,000	1.3
10	5	7.5	150,000	2.5
10	1	7.5	90,000	1.5
10	0.4	7.3	200,000	3.2
5	10	7.5	162,000	2.6
1	0.5	7.5	55,000	0.9
10 (blank)	None	3.5	41,000	—
10 (blank)	None	7.5	62,000	—

(2) Other Reagents

Many polyfunctional alkylating agents have been reacted with wool, including those discussed previously for crosslinking by disulfide expansion. In these cases, the wool is not reduced prior to reaction. Some typical compounds used and properties of the treated protein are shown in Table VI-38 (243). All derivatives had reduced solubility in alkali, and a decreased tendency toward supercontraction. Esterification of the wool prior to reaction (243) did not block the subsequent crosslinking reaction; acetylated wool, on the other hand did not show the crosslinking reaction with these reagents. This indicates that the amino group is involved in the crosslinking; it does not preclude, however, some reaction with —COOH or —OH, when these groups are not blocked prior to the alkylation reaction.

Various diepoxides (other than those in Table VI-38) have also been employed (287,288) on wool. Since deaminated wool reacts equally well with the diepoxide, the carboxyl group is probably involved. The crosslinking reaction is inhibited, in fact, by inclusion of a small monocarboxylate ion in the reaction medium. Zahn employed difluorodinitrodiphenyl sulfone (XIII) with a variety of proteins,

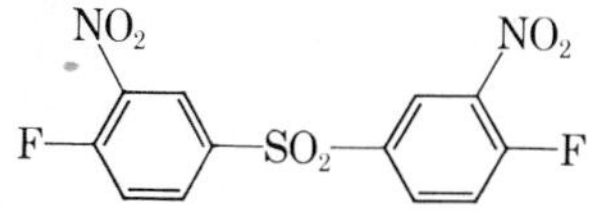

(XIII)

TABLE VI-38
Crosslinking of Wool by Alkylating Agents

Alkylating agent	Supercontraction, %: With bisulfite	Supercontraction, %: With peracetic acid	Peracetic acid–NH_3 solubility, %
None	30.0	12.5	12
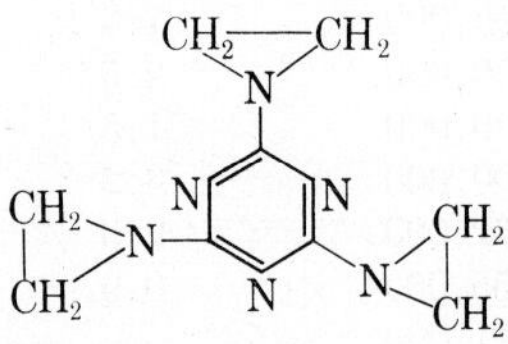	1.8	2.4	86
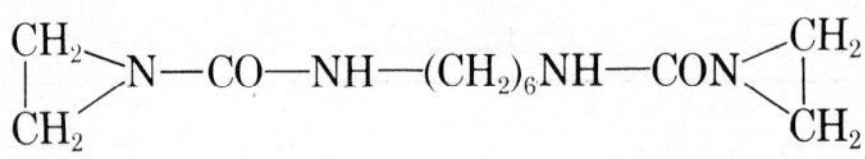	12.9	6.1	68
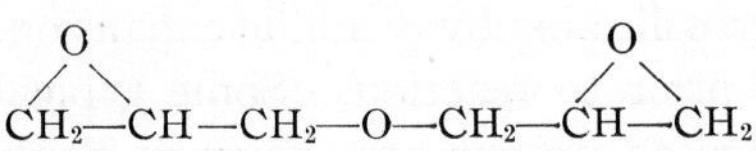	0.9	1.5	78
	3.8	2.3	75
$CH_3SO_2O(CH_2)_3OSO_2CH_3$	6.5	3.5	76
$CH_3SO_2O—CH_2—C{\equiv}C—CH_2—OSO_2CH_3$	0.0	1.4	74
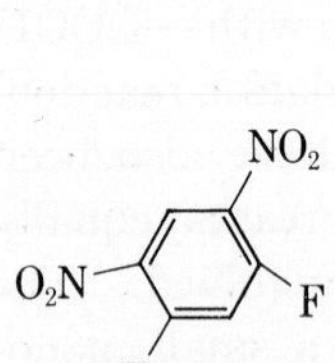	5.6	9.0	80
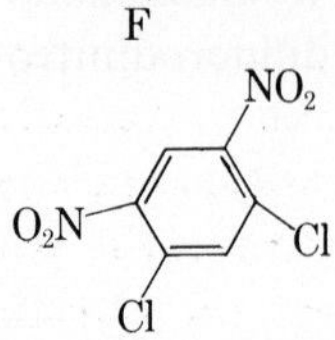	12.8	11.3	73

including wool, silk fibroin, and collagen (289,250). This reagent is particularly useful for isolation, characterization, and identification of the bridged amino acid pairs of the crosslinks.

Bifunctional diazo compounds and chloromethyl ethers (285), ninhydrin (290), and hexamethylene diazide (250) have been used to crosslink fibrous proteins.

Zahn (250) has reviewed the strategy and type of results to be derived from the classical organic chemical approach for studying of crosslinking in proteins. The actual isolation, characterization, and identification of the bridged amino acid pairs constituting the crosslink, and the further confirmation of structure by synthesis and comparison of the known compound with the degradatively derived crosslink, constitutes one of the most reliable methods for identification of the existence of the crosslink and of its actual molecular structure. Zahn demonstrates in some detail the types of results achievable by examples from crosslinked wool, silk, and collagen.

E. GRAFT POLYMERS OF PROTEINS

1. Reactions Involving Sulfur

The role of sulfur compounds in modifying, initiating, or promoting polymerization has been recognized for many years. It is, therefore, natural that efforts would be made to see whether the sulfur in proteins would behave in a similar manner in initiating or modifying polymerization. Graft polymerization to wool protein, through reactions involving sulfur, has been extensively studied. In the presence of a ferrous–peroxide redox system or persulfates, the polymerization is initiated on the wool molecule, presumably as a result of the formation of RS· radicals derived from initiation attack at the disulfide bond (291–294).

In 1949 Lipson reported graft polymerization in wool through —SH formed by reduction of cystine in the protein (295). Three 2–5 g. samples of purified all-wool flannel were treated respectively as follows: (*a*) one sample was immersed in 30 ml. of a 10% aqueous solution of thiolacetic acid for 3 hr. at 30°C.; (*b*) another sample was immersed in 50 ml. of 2% aqueous solution of sodium bisulfite and boiled for 8 min.; (*c*) the third sample was boiled for 8 min. in 50 ml. of 2% sodium hydrosulfite ($Na_2S_2O_4$). Following this reducing treatment, each wool sample was washed and then immersed for 16 hr. at 22°C. in 50 ml. of 4% solution of methacrylic acid. The samples were then washed, conditioned, and weighed; the reported weight increases were, respectively, (*a*) 14.5%; (*b*) 10.7%; (*c*) 3.1%.

Untreated wool showed little or no weight increase, and Lipson concluded that the treated wool provided its own polymerization catalyst in the form of reduced cystine.

The probable role of cysteine in the polymerization occurring in the presence of sulfur-containing proteins was illustrated further in the research of Lipson and Hope (292), who showed that methacrylic acid polymerizes in the presence of cysteine and ammonium persulfate. Thus, it is not surprising that wool which contains cystine, with its easily reduced —S—S—, can take part in suitable redox systems for initiating polymerization. In 1949, Lipson and Speakman (288) reported the polymerization of methacrylic acid in wool which previously had been impregnated with a dilute solution of ferrous ammonium sulfate and dried. Polymerization was reported to proceed best at low pH, in the absence of oxygen and in the presence of a trace of hydrogen peroxide.

Lipson's ferrous ion redox system has been used for the grafting of quite a few different polymers onto wool, among them being methacrylic acid (288), vinylidene chloride (288), methacrylamide (296), methyl (288,297), ethyl (297), and butyl (297) methacrylates, methyl and ethyl acrylates (297), and acrylonitrile (298).

Recent work by Schöberl and Wagner (299) elaborated the mechanism and further pointed to the role of the —SH in the reaction. Wool was reduced with thioglycolate and subsequently treated with alkyl halides. Acrylonitrile or methacrylic acid were added to the reduced wool, and polymerization was initiated with ferrous sulfate and/or peroxide, according to the method of Lipson and Speakman (291) or with potassium persulfate. It was found that alkylation of the —SH in reduced proteins prevents grafting, as was to be expected. However, in the presence of reduced (but not alkylated) wool, containing a protein —SH, polymerization proceeded at a much faster rate than in the presence of unmodified wool.

Proof of the reaction with protein-sulfur was found in the isolation of *S*-(β-carboxy)propylcysteine after treatment of reduced wool with methacrylic acid. However, an additional very interesting observation was reported by Schöberl and Wagner (299), who found that reduced wool, where practically all the S—S bridges were reduced to —SH, merely added a molecule of monomer onto the —SH group but did not show evidence of graft polymerization at this site. They concluded, therefore, that the bulk of the polymer formed in this instance was not grafted.

The use of persulfate in initiating graft polymerization in proteins was illustrated by Madaras and Speakman (296) who found that when wool is treated with persulfate and methacrylic acid at 25°C. for 1 hr., large amounts of polymer are formed, the weight increase in the wool being as high as 49%. For example, 1.5 g. of wool was treated with 50 ml. of 0.2*N* sulfuric acid, 2.5 ml. of methacrylic acid, and 0.027 g. of potassium persulfate for 1 hr. at 25°C. The wool was put into a flask immersed in a thermostat and connected to a vacuum line and supply of oxygen-free nitrogen. Distilled water was added and the pressure was reduced to 12 mm. of mercury for 10 min. Then, nitrogen was allowed to stream through the flask while the methacrylic acid and the persulfate were added. After 1 hr. at 25°C., the wool weight increase was 49.4%.

With persulfate as initiator, acrylonitrile can be polymerized in wool fibers in a short time (293). In 4 hr., the weight increase of the wool indicated the presence of 27% polymer when the reaction was carried out in the presence of air, and 39% when the reaction was carried out under nitrogen. Persulfates, however, alter the mechanicochemical properties of the wool to a much greater extent than does the H_2O_2–ferrous ion initiator system, which has little or no effect on these properties. A subsequent publication from Speakman's laboratory (300) discussed the mechanism of the polymerization which occurs within wool fibers impregnated with persulfate. The hypothesis that polymerization was initiated within the protein by free radicals formed by the action of persulfate on cystine (eqs. 53–56) was seriously questioned, and strong evidence was given sup-

$$R—S—S—R \rightarrow 2\ R—S\cdot \tag{53}$$

$$R—S\cdot + S_2O_8^{=} \rightarrow R—S—O—SO_3^- + \cdot SO_4^- \tag{54}$$

$$R—S—O—SO_3^- \rightarrow R—S\cdot + \cdot SO_4^- \tag{55}$$

$$\cdot SO_4^- + H_2O \rightarrow HSO_4^- + \cdot OH \tag{56}$$

porting the hypothesis that the polymerization was initiated by a different mechanism. It was Wolfram and Speakman's conclusion that the persulfate ion concentration inside the fibers greatly exceeded that in the surrounding solution, and thus free radicals were formed preferentially inside the fibers, $S_2O_8^{=} \rightarrow 2SO_4^-\cdot$ leading to preferential internal deposition of polymer. The same authors showed that acrylonitrile polymerized readily within regenerated protein fiber (Fibrolane) impregnated with persulfate but not in wool in which basic groups have been blocked nor in wool which has been oxidized by peracetic acid.

Persulfate-catalyzed polymerization has been used to modify casein with various vinyl compounds, including methacrylates, styrene, butadiene, and acrylonitrile, but whether a graft polymer was obtained is not clear (301). When a 15% solution of casein was reacted for 5 hr. at 80°C. with methyl methacrylate and sodium persulfate the product was a viscous solution.

Many other redox systems have been employed in making polymers in or on proteins One example is a novel application of hydrazine and hydrogen peroxide for polymerization of *N,N'*-methylenebisacrylamide on wool, described by Pardo and Lundgren (302). Wool was impregnated with a 0.5% solution of hydrazine sulfate and 0.05% wetting agent. The wool was next immersed in 0.3–5% solution of *N,N'*-methylenebisacrylamide containing 0.05% hydrogen peroxide and 0.05% wetting agent. After about 1 hr. at 60°C., the weight increase of the wool was 5–20%.

Another interesting example of the use of the sulfur in proteins to bring about grafting was given by Pierce (303), who found that sulfur-vulcanizable unsaturated polymers can be grafted onto wool so that they are not extractable in 16 hr. in boiling solvent. It was postulated that cystine was cleaved to give R—S· sites to which it was possible to attach natural rubber and various butadiene polymers. The cystine splitting was brought about by chemical treatment or by exposure to sunlight or ultraviolet light.

2. Reactions Involving Amino, Hydroxyl, or Carboxyl Groups

As polymers with built-in sites for grafting, proteins are unexcelled by most man-made polymers. In addition to the RSH and RS· sites derivable from cystine and cysteine, proteins are endowed with amine, hydroxyl, and carboxyl groups which can serve as sites for grafting.

Several examples will illustrate the reactivity of amine groups in polymer-forming reactions. The polymerization of dihydroxyacrolein, HOCH=C(OH)—CHO (reductone), (304–306) at 50°C. in the presence of keratin was considered by Speakman and co-workers to produce a graft polymer through the protein amine groups. Evidence that the polymer is grafted is that the polymer formed on the keratin resists extraction by 0.1*N* hydrochloric acid. It is assumed that the polymer reacts with amine groups in the keratin, since von Euler, Glaser, and Hasselquist (307) showed that reductone reacts with *p*-nitroaniline to give NO_2—C_6H_4—NH—CH=C(OH)—CHO. Stronger evidence of the grafting onto the protein amine groups is the fact that reductone has no effect upon deaminated keratins.

Grafting of a variety of polymers to the amine group of proteins through a novel polycondensation reaction has been reported (308,309). In an adaptation of interfacial polymerization, involving diamines and diacid chlorides, the polyamides formed are chemically anchored to the amine groups in protein substrates. When wool was treated with an aqueous solution of hexamethylenediamine and then a water-immiscible solution of sebacoyl chloride, the linear polyamide formed was found to be anchored to the wool fiber, presumably through reaction of the protein amine groups with acid chloride at one end of the polymer chain. As evidence of grafting under the above conditions, the polyamides thus formed are not extractable with the usual solvents for nylon, while, on the other hand, preformed polymers, deposited on the wool fibers from solution, were found to be easily extractable, as was to be expected. Blocking of the amine groups of the wool by acetylation prevents the polymers from grafting at these sites, and the polyamides formed in the presence of acetylated wool are readily extractable with solvents.

The grafting of polymers onto wool through the application of interfacial polymerization has been extended to include polyureas, polyurethanes, polyesters, polycarbonates, and various copolymers. For example, when diamines and bischloroformates are consecutively applied, polyurethanes are formed; when diamines and diisocyanates are used, polyureas are formed.

The reaction of β-propiolactone with proteins was first reported by Jones and Lundgren (310) who described the reaction with wool. They expected that the lactone would react with serine, lysine, histidine, and glutamic acid residues, and that once initiated, polymerization would continue, with the formation of grafted polymers. When wool was treated with a 3% solution of propiolactone in dry carbon tetrachloride for 5 hr. at 65°C. with a lactone to wool ratio (by weight) of 3, the weight increase of the wool was 185%. Even greater uptakes were reached in other experiments. The modified wool was found to be softer and whiter than untreated wool and to have somewhat greater luster. It was found that partial methylation or acetylation did not prevent the uptake of propiolactone in wool. It was concluded, therefore, that the amino and carboxyl groups are not necessary anchoring sites for modification with propiolactone. However, starting with unmodified protein, treatment with propiolactone does appear, on the basis of amino acid assay, to involve extensive reaction with histidine, methionine, cystine and lysine, and somewhat less with glutamic acid, serine, and threonine.

In subsequent research, Rose and Lundgren (311) found that traces of water either in the solvent, carbon tetrachloride, or in the wool, greatly accelerated the polymerization of the propiolactone. The maximum rate of uptake of propiolactone by wool in a mixture of water with amyl, oleyl, or dodecyl alcohol was 30% greater than the maximum with water and carbon tetrachloride. The influence of water and the lower alcohols, methyl or ethyl, in promoting the interaction of propiolactone within the fiber appears to be the result of swelling the fiber to permit penetration by propiolactone. In the presence of water, the higher alcohols, amyl and dodecyl, can penetrate to cause further swelling and increase the rate of modification within the fiber. Since it would be expected that the water in the solvent would initiate polymerization of propiolactone, it is interesting that no polymerization was observed in these solvents in the absence of the wool. Similar observations on the necessity of having traces of water present to increase the rate of reaction of wool with propiolactone were reported by Fearnly and Speakman (312).

The reaction of proteins with epoxides has been discussed in earlier sections, with special reference to the work of Fraenkel-Conrat. In the formation of protein graft polymers, the application of polyether epoxides is illustrated in the patent of Schroeder (313). In an example, wool was treated with an epoxide prepared from glycerol and epichlorohydrin and having a molecular weight of 324 and epoxy equivalent of 2.13. An amine curing agent, diethylenetriamine, was found to be effective, while an acid-type catalyst, zinc fluoborate, was much less effective, as judged by the shrink resistance of the treated fabrics. The actual mechanism of the polymerization reaction in or on the wool is not elucidated in the patent, though in view of Fraenkel-Conrat's work it would be expected that at least some of the polymer should be grafted to the protein through epoxide-amine reactions. The use of polymeric polyamide curing agents in the treatment of wool with epoxides is described in the patent of Pardo and O'Connell (314), and the treatment of wool with a variety of epoxy resins and curing agents has been the subject of numerous other patents (315,316).

A novel application of the reaction of polyepoxides with collagen is the treatment of leather with poly(glycidyl ethers) (321). Ordinary vegetable tanned leather has a characteristic shrink temperature of about 80°C. and if heated above this point undergoes an irreversible shrinkage, hardening, and embrittling. In contrast, when the leather is reacted with poly(glycidyl ethers) of the general formula XIV and then heated above the

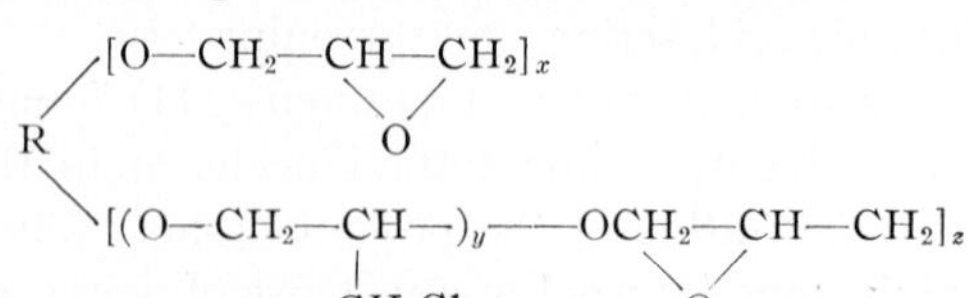

(XIV)

normal shrink temperature, the shrinkage is reversible. The reaction is carried out at room temperature in alkaline solutions, between pH 8 and 12.

The polymerization of *N*-carboxyamino acid anhydrides in the presence of proteins and poly(amino acids) leads to the formation of interesting graft polymers. Despite the fact that most of the work on the modification of proteins with *N*-carboxyamino acid anhydrides, has given evidence of direct bonding of the polypeptide to the treated protein, considerable controversy has existed concerning the nature of this type of reaction with wool. The reaction of wool with anhydrocarboxyglycine was first investigated by Baldwin, Barr, and Speakman (322,323), who were interested in the shrinkproofing effect. Speakman and co-workers suggested that the film of polyglycine which was formed was anchored to the wool fibers by reaction of the polymer with wool's basic side chains derived from arginine and lysine. They found, however, that successful shrinkproofing treatments were impossible in aqueous solution because water initiates the polymerization of the anhydrocarboxyglycine; satisfactory results were obtained from ethyl acetate solution. In an attempt to find a more stable monomer, Alexander, Bailey, and Carter (324) tested a series of *N*-carboxyamino acid anhydrides of the general formula XV, where R_1

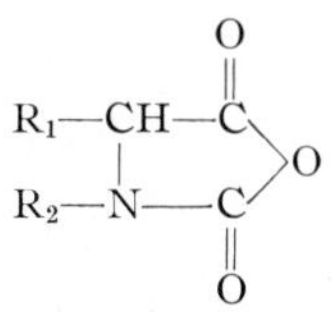

(XV)

and R_2 were hydrogen, alkyl, or phenyl groups. Examples include the *N*-carboxyanhydrides of glycine, DL-alanine, DL-α-aminovaleric acid, α-aminocapric acid, α-aminolauric, α-aminostearic, sarcosine, and phenylglycine. In addition, sulfur analogues were prepared, since the corresponding thiazolidines would be expected to be more stable than the carboxyanhydrides. This assumption was based on the fact that oxazoles are susceptible to acid hydrolysis while thiazoles have exceptional stability. Furthermore, the greater stability of isothiocyanates as compared with isocyanates is reflected in the slow rate of reaction of the former with alcohols or water. For these reasons, Alexander et al. prepared 3,4-dihydrodithiazole-5-one (XVI) and 2-thio-5-oxazolidone (XVII). These sulfur compounds, however, had little effect on wool when applied under conditions found suitable for shrinkproofing wool with anhydrocarboxy-

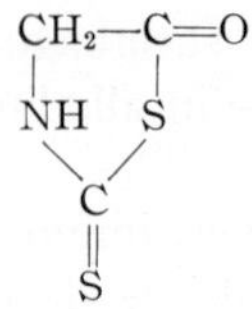

(XVI)

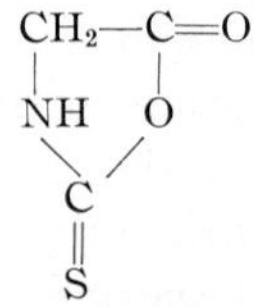

(XVII)

glycine. They came to the conclusion that the hypothesis of chemical anchoring of the polyglycine to the wool was untenable and believed that the water present simply initiated the polymerization of anhydrocarboxyglycine to polyglycine which would not be covalently attached to the wool.

The reaction of wool with anhydrocarboxyglycine was studied further by Bradbury and Shaw (325), who had found also that the polymerization of the sulfur analog of *N*-carboxyaminoglycine, thiazolid 2:5-dione (XVIII)

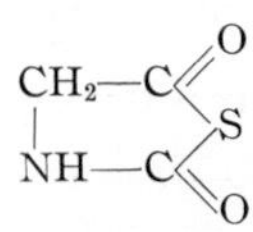

(XVIII)

was initiated by water (326). Their research showed that no shrinkproofing of wool with anhydrocarboxyglycine can occur in the absence of water, in agreement with the earlier work cited (322,323). They showed further that the rate of shrinkproofing is not altered by pretreatment of the fabric with buffers in the range of pH 6–9, while it had been found earlier that the ε-amino group of lysine in the positively charged form which exists at pH 6 does not initiate polymerization (326). The uncharged form which does initiate polymerization in soluble proteins in aqueous solution (327,328) exists in equilibrium with the charged form at pH 9, according to Bradbury et al., who concluded that the polymerization of anhydrocarboxyglycine is indeed initiated by the water present and that the polyglycine is bound to the wool by intermolecular hydrogen bonds, although it is recognized that initiation by ε-amino groups of lysine occurs in aqueous solutions at pH 7–9, even at 2°C., with soluble proteins (327,

328). Undoubtedly, further work will shed more light on the mechanism of the interesting reactions of wool with *N*-carboxyamino acid anhydrides.

Although the reaction of *N*-carboxyanhydrides with wool has been the subject of considerable interest and controversy, there has been even more extensive study of this reaction with other proteins and with model compounds including many synthetic polypeptides of high molecular weight (329–331). Multichain poly(amino acids) were obtained from *N*-carboxyaminoacid anhydrides by polymerization initiated by poly(amino acids) such as polylysine or polyornithine (332). Polymerizations were carried out in a 1:1 mixture of dioxane and dilute phosphate buffer of pH 7. In one example, polylysine of an average DP of 36 was used as the initiator for the polymerization of *N*-carboxy-DL-alanine anhydride. The average number of alanine residues per side chain was 25, and thus, with a few assumptions, it was calculated that the average molecular weight of the derived multi-poly-DL-alanyl-poly-L-lysine was about 68,500.

The use of proteins, instead of poly(amino acids), as multifunctional initiators for the polymerization of *N*-carboxyamino acid anhydrides was first described by Becker and Stahmann (333) and has been the subject of a great many papers (327,328,333–336). (References included here are only representative, not an exhaustive survey of the literature.) The polymerization proceeds under mild conditions. Becker and Stahmann (333) indicated that the initiation of the polymerization of *N*-carboxyamino acid anhydrides by proteins results in grafting of the polyamino acids to the proteins. Crystalline bovine plasma albumin and crystalline chymotrypsin were treated with *N*-carboxyglycine anhydride in phosphate-buffered solution at pH 7.3–7.4. Analysis of the modified protein showed an increase of 171 moles of glycine per mole of albumin and 65 moles of glycine per mole of chymotrypsin. The yields were quantitative, based on protein. Both proteins thus modified remained completely soluble with no evidence of denaturation. The chymotrypsin retained enzymatic activity, and the polyglycyl albumin was precipitated by antiserum prepared against normal plasma albumin. It was indicated that the glycine was attached as peptides containing an average of seven amino acid residues.

A study of albumins which had been modified by attachment of polypeptides of glycine, leucine, phenylalanine, glutamic acid, or lysine was reported by Van Kley (328), who obtained up to 24 new polypeptide chains per mole of protein. These polypeptide grafts contained from 3 to 30 amino acid residues per chain. Polytyrosyltrypsin and polytyrosylchymotrypsin (339) have been synthesized and shown to retain proteolytic activity despite the grafting of the polytyrosyl chains. Polypeptidyl gelatins to which were grafted amino acid residues unlike the parent protein were shown to have antigenicity (340–342).

In the study of the reaction of *N*-carboxyaminoacid anhydrides on proteins, C^{14}-labeled compounds have been employed by several workers. Fraenkel-Conrat (343) reacted C^{14} *N*-carboxyleucine anhydride in dioxane with a phosphate-buffered solution of proteins. In tests with tobacco mosaic virus, insulin, lysozyme, egg albumin, bovine serum albumin, ovomucoid, and conalbumin it was noted that (*a*) the reaction is almost complete after 1 min. at pH 7 at 0°C.; (*b*) with all proteins containing identifiable chain-end amino groups, these become partly substituted by leucine, and in some cases the original groups are no longer detectable in the derivative; and (*c*) the ε-amino groups of lysine are only partially blocked in all proteins studied. Extensively reacted insulin maintained most of its activity, whereas lysozyme was progressively inactivated.

The preparation of C^{14} polypeptidyl proteins was also described by Konigsberg and Becker in 1959 (327). Albumins, chymotrypsin, and lysozyme, among other proteins, were modified by reaction either with *N*-carboxyglycine-1-C^{14} anhydride or *N*-carboxy-L-phenylalanine-1-C^{14} anhydride. The effect of pH on the number of sites acylated and the average length of the added peptides indicated an increase in both factors with increasing pH between 6.3 and 9. Quantitative determinations of endgroups indicated that the reaction favors acylation of the reactive amino groups, as might be expected.

Polyvalyl protein grafts have been described by Stracher and Becker (344). From carbobenzyloxy-DL-valine the *N*-carboxy anhydride was formed and the latter was used to treat chymotrypsin, lysozyme and insulin. The number of valine residues and the number of protein sites acylated were determined by the FDNB method. The polyvalyl chymotrypsin retained about 60% of the esterolytic activity of the parent enzyme. In studies of the structure of the modified proteins, lysine residues were found to have polyvalyl chains attached to the epsilon amino group. Since the only *N*-terminal group found in hydrolyzates of DNP-poly-DL-valyl-lysozyme was DNP-valine, the ω-amino groups of the *N*-terminal lysine must have been acylated in the modification. The isolation of several other polypeptidyl-ε-lysine peptides from modified proteins has also been described (345).

The formation of graft polymers involving proteins can be brought about not only by polymerization in the presence of the protein, with concomitant grafting, but also through the grafting of preformed polymers onto proteins. One example is the reaction of polyalkylimines with proteins, as illustrated in the work of Pardo and Moore (346). Wool was immersed in a 5% aqueous solution of polyethyleneimine of molecular weight about 20,000–30,000 at pH 11.3, and the impregnated wool was baked at 120°C. for 60 min. The uptake of imine was 4.25%. This would appear to be grafting of an unconventional type. The grafting polyimine probably reacts at more than a single site on the backbone polymer, the protein. Information of the structure of this graft is not available.

Yet another method of anchoring, possibly grafting, of certain copolymers onto protein fibers was suggested in a British patent (347) on the stabilization of proteinaceous textile materials, including not only silk, wool, and mohair, but also fibers from casein, soy-protein, or collagen. When the protein is impregnated with, for example, a copolymer of butyl acrylate and vinylpyridine (90:10) and then heated above 100°C., "a chemical reaction is believed to take place between the proteinaceous textile and the copolymer." It is said that the copolymer appears to be anchored to the textile and not merely deposited as a dry coating on the fibers. In an example, a dispersion of a copolymer was prepared by emulsifying 90 parts by weight of *n*-butyl acrylate with 10 parts of 4-vinylpyridine in 300 parts of water, plus some nonionic emulsifier. To this emulsion was added 0.3% (by weight of monomers) of ammonium persulfate, 1% triethanolamine, and 0.6% sodium hydrosulfite. Polymerization took place in 17 min., at 20–46°C. The resin dispersion thus formed was diluted to 13.5% solids and applied to a fabric. Drying at 10 min. at 240°F. was followed by curing for 10 min. at 300°F. to "anchor" the copolymer onto the fibers.

If one thinks of proteins as polymers, as indeed they are, it is then apparent that another type of graft polymer would be protein-to-protein grafts. This type of problem has attracted much attention in biological research. Several reactions have been worked out for establishing a link between similar or dissimilar protein molecules.

The crosslinking of proteins such as bovine plasma albumin and wool keratin (163) was mentioned in an earlier section in connection with the reactions of sulfhydryl groups with bismaleimides. The use of carbodiimides to crosslink gelatin was also discussed earlier (348). Crosslinking of two proteins, albumin and keratin, was studied extensively by Alexander, Fox, Stacey, and Smith (243), who presented data on 21 crosslinking agents which were shown to react through the amine groups of the proteins. The soluble protein, albumin, was treated in aqueous solution and crosslinking was measured directly by determining the changes in molecular weight by light scattering. On the other hand, in wool, which is naturally crosslinked by disulfide bonds, the formation of additional crosslinks could be determined after the original disulfide bonds were broken.

The reaction of formaldehyde with proteins (150,318,319) normally involves formation of crosslinks between molecules to give an increase in molecular weight and finally an insoluble product. The most probable reaction is the crosslinking through primary amino groups. The removal of amino groups through reaction with nitrous acid or blocking by acetylation gives products which are not crosslinked by formaldehyde, according to Davis and Tabor (320). They postulate that the crosslinking of two gelatin molecules involves (*a*) formation of methylol compounds which then react to form a crosslink (eq. 57) and (*b*) formation of a dimethylol amino

$$2\ \text{Gel—NH—CH}_2\text{OH} \rightarrow \text{crosslinked product} \qquad (57)$$

compound which then reacts with a gelatin molecule to produce a crosslink (eq. 58). The methylene bridges (—CH_2—) usually proposed for

$$\text{Gel—N}\begin{matrix}\diagup \text{CH}_2\text{OH} \\ \diagdown \text{CH}_2\text{OH}\end{matrix} + \text{Gel—H} \rightarrow \text{crosslinked product} \qquad (58)$$

crosslinking proteins with formaldehyde may be sterically difficult with such a short crosslink (2.4–2.5 A.) (355). Methylene ether crosslinks (—CH_2—O—CH_2) (317) would be about twice as long as the methylene link, and the kinetics of the reaction, as reported by Davis and Tabor, support the initial formation of methylene ether type crosslinks.

The crosslinking of two dissimilar proteins through reaction with formaldehyde appears also to be a possibility. It has been shown that coatings of soluble proteins such as casein (337) or gelatin (338) can be hardened on wool and are essentially permanently anchored by treatment with formaldehyde. It can be argued, of course, that the formaldehyde simply renders the casein or gelatin insoluble, but crosslinking to the wool protein is not ruled out; the course of the reaction is yet to be proved.

Further work on protein–protein crosslinking through the use of diisocyanates has been described (349). Several other interesting examples of protein-polymer grafting involve isocyanate–amine reactions. Kropa and Nyquist (350) showed that wool reacts with a copolymer of 90% ethyl acrylate–10% allyl isocyanate when the polymer is applied from a toluene solution and heated for a short time at 290°F. Polymers obtained from monomers of the formula CH_2═CH—Ar—NCO react similarly with proteins in textiles (351) and in leather (352).

Isocyanato compounds were used, indirectly, in another novel scheme for attaching polymers to proteins. The isocyanato–alkyl vinyl ethers were reacted first with ethyleneimine to give the corresponding *N,N'*-ethyleneureido derivatives (353), which react with wool and silk to impart permanent finishes.

3. Chemically Modified Proteins

Besides grafting to natural or derived functional groups in proteins, grafting can be accomplished through groups introduced by chemical modification of the protein. For example, proteins can be reacted with maleic anhydride, acrylyl chloride, and other substances which will introduce vinyl groups (354), and subsequent polymerization of vinyl monomers in the presence of the vinylated protein should establish graft polymers. The treatment of wool with maleic anhydride was described by Speakman and co-workers (304,306). Wool was impregnated with a solution of maleic anhydride in an inert solvent and then heated for 30 min. at 85°C. Subsequently it was impregnated with a solution of methyl methacrylate and benzoyl peroxide (0.5% on weight of monomer). Heating at 85°C. led to the formation of an anchored film of copolymer on the surface of the fibers.

Proteins can also be treated with preformed polymers containing maleic anhydride, and the reaction leads to grafted products (357). A 90:10 mixture of maleic anhydride and an acrylic ester were copolymerized with benzoyl peroxide to produce a copolymer with an acid number of about 108. Wool or other protein material was treated with a solution of this copolymer and heated to complete the reaction of the anhydride with available reactive groups of the protein.

Reaction with isocyanates introduces into proteins groups which will subsequently enter into polymerization reactions (358). One mole of HCNO is used per equivalent of free —NH_2 in the protein. For example, 500 g. of acid-cured gelatin liquor containing 10% solids was warmed to 120°F., adjusted to pH 6.0–6.8, and treated with 1 g. of potassium cyanate. The proteinyl urea which is formed may be treated with aldehydes, forming modified aldehyde–urea polymers (359).

4. Organosilicon Polymers

Organosilicon polymers have been applied to proteins, particularly wool, to achieve a variety of effects, from water repellancy to shrink resistance. It is, however, open to some question as to whether a true graft is obtained between the organosilicon polymer and the protein. In 1949, Alexander and co-workers (360) found that silicon monomers containing Si—Cl groups gave rise to polymers chemically anchored on wool. The polymer is initially anchored to the protein by Si—NH linkage, but this bond is easily hydrolyzed on immersion in water or soap solution. A wide variety of silicon compounds was used, silicon tetrachloride, alkylsilicon halides, dialkyldialkoxysilanes, and one dialkoxydiaminosilane. Alexander and co-workers concluded that for wool to be made shrink-resistant by the deposition of small quantities of a silicone polymer on the wool surface, three conditions must be fulfilled: (*a*) the silicone polymer must be a hard solid; (*b*) the polymer must be formed *in situ;* (*c*) the monomer from which it is formed must contain reactive groupings such as Si—Cl. Groupings such as Si—OC_2H_5 and Si—NH_2 are not satisfactory.

The reactions of wool with the chlorosilanes were indicated by Alexander to be as shown in eqs. (59) and (60). The Si—Cl bond would then

$$\text{Wool—NH}_2 + \text{RSiCl}_3 \rightarrow \text{Wool—NH—SiRCl}_2 \quad (59)$$

$$\text{Wool—OH} + \text{RiSCl}_3 \rightarrow \text{Wool—O—SiRCl}_2 \quad (60)$$

hydrolyze and condense to produce an anchored polymer (XIX or XX).

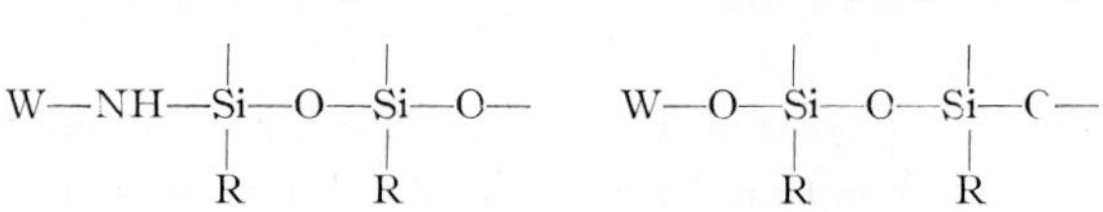

(XIX) (XX)

The question of these linkages between wool and polymer was investigated. R_3SiNHR compounds are readily hydrolyzed; Si—OR linkages are stable under mild conditions such as would be encountered in washing of fabric. Alexander's extraction experiments showed that if wool treated with dimethyldichlorosilane were given an aqueous treatment before ether extraction, the extraction would remove all the polymer. This indicated that the polymer was probably all anchored via Si—NH (easily hydrolyzed) linkages. On the other hand, a treatment is described in a patent by Robbart (361) in which it is claimed that the silicone polymer is effectively bound to the protein so that the wool may be washed in water without destroying the water-repellant characteristics. No proof of grafting of the organosilicon polymer is given. It may be that, as with the polymers described by Alexander, an oriented, durable deposit of polymer is formed and retained on the fiber surfaces. However, in view of the instability of the protein —NH—Si— linkage, durability to laundering would be unexpected.

F. EFFECTS OF HIGH ENERGY RADIATION

1. Introduction

The effects of high energy radiation on proteins is an area of increasingly great interest in relation to polymer chemistry. Charlesby's discovery (365) that crosslinking of polyethylene can be effected by ionizing radiation stimulated the whole field of high polymer radiation physics. It is now well established that radicals formed in polymers by high energy radiation are capable of combining to form crosslinks between adjacent chains. However, the degradation of polymers by high energy radiation is also well known, and in one example in polyethylene, the sum of the double bonds and the number of primary chain bonds cleaved equaled the crosslinks produced (380). The exposure of proteins to ionizing radiation has been shown to disrupt disulfide bonds (364,371), peptide bonds (366), and hydrogen bonds (367). The interactions of proteins with x-radiation, γ-radiation, electrons, neutrons, protons, deuterons, and alpha particles were covered by Bovey in 1958 (362). An earlier review by McLaren (363) discussed the most important contributions in this field up to 1949.

Radiation-generated free radicals provide potential sites for graft polymerization on proteins, and since electron spin resonance evidence shows that these radicals are long-lived, a wide range of applications should be possible. Studies of the chemical effects of radiation on proteins (368–372) are of practical as well as theoretical importance.

A comparison of the effects of x-rays and α-rays on proteins in dilute aqueous solution was made by Alexander and Rosen (373), who found that the changes produced by x- and α-rays differed qualitatively. It appeared that the effects of x-rays are due to OH· radicals reacting with all the common amino acids, whereas the effects of the α-rays are due to an activated hydrogen peroxide interacting preferentially with tryptophan. Irradiation of proteins with x- or β-radiation produced changes which were essentially identical.

Aggregation of albumin molecules in solution is caused by both x- and γ-radiations (374,375). At high doses this aggregation leads to precipitation; at lower doses it can be detected by ultracentrifugation. The same effect was produced by β-radiation (373). On α-irradiation, however, no precipitation and no changes in sedimentation were observed, even at doses up to 3 Mrad in a 1% protein solution.

From a detailed study of the effect of 2 M.e.v. electrons on solid bovine serum albumin in the absence of oxygen, Alexander and Hamilton (376) concluded that with this protein there were two types of damage: first, an opening up of the molecule due to the breaking of hydrogen bonds; and second, covalent changes recognized by the disappearance of amino acid side chains and the appearance of carbonyl groups and groups which released ammonia on mild hydrolysis. The opening of the albumin molecule can be followed by measuring the fraction of disulfide bonds available for reaction. In the native protein, all the seventeen disulfides per molecule are inaccessible at the isoelectric point (377). With increasing doses of radiation, up to 50% of the disulfides becomes available for reaction. However, Alexander and Hamilton found that there was no extensive formation of intermolecular —S—S— crosslinks by the oxidation of sulfhydryl groups.

Recent work on the high energy irradiation (2 M.e.v. electrons) of amides leads to the generalization that this type of treatment produces free radicals by the removal of a hydrogen atom from the CH group adjacent to the amide nitrogen atom (378). This position α to the amide nitrogen in proteins is analogous to that shown to be affected in irradiation of nylon (379); this is consistent with the mechanism suggested by Garrison and co-workers (366,381–384) for the degradation of proteins by irradiation.

2. Evidence for Free Radical Formation

Electron spin resonance patterns produced by x-irradiation of 25 amino acids, a comparable number of di- or tripeptides, and several proteins have been reported by Gordy and co-workers (385,386). These electron spin resonance studies of the effects of x-radiation on proteins show that generally only two types of patterns are produced. One of these patterns is characteristic of cysteine or cystine, and the other is a doublet similar to that of irradiated polyglycine. From the many types of long-lived electron spin resonances obtained for the amino acids and the simpler peptides, one might predict extremely complex, probably unresolvable patterns for all proteins. The fact that this does not occur reveals a property of proteins which may be important to the understanding of their reaction to ionizing radiation.

The irradiation of insulin is of particular interest because the sequence of amino acids in insulin is known (see Fig. VI-1). There are 17 different amino acid residues and a total of 51 amino acid units in the molecule. Of these 51 residues, only three contain sulfur, i.e., cystine units. Two of the cystine units form disulfide bridges between two polypeptide chains of the molecule, and the third forms an intrachain disulfide bridge along one of the chains. Between the cystine units on one of the polypeptide chains there are eleven other amino acid residues, eight of them different. On the other chain there are eight different units. Nevertheless, Gordy found that the electron spin resonance of x-irradiated insulin is predominantly that of the x-irradiated cystine.

It is obvious to consider the possibility of using organic sulfur compounds as protective agents against radiation damage to proteins and the role of —SH compounds in decreasing radiation injury has been reviewed extensively (388–391). Their role as free radical scavengers is supported by studies on the radiation chemistry of these compounds (392,393). Apparently, the avidity with which the —SH compounds combine with free radicals protects the most radiation-labile amino acids of the protein. The evidence is not unclouded, however, for experiments of Pihl (388) and Gordy and Miyagawa (391) would favor the theory of mixed disulfide formation between the —SH compound and the protein. From the work reported by Kumta et al. (394) the general protection of amino acid can be ascribed mainly to free radical scavenger effects.

Recent work by Kumta, Shimazu, and Tappel (394) on sulfhydryl "protectors" against radiation damage in proteins showed that cysteine offers considerable protection to radiation-labile amino acids. From the data on amino acid destruction in three proteins, it appeared that the protective effect of cysteine is not specific for any particular amino acid.

The notable ability of cysteine to absorb high energy radiation was further studied by Gordy and Miyagawa (391), who believed they had evidence that cysteine, as well as cysteamine and glutathione, could form complexes with proteins and thus act as a protective agent, absorbing the ionizing damage that would otherwise occur in the unprotected protein.

3. Grafting to Irradiated Proteins

As has been shown, there is ample evidence of the formation of radicals in irradiated proteins. These sites can be used to initiate graft polymerization. In wool there appears to be a safe margin between the radiation dose required for radical formation to initiate polymerization and the radiation dose required to produce detectable damage to fiber properties.

In their classical studies on the structure of fibrous proteins, Astbury and Woods (395) reported that wool fibers contracted more readily in steam after having been exposed to x-rays for many hours. More recently O'Connell and Walden (396) reported a decrease in strength and extensibility of wool after exposure to very large doses of ionizing radiation. They found no evidence of the introduction of new crosslinks in the wool protein. Although wool fibers showed progressive damage with increased

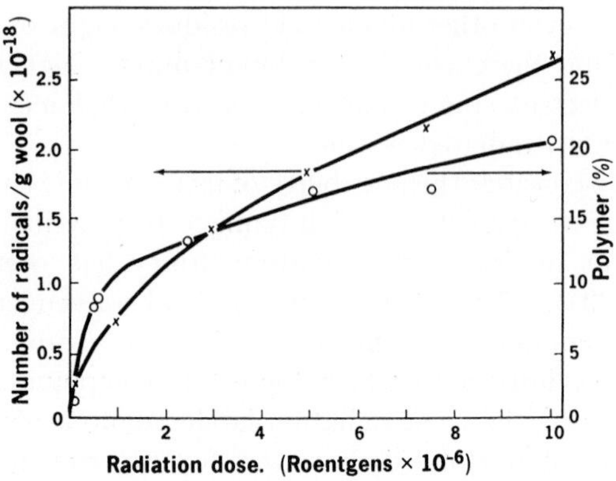

Fig. VI-5. Radical concentration and per cent polymer formed in wool irradiated with γ-rays: (X) number of radicals; (O) per cent polymer. (Taken from ref. 397.)

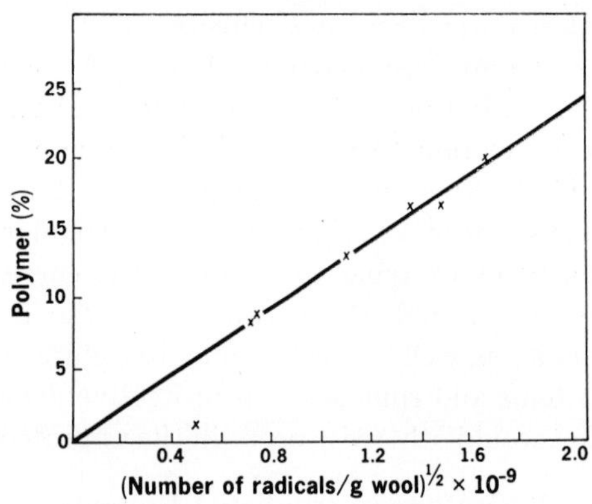

Fig. VI-6. Relationship between polymer formation and radical concentration in wool irradiation with γ-rays. (Taken from ref. 397.)

radiation, there was no appreciable damage when the radiation dose was less than 5 Mrep. It is therefore not surprising that radiation can be used safely to catalyze polymerization reactions in wool, and possibly in other ways to facilitate textile processing. At least 10^7 rads is required before degradation in wool can be detected by the chemical and physical method normally used to measure wool damage.

The presence of radicals in wool, sufficient to initiate graft polymerization, after radiation doses insufficient to degrade the fiber, was demonstrated by Nicholls and co-workers through electron spin resonance spectroscopy (397). They described the relation between radiation dose and the number of radicals detected in wool, and between the radiation dose and per cent polymer formed, as shown in Figure VI-5. It was found that the amount of acrylonitrile polymerized within irradiated wool was directly proportional to the square root of the radical concentration (Fig. VI-6). The γ-irradiation of the wool under air-free conditions produced free radicals which were stable only in the absence of oxygen; when air was admitted to the irradiated samples the radicals decayed rapidly, decreasing 12% in the first 30 minutes after the admission of the air.

γ-Radiation has also been used to initiate grafting of acrylonitrile and styrene onto silk (398). The best solvents for carrying out the radiation-induced grafting were water and ethyl alcohol. The optimum radiation dose was reported to be 10^6 r.

4. Hydrogen Bonding in Proteins

Under some conditions high energy radiation acts primarily to break hydrogen bonds in proteins; evidence is, however, somewhat indirect. Wool consists of micelles of high molecular weight polymer (protein) held together by hydrogen bonds, and surrounded by a matrix of lower molecular weight protein, intimately crosslinked by the disulfide bonds of cystine, a structure confirmed both by Lennox (399) and by Lundgren and Ward (26).

It has long been known that wool fiber contracts spontaneously if placed in a solution capable of breaking hydrogen bonds or if treated with a reagent which disrupts disulfide bonds. On removal of the reagent which breaks the hydrogen bonds such as lithium bromide, the fiber returns to its original length and the micellar structure is re-formed (400). On the other hand, supercontraction of wool fibers through disulfide bond breaking involves the noncrystalline matrix which maintains its structure by disulfide bonds, and 80% or more must be broken before contraction occurs (400). However, Allen and Alexander (401) assert that the observed effect of ionizing radiation on wool fiber is due not so much to breaks in the main chain or to disulfide cleavage, but more to disruption of hydrogen bonds. Although the radiation-induced changes in wool can be simulated, in part at least, by chemical treatments that break disulfide or peptide bonds, the number of such bonds that must be broken by chemical treatment is many times as great as the number that are destroyed by a dose of radiation that gives a comparable effect. It would therefore appear that under these conditions the changes produced by radiation lie in the hydrogen bonding and that radiochemical changes involving covalent bonds in wool are not principally responsible. Allen and Alexander (401) conclude, therefore, that the changes produced by radiation in the secondary structure of proteins may have more far reaching effects than covalent radiochemical changes involving individual amino acid residues.

Chemical reagents known to affect hydrogen bonding have a profound effect in reducing the shrinkage temperature of collagen (402), and the mechanism of the action of radiation may be similar (403). There may also be rupture of the protein chain, as Little (404) found that the crystalline areas of collagen became disordered at relatively low doses compared with silk, keratin and other proteins.

When Bailey, Bendall, and Rhodes (403) exposed collagen fibers in normal saline solution at 0°C. to doses of ionizing radiation up to 40 Mrad, they found that the hydrothermal shrinkage temperature decreased progressively with dose. After 5 Mrad the value dropped from 61 to 47°C. and after 40 Mrad it was about 25°C., agreeing well with the figures given by Cassel (368) for kangaroo tail fibers. Bailey et al. calculated that at a dose of 6 Mrad, an average of five ionizing events occur in the volume occupied by the postulated collagen triple helix unit, assuming the expenditure of 50 e.v. per event. This could account for the rupture of 50 hydrogen bonds, and since the triple structure requires about 300 such bonds, these figures suggest that ample energy is available for the destruction of a considerable portion of the secondary bonding structure.

Studies of the effects of radiation on collagen have practical importance in connection with the possible sterilization by radiation of raw meats. This sterilization process is accompanied by side effects on color, odor, flavor, and texture. It is generally agreed that the irradiated meat becomes softer and more tender during cooking than fresh meat. Since toughness of meat depends to a large extent upon the collagen, the effect of radiation upon collagen is of interest in this regard.

5. Cleavage of Peptide and Disulfide Bonds

Besides breaking of hydrogen bonds, other changes have also been found to occur in collagen after irradiation with doses of 5 Mrad (372). Low viscosity and gelling power of the irradiated collagen extracts suggests that there has been considerable breakdown of the polypeptide chains in this protein. The increase in terminal amino groups is relatively small and insufficient to account for the low molecular size indicated by the properties of the solution. The increase in amide nitrogen and the detection of carbonyl compounds in irradiated collagens fits into the scheme of —N—C— bond breakage proposed by Garrison and co-workers (366, 381–384).

Individual losses of amino acids in collagen varied with condition of irradiation, but in general the most affected were phenylalanine, tyrosine and histidine; leucine, isoleucine, valine, serine, and threonine were almost completely unattacked (372). These effects noted in the irradiation of collagen are quite different from the effects observed in the irradiation of keratins and other proteins rich in cystine. Phenylalanine, tyrosine, and histidine can accommodate electron-deficient centers of positive charge, which may be created by direct interaction with the high energy radiation or by reaction with electrophilic species created by the radiation. As discussed earlier, the oxygen atom of the peptide carbonyl may interact intramolecularly with these centers of positive charge in the side chain groups to yield unstable cyclic intermediates which subsequently decompose to yield the degradative products. This may account for these amino acids being among those most affected by the irradiation. On the other hand, leucine, isoleucine and valine have a marked steric hindrance to attack on their peptide bonds, and this may explain in part their resistance to attack by reactive species created by the irradiation.

6. Crosslinking of Proteins

Although moderate irradiation does not crosslink wool protein, radiation has been shown to crosslink a number of other proteins. On the irradiation of wool keratin with 1×10^7 rads, Zahn et al. (364) found a 3.6% loss of cystine; Allen and Alexander (401) reported a loss of 17% of the cystine in wool after a dose of 1×10^8 rads. However, the latter found no evidence for the formation of crosslinks in the wool due to the direct action of the radiation, which is in agreement with Alexander's previous findings with serum albumin (367), but contrary to the observation of Rosen (375), who reported that covalent crosslinks are indeed introduced into serum albumin when this protein is irradiated in dilute solution. Rosen postulated that x-rays affect proteins in solution by a two-stage process: the first step is the reaction between the protein molecule and a free radical formed in the radiolysis of the solvent; the second stage is the reaction of this activated protein either inter- or intramolecularly. This situation thus resembles the crosslinking of conventional polymers under irradiation.

From work on gelatin films, it appears that hydroxyl radicals are involved as intermediates in the crosslinking of polymers and proteins by γ-radiation (387). Gelatin films were irradiated with Co^{60} γ-rays at 4.2×10^4 r/hr. at 10°C. in the presence of oxygen, nitrogen, several organic liquids, and water. Only in the presence of water was the gelatin crosslinked. When the gelatin film was covered by an organic liquid such as methanol or glycerol, the crosslinkage was reduced in areas where the organic liquid penetrated. It was felt that the crosslinking of the gelatin induced by radiation is dependent upon the generation of free radicals by the action of the γ-radiation on water, and that these radicals react on the gelatin chains to form crosslinking sites.

7. Ultraviolet Light

The effects of ultraviolet light on proteins and the differences between the effects of ultraviolet light and the effects of ionizing radiation have been discussed by Setlow (429). The absorption of photons is not a random affair, as is the ionization by fast-charged particles. Photons are preferentially absorbed, in the long wavelength ultraviolet, by the aromatic groups in molecules, whereas sites at which ionizations occur are determined primarily by the electron density (429). Insofar as the electron density is constant, the ionizations are distributed randomly. The nonrandom localization of the absorption of light is apparent in the relative effectiveness of different wavelengths of light. The magnitudes of the effects of ionizing radiation and ultraviolet light are also different. However, both ultraviolet light and ionizing radiation studies give indications that cystine is the weak link in proteins (421).

It is well known that irradiation by ultraviolet light causes extensive physical and chemical changes in proteins. Examples are changes in viscosity, in optical rotation, in ultraviolet absorption spectra, in pH, in surface tension, in electrical conductivity, and in molecular weight. Some chemical changes directly observable include oxidation and reduction, formation of ammonia, loss of sulfhydryl groups, cleavage of disulfide links, and the opening of hydrogen bonds (253). Effects on the viscosity, on crosslinking, and on the formation of potential sites for initiating graft polymerization are naturally of particular interest in a consideration of the polymer chemistry of proteins.

The effects of ultraviolet light on the viscosity of proteins are by no means simple. The viscosity of gelatin solutions decreases with exposure to ultraviolet light (409). On the other hand, increases in viscosity have been observed with euglobulins and albumins (410), while yet other proteins, for example, tobacco mosaic virus, may be completely inactivated by ultraviolet light without showing any change in viscosity (411). It might be of interest to consider the effects of ultraviolet light on another natural polymer, deoxyribose nucleic acid (DNA), where the effects have been fairly well clarified. The decrease in viscosity and streaming birefringence in DNA were attributed by Hollaender (406) to main chain scission. The viscosity of a solution of large molecules, such as DNA or a protein, can be lowered both by reducing the average end-to-end distance by breaks in the main chain or by making the molecule more flexible so that it can assume a more compact configuration. By means of light scattering, Moroson and Alexander (408) were able to separate these two effects in the case of DNA, and found that both occur after irradiation of DNA with ultraviolet light. In the absence of oxygen, the primary effect of 2540 A. light is to disrupt hydrogen bonds; in the presence of oxygen main chain scission takes place immediately. With unfiltered ultraviolet light, both coiling and main chain scission occur in the absence of oxygen; in its presence the number of breaks is greatly enhanced.

Turning to the chemical effects of ultraviolet light upon proteins, Lieben (412,413) showed that exposure of amino acids and proteins, such as globulins, gelatin, and casein to the light of a mercury vapor lamp at temperatures below 35°C. results in the liberation of ammonia; in some other instances, tryptophan disappeared entirely, and the amount of histidine and tyrosine declined (414–416).

McLaren has shown that if all the light is converted into vibrational energy at some bond in the molecule, sufficient energy is available at wavelengths shorter than 2850 A. to break any single bond present in proteins (363) as shown in Table VI-39. The quantum efficiencies of ultraviolet photolysis of peptide bonds were measured by McLaren (417) and the values varied from 0.0004 to 0.004. An inverse relationship between quantum yield and the molecular weight of the protein was observed.

TABLE VI-39
Wavelength–Bond Energy Relationships[a]

Wavelength, A.	Light energy, kcal./mole	Bond	Bond energy, kcal./mole
4000	71	C—C	80
2850	100	C—N peptide	45
2537	112	C—N amine	66
		C—S	55
		S—S	64
		C—H	87–100
		C—O	70–82

[a] Taken from ref. 363.

Since ultraviolet quanta are sufficiently energetic to abstract hydrogen atoms from the backbone structure of synthetic polymers and it has been shown (418–420) that ultraviolet radiation is capable of crosslinking and grafting of high polymers, it might be assumed that proteins would be similarly crosslinked. However, proteins, especially keratins which are relatively rich in cystine, are easily degraded by ultraviolet radiation.

The work of Augenstine and Ghiron (421) on the effects of ultraviolet light on trypsin confirmed the hypothesis that cystine is the weak link, the first to be disrupted by the ultraviolet radiation. Trypsin solutions were exposed to 2537 A. ultraviolet irradiation. Subsequently the —SH groups and the trypsin activity were determined. When the enzyme activity was reduced to 50% by irradiation, the half cystine content dropped 40%, but other amino acid residues remained constant. This preferential disruption of cystine is essentially in agreement with the earlier observations of Stearn (422) and Setlow (423). Indeed, the liberation of —SH groups in ultraviolet-irradiated ovalbumin was reported as early as 1935 (424).

The chemical effects of ultraviolet light on sulfur-containing proteins has been summarized by Cecil and McPhee (253) in eqs. (61)–(65). It is obvious that the possibilities for graft polymerization onto ultraviolet-irradiated proteins provide a fertile field for research.

$$\mathrm{RSH} \overset{h\nu}{\rightleftharpoons} \mathrm{RS\cdot} + \mathrm{H\cdot} \tag{61}$$

$$\mathrm{RS\cdot} + \mathrm{RSH} \rightleftharpoons \mathrm{RSSR} + \mathrm{H\cdot} \tag{62}$$

$$\mathrm{RSH} + \mathrm{H\cdot} \rightleftharpoons \mathrm{RS\cdot} + \mathrm{H_2} \tag{63}$$

$$\mathrm{H\cdot} + \mathrm{H\cdot} \rightleftharpoons \mathrm{H_2} \tag{64}$$

$$\mathrm{RS\cdot} \quad \mathrm{RS\cdot} \rightleftharpoons \mathrm{RSSR} \tag{65}$$

From the mass of evidence there can be little doubt that the S—S bond is indeed the weak link with respect to ultraviolet radiation. However, in the absence of sufficient disulfide linkages, other easily ruptured bonds may be affected. An example of this is an ovalbumin in which the rupture of its single S—S bond (425) does not fully explain the degradation caused by the ultraviolet energy.

Upon prolonged exposure of wool to ultraviolet light (2480–4360 A., with maximum energy between 3000 and 3600 A.) the most marked effect on polymer properties results from the rapid destruction of cystine, with accompanying loss of interchain crosslinks. However, there is also an increase in the alkali solubility of the protein, from 12 to 28%, and a

TABLE VI-40
Effect of Ultraviolet Light on Amino Acids in Merino Wool[a]
(Amino acid content, wt.-% on dry weight of wool)

	22 Hr. hydrolysis[b]		44 Hr. hydrolysis[b]	
Amino acid	Untreated control	Irradiated[c] 40 hr.	Untreated control	Irradiated[c] 160 hr.
Aspartic acid	6.8	7.0	6.5	5.6
Threonine	6.3	5.9	6.2	5.1
Serine	9.8	9.1	9.2	8.1
Glutamic acid	15.2	15.0	13.6	13.2
Proline	7.2	6.1	7.1	3.1
Glycine	5.4	6.0	5.8	4.4
Alanine	4.6	4.2	4.5	4.4
Valine	5.5	5.9	5.4	4.2
Isoleucine	3.5	3.4	3.2	3.2
Leucine	8.9	8.7	8.7	6.7
Tyrosine	6.6	4.9	5.1	4.5
Phenylalanine	3.6	3.3	2.7	4.2
Lysine	3.8	3.9		
Histidine	0.9	1.0		
Arginine	10.0	9.5		
Cystine	13.0	7.6		

[a] Taken from ref. 426.
[b] In 6*N* HCl at 105°C.
[c] Mercury vapor lamp (2480–4360 A., with maximum energy in the 3000–3600 A. range); wool temperature, 20–22°C.

decrease in the content of proline, tryptophan, and tyrosine (Table VI-40) (426).

Moderate exposure to ultraviolet light, particularly in the presence of activators, can be used to initiate graft polymerization to proteins. Many applications of ultraviolet light as the initiator of graft polymerization have been described by Oster who has included the grafting to proteins (427). In the treatment of proteins the mechanism was not defined, but the method was said to be applicable to both keratins and collagens, silk, hair, and leather. The grafting is effected by irradiating the protein with ultraviolet light in the 1700–3000 A. range, in the presence of the monomer. The presence of activators greatly increases the rate of grafting.

Finally, the possibilities in simple ultraviolet irradiation of wool as a textile treatment have not been overlooked. Indeed, it is claimed (428) that wool that has been irradiated with ultraviolet light absorbs dye more rapidly and in greater quantity than does untreated wool and has improved shrinkproofing characteristics. For this treatment wool is exposed to the radiation from a mercury vapor lamp for about 20 min.

References

1. Hofmeister, F., *Ergeb. Physiol. Biol. Chem. Exp. Pharmakol.*, **1,** 759 (1902).
2. Fischer, E., *Ber.*, **35,** 1095 (1902); **36,** 2094, 2982 (1903); *Chemiker Ztg.*, **26,**939 (1902).
3. Tristram, G. R., in *The Proteins*, H. Neurath and K. Bailey, eds., Vol. I, Part A, Academic Press, New York, 1953, chap. 3.

4a. Sanger, F., and H. Tuppy, *Biochem. J.*, **49,** 463 (1951).

4b. Sanger, F., and E. O. P. Thompson, *Biochem. J.*, **53,** 353 (1953).

4c. Sanger, F., L. F. Smith, and R. Kitai, *Biochem. J.*, **58,** vi (1954).

5. Margoliash, E., and E. L. Smith, *Nature*, **192,** 1121 (1961).
6. Kreil, G., and H. Tuppy, *Nature*, **192,** 1123 (1961).
7. Margoliash, E., E. L. Smith, G. Kreil, and H. Tuppy, *Nature*, **192,** 1125 (1961).
8. Tsugita, A., D. T. Gish, J. Young, H. Fraenkel-Conrat, C. A. Knight, and W. M. Stanley, *Proc. Natl. Acad. Sci. U. S.*, **46,** 1463 (1960); *Chem. Abstr.*, **55,** 6595e (1961).

9a. Gish, D. T., *J. Am. Chem. Soc.*, **82,** 6329 (1960).

9b. Gish, D. T., *J. Am. Chem. Soc.*, **83,** 3303 (1961).

10. Anderer, F. A., H. Uhlig, E. Weber, and G. Schramm, *Nature*, **186,** 922 (1960).
11. Hirs, C. H. W., *J. Biol. Chem.*, **235,** 625 (1960).
12. Hirs, C. H. W., S. Moore, and W. H. Stein, *J. Biol. Chem.*, **235,** 633 (1960).
13. Spackman, D. H., W. H. Stein, and S. Moore, *J. Biol. Chem.*, **235,** 648 (1960).
14. Braunitzer, G., R. Gehring-Müller, N. Hilschmann, K. Hilse, G. Hobom, V. Rudloff, and B. Wittmann-Liebold, *Z. Physiol. Chem.*, **325,** 283 (1961); *Chem. Abstr.*, **56,** 7676b (1962).
15. Hill, R. J., and W. Konigsberg, *J. Biol. Chem.*, **236,** PC7 (1962).
16. Edmundson, A. B., and C. H. W. Hirs, *Nature*, **190,** 663 (1961).
17. Kendrew, J. C., H. C. Watson, B. E. Strandberg, R. E. Dickerson, D. C. Phillips, and V. C. Shore, *Nature*, **190,** 666 (1961).
18. Watson, H. C., and J. C. Kendrew, *Nature*, **190,** 670 (1961).
19. Bell, P. H., *J. Am. Chem. Soc.*, **76,** 5565 (1954).
20. Howard, K. S., R. G. Shepherd, E. A. Eigner, D. S. Davies, and P. H. Bell, *J. Am. Chem. Soc.*, **77,** 3419 (1955).
21. Li, C. H., I. I. Geschwind, R. D. Cole, I. D. Raacke, J. I. Harris, and J. S. Dixon, *Nature*, **176,** 687 (1955).
22. Bromer, W. W., L. G. Sinn, and O. K. Behrens, *J. Am. Chem. Soc.*, **79,** 2807 (1957).
23. Elmore, D. T., *Ann. Rept. Progr. Chem. (Chem. Soc. London)*, **58,** 300 (1961).
24. Linderstrøm-Lang, K., *Lane Medical Lectures: Proteins and Enzymes*, Stanford University Press, Stanford, California, 1952, p. 58.

25a. Kauzmann, W., in *Advances in Protein Chemistry*, C. B. Anfinsen, Jr., M. L. Anson, K. Bailey, and J. T. Edsall, eds., Vol. 14, Academic Press, New York, 1959, p. 1.

25b. Kauzmann, W., in *Annual Review of Physical Chemistry*, H. Eyring, C. J. Christensen, and H. S. Johnston, eds., Vol. 8, Annual Reviews, Inc., Palo Alto, Calif., 1957, p. 413.

26. Lundgren, H. P., and W. H. Ward, *Arch. Biochem. Biophys. Suppl. 1*, 78–111 (Sept. 1962).
27. Scheraga, H. A., *Protein Structure*, Academic Press, New York, 1961.
28. Katchalski, E., in *Annual Review of Physical Chemistry*, H. Eyring, C. J. Christensen, and H. S. Johnston, eds., Vol. 12, Annual Reviews, Inc., Palo Alto, Calif., 1961, p. 433.
29. Neuberger, A., *Symposium on Protein Structure*, Wiley, New York, 1958.
30. Low, Barbara, W., in *The Proteins*, H. Neurath and K. Bailey, eds., Vol. I, Part A, Academic Press, New York, 1953.
31. Harrap, B. S., W. G. Gratzer, and P. Doty, in *Annual Reviews of Biochemistry*, J. M. Luck, F. W. Allen, and G. MacKinney, eds., Vol. 30, Annual Reviews, Inc., Palo Alto, Calif., 1961, p. 269.
32a. Perlmann, G. E., and R. Diringer, in *Annual Reviews of Biochemistry*, J. M. Luck, F. W. Allen, and G. M. MacKinney, eds., Vol. 29, Annual Reviews, Inc., Palo Alto, Calif., 1960, p. 151.
32b. Hill, R. L., J. R. Kimmel, and E. L. Smith, *Ann. Rev. Biochem.*, **28,** 97 (1959).
33. William of Occam (1270–1349). "The Invincible Doctor." Occam's razor: a method of argumentation adopted by William of Occam, consisting of eliminating all unnecessary facts or constituents from a question under analysis.
34a. Swain, C. G., and C. B. Scott, *J. Am. Chem. Soc.*, **75,** 141 (1953).
34b. Swain, C. G., and R. B. Mosely, *J. Am. Chem. Soc.*, **77,** 3727 (1955).
34c. Swain, C. G., R. B. Mosely, and D. E. Bown, *J. Am. Chem. Soc.*, **77,** 3731 (1955).
35. Hine, J., *Physical Organic Chemistry*, McGraw-Hill, New York, 1956.
36. Ingold, C. K., *Structure and Mechanism in Organic Chemistry*, Cornell University Press, Ithaca, New York, 1953.
37. Hammett, L. P., *Physical Organic Chemistry*, McGraw-Hill, New York, 1940.
38a. Barnard, E. A., and W. D. Stein, *J. Mol. Biol.*, **1,** 339 (1959); *Chem. Abstr.*, **54,** 21213e (1960).
38b. Stein, W. D., and E. A. Barnard, *J. Mol. Biol.*, **1,** 350 (1959); *Chem. Abstr.*, **54,** 21213 (1960).
39. Korman, S., and H. T. Clarke, *J. Biol. Chem.*, **221,** 133 (1956).
40. Sela, M., F. H. White, Jr., and C. B. Anfinsen, *Biochim. Biophys. Acta*, **31,** 417 (1959); *Chem. Abstr.*, **53,** 10329d (1959).
41. Gundlach, H. G., W. H. Stein, and S. Moore, *J. Biol. Chem.*, **234,** 1754 (1959).
42. Rosner, L., *J. Biol. Chem.*, **132,** 657 (1940).
43. Anson, M. L., *J. Gen. Physiol.*, **23,** 321 (1940); *Chem. Abstr.*, **34,** 4752^2 (1940).
44. Pillemer, L., E. E. Ecker, and E. W. Martiensen, *J. Exptl. Med.*, **70,** 387 (1939).
45. Goddard, D. R., and L. Michaelis, *J. Biol. Chem.*, **112,** 361 (1936).
46. Anson, M. L., and W. M. Stanley, *J. Gen. Physiol.*, **24,** 679 (1941); *Chem. Abstr.*, **36,** 122^4 (1942).
47. Gillespie, J. M., and P. H. Springell, *Biochem. J.*, **79,** 280 (1961).
48. Balls, A. K., and H. Lineweaver, *J. Biol. Chem.*, **130,** 669 (1939); *Nature*, **144,** 513 (1939).
49. Michaelis, L., and M. Schubert, *J. Biol. Chem.*, **106,** 331 (1934).
50. Olcott, H. S., and H. Fraenkel-Conrat, *Chem. Rev.*, **41,** 151 (1947).
51. Oku, M., and H. Ishibashi, *J. Textile Inst.*, **51,** T642 (1960).
52. Sanger, F., *Biochem. J.*, **39,** 507 (1945); **40,** 261 (1946).
53a. Porter, R. R., *Biochim. Biophys. Acta*, **2,** 105 (1948); *Chem. Abstr.*, **42,** 6863b (1948).

53b. Porter, R. R., *Biochem. J.*, **46**, 304 (1950); *Chem. Abstr.*, **44**, 1006b (1950).
54. Putnam, F. W., in *The Proteins*, H. Neurath and K. Bailey, eds., Vol. 1, Part B Academic Press, New York, 1953.
55. Herriott, R. M., M. L. Anson, and J. H. Northrop, *J. Gen. Physiol.*, **30**, 185 (1946); *Chem. Abstr.*, **41**, 1259h (1947).
56. Fraenkel-Conrat, H., in *Amino Acids and Proteins*, D. M. Greenberg, ed., Thomas, Springfield, Ill., 1951.
57. Bose, S. M., and K. T. Joseph, *Arch. Biochem. Biophys.*, **74**, 46 (1958); *Chem. Abstr.*, **52**, 9257g (1958).
58. Gordon, W. G., A. E. Brown, and R. W. Jackson, *Ind. Eng. Chem.*, **38**, 1239 (1946).
59. Gordon, W. G., A. E. Brown, and C. M. McGrory, *Ind. Eng. Chem.*, **38**, 90 (1946).
60. Baddiley, J., R. A. Kekwick, and E. M. Thain, *Nature*, **170**, 968 (1952).
61. Fraenkel-Conrat, H., R. S. Bean, and H. Lineweaver, *J. Biol. Chem.*, **177**, 385 (1949).
62. Green, R. W., K. P. Ang, and L. C. Lam, *Biochem. J.*, **54**, 181 (1953).
63. Alexander, P., R. F. Hudson, and M. Fox, *Biochem. J.*, **46**, 27 (1950).
64. Gould, E. S., *Mechanism and Structure in Organic Chemistry*, Holt, Rinehart, and Winston, New York, 1959, chap. 9.
65. Fraenkel-Conrat, H., and H. S. Olcott, *J. Biol. Chem.*, **161**, 259 (1945).
66. Fraenkel-Conrat, H., *J. Biol. Chem.*, **154**, 227 (1944).
67. Goodlad, G. A. J., *Biochim. Biophys. Acta*, **24**, 645 (1957); *Chem. Abstr.*, **51**, 13968c (1957).
68. Wilcox, P. E., *Abstr. Intern. Congr. Pure and Applied Chem.*, 12th Congress, New York, 1951, pp. 60–61.
69. Doscher, M. S., and P. E. Wilcox, *J. Biol. Chem.*, **236**, 1328 (1961).
70. Windmueller, H. G., C. J. Ackerman, and R. W. Engel, *J. Biol. Chem.*, **234**, 895 (1959).
71. Alexander, P., D. Carter, C. Earland, and O. E. Ford, *Biochem. J.*, **48**, 629 (1951).
72. Reitz, H. C., R. E. Ferrel, H. Fraenkel-Conrat, and H. S. Olcott, *J. Am. Chem. Soc.*, **68**, 1024 (1946).
73. Suter, C. M., *Organic Chemistry of Sulfur Compounds*, Wiley, New York, 1943.
74. Uchino, T., *J. Biochem. (Tokyo)*, **20**, 65 (1934).
75. Ferrel, R. E., H. S. Olcott, and H. Fraenkel-Conrat, *J. Am. Chem. Soc.*, **70**, 2101 (1948).
76. Kampfhammer, J., and H. Muller, *Z. Physiol. Chem.*, **225**, 1 (1934); *Chem. Abstr.*, **28**, 4707^1 (1934).
77. Greenstein, J. P., *J. Biol. Chem.*, **109**, 541 (1935).
78. Hughes, W. L., Jr., H. A. Saroff, and A. L. Carney, *J. Am. Chem. Soc.*, **71**, 2476 (1949).
79. Roche, J., M. Mourgue, and R. Baret, *Bull. Soc. Chim. Biol.*, **36**, 85 (1954); *Chem. Abstr.*, **48**, 10074f (1954).
80. Chervenka, C. H., and P. E. Wilcox, *J. Biol. Chem.*, **222**, 621, 635 (1956).
81. Klee, W. A., and F. M. Richards, *J. Biol. Chem.*, **229**, 489 (1957).
82. Geschwind, I. I., and C. H. Li, *Biochim. Biophys. Acta*, **25**, 171 (1957); *Chem. Abstr.*, **51**, 15649c (1957).
83. Evans, R. L., and H. A. Saroff, *J. Biol. Chem.*, **228**, 295 (1957).

84. Ramachandran, L. K., *Biochim. Biophys. Acta*, **32**, 557 (1959); *Chem. Abstr.* **53**, 15155i (1959).
85. Komimz, D. R., and K. Laki, paper presented at the 126th meeting of the American Chemical Society, New York, Sept. 12–17, 1954.
86a. Maekawa, K., and I. E. Liener, *Arch. Biochem. Biophys.*, **91**, 101 (1960); *Chem. Abstr.*, **55**, 5607h (1961).
86b. Maekawa, K., and I. E. Liener, *Arch. Biochem. Biophys.*, **91**, 108 (1960); *Chem. Abstr.*, **55**, 5607i (1961).
87. Micheel, F., and W. Berlenbach, *Chem. Ber.*, **85**, 189 (1952).
88. Micheel, F., and B. Herold, *Z. Physiol. Chem.*, **293**, 187 (1953).
89. Schutte, E., *Z. Physiol. Chem.*, **279**, 52, 59 (1943).
90. Ramachandran, L. K., *Chem. Rev.*, **56**, 199 (1956).
91. Roche, J., and R. Michel, in *Advances in Protein Chemistry*, M. L. Anson and J. T. Edsall, eds., Vol. 6, Academic Press, New York, 1951, p. 253.
92. Reineke, E. P., *Vitamin Hormone*, **4**, 207 (1946); *Chem. Abstr.*, **41**, 2480a (1947).
93. Li, C. H., *J. Am. Chem. Soc.*, **67**, 1065 (1945).
94. Neuberger, A., *Biochem. J.*, **28**, 1982 (1934).
95a. Herriott, R. M., *J. Gen. Physiol.*, **20**, 335 (1936); *Chem. Abstr.*, **31**, 2241 (1937).
95b. Herriott, R. M., *J. Gen. Physiol.*, **25**, 185 (1941); *Chem. Abstr.*, **36**, 4529[2] (1942).
96. Li, C. H., W. R. Lyons, and H. M. Evans, *J. Bi-l. Chem.*, **139**, 43 (1941).
97. Harington, C. R., and A. Neuberger, *Biochem. J.*, **30**, 809 (1936).
98. Richards, H. R., and J. B. Speakman, *Nature*, **171**, 751 (1953).
99a. Bauer, H., and E. Strauss, *Biochem. Z.*, **211**, 163 (1929); *Chem. Abstr.*, **23**, 5204 (1929).
99b. Bauer, H., and E. Strauss, *Biochem. Z.*, **284**, 197, 231 (1936); *Chem. Abstr.*, **30**, 3449[9] (1936).
100. Fraenkel-Conrat, H., *Arch. Biochem.*, **27**, 109 (1950); *Chem. Abstr.*, **44**, 10749c (1950).
101. Li, C. H., *J. Am. Chem. Soc.*, **64**, 1147 (1942).
102. Hughes, W. L., and R. Straessle, *J. Am. Chem. Soc.*, **72**, 452 (1950).
103. Li, C. H., *J. Am. Chem. Soc.*, **66**, 225 (1944).
104. Johnson, T. B., and E. F. Kohmann, *J. Am. Chem. Soc.*, **37**, 1863, 2164 (1915).
105. Johnson, T. B., *J. Am. Chem. Soc.*, **37**, 2598 (1915).
106. Johnson, T. B., and A. J. Hill, *J. Am. Chem. Soc.*, **38**, 1392 (1916).
107a. Lieben, F., *Biochem. Z.*, **145**, 535 (1924); *Chem. Abstr.*, **19**, 84 (1925).
107b. Lieben, F., *Biochem. Z.*, **145**, 555 (1924).
108. Roche, J., M. Mourgue, *Bull. Soc. Chim. Biol.*, **30**, 322 (1948); *Chem. Abstr.*, **43**, 256f (1949).
109. Roche, J., and M. Mourgue, *Compt. Rend.*, **226**, 1848 (1948); *Chem. Abstr.*, **42**, 7347a (1948).
110. Kossel, A., and F. Weiss, *Z. Physiol. Chem.*, **84**, 1 (1913); *Chem. Abstr.*, **7**, 2229 (1913).
111. Zahn, H., and K. Kohler, *Z. Naturforsch.*, **5b**, 137 (1950); *Chem. Abstr.*, **44**, 7906b (1950).
112. Robinson, E. A., and J. Robinson, *J. Soc. Dyers Colourists*, **77**, 351 (1961); *Chem. Abstr.*, **56**, 11833h (1962).
113. Fröhlich, H. G. *J. Textile Inst.*, **51**, T1237 (1960).

114. Wormall, A., *J. Expl. Med.*, **51,** 295 (1930); *Chem. Abstr.*, **24,** 1422 (1930).
115. Ehrenberg, L., I. Fischer, and N. Löfrem, *Nature*, **157,** 730 (1946).
116. Conant, J. B., and W. D. Peterson, *J. Am. Chem. Soc.*, **52,** 1220 (1930).
117. Wistar, R., and P. D. Bartlett, *J. Am. Chem. Soc.*, **63,** 413 (1941).
118. Hauser, C. R., and D. S. Breslow, *J. Am. Chem. Soc.*, **63,** 418 (1941).
119. Ridd, J. H., *Quart Rev. (London)*, **15,** 418 (1961).
120. Landsteiner, K., *The Specificity of Serological Reactions*, 2nd ed., Harvard University Press, Cambridge, Massachusetts, 1946.
121. Kabat, E. A., in *Annual Reviews of Biochemistry*, J. M. Luck., F. W. Allen, and G. MacKinney, eds., Vol. 15, Annual Reviews, Inc., Palo Alto, Calif., 1946, p. 505.
122. Boyd, W. C., *Fundamentals of Immunology*, Interscience, New York, 1943.
123. Higgins, H. G., and K. J. Harrington, *Arch. Biochem. Biophys.*, **85,** 409 (1959); *Chem. Abstr.*, **54,** 9780c (1960).
124. Higgins, H. G., and D. Fraser, *Australian J. Phys.*, **A5,** 736 (1952); *Chem. Abstr.*, **47,** 3118d (1953).
125. Gelewitz, E. W., W. L. Riedeman, and I. M. Klotz, *Arch. Biochem. Biophys.*, **53,** 411 (1954); *Chem. Abstr.*, **49,** 4749c (1955).
126. Fitzgerald, J. E., and W. L. Koltun, *J. Am. Chem. Soc.*, **79,** 6383 (1957).
127. Koltun, W. L., *J. Am. Chem. Soc.*, **79,** 5681 (1957).
128. Higgins, H. G., and E. J. Williams, *Australian J. Chem.*, **6,** 195 (1953); *Chem. Abstr.*, **47,** 10976c (1953).
129. Higgins, H. G., *Australian J. Chem.*, **10,** 99 (1957); *Chem. Abstr.*, **51,** 12611i (1957).
130. Pauly, H., *Z. Physiol. Chem.*, **44,** 159 (1905); *Chem. Zentr.*, **76,** 1163 (1905).
131. Pauly, H., *Z. Physiol. Chem.*, **94,** 284 (1915); *Chem. Abstr.*, **9,** 2905 (1915).
132. Busch, M., N. Patrascamu, and W. Weber, *J. Prakt. Chem.*, **140,** 117 (1934); *Chem. Abstr.*, **28,** 5425[7] (1934).
133. Eagle, H., and P. Vickers, *J. Biol. Chem.*, **114,** 193 (1936).
134. Jacobs, W. A., and M. Heidelberger, *J. Am. Chem. Soc.*, **43,** 1632 (1921).
135. Markush, E. A., U. S. Patent 1,982,681 (to Pharma Chemical Corp.), Dec. 4, 1933; *Chem. Abstr.*, **29,** 555[8] (1935).
136. Boyd, W. C., and S. B. Hooker, *J. Biol. Chem.*, **104,** 329 (1934).
137. Boyd, W. C., and P. Mover, *J. Biol. Chem.*, **110,** 457 (1935).
138. Kapeller-Adler, R., and G. Boxer, *Biochem. Z.*, **285,** 55 (1936); *Chem. Abstr.*, **30,** 4881[4] (1936).
139. Zahn, H., B. Wollemann, and O. Waschka, *Z. Physiol. Chem.*, **294,** 100 (1953); *Chem. Zentr.*, **125,** 7628 (1954).
140. Howard, A. N., and F. Wild, *Biochem. J.*, **65,** 651 (1957).
141. Hantzsch, A., *Ber.*, **31,** 340 (1898).
142. Walther, R. V., and W. Grieshammer, *J. Prakt. Chem.*, **92,** 209 (1915); *Chem. Abstr.*, **10,** 592 (1916).
143. Fraser, D., and H. G. Higgins, *Nature*, **172,** 459 (1953).
144. Herriott, R. M., in *Advances in Protein Chemistry*, M. L. Anson and J. T. Edsall, eds., Vol. 3, Academic Press, New York, 1947, p. 169.
145. Philpot, J. St. L., and P. A. Small, *Biochem. J.*, **32,** 534, 542 (1938).
146. Leveau, M., M. Caillet, and N. Demonmerot, *Bull. Inst. Textile France*, **90,** 7 (1960); *Chem. Abstr.*, **55,** 3068b (1961).

147. Leveau, M., *Bull. Inst. Textile France*, **93**, 75 (1961); *Chem. Abstr.*, **55**, 19253b (1961).
148. Cadwallader, C. J., and S. G. Smith, *J. Textile Inst.*, **47**, T489 (1956).
149. Sorensen, S. P. L., *Biochem. Z.*, **7**, 45 (1908).
150. French, D., and J. T. Edsall in *Advances in Protein Chemistry*, M. L. Anson and J. T. Edsall, eds., Vol. 2, Academic Press, New York, 1945, p. 277.
151. Fraenkel-Conrat, H., M. Cooper, and H. S. Olcott, *J. Am. Chem. Soc.*, **67**, 950 (1945).
152. Fraenkel-Conrat, H., B. A. Brandon, and H. S. Olcott, *J. Biol. Chem.*, **168**, 99 (1947).
153. Fraenkel-Conrat, H., and H. S. Olcott, *J. Am. Chem. Soc.*, **70**, 2673 (1948).
154. Fraenkel-Conrat, H., and H. S. Olcott, *J. Biol. Chem.*, **174**, 827 (1948).
155. Fraenkel-Conrat, H., and D. K. Mecham, *J. Biol. Chem.*, **177**, 477 (1949).
156. Fraenkel-Conrat, H., and H. S. Olcott, *J. Am. Chem. Soc.*, **68**, 34 (1946).
157. Anson, M. L., *J. Gen. Physiol.*, **24**, 399 (1941); *Chem. Abstr.*, **36**, 103[7] (1942).
158. Ross, A. F., and W. M. Stanley, *J. Gen. Physiol.*, **22**, 165 (1938); *Chem. Abstr.*, **33**, 2179[8] (1939).
159. Fraenkel-Conrat, H., J. C. Lewis, K. P. Dimick, B. Edwards, H. C. Reitz, R. E. Ferrel, B. A. Brandon, and H. S. Olcott, *Proc. Soc. Exp. Biol. Med.*, **63**, 302 (1946); *Chem. Abstr.*, **41**, 1258a (1947).
160. Mohammad, A., H. Fraenkel-Conrat, and H. S. Olcott, *Arch. Biochem.*, **24**, 157, 270 (1949); *Chem. Abstr.*, **44**, 2045f (1950).
161. Friedmann, E., D. H. Marrian, and I. Simon-Reuss, *Brit. J. Pharmacol.*, **4**, 105 (1949); *Chem. Abstr.*, **43**, 7591b (1949).
162. Moore, J. E., and H. P. Lundgren, *Proc. Intern. Wool Textile Res. Conf., Australia*, **1955**, C355.
163. Moore, J. E., and W. H. Ward, *J. Am. Chem. Soc.*, **78**, 2414 (1956).
164. Kovacic, P., and R. W. Hein, *J. Am. Chem. Soc.*, **81**, 1187 (1959).
165. Schöberl, A., *J. Textile Inst.*, **51**, T613 (1960).
166. Moore, J. E., U. S. Patent 2,955,016, Oct. 4, 1960; *Chem. Abstr.*, **55**, 3085h (1961).
167. Grant, W. M., and V. E. Kinsey, *J. Biol. Chem.*, **165**, 485 (1946).
168. Stahmann, M. A., C. Golumbic, W. H. Stein, and J. S. Fruton, *J. Org. Chem.*, **11**, 719 (1946).
169. McPhee, J. R., and M. Lipson, *Australian J. Chem.*, **7**, 387 (1954); *Chem. Abstr.*, **49**, 1332a (1955).
170. Bikales, N. M., J. J. Black, and L. Rapoport, *Textile Res. J.*, **27**, 80 (1957).
171. Oku, M., and H. Ishibashi, *J. Textile Inst.*, **51**, T637 (1960).
172. Tomimatsu, Y., J. J. Bartulovich, and W. H. Ward, *Textile Res. J.*, **29**, 593 (1959).
173. Bartulovich, J. J., Y. Tomimatsu, and W. H. Ward, *J. Textile Inst.*, **51**, T628 (1960).
174. Weil, L., and T. S. Seibles, *Arch. Biochem. Biophys.*, **95**, 470 (1961); *Chem. Abstr.*, **56**, 7670d (1962).
175. *The Chemistry of Acrylonitrile*, 2nd ed., American Cyanamid Co., New York, 1959, p. 28.
176a. Hopkins, S. J., and A. Wormall, *Biochem. J.*, **27**, 740 (1933).
176b. Hopkins, S. J., and A. Wormall, *Biochem. J.*, **27**, 1706 (1933).

176c. Hopkins, S. J., and A. Wormall, *Biochem. J.*, **28,** 2125 (1934).
177. Guant, W. E., and A. Wormall, *Biochem. J.*, **30,** 1915 (1936).
178a. Desnuelle, P., and M. Rovery, *Biochim. Biophys. Acta*, **1,** 497 (1947); *Chem. Abstr.*, **42,** 4215c (1948).
178b. Desnuelle, P., and M. Rovery, *Biochim. Biophys. Acta*, **3,** 26 (1949); *Chem. Abstr.*, **43,** 5062g (1949).
179. Miller, G. L., and W. M. Stanley, *J. Biol. Chem.*, **141,** 905 (1941).
180. Fraenkel-Conrat, H., *J. Biol. Chem.*, **152,** 385 (1944).
181. Rodney, G., and N. Fell, *J. Immunol.*, **47,** 251 (1943); *Chem. Abstr.*, **38,** 156^3 (1944).
182. Creech, H. J., and R. N. Jones, *J. Am. Chem. Soc.*, **62,** 1970 (1940).
183. Fraenkel-Conrat, H., M. Cooper and H. S. Olcott, *J. Am. Chem. Soc.*, **67,** 314 (1945).
184. Farnsworth, A. J., *Biochem. J.*, **59,** 529 (1955).
185. Moore, J. E., *Textile Res. J.*, **26,** 936 (1956).
186. Moore, J. E., and R. A. O'Connell, *Textile Res. J.*, **27,** 783 (1957).
187. Koenig, N. H., *Textile Res. J.*, **31,** 592 (1961); **32,** 117 (1962).
188. Fraenkel-Conrat, H., J. I. Harris, and A. L. Levy, in *Methods of Biochemical Analysis*, D. Glick, ed., Vol. 2, Interscience, New York, 1955, pp. 359–425.
189. Reyerson, L. H., and K. Kobe, *Chem. Rev.*, **7,** 479 (1930).
190. Ross, W. F., and L. A. Green, *J. Biol. Chem.*, **137,** 105 (1941).
191. Tracy, A. H., and W. F. Ross, *J. Biol. Chem.*, **146,** 63 (1942).
192. Ross, W. F., and H. N. Christensen, *J. Biol. Chem.*, **137,** 89 (1941).
193. Tracy, A. H., and W. F. Ross, *J. Biol. Chem.*, **142,** 871 (1942).
194. Fraenkel-Conrat, H., *J. Biol. Chem.*, **154,** 227 (1944).
195. Cook, A. H., I. Heilbron, and A. L. Levy, *J. Chem. Soc.*, **1948,** 201.
196. Levy, A. L., *J. Chem. Soc.*, **1950,** 404.
197. Leonis, J., and A. L. Levy, *Bull. Soc. Chim. Biol.*, **33,** 779 (1951); *Chem. Abstr.*, **46,** 4595d (1952).
198. Leonis, J., *Compte Rend. Trav. Lab. Carlsberg.*, **26,** 315 (1948); *Chem. Abstr.*, **43,** 2247f (1949).
199. Levy, A. L., and C. H. Li, *J. Biol. Chem.*, **213,** 487 (1955).
200. Porter, R. R., and F. Sanger, *Biochem. J.*, **42,** 287 (1948).
201. Sanger, F., *J. Polymer Sci.*, **49,** 3 (1961).
202. Sanger, F., in *Advances in Protein Chemistry*, M. L. Anson and J. T. Edsall, eds., Vol. 7, Academic Press, New York, 1952, p. 1.
203. Harris, J. I., and V. M. Ingram, in *Analytical Methods of Protein Chemistry*, P. Alexander and R. J. Block, eds., Vol. II, Pergamon Press, New York, 1960, pp. 424–499.
204. Thompson, E. O. P., in *Advances in Organic Chemistry*, R. A. Raphael, E. C. Taylor, and H. Wynberg, eds., Vol. 1, Interscience Publishers, New York, 1960, pp. 149–238.
205. Edman, P., *Acta Chem. Scand.*, **4,** 277, 283 (1950); *Chem. Abstr.*, **45,** 612c (1951).
206. Fox, S. W., in *Advances in Protein Chemistry*, M. L. Anson and J. T. Edsall, eds., Vol. 2, Academic Press, New York, 1945, p. 155.
207. Akabori, S., K. Ohno, and K. Narita, *Bull. Chem. Soc. Japan*, **25,** 214 (1952); *Chem. Abstr.*, **48,** 1468b (1954).
208. Niu, C., and H. Fraenkel-Conrat, *J. Am. Chem. Soc.*, **77,** 5882 (1955).

209. Braunitzer, G., *Chem. Ber.*, **88,** 2025 (1955).
210. Loening, K. L., A. B. Garrett, and M. S. Newman, *J. Am. Chem. Soc.*, **74,** 3929 (1952).
211. Newman, M. S., *Steric Effects in Organic Chemistry*, Wiley, New York, 1956, chap. 4.
212. Synge, R. L. M., *Biochem. J.*, **39,** 351 (1945).
213. Heyns, K., W. Walter, and H. F. Grützmacher, *J. Polymer Sci.*, **30,** 573 (1958).
214. Whitfield, R. E., *Science*, **142,** 577 (1963).
215. Christensen, H. N., *J. Biol. Chem.*, **151,** 319 (1943).
216. Elliott, D. F., in *The Chemical Structure of Proteins*, G. E. W. Wolstenholme and M. P. Cameron, eds., Little, Brown, Boston, Mass., 1953.
217. Blout, E. R., in *Polyamino Acids, Polypeptides, and Proteins*, M. Stahmann, ed., University of Wisconsin Press, Madison, Wisconsin, 1962, p. 275.
218. Stein, W. H., S. Moore, and M. Bergmann, *J. Biol. Chem.*, **154,** 191 (1944).
219. Fischer, E., and E. Abderhalden, *Ber.*, **40,** 3544 (1907).
220. Abderhalden. E., and H. Brockmann, *Biochem. Z.*, **225,** 386 (1930); *Chem. Abstr.*, **24,** 5758 (1930).
221. Desnuelle, P., and A. Casal, *Biochim. Biophys. Acta*, **2,** 64 (1948); *Chem. Abstr.* **43,** 2943h (1949).
222. Desnuelle, P., and G. Bonjour, *Biochim. Biophys. Acta*, **7,** 451 (1951); *Chem. Abstr.*, **46,** 6675d (1952).
223. Elliott, D. F., *Biochem. J.*, **50,** 542 (1952).
224. Lucas, F., J. T. B. Shaw, and S. G. Smith, *Biochem. J.*, **66,** 468 (1957).
225. Ramachandran, L. K., and W. B. McConnell, *Can. J. Chem.*, **33,** 1638 (1955).
226. Wiseblatt, L., L. Wilson, and W. B. McConnell, *Can. J. Chem.*, **33,** 1295 (1955).
227. Bock, R. M., and V. Thakur, *Federation Proc.*, **18,** 194 (1959).
228a. Hille, E., and H. Zahn, *J. Textile Inst.*, **51,** T1162 (1960).
228b. Hille, E., and H. Zahn, *J. Textile Inst.*, **51,** T1171 (1960).
229. Zahn, H., *J. Soc. Dyers Colourists*, **76,** 226 (1960).
230. Fasman, G. D., *Science*, **131,** 420 (1960).
231. Witkop, B., in *Advances in Protein Chemistry*, C. B. Anfinsen, Jr., M. L. Anson, K. Bailey, and J. T. Edsall, eds., Vol. 16, Academic Press, New York, 1961, p. 221.
232. Linderstrøm-Lang, K., *Chem. Soc. (London), Spec. Publ.*, No. 2 (1955).
233. Hvidt, A., and K. Linderstrøm-Lang, *Biochim. Biophys. Acta*, **14,** 574 (1954); *Chem. Abstr.*, **48,** 12838g (1954).
234. Linderstrøm-Lang, K., in *Symposium on Protein Structure*, A. Neuberger, ed., Wiley, New York, 1958.
235. Leach, S. J., *Rev. Pure Appl. Chem.*, **9,** 33 (1959); *Chem. Abstr.*, **53,** 21695g (1959).
236. Scheraga, H. A., in "Protein Structure and Function," *Brookhaven Symp. Biol.*, **13,** 71 (1960).
237. Lenormant, H., and E. R. Blout, *Nature*, **172,** 770 (1953).
238a. Haggis, G. H., *Biochim. Biophys. Acta*, **19,** 545 (1956); *Chem. Abstr.*, **50,** 10154b (1956).
238b. Haggis, G. H., *Biochim. Biophys. Acta*, **23,** 494 (1957); *Chem. Abstr.*, **51,** 8162h (1957).
239. Wishnia, A., and M. Saunders, *J. Am. Chem. Soc.*, **84,** 4235 (1962).
240a. Fraser, R. D. B., and T. P. MacRae, *J. Chem. Phys.*, **28,** 1120 (1958).

240b. Fraser, R. D. B., and T. P. MacRae, *J. Chem. Phys.*, **29,** 1024 (1958).
240c. Fraser, R. D. B., and T. P. MacRae, *J. Chem. Phys.*, **31,** 122 (1959).
241. Harris, M., and A. L. Smith, *J. Res. Natl. Bur. Std.*, **17,** 577 (1936); *Chem. Abstr.*, **31,** 544[5] (1937).
242. Zahn, H., and A. Würz, *J. Textile Inst.*, **45,** 88 (1954).
243. Alexander, P., M. Fox, K. A. Stacey, and L. F. Smith, *Biochem. J.*, **52,** 177 (1952).
244. Lees, K., and F. F. Elsworth, *Proc. Intern. Wool Textile Res. Conf., Australia,* **1955,** C363.
245. Astbury, W. T., and H. J. Woods, *Phil. Trans. Roy. Soc. London,* **A232,** 333 (1933); *Chem. Abstr.*, **28,** 3238[1] (1934).
246. Speakman, J. B., *J. Soc. Chem. Ind.*, **50,** T1 (1931); *Nature,* **152,** 930 (1930); *Chem. Abstr.*, **25,** 1388 (1931).
247a. Elöd, E., and H. Zahn, *Melliand Textilber.*, **29,** 17 (1948); *Chem. Abstr.*, **43,** 9457e (1949).
247b. Elöd, E., and H. Zahn, *Kolloid-Z.*, **108,** 94 (1944); *Chem. Abstr.*, **40,** 6903[8] (1946).
248. Speakman, J. B., *J. Soc. Dyers Colourists,* **52,** 335 (1936); *Chem. Abstr.*, **30,** 8629[2] (1936).
249. Speakman, J. B., *J. Textile Inst.*, **37,** T102 (1947).
250. Zahn, H., *Proc. Intern. Wool Textile Res. Conf. Australia,* **1955,** C425.
251. Flory, P. J., *Principles of Polymer Chemistry,* Cornell University Press, Ithaca, New York, 1953, chaps. 10, 13.
252. Alexander, P., and R. F. Hudson, *Wool: Its Chemistry and Physics,* Reinhold, New York, 1954. chaps. 3, 8, and 10.
253. Cecil, R., and J. R. McPhee, in *Advances in Protein Chemistry,* C. B. Anfinsen, M. L. Anson, K. Bailey, and J. T. Edsall, eds., Vol. 14, Academic Press, New York, 1959, p. 255.
254. Parker, A. J., and N. Kharasch, *Chem. Rev.*, **59,** 583 (1959).
255. Benesch, R., R. E. Benesch, P. D. Boyer, I. M. Klotz, W. R. Middlebrook, A. G. Szent-Györgyi, and D. R. Schwartz, eds., *Sulfur in Proteins,* Academic Press, New York, 1959.
256. Pryor, W. A., *Mechanism of Sulfur Reactions,* McGraw-Hill, New York, 1962.
257. Kharasch, N., *Organic Sulfur Compounds,* Pergamon Press, New York, 1961.
258. Rosenthal, N. A., and G. Oster, *J. Soc. Cosmetic Chemists,* **5,** 286 (1954).
259. Alexander, P., M. Fox, and R. F. Hudson, *Biochem. J.*, **49,** 129 (1951).
260. Fox, M., Ph.D. Thesis, University of London, 1951.
261. Alexander, P., D. Carter, and C. Earland, *J. Soc. Dyers Colourists,* **67,** 23 (1951); *Chem. Abstr.*, **45,** 2674a (1951).
262. Blackburn, S., and A. G. Lowther, *Biochem. J.*, **49,** 554 (1951).
263. Gillespie, J. M., I. J. O'Donnell, E. O. P. Thompson, and E. F. Woods, *J. Textile Inst.*, **51,** T703 (1960).
264a. Smith, A. L., and M. Harris, *J. Res. Natl. Bur. Std.*, **16,** 301, 309 (1936).
264b. Smith, A. L., and M. Harris, *J. Res. Natl. Bur. Std.*, **17,** 97, 577 (1936).
264c. Smith, A. L., and M. Harris, *J. Res. Natl. Bur. Std.*, **18,** 623 (1937).
265. Elod, E., H. Nowotny, and H. Zahn, *Melliand Textilber.*, **23,** 313 (1942); *Chem. Zentr.*, **113**(2), 1979 (1942).
266. Consden, R., A. H. Gordon, and A. J. P. Martin, *Biochem. J.*, **40,** 570 (1946).

267. Alexander, P., and D. Gough, *Biochem. J.*, **48,** 504 (1951).
268. Alexander, P., and M. Fox, *Proc. Intern. Wool Textile Res. Conf. Australia,* 1955.
269. Blackburn, S., and H. Phillips, *J. Soc. Dyers Colourists,* **61,** 100 (1945); *Chem. Abstr.,* **39,** 2883i (1945).
270. Patterson, W. I., W. B. Geiger, L. Mizell, and M. Harris, *J. Res. Natl. Bur. Std.,* **27,** 89 (1941).
271. Harris, M., L. R. Mizell, and L. Fourt, *Ind. Eng. Chem.,* **34,** 833 (1942).
272. Cecil, R., and J. R. McPhee, *Biochem. J.,* **60,** 496 (1955).
273. Stricks, W., I. M. Kolthoff, and R. C. Cooper, *J. Am. Chem. Soc.,* **77,** 2057 (1955).
274. Swan, J. M., Ref. 255, pp. 3–14.
275. Stoves, J. L., *Trans. Faraday Soc.,* **38,** 261 (1942).
276. Schöberl, A., and R. Hamm, *Biochem. Z.,* **318,** 331 (1948); *Chem. Abstr.,* **42,** 9184c (1948).
277. Cuthbertson, W. R., and H. Phillips, *Biochem. J.,* **39,** 7 (1945).
278. Moore, S., R. P. Cole, H. G. Gundlach, and W. H. Stein, *Proc. Intern. Congr. Biochem. 4th, Vienna 1958,* Pergamon, New York, 1960.
279. Gillespie, J. M., *Nature,* **183,** 322 (1959).
280. Zahn, H., *Melliand Textilber,* **31,** 481 (1950); *Chem. Abstr.,* **44,** 9157c (1950).
281. Benesch, R., and R. E. Benesch, Ref. 255, pp. 15–24.
282. Geiger, W. B., F. F. Kobayashi, and M. Harris, *J. Res. Natl. Bur. Std.,* **29,** 381 (1942).
283. Speakman, J. B., British Patent 453,701, Sept. 10, 1936.
284. Brown, A. E., and M. Harris, *Ind. Eng. Chem.,* **40,** 316 (1948).
285a. Kirst, W., *Melliand Textilber.,* **28,** 169 (1947).
285b. Kirst, W., *Melliand Textilber.,* **28,** 314 (1947).
285c. Kirst, W., *Melliand Textilber.,* **28,** 394 (1947).
285d. Kirst, W., *Melliand Textilber.,* **29,** 236 (1948).
286. Speakman, J. B., and P. L. D. Peill, *J. Textile Inst.,* **34,** T70 (1943).
287. Speakman, J. B., *J. Soc. Leather Trades Chemists,* **37** (1953); *Chem. Abstr.,* **47,** 5708i (1953).
288. Lipson, M., and J. B. Speakman, *J. Soc. Dyers Colourists,* **65,** 390 (1949); *Chem. Abstr.,* **43,** 8142d (1949).
289. Zahn, H., and D. Wegerle, *Leder,* **5,** 121 (1954); *Chem. Abstr.,* **48,** 14269h (1954).
290. Cockburn, R., and J. B. Speakman, *Proc. Intern. Wool Textile Res. Conf., Australia,* **1955,** C315.
291. Lipson, M., and J. B. Speakman, *Nature,* **157,** 590 (1946).
292. Lipson, M., and R. Hope, *Australian J. Chem.,* **3A,** 324 (1950); *Chem. Abstr.,* **45,** 360g (1951).
293. Lohani, B., L. Valentine, and C. S. Whewell, *J. Textile Inst.,* **49,** T265 (1958).
294. Valentine, L., *J. Textile Inst.,* **46,** T270 (1955).
295. Lipson, M., *Nature,* **164,** 576 (1949).
296. Madaras, G. W., and J. B. Speakman, *J. Soc. Dyers Colourists,* **70,** 112 (1954); *Chem. Abstr.,* **48,** 6703f (1954).
297. Boardman, N. K., and M. Lipson, *J. Soc. Dyers Colourists,* **69,** 335 (1953); *Chem. Abstr.,* **47,** 12821c (1953).
298. Valentine, L., *J. Textile Inst.,* **47,** T1 (1956).

299. Schöberl, A., and D. Wagner, *Melliand Textilber.*, **41**, 984 (1960); *Chem. Abstr.*, **54**, 25846b (1960).
300. Wolfram, L. J., and J. B. Speakman, *J. Soc. Dyers Colourists*, **77**, 477 (1961); *Chem. Abstr.*, **56**, 3672a (1962).
301. Bělohradský, F., M. Kulhánek, and L. Blažek, Czech. Patent 87,983, Dec. 15, 1958; *Chem. Abstr.*, **54**, 5176b (1960).
302. Pardo, C. E., and H. P. Lundgren, U. S. Patent 3,005,730 (to U. S. Dept. of Agriculture), Oct. 24, 1961; *Chem. Abstr.*, **56**, 3690e (1962).
303. Pierce, G. W., U. S. Patent 2,737,434, Mar. 6, 1956; *Chem. Abstr.*, **50**, 9034d (1956).
304. Ghosh, R. C., J. R. Holker, and J. B. Speakman, *Textile Res. J.*, **28**, 112 (1958).
305. Speakman, J. B., *J. Soc. Leather Trades Chemists*, **42**, 135 (1958); *Chem. Abstr.*, **52**, 13271f (1958).
306. Speakman, J. B., *J. Am. Leather Chemists Assoc.*, **53**, 492 (1958); *Chem. Abstr.*, **52**, 19147f (1958).
307. von Euler, H., H. Hasselquist, and A. Glaser, *Arkiv. Kemi.*, **3**, 81 (1950); *Chem. Zentr.*, **123**, 1304 (1952).
308. Whitfield, R. E., L. A. Miller, and W. L. Wasley, *Textile Res. J.*, **31**, 704 (1961).
309. Whitfield, R. E., L. A. Miller, and W. L. Wasley, *Textile Res. J.*, **32**, 743 (1962).
310. Jones, H. W., and H. P. Lundgren, *Textile Res. J.*, **21**, 620 (1951).
311. Rose, W. G., and H. P. Lundgren, *Textile Res. J.*, **23**, 930 (1953).
312. Fearnley, C., and J. B. Speakman, *J. Soc. Dyers Colourists*, **68**, 88 (1952).
313. Schroeder, C. W., U. S. Patent 2,829,071 (to Shell Development Co.), Apr. 1, 1958; *Chem. Abstr.*, **52**, 15084e (1958).
314. Pardo, C. E., and R. A. O'Connell, U. S. Patent 3,019,076 (to U. S. Dept. of Agriculture), Jan. 30, 1962.
315. Pardo, C. E., U. S. Patent 2,817,602 (to U. S. Dept. of Agriculture), Dec. 24, 1957; *Chem. Abstr.*, **52**, 4202a (1958).
316a. Coe, T. J., U. S. Patent 2,869,971 (to U. S. Dept. of Agriculture), Jan. 20, 1959; *Chem. Abstr.*, **53**, 8655i (1959).
316b. Coe, T. J., U. S. Patent 2,866,402 (to U. S. Dept. of Agriculture), May 12, 1959; *Chem. Abstr.*, **53**, 16554g (1959).
316c. Coe, T. J., U. S. Patent 2,890,097 (to U. S. Dept. of Agriculture), June 9, 1959; *Chem. Abstr.*, **53**, 17523f (1959).
316d. Coe, T. J., U. S. Patent 2,933,366 (to U. S. Dept. of Agriculture), Apr. 19, 1960; *Chem. Abstr.*, **54**, 15953g (1960).
316e. Coe, T. J., U. S. Patent 2,975,077 (to U. S. Dept. of Agriculture), Mar. 14, 1961; *Chem. Abstr.*, **55**, 15952e (1961).
317. Wormell, R. L., *New Fibers from Proteins*, Butterworths, London, 1954, p. 93.
318. Fraenkel-Conrat, H., M. Cooper, and H. S. Olcott, *J. Am. Chem. Soc.*, **67**, 950 (1945).
319. Gustavson, K. H., in *Advances in Protein Chemistry*, M. L. Anson and J. T. Edsall, eds., Vol. 5, Academic Press, New York, 1949, p. 353.
320. Davis, P., and B. E. Tabor, *J. Polymer Sci.*, **A1**, 799 (1963).
321. Filachione, E. M., and E. H. Harris, U. S. Patent 2,829,943 (to U. S. Dept. of Agriculture), Apr. 8, 1958; *Chem. Abstr.*, **52**, 12439h (1958).
322. Baldwin, A. W., T. Barr, and J. B. Speakman, and Imperial Chemical Industries Ltd., British Patent 567,501, Feb. 16, 1945; *Chem. Abstr.*, **41**, 2585e (1947).

323. Baldwin, A. W., T. Barr, and J. B. Speakman, *J. Soc. Dyers Colourists*, **62**, 4 (1946); *Chem. Abstr.*, **40**, 2003[9] (1946).
324. Alexander, P., J. L. Bailey, and D. Carter, *Textile Res. J.*, **20**, 385 (1950).
325. Bradbury, J. H., and D. C. Shaw, *Textile Res. J.*, **30**, 976 (1960).
326. Bradbury, J. H., and D. C. Shaw, *Textile Res. J.*, **30**, 118 (1960).
327. Konigsberg, W. H., and R. R. Becker, *J. Am. Chem. Soc.*, **81**, 1428 (1959).
328. Van Kley, H., S. G. Korngutli, and M. A. Stahmann, *J. Am. Chem. Soc.*, **81**, 4370 (1959).
329. Sela, M., and R. Arnon, *Biochim. Biophys. Acta*, **40**, 382 (1960); *Chem. Abstr.*, **54**, 21441h (1960).
330. Sela, M., and E. Katchalski, *Experientia*, **11**, 62 (1955).
331. Katchalski, E., and M. Sela, in *Advances in Protein Chemistry*, C. S. Anfinsen, Jr., M. L. Anson, K. Bailey, and J. T. Edsall, eds., Vol. 13, Academic Press, New York, 1958, p. 243.
332. Sela, M., E. Katchalski, and M. Gehatia, *J. Am. Chem. Soc.*, **78**, 746 (1956).
333. Becker, R. R., and M. A. Stahmann, *J. Biol. Chem.*, **204**, 745 (1953).
334. Green, M., and M. A. Stahmann, *J. Biol. Chem.*, **213**, 259 (1955).
335. Stahmann, M. A., and R. R. Becker, *J. Am. Chem. Soc.*, **74**, 2695 (1952).
336. Tsuyuki, H., H. Van Kley, and M. A. Stahmann, *J. Am. Chem. Soc.*, **78**, 764 (1956).
337. Jackson, D. L. C., and A. R. A. Blackwell, *Australian J. Appl. Sci.*, **6**, 244 (1955); *Chem. Abstr.*, **49**, 13653i (1955).
338. Jackson, D. L. C., *Australian J. Appl. Sci.*, **8**, 130, 136 (1957); *Chem. Abstr.*, **51**, 11724[2] (1957).
339. Bar-Eli, A., and E. Katchalski, *Nature*, **188**, 856 (1960).
340. Arnon, R., and M. Sela, *Biochem. J.*, **75**, 103 (1960).
341. Sela, M., and R. Arnon, *Biochem. J.*, **75**, 91 (1960).
342. Sela, M., and R. Arnon, *Biochem. J.*, **77**, 394 (1960).
343. Fraenkel-Conrat, H., *Biochim. Biophys. Acta*, **10**, 180 (1953); *Chem. Zentr.*, **125**, 2637 (1954).
344. Stracher, A., and R. R. Becker, *J. Am. Chem. Soc.*, **81**, 1432 (1959).
345. Stracher, A., W. H. Konigsberg, and R. R. Becker, *Biochim. Biophys. Acta*, **20**, 595 (1956); *Chem. Abstr.*, **50**, 15641h (1956).
346. Moore, J. E., and C. E. Pardo, U. S. Patent 2,925,317 (to U. S. Dept. of Agriculture), Feb. 16, 1960; *Chem. Abstr.*, **54**, 12606h (1960).
347. Rohm and Haas Co., British Patent, 801,987, Sept. 24, 1958; *Chem. Abstr.*, **53**, 3727h (1959).
348. Sheehan, J. C., and J. J. Hlavka, *J. Am. Chem. Soc.*, **79**, 4528 (1957).
349. Schick, A. F., and S. J. Singer, *J. Biol. Chem.*, **236**, 2477 (1961).
350. Kropa, E. L., and A. S. Nyquist, U. S. Patent 2,537,064 (to American Cyanamid Co.), Jan. 9, 1951; *Chem. Abstr.*, **45**, 8262a (1951).
351. Nyquist, A. S., and E. L. Kropa, U. S. Patent 2,468,716 (to American Cyanamid Co.), Apr. 26, 1949; *Chem. Abstr.*, **43**, 6428b (1949).
352. Bortnick, N. M., U. S. Patent 2,718,516 (to Rohm and Haas Co.), Sept. 20, 1955; *Chem. Abstr.*, **50**, 1371c (1956).
353. Melamed, S., U. S. Patent 2,694,696 (to Rohm and Haas Co.), Nov. 16, 1954; *Chem. Abstr.*, **49**, 3576f (1955).
354. Miller, L. A., and R. E. Whitfield, *Textile Res. J.*, **31**, 451 (1961).

355. Carpenter, D. C., *Arch. Biochem. Biophys.*, **9**, 159 (1946); *Chem. Abstr.*, **40**, 4399[7] (1946).
356. Bartlett, P. D., and R. H. Jones, *J. Am. Chem. Soc.*, **79**, 2153 (1957).
357. Kropa, E. L., and A. S. Nyquist, U. S. Patent 2,499,653 (to American Cyanamid Co.), Mar. 7, 1950; *Chem. Abstr.*, **44**, 8671f (1950).
358. Young, H. H., and E. F. Christopher, U. S. Patent 2,816,099 (to Swift and Co.), Dec. 10, 1957; *Chem. Abstr.*, **52**, 5867a (1958).
359. Young, H. H., and E. F. Christopher, U. S. Patent 2,923,691, (to Swift and Co.), Feb. 2, 1960; *Chem. Abstr.*, **54**, 10366g (1960).
360. Alexander, P., D. Carter, and C. Earland, *J. Soc. Dyers Colourists*, **65**, 107 (1949); *Chem. Abstr.*, **43**, 4017a (1949).
361. Robbart, E., U. S. Patent 2,961,338, Nov. 22, 1960; *Chem. Abstr.*, **55**, 4981i (1961).
362. Bovey, F. A., *The Effects of Ionizing Radiation on Natural and Synthetic High Polymers*, Polymer Reviews Series, Vol. I, Interscience, New York, 1958.
363. McLaren, A. D., in *Advances in Enzymology*, F. F. Nord, ed., Vol. IX, Interscience, New York, 1949, p. 75.
364. Zahn, H., E. R. Fritze, H. Pfannmuller, and G. Satlow, *Proc. 2nd Intern. Conf. Peaceful Uses Atomic Energy, Geneva, 1958*, Vol. 29, United Nations, 1959, p. 233.
365. Charlesby, A., *Proc. Roy. Soc. (London)*, **A215**, 187 (1952); *Chem. Abstr.*, **47**, 4759a (1953).
366. Jayko, M. E., and W. M. Garrison, *Nature*, **181**, 413 (1958).
367. Alexander, P., L. D. G. Hamilton, and K. A. Stacey, *Radiation Res.*, **12**, 510 (1960); *Chem. Abstr.*, **54**, 21248a (1960).
368. Cassel, J. H., *J. Am. Leather Chemists' Assoc.*, **54**, 432 (1959); *Chem. Abstr.*, **54**, 21819a (1960).
369. Drake, M. P., J. W. Giffee, D. A. Johnson, and V. L. Koenig, *J. Am. Chem. Soc.*, **79**, 1395 (1957).
370. Caputo, A., and K. Dose, *Z. Naturforsch.*, **12**, 172 (1957); *Chem. Abstr.*, **51**, 10601h (1957).
371. Alexander, P., and L. D. G. Hamilton, *Radiation Res.*, **13**, 214 (1960); *Chem. Abstr.*, **55**, 1748a (1961).
372. Bowes, J. H., and J. A. Moss, *Radiation Res.*, **16**, 211 (1962).
373. Alexander, P., and D. Rosen, *Radiation Res.*, **15**, 475 (1961); *Chem. Abstr.*, **57**, 6276e (1962).
374. Rosen, D., S. Brohult, and P. Alexander, *Arch. Biochem. Biophys.*, **70**, 266 (1957); *Chem. Abstr.*, **51**, 16627e (1957).
375. Rosen, D., *Biochem. J.*, **72**, 597 (1959).
376. Alexander, P., and L. D. G. Hamilton, *Radiation Res.*, **15**, 193 (1961); *Chem. Abstr.*, **56**, 6325c (1962).
377. Katchalski, E., G. S. Benjamin, and V. Gross, *J. Am. Chem. Soc.*, **79**, 4096 (1957).
378. Burrell, E. J., *J. Am. Chem. Soc.*, **83**, 574 (1961).
379. Zimmerman, J., *J. Appl. Polymer Sci.*, **2**, 181 (1959).
380. Black, R. M., and B. J. Lyons, *Nature*, **180**, 1346 (1957).
381. Bennett, W., and W. M. Garrison, *Nature*, **183**, 889 (1959).
382. Jayko, M. E., B. M. Weeks, and W. M. Garrison, *Proc. 2nd Intern. Conf. Peaceful Uses Atomic Energy, Geneva, 1958*, Vol. 22, United Nations, 1959, p. 488.

383. Garrison, W. M., M. E. Jayko, and W. Bennett, *Radiation Res.*, **16**, 483 (1962).
384. Garrison, W. M., and B. M. Weeks, *Radiation Res.*, **17**, 341 (1962).
385. Gordy, W., W. B. Ard, and H. Shields, *Proc. Natl. Acad. Sci. U. S.*, **41**, 983 (1955); *Chem. Abstr.*, **50**, 11816g (1956).
386. Gordy, W., *Radiation Res. Suppl.*, **1**, 491 (1959); *Chem. Abstr.*, **53**, 10318i (1959).
387. Tomoda, Y., and M. Tsuda, *Nature*, **190**, 905 (1961).
388. Pihl, A., and L. Eldjarn, *Pharmacol. Rev.*, **10**, 437 (1958); *Chem. Abstr.*, **53**, 3481b (1959).
389. Patt, H. M., *Federation Proc.*, **19**, 549 (1960); *Chem. Abstr.*, **54**, 21219f (1960).
390. Maisin, T. R., and D. G. Doherty, *Federation Proc.*, **19**, 564 (1960); *Chem. Abstr.*, **54**, 21219g (1960).
391. Gordy, W., and I. Miyagawa, *Radiation Res.*, **12**, 211 (1960); *Chem. Abstr.*, **54**, 22024c (1960).
392. Bacq, Z. M., and P. Alexander, *Fundamentals of Radiobiology*, Academic Press, New York, 1955.
393. Shapiro, B., and E. A. Dickens, *Radiation Res.*, **13**, 857 (1960); *Chem. Abstr.*, **55**, 10540c (1961).
394. Kumta, U. S., F. Shimazu, and A. L. Tappel, *Radiation Res.*, **16**, 679 (1962); *Chem. Abstr.*, **57**, 8853a (1962).
395, Astbury, W. T., and H. J. Woods, *Phil. Trans. Roy. Soc. London*, **A232**, 333 (1933).
396. O'Connell, R. A., and M. K. Walden, *Textile Res. J.*, **27**, 516 (1957).
397. Burke, M., P. Kenny, and C. H. Nicholls, *J. Textile Inst.*, **53**, T370 (1962).
398. Azimov, S. A., K. U. Usmanov, N. V. Kordub, and S. I. Slepakova, *Vysokomolekul. Soedin.*, **2**, 1459 (1962).
399. Lennox, F. G., *Research (London)*, **12**, 82 (1959).
400. Alexander, P., *Ann. N. Y. Acad. Sci.*, **53**, 653 (1951); *Chem. Abstr.*, **45**, 7796i (1951).
401. Allen, E., and P. Alexander, *Radiation Res.*, **15**, 390 (1961); *Chem. Abstr.*, **56**, 6195e (1962).
402. Gustavson, K. H., *The Chemistry and Reactivity of Collagen*, Academic Press, New York, 1956.
403. Bailey, A. J., J. R. Bendall, and D. N. Rhodes, *Intern. J. Appl. Radiation Isotopes*, **13**, 131 (1962); *Chem. Abstr.*, **57**, 7431f (1962).
404. Little, K., *Proc. Intern. Conf. Electron Microscopy, 3rd London, 1954*, Royal Microscopical Society, London, 1956, pp. 165–171.
405. Boyer, P. D., *J. Am. Chem. Soc.*, **76**, 4331 (1954).
406. Hollaender, A., J. P. Greenstein, and W. V. Jenrette, *J. Natl. Cancer Inst.*, **2**, 23 (1941); *Chem. Abstr.*, **35**, 7989[1] (1941).
407. Butler, J. A. V., and B. E. Conway, *Proc. Roy. Soc. (London)*, **B141**, 562 (1953); *Chem. Abstr.*, **47**, 11272d (1953).
408. Moroson, H., and P. Alexander, *Radiation Res.*, **14**, 29 (1961); *Chem. Abstr.*, **55**, 16692e (1961).
409. Ponthus, P., *Compt. Rend.*, **196**, 1248 (1933); *Chem. Abstr.*, **27**, 3670 (1933).
410. Spiegel-Adolph, M., *Die Globuline*, Steinkopff, Leipzig, 1930.
411. Oster, G., and A. D. McLaren, *J. Gen. Physiol.*, **33**, 215 (1950); *Chem. Abstr.*, **44**, 3095d (1950).
412. Lieben, F., and F. Urban, *Biochem. Z.*, **239**, 250 (1931); *Chem. Abstr.*, **26**, 159 (1932).

413. Eckstein, H. C., and F. Lieben, *Biochem. Z.*, **263,** 366 (1933); *Chem. Abstr.*, **27,** 5350 (1933).
414. Lieben, F., *Biochem. Z.*, **184,** 453 (1927); **187,** 307 (1927); *Chem. Abstr.*, **21,** 2434 (1927).
415. Lieben, F., and G. Ehrlich, *Biochem. Z.*, **222,** 221 (1930); *Chem. Abstr.*, **24,** 4312 (1930).
416. Leiben, F., and H. Jesserer, *Biochem. Z.*, **275,** 367 (1935); *Chem. Abstr.*, **29,** 2983[5] (1935).
417. McLaren, A. D., P. Gentile, D. C. Kirk, and N. A. Levin, *J. Polymer Sci.*, **10,** 333 (1953).
418. Oster, G., *J. Polymer Sci.*, **22,** 185 (1956).
419. Oster, G., and O. Shibata, *J. Polymer Sci.*, **26,** 233 (1957).
420. Oster, G., G. K. Oster, and H. Moroson, *J. Polymer Sci.*, **34,** 671 (1959).
421. Augenstine, L. H., and C. A. Ghiron, *Proc. Natl. Acad. Sci. U. S.*, **47,** 1530 (1961); *Chem. Abstr.*, **56,** 9111c (1962).
422. Stearn, A. E., in *Advances in Enzymology*, F. F. Nord, ed., Vol. 9, Interscience, New York, 1949, p. 25.
423. Setlow, R., *Biochim. Biophys. Acta*, **16,** 444 (1955).
424. Guillaume, A., and G. Tanret, *Compt. Rend.*, **201,** 1057 (1935).
425. Tristram, G. R., in *Advances in Protein Chemistry*, M. L. Anson and J. T. Edsall, eds., Vol. 5, Academic Press, New York, 1949, p. 83.
426. Hildebrand, D., and H. Kersten, *Biochem. Z.*, **332,** 67 (1959).
427. Oster, G., British Patent 856,884, Dec. 21, 1960; *Chem. Abstr.*, **55,** 13907f (1961).
428. Commonwealth Scientific and Industrial Research Organization, Australian Patent 229,835 (by A. R. Haly), Aug. 11, 1960; *Chem. Abstr.*, **55,** 25278a (1961).
429. Setlow, R. B., *Radiation Res. Suppl.*, **2,** 276 (1960); *Chem. Abstr.*, **55,** 5609i (1961).

Chapter VII

INTERCHANGE REACTIONS

A. POLYESTERS

T. Davies

Imperial Chemical Industries, Ltd.

1. Introduction

A molecule of an addition polymer, once formed by a chain reaction, is a stable macromolecule which does not normally react further with its neighbors. When a macromolecule such as a polyester has been formed by a condensation reaction, however, the ester links which have been formed in the polycondensation are still reactive, and molecules of different sizes can continue to react together in different ways. Such interchange reactions between polymeric molecules have been recognized since condensation polymers were first made.

We may define interchange reactions in polyesters as those reactions which take place between two ester links or endgroups and which lead to the formation of two *identical* groups. As a result of the reaction, the parts of the molecules attached to the reacting groups are interchanged. Such reactions are always reversible and can be both intermolecular and intramolecular. In polyesters, where chains are terminated by hydroxyl or carboxyl groups, three types of interchange are possible, and each type can be exemplified in nonmacromolecular systems.

In type I, there is interchange between an ester group and a terminal hydroxyl group (eq. 1).

$$\begin{matrix} \sim R_1C{=}O \\ | \\ OR_2\sim \end{matrix} + \sim R_3OH \rightleftarrows \begin{matrix} \sim R_1C{=}O \\ | \\ OR_3\sim \end{matrix} + \sim R_2OH \qquad (1)$$

This type of interchange has been demonstrated in simple aliphatic esters by the reaction between ethyl acetate and butanol to give butyl acetate and ethanol (1) and was shown to occur in the ester of a phenol in the reaction between β-naphthyl esters and various aliphatic alcohols (2).

In type II, the interchange is between an ester group and a terminal carboxyl group (eq. 2).

$$\begin{array}{l}\sim R_1C{=}O\\ \quad|\\ \quad OR_2\sim\end{array} + \sim R_3COOH \rightleftarrows \begin{array}{l}\sim R_3C{=}O\\ \quad|\\ \quad OR_2\sim\end{array} + \sim R_1COOH \qquad (2)$$

Korshak and Vinogradova have shown that such a reaction takes place between ethyl stearate and either acetic acid (3) or adipic or succinic acids (4); they have also examined the kinetics of these reactions.

Type III involves interchange between two ester groups (eq. 3).

$$\begin{array}{l}\sim R_1C{=}O\\ \quad|\\ \quad OR_2\sim\end{array} + \begin{array}{l}\sim R_3C{=}O\\ \quad|\\ \quad OR_4\sim\end{array} \rightleftarrows \begin{array}{l}\sim R_1C{=}O\\ \quad|\\ \quad OR_4\sim\end{array} + \begin{array}{l}\sim R_3C{=}O\\ \quad|\\ \quad OR_2\sim\end{array} \qquad (3)$$

Ethyl stearate and cetyl acetate have been shown to be partially converted, above 120°C., into cetyl stearate and ethyl acetate at easily measurable rates (5).

2. Evidence for Occurrence of Interchange Reactions

We first consider the evidence for each of the three types of interchange reactions, and then consider evidence which is less specific for any one of the reactions.

a. Evidence for Reactions of Type I (Ester/Hydroxyl)

Although linear polyesters other than those derived from hydroxycarboxylic acids may be prepared from equivalent quantities of dibasic acid and glycol, an excess of one of the components (usually the glycol) is often used to ensure the attainment of a high molecular weight. To this end, the hydroxyl-ended "monomer" formed from the acid and two moles of glycol frequently forms the starting material. The subsequent polycondensation to give polyester and free diol is a special and important form of a type I interchange reaction, of which the first step is:

$$2HOR_1OOCR_2COOR_1OH \rightleftarrows HO(R_1OOCR_2COO)_2R_1OH + HOR_1OH \qquad (4)$$

Further steps in which molecules of steadily increasing size are condensed then follow.

The polycondensation is usually carried out by heating the material at a temperature above the melting point of the resultant polymer, although polycondensation in the solid state just below the melting point can also take place (6). Heating at a temperature above 200°C. for several hours and under a vacuum of less than 1 mm. is commonly required. Under these conditions, diol formed in reaction (4) volatilizes, and the chemical equilibrium is disturbed. An excess of diol is generally used because its volatility is much greater than that of the acid component.

This method of polycondensation is not limited to aliphatic diols or to linear polyesters. Bisphenol esters with dicarboxylic acids condense in a similar way (7), and the reaction has also been used to polycondense poly(ethylene terephthalate) with polymethylphenylethoxysiloxanes (8). By reacting hydroxyl-ended poly(ethylene adipate) with polyols such as pentaerythritol, Youngson and Melville (9) were able to prepare branched chain polyesters of definite composition.

The reverse of reaction (4) is also well known, because of its retarding effect on the rate of polyester formation by the method described above. Attempts to carry out the reaction at too low a temperature for effective glycol removal result for this reason in a severe molecular weight limitation. At 200°C. and a pressure of 2 mm., the polyester from sebacic acid and 1,6-hexanediol has a maximum molecular weight of 4000, whereas an increase in temperature to 260°C. enables the molecular weight to be increased to 5450 (10). The reaction with alcohols has also been used to degrade high polymers with monohydric alcohols. Flory (11) studied the kinetics of the degradation of poly(decamethylene adipate) by lauryl alcohol, while Korshak and co-workers examined the reaction of poly(hexamethylene sebacate) with cetyl alcohol (12) and the reaction of poly(ethylene terephthalate) with cresol (13). The reaction has also proved to be of commercial value in the recovery of dimethyl terephthalate from poly(ethylene terephthalate) by reacting it with methanol (14). In carrying out this alcoholysis reaction it is necessary to work at a high temperature, and a sealed system must be used in order to prevent premature evaporation of the degrading alcohol.

It is most difficult to prove that random attack by a terminal hydroxyl group of a polymer molecule on ester links of other macromolecules occurs in a similar way, for it is difficult to isolate this particular reaction. The general evidence below will suggest that this does happen, however.

b. *Evidence for Reactions of Type II (Ester/Carboxyl)*

This is a similar reaction, but is much less frequently described. The special case which is the polycondensation of carboxyl-ended units with elimination of dicarboxylic acid has been found to occur (15) when the ethylene ester of *o*-phthalic acid is heated, for free acid is generated in the reaction shown in eq. (5).

$$2HOOCC_6H_4COOCH_2CH_2OOCC_6H_4COOH \rightleftarrows$$
$$H(OOCC_6H_4COOCH_2CH_2)_2OOCC_6H_4COOH + C_6H_4(COOH)_2 \quad (5)$$

Similarly, the carboxyl-ended ethylene diadipate undergoes slow elimination of adipic acid at 200°C. and 1–2 mm. pressure, with formation of low molecular weight polyester (16).

The reverse degradation of poly(ethylene terephthalate) by adipic acid has also been shown to take place at 200°C. (13).

c. *Evidence for Reactions of Type III (Ester/Ester)*

Kursanov, Korshak, and Vinogradova (17) have used an isotope exchange method to demonstrate the interchange reaction between carboxyl-ended poly(hexamethylene sebacate) of molecular weight 3400 and deuterated diethyl succinate, $C_2H_5OOCCHDCHDCOOC_2H_5$. They took equimolar amounts of the polyester repeat units and the diethyl succinate, and held the mixture molten for 10 hr. at 250°C. After cooling, the polyester was purified by petroleum ether precipitation from benzene solution. The purification was repeated five times until the unchanged diethyl succinate was completely removed. The deuterium content of the polyester, determined by combustion to water and subsequent density determination, was such that about 30% exchange between the two compounds had taken place.

A further general method for the demonstration of this type of interchange is to cause materials with no reactive hydroxyl or carboxyl end-groups to polymerize. Bis(2-acetoxyethyl) terephthalate and bis(2-benzoxyethyl) terephthalate have been shown to polymerize at 305°C. to give poly(ethylene terephthalate) (18). Goodman and Nesbitt (19) describe how, by heating to 250°C. poly(ethylene terephthalate) with 1,4-dibenzoyloxybutane, and poly(tetramethylene terephthalate) with 1,2-dibenzoyloxyethane they could extract from the product 1,2-dibenzoyloxyethane and 1,4-dibenzoyloxybutane, respectively, showing that in each case interchange had taken place. The same authors also heated the cyclic ethylene terephthalate trimer, $(C_6H_4COOCH_2CH_2OCO)_3$ with a catalyst at 306°C. and thereby formed poly(ethylene terephthalate). This reaction did not take place after intensive drying of the trimer, however, and there is the possibility that some ring opening by hydrolysis may first be necessary, followed by interchange reactions of type I.

d. General Evidence

Finally, there is unspecific evidence for the occurrence of interchange reactions. Usually, it can be seen that two of the possible types can be involved, but no differentiation can be made between them.

When two samples of poly(decamethylene adipate) were mixed (20), a fall in viscosity was obtained which corresponded to a fall in weight-average molecular weight, though there was no change in the number-average molecular weight. The fall was doubtless caused by molecular weight equilibration brought about by the interchange reaction. Similarly, Kresse (21) mixed poly(ethylene terephthalate) with 10–20 mole-% of a second polyester in which the acid component was phthalic, isophthalic, hexahydroterephthalic, succinic, adipic, or sebacic acid. On first adding any of these second components a polyester was obtained of a given softening point, but on holding the mixture for about an hour the softening point gradually fell, usually by about 20–30°C. The fall was caused by the slow randomization by ester interchange of the first formed block copolymer, with a consequent gradual fall in the softening point. Rafikov, Korshak, and Chelnokova (22) took a narrow molecular weight fraction of poly(ethylene adipate) of molecular weight 1100 which could not be fractionated further. After heating this material for 42 hr. at 170°C. in a sealed tube, they obtained a product which could again be fractionated and which had a molecular weight distribution very similar to the original polyester. Yet another demonstration of the reaction was also made by Korshak and his school (23) by the preparation of two polyesteramides. The first, from 2-aminoethanol and sebacic acid, had the repeat unit —OCH_2-$CH_2NHCO(CH_2)_8CO$—, while the second was made by polycondensing *N,N′*-bis(2-hydroxyethyl)decanediamide with sebacic acid. With no interchange and by simple elimination of water by esterification, the reaction would have been

$$x\mathrm{HO(CH_2)_2NHCO(CH_2)_8CONH(CH_2)_2OH} + x\mathrm{HOOC(CH_2)_8COOH} \rightarrow \\ \text{—}[\mathrm{O(CH_2)_2NHCO(CH_2)_8CONH(CH_2)_2OOC(CH_2)_8CO}]_x\text{—} + x\mathrm{H_2O} \quad (6)$$

However, when the physical properties and electron diffraction patterns of the two products were compared, they were found to be identical, and to have the expected size of repeat unit, a result which could only have been brought about by interchange reactions.

The varied evidence for these reactions which has been given illustrates their practical importance. They are essential in the preparative polycondensation process, and enable the molecular weight distribution in the polymer to be re-established after a disturbance. They also enable block copolymers to be made, but also lead to eventual copolymer randomization. They are finally the source of degradation of polyesters by alcoholysis.

3. Catalysis of Interchange

Although measurements of uncatalyzed polycondensation reaction rates have been described (24), high molecular weight polyesters cannot be made without catalysts, for in their absence thermal degradation severely limits the attainable molecular weight. Consequently, interchange reactions in high molecular weight polyesters must of necessity always be examined in the presence of catalysts.

The interchange reactions are formally similar to esterification and hydrolysis, and as might be expected are catalyzed both by strong acids, such as *p*-toluenesulfonic acid, and by strong bases, such as sodium hydroxide. These catalysts are of limited use, nevertheless, because the former catalyze the dehydration of glycols, with incorporation of the resulting polyglycols as impurities into the polyester chain, while the latter are quickly inactivated by salt formation. A large number of metal oxides, hydroxides, alkoxides and salts with *weak* acids are, however, also known to be active as polycondensation catalysts. Examples can be briefly cited from every group of the Periodic Table: compounds of lithium (25), zinc, aluminum (26), titanium (27), antimony (28), uranium (29), manganese, and cobalt (26) have all been described. A recent compilation gives a comprehensive list (30); it is clear that compounds of very many metals catalyze the reaction, and some of the most useful are not strongly basic. However, other considerations such as the elimination of unwanted side reactions narrow the practical choice of catalysts in the preparation of polyesters, particularly when they are to be used for fiber or film manufacture. A compromise must usually be made between the useful activity of the catalyst and its activity in promoting degradative reactions. The final choice is usually very restricted, and is dependent on the end use to which the polyester is to be put.

The mode of action of these metal compounds is not known with certainty. Catalysis by strong acids and bases probably involves similar mechanisms to those found in esterification and hydrolysis, though the medium, particularly in the later stages of the reaction, is not strongly ionizing. Ester interchange reactions with edible oils, catalyzed by many compounds, including an alkali metal alcoholate such as sodium ethoxide, are known (31). The close parallel between these reactions and polyester interchange reactions suggests that a metal alcoholate may again be the active catalyst. There is experimental support for this view, for when oxides of boron or antimony are heated with ethylene glycol, glycoloxides of formulae $B_2(OCH_2CH_2O)_3$ and $Sb_2(OCH_2CH_2O)_3$ are formed with elimination of water (32). These glycoloxides are active as catalysts for polycondensation. Berner and Aaberg (33) examined the interchange reaction between bornyl acetate and methanol by salts of weak acids using as catalysts weak acid salts of cadmium, lead, thallium, zinc and calcium. From their reaction vessel when cadmium acetate was used as catalyst, an unstable compound, $Cd(OCH_3)OOCCH_3$ separated, and they were also able to prepare the corresponding cadmium methoxybenzoate from cadmium benzoate and methanol. In the case of lead benzoate, a basic salt, $Pb(OH)OOCC_6H_5$ was obtained which also was catalytically active. Similar mixed salts could not be prepared from salts of mineral acids, which were not in any case catalytically active.

If similar compounds are the active catalyst species in the catalysis of polycondensation, a possible scheme for the catalysis is as shown in eq. (7)

$$\sim\!\!\sim R_1OH + M(OR_2OH)_n \rightleftarrows \sim\!\!\sim R_1OM(OR_2OH)_{n-1} + HOR_2OH$$

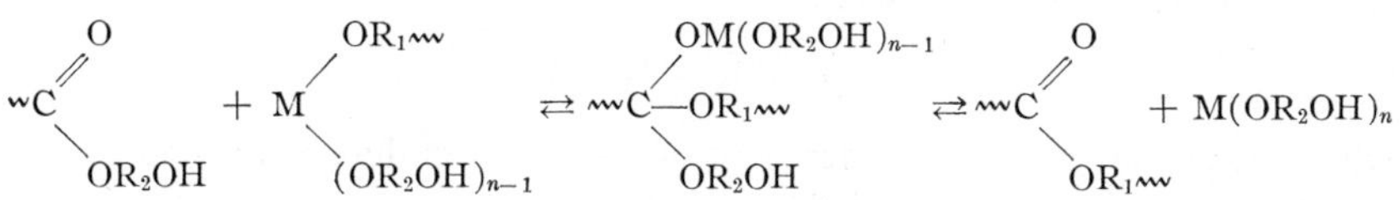

(7)

Analogous mechanisms would apply to the other possible forms of the polyester interchange reaction.

This nonionic mechanism may exaggerate the lack of charge separation, particularly in the early stages of polycondensation, while hydroxyl and carboxyl terminal group concentrations remain high, and in reality there may be a gradual change from the similar ionic to this nonionic mechanism.

4. Kinetics of Interchange

a. Polycondensation

Kinetic studies have been predominantly concerned with the preparative polycondensation reaction (4).

If diol and acid are reacted at a given temperature, the rate of increase of molecular weight can be followed by measuring the rate of increase of viscosity or the rate of change of endgroup concentrations. However, the results are very difficult to interpret because both esterification and polycondensation reactions are proceeding simultaneously. Little attempt has been made to measure the kinetics of polycondensation in this way, though several workers, for example Flory (34), have studied the kinetics of polyesterification in this way.

This difficulty is overcome by starting with a monomer such as bis(2-hydroxyethyl) terephthalate in which the whole of the esterification has been completed and in which polycondensation alone can increase the molecular weight. Again, the material is heated at a fixed temperature with a catalyst, and an inert gas may be passed through the molten mass to remove the diol as it is formed. The extent of the reaction can be followed by measurements of endgroup concentrations, molecular weight, or mass of diol evolved.

If the reverse reaction and volume changes in the system are neglected, the rate of polycondensation may be expressed as

$$da/dt = -ka^n \tag{8}$$

where a is the concentration of hydroxyl endgroups after time t, k is the rate constant for the reaction, and n is an integer determining the order of the reaction, with respect to hydroxyl endgroups. If p is the fraction of the reaction that has taken place,

$$p = 1 - (a/a_0) \tag{9}$$

where a_0 is the initial concentration of hydroxyl endgroups at zero time.

Integrating eq. (8) we find, for $n = 1$:

$$t = (1/k) \ln [1/(1 - p)] \tag{10}$$

for $n = 2$,

$$t = (1/ka_0) \{[1/(1 - p)] - 1\} \tag{11}$$

and for $n = 3$,

$$t = (1/2ka_0^2) \{[1/(1 - p)^2] - 1\} \tag{12}$$

The order of the reaction may then be determined by plotting t against each of $\ln [1/(1 - p)]$, $1/(1 - p)$, and $1/(1 - p)^2$, and observing which graph most nearly gives a straight line.

Korshak, Bekasova, and Zamyatina (25) examined the polycondensation of bis(2-hydroxyethyl) terephthalate in this way, using lithium hydroxide and aluminum oxide as catalysts. They followed the reaction both by determining the hydroxyl content of the polymer and also by measuring the rate of distillation of ethylene glycol. They found that a second-order reaction with an activation energy of 35 kcal./mole best fitted their results between 242 and 285°C. and up to a molecular weight of about 2000. Griehl and Schnock (26,35) examined the same reaction up to a molecular weight of about 20,000, although they used as starting material the esterification product of terephthalic acid and ethylene glycol without further purification, and followed the polycondensation by measurements of the solution viscosity of the polymer. They found that the first-order equation (eq. 10) best fitted their results, although in two of their three experiments for which graphs were shown, there was little to choose between the fit for both first- and second-order expressions. They compared the rates obtained with a number of metal oxides and weak acid salts as catalysts. Skwarski (36), by measuring the rate of glycol evolution, reported that the same reaction was of the third-order and measured an activation energy of 37 kcal./mole between 240 and 280°C., when magnesium methoxide was used as catalyst. The polycondensation was taken to a molecular weight of about 2000 at atmospheric pressure, and to about 7000 at 3 mm. pressure.

The major disadvantage of this experimental approach is that the reverse reaction is, of necessity, neglected. This is quite unrealistic, particularly at the higher molecular weights, since for a given concentration of diol in solution the reverse reaction becomes progressively more important. The concentration of diol in solution at any temperature is determined by an equilibrium with diol in the vapor phase, and the polyester molecular weight is in turn determined by its chemical equilibrium with diol in solution. The resultant equilibrium between poly(ethylene terephthalate) and glycol vapor has been measured directly by Griehl and Förster (37) at various glycol pressures by passing a current of nitrogen containing a known partial pressure of ethylene glycol through the molten polyester and determining the resulting constant polyester molecular weight. They confirmed that the higher the vapor pressure of glycol, the lower was the molecular weight: at a molecular weight of 20,000 the glycol vapor pressure was about 2.5 mm. They found a mean value of 4.9 for the equilibrium constant K of the reaction

$$2 \sim\!\!\sim COOCH_2CH_2OH \rightleftarrows \sim\!\!\sim COOCH_2CH_2OOC \sim\!\!\sim + HOCH_2CH_2OH \qquad (13)$$

where

$$K = [\sim\!\!\sim COOCH_2CH_2OOC \sim\!\!\sim][HOCH_2CH_2OH]/[\sim\!\!\sim COOCH_2CH_2OH]^2 \qquad (14)$$

Unfortunately, this result cannot be used to correct the work described above, for the glycol evolved in those experiments was not in equilibrium with the reacting mixture. There is, too, another complication, for in molten viscous polymers diffusion of the volatile diol to the surface is a slow process and a concentration gradient of the diol in solution is set up within the reacting mass. The actual net forward reaction rate will thus vary throughout the mass of the polyester.

This hindrance to polycondensation not only makes kinetic measurements of this kind unreliable, but also makes the preparation of high molecular weight polyesters difficult. The need to maximize the rate of removal of by-product either by repeatedly renewing the polymer surface (38) or by generating a very large surface area in some other way (39) is well known. This point has been emphasized by the study (40) of the rate of polycondensation of poly(ethylene terephthalate) in static layers of various thicknesses by passing nitrogen at various pressures over the polyester. It was found that even in layers between 0.35 and 1.3 mm. thick the rate of rise of molecular weight was greater, the thinner the layer. In this work, in which the effect of the reverse reaction was again neglected, a second-order expression with respect to hydroxyethyl endgroups was found to fit the measurements on the reaction catalyzed by compounds of lead, calcium, zinc, and aluminum. Korshak and Vinogradova (41) demonstrated the importance of the volatility of the by-product diol on the rate of polycondensation by preparing both a carboxyl-ended (I) and a hydroxyl-ended (II) polymer from sebacic acid and 1,6-hexanediol, and a polyester from ethylene glycol and diethyl sebacate, with terminal ethyl groups (III). Mixtures of the three possible pairs of polymers were then heated for 10 hr. at 200°C. and 2 mm. pressure, and molecular weights of the mixtures were redetermined. The mixtures of I and II and of II and III increased in molecular weight, for in both of these mixtures the polycondensation by-product was volatile (either 1,6-hexanediol, ethanol, or water). The molecular weight of the mixture of I and III did not change, because the sebacic acid which would be formed as by-product in the polycondensation was not sufficiently volatile to disturb the equilibrium.

The only way of making unambiguous measurements of the rate of polycondensation is, therefore, to prevent the removal of diol, and make allowance for its presence, rather than to try to remove it completely and instantaneously. Challa (24,42,43) has done this, by completely filling small glass tubes with bis(2-hydroxyethyl) terephthalate or with low molecular weight polycondensate from it. After heating for various times, the tubes were broken open, and the contents analyzed for free glycol and unchanged bis(2-hydroxyethyl) terephthalate. In this way, by heating the tubes until equilbrium was established, the equilibrium constant K for the above reaction was directly determined, and allowance could then be made for the reverse glycolysis reaction by including a term into eq. (8) to represent it, and then integrating the modified expression. No catalyst was used in this work, and it was found that both the forward and the reverse reactions had about the same dependence on temperature, the activation energy being 23 kcal./mole. This implies that the heat of reaction, the difference between the activation energies is very small, as is expected for interchange in which the reacting groups before and after the interchange are identical. The good fit found for the integrated reversible second-order expression suggests that this is, in fact, the correct expression under these conditions.

For higher molecular weights than could be covered by this method, recourse must be to viscosity changes in the polyester melt, for endgroup concentration changes become too small for the even smaller differences with time to be measured. Results obtained in this way are always difficult to relate to fundamental rate constants, for side reactions leading to thermal scission of polymer chains can play havoc with the calculated endgroup concentrations; the most reliable estimates of rate constants are bound to be those determined at the lower degrees of polymerization.

b. Other Interchange Reactions

Flory (11) investigated the kinetics of alcoholysis of poly(decamethylene adipate) by 1,10-decanediol and by lauryl alcohol, by measuring changes in the melt viscosity during reaction. Such a reaction is much more rapid than the corresponding polycondensation in the molecular weight range that was used, and can thus be followed quite reliably by this method. By assuming that the rate of removal of the degrading alcohol was proportional to the concentrations of ester links, alcohol, and catalyst, and that all ester links were equally available for attack by alcohol, Flory developed an expression for the expected change of melt viscosity with time with which the experimental results were in excellent agreement. He also found, as expected, that the reaction was catalyzed by *p*-toluenesulfonic acid and that the rate constant was proportional to catalyst concentration. From measurements with 1,10-decanediol made over the temperature range 82–130°C., with this catalyst (44), the activation energy was found to be 12.2 kcal./mole. Similar work (45) on the degradation of poly(ethylene isophthalate) by ethylene glycol has resulted in identical conclusions about the nature of the reaction.

A basic assumption in methods of this kind is that although other interchange reactions are taking place simultaneously with that under investigation (that is, the polycondensation reaction or its reverse), they have no effect on the overall viscosity, or on the terminal group concentrations. It is much more difficult to measure the rates of these other reactions. Challa (43) investigated the rate of the type I interchange reaction in poly(ethylene terephthalate) for the special case in which bis(2-hydroxyethyl) terephthalate is formed:

$$\sim COO(CH_2)_2OH + HO(CH_2)_2OOCC_6H_4COO(CH_2)_2OOC\sim \rightleftarrows HO(CH_2)_2OOCC_6H_4COO(CH_2)_2OH + \sim COO(CH_2)_2OOC\sim \quad (15)$$

This is similar to the polycondensation already described, bis(2-hydroxyethyl) terephthalate being eliminated instead of glycol. The technique was to determine the bis(2-hydroxyethyl) terephthalate by vacuum sublimation; the starting material (low molecular weight polymer) already having had this substance and ethylene glycol removed from it. The rate constant, deduced from direct measurement of the rate of formation of bis(2-hydroxyethyl) terephthalate was of the same order of magnitude between 223 and 254°C. as the polycondensation reaction rate constant, but the activation energy of the reaction, 31 kcal./mole, was appreciably higher.

To summarize the available results, the kinetics of the interchange reactions are probably best described by second-order expressions. Measured activation energies are very variable, and are probably dependent on the nature of the reaction, of the polyester, and of the catalyst used. For the uncatalyzed reactions, however, the activation energy is not less than 25 kcal./mole, and this is much higher than the 12–15 kcal./mole usually found for acid- and base-catalyzed esterification and hydrolysis reactions, with which the result for the acid-catalyzed polyester glycolysis is in good agreement.

c. *Dependence of Rate on Chain Length*

It is almost impossible to measure directly the dependence of interchange rates on chain length, because it is extremely difficult to isolate reactions involving single molecular species. Challa (42) has examined the simplest form of the problem in the polycondensation leading to poly(ethylene terephthalate) by measuring the concentration of the monomer in low molecular weight polyesters at equilibrium, and comparing it with that deduced from the Flory relationship (46) shown in eq. (16)

$$N_n = N_0\, p^{(n-1)}\, (1 - p)^2 \quad (16)$$

where N_n and N_0 are the numbers of n-mer molecules and initial monomer molecules, respectively, and p is the fraction of endgroups that have polycondensed. The derivation of the relationship assumes that all molecules are equally reactive. For monomer, $n = 1$, and the number of monomer molecules at any degree of reaction p should thus be proportional to $(1 - p)^2$. Challa found that the monomer content was up to 1.6 times greater than expected by this relation. He also measured the rate constant for the uncatalyzed forward reaction in polyesters of progressively increasing molecular weight, and found it to increase. The rate constant for the reverse (glycolysis) reaction remained constant, however, and consequently the reaction equilibrium constant also increased from 0.4 at a degree of polymerization of 1.7 to 1.1 at a degree of polymerization of 6.2.

He was able to explain both results by postulating a rate constant for polycondensation between polymer molecules 1.8 times greater than that for polycondensation involving one or more monomer molecules. The difference was ascribed to the lower activation entropy for reactions involving monomer.

In order to resolve the problem at higher molecular weights, the molecular weight distribution can be determined for linear polyesters, and a comparison made between the distribution found and that theoretically predicted on the basis of reactivity being independent of molecular size. Measurement of molecular weight distributions which substantially confirm those predicted by the formula above have been made (47,48) but in recent years Korshak and his co-workers (49–51) have described polyester fractionations which show a much narrower molecular weight distribution than would be expected from Flory's theory. These workers have also deduced an alternative distribution function which predicts a much less heterogeneous distribution than does Flory's, but a fallacy in their argument has been pointed out (52). One concludes that if this experimentally found distribution were correct, there would be considerable doubt cast on the principle of equal reactivity. However, an examination of the published data of these workers suggests that much of their experimental evidence for polyester distributions is based on fractionations of poly(ethylene adipate) and poly(decamethylene adipate) reported in a single paper (50) in which each polyester was only fractionated into five or six fractions. Since incomplete fractionation leads to a narrowing of the apparent molecular weight distribution, and in view of the evidence for the broader distribution predicted by eq. (16) and of other evidence in favor of equal reactivity of all links already mentioned (11), we may conclude that there is insufficient evidence to disprove the equal interchange reactivity of ester groups in molecules of all sizes, other than between monomer and higher polymers in poly(ethylene terephthalate).

5. Cyclic Oligomers

Polyesters consist not only of linear and branched molecules, but may also contain small cyclic molecules, and probably, in addition, larger cyclic molecules which cannot be isolated. Thus, a cyclic dimer has been obtained from poly(ethylene isophthalate) during the later stages of polycondensation (53), and similar cyclic trimer (19,54) and cyclic tetramer and pentamer (19) molecules have been found in poly(ethylene terephthalate).

Such cyclic oligomers could be formed by any of the three types of interchange reaction, but since they are found in equilibrium with molecules of other sizes in high molecular weight polyesters, even to the extent of being reformed in polyesters from which they have been removed (19), they are probably not produced by closure of the ends of a short chain. Although the endgroup concentrations are small the reaction rate constants for reactions of types I and II may well be higher than that for type III, and either the process by which a polymer endgroup undergoes an intramolecular interchange with another group near the chain end, or that in which a small portion of the middle of the chain is cut out by the interchange reaction (3) is a possible way of forming the ring compound.

Not only can these rings be formed in this way, but as already mentioned, the cyclic trimer from poly(ethylene terephthalate) can also be polymerized in presence of any one of several interchange catalysts. This behavior is akin to the reversible lactone polymerization (55,56) which itself is presumably an interchange reaction of this kind, and which can lead to formation of a high molecular weight polyester.

B. SILICONES

E. E. Bostick

General Electric Co.

1. Introduction

The field of organosilicon chemistry has developed rapidly during the past twenty-five years. The greatest application of the developed chemical knowledge is in the synthesis and technology of polyorganosiloxanes. The generic term "silicone" is used to describe the entire area. The term will be used in this discussion to imply those organosilicon compounds that are polymeric with a majority of the units connected by silicon–oxygen bonds. Both linear and nonlinear polymers will be discussed.

Polyorganosiloxanes, silicones, are further characterized by the lack of an isolable stable monomer, i.e., $R_2Si{=}O$. The smallest stable difunctional compound that has been isolated yet is the cyclic trimer, which is a six-membered ring of stoichiometry $(R_2SiO)_3$. Larger cyclics, tetramers, pentamers, hexamers, etc., have also been isolated and, in some cases, well characterized (57,58). For the dimethyl-substituted siloxanes this is especially true (59–62).

Usually, the conversion of these low molecular weight cyclics to high molecular weight polymers involves equilibration or interchange reactions. In almost all cases very few or no new bonds are formed. The polymers formed may range from low molecular weight liquids to high molecular weight gums, elastomers or crosslinked resins. These interchange reactions may be acid- or base-catalyzed. The catalysts used to promote polymerization may also cause chain scission and, ultimately, depolymerization.

Some interchange and equilibration may be effected thermally. The thermal equilibration of polydimethylsiloxane has been studied (58). A nonvolatile polymer was found to rearrange and yield distillable dimethylcyclosiloxanes upon heating to 400°C. The depolymerization was found to be a clean reaction with only traces of residual polymer. Further work has revealed that no radicals are formed, and that only silicon–oxygen bonds are involved (63). Other organosiloxanes also show this behavior.

2. Base-Catalyzed Reactions

Some of the processes for the preparation of high molecular weight linear silicone polymers are base-catalyzed (64–66).

Most studies have been done with dimethylsiloxane systems. A reactivity series of low molecular weight compounds towards bases has been established (67):

$$D_3 > D_4 > MD_2M > MDM > MM$$

where D denotes a difunctional dimethylsiloxane and M a monofunctional trimethylsiloxane. The series of reactions is represented eqs. (17)–(20) as follows, where D = $(CH_3)_2SiO$; M = $(CH_3)_3SiO$.

$$D_x + D_4 \xrightarrow{k_1} D_{x+4} \tag{17}$$

$$D_x + MM \xrightarrow{k_2} MD_xM \tag{18}$$

$$MD_xM + MM \xrightarrow{k_3} MD_{x-z}M + MD_zM \tag{19}$$

$$MD_xM + MD_yM \xrightarrow{k_4} MD_{x-w}M + MD_{y+w}M \tag{20}$$

The active species was reasoned to be a silanolate anion with an alkali metal counterion, i.e., K^+. The greater reactivity of D units than M units towards bases was proposed as due to electron withdrawal from silicon by the oxygens on each side. The net effect of the reactivity differences is to cause the average molecular weight to go through a maximum during equilibration ($k_1 \gg k_2, k_3$; $k_4 > k_2, k_3$; $k_2 = k_3$). Eventually, a true thermodynamic equilibrium is established.

Experiments with alkali metal hydroxides have shown their order of reactivity towards octamethylcyclotetrasiloxane, D_4, to be (68):

$$CsOH > RbOH > KOH > NaOH > LiOH$$

Conductivity measurements on the systems were found to be erratic although some evidence for the presence of ions was found. The increase in catalytic reactivity with size of cation was believed to be due to enhanced ionization of the silanolate.

Kinetic studies of the polymerization of octamethylcyclotetrasiloxane have revealed some interesting aspects of the reaction. One of these has shown that the rate is proportional to the square root of added KOH catalyst (69). An apparent activation energy of 19.6 kcal./mole was found. Experiments also showed preformed potassium silanolate to be equivalent to KOH in catalytic effect. An ionic mechanism was proposed according to the scheme shown in eqs. (21)–(23),

$$KOH + [(CH_3)_2SiO]_4 \xrightarrow{k_i} HO[(CH_3)_2SiO]_3{-}O(CH_3)_2SiO^- + K^+ \quad (21)$$

$$HO[(CH_3)_2SiO]_x^- + K^+ + [(CH_3)_2SiO]_4 \underset{k_d}{\overset{k_p}{\rightleftharpoons}} HO[(CH_3)_2SiO]_{x+4}^- + K^+ \quad (22)$$

$$HO[(CH_3)_2SiO]_x^- + K^+ \underset{k_i}{\overset{k_t}{\rightleftharpoons}} HO[(CH_3)_2SiO]_xK \quad (23)$$

As can be seen, this mechanism postulates an ionization step as the rate-controlling process with reversible termination by association. The reverse reaction is shown to produce tetramer but may also produce other cyclics and chain scission products. Further, a secondary reaction involving condensation of terminal hydroxyl groups is possible.

The rate dependence on the square root of base catalyst concentration was attributed to the ionization equilibrium. Thus,

$$SiOK \underset{k_2}{\overset{k_1}{\rightleftharpoons}} SiO^- + K^+$$

with

$$K_e = [SiO^-][K^+]/[SiOK] = [SiO^-]^{+2}/[SiOK] \quad (24)$$

and

$$[SiO^-] = K_e^{1/2}[SiOK]^{1/2} = K_e^{1/2}[KOH]^{1/2} \quad (25)$$

The rate constant will then be proportional to $[KOH]^{1/2}$.

$$k = A[KOH]^{1/2} \quad (26)$$

where A is a factor depending on temperature, monomer concentration, etc.

More recent studies reveal that the equilibrium state of the reaction is a function of both monomer concentration and temperature (70). The rate was found to be half-order with monomer and catalyst concentration. The relationship applies to mixtures containing nitrobenzene and toluene as well. Further, the reverse reaction is half-order in catalyst concentration. Stoichiometric measurements indicate that the number of growing chains remains constant throughout the reaction. A mechanism was proposed in which the opening of a cyclosiloxane ion-pair at the end of the chain determines the rate of polymerization.

The differences between these two proposed mechanisms may not be striking. Kinetic studies in media of different dielectric constant have, in part, confirmed the ionic effect (71). As the dielectric constant of the medium was increased by selective solvents, the rate was found to increase, indicating a higher degree of ionization and/or solvation. Other solvent effects on the rate of base-catalyzed polymerization of octamethylcyclotetrasiloxane are known. For instance, the use of a good Lewis base such as tetrahydrofuran will allow polymerization at room temperature (72). Apparently, the Lewis base is stabilizing the alkali metal cation, thereby increasing the concentration of active species and creating a low energy path for polymerization to occur. A reference to the use of amides and nitriles as solvents for polymerization is in the patent literature (73).

The effects of other additives on the equilibration reactions of dimethylsiloxanes have also been observed and reported. For instance, polymerization of octamethylcyclotetrasiloxane is readily accomplished in the presence of a mixture of methyl and ethyl alcohols when catalyzed by strong bases: K_2O, KOH, CsOH, RbOH, R_4NOH (68). The polymer formed is insoluble and separates, but polymerization occurs in the homogeneous phase. More recently, the effects of other additives on the polymerization catalyzed by potassium hydroxide have been observed and reported (74). Carbon dioxide, anisole, diphenylamine, phenol, lithium hydroxide, and sodium hydroxide were included in the additives studied. Carbon dioxide exerts a temporary retardation on the rate. The other compounds also affect both rate and molecular weight of polymer formed. Sodium hydroxide and lithium hydroxide provide two very interesting effects. Both suppress rate of equilibration of KOH-catalyzed systems with lithium hydroxide as the most effective inhibitor. The authors invoke a stable pentacovalent silicon complex as the termination site, or dead end. The stability of the complex determines its efficiency in retardation of polymerization. A scale of stabilities of pentacovalent silicon complexes with inorganic bases was reported. They are as follows:

$$\mathrm{Na} < \mathrm{Li} < \mathrm{Zn} < \mathrm{Fe} < \mathrm{Al} < \mathrm{Be}$$

The effect of basic suppression is called "isobasic termination." Extension of this type of experiment may be necessary in order to differentiate between complexing effects and ionic association and to define the complexes more quantitatively. Such information is important with respect to silicone polymer stabilization and subsequent reactions of the polymer.

Poly(dimethylsiloxane) prepared by catalysis with potassium hydroxide is a heterodisperse material which contains, in addition to high molecular weight polymer, 13–15% of low molecular weight siloxanes which are volatile at <250°C. (68). If the potassium hydroxide remains, the entire polymer will depolymerize rapidly at 250°C. (90% in 20 hr.) (75).

Experiments have been conducted to determine the effect of residual catalyst and various neutralizing reagents on the mechanical properties of the polymer (76–79). An activation energy for stress relaxation of 5.1 kcal./mole was reported for polymer which contained 0.01% KOH, while polymer which had been decatalyzed with iodine required an apparent energy of 22.8 kcal./mole for stress relaxation. Treatments and materials which improve the stability of KOH-catalyzed polydimethylsiloxane include extraction with water, or addition of iodine, triaryl phosphate or phosphite, benzoic acid, or aluminum hydroxide.

Transient catalyst systems have been reported in the literature (75). For instance, the solid hydrate of tetramethylammonium hydroxide will polymerize octamethylcyclotetrasiloxane at temperatures of 70–130°C. The rate is comparable to that obtained with cesium hydroxide. Above 130°C., the quaternary hydroxide decomposes to trimethylamine and methanol. Other quaternary ammonium hydroxides are effective with the exception of those having alkyl substituents with β-hydrogens. Tetrabutylphosphonium hydroxide is also effective in catalyzing polymerization of dimethylsiloxanes from 20–130°C. Above 130°C., the hydroxide decomposes to tributylphosphine oxide and hydrocarbons. The active species in this case was postulated to be a silanolate anion with tetrabutylphosphonium counterion. Polymers prepared with this class of catalysts are much more stable to hydrolytic and base-catalyzed interchange.

Crosslinked elastomeric networks (I) may also be prepared *in situ* by this method through the introduction of tetrafunctional cyclics:

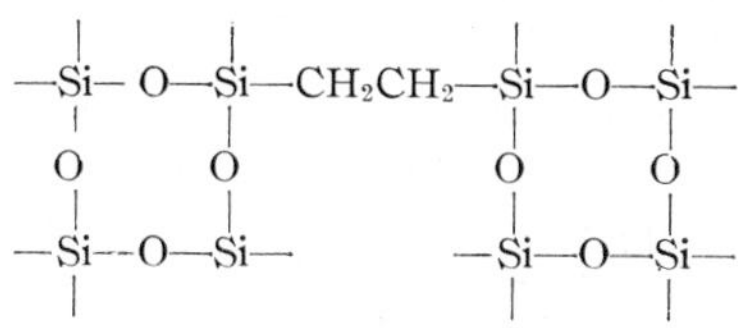

(I)

3. Organometallic Catalysts

Organometallic reagents add to the Si—O bond in polyorganosiloxanes in much the same manner as they add to ketone carbonyls. Di- and trifunctional organosiloxanes react by addition of the organic moiety of Grignard reagent, but monofunctional or triorganosiloxanes do not (80).

$$(C_6H_5SiO_{1.5})_x + C_6H_5MgBr \rightarrow (C_6H_5)_3SiOMgBr \xrightarrow{HOH} (C_6H_5)_3SiOH \qquad (27)$$

In a similar manner (81):

$$[(CH_3)_2SiO]_x + CH_3MgI \rightarrow (CH_3)_3SiOMgBr \xrightarrow{HOH} (CH_3)_3SiOH \qquad (28)$$

These reactions were accomplished on low molecular weight polymer in order to achieve adequate mixing. However, it is reasonable to assume that high molecular weight polymers will react likewise if properly dissolved.

Electron-transfer complexes have been used to polymerize methylsiloxanes. Complexes prepared from either sodium or potassium with naphthalene were found to effect polymerization of octamethylcyclotetrasiloxane at 25°C. (82) as shown in eq. (29). The reaction appears to be a

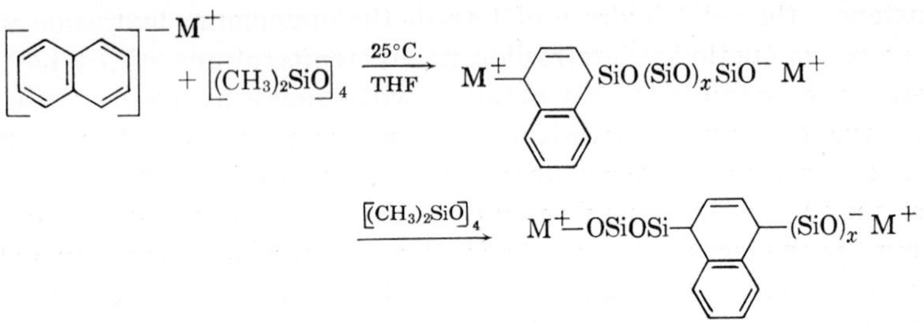

(29)

two-step initiation with both 1,2- and 1,4- dihydronaphthalene residues incorporated in the siloxane chain. For every complete interaction, there is a molecule of naphthalene regenerated. Likewise, carbanions were found to add to and then catalyze polymerization of methyl tetramer. By use of this technique, block copolymers were prepared having segments of polystyrene and polyisoprene incorporated with segments of polyorganosiloxanes. Properties of the polymers could be altered by varying the length of the segments.

Trialkyl aluminum compounds are reported further to polymerize dialkyl-polysiloxanes at ≤ 60°C. in 1 hr. to materials suitable for silicone rubber compounding (83,84).

4. Acid-Catalyzed Reactions

Acid-catalyzed rearrangements of siloxane bonds have not received the detailed investigation as have the base-catalyzed systems. Studies on acidic catalysts include the effects of both mineral acids and Lewis acids, but only one or two organic acids.

Sulfate esters of methylsiloxanes were prepared early and found to be easily hydrolyzed to siloxanes (58). Sulfuric acid-catalyzed rearrangements of low molecular weight methylsilicone fluids have been conducted (85). The reaction path postulated was as shown in eq. (30). The intermediate II was proposed as being capable of condensation

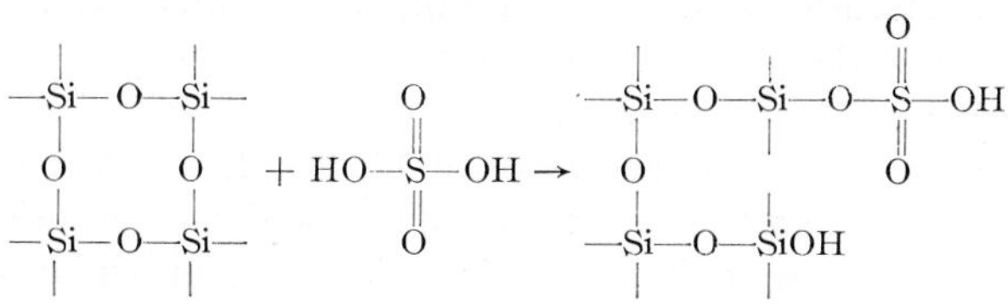

(II) (30)

at the terminal SiOH groups with the elimination of a molecule of water. The resulting water is then capable of regenerating sulfuric acid through hydrolysis. Chain growth is by a continuation of these exchange and hydrolytic steps. Molecular weight control is accomplished by the addition of monofunctional groups.

A systematic study of such a system has shown that the same equilibrium is attained with either sulfuric acid or antimony pentachloride (86). By applying Flory's statistical treatment (87) to the system, an equilibrium constant for the concentration of cyclic structures with y units was found to be:

$$K_y = (11.0)\,(0.40)^y \qquad y \geq 4 \qquad (31)$$

The calculated and experimental number-average molecular weights of the two systems corresponded very closely. The particular significance of such an experiment is that a minimum molar concentration of units, $(CH_3)_2$-SiO, is required in the form of rings before chain formation will occur. This concentration has been found to be 2.34M in tetrahydrofuran at room temperature (82).

Later observations have been made on the sulfuric acid–dimethylsiloxane system (88). The formation of a protonated siloxonium ion complex has been advanced as the route for siloxane bond activation and subsequent interchange. As the result of another study, a stepwise reaction has been proposed for polymerization of siloxane tetramers having both phenyl and methyl substituents on silicon (89). The active species was believed to be a siliconium ion, e.g.,

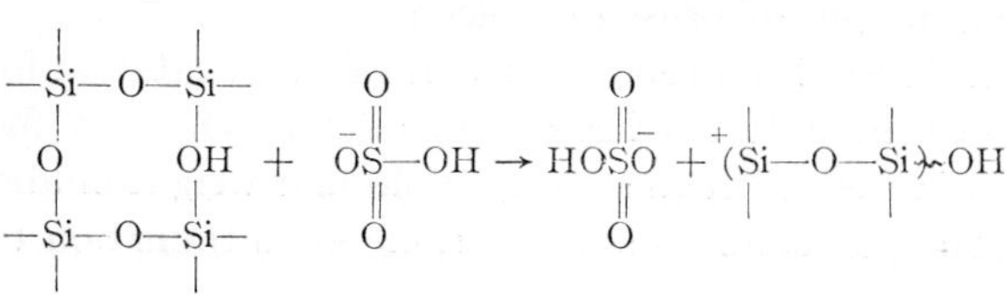

(32)

Molecular weight was found to increase with conversion to polymer which was a first-order process. Activation energy was reported to be 35.5 kcal./mole. Ethyl sulfuric acid was found to cause polymerization but not as effectively as sulfuric acid. Phenyl substitution and chlorophenyl substitution decrease the polymerization rate.

Oxygen has been found to accelerate the acid catalysis of methylsiloxane rearrangement and polymerization (90,91). On the basis of this effect, it has been suggested that the mechanism of interaction of sulfuric acid, ferric chloride, and aluminum sulfate dihydrate involves an oxidation-reduction process of the catalyst. Active species were proposed to be the lower and higher oxide and peroxide forms of the catalyst (90). There seems to be a need for further investigation in order to define this type of interaction more clearly.

Sulfuric acid has also been used as a depolymerization catalyst for methylsiloxane polymers (92). Octamethylcyclotetrasiloxane is generated by treating methylsilicone polymers with sulfuric acid in the presence of a volatile solvent. Hydrogen chloride and hydrogen bromide also react with polyorganosiloxanes to cause equilibration.

Aqueous hydrogen bromide has been claimed as a catalyst for the polymerization of dimethylsiloxanes (DP $\leq$ 10) with CH_3/Si ratio of 1–3 (93). Anhydrous hydrogen chloride is also effective as a reagent for breaking siloxane linkages to form chlorosilane and silanol endgroups at the scission point (94), as shown, for example, in eqs. (33)–(35). Most of the applica-

$$-\overset{|}{\underset{|}{\mathrm{Si}}}\mathrm{O}\overset{|}{\underset{|}{\mathrm{Si}}}- + \mathrm{HCl} \rightarrow -\overset{|}{\underset{|}{\mathrm{Si}}}\mathrm{Cl} + \mathrm{HO}\overset{|}{\underset{|}{\mathrm{Si}}}- \qquad (33)$$

$$-\overset{|}{\underset{|}{\mathrm{Si}}}\mathrm{OH} + -\overset{|}{\underset{|}{\mathrm{Si}}}\mathrm{OH} \rightarrow -\overset{|}{\underset{|}{\mathrm{Si}}}\mathrm{O}\overset{|}{\underset{|}{\mathrm{Si}}}- + \mathrm{H_2O} \qquad (34)$$

$$-\overset{|}{\underset{|}{\mathrm{Si}}}\mathrm{Cl} + \mathrm{H_2O} \rightarrow -\overset{|}{\underset{|}{\mathrm{Si}}}\mathrm{OH} + \mathrm{HCl} \qquad (35)$$

tions involve alkyl or alkyl functional-substituted siloxanes since aromatic groups are susceptible to cleavage in acid media (95,96).

In addition to protonic acid catalysis, there are many applications of Friedel-Crafts (Lewis acids) reagents. These include halides of boron, aluminum, iron, tin, phosphorus, and silicon.

Stannic chloride has been reported as an effective catalyst for the polymerization of octamethylcyclotetrasiloxane at temperatures above 100°C. (97). Linear polymers with an average molecular weight of about 350,000 are formed. The polymers possess the same glass transition temperature as that of a specimen of methylsilicone rubber of the same molecular weight. The polymerization is postulated to proceed through formation of an intermediate active complex (III) between stannic chloride and siloxane. For example,

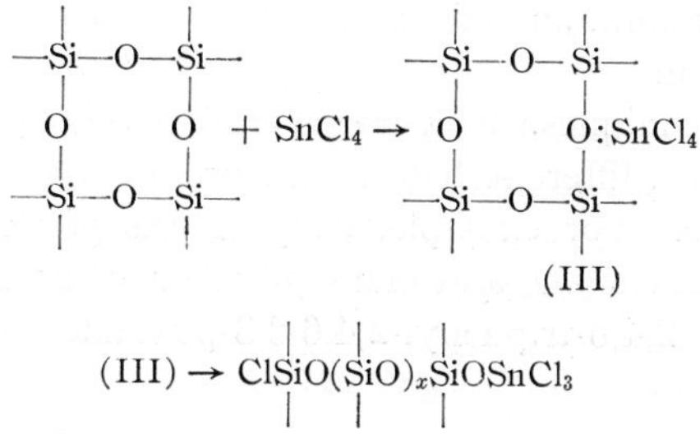

(36)

The covalent halides are all believed to react with SiO bonds in more or less the same manner as illustrated above. A cyclic transition state (IV) involving four centers is usually postulated (98)

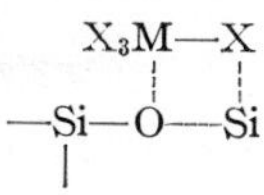

(IV)

where X is halogen. The interactions of organohalosilanes provide great interest due to their availability. Depolymerization of dimethylsilicone rubber by $(CH_3)HSiCl_2$ and $SiHCl_3$ in 5 hr. at 300–350°C. has been claimed (99). Products are alkylchlorosilanes and higher boiling compounds.

5. Copolymerization

Silicone copolymers may be generally divided into three groups. There are those which have siloxane units along the chain with different alkyl or aryl substituents, those which have other metal or organometallic units, and those which include organic polymer units and segments in the main chain or grafted to the main chain. This discussion will be primarily concerned with those copolymers prepared by reactions involving the chain backbone.

The incorporation of siloxane units having different substituents on silicon in methylsilicone fluids, gums and resins has been accomplished since the early days of industrial silicone technology. These units include vinyl, ethyl, trifluoropropyl, β-cyanoethyl, phenyl, biphenyl, and carbon functional substituents. The compositions are generally improved in specific properties such as oil resistance, high strength and toughness, flame resistance, low stress relaxation characteristics, and compatibility. The concentrations of units vary and usually depend on two major factors. First, the rates of polymerization and copolymerization to an equilibrium may determine the composition. Second, the economics of achieving the desired properties with a minimum concentration of comonomer may dictate the product composition.

There are two techniques which are generally used to prepare copolymers. The cohydrolysis of different halosilanes produces cyclosiloxanes having mixed substituents. For example, cohydrolysis of three equivalents of methylphenyldiethoxysilane and one equivalent of dimethyldichlorosilane in toluene gives 2,4,6-triphenyl-2,4,6,8,8-pentamethylcyclotetrasiloxane (100):

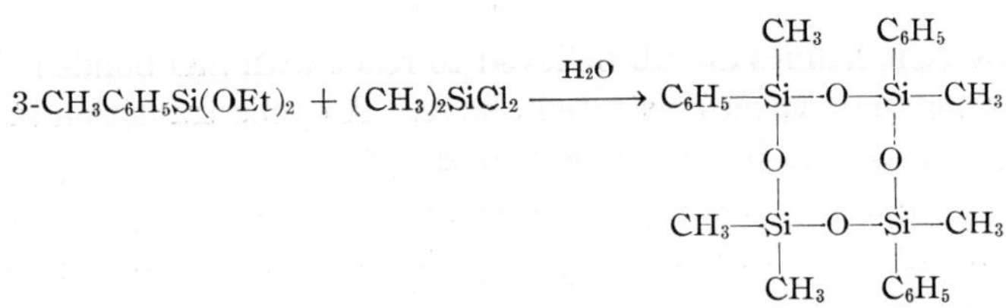
(37)

Cyclics such as this may then be subjected to equilibration to produce a copolymer with random units of phenylmethylsiloxane and dimethylsiloxane.

The other approach is to copolymerize different organocyclosiloxanes. There are many examples of this technique in the literature. Methylvinylpolysiloxanes have been copolymerized with dimethylsiloxanes by base catalysis to produce copolymers having up to 5% vinylmethylsiloxane (101,102). These copolymers exhibited improved stabilities and could be covulcanized with unsaturated organic elastomers. Likewise diphenyl–phenylmethylsiloxane copolymers have been prepared by copolymerizing hexaphenylcyclotrisiloxane with triphenyltrimethylcyclotrisiloxane and tetraphenyltetramethylcyclotetrasiloxane in the presence of basic catalysts (103). There are limitations to this technique. Probably the most severe is the tendency for some cyclics to polymerize extremely fast, and to then depolymerize extremely fast to a more stable cyclic isomer. This characteristic is exemplified by the fluoroalkylsiloxanes (104). The trimer, 2,4,6-tris(4,4,4-trifluoropropyl)-2,4,6-trimethylcyclotrisiloxane was found to follow this reaction path at 150°C in the presence of sodium hydroxide.

$$\underset{A}{\text{Cyclotrisiloxane}} \rightarrow \underset{B}{\text{Linear polymer}} \rightarrow \underset{C}{\text{Cyclotetrasiloxane}} \qquad (38)$$

Step A → B is irreversible and Step B → C is only slightly reversible. Therefore, one must stop the reaction at an opportune time in order to isolate polymer.

A comprehensive study of siloxane copolymerization has been conducted for only a few of the possible cyclics available. One such investigation has been conducted by copolymerizing different cyclosiloxanes with a series of five-membered silethylene–siloxane cyclics (105), for example, V.

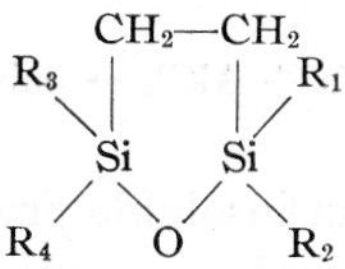

(V)

where R_1, R_2, R_3, R_4 are methyl or phenyl. All six members of this series were examined. This particular structure was considered ideal for one of the monomers, since the strain energy in the ring was estimated at about 8–12 kcal./mole (106). Thus, the reverse reaction in polymerization will be extremely slow. In comparison, the strain energy of hexamethylcyclotrisiloxane has been estimated at 3–4 kcal./mole. Reactions were base-catalyzed, i.e., potassium silanolate. The comonomers investigated were hexamethylcyclotrisiloxane and hexaphenylcyclotrisiloxane. The Mayo and Lewis (107) reactivity ratio concept was found to apply to the treatment of the data. The products of the reactivity ratios for several of the monomer pairs approached unity, indicating very little specificity of catalyst. Reactivity increased with increased ring strain and increased degree of phenyl substitution. Reactivity ratios were found to be temperature-dependent, $r_1r_2 \rightarrow 1$, which suggests large differences in activation energy. The tetraphenylsilethylene–siloxane cyclic, the cyclic most reactive to base-catalyzed polymerization, was found to be about 160-fold more reactive than the least reactive cyclic, hexamethylcyclotrisiloxane. This is in contrast to the results of Andrianov with acid catalysis (89). In that case, the polymerization rate decreased as degree of phenyl substitution increased.

In addition to copolymeric siloxanes with variation in organic substituent, copolymers have been prepared which have other metalloorganic units in the chain backbone. Most of the effort and accomplishment in this area has been led by Andrianov, who has reviewed the subject (108). The metal atoms that have been incorporated in siloxane polymer chains and networks are aluminum, titanium, tin, lead, and germanium. The preparation of high molecular weight polymers with these metals in the chain presents some difficulties. Due to the variable oxidation state and the extraordinary thermal stability of the M—O—Si bonds in the polymer, only complex polymers have been obtained. The separation of a pure cyclic structure which can then be polymerized to high molecular weight linear polymer has not been found in the open literature for polymers containing titanium and aluminum.

Polyalumodimethylsiloxanes have been prepared by reacting the sodium salt of polydimethylsiloxane with $AlCl_3$ (109):

$$\mathrm{NaO\overset{|}{\underset{|}{Si}}O(\overset{|}{\underset{|}{Si}}O)_{x}Na + AlCl_3 \rightarrow polymer + NaCl} \qquad (39)$$

If aluminum content is high, an insoluble product is obtained. As aluminum content is reduced, polymers become more soluble. Thus, the Al^{+3} is assumed to be providing branching and crosslinking sites. Polydimethylgermanosiloxanes have been prepared by acid-catalyzed rearrangement of hybrid cyclics (110). Cyclics containing 1.93–7.48% Ge were prepared by cohydrolysis of dimethyldichlorosilane and dimethyldibromogermane. Polymerization with 2–6% sulfuric acid was found to occur in two stages. First, a white precipitate forms, which is presumably due to germanoxane fragments. These fragments then interchange with siloxane fragments to produce a clear homogeneous reaction mass. The overall rate was found to be less than a comparable reaction with octamethylcyclotetrasiloxane. The molecular weight of the polymer produced was found to be in the range of 360,000–820,000.

In both the aluminum and titanium cases, the soluble polymer is probably branched. Of course, the insoluble polymer is highly branched and crosslinked. A structure similar to VI is postulated for titanium trifunctional organosiloxane copolymers. Similar structures (VII) may be drawn for the

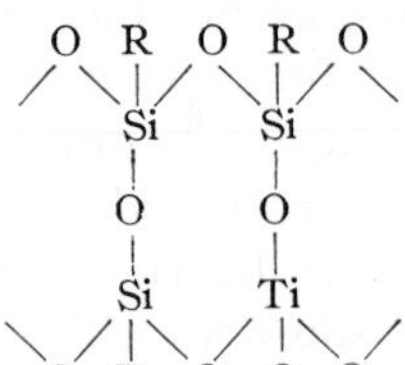

(VI)

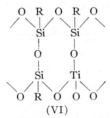

aluminum copolymer with $(C_6H_5SiO_{1.5})_x$. These structures are similar to those (VIII) postulated for the polyphenylsilsesquioxanes (111–113). These polymers were prepared by base catalysis from the hydrolysis products of phenyltriethoxysilane and phenyltrichlorosilane. Ordinarily, when trifunctional siloxanes are present in substantial concentrations in an

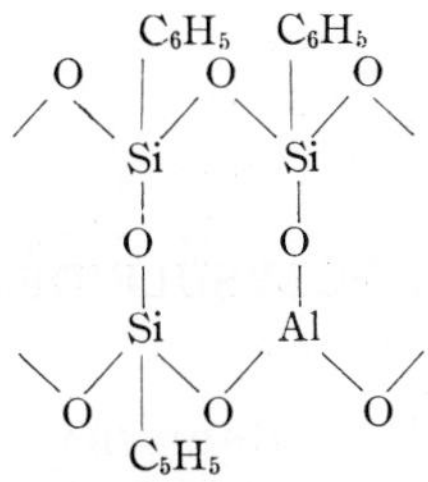

(VII)

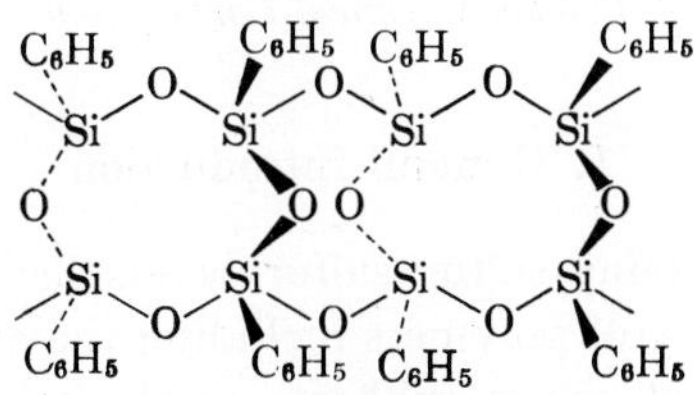

(VIII)

equilibration, a crosslinked structure finally results. The preparation of a soluble material with fully reacted trifunctional systems is therefore unique.

As has been mentioned previously, organosiloxane polymers may be copolymerized with organic systems (82). Many other systems are known. Silicones have been used in the modification of alkyds, polyethers, phenolics, and vinyl polymers (113–115). However, most of these polymer systems involve addition to functional groups on silicon rather than rearrangement. The possible exception is the incorporation of polyalkylene oxides with polysiloxanes wherein the silanolate anion opens the cyclic ether ring, for example,

$$RO(\overset{|}{\underset{|}{Si}}O)_x\overset{|}{\underset{|}{Si}}ORO(RO)_xH$$

(IX)

The silicone-modified organics exhibited new and improved properties for specialized applications.

C. POLYSULFIDES

M. B. Berenbaum

Thiokol Chemical Corporation

1. General Introduction

Redistribution involving sulfur–sulfur bonds has been used to explain phenomena in a variety of polymers including the alkyl polysulfide elastomers, sulfur-vulcanized diene rubbers, wool, hair and other proteins. Depending on the reaction environment, the interchange reactions have been shown to proceed via anionic or cationic processes or through radical intermediates. The major part of this section will deal with the alkyl polysulfide polymers. The chemistry of these products is somewhat better understood since it closely parallels the chemistry of simple organic molecules. The production and utilization of the commercial alkyl polysulfide polymers is markedly dependent on a series of interchange processes of different types which play key roles in various stages from polymer synthesis to performance in the field. Formation of the high molecular weight polymer takes place through a condensation reaction in which a number of side reactions limiting molecular weight can occur. Achieving high molecular weight requires interchange reactions to eliminate the chain-stopping terminals. Similarly, the facile reduction of these polymers to the commercially important thiol-terminated liquid polymers depends on interchange at the disulfide bond. In use, the relatively poor resistance to compression set of the cured product can be attributed to chemorheologic flow involving anionic interchange at these disulfide linkages. Another degradative side reaction results from cyclodepolymerization initiating at a mercaptide terminal and propagating by interchange displacement at an adjacent disulfide bond by the reactive terminal.

Despite the importance in terms of the life processes and the economically significant fields of wool and hair waving, the atypical chemistry in these systems arising from the greater reactivity of the disulfides derived from sulfur-containing amino acids requires explanation different from that for aliphatic polysulfide compounds. A useful review of the thiol–disulfide interchange in biological processes such as protein denaturation, blood clotting, and mitosis is presented by Jensen (116).

2. Interaction with Inorganic Sulfides

Otto and Rossing (117) in 1886 showed that organic disulfides could be converted to mercaptans by reaction with potassium monosulfide.

$$RSSR + S^{=} \rightleftharpoons RS^{-} + SSR \quad (40)$$

$$RSSR + 2S^{=} \rightleftharpoons 2RS^{-} + S_2^{=} \quad (41)$$

This reaction served as the basis for a preparative technique in a synthesis of mercaptans. With excess potassium sulfide, acidification of the equilibrium mixture followed by steam distillation results in fair yields of the mercaptan from the corresponding disulfide. In fact, this interchange reaction has been of economic importance for a long time since it serves as the basis for the process to dehair hides by reaction with calcium sulfide preparatory to tanning operations. The use of alkaline monosulfides in the solution of keratinaceous proteins is based on the reaction of the sulfide ion with the disulfide groups in the cystine of the protein cleaving the cross-links to form the cysteine salt thus solubilizing the protein. Aqueous inorganic monosulfides are particularly effective agents for cleaving the disulfide bonds in dispersions of the alkyl disulfide polymers (118).

In the manufacture of thiol-terminated polysulfide polymers, a reaction similar to this is used to reduce the high molecular weight disulfide polymer to the desired low molecular weight reactive products. The reagent used is sodium hydrosulfide, which reacts as in eq. (42) to form an equilibrium mixture of the mercaptide and a thiomercaptide. Since steam distillation cannot be used to isolate the product after acidification, it is necessary to use a reagent to react with the excess sulfur present in the thiomercaptide terminal. If not employed, the thiomercaptide terminals will react with the thiol terminals to form H_2S and reform the high molecular weight product. The reagent commonly used to eliminate this reaction is sodium sulfite, which "strips" the excess sulfur down to the thiol group while forming sodium thiosulfate.

$$—SRSSRSSRSSR— + {}^{-}SH \rightleftharpoons —RSSRS^{-} + HSSRSSR— \quad (42)$$

$$—RSSRSSH + {}^{=}SO_3 \rightleftharpoons —RSSRSH + {}^{=}S_2O_3 \quad (43)$$

The reaction of an alkyl disulfide polymer with disulfide ions proceeds in an essentially similar fashion (eq. 44). This equilibrium plays an important

$$—RSSR— + S_2^{=} \rightleftharpoons 2\ —RSS^{-} \quad (44)$$

role in the production of alkyl polysulfide polymers. If this polymerization were considered as a conventional condensation reaction between a difunctional halide and an inorganic disulfide, then great care would be necessary to react exact stoichiometric proportions of reagents in order to obtain a high molecular weight product. In theory, hydrolytic side reactions to which organic halides are susceptible would prevent the formation of anything beyond an intermediate molecular weight product. In actual practice, however, high molecular weights are easily obtained by using a substantial excess of the inorganic polysulfide. A brief review of the steps involved serves to explain these anomalous results.

$$\text{ClRCl} + \text{S}_2^{=}\ (\text{excess}) \rightarrow {}^{-}\text{S(SRS)}_n\text{S}^{-} \quad (45)$$

$$\text{—S(SRS)SRCl} + \text{OH}^{-} \rightarrow \text{—S(SRS)SROH} + \text{Cl}^{-} \quad (46)$$

Reaction (45) results in polymer formation with the molecular weight limited by the mole ratio of the excess inorganic polysulfide. Since reaction as in eq. (46) results in some chain-stopping with hydroxyl groups, the excess of inorganic polysulfide insures the essentially complete conversion of the halide terminals. The intermediate product is predominantly a thiomercaptide-terminated polymer of moderate molecular weight containing some proportion of the undesired hydroxyl terminals. In the later stages of the polymerization process, when most of the halide is consumed, the excess sodium polysulfide is continuously interchanging with the disulfide bonds in the polymer. When this occurs in the middle of a high molecular weight chain, relatively little effect would be observed, since two fairly high molecular weight fragments are formed. However, when the interchange occurs near the terminals, soluble low molecular weight fragments are formed.

$$\text{—SRSSRSSRSSRS—} + \text{S}_2^{=} \rightleftharpoons \text{—SRSSRSS}^{-} + {}^{-}\text{SSRSSRS—} \quad (47)$$

$$\text{—SRSSRSSRSSROH} + \text{S}_2^{=} \rightleftharpoons \text{—SRSSRSSRSS}^{-} + {}^{-}\text{SSROH} \quad (48)$$

The hydroxyl-terminated segments accumulate in the aqueous phase and are ultimately decanted from the polymer latex at the end of the reaction. The intermediate polymer is brought to the high molecular weight stage during the washing process used to remove the salts formed as by products of the reaction. The disulfide ion formed in reversal of the equilibrium of eq. (47) is also washed out, driving the equilibrium back in a chain-extension process. This phenomenon can be readily observed by washing under running water a ball of the soft gum formed by reaction of bis(2-chloroethyl) formal with 25% excess of sodium disulfide and observing its gradual conversion to a tough rubber.

The efficiency of the solubilization process to remove dead terminals is markedly affected by the nature of the terminal. Fettes and Mark (118) have shown by deliberate introduction of inert nonpolar terminals that the expected low molecular weight polymer is formed, and efforts to chain-extend the product by solubilizing these fragments were relatively unsuccessful. Conversely, deliberate incorporation of hydroxyl-containing chain stoppers by the use of ethylene chlorohydrin yielded a product which could be readily converted to a high molecular weight polymer by treatment with excess aqueous sodium polysulfide solution followed by the usual wash treatment.

The reaction of inorganic polysulfide species of rank* higher than two presents a somewhat complex picture. Equation (41) earlier described the equilibrium between alkyl disulfides with monosulfide ion and the alkyl mercaptide with disulfide ion. Trisulfide ion and higher rank species drive the equilibrium to formation of the oxidized product. In fact, this reaction has been used to prepare polymers from dimercaptans (121).

$$2RS^- + 2S_3^= \rightarrow RSSR + 3S_2^=$$
$$2RS^- + S_4^= \rightarrow RSSR + 2S_2^= \quad (49)$$

If excess amounts of the high rank polysulfide ion are present, the alkyl disulfide is thionated.

$$RSSR + S_4^= \rightarrow RS_3R + S_3^= \quad (50)$$

The identity in rank between the organic and ionic polysulfide compounds holds to a first approximation. Actually, the rank of the organic polysulfide tends to be somewhat less than that of the ionic species (122).

$$RS_4R + S_4^= \rightarrow RS_{3.2}R + S^=_{4.8} \quad (51)$$

3. Thiol–Disulfide Interchange: Monomeric Systems

The interchange reaction of a thiol with a disulfide was first described in 1920 by Lecher (123) working with sodium thiophenate and *o*-nitrophenyl phenyl disulfide.

$$C_6H_5S^- + C_6H_5SSC_6H_4{-}NO_2 \rightarrow NO_2{-}C_6H_4S^- + C_6H_5SSC_6H_5 \quad (52)$$

* The rank of polysulfide compounds is defined as the number of aggregated sulfur atoms in a bond or ionic species. This nomenclature is necessary since polysulfide compounds are frequently mixtures of the various sulfide species with an average value that is not necessarily an integer. Thus, while a disulfide corresponds to a rank of 2 and a trisulfide to a rank of 3, it is possible to have compounds with an average rank somewhere between these limits with a decimal value.

Subsequent studies (124–127) with proteins and amino acids showed that cystine was readily "reduced" to cysteine by thioglycolic acid treatment. In the absence of base, these reactions proceeded quite slowly. This was particularly true with simpler aliphatic systems. For example, heating dodecyl mercaptan with propyl disulfide for 1 hr. at 138°C. resulted in 50% conversion to the mixed disulfide (128). This technique has been used as a synthetic tool for the preparation of mixed disulfides from high boiling mercaptans. However, it was found necessary to accelerate the process by addition of sodium hydroxide (129). The reaction was driven to completion by removing the lower boiling thiol as formed through a fractionating column.

$$\mathrm{RSSR} + \mathrm{R'SH} \xrightleftharpoons{^{-}\mathrm{OH}} \mathrm{RSSR'} + \mathrm{RSH} \quad (53)$$

Fava and Iliceto observed that the polarity of the solvent affected the reaction rate (130). Using radioactive tracer techniques, they found that the interchange of butyl mercaptan with butyl disulfide was negligible in absolute alcohol, faster in aqueous alcohol and very rapid in the presence of sodium hydroxide. Monosulfides did not enter into the exchange even under extreme conditions. Extending this work to quantitative kinetic studies (131), they showed that in methanol at 0–35°C. the interchange rate is first-order in disulfide and in mercaptide ion concentration. For simple aliphatic or aromatic systems the apparent activation energy was approximately 15 kcal./mole. The interchange rate of the sterically hindered *tert*-butyl thiol/*tert*-butyl disulfide system was much slower and the apparent activation energy was considerably higher at 22 kcal./mole.

In the reaction of the butyl mercaptide ion with a cyclic disulfide, trimethylene disulfide (eq. 54), interchange proceeded very rapidly with an activation energy of about 13 kcal./mole, slightly lower than for linear systems. This probably was due to improved accessibility at the cyclic disulfide as well as release of some ring strain.

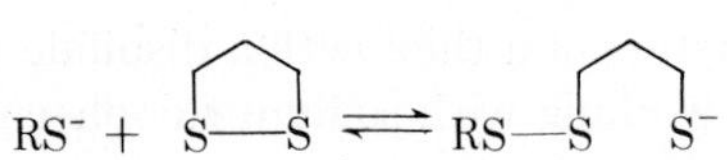

(54)

With this five-membered ring compound, it was necessary to use a large excess of thiol to achieve a substantial degree of conversion. In larger ring compounds such as 1-oxa-4,5-dithiacycloheptane or 1,3-dioxa-6,7-dithiacyclononane, Tobolsky, Leonard, and Roeser (132) found that trace amounts of mercaptide ion bring about rapid polymerization to a polymeric disulfide as the mercaptide ion formed in ring-opening continues to react with additional cyclic monomer.

RS^- + 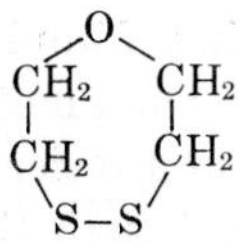 → $RS(SCH_2CH_2OCH_2CH_2S)_nSCH_2CH_2OCH_2CH_2S^-$ (55)

Guryanova, Vasilyeva, and Kuzina (133) carried out similar tracer studies in aromatic solvents. Results in the nonpolar media were quite different from the above. Butyl thiol–butyl disulfide exchange was quite slow, even at temperatures up to 200°C. In addition, the activation energy for the process was high (28 kcal./mole) compared with 15 kcal./mole observed in the anionic exchange in polar media. On the other hand, thiophenol–phenyldisulfide exchange proceeded readily at much lower temperatures with an activation energy of only 10 kcal./mole. Extrapolation of rate data for the two systems to 100°C. indicated the rate constant for the aliphatic system to be 4.6×10^{-5} that of the aromatic system.

In the nonpolar solvents, the exchange reaction was shown to be proportional to the square root of the disulfide concentration but independent of the thiol concentration. A radical mechanism was proposed in which homolytic scission of the disulfide formed sulfenyl radicals which abstract hydrogen atoms from the mercaptans (eqs. 56–57). The radicals recombine to form the new disulfide (eq. 58).

$$RSSR \xrightarrow{\Delta} 2RS\cdot \quad (56)$$

$$RS\cdot + RS^*H \rightarrow RS^*\cdot + RSH \quad (57)$$

$$RS\cdot + RS^*\cdot \rightarrow RS^*SR \quad (58)$$

The slowest and rate-determining step is the initiating scission of the disulfide into radicals. This was confirmed by observing that the rate of exchange and the activation energy in mixtures of a thiol with a disulfide having different substituents is independent of the nature of the thiol but is almost the same as that observed for the exchange of the disulfide component with a thiol of the same system. Thus the constants for a mixture of thiophenol and butyl disulfide are almost identical with those for the butyl thiol–butyl disulfide interchange.

The presence of radicals was confirmed by the accelerating effect of ultraviolet radiation and by purely chemical methods of detection of the presence of radicals by reaction with 2,2-diphenyl-1-picryl hydrazyl.

Fava and co-workers (134) have examined the data of Guryanova and claim that recalculation showed the conclusions of the latter to be in error. Rather, the data indicated the interchange to be roughly half-order in thiol and first-order in disulfide. Carrying out a careful study of the thiophenol–

phenyl disulfide system in hydrocarbon solvents, they found the rate of interchange to be very low in the absence of oxygen, the kinetics showing half-order dependence in oxygen as well as thiol and first-order in disulfide. The mechanism of oxygen catalysis is not clear. Although the exchange reaction seems to be a free radical process accelerated by benzoyl peroxide, by azobisisobutyronitrile, or by metal salts, some inhibitors of radical reactions like benzoquinone or trinitrobenzene enhance the reaction, while other inhibitors such as hydroquinone have no effect.

Despite the obscure initiation mechanism which appears to involve one molecule each of mercaptan and oxygen, the exchange reaction process was considered to follow a conventional radical chain in which the propagation steps are a slow displacement of the sulfenyl radical on the disulfide and a fast hydrogen transfer process with the thiophenol. Termination is by radical coupling.

4. Disulfide–Disulfide Interchange: Monomeric Systems

In the absence of catalysts, exchange reaction between simple organic disulfides is very slow at normal temperatures. This observation has been confused by the difficulty in eliminating adventitious catalysts or light, but if rigorously purified reagents are heated in the dark, interchange is essentially negligible.

Particular care is necessary to remove all traces of thiol which can bring about the facile thiol–disulfide interchange. As a consequence of the latter, the most effective catalytic agents are mercaptide salts. Alkaline inorganic polysulfides or caustic, which can cleave disulfides to form mercaptide salts, are also quite effective. Obviously, these ionic catalysts are most effective in polar media. This interchange has been used as a technique for preparing mixed disulfides. The usual procedure is to reflux the two parent symmetrical disulfides in alcoholic solution containing sodium sulfide (135, 136) or thiol plus potassium hydroxide (129). Starting with an equimolar mixture, the final product at equilibrium is usually a statistical mixture containing two parts of the desired mixed disulfide to one part of each of the parent disulfides.

$$2RSSR + 2R'SSR' \xrightleftharpoons{RS^-} 2RSSR' + RSSR + R'SSR' \qquad (59)$$

Care must be taken to exclude light during isolation of the product since ultraviolet light will activate the interchange reaction and the mixed disulfide will disproportionate to a product mixture containing the symmetrical disulfides. Birch, Cullum, and Dean (137) have proposed a radical chain reaction to explain the extent of reaction on relatively limited exposure.

$$RSSR' \xrightarrow{h\nu} RS\cdot + R'S\cdot \tag{60}$$

$$R'S\cdot + RSSR' \rightarrow R'SSR' + R'S\cdot \tag{61}$$

$$RS\cdot + RSSR' \rightarrow RSSR + RS\cdot \tag{62}$$

They found this photosynthetic process worked readily for disproportionation of asymmetrical disulfides or the synthesis of mixed disulfides from the symmetrical compounds with the exception of *tert*-alkyl derivatives. The failure of the exchange reactions with the latter was attributed to steric hindrance in reactions (61) and (62).

Leandri and Tundo (138) observed that asymmetric aromatic disulfides would rearrange to symmetrical disulfides when irradiated with ultraviolet light or heated to 170°C. in dioxane. Lecher (139) had found that aryl disulfides would not interchange or disproportionate in aromatic solvents at temperatures as high as 200°C.

Birch (137) confirmed his proposed free radical mechanism for the photoactivated disulfide redistribution by observing polymerization of acrylonitrile when this monomer was added to the disulfide mixture under irradiation. In the dark, polymerization did not occur at 100°C. Formation of polymer at 150°C. indicated that some homolytic scission can take place at higher temperatures.

Similar results were obtained by Kharasch, Nudenberg, and Meltzer (140) with aromatic disulfides. Photoinitated polymerization of vinyl monomers occurred readily while the thermal process was essentially negligible at moderate temperatures.

Otsu (141) found that aromatic, benzyl, or acyl disulfides would not cleave thermally to initiate polymerization at temperatures up to 120°C. but did so readily at 30°C. in sunlight.

As might be expected, cyclic disulfides can be polymerized by photoinitiation. Trimethylene disulfide will photopolymerize at very low temperatures (142).

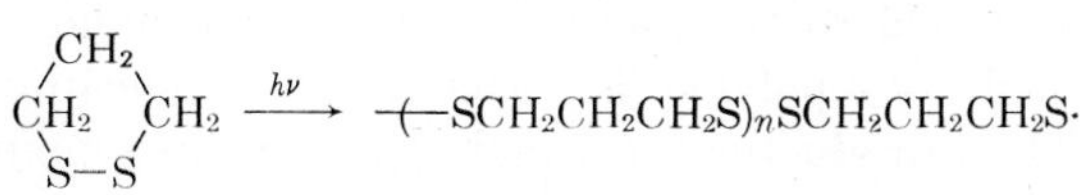

(63)

The cyclic disulfides will also copolymerize with vinyl monomers under the action of heat (143), light (144), or conventional free radical catalysts (145).

Very little information is available on interchange between polysulfides of ranks higher than two. Guryanova (133), in the tracer study mentioned above, observed that organic polysulfides in xylene readily picked up activity on being treated with radioactive sulfur either thermally or with ultraviolet radiation. The middle sulfur atoms of a polysulfide bond exchange with elemental sulfur or with the middle sulfur atom of another organic polysulfide. No activity is observed in the sulfur atoms attached to carbon. For example, treating tolyl trisulfide containing an active central sulfur with inactive ethyl trisulfide results in incorporation of activity in the central sulfur atom of the latter. The mechanism was indicated as proceeding by exchange of the RS— groups.

The nature of the organic substituents plays a significant role in the exchange reaction. The activation energy for elemental sulfur exchange with tolyl trisulfide is 14.5 kcal./mole, while the value for ethyl trisulfide–sulfur exchange is 27.3 kcal./mole. Interestingly, these values are not too different from those reported for the disulfide–thiol exchange cited above.

Acid-catalyzed interchange is also feasible. Benesch and Benesch (146) studied cystine–bis(2,4-dinitrophenyl)cystine interchange in strongly acidic solutions at 35°C. The rate was fast in concentrated HCl but fell off rapidly on dilution. Aliphatic disulfides will also undergo interchange when heated in the presence of Lewis acids (147). Presumably, formation of sulfenium ion is involved as the active intermediate. Another indication of this mechanism is the Lewis acid-catalyzed polymerization of the cyclic disulfide, 1-oxa-4,5-dithiacycloheptane, observed by Tobolsky, Leonard, and Roeser (132).

5. Interchange Reactions: Alkyl Polysulfide Polymers

The behavior of the model monomeric polysulfides is paralleled in the polymeric alkyl polysulfides. The interchange or redistribution of polymer segments in aqueous suspension is particularly susceptible to the anionic mercaptide-disulfide reaction. Bertozzi, Davis, and Fettes (148) studied the softening of a high molecular weight polymer which occurred when butyl thiol was added to a slightly alkaline dispersion of a polymer formed by reaction of bis(2-chloroethyl) formal with sodium disulfide. The change in molecular weight of a polymer is a very sensitive indicator of the degree of reaction. The introduction of 5 mole-% of chain-stopping monofunctional thiol results in reduction of a polymer of infinite molecular weight to a liquid of 4000 to 5000 molecular weight. Any system which could form butyl mercaptide in the reaction environment behaved similarly. Thus, heating 5 mole-% of butyl disulfide or butyl chloride in the presence of 10 mole-% of sodium disulfide with 1 mole of the aforementioned formal disulfide polymer in aqueous dispersion again yielded liquid products. As would be expected, butyl monosulfide which cannot be cleaved to the mercaptide had no action under the same conditions.

$$\text{—RSSR—} + C_4H_9S^- \rightarrow \text{—RSSC}_4H_9 + {}^-\text{SR—} \quad (64)$$

$$C_4H_9SSC_4H_9 + S_2^{=} \rightleftharpoons C_4H_9S^- + C_4H_9S_3^- \quad (65)$$

$$2C_4H_9Cl + S_2^{=} \rightarrow C_4H_9SSC_4H_9 \quad (66)$$

Fettes (119) studied the effect on a formal disulfide polymer dispersion of a number of thiols of widely different structures both in the presence and absence of sodium disulfide. Primary aliphatic thiols and benzyl mercaptan were essentially of equal activity, while the sterically hindered *tertiary*-butyl thiol was very much less effective. Thiophenol and substituted thiophenols surprisingly showed greater ability to cleave the polymer in the absence of sodium disulfide. These, also, were reasonably effective in softening the polymer. Mercaptobenzothiazole behaved in a fashion similar to the thiophenol modifiers.

The study was extended to the action of alkyl disulfides on the polymer dispersion (120). Rigorous purification was necessary to remove traces of thiol which otherwise caused the interchange to behave more like the mercaptide–disulfide rather than the disulfide-disulfide reaction being studied. No exchange with the polymer was observed in the absence of sodium disulfide. As mentioned above, addition of sodium disulfide to a mixture of the polymer with 5 mole-% of butyl disulfide resulted in reduction of the high molecular weight elastomeric product to a liquid polymer. Sterically hindered *tertiary*-butyl disulfide had very slight effect. Aromatic and benzyl disulfides in the presence or absence of sodium disulfide displayed relatively little activity. Apparently, the equilibrium in the reaction of thiophenol with the alkyl disulfide groups was such that the interchange reaction was not favored. Consequently, the action of the inorganic disulfide to form small quantities of the thiophenolate ion which would normally act as a catalyst was not adequate to bring about a significant degree of reaction.

The interchange action can be seen quite clearly in a series of studies (148) in which a chain-stopped polymer was prepared from bis-(2-chloroethyl) formal and 5 mole-% of butyl chloride by reaction with sodium disulfide. In the first experiment, the two monomers were combined and reacted simultaneously to form the liquid product. In the second study, the difunctional formal monomer was reacted completely before the butyl chloride was added. Again, the final product was a liquid identical with that formed in the first test. In the third experiment, butyl chloride was first reacted completely to the disulfide and then the formal monomer added. The results duplicated the others exactly. Clearly, it made no difference which of the disulfide components was formed first or whether the product was formed in one single co-reaction; interchange caused the ultimate product to be identical in all cases.

$$2C_4H_9Cl + nClFCl + (n + 2)Na_2S_2 \rightarrow C_4H_9S(SFS)_nSC_4H_9 \quad (67)$$

$$2C_4H_9Cl + (n + 2)Na_2S_2 \rightarrow C_4H_9SSC_4H_9 + nNa_2S_2 \quad (68)$$

$$C_4H_9SSC_4H_9 + nNa_2S_2 + nClFCl \rightarrow C_4H_9S(SFS)_nSC_4H_9 \quad (69)$$

$$nClFCl + (n + 2)Na_2S_2 \rightarrow ({}^-SFS^-)_n + 2Na_2S_2 + 2C_4H_9Cl \rightarrow C_4H_9S(SFS)_nSC_4H_9 \quad (70)$$

Practical use can be made of this phenomenon to incorporate active terminals on polysulfide polymers. For example, treatment of a high molecular weight alkyl disulfide polymer with bis(2-mercaptoethyl) formal resulted in formation of a thiol-terminated polysulfide liquid polymer. Similarly, reaction with mercaptoethanol or mercaptoethylamine resulted in the formation of low molecular weight polymer terminated with thiol, and the other added functional group. Mild oxidation to reconvert the thiol groups to disulfide yielded polymers with the desired reactive terminals (149). Similar results can be obtained by treatment of the high molecular weight polymer dispersion with disulfides carrying reactive terminals (150). The water soluble modifiers such as mercaptoethanol or dithiodiglycol were less efficient than the other reagents presumably because of the partition between the aqueous phase and the polymer particle (118). In fact in the presence of excess sodium disulfide, these reagents are completely water solubilized and very little modification is observed. Hydroxyl-containing polymers derived by interchange can be reconverted to the high molecular weight starting material by treatment with sufficient sodium disulfide to remove these terminals as described in eq. (48). Another practical application of this interchange phenomenon is in the preparation of copolymers derived from two alkyl dihalides. Because of differences in water solubility that can exist between the many potential dihalide monomers, it is occasionally difficult to prepare copolymers of accurately known composition since the more soluble component tends to remain in the mother liquor containing the excess sodium polysulfide normally used in order to obtain the high molecular weight product. By taking two high molecular weight polymer dispersions and redistributing them in the presence of catalytic amounts of sodium disulfide, the resulting product is quite close in composition to that predicted from the ratio of the components initially blended together. An example of this technique is given by Bertozzi, Davis, and Fettes (148), as cited above. Dispersions of a hard plastic ethylene disulfide polymer, $(\text{—}CH_2CH_2CH_2S_2\text{—})_n$ and a liquid chain-stoppered triglycol disulfide polymer, $(\text{—}CH_2CH_2OCH_2CH_2OCH_2CH_2\text{-}S_2\text{—})_n$ were blended in equal quantities and the mixture heated at 90°C. in the presence and absence of a small amount of sodium disulfide. Recovery of the polymer by the usual procedure from the two systems resulted in a homogeneous liquid polymer of significantly higher viscosity than the triglycol disulfide liquid from the experiment in which the sodium disulfide was present, while the other product was an inhomogeneous mixture of fine particles of the hard ethylene disulfide polymer suspended in the liquid triglycol polymer.

The above information demonstrates that earlier attempts cited in the literature to prepare polysulfide block copolymers by producing the first component in a conventional polymerization and then attempting to add the second monomer subsequently to have it propagate from the terminals of the first moiety could not have succeeded. Obviously, as long as any sodium polysulfide is present, the interchange reaction will convert the final product to something approximating a random copolymer. The only way in which a reasonably close approximation to a block copolymer could be prepared would be to use general oxidation techniques to oxidize a blend of liquid polymers derived from the two components desired for the block copolymer.

$$HS(SRS)_nSRSH + HSR'S(SR'S)_mSR'SH \xrightarrow{[O]} \text{—}(SRS)_n(SR'S)_m(SRS)_n, \text{ etc.} \quad (71)$$

In nonaqueous environments, the nature of the exchange reaction is less clear-cut. Fettes and Mark found (119) that butyl mercaptan took about one-fourth the time to react with formal disulfide polymer at 85°C. in dioxane solution when 1% of sodium phenolate was added to activate the reaction. However, efforts to study redistribution between alkyl polysulfide polymers in bulk gave rather erratic results. Mercaptan-terminated disulfide liquid polymers of substantially different molecular weight were blended and treated under a variety of conditions. It was expected that the mercaptan terminals would enter into the exchange reaction with the disulfide bonds in the polymer backbone. Ultimately, when the reaction was complete, it was expected that a distribution in polymer molecular weights would be achieved approximating the distribution predicted in theory developed by Flory (151) for interchange of this type in polyesters. For such a random distribution of molecular weight species, the ratio of the weight-average molecular weight $\bar{M}_w$ to the number-average molecular

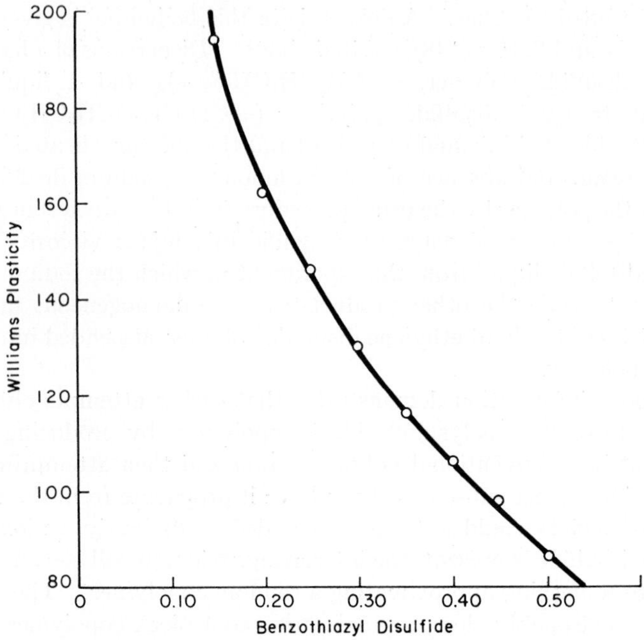

Fig. VII-1. Effect of benzothiazyl disulfide on molecular weight as measured by Williams plasticity. (Taken from ref. 152.)

weight $\bar{M}_n$ should be 2.00. The results observed did not confirm these expectations. In the presence of a tertiary aliphatic amine, *n*-methyl morpholine, as an activating base, treatment for as long as 100 hours at 100°C. brought the $\bar{M}_w/\bar{M}_n$ ratio from an initial value of 4 down to 3. It is possible that the somewhat unexpected results would arise from the low degree of ionization of the mercaptide salt in the polysulfide polymer in the absence of solvent. Addition of small amounts of water to promote ionization was ineffective, probably because of the essential insolubility of water in these polymers.

Xanthogen disulfides and thiuram disulfides behave as particularly reactive disulfides and these compounds interchange with the polysulfide polymers quite readily, even in the absence of mercaptide terminals, although addition of small amounts of a strong base such as diphenylguanidine will greatly accelerate the redistribution process. Figure VII-1 shows the interaction of benzothiazyl disulfide with Thiokol FA (a copolymer of ethylene dichloride and dichloroethyl formal with a rank of approximately 2.0) incorporated by mastication on a hot rubber mill. As can be seen, the molecular weight as measured by Williams plasticity drops very rapidly with incorporation of trace amounts of the modifier (152). This technique is used commercially to reduce the molecular weight of the rubber to a range suitable for convenient processing.

These polymers terminated with the benzothiazyl group can be vulcanized by treatment at elevated temperatures with zinc oxide. The heterocyclic terminal splits out as the zinc salt, while the polymer residues combine to reform the high molecular weight product. Since this process is not completely effective and some zinc is incorporated in the polymer as a mercaptide salt, the resulting vulcanized product has poor compression set resistance. This behavior is paralleled in aqueous dispersion systems (120). Benzothiazyl disulfide or tetramethylthiuram disulfide readily interchange with polymer dispersions in the absence of sodium disulfide When the polysulfide ion is introduced, the modifying terminals are solubilized and are stripped from the polymer chain, while the polymer is reconverted to its orginal molecular weight.

Pioneering quantitative studies were carried out by Tobolsky (153,154) using the elegant stress relation technique to follow the interchange process. An excellent review (155) is available on this technique and its application to the polysulfide polymers. This classic work antedates many of the quantitative studies on simple monomeric compounds described previously in this chapter. A wide variety of polysulfide elastomers of different backbone structure and sulfur rank were investigated. It was found that all of these polymers obeyed a simple Maxwellian function,

$$f/f_0 = e^{-k't}$$

in relaxation of stress, indicating that some common type of bond was responsible for the relaxation behavior. Intermittent relaxation tests indicated that the rates of bond breaking and bond formation were exactly equal confirming that some specific structure was involved in this process. Oxidative scission was not a factor as with hydrocarbon rubbers, since tests carried out in high vacuum were identical with those carried out in air. The observed cold flow was not simple molecular flow similar to that observed in unvulcanized rubbers or rubbery linear polymers, as can be noted in Figure VII-2. The conditions required for the complete relaxation of a polymer were sufficiently mild that heating the polymer for a period sufficient to cause complete stress decay resulted in no apparent change in such polymer properties as elongation, tensile strength, and modulus. In fact, it was possible to take a sample of polymer after a relaxation test and repeat the test several times on the same sample with the stress decay curves for all of the experiments completely superimposable.

The distinction between chemorheologic flow resulting from interchange and simple plastic flow can readily be seen in the behavior of a crosslinked polysulfide polymer. Disulfide copolymers of bis(2-chloroethyl) formal and polyfunctional monomers to bring about network formation still relaxed at much the same rate as the linear formal homopolymer. These crosslinked polymers were true three-dimensional network gels, as indicated by their

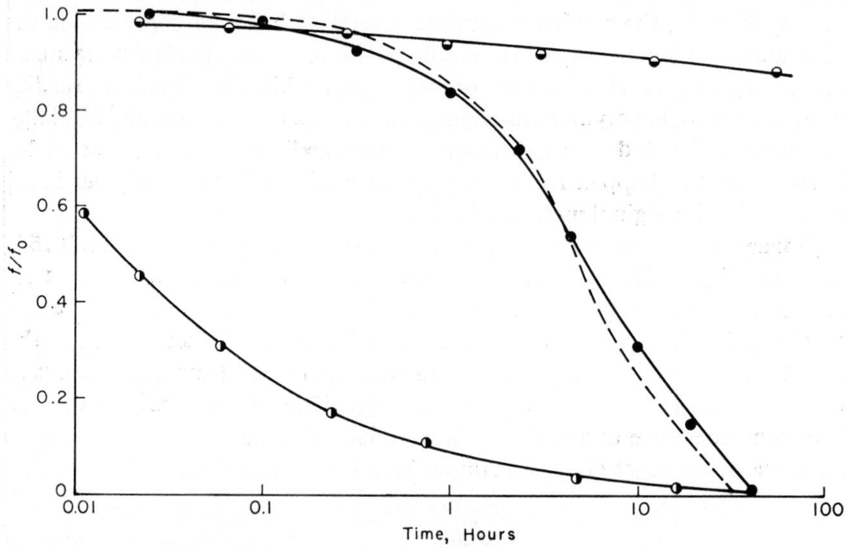

Fig. VII-2. Relaxation curves of cured and uncured compounded Hevea gum stock (35°C., 50% elongation) and tetrasulfide polymer from bis-2-chloroethyl ether (35°C., 20% elongation) compared with Maxwell function: (◑) uncured Hevea; (◒) Hevea cured for 1 hr. at 130°C.; (●) polysulfide rubber; (- -) Maxwell function ($f/f_0 = e^{-k't}$). (Taken from ref. 154.)

insolubility in solvents which would completely dissolve the linear homopolymer. Because of the relatively high activation energy of 24 kcal./mole for this chemorheologic flow process, these crosslinked polymers can show adequate compression set performance at lower temperatures (below 70°C.). This value for the activation energy was essentially the same for all of the disulfide and tetrasulfide polymers studied, with or without a crosslinking comonomer. Since the value for simple molecular flow is seldom much greater than 10 kcal./mole, the distinction is again evident.

Incorporation of different types of carbon black had essentially no effect on the relaxation rate of a lightly crosslinked formal disulfide polymer. This is further evidence that the apparent thermoplastic behavior of the polysulfide polymers is not due to molecular flow, since the reinforcing effect of the carbon back would have an important retarding action.

Although the activation energy for interchange in the polysulfide polymers is essentially the same for the various rubbers studied, the actual rates of relaxation varied very widely. The effect of increase in rank of the polymer was not clear, although it is apparent that the very high rank polymers, about rank 4.0, do relax much more rapidly than the disulfides. Polymers of intermediate rank, 2.2 to 2.4, appear to relax at a somewhat lower rate than the disulfide. This may possibly be due to a difference in the mechanism of the interchange. At very high ranks, the interchange may be a free radical type, as indicated by the work of Guryanova, while at the lower ranks the mercaptide-disulfide interchange is probably taking place. In that event, the sulfur present in slightly higher rank polymers might serve to scavenge any thiol terminals by oxidation, as indicated in eq. (49). The enormous effect of small amounts of thiol on the relaxation rate was shown by incorporation of butyl thiol into a cured test specimen by exposure to the thiol vapor. As little as 0.65% by weight of bound thiol increased the relaxation rate several hundredfold. By extrapolation of the effect of various levels of bound thiol, Tobolsky calculated that the rate observed in untreated cured polymer could be caused by 10^{-4}–10^{-5} g. thiol/g. rubber. Efforts to eliminate this last residue of thiol by adding scavengers to the vulcanization recipes produced only slight effects.

Free sulfur also had a very significant impact on the relaxation behavior. Incorporation of a few per cent of sulfur into a cured test specimen resulted in a 50-fold increase in the relaxation rate. Addition of free sulfur to the vulcanization recipe had a similar effect. This study indicated a somewhat lower activation energy in the presence of free sulfur. A different reaction mechanism may be involved.

Thin films of the polysulfide rubber were exposed to ultraviolet light, and very rapid relaxation was observed. Here, where a free radical interchange mechanism is undoubtedly occurring, the activation energy was approximately 5.7 kcal./mole, considerably lower than observed for the other studies.

The stress relaxation technique was also used to examine the effect of the type of cures used with the polysulfide polymers. It was long known that polymers with mercaptan or even hydroxyl terminals could be converted to solid elastomers by cure with metal oxides like zinc oxide, lead oxide, or magnesium oxide. However, these products all show little or no compression set resistance at 60–70°C. This had been attributed to the saltlike nature of the cure, with interchange occurring at the ionic bonds or by mercaptide–disulfide exchange. Even the metal peroxide cures tend to show limited compression set resistance unless properly formulated, since some metal salt is incorporated into the polymer chain from the lower valence forms of the curing agent resulting from the oxidative process.

Cured products of this type are particularly susceptible to weight loss on heat aging. For example, mercaptide-containing formal disulfide polymers can form cyclic compounds by cyclodepolymerization occurring via mercaptide–disulfide interaction at the ionic terminals. Prolonged heat treatment can result in almost complete volatilization of the polymer.

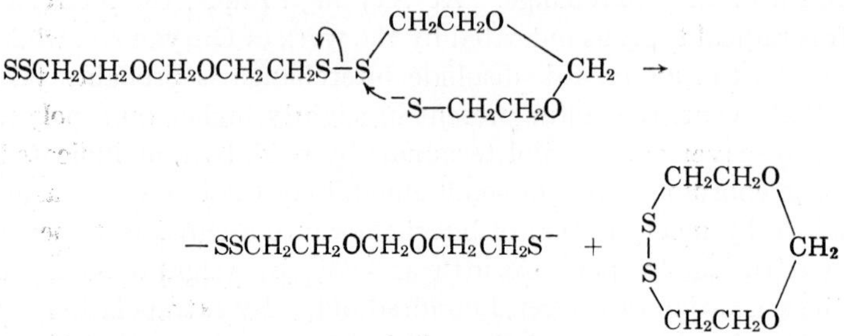

(72)

Tobolsky and Colodny (156) studied the stress relaxation behavior at 80°C. of the commercial thiol-terminated ethyl formal disulfide liquid polymer, Thiokol LP-2, when cured by wide variety of oxidizing agents, including the metal peroxides, PbO_2 and MnO_2, organic hydroperoxides, and *p*-quinone dioxime. In addition, a number of diisocyanate cures were evaluated. These last were different in type since the cure is by addition rather than oxidation.

Vulcanization with lead peroxide at room temperature without an additive to tighten the cure yielded products that show relatively rapid stress decay at 80°C. Postcure at 75°C. did not change the degree of cure as indicated by an essentially equivalent modulus but resulted in a 20-fold increase in relaxation time. This confirmed the theory previously proposed that the saltlike lead mercaptide bonds are converted to monosulfide bonds with elimination of the lead as PbS (Chapter XI-A).

The manganese dioxide cure was somewhat sluggish, requiring heat plus manganous ion and base as activators. With this system, a relatively high relaxation time was observed. Either relatively few mercaptide bonds were formed or those formed were eliminated as the cure proceeded.

Cumene hydroperoxide and *tertiary*-butyl hydroperoxide required magnesium oxide for activation in order to obtain room temperature cures. These showed low relaxation rates. Activation of the *tert*-butyl hydroperoxide cure with cobalt naphthenate decreased the relaxation time by a factor of 20. Presumably, a free radical-catalyzed interchange brought about the rate increase observed.

The *p*-quinone dioxime heat cure was studied in some detail. Diphenylguanidine was used as activator together with variable amounts of sulfur. Small amounts of added sulfur had a retarding action on the relaxation rate, possibly by scavenging ionic impurities which could catalyze the mercaptan-disulfide interchange. However, addition of relatively large amounts of sulfur yielded cures with appreciably greater chemorheologic flow. The rate increase was believed to occur by a trisulfide–trisulfide interchange which had been shown by Guryanova to proceed more readily than the disulfide–disulfide reaction. The trisulfide bonds are formed by diphenylguanidine-catalyzed thionation.

The additive diisocyanate cures were of particular interest. Relaxation times for these systems were substantially greater than for the oxidative cures. In addition, the activation energy for the relaxation process was 37 kcal./mole, compared with 24 kcal./mole found earlier for ionic interchange in these polymers. In the absence of ionic impurities, it was proposed that disulfide interchange proceeds so slowly that the rate-determining step in the relaxation process is interchange at the isothiourethane linkages.

References

A. Polyesters

1. Farkas, L., O. Schächter, and B. H. Vromen, *J. Am. Chem. Soc.*, **71,** 1991 (1949).
2. Harfenist, M., and R. Baltzly, *J. Am. Chem. Soc.*, **69,** 362 (1947).
3. Korshak, V. V., and S. V. Vinogradova, *Izv. Akad. Nauk SSSR Otd. Khim. Nauk*, **1951,** 179; *Chem. Abstr.*, **45,** 8975g (1951).
4. Korshak, V. V.,and S. V. Vinogradova, *Izv. Akad. Nauk SSSR Otd. Khim. Nauk*, **1952,** 180; *Bull. Acad. Sci. USSR, Div. Chem. Sci.* (*English Transl.*) **1952,** 193; *Chem. Abstr.*, **47,** 1591a (1953).
5. Korshak, V. V., and S. V. Vinogradova, *Izv. Akad. Nauk SSSR Otd. Khim. Nauk*, **1951,** 334; *Chem. Abstr.*, **46,** 1440d (1952).
6. Coover, H. W., F. B. Joyner, and N. H. Shearer, South African Patent 61,966 (to Eastman Kodak Company) 1961.
7. Levine, M., and S. C. Temin, *J. Polymer Sci.*, **28,** 179 (1958).
8. Andrianov, K. A., O. I. Gribanova, A. G. Prelkova, N. N. Sokolov, and S. M. Sung, *Vysokomolekul. Soedin.*, **2,** 521 (1960); *Chem. Abstr.*, **55,** 5013i (1961).
9. Youngson, G. W., and H. W. Melville, *J. Chem. Soc.*, **1950,** 1613.

10. Korshak, V. V., and S. V. Vinogradova, *Zh. Obshch. Khim.*, **22**, 1176 (1952); *Chem. Abstr.*, **47**, 6883e (1953).
11. Flory, P. J., *J. Am. Chem. Soc.*, **62**, 2255 (1940).
12. Korshak, V. V., and S. V. Vinogradova, *Izv. Akad. Nauk SSSR Otd. Khim. Nauk*, **1951**, 756; *Chem. Abstr.*, **46**, 7527d (1952).
13. Korshak, V. V., N. I. Bekasova, and V. A. Zamyatina, *Izv. Akad. Nauk SSSR Otd. Khim. Nauk*, **1958**, 614; *Chem. Abstr.*, **52**, 20028d (1958).
14. Vereinigte Glanzstoff-Fabriken A.-G., British Patent 755,071, Aug. 15, 1956; *Chem. Abstr.*, **51**, 7057h (1957).
15. Zeidler, I. I., and E. E. Shkol'man, *Zh. Prikl. Khim.*, **26**, 410 (1953); *Chem. Abstr.* **48**, 7587a (1954).
16. Korshak, V. V., and S. V. Vinogradova, *Izv. Akad. Nauk SSSR Otd. Khim. Nauk*, **1953**, 951; *Bull. Acad. Sci. USSR, Div. Chem. Sci.* (*English Transl.*), **1953**, 847; *Chem. Abstr.*, **49**, 866d (1955).
17. Kursanov, V. N., V. V. Korshak, and S. V. Vinogradova, *Izv. Akad. Nauk SSSR Otd. Khim. Nauk*, **1953**, 140; *Bull. Acad. Sci. USSR Div. Chem. Sci.* (*English Transl.*) **1953**, 125; *Chem. Abstr.*, **48**, 3912g (1954).
18. Imperial Chemical Industries, Ltd., British Patent 760,125 (by W. R. Burton and D. S. Davies), Oct. 31, 1956; *Chem. Abstr.*, **51**, 7733a (1957).
19. Goodman, I., and B. F. Nesbitt, *Polymer*, **1**, 384 (1960).
20. Flory, P. J., *J. Am. Chem. Soc.*, **62**, 1057 (1940).
21. Kresse, P., *Faserforsch. Textiltech.*, **11**, 353 (1960); *Chem. Abstr.*, **54**, 23340c (1960).
22. Rafikov, S. R., V. V. Korshak, and G. N. Chelnokova, *Izv. Akad. Nauk SSSR Otd. Khim. Nauk*, **1953**, 743; *Bull. Acad. Sci. USSR, Div. Chem. Sci.* (*English Transl.*) **1953**, 669; *Chem. Abstr.*, **48**, 12674g (1954).
23. Korshak, V. V., G. N. Chelnokova, and G. I. Distler, *Dokl. Akad. Nauk SSSR*, **82**, 589 (1952); *Chem. Abstr.*, **46**, 6465a (1952).
24. Challa, G., *Makromol. Chem.*, **38**, 123 (1960).
25. Korshak, V. V., N. I. Bekasova, and V. A. Zamyatina, *Izv. Akad. Nauk SSSR, Otd. Khim. Nauk*, **1958**, 486; *Chem. Abstr.*, **52**, 17167f (1958).
26. Griehl, W., and G. Schnock, *Faserforsch. Textiltech.*, **8**, 408 (1957); *Chem. Abstr.*, **52**, 11781b (1958).
27. Caldwell, J. R., and J. W. Wellman, U. S. Patent 2,727,881 (to Eastman Kodak Co.), Dec. 20, 1955; *Chem. Abstr.*, **50**, 15126h (1956).
28. Billica, H. R., U. S. Patent 2,647,885 (to E. I. du Pont de Nemours & Co.), Aug. 4, 1953; *Chem. Abstr.*, **47**, 10278d (1953).
29. Goodyear Tire and Rubber Co., British Patent 861,712, Feb. 22, 1961; *Chem. Abstr.*, **55**, 24106h (1961).
30. Wilfong, R. E., *J. Polymer Sci.*, **54**, 385 (1961).
31. Eckey, E. W., *Ind. Eng. Chem.*, **40**, 1183 (1948).
32. Gevaert Photo-Produkten N. V., British Patent 805,534 (by F. L. Schouteden), Dec. 10, 1958; *Chem. Abstr.*, **53**, 7673g (1959).
33. Berner, E., and E. Aaberg, *Suomen Kemistilehti*, **31B**, 53 (1958); *Chem. Abstr.*, **53**, 269i (1959).
34. Flory, P. J., *J. Am. Chem. Soc.*, **61**, 3334 (1939).
35. Griehl, W., and G. Schnock, *J. Polymer Sci.*, **30**, 413 (1958).
36. Skwarski, T., *Zeszyty Nauk Politech. Lodz. Chem.* **12**, (4), 41 (1956); *Chem. Abstr.*, **51**, 1704e (1957).

37. Griehl, W., and P. F. Förster, *Faserforsch. Textiltech.*, **7**, 463 (1956); *Chem. Abstr.*, **51**, 3179b (1957).
38. Ryder, D. F., U. S. Patent 2,869,838 (to E. I. du Pont de Nemours & Co.), Jan. 20, 1959.
39. Toyo Rayon Co., Ltd., Japanese Patent 4993 ('60) May 12 (by P. Nakanishi), *Chem. Abstr.*, **54**, 25982e (1960).
40. Korshak, V. V., V. A. Zamyatina, and N. I. Bekasova, *Vysokomolekul. Soedin.*, **1**, 1586 (1959); *Chem. Abstr.*, **54**, 14762c (1960).
41. Korshak, V. V., and S. V. Vinogradova, *Izv. Akad. Nauk SSSR, Otd. Khim. Nauk*, **1954**, 376; *Bull. Acad. Sci. USSR, Div. Chem. Sci. (English Transl.)*, **1954**, 311; *Chem. Abstr.*, **48**, 9919d (1954).
42. Challa, G., *Makromol. Chem.*, **38**, 105 (1960).
43. Challa, G., *Makromol. Chem.*, **38**, 138 (1960).
44. Flory, P. J., *J. Am. Chem. Soc.*, **62**, 2261 (1940).
45. Sumoto, M., A. Kito, and R. Inoue, *Kobunshi Kagaku*, **15**, 664 (1958); *Chem. Abstr.*, **54**, 16001e (1960).
46. Flory, P. J., *J. Am. Chem. Soc.*, **58**, 1877 (1956).
47. Koepp. H. M., and H. Werner, *Makromol. Chem.*, **32**, 79 (1959).
48. Turska, E., T. Skwarski, and S. Szapiro, *J. Polymer Sci.*, **30**, 391 (1958).
49. Rafikov, S. R., V. V. Korshak, and G. N. Chelnokova, *Dokl. Akad. Nauk SSSR*, **57**, 357 (1947).
50. Rafikov, S. R., V. V. Korshak, and G. N. Chelnokova, *Izv. Akad. Nauk SSSR Otd. Khim. Nauk*, **1948**, 642; *Chem. Abstr.*, **43**, 4228a (1949).
51. Korshak, V. V., *Faserforsch. Textiltech.*, **6**, 241 (1955); *Chem. Abstr.*, **49**, 13741h (1955).
52. Howard, G. J., in *Progress in High Polymers*, J. C. Robb and F. W. Peaker, eds., Vol. I, Heywood & Co., London, 1961, p. 185.
53. Berr, C. E., *J. Polymer Sci.*, **15**, 591 (1955).
54. Ross, S. D., E. R. Coburn, W. A. Leach, and W. B. Robinson, *J. Polymer Sci.*, **13**, 406 (1954).
55. Zaugg, H. E., in *Organic Reactions*, R. Adams, ed., Vol. VIII, Wiley, New York, 1954, p. 326.
56. Hall, H. K., Jr., and A. K. Schneider, *J. Am. Chem. Soc.*, **80**, 6409 (1958).

B. Silicones

57. Hyde, J. F., and R. C. DeLong, *J. Am. Chem. Soc.*, **63**, 1194 (1941).
58. Patnode, W., and D. Wilcock, *J. Am. Chem. Soc.*, **68**, 358 (1946).
59. Frevel, L. K., and M. J. Hunter, *J. Am. Chem. Soc.*, **67**, 2275 (1945).
60. Hunter, M. J., J. F. Hyde, E. L. Warrick, and H. J. Fletcher, *J. Am. Chem. Soc.*, **68**, 667 (1946).
61. Osthoff, R. C., W. T. Grubb, and C. A. Burkhard, *J. Am. Chem. Soc.*, **75**, 2227 (1953).
62. Osthoff, R. C., and W. T. Grubb, *J. Am. Chem. Soc.*, **76**, 399 (1954).
63. Scott, D. W., *J. Am. Chem. Soc.*, **68**, 356 (1946).
64. Hyde, J. F., U. S. Patent 2,490,357 (to Corning Glass Works), Dec. 6, 1949; *Chem. Abstr.*, **44**, 4490d (1950).

65. Hyde, J. F., U. S. Patent 2,567,110 (to Corning Glass Works), Sept. 4, 1951; *Chem. Abstr.*, **45,** 10676d (1951).
66. Kantor, S. W., and A. R. Gilbert, U. S. Patent 2,883,366 (to General Electric Co.), Apr. 21, 1959; *Chem. Abstr.*, **53,** 20886e (1959).
67. Kantor, S. W., W. T. Grubb, and R. C. Osthoff, *J. Am. Chem. Soc.*, **76,** 5190 (1954).
68. Hurd, D. T., R. C. Osthoff, and M. L. Corrin, *J. Am. Chem. Soc.*, **76,** 249 (1954).
69. Grubb, W. T., and R. C. Osthoff, *J. Am. Chem. Soc.*, **77,** 1405 (1955).
70a. Veselý, K., and M. Kučera, Intern. Symp. Macromol. Chem. (UPAC), Wiesbaden, 1959; Preprints Section IV, B3.
70b. Veselý, K., and M. Kučera, Paper Presented at 135th Meeting of American Chemical Society, Boston, Mass., Apr. 5–10, 1959.
71. Morton, M., and M. A. Deisz, Paper Presented at 130th Meeting of American Chemical Society, Atlantic City, N. J., Sept. 16–20, 1956.
72. Morton, M., A. Rembaum, and E. E. Bostick, *J. Polymer Sci.*, **32,** 530 (1958).
73. Hyde, J. F., U. S. Patent 2,634,284 (to Dow Corning Corp.), Apr. 7, 1953; *Chem. Abstr.*, **47,** 6697g (1953).
74. Kučera, M., M. Jelínek, J. Láníková, and K. Veselý, *J. Polymer Sci.*, **53,** 311 (1961).
75. Gilbert, A. R., and S. W. Kantor, *J. Polymer Sci.*, **40,** 35 (1959).
76. Osthoff, R. C., A. M. Bueche, and W. T. Grubb, *J. Am. Chem. Soc.*, **76,** 4659 (1954).
77. St. Pierre, L. E., and A. M. Bueche, *J. Phys. Chem.*, **63,** 1338 (1959).
78. Kučera, M., J. Láníková, and M. Jelínek, *J. Polymer Sci.*, **53,** 301 (1961).
79. Linville, R. G., U. S. Patent 2,739,952 (to General Electric Co.), Mar. 27, 1956; *Chem. Abstr.*, **50,** 9784g (1956).
80. Kipping, F. S., and J. E. Hackford, *J. Chem. Soc.*, **99,** 138 (1911).
81. Sauer, R. O., *J. Am. Chem. Soc.*, **66,** 1707 (1944).
82. Bostick, E. E., Doctoral Dissertation, The University of Akron, Akron, Ohio (1959); *Dissertation Abstr.*, **21,** 2501(1960–61).
83. Kali-Chemie Akt.-Ges, German Patent 1,018,226 (by H. Jenkner), Oct. 24, 1957; *Chem. Abstr.*, **54,** 8136e (1960).
84. Kali-Chemie Akt.-Ges, British Patent 797,235, June 25, 1958; *Chem. Abstr.*, **53,** 17568h (1959).
85. Patnode, W. I., and F. C. Schmidt, *J. Am. Chem. Soc.*, **67,** 2272 (1945).
86. Scott, D. W., *J. Am. Chem. Soc.*, **68,** 2294 (1946).
87. Flory, P. J., *J. Chem. Phys.*, **12,** 425 (1944).
88. Hurd, D. T., *J. Am. Chem. Soc.*, **77,** 2998 (1955).
89. Andrianov, K. A., and S. E. Yakushkina, *Vysokomolekul. Soedin.*, **1,** 613 (1959); *Polymer Sci. (USSR) (English Transl.)*, **1,** 221 (1960).
90. Gruber, V. N., and L. S. Mukhina, *Vysokomolekul. Soedin.*, **1,** 1194 (1959); *Polymer Sci. (USSR) (English Transl.)*, **1,** 577 (1960); *Chem. Abstr.*, **54,** 20281g (1960).
91. Gruber, V. N., M. M. Fomicheva, and L. S. Mukhina, U.S.S.R. Patent 116,350, Jan. 19, 1959; *Chem. Abstr.*, **53,** 19432c (1959).
92. Baranovskaya, N. B., U.S.S.R. Patent 125,252, Jan. 8, 1960; *Chem. Abstr.*, **54,** 12651e (1960).
93. Britton, E. C., and H. C. White, U. S. Patent 2,476,132 (to Dow Chemical Co.,) July 12, 1949; *Chem. Abstr.*, **43,** 8210c (1949).

94. Mayo, F. R., *J. Polymer Sci.*, **55**, 57 (1961).
95. Eaborn, C., *J. Chem. Soc.*, **1953**, 3148.
96. Eaborn, C., *J. Chem. Soc.*, **1956**, 4859.
97. Andrianov, K. A., and S. E. Yakushkina, *Vysokomolekul. Soedin.*, **2**, 1508 (1960); *Chem. Abstr.*, **55**, 19301e (1961).
98. Eaborn, C., *Organosilicon Compounds*, Academic Press, New York, 1960, p. 264ff.
99. Maeda, S., and E. Nojimoto, Japanese Patent 3741 (to Nippon Silicone Resin Co.), May 14, 1958; *Chem. Abstr.*, **53**, 5735g (1959).
100. Sasin, M., and J. Cermak, *Chem. Listy*, **51**, 1766 (1957); *Chem. Abstr.*, **52**, 4534f (1958).
101. Kantor, S. W., R. C. Osthoff, and D. T. Hurd, *J. Am. Chem. Soc.*, **77**, 1685 (1955).
102. Hurd, D. T., U. S. Patent 2,878,195 (to General Electric Co.), March 17, 1959; *Chem. Abstr.*, **53**, 12739a (1959).
103. Midland Silicones, Ltd., British Patent 790,182, Feb. 15, 1958; *Chem. Abstr.*, **52**, 17793d (1958).
104. Pierce, O. R., G. W. Holbrook, O. K. Johannson, J. C. Saylor, and E. D. Brown, *Ind. Eng. Chem.*, **52**, 783 (1960).
105. Merker, R. L., and M. J. Scott, *J. Polymer Sci.*, **43**, 297 (1960).
106. Piccoli, W. A., G. G. Haberland, and R. L. Merker, *J. Am. Chem. Soc.*, **82**, 1883 (1960).
107. Mayo, F. R., and F. M. Lewis, *J. Am. Chem. Soc.*, **66**, 1594 (1944).
108. Andrianov, K. A., *J. Polymer Sci.*, **52**, 257 (1961).
109. Andrianov, K. A., and A. I. Petrashko, *Vysokomolekul. Soedin.*, **1**, 1514 (1959); *Polymer Sci. (USSR) (English Transl.)*, **2**, 39 (1961); *Chem. Abstr.*, **54**, 14106e (1960).
110. Stavitskii, I. K., S. N. Borisov, V. A. Ponomarenko, N. G. Sviridova, and G. Ia. Zueva, *Vysokomolekul. Soedin.*, **1**, 1502 (1959); *Polymer Sci. (USSR) (English Transl.)*, **2**, 24 (1961); *Chem. Abstr.*, **54**, 14106g (1960).
111. Sprung, M. M., and F. O. Guenther, *J. Polymer Sci.*, **28**, 17 (1958).
112. Brown, J. F., Jr., L. H. Vogt, Jr., A. Katchman, J. W. Eustance, K. M. Kiser, and K. W. Krantz, *J. Am. Chem. Soc.*, **82**, 6194 (1960).
113. Patterson, J. R., *Ind. Eng. Chem.*, **39**, 1376 (1947).
114. Hatcher, D. B., and R. H. Bunnell, U. S. Patent 2,624,720 (to Libbey-Owens-Ford Glass Co.), Jan. 6, 1953; *Chem. Abstr.*, **47**, 3614c (1953).
115. Greber, G., and E. Reese, *Makromol. Chem.*, **47**, 228 (1961).

C. Polysulfides

116. Jensen, E. V., *Science*, **130**, 1319 (1959).
117. Otto, R., and A. Rossing, *Chem. Ber.*, **19**, 3129 (1886),
118. Fettes, E. M., and H. Mark, *J. Appl. Polymer Sci.*, **5**, 7 (1961).
119. Fettes, E. M., and H. Mark, *J. Appl. Polymer Sci.*, **7**, 2239 (1963).
120. Fettes, E. M., and H. Mark, *J. Appl. Polymer Sci.*, **8**, 603 (1964).
121. Patrick, J. C., and H. R. Ferguson, U. S. Patent 2,466,963 (to Thiokol Chemical Corp.), Apr. 12, 1949; *Chem. Abstr.*, **43**, 5636h (1949).
122. Berenbaum, M. B., and E. Bobe, unpublished work, Thiokol Chemical Corp.
123. Lecher, H. Z., *Chem. Ber.* **53B**, 591 (1920).
124. Goddard, D. R., and L. Michaelis, *J. Biol. Chem.*, **106**, 605 (1934); *Chem. Abstr.*, **28**, 6740^2 (1934).

125. Toennies, G., *J. Biol. Chem.*, **120,** 297 (1937); *Chem. Abstr.*, **31,** 7849[8] (1937).
126. Fredga, A., *Arkiv Kemi Mineral. Geol.*, **12A,** 13 (1937); *Chem. Abstr.* **31,** 3451[5] (1937).
127. Bersin, T., and J. Steudel, *Chem. Ber.*, **71B,** 1015 (1938).
128. Gorin, G., G. Dougherty, and A. V. Tobolsky, *J. Am. Chem. Soc.*, **71,** 3551 (1949).
129. McAllan, D. T., T. V. Cullum, R. A. Dean, and F. A. Fidler, *J. Am. Chem. Soc.*, **73,** 3627 (1951).
130. Fava, A., and A. Iliceto, *Ric. Sci.*, **23,** 839 (1953); *Chem. Abstr.*, **47,** 9814c (1953).
131. Fava, A., A. Iliceto, and E. Camera, *J. Am. Chem. Soc.*, **79,** 833 (1957).
132. Tobolsky, A. V., F. Leonard, and G. P. Roeser, *J. Polymer Sci.*, **3,** 604 (1948).
133. Guryanova, E. N., V. N. Vasilyeva, and L. S. Kuzina, *Rubber Chem. Technol.*, **29,** 534 (1956).
134. Reichenbach, G., U. Peron, and A. Fava, unpublished work.
135. Proell, W. A., U. S. Patent 2,521,870 (to Standard Oil of Indiana), Sept. 12, 1950; *Chem. Abstr.*, **45,** 8027f (1951).
136. Proell, W. A., and C. E. Adams, U. S. Patent 2,557,312 (to Standard Oil of Indiana), June 19, 1951; *Chem. Abstr.*, **46,** 1579g (1952).
137. Birch, S. F., T. V. Cullum, and R. A. Dean, *J. Inst. Petrol.*, **39,** 206 (1953); *Chem. Abstr.*, **48,** 4428e (1954).
138. Leandri, G., and A. Tundo, *Ric, Sci.*, **23,** 1646 (1953); *Chem. Abstr.*, **48,** 12699d (1954).
139. Lecher, H. Z., *Science*, **120,** 220 (1954).
140. Kharasch, M. S., W. Nudenberg, and T. H. Meltzer, *J. Org. Chem.*, **18,** 1233 (1953).
141. Otsu, T., *J. Polymer Sci.*, **21,** 559 (1956).
142. Barltrop, J. A., P. M. Hayes, and M. Calvin, *J. Am. Chem. Soc.*, **76,** 4348 (1954).
143. Tobolsky, A. V., and B. Baysal, *J. Am. Chem. Soc.*, **75,** 1757 (1953).
144. Tobolsky, A. V., and T. H. Meltzer, U. S. Patent 2,728,750 (to Thiokol Chemical Corp.), Dec. 27, 1955; *Chem. Abstr.*, **50,** 5097a (1956).
145. Stockmayer, W. H., R. O. Howard, and J. T. Clarke, *J. Am. Chem. Soc.*, **75,** 1756 (1953).
146. Benesch, R. E., and R. Benesch, *J. Am. Chem. Soc.*, **80,** 1666 (1958).
147. Berenbaum, M. B., unpublished work, Thiokol Chemical Corporation.
148. Bertozzi, E. R., F. O. Davis, and E. M. Fettes, *J. Polymer Sci.*, **19,** 17 (1956).
149. Fettes, E. M., U. S. Patent 2,606,173 (to Reconstruction Finance Corp.), Aug. 5, 1952; *Chem. Abstr.*, **47,** 349g (1953).
150. Fettes, E. M., U. S. Patent 2,676,165 (to Reconstruction Finance Corp.), Apr. 20, 1954; *Chem. Abstr.*, **48,** 9110c (1954).
151. Flory, P. J., *J. Am. Chem. Soc.*, **58,** 1877 (1936).
152. Fettes, E. M., and J. S. Jorczak, *Ind. Eng. Chem.*, **42,** 2217 (1950).
153. Stern, M. D., and A. V. Tobolsky, *J. Chem. Phys.*, **14,** 93 (1946).
154. Mochulsky, M., and A. V. Tobolsky, *Ind. Eng. Chem.*, **40,** 2155 (1948).
155. Tobolsky, A. V., *Properties and Structure of Polymers*, Wiley, New York, 1960.
156. Colodny, P. C., and A. V. Tobolsky, *J. Appl. Polymer Sci.*, **2,** 39 (1959).

Chapter VIII

CLEAVAGE REACTIONS

A. HYDROLYSIS

D. A. S. Ravens and Mrs. J. E. Sisley

Imperial Chemical Industries, Ltd.

1. Introduction

Although the hydrolytic degradation of polymers was first studied in the fields of protein and cellulose chemistry, recently the investigations have been extended to synthetic condensation polymers, particularly polyesters and polyamides. The technological importance of polymer hydrolysis lies in the deterioration of tensile properties, either in polymer processing or in the end uses. It is therefore desirable to know the mechanism of degradation for a particular polymer and to be able to compare the hydrolytic resistance of different polymers. In order to discover the reaction mechanism, the chemical reaction rate and the way in which the physical structure of a polymer influences the rate are required.

The hydrolysis of cellulose is dealt with in more detail in Chapter V of this book, but it is useful to look briefly at this reaction because it is one of the most widely studied of all polymer degradations, and the principles of the methods developed for attacking the problem have been applied to other polymers. During the hydrolysis of cellulose there is a decrease in molecular weight and in tensile strength, but in the early stages no appreciable amount of monomer is formed. This led Freudenberg and Kuhn (1) to suggest that chemically, the process was one of random chain scission. Nickerson and Habrle (2), Sharples (3), and other workers in investigating the effects of the physical properties of the polymer on the reaction have shown that the crystalline regions of cellulose are far more resistant to hydrolysis than the amorphous regions. Gibbons (4), by following the homogeneous hydrolysis of methyl cellulose in hydrochloric acid, has been able to suggest a mechanism for the hydrolysis of the ether linkage.

From this it can be seen that the questions to be asked when considering polymer hydrolysis are: (*1*) Is the reaction one of random chain scission? (*2*) What is the mechanism of the reaction and what catalysts influence the reaction? (*3*) How do the physical parameters of the polymer influence the reaction rate?

When the reaction is carried out under heterogeneous conditions a fourth question must be added: is the reaction rate governed by chemical factors or is it controlled by diffusion of some species through the polymer?

We shall be concerned here with linear polyesters and polyamides as it is on these commercially important materials that detailed studies have been made. The rate of hydrolysis may be followed by chemical methods, such as determination of the endgroup concentration and observation of the fall in viscosity in the solution of the polymer, or by physical methods such as measurement of the changes in physical properties. The results based on tensile measurements are, however, unsatisfactory, since no unique relationship exists between molecular weight and the tenacity or extensibility of the degraded fiber. We shall, therefore, consider only reaction rates based on molecular weight measurements.

2. Statistics of Random Scission

There are several reviews of random chain scission statistics such as that of Grassie (5), but it is convenient to outline briefly some of the treatments here. Kuhn (6) used a statistical method and assumed that all bonds are equally reactive, independent of their position in the chain and of the length of the chain.

If a polymer chain of N_0 monomer units with $N_0 - 1$ bonds undergoes reaction so that in time t, p bonds are broken, then the degree of degradation α is given by

$$\alpha = p/(N_0 - 1) \tag{1}$$

and this is the probability that any particular bond is broken. The number of bonds broken at time t, will also be given by

$$p = (N_0 - 1)(1 - e^{-kt}) \tag{2}$$

where

$$\alpha = 1 - e^{-kt}$$

and k is the unimolecular rate constant for chain scission. The number-average chain length at this time, N_t, is given by

$$N_t = N_0/(p + 1) \tag{3}$$

If the process is completely random then p can be eliminated from eq. (2) and (3) giving

$$(N_t - 1)/N_t = [(N_0 - 1)/N_0] (e^{-kt})$$

or

$$kt = \ln [(N_0 - 1)/N_0] - \ln [(N_t - 1)/N_t] \tag{4}$$

When $1/N_t$ is small, eq. (4) reduces to

$$(1/N_t) - (1/N_0) = kt \tag{5}$$

If the endgroup concentration is initially n_0, and becomes n_t at time t, then since $n \propto 1/N$

$$n_t - n_0 = k' t \tag{6}$$

Thus Kuhn's treatment may be used where the extent of degradation is not great and the concentration of endgroups should increase linearly with time for a random chain scission process. For unbranched polymer chains (such as those we shall consider) the number-average chain length, the number-average molecular weight or the endgroup concentration can be related to the intrinsic viscosity of the polymer in solution. A more detailed statistical treatment involving both number-average and weight-average molecular weights is given by Montroll and Simha (7), who include in their paper theoretical calculations of the size distribution of the degraded fragments. They assume however that all initial molecules have the same molecular weight, but such a homogeneous system is seldom obtained. Montroll (8) later extended the treatment to include a normal molecular distribution curve for the initial polymer.

3. Polyesters

a. *Poly(ethylene Terephthalate): Introduction*

Although many polyesters are mentioned in the literature, only poly(ethylene terephthaalte) has been studied from the viewpoint of hydrolysis kinetics. In order to understand the reaction fully it is necessary to first discuss briefly some of the physical properties of the polymer. Poly-

(ethylene terephthalate) may be obtained in either an amorphous or partially crystalline state, in either case with various levels of molecular orientation, and the number-average molecular weight range of commercial products is about 15,000–20,000.

The degree of crystallinity of the polymer may be measured by the x-ray method described by Farrow and Preston (9) who have followed the general procedure of Matthews, Peiser, and Richards (10). The infrared methods of Cobbs and Burton (11) and Miller and Willis (12) and the density method (13) have serious disadvantages for reasons discussed fully by Farrow and Ward (14). For the determination of the degree of molecular orientation an optical birefringence method (15) or dichroic dyestuffs devised by Patterson and Ward (16) can be used. There are several papers correlating the intrinsic viscosity of polymer solutions with the number-average molecular weight. Conix (17) estimated carboxyl and hydroxyl endgroups by titration, Marshall and Todd (18) used an osmometric calibration, and Ward (19) an infrared method of determining endgroup concentrations based on a deuteration technique. This last method (20) gives the relationship

$$[\eta] = 1.7 \times 10^{-4} \bar{M}_n^{0.83} \tag{7}$$

where $[\eta]$ is the intrinsic viscosity of poly(ethylene terephthalate) in *o*-chlorophenol and $\bar{M}_n$ is the number-average molecular weight. It should be noted that, although cyclic oligomers occur in the polymer (21), these do not invalidate the relationship, since the calibration is purely empirical. As the physical state of the polymer influences the rate of hydrolysis the above rapid characterization techniques enable the reaction to be followed easily and facilitate the interpretation of results.

The hydrolysis of poly(ethylene terephthalate) can be carried out under neutral, acid, or alkaline conditions. We shall consider first the neutral and acid cases which are similar, and then the very different case of alkaline hydrolysis. All the studies so far reported have been of heterogeneous hydrolysis, although as will become clear later, for neutral and acid hydrolysis the reaction within the polymer network is homogeneous, the polymer acting as the solvent.

b. Neutral and Acid-Catalyzed Hydrolysis

(1) Random Nature of the Reaction

The limitations of the intrinsic viscosity method make it possible to measure values of $[\eta]$ only down to about 0.1 with reliable accuracy, and

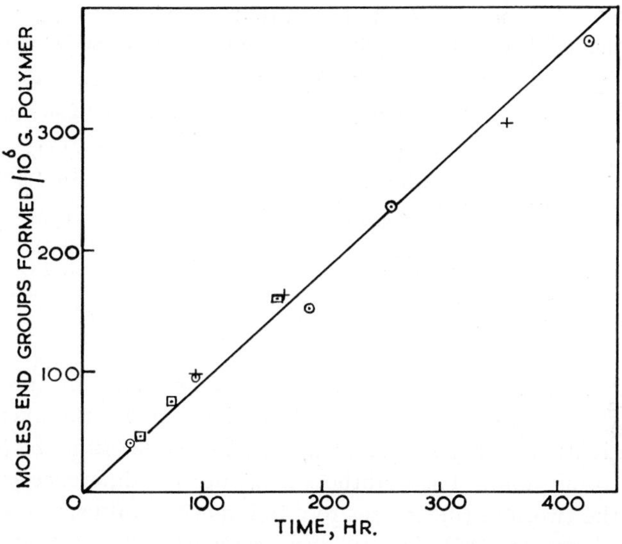

Fig. VIII-1. Effect of filament denier on the hydrolysis rate of amorphous poly(ethyleneterephthalate) in 5N HCl at 70°C.: (⊙) 2 den.; (⊡) 3 den.; (+) 6 den. (Takenfrom ref. 30.)

since the value for undegraded polymer is about 0.6, only about two cuts per chain can be reliably measured. It is therefore possible to apply Kuhn's treatment which for random scission requires that the increase in the number of endgroups should be linear with time. This is shown to be the case with the hydrochloric acid-catalyzed hydrolysis (Fig. VIII-1) and with neutral hydrolysis, but there is evidence (22) that hydrolysis by concentrated sulfuric acid is not random since terephthalic acid can be isolated early in the reaction.

(2) Diffusion of Water Through Poly(ethylene Terephthalate)

The possibility of the diffusion of water into the polymer becoming the rate-determining step has been considered by several groups of workers but with conflicting conclusions. McMahon et al. (23) studied the hydrolysis of poly(ethylene terephthalate) film over a wide temperature range and investigated the rate of reaction for a relative humidity range of 20–100% and for a 20-fold difference in film thickness, following the reaction rate by intrinsic viscosity measurements. Some of their results are shown in Table VIII-1.

TABLE VIII-1
Effect of Film Thickness on the Hydrolysis Rate of Poly(ethylene Terephthalate) at 100% R.H.[a]

Temp., °C.	Rate constants, $days^{-1} \times 10^{-4}$ for various film thickness	
	10 mil film of density 1.395	0.5 ml film of density 1.389
90	0.692	1.29
99	1.83	3.53
130	26.5	39.1

[a] Taken from ref. 23.

For a 20-fold decrease in film thickness they found an approximately 2-fold increase in rate. Also between 50–100% R.H. the average value for the activation energy is 26.2 kcal./mole for 0.5 mil film and 30.9 kcal./mole for 10 mil film. These authors attribute the difference in rate constant for the two film thicknesses to a difference in diffusion rates. They also note, however, that density measurements indicate that the 10 mil sample may have a higher degree of crystallinity and the thinner sample a higher degree of orientation.

A more elaborate treatment of the diffusion problem has been given by Golike and Lasoski (24), who have derived a theoretical equation for the hydrolysis kinetics assuming that diffusion of water into the polymer is the rate controlling step. If n is the number of moles of ester links hydrolyzed/mole of polymer, A is the initial number of ester links/mole of polymer, B is the initial number of moles of water in polymer/mole of polymer, C_0 is the water concentration at the polymer surface, D is the diffusion coefficient, $2l$ is film thickness, and t is time, then $B - n = \mathrm{C}$ is the effective water concentration, and

$$n/\mathrm{A} = kCt = k't \tag{8}$$

For diffusion-controlled hydrolysis it is shown that

$$k't = n/A = \left[kC_0 \frac{\tanh\,(kA/D)^{1/2}l}{(kAD)/^{1/2}l} \right] t \tag{9}$$

Making the approximation that $\tanh x/x = 1 - (x^2/3)$ for $x < \pi/2$ then

$$k' = C_0k - (kC_0l^2/3)\,(kA/D) \tag{10}$$

By plotting k' (from intrinsic viscosity measurements) against l^2, Golike and Lasoski obtained values of $(kA/D)^{1/2}$ from the slopes of the graphs. They say that the agreement between experimental data and the equations they have developed confirms that the reaction is diffusion controlled; however the validity of their conclusions has recently been questioned by Davies et al. (25), both on chemical and mathematical grounds.

The chemical objections are 2-fold. First, there is a back reaction of esterification which becomes increasingly important at low relative humidity values, and therefore the measured hydrolysis rate is smaller than the true value. This may explain the discrepancy between their value for an activation energy of 22.6 kcal./mole and the value of 26–27 kcal./mole found by McMahon (23) and Ravens and Ward (20). Second, measurements of the rate of diffusion of water into poly(ethylene terephthalate) by Small (26) using a gain in weight method, and by Ward (27) determining the rate of deuteration of the endgroups by D_2O, show that the diffusion rate is at least 1000-fold greater than the reaction rate, so the reaction will not be diffusion-controlled. Both Small and Ward agree that the activation energy for diffusion is about 14 kcal./mole, which is considerably smaller than the value for the hydrolysis reaction. On mathematical grounds, Davies points out that the approximation $(\tanh x)/x \simeq 1 - (x^2/3)$ has been used for values of $x > \pi/2$, i.e., where $(kA/D)^{1/2}l > 1.57$, and the quantities derived from these conditions are therefore incorrect.

The rate of diffusion of the reagent into the polymer does not therefore seem to be the rate-controlling factor in the hydrolytic degradation of poly(ethylene terephthalate), and where slower rates of reaction are found for thicker films, other physical parameters may well be the major influence.

(3) Reaction Mechanism and Polymer Structure

The hydrolysis of simple esters in neutral or acid media generally proceed through one of two mechanisms. There is a rapidly established initial equilibrium:

$$\mathrm{R{-}\overset{\overset{\displaystyle O}{\|}}{C}{-}OR' + H^+ \rightleftharpoons R{-}\overset{\overset{\displaystyle O}{\|}}{C}{-}\overset{+}{O}HR'} \qquad (11a)$$

which may be followed by either of two reactions:

$$\mathrm{R{-}\overset{\overset{\displaystyle O}{\|}}{C}{-}\overset{+}{O}HR' \rightleftharpoons R{-}\overset{\overset{\displaystyle O}{\|}}{C}{}^{+} + R'OH} \qquad (11b)$$

or

$$R\text{—}\overset{\overset{\large O}{\|}}{C}\text{—}\overset{+}{O}HR' + H_2O \overset{k'}{\rightleftharpoons} R\text{—}\overset{\overset{\large O}{\|}}{C}\text{—}OH_2^{\,+} + R'OH \qquad (11c)$$

When the rate-controlling step is reaction (11b), the reaction rate is given by the rate equation,

$$r = k[\mathrm{E}]\,[\mathrm{H}^+] \qquad (12)$$

and log k is linearly related to the Hammett acidity function (28). When reaction (11c) is the rate-determining step, then the rate depends on $[\mathrm{H}^+]$ and on the water concentration, since water is involved in the transition state complex (29). Thus,

$$r = k'[\mathrm{E}][\mathrm{H}^+]\,[\mathrm{H_2O}] \qquad (13)$$

McMahon (23) has shown how for poly(ethylene terephthalate) the hydrolysis rate is dependent on the relative humidity, and these results taken in conjunction with the adsorption isotherm reported by Ravens and Ward (20) show that the rate of hydrolysis is directly proportional to the concentration of water in the polymer (Fig. VIII-2).

Hydrolysis in hydrochloric acid (30) shows several interesting features from which both the nature of acid catalysis and the effects of the physical

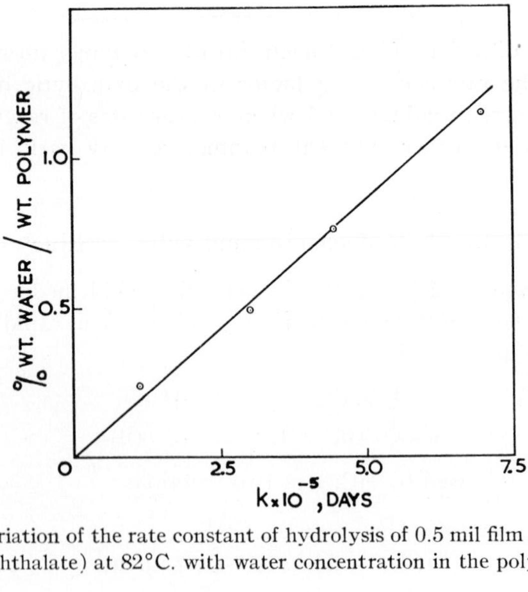

Fig. VIII-2. Variation of the rate constant of hydrolysis of 0.5 mil film of poly(ethylene terephthalate) at 82°C. with water concentration in the polymer.

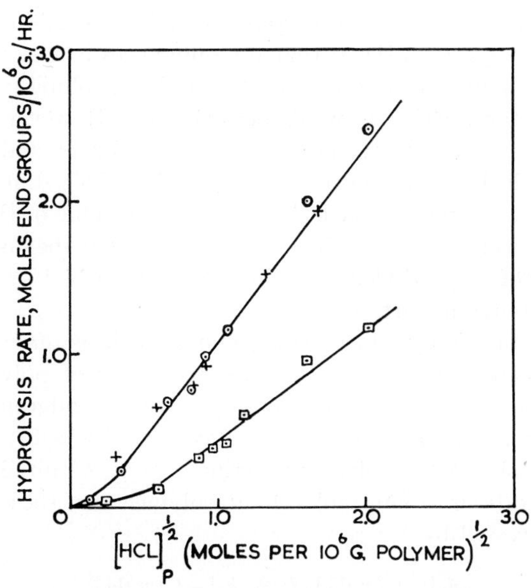

Fig. VIII-3. Effect of $[HCl]_p$ on the hydrolysis rate of poly(ethylene terephthalate) at 70°C.: (+) amorphous, unoriented; (⊙) 48% crystalline, unoriented; (⊡) 30% crystalline, oriented. (Taken from ref. 30.)

structure of the polymer have been inferred. The reaction rate is little influenced by acid concentration below 3*N* but increases rapidly at concentrations above this value. This effect may be explained by considering not the concentration of the acid in the aqueous phase but in the polymer itself. This may be done by assuming that because of the low dielectric constant of the polymer (31) only undissociated hydrogen chloride diffuses into the polymer and not hydrogen ions. To examine this theory the adsorption isotherms for hydrogen chloride were determined with a manometric method in the pressure range 1–30 mm. Hg, which is the range of HCl partial pressures above the aqueous solution at 70°C. for concentrations of 1–7*N* HCl. When the rate of reaction is plotted against the concentration of HCl in the polymer at the pressures corresponding to the partial pressures of the undissociated acid, it is found that the rate is approximately proportional to $[HCl]_p^{1/2}$ where $[HCl]_p$ is the concentration of hydrogen chloride in the polymer. Since, in the low dielectric medium of the polymer the hydrogen chloride will be weakly dissociated, the rate equation in excess water and ester becomes

$$r = \text{const. } [H^+]_p \qquad (14)$$

When this is applied to amorphous, partially crystalline and oriented samples it is seen (Fig. VIII-3) that the differences in rate for amorphous and crystalline polymer are due almost entirely to solubility effects in the early stages of the reaction, as would be expected. However, orientation of the polymer causes a decrease in the true chemical rate, and this has been attributed to the lower dielectric constant of the oriented material causing a smaller dissociation of the acid, hence a smaller value of $[H^+]$. It must be noted, however, that McMahon (23) suggests that the faster rate found for hydrolysis of poly(ethylene terephthalate) in 0.5×10^{-3} mil thick film might be attributed in part, to higher orientation.

Although catalysis by added strong mineral acid is quite clearly established, the possibility that the aqueous hydrolysis of poly(ethylene terephthalate) may be autocatalyzed by the carboxylic endgroups in the polymer has only recently been examined. Ravens and Ward (20) have shown by taking samples of the polymer covering a range of initial carboxyl endgroup concentrations of 8–97 moles/10^6 g. polymer, that the rate of hydrolysis can be expressed by

$$d\,[-\text{COOH}]/dt = k\,[-\text{COOH}]^{1/2} \tag{15}$$

where the square root term arises from the weak acidic nature of the carboxyl group. This is a genuine catalytic effect and is not due to adsorption of water in the polymer at carboxylic endgroups only, since the authors have also shown that the adsorption isotherm is independent of the —COOH endgroup concentration. McMahon et al. (23) in their study have also found that the hydrolysis rate increases as the reaction proceeds but attribute this to the formation of voids due to an increase in sample crystallinity. This theory of void formation on drawing is described by Thompson and Woods (32), but Farrow and Ward (14) suggest that voids are not formed, the increase in density being due to molecular orientation (without the formation of crystallinity) and that this is far in excess of the reduction in density caused by the formation of voids. It can be seen therefore that the increase in reaction rate described by McMahon is more probably due to autocatalysis.

c. Alkaline Hydrolysis

Compared with other hydrolysis studies on poly(ethylene terephthalate), very little published work has appeared on the alkaline hydrolysis, in spite of the importance of the reaction when fibers from the polymer are treated in alkaline dyeing processes.

The hydrolysis of poly(ethylene terephthalate) by 20% potassium hydroxide solution at 98°C. has been reported by Waters (33), who found that, unlike neutral and acid hydrolysis, the reaction is not homogeneous with respect to the polymer. He found that the polymer, as fiber, is attacked on the surface only, causing a loss in weight as ethylene glycol and terephthalate ions are removed into solution. The explanation of this would seem to be that hydroxyl ions cannot penetrate the polymer structure because of the dielectric properties of the polymer, and also that the formation of negatively charged carboxylate ions on the surface of the polymer may repulse attacking hydroxyl ions.

4. Polyamides

a. Introduction

The hydrolysis of polyamides results in a splitting of the molecular chain with the production of an amine and a carboxylic acid for each bond broken.

$$R-N(H)-C(=O)-R' \xrightarrow{H_2O} RNH_2 + R'COOH \qquad (16)$$

Although from a technical point of view heterogeneous hydrolysis is important, the reaction kinetics may be complicated by the rate of diffusion of the reagent to the amide bond becoming the rate-determining step. Investigations in homogeneous solution where the physical effect of the fiber is eliminated are therefore more satisfactory for elucidating the kinetic mechanism of the cleavage reaction.

b. Mechanism of the Reaction

The acid hydrolysis of polyamides has been investigated in homogeneous solution by Myagkov and Pakshver (34). The rates of hydrolysis of caprolactam and an unspecified polyamide resin of molecular weight ~2000 were measured in 0.128M and 1.2M H_2SO_4 at 70, 80, and 102°C. In the more dilute acid they found the reaction rate was dependent on [lactam] $[H_3O^+]$; in excess of hydrolyzing agent, 1.2M H_2SO_4, where $[H_3O^+]$ changes little during the hydrolysis, the reaction was best explained by a first-order rate equation. This confirmed the role of H_3O^+ in the hydrolysis and the mechanism of eqs. (17) was postulated, where the addition

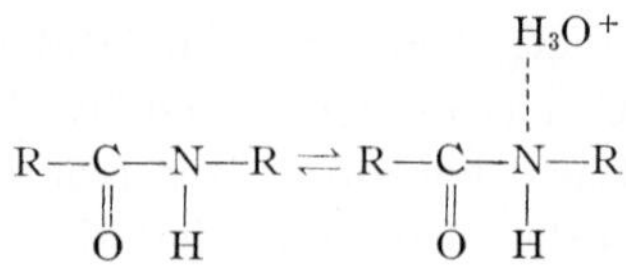 (17a)

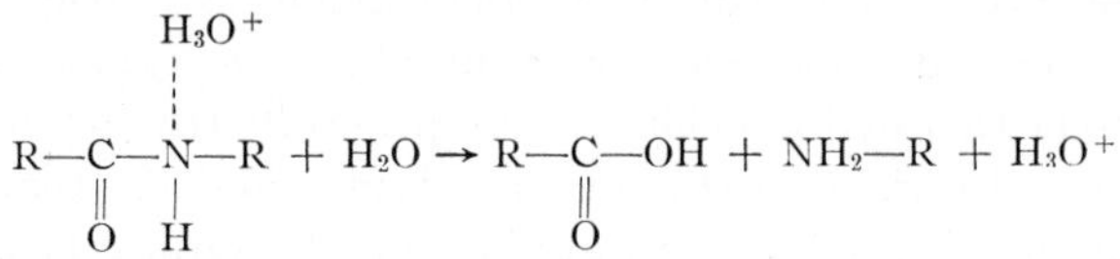 (17b)

of H_3O^+ to the amide is the rate-determining step. The apparent activation energy of 20 kcal./mole for both caprolactam and polyamide resin suggests that the rate of hydrolysis is independent of the length of the polymer chain.

The mechanism of the alkaline hydrolysis of poly(ethylene terephthalate) differs from the neutral and acid type, but according to Myagkov and Pakshver (34), in the homogeneous alkaline hydrolysis of caprolactam with $1.2M$ NaOH, OH^- has an analogous role to H_3O^+ adding on to the —C═O group. The apparent activation energy of the reaction is 16.6 kcal./mole. No results for the alkaline hydrolysis of polyamides are quoted.

c. Random Nature of the Reaction

The random nature of the hydrolytic scission of polyamides has aroused the interest of several workers. The statistical treatment of Kuhn (6) has shown that the number of endgroups formed in hydrolysis should increase linearly with time, assuming that the scission of a bond is independent of its position in the chain, and of the length of the chain in which it is found.

Heikins (35) confirmed this theory when he hydrolyzed linear oligomers of ε-aminocaproic acid at 72°C. with $7.72N$ HCl. The dimer, trimer, and an oligomer of average degree of polymerisation ($\overline{DP}$) = 15 from which the pentamer and lower molecular weight material has been carefully removed were investigated. All followed a first-order reaction with respect to amide concentration, giving a rate constant $k = 0.36$ hr.$^{-1}$ There are, however, remarkable differences in the rate of hydrolysis of cyclic polyamides. Rate constants for the hydrolysis of cyclic oligomers of ε-caprolactam and nylon 66 cyclic diamide by $7.72N$ HCl at 110°C. (36) are evidence of this. The amide bond in the seven-membered ring of caprolactam hydrolyzed at a rate ten times that in linear molecules, a possible explanation of this being that on steric grounds the seven-membered ring assumes the *cis* form

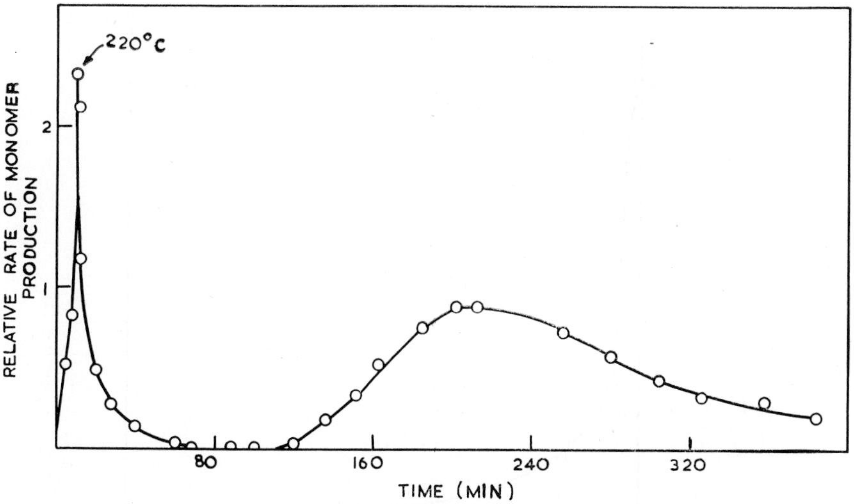

Fig. VIII-7. Rate of evolution of monomer at 220°C. from a methyl methacrylate–acrylonitrile copolymer containing 0.24 mole-% acrylonitrile (molecular weight = 617,000). (Taken from ref. 51.)

and rotating sector techniques they were able to derive rate constants and energies of activation for the depropagation and termination processes. The termination rate constant is very much larger than the value for the same process in the polymerization reaction and its energy of activation is 21 kcal./mole compared with only 2–3 kcal./mole in polymerization. These high values are undoubtedly due to the fact that the reaction is diffusion-controlled due to the high viscosity of the molten medium in which it occurs. Unfortunately, the temperature range in which these experiments could be made was limited to 160–180°C., the lower limit being determined by the softening point of the polymer and the upper limit by the tendency for thermal degradation to occur.

At temperatures below 160°C. diffusion of monomer from the polymer is severely restricted, so that high concentrations of monomer can be retained in the degrading polymer thus the propagation process in the reversible reaction

$$P_n \underset{\text{Propagation}}{\overset{\text{Depropagation}}{\rightleftharpoons}} P_{n-1} + M \tag{34}$$

plays an important role in determining the overall characteristics of the reaction (45,81).

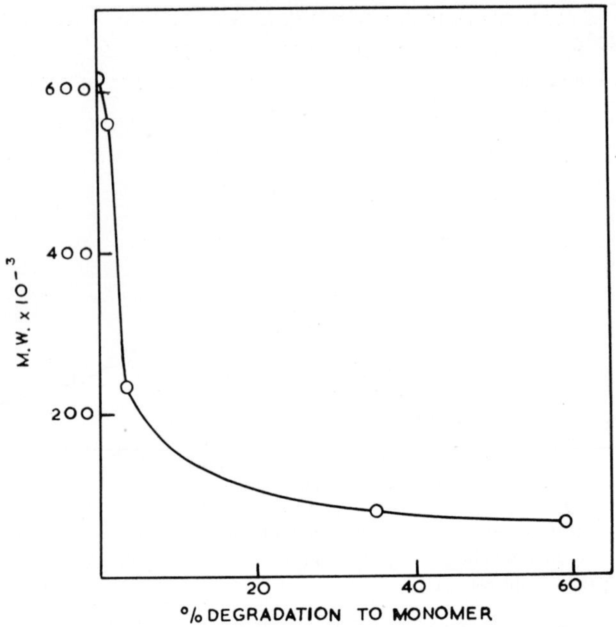

Fig. VIII-8. Effect of thermal degradation at 220°C. on the molecular weight of a methyl methacrylate–acrylonitrile copolymer containing 0.24 mole-% acrylonitrile (molecular weight = 617,000). (Taken from ref. 51.)

The stability of poly(methyl methacrylate) may be increased not only through the initiation process by modification of the chain ends but also by interfering with the depropagation process. Thus a startling increase in stability is achieved by copolymerization with small concentrations of a second monomer which is incapable of being liberated from the polymer chain by depolymerization. Certain acrylates are particularly effective and have been used industrially for this purpose.

As little as one part in 400 parts of copolymerized acrylonitrile inhibits the reaction completely, as shown in Figure VIII-7. The initial peak represents the elimination of nonmonomeric volatile material as the polymer is heating up and the point at which the temperature reaches the reaction temperature, 220°C., is indicated. Stabilization is not permanent in this case, however, the rate ultimately increasing and passing through a maximum.

While the reaction is fully inhibited, rapid chain scission is occurring, as illustrated in Figure VIII-8, the molecular weight tending to a limiting value close to the average distance between acrylonitrile units in the chains. The characteristics of the overall reaction suggest that the acrylonitrile units introduce "weak links" into the polymer molecules such that chain scission occurs by disproportionation, for example,

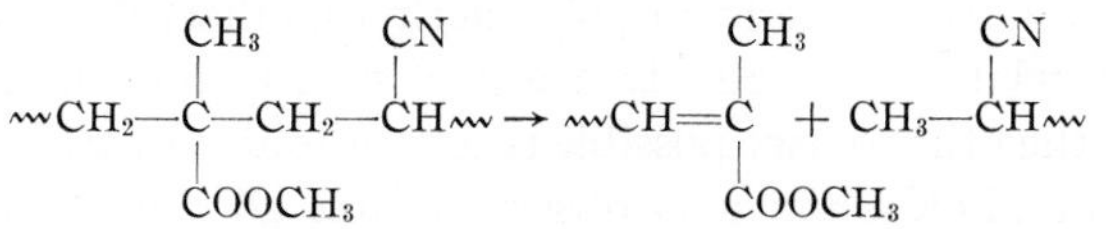

(35)

It has been suggested that scission results in radicals capable of depolymerizing but this would result in a high initial rate. Alternatively, it has been proposed that scission is a result of transfer at the tertiary hydrogen atoms of the acrylonitrile units by the depolymerizing radical, but this would imply considerable monomer production during the chain scission phase of the reaction. Chain scission as depicted in eq. (35) not only explains the decrease in molecular weight, but also the inhibition period and subsequent reaction since as a result of chain scission degradable unsaturated chain ends are being produced.

These characteristics of the depolymerization of methyl methacrylate/acrylonitrile copolymers are strikingly similar to those of pure polystyrene to be discussed.

e. Higher Polymethacrylates

Crawford (82) has shown that from the lower poly(alkyl methacrylates) monomer is the only significant product of thermal degradation at temperatures up to 250°C. Poly(*tert*-butyl methacrylate) is a notable exception, giving quantitative yields of isobutene. Grant and Grassie (83,84) studied this latter reaction, which is described below (see part 3d 3), showing that while ester decomposition is indeed the predominating primary reaction, about 1% of the polymer decomposes to monomer. This monomer is in fact the first product of decomposition, monomer production ceasing as soon as significant amounts of isobutene have appeared.

Later, Grassie and MacCallum (85) examined the thermal decomposition of some primary alkyl methacrylates, focusing their attention in particular upon poly(*n*-butyl methacrylate). They revealed that while 30–50% yields of almost pure monomer could easily be obtained at 200–250°C., insolubility developed, and the residue became progressively more resistant to thermal breakdown to monomer. On closer examination, the ester decomposition reaction in poly(*tert*-butyl methacrylate) having supplied the vital clue, acid and anhydride structures were discovered in the insoluble residue by use of infrared spectroscopic methods, while traces of butene were revealed by gas–liquid chromatographic examination of the volatile fraction. Thus the production of almost quantitative yields of monomer and isobutene from poly(methyl methacrylate) and poly(*tert*-butyl methacrylate), respectively are now seen to represent situations in which one or the other of two possible reactions is able to predominate.

Grassie and MacCallum also observed that all the polymethacrylates which they examined, including poly(*tert*-butyl methacrylate), are completely volatilized to monomer by ultraviolet irradiation (2537 A.) at 170°C. All this information has led these authors to the conclusion that thermal depolymerization to monomer is probably common to all polymethacrylate esters. As the series of primary alkyl esters is ascended, and particularly on passing to secondary and tertiary esters, the tendency for ester decomposition to occur increases, the products of ester decomposition preventing the free passage of the depolymerization process along the polymer chains.

This theory of the interaction of the two possible degradation processes has been tested by studying the thermal and photodegradation of copolymers of *n*-butyl methacrylate with small amounts of methacrylic acid, the primary product of ester decomposition. These copolymers, as expected, give very much smaller yields of monomer than does the homopolymer at 250°C. At 170°C. under 2537 A. irradiation, however, the rates of depolymerization of copolymers containing 1 and 10% of methacrylic acid are, within experimental error, identical with that of homopolymers. Furthermore, methacrylic acid appears among the volatile products. As the period of preheating the polymer at 170°C. is increased, however, the rate of depolymerization on subsequent exposure to 2537 A. radiation is progressively decreased as shown in Figure VIII-9 (86).

Infrared spectral measurements have revealed that anhydride structures are being produced in the copolymer during the preheating period. Thus methacrylic acid can participate in a radical depolymerization process, methacrylic anhydride being the true inhibitor of monomer production in polymethacrylates. The conversion of poly(methacrylic acid) to anhydride, which is discussed below (see Part 3c), occurs at a lower temperature than either ester decomposition or depolymerization to monomer. Thus the depolymerization of poly(methacrylic acid) can only be observed in photoinitiated decompositions at relatively low temperatures and even so only in copolymers since the depolymerization reaction in pure poly(methacrylic acid) is not initiated by ultraviolet radiation.

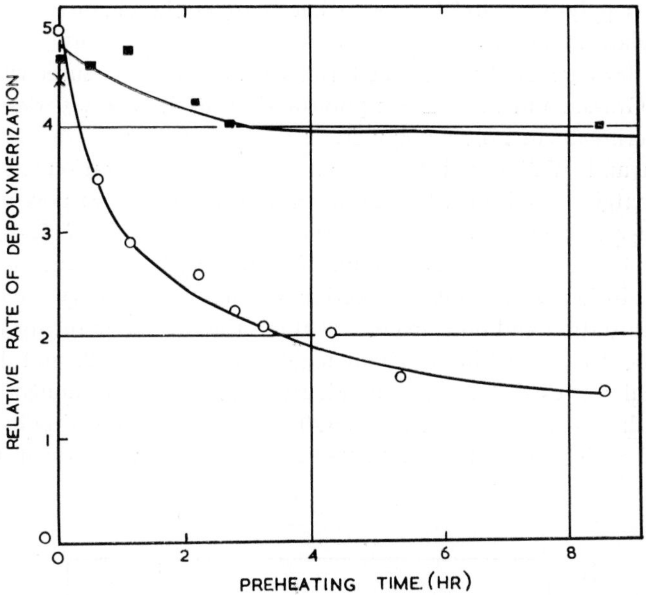

Fig. VIII-9. Effect of preheating on the initial rate of photodepolymerization of poly(*n*-butyl methacrylate) at 170°C.: (×) homopolymer; (■) 1% methacrylic acid copolymer; (O) 10% methacrylic acid copolymer. (Taken from ref. 86.)

Since the alcohol residue in poly(methyl methacrylate) has no β hydrogen atoms, ester decomposition in its polymer is impossible. It is for this reason that poly(methyl methacrylate) is the only member of the series so far studied in detail from which quantitative yields of monomer may be obtained thermally. It is interesting to speculate that the next higher member of the series with the necessary structural features is neopentyl methacrylate.

f. Poly-α-methylstyrene

There are strong similarities between poly-α-methylstyrene and poly(methyl methacrylate). Both are derived from α,α-disubstituted monomers, and the data in Table VIII-2 show that they are relatively unstable thermally and break down to give almost pure monomer. There are, however, a number of marked differences in the characteristics of their thermal decomposition reactions which were shown by Brown and Wall (87) to be the result of initiation of the chain depolymerization process at random in poly-α-methylstyrene rather than at the chain ends as in the methacrylates. Later experiments in solution by Grant, Vance, and Bywater (88) generally confirmed Brown and Wall's results which, like those of Grassie and Melville on poly(methyl methacrylate), were derived from experiments in molten polymer.

Brown and Wall found the initial rate of volatilization to increase approximately 4-fold for a 15-fold increase in the degree of polymerization of polymer fractions as shown by the points in Figure VIII-10. They were able to account for this in terms of Simha, Wall, and Blatz's quantitative description of the chain reaction mechanism in Part 2a assuming random initiation and no transfer. Taking the rate constant for initiation as 3.42×10^{-6} and kinetic chain lengths of 1476, 1342, and 1208, the theoretical curves *A*, *B*, and *C* in Figure VIII-10 were obtained. On the basis of the change in molecular weights during reaction of polymer with an initial molecular weight of 97,000 a kinetic chain length of 1230 was derived.

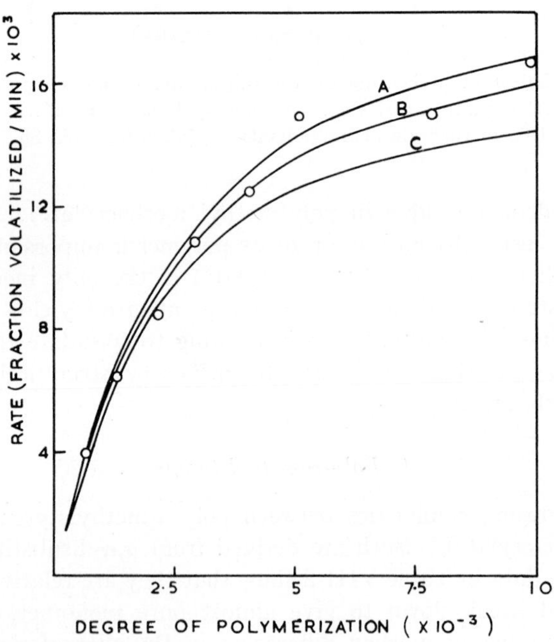

Fig. VIII-10. Initial rates of volatilization as a function of degree of polymerization for poly-α-methylstyrene fractions. (Taken from ref. 87.)

The experiments of Grant, Vance, and Bywater were carried out in solution in decalin and diphenyl ether. The rate of production of monomer was found to be directly proportional to the molecular weight and concentration of the polymer and quite independent of the solvent. Both anionically and cationically initiated materials were used, and one series prepared using sodium naphthenide in tetrahydrofuran solution was found after 9% depolymerization to retain the extremely sharp molecular weight distributions of the original materials. It was pointed out that these features could be accounted for again in terms of the mechanism described above (see Part 2a) assuming random initiation, no transfer, and a kinetic chain length long compared with the molecular chain length of the polymer. On these assumptions the termination reaction can be neglected since most chains will have depolymerized completely before termination can occur. Thus the rate of the reaction is given by the rate of initiation times the chain length of the polymer, that is,

$$\text{Rate} = k_i \, [\text{P}_N] \, N \tag{36}$$

in which $[\text{P}_N]$ is the concentration of the polymer in base moles per liter and N is the chain length of the polymer. This is in accordance with the experimental findings. For kinetic chains very much shorter than the molecular chain length, on the other hand, in the stationary state,

$$d[\text{P}]/dt = 0 = 2k_i \, [\text{P}_N] - k_t]\text{P}^2] \tag{37}$$

$$\therefore \quad [\text{P}] = (\sqrt{2}k_i^{1/2}/k_t^{1/2}) \, [\text{P}_N]^{1/2} \tag{38}$$

$$\therefore \quad \text{Rate} = k_d[\text{P}] = (\sqrt{2}k_d k_i^{1/2}/k_t^{1/2}) \, [\text{P}_N]^{1/2} \tag{39}$$

in which case the rate would be independent of chain length and proportional to the square root of the polymer concentration.

Grant, Vance, and Bywater believed that the molten polymer experiments of Brown and Wall showed a more complex dependence of rate on chain length because they were carried out under conditions in which kinetic and molecular chain lengths were comparable. This implies that the kinetic chain length in solution is appreciably greater than in the molten state and this has recently been confirmed by Cowie and Bywater (89). This is reasonable, since the lower concentration of polymer in solution and the lower temperature at which the solution experiments were carried out (approximately 230°C. compared with 282.5°C. in bulk) both imply a lower radical concentration so that bimolecular kinetic chain terminating reactions such as transfer or mutual interaction of radicals will be relatively less important compared with depropagation.

Grant, Vance, and Bywater's mechanism implies that whole molecules are eliminated from the system so that the retention of the sharp molecular weight distribution during degradation is reasonable. However, they admit that there is a decrease in molecular weight, which implies some chain termination either by transfer or mutual interaction of pairs of radicals, and this should result in a broad band of lower molecular weight material in the distribution. They attribute this discrepancy to experimental error in the fractionation procedure.

g. *Polystyrene*

The principal features of the thermal degradation of polystyrene are firstly, that the volatile product is approximately 42% monomer with decreasing amounts of dimer, trimer, and tetramer and traces of pentamer (59,90) but no other significant products and, secondly, a sharp but limited decrease in molecular weight occurs early in the reaction. Jellinek (74) explained the decrease in molecular weight as being due to the scission of a limited number of weak links distributed at random in the polystyrene chains. He also demonstrated the radical nature of monomer production by comparing the loss in weight of polystyrene degraded in naphthalene and in tetralin solutions (91). The rapid production of volatile material in the former which is an inert solvent is completely inhibited in the latter, the radicals being deactivated by transfer to the reactive α-methylenic hydrogen atoms before any appreciable depropagation can occur. The production of volatile material is thus clearly a radical reaction, fragments larger than monomer being produced by intramolecular transfer as illustrated in Part 2b. It was a reasonable additional assumption that the decrease in molecular weight is due to intermolecular transfer. The theoretical consequences of such a mechanism have already been referred to (see Part 2a), and Figures VIII-11 and VIII-12 illustrate the excellent agreement which Gordon (55) has been able to achieve by the application of curve-fitting methods to Grassie and Kerr's (92) experimental results.

There did however, appear to Grassie and Kerr (92) to be certain discrepancies in the intermolecular transfer explanation for the decrease in molecular weight. Once the initial rapid decrease is complete, at the points X in Figure VIII-13 for example, the subsequent parts of the curves always lie between the horizontal and the diagonal running from point X

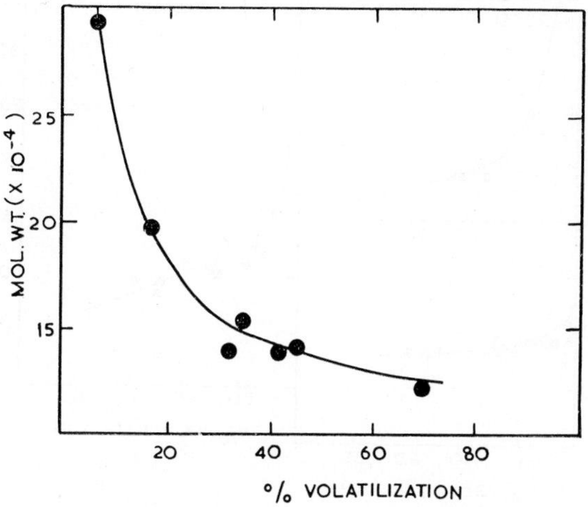

Fig. VIII-11. Application of Gordon's theory (continuous line) to Grassie and Kerr's experimental points for the molecular weight changes during depolymerization of polystyrene. (Taken from ref. 55.)

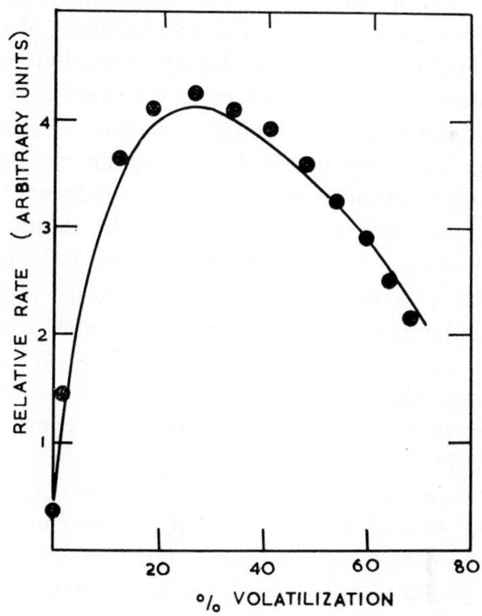

Fig. VIII-12. Application of Gordon's theory (continuous line) to Grassie and Kerr's experimental points for rate changes during depolymerization of polystyrene. (Taken from ref. 55.)

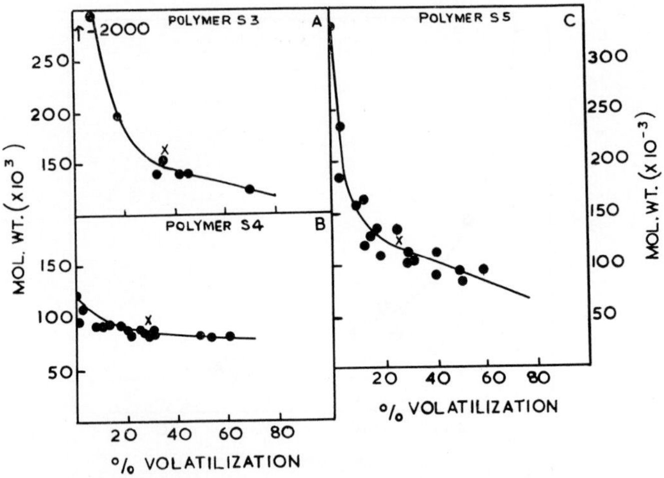

Fig. VIII-13. Dependence of molecular-weight changes upon extent of volatilization in various polystyrenes. (Taken from ref. 82.)

to zero molecular weight and 100% volatilization. It follows (Part 2d) that intermolecular transfer is negligible in this phase of the reaction, and that the kinetic chain length of the depolymerization process (including monomer units produced in intramolecular transfer) is of the order of the molecular chain length of the residual material at point X. If intermolecular transfer did account for the molecular weight changes in the initial stages of the reaction, it is difficult to explain why its effect should cease so abruptly and why the molecular weight should not continue to fall to very low values. It is clear from Figure VIII-13 that the rapid initial chain scission is complete at approximately 30% volatilization. Up to that point, therefore, the number of molecules, that is, the number of chain ends, in the system is increasing. The fact that the rate of volatilization passes through a maximum in this region (Fig. VIII-14) supports the view that the reaction is initiated at chain ends like that in poly(methyl methacrylate).

These doubts about the existence of intermolecular transfer led to a reconsideration of Jellinek's proposal that "weak links" are responsible for the initial molecular weight decrease, and a decision between the two possibilities was finally obtained by a further comparison of experiments in bulk and in naphthalene and tetralin solution (73).

Figure VIII-15 illustrates the changes in molecular weight which occur in each of the three media at 325°C. The rates of the initial rapid fall

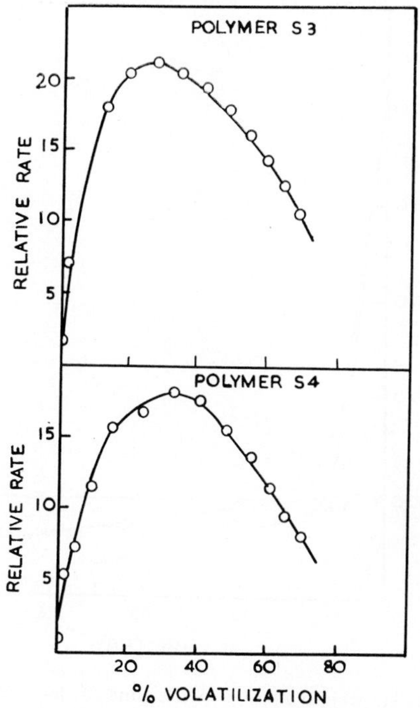

Fig. VIII-14. Dependence of rate upon extent of volatilization at 360°C. for two polystyrene samples. (Taken from ref. 92.)

in molecular weight are, within experimental error, the same in each case. On the other hand, the subsequent decrease in molecular weight is less in naphthalene and is completely inhibited in tetralin. Nevertheless, the values of molecular weight obtained by extrapolating this later part of the curve back to zero time are identical within experimental error, which emphasizes the close similarity of the extent as well as the rate of the initial molecular weight decrease by contrast with the divergent behavior in the later stages of the reaction.

The reason for this divergent behavior is explained by the data in Figure VIII-16, no volatilization taking place in tetralin solution. The radical chain depolymerization process is retarded in naphthalene and completely inhibited in tetralin. Tetralin is a radical chain inhibitor by virtue of the relatively high reactivity of the methylene groups adjacent to the aromatic ring. The reactivity of the hydrogen atoms in naphthalene may be great enough to account for its retardation activity. Alternative explanations are the presence of trace retarders or the greater mobility of

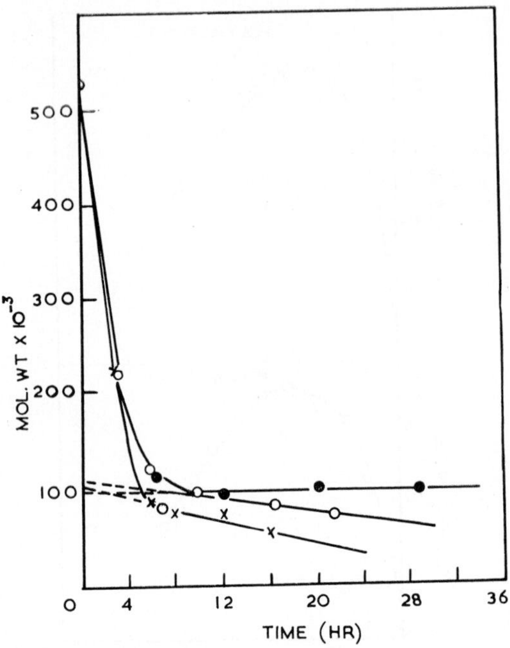

Fig. VIII-15. Molecular weight changes with time of degradation of polystyrene at 325°C.: (×) in bulk; (O) in naphthalene solution; (●) in tetralin solution. (Taken from ref. 73.)

the depolymerizing radicals in solution facilitating the disproportionation termination process. This latter explanation seems the more reasonable since it has also been shown to account, under similar experimental conditions, for the gel effect which may be observed during polymerization.

By plotting the molecular weight change against the extent of volatilization as in Figure VIII-17 the lower rate of volatilization in naphthalene solution relative to the constant rate of molecular weight decrease in each medium is clearly illustrated. In this figure the behavior of the polystyrene in tetralin is represented by the molecular weight axis.

This illustration of the complete inhibition of volatilization while the rate of initial molecular weight decrease remains constant is in complete accordance with, and is indeed strong evidence in support of, the weak link theory. It is unaccountable in terms of the transfer theory, which requires that the inhibition of molecular weight changes and volatilization should run parallel. There might well be a difference in the relative rates of these two component processes in bulk polymer and solution,

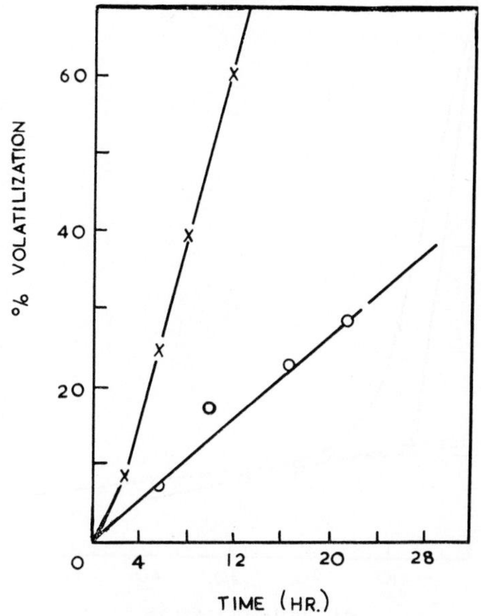

Fig. VIII-16. Extent of volatilization versus time relationship for polystyrene at 325°C.: (×) in bulk; (O) in naphthalene solution. (Taken from ref. 73.)

although it is inconceivable that one should be completely inhibited while the other proceeds at its full rate.

The close similarity of the overall depolymerization of polystyrene with that of methyl methacrylate–acrylonitrile copolymers has already been mentioned (see Part 2d), when it was pointed out that the acceleration in the rate of production of monomer while the molecular weight is rapidly decreasing is evidence that chain scission results in molecules rather than radicals capable of depolymerization. Grassie and Kerr (92) confirmed this by an analysis of the rates of monomer production and chain scission in the early parts of the reaction.

In spite of the fact that intermolecular transfer is not significantly important in the thermal degradation of polystyrene, the potential transfer process between polystyryl radicals and the tertiary hydrogen atoms in polystyrene chains is of considerable interest. These tertiary hydrogen atoms might reasonably be expected to be highly reactive toward radicals. Polystyrene may be regarded in this connection as a substituted isopropylbenzene (cumene) which is a powerful transfer agent in radical processes.

If transfer occurred during depolymerization then it should also occur during polymerization and result in chain branching in view of the high

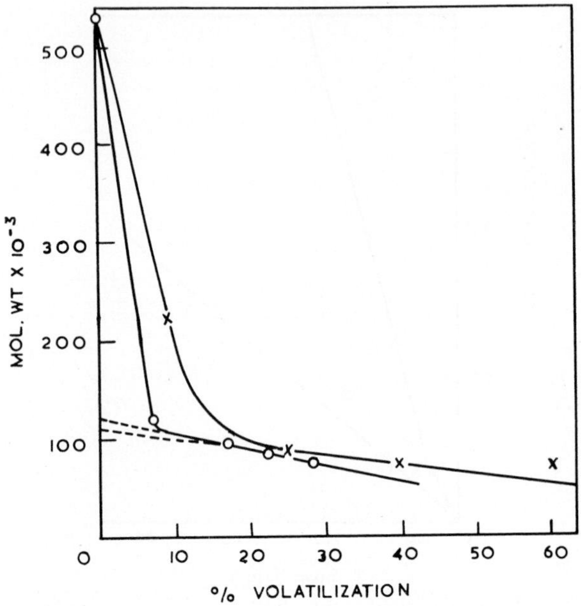

Fig. VIII-17. Molecular weight changes versus extent of volatilization of polystyrene at 325°C.: (×) in bulk; (O) in naphthalene solution. (Taken from ref. 73.)

concentration of monomer present. But Wall and Brown (93) have found no evidence for branching in polystyrene prepared in bulk at 70°C., so there seems to be a fundamental difference in behavior in this respect between polystyrene and the parent cumene structure. It has been suggested that transfer does indeed occur during polymerization, but that the radical so formed throws off a hydrogen atom from an adjacent main chain carbon atom to form a double bond. If this occurred, the resulting hydrogen atom would initiate a new molecular chain so that the molecular weight of polystyrene should be strongly dependent upon the extent of conversion of monomer to polymer, being lower at higher conversions. Such an effect does not exist.

The molar proportions in which the volatile products appear are approximately, monomer:dimer:trimer:tetramer = 40:10:8:1. According to the intramolecular transfer mechanism (see Part 2b), the transition states for dimer, trimer, and tetramer formation should involve four-, six-, and eight-membered rings, respectively. Thus, on this basis alone, trimer might reasonably be expected to be very much more abundant than either dimer or tetramer. That dimer is even more abundant than trimer may be an indication that the most important factor in facilitating this intramolecular transfer process of chain ends is the proximity of the radical chain end to the center at which transfer occurs. The greater the proximity in the same molecule, the greater will be the possibility of internal energy transfer between the bonds made and those broken so that the overall energy requirements for the reaction to occur are very much less than would be necessary for an intermolecular process.

The concentration of these weak links is apparently too low to give any hope of direct chemical or spectroscopic identification. Jellinek (74) had speculated that they might be oxygenated structures in the polymer chains. Grassie and Kerr (94) showed, however, that polymers prepared in vacuum from carefully purified monomer still contained weak links. Thus they must be built into the polymer chains during polymerization. This being so, it seemed reasonable that their concentration might depend upon one or other of the variables in the polymerization process. With this in mind Grassie and Kerr determined the number of weak links by measuring the extent of the initial steep fall in molecular weight during thermal degradation in a variety of polystyrene samples: (*a*) those prepared by different initiation methods (thermal, photochemical, and catalytic); (*b*) those polymerized to different conversions (to investigate the possible effect of branching); (*c*) those polymerized at different temperatures. The first two of these have no significant influence, but the proportion of weak links is found to increase with the temperature of polymerization as illustrated in Figure VIII-18. There is also a molecular weight effect, but considering the range of molecular weights investigated this is relatively small. The most reasonable assumption from this evidence is that the weak links are formed in an abnormal propagation step in direct competition with and with a slightly higher energy of activation than normal head-to-tail addition.

Thus it is reasonable to speculate that they are associated with structures of the type II derived from occasional head-to-head addition of styrene

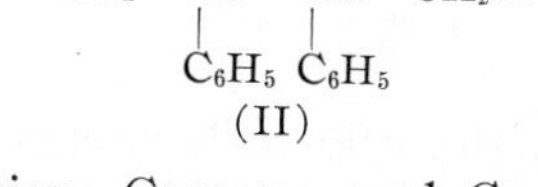

(II)

units during polymerization; Cameron and Grassie (95) tested this by examination of copolymers of styrene and stilbene which contain the same structural elements.

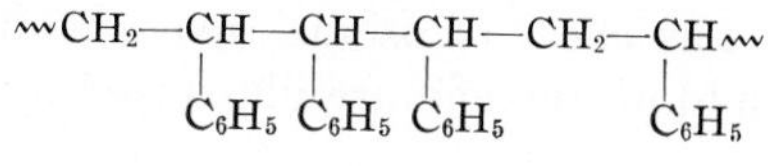

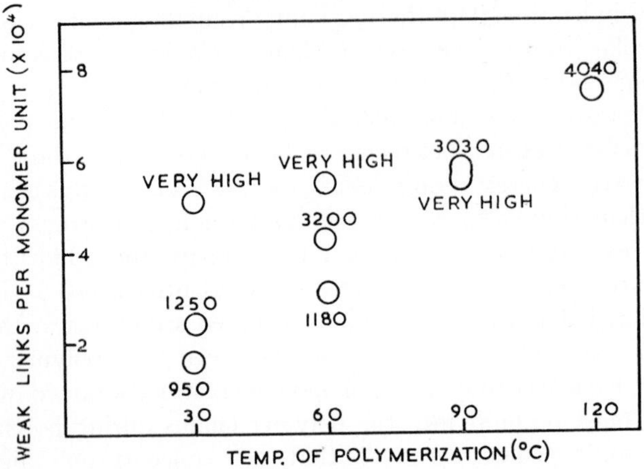

Fig. VIII-18. Effect of temperature of polymerization and initial chain length on the concentration of weak links in polystyrene (figures indicate initial chain lengths). (Taken from ref. 94.)

Their concentration in the polymer was measured by the use of tritium-labeled stilbene monomer, but, in spite of the fact that relatively high concentrations could be introduced into polystyrene molecules, there was no consequent increase in the proportion of weak links.

Since the high stability of the polystyryl radical is attributed to resonance structures with the radical center in the benzene ring, Cameron and Grassie (96) have suggested that these may add monomer to result in structures of the types III and IV which are analogous to the ketene-

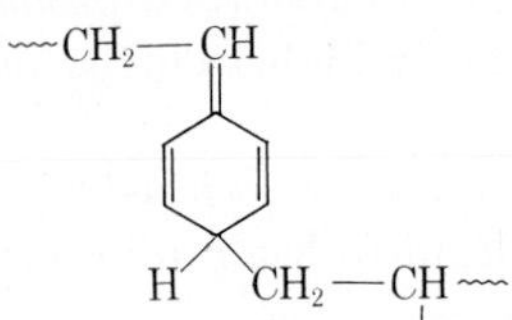

(III)

and

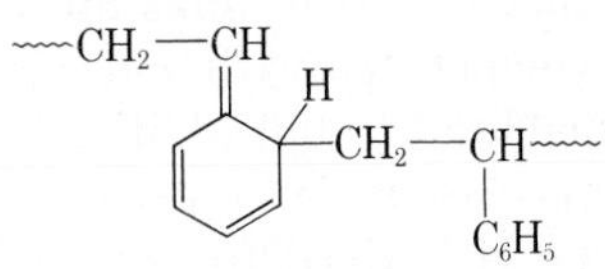

(IV)

imine structures in polymethacrylonitrile discussed below (see Part 2i) and which constitute weak links in that polymer. If the weak links in polystyrene are associated with such structures, then molecular weight measurements represent a sensitive method of estimating them if they can be broken chemically. The effect of ozonization and subsequent scission of the ozonide by zinc and acetic acid are illustrated by the top and middle

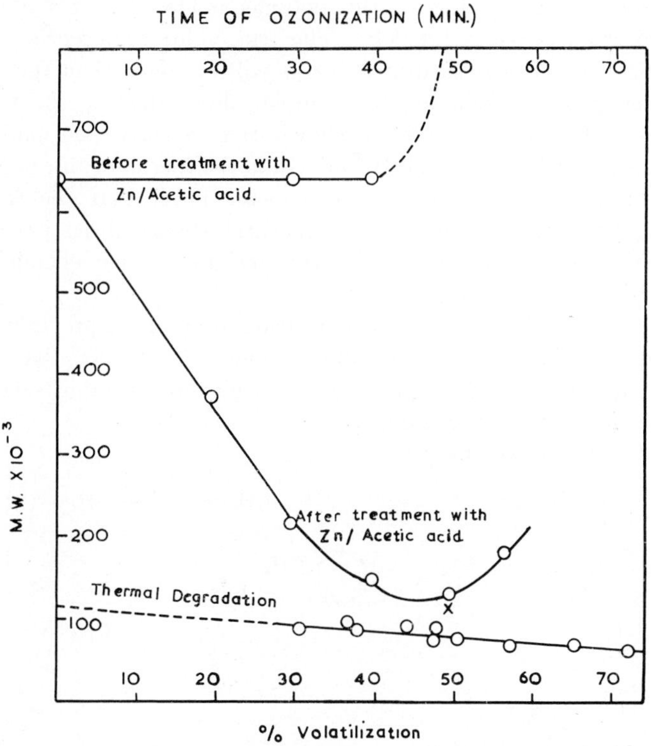

Fig. VIII-19. Thermal and ozonolytic degradation of polystyrene. (Taken from ref. 96.)

curves in Figure VIII-19. That the structures broken down by this treatment are associated with the thermally weak links is proved by the observation that polymer pyrolyzed to beyond 30% volatilization, so that all weak links are destroyed, does not suffer a further fall in molecular weight on subsequent ozonization and treatment with zinc and acetic acid.

The evidence in favor of associating weak links with main chain unsaturation is even more convincing when a quantitative comparison of the molecular weight change in thermal and ozone degradation is made. The bottom curve in Figure VIII-19 is a straight line through points representing the molecular weights of thermally degraded polymer at advanced stages of volatilization. The intercept on the molecular weight axis represents, to a good approximation, the molecular weight obtained on scission of all the weak links but in absence of the quite separate volatilzation process. The value for this polymer is 118,000. The minimum in the ozonization curve is 126,000. The true value representing complete ozonolytic scission of unsaturated bonds will be lower than this owing to the tendency for crosslinking to occur, as illustrated by the top curve. Cameron and Grassie (96) have shown that a correction made on this basis leads to a value only slightly lower than the thermal value of 118,000.

While this evidence represents conclusive proof that the weak links in polystyrene are associated with structural abnormalities incorporating unsaturation it gives no further information about their chemical nature or mode of formation.

Speculating further, however, and bearing in mind the previous evidence that thermal chain scission results in molecules rather than radicals, Cameron and Grassie have proposed the following reaction scheme (eqs. 40 and 41) for weak link scission.

For *ortho*-type weak links:

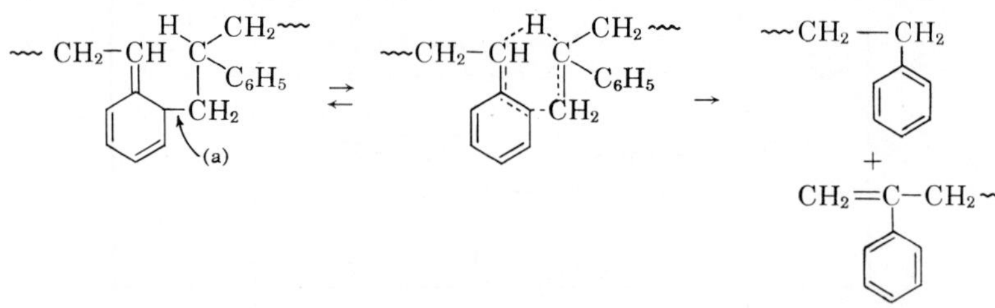

(40)

For *para*-type weak links:

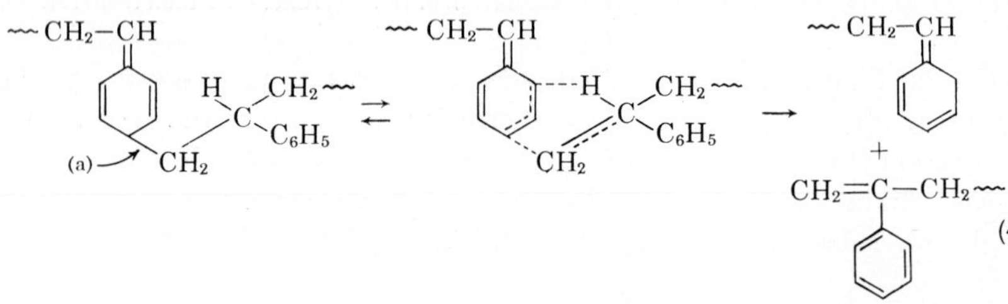

(41)

This reaction scheme is similar to the Hurd and Blunck mechanism for decomposition of esters into olefin and acid (97) and to the mechanism proposed to account for the decomposition of vinyl isopropyl ether into propylene and acetaldehyde (98). It involves scission of the weakest carbon–carbon bond (a) in the system, and also α-hydrogen transfer which, once accomplished, would be irreversible and could well be the rate-determining step in the process.

h. Polyethylene and Polypropylene

High pressure polyethylene is thermally stable to about 290°C. Above this temperature a decrease in molecular weight can be detected, although without much volatile material being produced. Above 360°C. volatilization becomes rapid. From viscosity changes in the intermediate range, 290–360°C, Oakes and Richards (99) have calculated the number of bonds broken as shown in Figure VIII-20. Instead of continuing at a constant value as in a completely random process, the rate of chain scission is seen to decrease continuously. Since shorter chain linear hydrocarbons are stable to much higher temperatures, something other than carbon–carbon bonds between pairs of methylene groups are being broken in this phase of the reaction, and the situation is reminiscent of the scission of weak linkages in polystyrene. Two possible weak structures are known to exist in polyethylene, namely, carbonyl groups and chain branches.

While the viscosity is decreasing the polymer becomes unsaturated at the rate of one double bond per chain scission, but infrared measurements show that this unsaturation is of three types, namely, RCH═CHR′, RR′C ═CH_2, and RCH═CH_2. All are formed in the initial stages of the reaction but the concentrations of the first two soon reach a maximum and only the third continues to be formed as shown in Table VIII-4

TABLE VIII-4
Effect of Thermal Degradation on Unsaturation in Polyethylene[a]

	Optical density		
M.W.	RCH═CH_2 (11.0 μ)	RCH═CHR′ (10.35 μ)	RR′C═CH_2 (11.26 μ)
13,000 (original)	<0.1	<0.1	<0.1
5,000	0.25	0.17	0.17
1,100	0.40	0.22	0.24
700	0.52	0.27	0.28
500	0.90	0.27	0.30

[a] Taken from ref. 99.

RCH═CHR′ and RR′C═CH_2 are clearly formed by scission at chain branches. But even if all chain scission at 315°C. occurs at weak links it can be deduced from Figure VIII-20 that only one chain break has occurred on the average for every four polymer molecules, in spite of the fact that approximately 20 branches exist per molecule. Oakes and Richards therefore suggested that oxygenated structures are the true weak

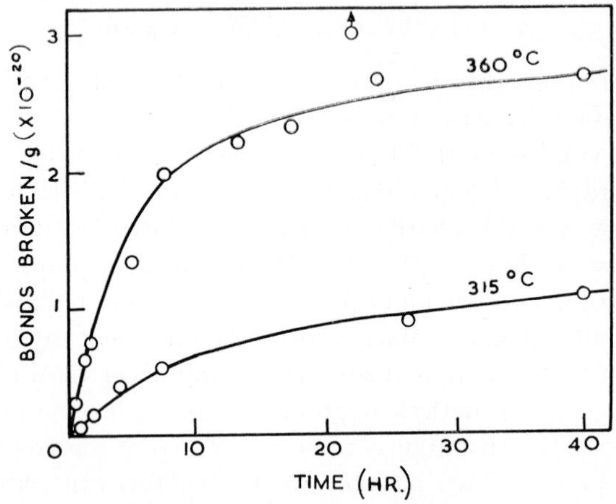

Fig. VIII-20. Time dependence of bond scission in polyethylene at 315 and 360°C. (Taken from ref. 99.)

links and that the depolymerization in this temperature range is a chain reaction initiated at these structures and propagated through the points of branching. The apparent number of weak links will therefore be the product of the number of oxygenated structures and the chain length of the reaction. The increase, with temperature of degradation, of the measured number of weak links could be the result of a greater chain length at higher temperatures or of the existence of a variety of oxygenated structures of different stabilities.

In order to account for the infrared evidence in Table VIII-4 radicals formed in the initiation process must abstract hydrogen atoms either in the unbranched parts of the molecules (eq. 42) or at or near branches (eqs. 43 and 44) the resulting radicals decomposing thus:

$$R{-}\dot{C}H{-}CH_2{-}R' \rightarrow R{-}CH_2{=}CH_2 + R' \quad (42)$$

$$(R)(R')\dot{C}{-}CH_2{-}R'' \rightarrow (R)(R')C{=}CH_2 + R'' \quad (43)$$

$$(R)(R')CH{-}\dot{C}H{-}CH_2R'' \rightarrow (R)(R')CH{-}CH{=}CH_2 + R'' \quad (44)$$

$$\searrow RCH{=}CH{-}CH_2R'' + R'$$

Table VIII-4 indicates that reactions (43) and (44) are most probable. There is no apparent reason why the methylenic center at which the radical appears in reaction (44) should be more reactive than any other methylene group in the molecule, but since tertiary hydrogen atoms are known to be most reactive and because of the obvious parallelism of the production of R—CH=CH—R′ and RR′C=CH_2 it seems most likely that the primary process in the production of R—CH=CHR′ is also the removal of the tertiary hydrogen atom which is followed by an intramolecular rearrangement before chain scission takes place.

The molecular weight of polypropylene is found to decrease in very much the same way as that of polyethylene at temperatures (230–300°C.) lower than those at which volatilization occurs. Van Schooten and Wijga (100) proposed that this is due to weak links in the polymer. They demonstrated that these could be destroyed without chain scission by preheating at 180°C. and that contamination with traces of copper greatly accelerates the rate of decrease of viscosity. This evidence, together with activation energy data, led them to propose that these weak links are hydroperoxide structures.

The volatile products of thermal degradation of polyethylene emphasize the random nature of the reaction since they consist of an apparently continuous spectrum of hydrocarbons from C_1 to C_{70} (60). The C_1–C_7 fraction, which constitutes a relatively small part of the total products, has been analyzed mass spectroscopically and includes almost all possible paraffins, monoolefins, and dienes. In spite of this, and as pointed out above (see Part 2a), the rate maximum for a random scission reaction which is predicted to be in the region of 25% volatilization, is not observed. Instead the rate decreases continuously from a high initial value (60,65). Wall and his colleagues suggested that this behavior must be associated with the branched structure of polyethylene, since polymethylene, prepared from diazomethane, exhibits the predicted rate maximum (52). Yet this absence of a maximum cannot be accounted for in terms of more rapid cleavage at points of branching since, according to Wall and Florin (65), "Theoretical treatment of the degradation of branched structures on a statistical basis and the use of various ratios for the rate constant for breaking bonds at or near the branched points versus those between branched points could not eliminate the maximum in the rate curves without going to unreasonable values for the ratios of constants for bond cleavage" (101).

Wall and Straus (53,54) have therefore compared the shapes of the degradation rate curves for a wide variety of well characterized branched polyethylenes. Not only linear polyethylene but also linear polypropylene and linear copolymers of ethylene and propylene exhibit rate maxima. These disappear not only in branched polyethylene and polypropylene but also in copolymers prepared by direct copolymerization of ethylene with 1-butene and 1-pentene and from diazomethane–diazohexane mixtures. The maxima reappear in copolymers from diazomethane–diazoethane mixtures. Thus random behavior, in so far as it is revealed by rate maxima, exists only when branches are methyl groups, while ethyl and longer branches result in nonrandom behavior typified by continuously decreasing rates.

From the general theory of radical depolymerization it is clear that random chain scission results from the predominance of intermolecular transfer at the expense of the production of volatiles by depropagation and intramolecular transfer. Wall and Straus therefore believe that the absence of rate maxima in branched polyethylene is due to the occurrence of relatively more intramolecular transfer at the expense of intermolecular transfer as a result of the more spherical shape of the molecules of highly branched material, particularly when the branches are long.

i. Polymethacrylonitrile

Three quite separate thermal degradation processes have been shown to occur in this material (102–106). These are, decomposition of ketene-imine structures, coloration, and radical depolymerization, which have been studied in the temperature ranges, 20–120°C., 120–220°C., and over 220°C., respectively. A different abnormality in the polymer structure is responsible for each and this polymer affords an excellent example of the way in which the nature and course of degradation processes can be affected by structural abnormalities. Ketene-imine decomposition and radical depolymerization are depolymerization processes, while coloration is a nonchain-scission or substituent reaction which is discussed later.

(1) Radical Depolymerization

In view of the α,α-disubstituted structure of polymethacrylonitrile it is not surprising that high yields of monomer can be obtained from it under suitable conditions. The coloration process, which tends to occur at a lower temperature, produces structures in the polymer (see Part 3b 1) which block the passage of depropagation along the polymer chains. The yields of monomer therefore depend inversely upon the extent to which coloration occurs (104). Since this latter reaction can be reduced to a minimum by careful purification of the monomer used in the preparation of the polymer, high monomer purity and a high temperature are the optimum conditions for high yields of monomer. By depolymerizing pure polymer at 300°C., yields approaching 100% can be obtained. From polymer which colors extensively at lower temperatures the ultimate yield at 220°C. is never greater than 50%, and this is reduced further by preheating for prolonged periods at coloration temperatures, for example at 150°C.

In spite of these high yields of monomer however, there are a number of complicating factors which make it difficult to interpret experiments designed to clarify the mechanism of the reaction. Firstly, there is a residual amount of coloration even in pure polymer which is most probably initiated at chain ends. Secondly, the polymer becomes insoluble, which prohibits a study of molecular weight changes except in the very early stages. Thus rate and molecular weight measurements, which were the two principal tools in the elucidation of the mechanism of the degradation to monomer of poly(methyl methacrylate), can only give approximate information. It has been possible to show, however, that for material with a molecular weight of the order of 20,000 there is no steep fall in the molecular weight of the soluble part of the residue up to 25% volatilization. This suggests that, as with poly(methyl methacrylate) and polystyrene, monomer is liberated from the chain ends, and this is supported by the fact that the rate of the reaction is also a direct function of the concentration of chain ends, being inversely related to the molecular weight of the polymer.

(2) Ketene-Imine Decomposition

Talât-Erben and Bywater (107) and Grassie and McNeill (103,104) demonstrated independently that absorption occurs in the region of 2012 cm.$^{-1}$ in the infrared spectrum of polymethacrylonitrile and disappears rapidly at slightly elevated temperatures as in Figure VIII-21. This is characteristic of compounds containing adjacent double bonds such as allenes, ketenes, and ketene-imines.

Talât-Erben and Bywater (108,109) have also demonstrated that while the principal product of decomposition of 2,2′-azobisisobutyronitrile is the radical combination product, tetramethylsuccinodinitrile, a labile second product, *N*-(2-cyano-2-propyl)dimethylketene-imine (V) is also

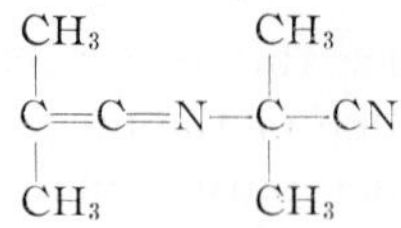

(V)

formed by reaction of the radical in the form

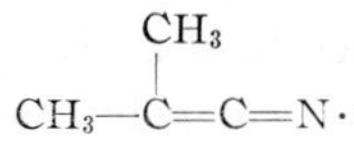

The similarity of the structure of the methacrylonitrile polymer radical allows of no doubt that the labile structures in polymethacrylonitrile are ketene-imines, and this was confirmed by Grassie and McNeill by chemical tests.

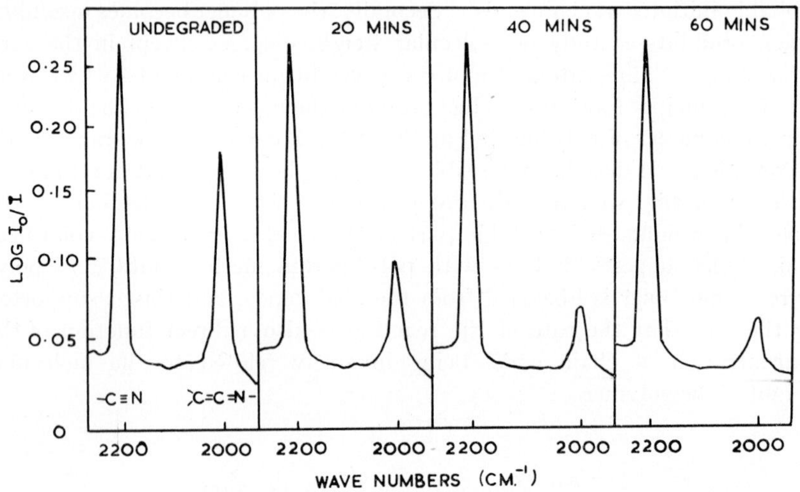

Fig. VIII-21. Disappearance of ketene-imine absorption at 2012 cm.$^{-1}$ on heating polymethacrylonitrile at 90°C. in cyclohexanone solution. (Taken from ref. 104.)

Using the 2012 cm.$^{-1}$ peak height as a measure of ketene-imine content, Grassie and McNeill were able to show that the disappearance of ketene-imine structures is a second-order reaction but that the rate constant increases as the polymer concentration is decreased. Since the ketene-imine structures are incorporated into the polymer chains, it is reasonable to visualize the process as being diffusion controlled in very much the same way as the bimolecular termination step in polymerization, which results in the well known "gel effect" or "peaking." In confirmation of this they were able to show that the rate constant is also depressed by addition of the "inert" polymer, poly(methyl methacrylate).

Grassie and McNeill also showed that these structures are produced almost entirely in the termination process during polymerization. It may therefore be deduced that the abnormal form of the radical is very much less reactive than the normal polymethacrylonitrile radical showing little tendency to add monomer and being able to react only with a second radical.

It is of interest to consider whether these ketene-imine groupings, formed during termination, result from a combination (VI) or disproportionation (VII) reaction. Among simple ketene-imines those of the

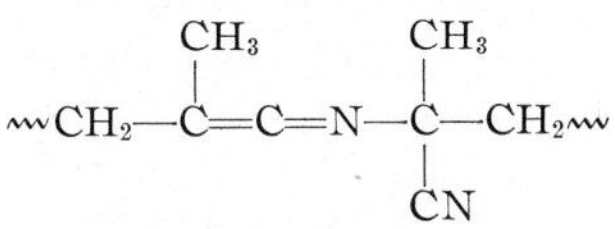

(VI)

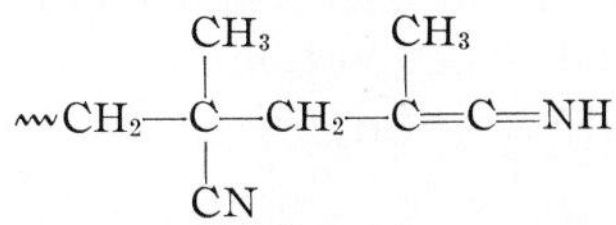

(VII)

second type are extremely unstable. Furthermore the thermal disappearance of ketene-imine structures is associated with a decrease in the molecular weight of the polymer which is difficult to explain if they are situated at chain ends. If both types were present, evidence of a double peak in the infrared spectrum would be expected rather than the single very sharply defined peak which appears. Since the ketene-imine form of the polymer radical is apparently not reactive enough to add monomer, it seems reasonable that it should not be capable of abstracting a hydrogen atom in a disproportionation process.

The strict second-order thermal disappearance of ketene-imine structures suggests a dimerization process analogous to the behavior of ketenes, and this seems even more likely in view of the formation from simple ketene-imines of products believed to be dimers.

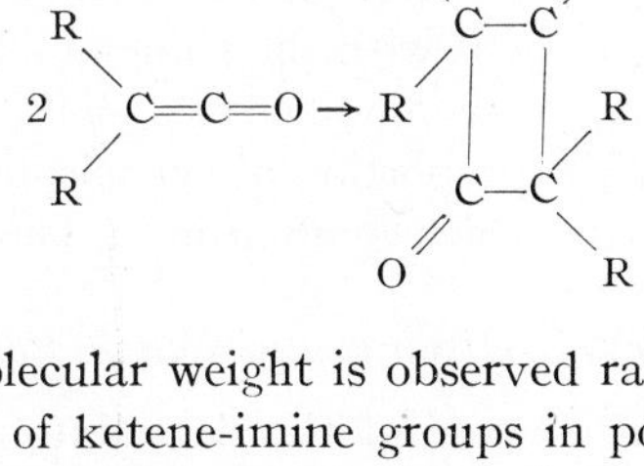

(45)

However, a fall in molecular weight is observed rather than the expected rise on disappearance of ketene-imine groups in polymer. This decrease in molecular weight is usually of the order of 20–40%; for example, the molecular weight of a typical polymer sample decreased from 17,750 to 11,000.

The data discussed so far refer to reaction at elevated temperatures (60–110°C.) at which initially formed dimer might decompose rapidly. In an attempt to detect dimer formation, a solution of the 17,750 polymer was allowed to stand at room temperature for two months in the course of which considerable reduction in ketene-imine absorption occurred. During this time the molecular weight decreased to 15,500, which was about the value predictable from the decrease in 2012 cm.$^{-1}$ absorption.

One possible simple mode of disappearance of ketene-imine structures involving a decrease in molecular weight consists of scission of the main chain carbon–nitrogen bond followed by rearrangement of the abnormal radical and disproportionation (eq. 46). It is not clear, however, why

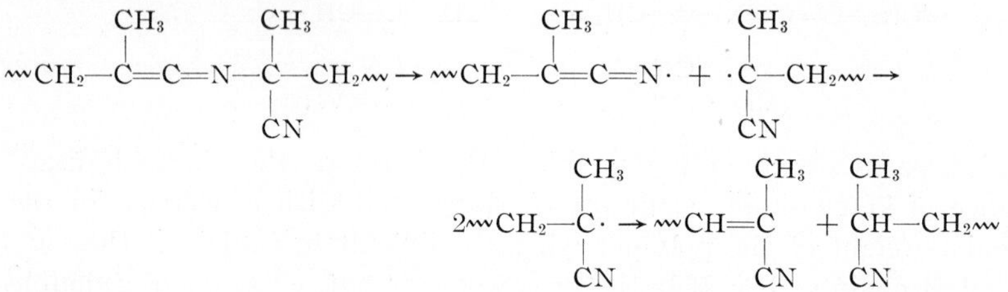
(46)

such a process should be second-order. The infrared spectrum of polymethacrylonitrile exhibits weak absorption at 1620 cm.$^{-1}$ which might be attributed to unsaturated end structures. The assignment cannot be made unambiguously, however, since polymers often exhibit slight absorption in this region due to traces of moisture. It may be significant, however, that this band increases slightly in intensity on thermal disappearance of ketene-imines. No other changes in the spectrum are observed.

Grassie and McNeill also calculated from their experimental data that the proportion of polymethacrylonitrile radicals reacting in the termination process in the ketene-imine form lies between 20 and 40%. This may be in significant agreement with the value of 30% obtained by Talât-Erben and Bywater and later modified to 54.4% by Talât-Erben and Isfendiyarŏglu (110) for the proportion of cyanoisopropyl radicals, derived from azobisisobutyronitrile, which combine in the ketene-imine form.

j. Other α,α-Disubstituted Nitrile Polymers

Brief studies have been made of the degradation of the polymers of a number of other α,α-disubstituted nitriles whose depolymerization behavior it is interesting to compare with that of polymethacrylonitrile. Thus poly(methyl α-cyanoacrylate) (111) colors and liberates monomer in qualitatively the same way as polymethacrylonitrile. Poly(vinylidene cyanide) liberates monomer in appreciable yields (112) while poly-α-chloroacrylonitrile behaves as a substituted poly(vinyl chloride), liberating almost quantitative yields of hydrogen chloride (113). If monomer is present it represents less that 1% of the initial polymer. In the first and third of these, evidence of ketene-imine structures was sought without success.

k. Polytetrafluoroethylene

The products of the thermal degradation of polytetrafluoroethylene were shown by Lewis and Naylor (114) to consist of monomer, a dimer, and a compound with the intermediate formula C_3F_6. The proportions of these products depend upon the pressure under which the degradation is carried out; at 760 mm., monomer comprises 15.9% of the total, but this increases as the external pressure is decreased until at 5 mm. the monomer yield is 97%. It was suggested that under all pressure conditions monomer is the primary product but that this reacts to an increasing extent to form the other products as the pressure is raised, because it remains longer in the high temperature surroundings of the reaction zone.

Madorsky and his colleagues (61) confirmed that under high vacuum conditions almost 100% conversion to monomer occurs. Thus it is a reasonable assumption that the reaction proceeds according to the normal depolymerization mechanism (see Part 2a), the zip length being long compared with the chain length of the polymer, transfer reactions being relatively unimportant. This is to be expected in view of the great strength of the carbon–fluorine bonds which would have to be broken in any transfer process. It is difficult to assess any small amounts of transfer or other chain scission reactions which may occur because there is no known solvent for this polymer in which molecular weight measurements may be carried out. There is some small molecular weight decrease, however, because the residue softens at about 50% conversion.

Polytetrafluoroethylene is the most stable of the vinyl-type polymers, yet, as pointed out by Florin, Wall, and their colleagues (115), its stability is only 100°C. higher than that of polyethylene, which is disappointing in view of the very much greater dissociation energies of its C—C and C—F bonds compared with the C—C and C—H bonds in polyethylene. With the structure and kinetics of thermal decomposition of polytetrafluoroethylene in mind, therefore, these authors suggested several methods for the improvement of its stability. In order to try to eliminate labile initiation centers at the chain ends they prepared polymers, using as initiators, perfluorodimethylmercury, perfluoromethyl iodide and fluorine gas as well as the conventional catalysts. They also considered that the depropagation process producing monomer might be blocked by the incorporation of chain transfer agents into the chains or simply admixed with the polymer. To this end they used sulfur, selenium, and a variety of hydrocarbon and fluorocarbon groups, mainly aromatic, added usually as dibromides to the polymerizing mixture. In none of these trials, however, was there any difference produced in the rate of thermal decomposition. They therefore came to the conclusion that any labile groups must be destroyed before the degradation temperature is reached and that degradation is always initiated by breaking the C—C bonds of the fluorocarbon.

Continuing to pursue possible methods of stabilizing this polymer, Wall and Michaelsen (116,117) investigated the effects of various gases on its decomposition on the principle that these should diffuse more readily than the above solid reactants to the degrading free radicals within the solid polymer. The gases studied could be divided into three groups: (*1*) oxygen, nitric oxide, water, and sulfur dioxide strongly catalyzed the degradation; (*2*) hydrogen, chlorine, carbon tetrachloride, and toluene acted as inhibitors; (*3*) nitrogen and benzotrifluoride had no effect. With oxygen, the polymer remains white and solid, the products being silicon tetrafluoride, carbon dioxide, carbon monoxide but no monomer. Thus the oxygen must react with the polymer radical (eq. 47) at a very high

$$\sim\!\sim CF_2—CF_2\cdot + O_2 \rightarrow \text{Products} \quad (47)$$

rate, the labile products reacting with the surface of the glass vessel.

In the presence of the inhibiting gases the nature of the reaction is completely changed. Thus the rate curves now exhibit maxima and the polymer rapidly becomes fluid. Both of these features are typical of random processes. The products are monomer as well as SiF_4 and CO_2. It has been suggested that this inhibition depends upon a termination reaction in which a molecule or atom of the gas combines with the degrading polymer radical (eq. 48). Inhibition is accompanied by a catalytic effect

$$R—CF_2—CF_2\cdot + H_2 \rightarrow R—CF_2—CF_2H + H\cdot \quad (48)$$

probably caused by reaction of some of these resulting atoms with the polymer chain (eq. 49) which results in chain scission. Thus the most

$$R{-}CF_2{-}CF_2{-}R + H\cdot \rightarrow HF + R{-}CF{=}CF_2 + R\cdot \quad (49)$$

effective inhibitor will be one (AB) which forms a strong bond (XA) in the inhibition reaction leaving a stable radical, B, which therefore does not readily induce the catalytic reaction (that is the compound BF is unstable). In agreement with predictions from bond dissociation energy data, fluorine or compounds which decompose to form fluorine (ClF_3 and IF_3) were found to be the best inhibitors, but even they are also too active in inducing chain scission.

l. Poly-p-xylylene

In the search for thermally stable materials considerable interest has been focussed on polymers containing rings in the main chains, and particular attention has been given to poly-*p*-xylylene (VIII) which has been

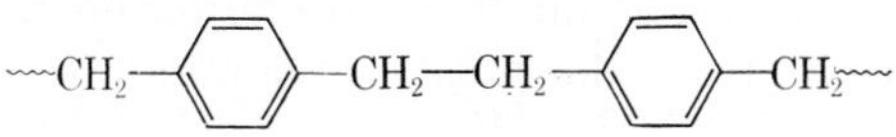

(VIII)

prepared both by the pyrolysis of xylene (120) and by treatment of *p*-methylbenzyltrimethylammonium chloride and bromide with hot aqueous alkali (121)

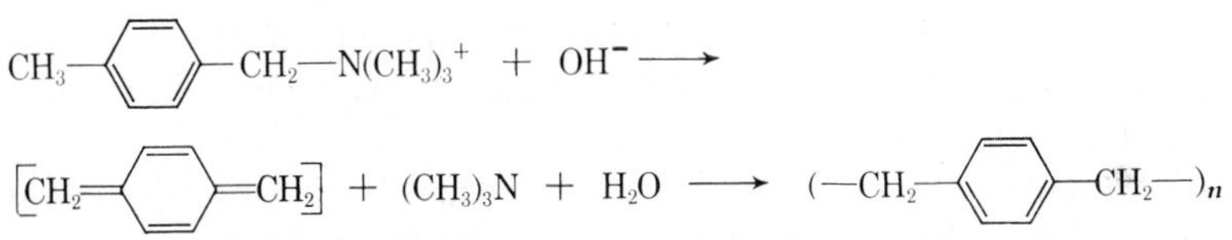

(50)

Table VIII-2 shows it to be slightly more stable than polyethylene although a good deal less stable than polytetrafluoroethylene. Madorsky and Straus (64) find it to give 10% monomer at 415–430°C., although Errede and Szwarc (122) found none at 400°C.

Schaefgen (121) has investigated its degradation at lower temperatures (285–321°C.) in solution in benzyl benzoate and chlorinated diphenyls. He considered that its degradation must be due primarily to the breaking of the bonds between the pairs of methylene groups. These should be the weakest bonds in the molecule since their scission results in two resonance-stabilized benzyl radicals. This primary scission could thus be followed either by elimination of monomer or stabilization by transfer with the hydrogen atoms of solvent or methylene groups elsewhere in the chain. He found no monomer and, on relating the viscosity decrease to chain scission, found the energy of activation for this process to be 58 kcal./mole. This is considered to be a reasonable value for the strength of the intermethylene carbon–carbon bond although for the gaseous decomposition of dibenzyl, 48 kcal./mole has been quoted (123). Thus the stability of this polymer is limited only by the strength of the weakest link in the chain.

m. Poly(ethylene Terephthalate)

The thermal degradation of poly(ethylene terephthalate) is not important in its common commercial applications. Goodings (124) has pointed out, however, that the main reason for its being available so cheaply is largely due to the fact that its decomposition temperature is high enough to allow it to be spun into fibers from the melt. Under conditions of melt spinning, however, small amounts of degradation do take place and this is critically important from the point of view of the manufacture of a consistent product.

Interest in the degradation of this polymer is reflected in two contributions to a recent symposium by Goodings (124) and Ritchie (125). In his paper Ritchie also describes similar studies on poly(ethylene fumarate). Ritchie discusses the reactions which occur in poly(ethylene terephthalate) at 440–550°C. while Goodings' experiments were carried out in the range 282–323°C. Their principal findings about the nature of the reaction are closely similar; minor differences probably being due to the different temperature ranges.

Carbon dioxide, acetaldehyde, and terephthalic acid are the major products, together with smaller amounts of anhydride groupings, benzoic acid, *p*-acetyl benzoic acid, acetophenone, vinyl benzoate, uncharacterized ketonic substances, water, methane, ethylene and acetylene. Owing to the complexity of the products both authors have studied model compounds to assist in interpreting results. Both have studied the decomposition of ethylene dibenzoate (IX)

$$C_6H_5-\overset{\overset{\displaystyle O}{\|}}{C}-O-CH_2-CH_2-O-\overset{\overset{\displaystyle O}{\|}}{C}-C_6H_5$$

(IX)

while Ritchie in addition has studied the following:

$$C_6H_5-\overset{\overset{\displaystyle O}{\|}}{C}-O-CH_2-CH_2-O-CH_2-CH_2-O-\overset{\overset{\displaystyle O}{\|}}{C}-C_6H_5$$

(X)

$$p\text{-X—C}_6\text{H}_4\text{—}\overset{\overset{\text{O}}{\|}}{\text{C}}\text{—O—CH}_2\text{—CH}_2\text{—O—}\overset{\overset{\text{O}}{\|}}{\text{C}}\text{—C}_6\text{H}_4\text{—}\overset{\overset{\text{O}}{\|}}{\text{C}}\text{—O—CH}_2\text{—CH}_2\text{—O—}\overset{\overset{\text{O}}{\|}}{\text{C}}\text{—C}_6\text{H}_4\text{—X-}p$$

(XI)

$$\text{C}_6\text{H}_5\text{—}\overset{\overset{\text{O}}{\|}}{\text{C}}\text{—O—CH}_2\text{—CH}_2\text{— OH}$$

(XII)

$$\text{C}_6\text{H}_5\text{—}\overset{\overset{\text{O}}{\|}}{\text{C}}\text{—O—CH=CH}_2$$

(XIII)

IX and XI represent segments from within the polyester chains and X represents the ether linkages which have become incorporated into the chains by virtue of diethylene glycol units. Chain endgroups are represented by XII while XIII represents the vinyl ester ends which result from primary scission of the chains.

As a result of the comparison of pyrolysis of IX and XIII with that of the polymer, a number of conclusions were arrived at. The initial scission process, which is random, results in carboxyl and vinyl groups,

$$\sim\text{C}_6\text{H}_4\text{—CO—O—CH}_2\text{—CH}_2\text{—O—CO—C}_6\text{H}_4\sim \rightarrow$$
$$\sim\text{C}_6\text{H}_4\text{—COOH} + \text{CH}_2\text{=CH—O—CO—C}_6\text{H}_4\sim \quad (51)$$

The vinyl ester endgroups are destroyed in a number of reactions;

$$\sim\text{C}_6\text{H}_4\text{—CO—O—CH=CH}_2 \rightarrow \begin{cases} \nearrow \sim\text{C}_6\text{H}_4\text{—COOH} + \text{CH}\equiv\text{CH} \\ \rightarrow \sim\text{C}_6\text{H}_4\text{—CH=CH}_2 + \text{CO}_2 \\ \searrow \sim\text{C}_6\text{H}_4\text{—CO—CH}_2\text{—CHO} \rightarrow \sim\text{C}_6\text{H}_4\text{—CO—CH}_3 + \text{CO} \end{cases} \quad (52)$$
$$\downarrow + \sim\text{COOH}$$
$$\sim\text{C}_6\text{H}_4\text{—CO—O—CH(CH}_3\text{)—O—CO}\sim \rightarrow$$
$$\sim\text{C}_6\text{H}_4\text{—CO—O—CO—C}_6\text{H}_4\sim + \text{CH}_3\text{CHO}$$

Thus terephthalic acid, vinyl benzoate, acetylene, ketones, carbon monoxide, anhydrides, and acetaldehyde are accounted for. Carbon monoxide may also be produced by decomposition of acetaldehyde which becomes appreciable at 400°C. In addition, pyrolysis of XI has shown that ester interchange occurs during pyrolysis which may account for the traces of cyclic trimer which have been observed during the pyrolysis of poly(ethylene terephthalate).

Ethereal linkages represent points of thermal lability in the polymer and decomposition of X indicates that they must be a source of additional carboxyl endgroups and acetaldehyde during the pyrolysis of the polymer.

Among the decomposition routes of XII the following disproportionation reaction occurs:

$$2\sim C_6H_4—CO—O—CH_2—CH_2—OH \rightarrow$$
$$\sim C_6H_4—CO—O—CO—C_6H_4\sim + HO—CH_2—CH_2—O—CH_2—CH_2—OH \rightarrow$$
$$H_2O + CH_2{=}CH—O—CH_2—CH_2—OH \rightarrow 2CH_3CHO \qquad (53)$$

This represents the only clue to the formation of water in the polymer pyrolysis, although some may also be produced by further polycondensation.

n. Polyamides

During the past 10 years or so a number of investigators have been concerned with the thermal decomposition of various polyamides. As in the case of poly(ethylene terephthalate) the basic reason for this interest is the small amount of degradation which can occur at melt spinning and molding temperatures and which can have a profound effect upon properties during subsequent use. The degradation reactions which occur during the normal life of the fabricated articles, on the other hand, appear to be predominantly oxidative and hydrolytic in nature.

Among the more recent work on the subject is that of Straus and Wall (126) who, on the basis of experiments in which extreme breakdown of the polymer is brought about, find that carbon dioxide and water are the principal volatile products. Unlike other investigators they did not find ammonia. They suggest that residual water in the polymer plays a large part in the decomposition, causing hydrolysis of peptide linkages which is followed by the liberation of carbon dioxide by decarboxylation of the resulting carboxyl groups. They believe that there is also a free radical process contributing to the overall decomposition, which is probably initiated at the bonds indicated (XIV) which must be the most labile in the molecule.

$$\sim CO—NH—(CH_2)_4—\vdots—CH_2—\overset{\overset{\displaystyle O}{\|}}{C}—NH—\vdots—CH_2—(CH_2)_4—CO—NH\sim$$

(XIV)

Rafikov and Sorokina (127) also believe that hydrolysis by residual water is important, the ultimate volatile products of this type of chain scission being carbon dioxide and ammonia. They do not believe that homolytic scission plays any significant part.

Quite recently, Kamerbeek, Kroes, and Grolle (128) have described a very thorough investigation of the thermal degradation of poly(hexamethylene adipamide) and polycaprolactam under comparatively mild conditions which are more closely comparable to those under which the polymers are processed, for example during polycondensation and melt spinning. They point out that the amount of water evolved is very much greater than that which can be originally present in the polymer or which can result from the decomposition of end groups. It must therefore be released from amide groups in the body of the chains. Kamerbeek and his colleagues divide the overall mechanism into a primary degradation reaction and a system of secondary reactions.

The primary reaction consists of homolytic scission at the $\sim NH—CH_2 \sim$ bond indicated above, resulting, from polycaprolactam, in

$$\sim CO—NH—CH_2—(CH_2)_4—CO—NH\cdot + \cdot CH_2—CH_2—CH_2—CH_2—CH_2—CO—NH\sim$$
$$\downarrow$$
$$\sim CO—NH—CH_2—(CH_2)_4—CO—NH_2 + CH_2{=}CH—CH_2—CH_2—CH_2—CO—NH\sim$$
$$\downarrow$$
$$\sim CO—NH—CH_2—(CH_2)_4—C{\equiv}N + H_2O \qquad (54)$$

$$\sim CO—NH—(CH_2)_5—CO—N\langle \; + CH_3—(CH_2)_4—CO—NH\sim \rightarrow$$
$$\sim CO—NH—(CH_2)_5—N{=}C{=}O \qquad (55)$$

Principally by means of infrared spectral evidence and the identification of the products of hydrolysis of partially degraded polymer, the existence of both these reaction sequences has been verified, the ratio of their rates being approximately 20:1 in favor of the former.

There is also some evidence of scission at the $\sim CH_2-CH_2 \sim$ bond indicated above, but this is of minor importance.

A number of secondary processes now become possible. The continuous source of water available in eq. (54) above allows amide groups to be hydrolyzed (eq. 56)

$$\sim NH-CO\sim + H_2O \rightarrow \sim NH_2 + \sim COOH \qquad (56)$$

which is followed by

$$2\sim COOH \rightarrow \sim \underset{\underset{O}{\|}}{C} \sim + CO_2 + H_2O \qquad (57)$$

(XV)

$$2\sim NH_2 \rightarrow \sim NH\sim + NH_3 \qquad (58)$$

(XVI)

XV may then react with an amino endgroup attached to a polymer chain,

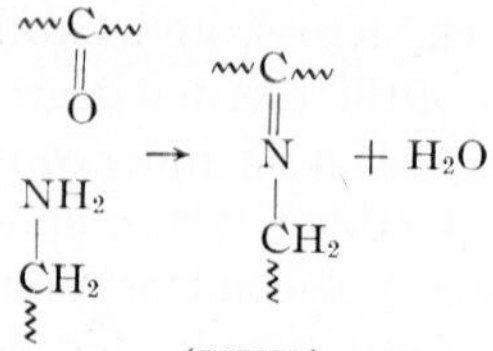

(59)

(XVII)

The structure XVII will have the environment,

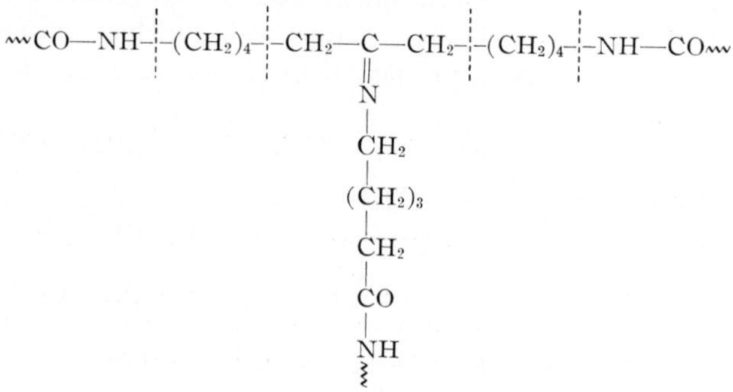

(XVIII)

the bonds most liable to undergo scission as in eqs. (54) and (55) being indicated. Certain of the products which would result from hydrolysis of polymers reacting in this way have been identified by Kamerbeek and his colleagues.

A similar analysis of the new structures (XIX) introduced by reaction of XVI with a carboxyl endgroup,

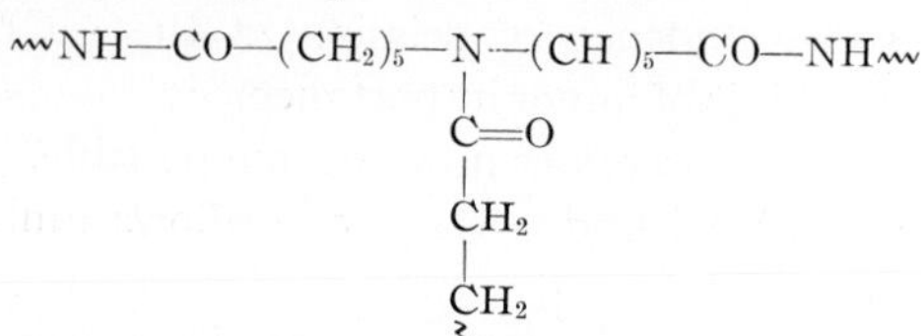

(XIX)

reveals no new type of weak links from which products of hydrolysis different from those obtained from a normal polymer chain, might arise.

The branched chain structures can also explain the gelation which has been observed to develop in polyamides under mild degradation conditions, although it has also been suggested that this may result in part at least from a radical process initiated by the radicals initially formed in the primary reaction above and possibly involving also the polymerization of the unsaturated materials which appear among the products.

3. Substituent Reactions

a. Introduction

Among depolymerization reactions there exists the outstanding unifying feature that whatever the detailed mechanism of the breakdown may be the reaction ultimately resolves itself into progressive breaking of the chain backbone. Since, in addition polymers at least, this usually consists almost entirely of carbon–carbon bonds it is perhaps not surprising that a single mechanism can, with only slight modification, be used to describe the depolymerization of a variety of materials. Substituents can modify these reactions profoundly but the essential features of main chain scission remain.

Substituent reactions, on the other hand, have no comparable unity since they depend entirely upon the chemical nature of the appendages to the polymer backbone. These reactions will occur in any given system only if they can be initiated at temperatures lower than that at which main chain bonds are broken. Thus substituent reactions are usually observed at relatively low temperatures. Thermal depolymerization seldom takes place below 200°C., even if structural features are most favorable. Substituent reactions, if they take place at all are frequently quite rapid at this temperature.

b. Coloration of Nitrile Polymers

It has been mentioned (see Part 2i 1) that the principal volatile product of the thermal degradation of polymethacrylonitrile is monomer. At similar temperatures (>200°C.) polyacrylonitrile has been reported to give HCN, NH_3, and a basic distillate (129), while Kennedy and Fontana (130) have recently described a drastic change in physical properties which occurs at 265°C. and which is accompanied by a reproducible weight loss of 31.6%. Below 200°C., coloration can occur in both polymers, and the essential features of the reaction are the same in each case. It is now known to be directly associated with the nitrile groups in these polymers. Since polyacrylonitrile is among the more important of the commercial polymers, its coloration process has been of particular interest because it intrudes during both the processing and subsequent use of both homopolymers and copolymers.

In spite of the fact that polyacrylonitrile is the more familiar and more readily available of the two materials, significant success in clarifying the nature of the coloration process was first achieved with polymethacrylonitrile.

This was because quantitative experimentation was facilitated by reason of its greater solubility and more favorable physical properties as well as the fact that the overall reaction is very much less complicated.

(1) Polymethacrylonitrile

While the thermal coloration of polymethacrylonitrile has always been regarded as characteristic of this polymer, Grassie and McNeill (102) observed that the ease and extent of the reaction in bulk were liable to vary widely from sample to sample. Closer investigation proved that the method of purification of the monomer, the nature of the polymerization catalyst and the method of polymerization may all have an effect. Thus monomer purified by distillation only, results in polymer which colors rapidly at 160°C. (A). If the monomer is washed with conc. ammonia prior to distillation, coloration at this temperature is still rapid if the polymerization is carried out in air (B), only slight if carried out in vacuum with benzoyl peroxide as catalyst (C), and does not occur at all at 160°C. if the polymerization is carried out in vacuum with azobisisobutyronitrile as catalyst (D). Infrared spectra of typical polymers (A)–(D) are shown in Figure VIII-22. The main difference between these spectra

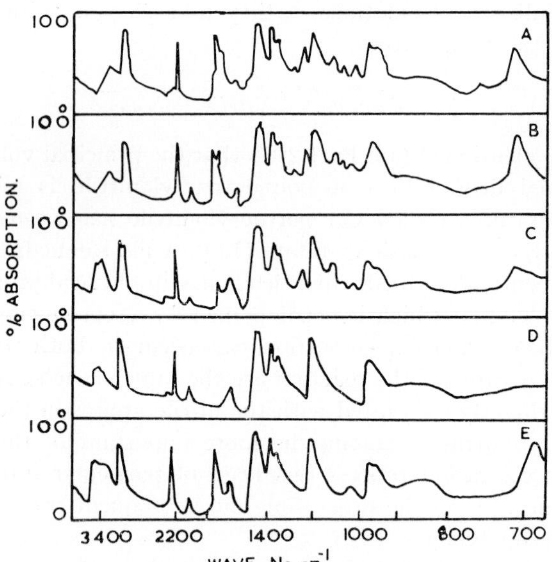

Fig. VIII-22. Infrared spectra of *A–D* polymethacrylonitriles prepared by various methods and (*E*) a methacrylonitrile–methacrylic acid copolymer. (Taken from ref. 102.)

resides in the band at 1720 cm.$^{-1}$, the intensity of which runs closely parallel to the ease of coloration of the polymers at high temperatures. The region of this band, the fact that it can be eliminated by washing the monomer with alkali, the obvious possibility of cyanide groups being converted into carboxyl, and the fact that reprecipitation of the polymers affects neither the intensity of the band nor the coloration properties, all suggest that the 1720 cm.$^{-1}$ band is due to carbonyl groups incorporated in one way or another into the molecular chains.

Strause and Dyer (131) have shown that oxygen readily copolymerizes with methacrylonitrile. Peroxidic structures are undoubtedly formed primarily. Being labile, however, these will decompose to produce other oxygenated structures including carbonyl groups. The double carbonyl peak in B is probably due to products of different modes of peroxide decomposition. The carbonyl groups in benzoyl peroxide-catalyzed polymers are also easily accounted for since they occur in the catalyst. Since monomer washed with alkali and polymerized in presence of an azo catalyst results in a polymer free from carbonyl groups, it is reasonable to suppose that polymer prepared from monomer not so washed is really a copolymer of methacrylonitrile with traces of methacrylic acid. Copolymers prepared from alkali-washed monomer with traces of methacrylic acid do in fact have identical thermal coloration properties and similar infrared spectra (Fig. VIII-22E).

Yet it seems most unlikely that a sufficient quantity of methacrylic acid could persist through a multiple distillation process during monomer purification (methacrylonitrile, b.p. 89°C.; methacrylic acid, b.p. 163°C.). Grassie and McNeill showed that the acidic constituent of distilled methacrylonitrile is acetic acid, which is a by-product in the preparation of methacrylonitrile by pyrolysis of acetone cyanhydrin acetate. With the aid of traces of water this acid hydrolyzes a proportion of nitrile groups to carboxyl at the elevated polymerization temperatures.

Since the color of degrading polymer progresses through the spectrum from yellow to red and since these impurities are present only in low concentration, it seems that they act only as centers of initiation for a process which results in conjugated structures which gradually increase in length and are characteristic of the methacrylonitrile units rather than of the carbonyl groups.

Polymer prepared by azobisisobutyronitrile initiation does develop color slowly at 250°C., but this represents a rate of reaction many orders of magnitude less than coloration initiated by traces of methacrylic acid. It does not appear to result from impurity and is probably due to some initiation process occurring within the methacrylonitrile units or possibly at chain terminal structures.

Since methacrylic acid can be incorporated into polymethacrylonitrile chains in closely controlled amounts by copolymerization techniques, Grassie and McNeill (103) made use of such copolymers to study the mechanism of the coloration reaction. They observed that while polymer colored to orange-red is still soluble, extreme coloration does ultimately result in insolubility. However, at no point is there evidence of an increase in molecular weight. This, together with the fact that no volatile material is produced during the reaction led them to believe that the reaction consists of an intramolecular rearrangement involving extensive configurational changes which are the direct cause of the insolubility. A small but definite decrease in molecular weight does occur in the earliest stages of reaction but this is due to the destruction of ketene-imine linkages already referred to (see Part 2i 2).

A series of infrared spectra of progressively colored polymethacrylonitrile is shown in Figure VIII-23. It is clear from these that the principal

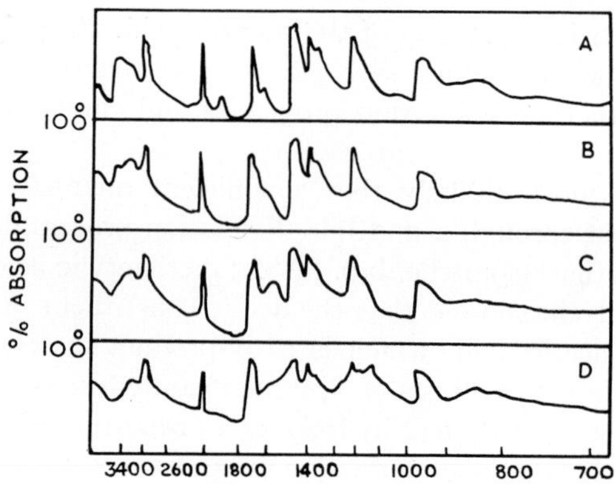

Fig. VIII-23. Changes in the infrared spectrum of polymethacrylonitrile during coloration: (*A*) undegraded, colorless; (*b*) 3 hr., at 140°C., yellow orange; (*C*) 9 hr. at 140°C., orange-red; (*D*) 23.5 hr. at 140°C., deep red. (Taken from ref. 103.)

changes, apart from a general intensification of background absorption, are a steady decrease in C≡N absorption at 2210 cm.$^{-1}$ and an increase in the region 1693–1490 cm.$^{-1}$. The 2012 cm.$^{-1}$ peak, which disappears as soon as the temperature is raised substantially above room temperature, is due to ketene-imine groups (>C=C=N–) in the polymer.

The changes which occur in the 1660–1490 cm.$^{-1}$ region are shown in greater detail in Figure VIII–24. The initial increase in absorption occurs at the higher frequency end of this region. As the color changes from yellow to red there is a gradual shift to lower frequencies as well as a general intensification. This behavior can be accounted for on the basis of the production of conjugated sequences gradually increasing in length. The movement of color through the visible spectrum rather than the inten-

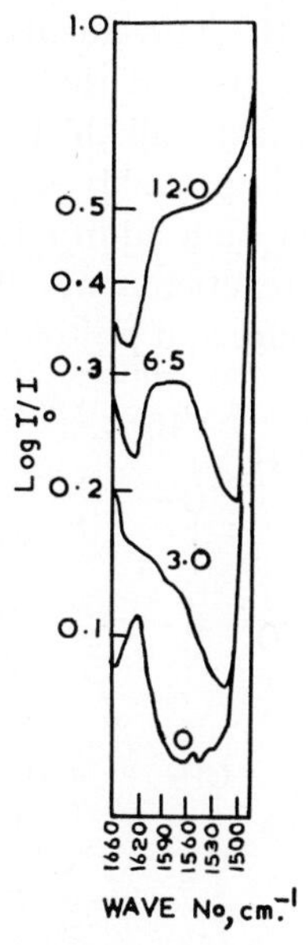

Fig. VIII-24. Changes in the 1660–1490 cm.$^{-1}$ region of the infrared spectrum of polymethacrylonitrile during coloration. (Figures denote percentage of C≡N groups which have reacted. (Taken from ref. 103.)

sification of a single spectral color is additional evidence for the gradual development of conjugation. Since nitrile groups are disappearing and also from the position of this absorption, it is clear that the nitrile groups are linking up into long carbon–nitrogen conjugated sequences and the sharp peak which develops quickly at 1693 cm.$^{-1}$ is due to the single unconjugated C═N linkage.

The structure which was thus proposed for colored polymer is XX, and this has more recently been supported by Skoda and Schurz (132).

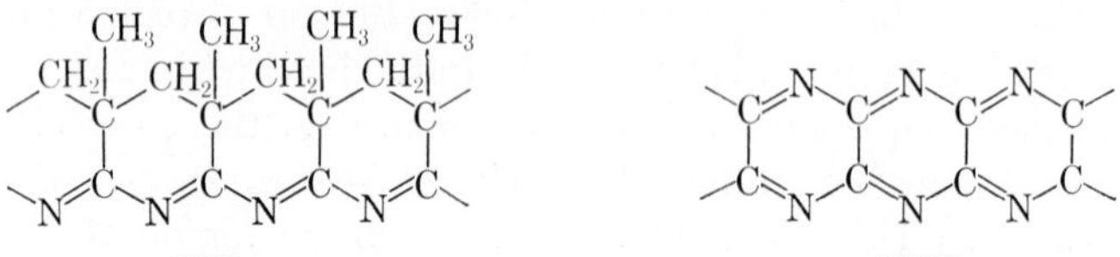

(XX) (XXI)

A similar interpretation has been made of absorption in the same region of the spectrum of paracyanogen (XXI).

The relative slowness of the movement of color through the visible spectrum in thermal experiments and the fact that a superficially similar reaction can be initiated by caustic alkalis leads to the conclusion that this is not a radical process but is probably ionic in nature and results in a stable molecular structure as each additional double bond is added to a conjugated sequence. The reaction may thus be simply represented as shown in eq. (60). Ring closure and proton migration would be facilitated

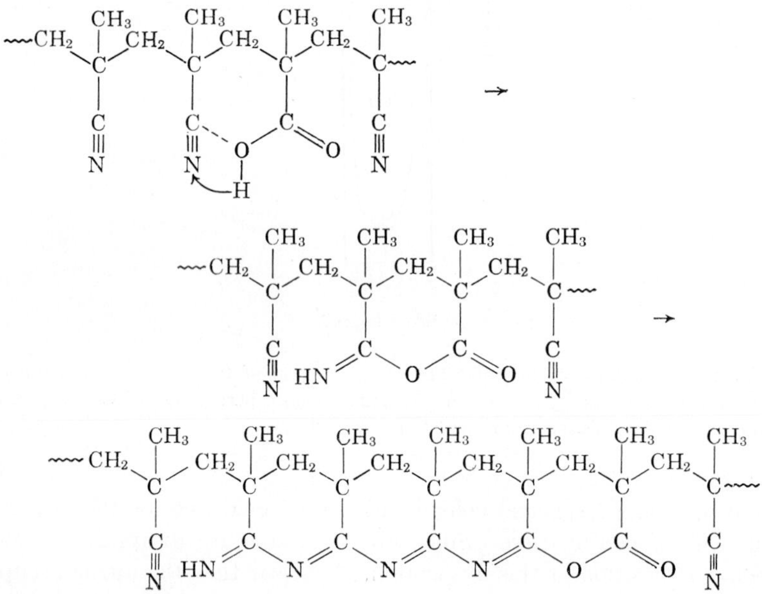

(60)

by the electromeric displacements in the nitrile and carboxyl groups. Interaction of this kind has been observed in *o*-cyanobenzoic acid, which can be converted to phthalimide via an isomer of this structure which can be isolated.

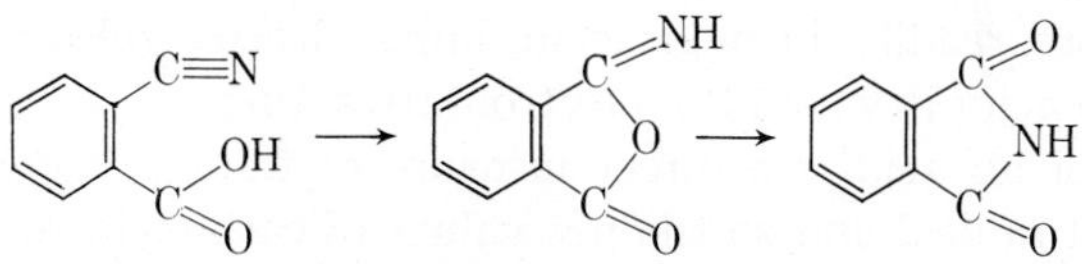

(61)

A similar initiation process should be possible, however, even when the carboxyl group is not attached to the polymer backbone, and a wide variety of organic acids have been shown to be efficient color initiators. This is not a property only of acids, however, since nucleophilic reagents generally have this activity; some typical examples are given in Table VIII-5.

TABLE VIII-5
Color Initiators[a]

(a) In the melt at 130–170°C.
Very reactive
Aromatic carboxylic acids (p$K > 2$)
Aliphatic carboxylic acids (p$K > 2$)
Phenols
Imides
Less reactive
Amides (e.g., acetamide, urea)
Aliphatic amines (butylamine), but not aromatic amines (aniline, *p*-toluidine)
(Some) ketones (acetophenone, cyclohexanone, but not acetone)
Alcohols (cyclohexanol)
Aldehydes (anisaldehyde)
(b) In solution at room temperature
Sodium hydroxide
Sodium ethoxide
Sodium amide
Lithium amide
Triphenylmethyl sodium
Butylmagnesium bromide

[a] Taken from ref. 106.

If nucleophilic attack is involved, then the initiation reaction may be represented more accurately as shown in eq. (62).

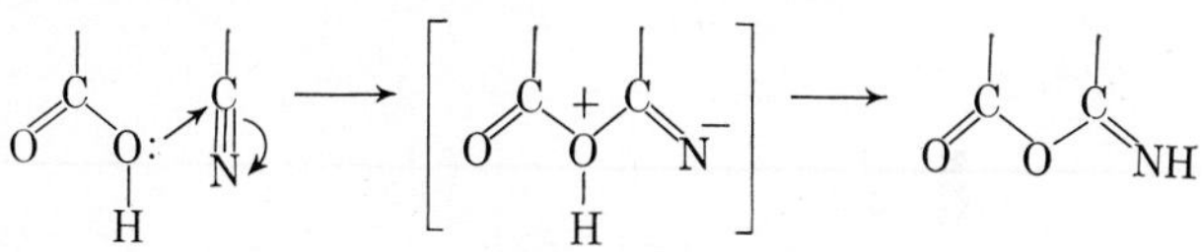

(62)

If this is correct, the first step should be strongly influenced by the nature of the group R in carboxylic acids R—COOH. In particular initiation should occur more readily in acids containing electron-releasing groups and less readily in acids in which R is electron-attracting.

The strength of an acid is a direct measure of the electron-attracting power of the acid radical and so the pK values of carboxylic acids should provide a convenient measure of the power to release electrons to the hydroxyl group which is the site of reaction, and ability to initiate coloration should increase with pK value.

Figure VIII-25 shows that for a series of aromatic acids these predictions are confirmed. k is a measure of the rate constant for initiation. Aromatic acids were chosen because they represent a series of compounds of suitable physical properties (nonvolatile at the reaction temperature) and have generally similar dimensions. The only acids which show a great deviation from the straight line are the *ortho* acids, *o*-chloro- and *o*-nitrobenzoic acids. Apparently steric effects intervene which affect the pK value but are not reflected in color initiation. The same sort of relationship can be shown qualitatively to apply also to the phenols.

Coloration may also be induced to occur in solution by sodium hydroxide. Polymer degraded in this way shows the same broad absorption in the region 1690–1490 cm.$^{-1}$ which is characteristic of thermally degraded

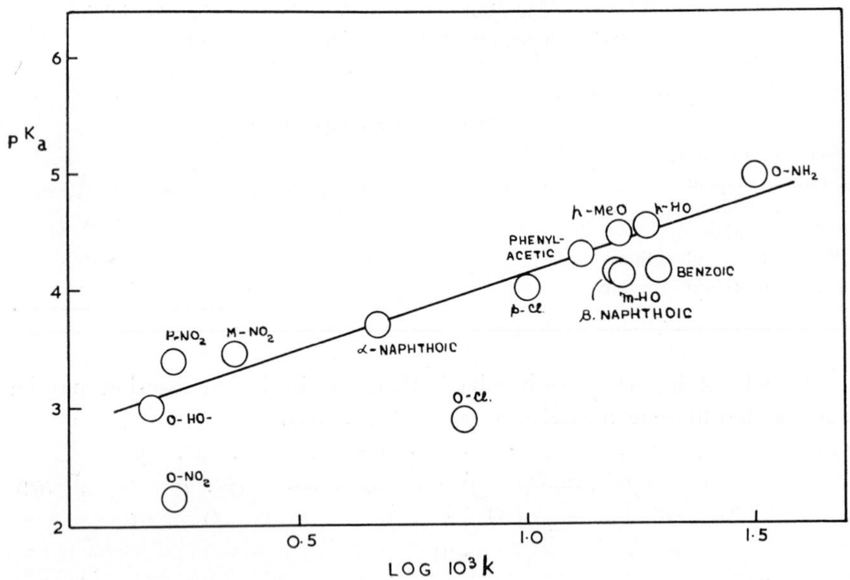

Fig. VIII-25. Effect of acid strength on the rate constant for color initiation in polymethacrylonitrile by aromatic carboxylic acids. (Taken from ref. 106.)

material. By analogy with the behavior of acids and phenols, the mechanism of alkali-induced coloration is probably as shown in eq. (63).

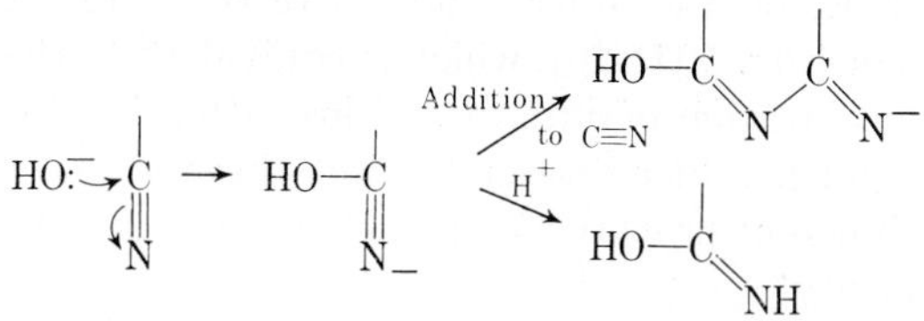

(63)

By comparison with polyene structures it seems probable that a minimum of about five conjugated carbon/nitrogen structures are necessary to produce color. On the other hand, it has been found possible to construct reasonably strain-free models of these color structures up to about four units in length; thereafter the strain increases. It may, therefore, be assumed that sequences of more than four rings become progressively more unstable. This is in line with certain experimental observations.

Thus, deep red coloration is only obtained in the melt. In cyclohexanone solution at the same temperature no coloration is observed (133). Furthermore, deep red material dissolved in cyclohexanone reverts slowly to yellow by way of orange-red and orange which implies a stepwise reduction in the length of conjugated sequences by the reverse of the above coloration process and is in keeping with the low stability of longer fused ring sequences. In addition, coloration can be induced in solution only by strong nucleophilic reagents and only to the extent of yellow-orange. This is to be expected, since the molecular motion possible in the low viscosity solution is much greater than in the viscous melt and would hinder formation of longer sequences. If this yellow polymer, produced by alkali initiation in solution, is isolated and heated to 140°C. its color deepens progressively to orange and red; the propagation process continues under conditions more favorable to the formation of longer sequences.

(2) Polyacrylonitrile

The changes which occur in the infrared spectrum of polyacrylonitrile as it colors thermally at 175°C. are essentially similar to those which occur in polymethacrylonitrile and are clearly due to the linking of nitrile groups to form conjugated carbon–nitrogen sequences (129,134–137). The reaction is also similarly induced by nucleophilic reagents, and acrylic acid copolymerized into the polymer chains is a powerful initiator. The relationship between acid concentration and rate of reaction illustrates, however, the first major difference between the behaviors of the two polymers. With polymethacrylonitrile the rate is closely proportional to the acid concentration reducing to zero in polymer completely free from acid. In polyacrylonitrile, on the other hand, there is a large residual rate at zero concentration (Fig. VIII-26), which is equivalent to that produced by a substantial concentration of initiator. Close attention to purification of both monomer and polymer does not affect this residual rate. It must therefore be an inherent property of the polyacrylonitrile itself rather than the result of impurity.

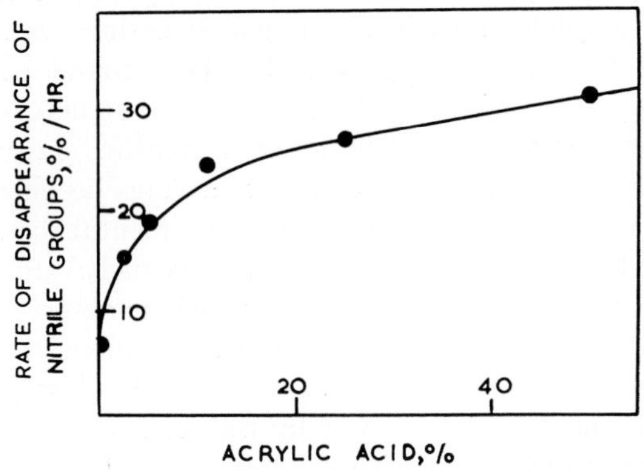

Fig. VIII-26. Effect of concentration of copolymerized acrylic acid on the rate of coloration of polyacrylonitrile. (Taken from ref. 136.)

By inspection of the structure of the two polymers it seems possible that the tertiary C—H structures in polyacrylonitrile may be responsible, reacting as —O—H and =N—H do.

$$-\underset{\displaystyle H}{\overset{|}{\underset{|}{C}}}- + \underset{\displaystyle N}{\overset{|}{\underset{|||}{C}}} \rightarrow -\overset{|}{\underset{|}{C}}-\overset{|}{C}=NH \qquad (64)$$

It is not immediately obvious whether this is most likely to be intermolecular or intramolecular. Both appear possible—the former because of the close contact which exists between adjacent chains in polyacrylonitrile, and the latter because one can represent graphically and by models an initiation reaction configuration closely analogous to that which must occur during initiation using an internal acidic initiator such as acrylic acid.

Models indicate than this intramolecular structure is more readily accommodated than the intermolecular one.

If polyacrylonitrile can initiate its own coloration in this way, then the reaction should also be accelerated by compounds with especially reactive —C—H groups. In view of the high concentration of these already present in pure polyacrylonitrile it was necessary to test the hypothesis with polymethacrylonitrile. Cumene (XXII), with its tertiary C—H bond activated by the phenyl group, and phenylacetonitrile (XXIII) in which it

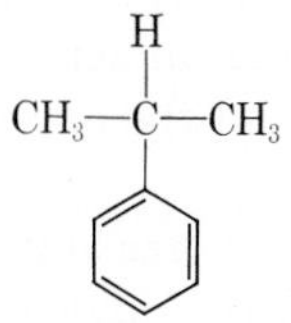

(XXII)

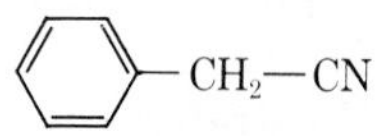

(XXIII)

is doubly activated are both initiators, although less active than hydroxyl compounds like benzoic acid. Acrylonitrile also proves to be a good initiator for reaction in polymethacrylonitrile.

A second great difference between the degradation behaviors of these two polymers resides in the fact that while polymethacrylonitrile remains soluble even when extensively colored (for example, to deep red), polyacrylonitrile becomes insoluble even before visible color develops.

This could be explained on the basis of self-initiation of coloration, provided at least some proportion of this initiation is intermolecular. If this explanation is completely adequate, then polymer colored with benzoic acid as initiator at temperatures below that at which self-initiation occurs, should remain soluble. But 3% benzoic acid gives, in 1 hr. at 120°C., a yellow polymer which is 74% insoluble.

It seems, therefore, that the more intimate packing of chains in polyacrylonitrile may allow reaction to move from molecule to molecule to produce "propagation crosslinks" (XXIV) much more readily than in polymethacrylonitrile. When the reaction is initiated by alkali in solution,

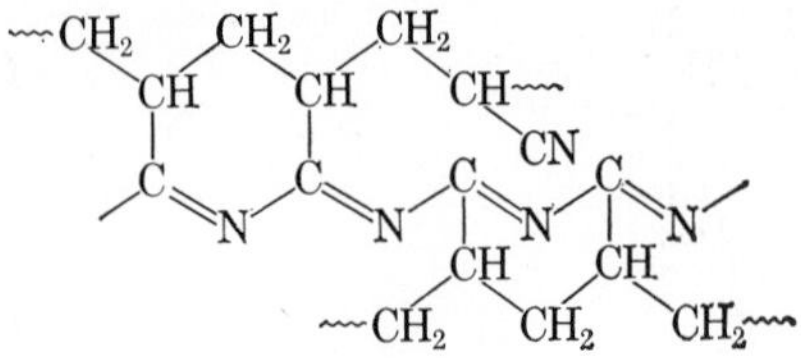

(XXIV)

this crosslinking process is inhibited owing to the separation of the molecules, and colored homogeneous solutions are obtained; it is clearly something additional to the conjugated structure which is causing insolubility.

If "propagation crosslinks" cause insolubility, then it should be possible to decrease the tendency to insolubilize by introducing bulky groups into the molecule. Groups of this type which also block the reaction by preventing its propagation along a single chain will also have the effect of decreasing the rate of coloration. Grassie and Hay (135,136) have therefore observed the effect of the second monomer in acrylonitrile copolymers upon both the development of insolubility and the overall rate of reaction of C≡N.

Figure VIII-27 illustrates the effect of increasing concentrations of styrene, methyl methacrylate, methacrylonitrile, and methyl vinyl ketone on the rate of disappearance of nitrile groups.

The propagation reaction should not be appreciably affected by the presence of methacrylonitrile. The increase in rate in polymers of higher methacrylonitrile content is probably a measure of the greater ease with which propagation can proceed through methacrylonitrile units. This could certainly be accounted for in terms of a steric effect, the additional methyl group in the methacrylonitrile structure restricting rotation about the main chain carbon–carbon bonds such that adjacent nitrile groups tend to be held in positions favorable for reaction. Molecular models support this view.

The decrease in overall rate brought about by low concentrations of methacrylonitrile is no more than is to be expected from the accompanying decrease in the acrylonitrile content of the system upon which the rate of initiation must depend. The initiation process itself can therefore not be much affected by the presence of the second monomer.

Figure VIII-28 shows that, in common with the other comonomers, increasing concentrations of methacrylonitrile progressively render the copolymer less insoluble on degradation, yet initiation must still be occurring through the tertiary centers of the acrylonitrile units. This lends

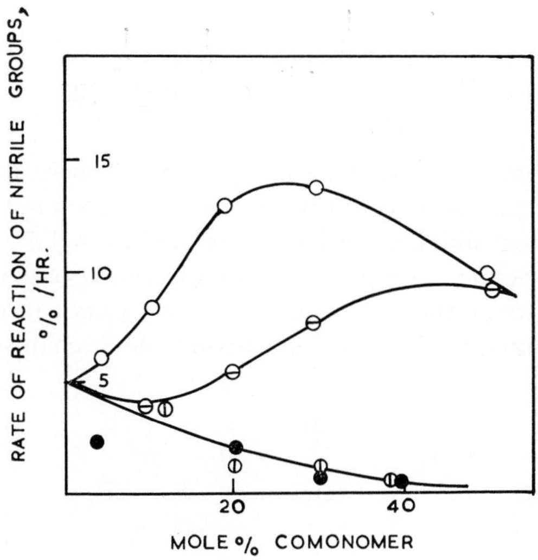

Fig. VIII-27. Effect of comonomers on the rate of coloration of polyacrylonitrile: (⊖) methacrylonitrile; (O) methyl vinyl ketone; (⦶) styrene: (●) methyl methacrylate. (Taken from ref. 136.)

further support to the proposition already made to the effect that intramolecular rather than intermolecular initiation is more likely, since the latter would lead to crosslinking and insolubility.

Both methyl methacrylate and styrene greatly reduce the overall reaction rate. With these monomers it seems unlikely that initiation should be affected any more than by methacrylonitrile, particularly at low concentrations of the second monomer. The effect must, therefore, be due principally to the blocking of the coloration reaction along a single molecule combined with the bulk effect of these groups in inhibiting transfer of the reaction to another molecule (propagation crosslinking).

The behavior of methyl vinyl ketone copolymers is at first sight rather surprising. The accelerating effect even at the lowest concentrations of this monomer can only be due to its behaving as a relatively weak initiator. This could result either from its reaction in the enol form (eq. 65) or as a result of hyperconjugative effects in the methyl group (eq. 66).

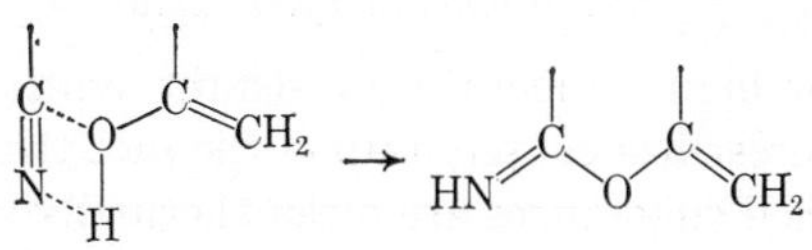

(65)

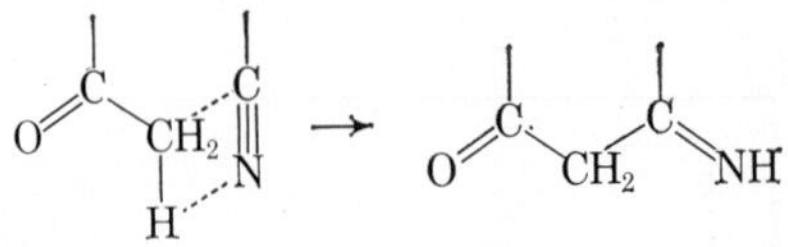

(66)

As in the styrene and methyl methacrylate copolymers, it seems that the possibilities for extensive conjugation should be severely restricted by methyl vinyl ketone units, but neither color nor infrared data give evidence of any such restriction. Propagation can apparently pass through methyl vinyl ketone units at the same time preserving conjugation and this can in fact be accounted for in terms of a reasonable mechanism (eqs. 67 and 68).

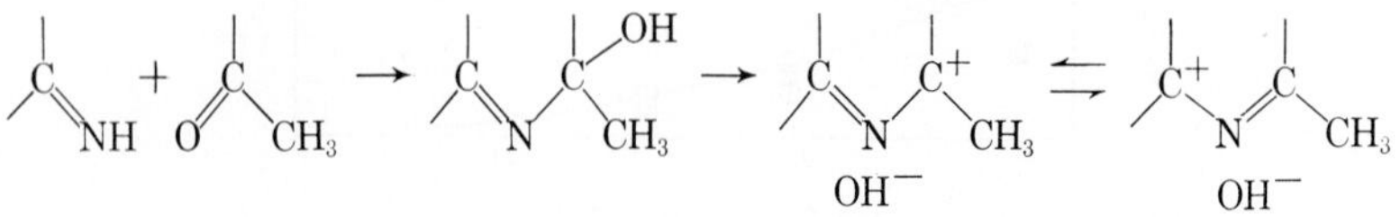

(67)

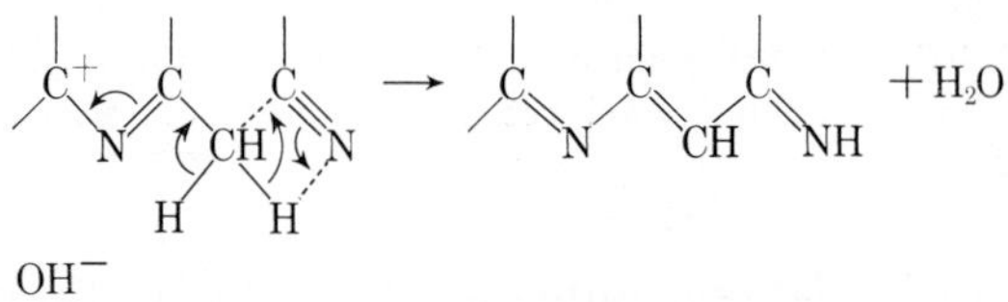

(68)

The effect of these four comonomers on the solubility of degraded polyacrylonitrile is illustrated in Figure VIII-28. The initial gradients of the curves give a measure of the relative abilities of these comonomers to prevent crosslinking, and it is interesting that this ability correlates qualitatively with the bulkiness (covalent radii) of the substituent groups on the various monomers as shown in Figure VIII-29.

Since initiation is probably little affected by the second monomer, this bulk effect would appear to result directly from the inhibition of the propagation crosslinking reaction.

While the deductions made from these measurements of copolymer rate and insolubility are admittedly only qualitative, they do provide fairly strong evidence in support of the suggestion that insolubility is due to propagation crosslinking.

c. *Polymethacrylic Acid*

In the search for high temperature-resistant synthetic materials a certain amount of interest has centered upon the fact that partially degraded or thermally modified substances are often thermally more stable than the

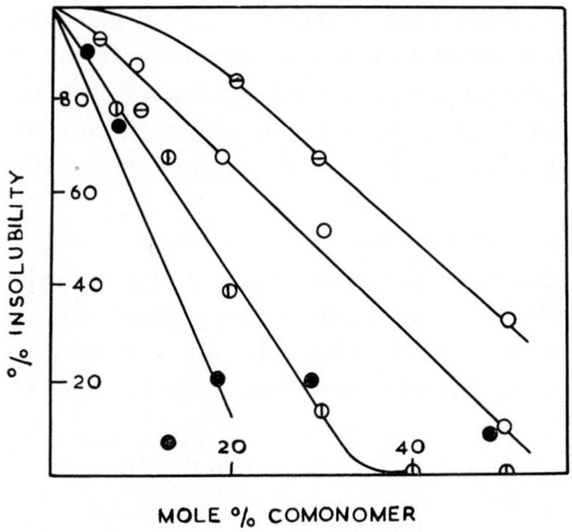

Fig. VIII-28. Effect of comonomers on the solubility of polyacrylonitrile heated at 200°C. for 1 hr.: (⊖) methacrylonitrile; (O) methyl vinyl ketone; (⦶) styrene: (●) methyl methacrylate. (Taken from ref. 136.)

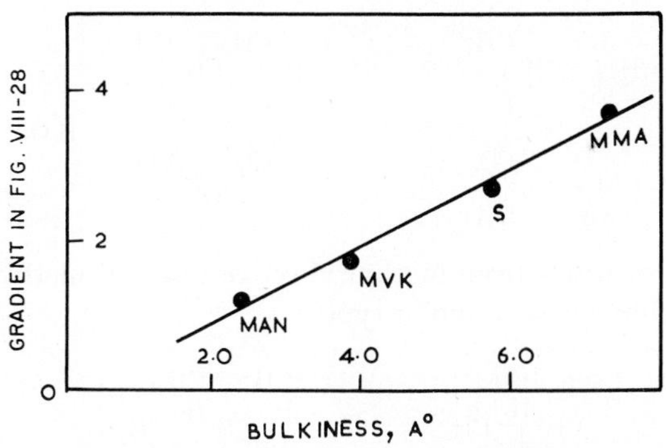

Fig. VIII-29. Effect of covalent radii of monomers on their ability to inhibit crosslinking in copolymers with acrylonitrile. (Taken from ref. 136.)

parent polymer. Madorsky and Straus (69,71) have carried out experiments at temperatures as high as 1200°C. but find that polymers which do not volatilize completely at lower temperatures leave, at these higher temperatures, a residue which is essentially a carbonaceous char which is quite useless as a possible structural material.

The nature of the various degradation reactions of polymethacrylonitrile, which have been discussed above, illustrate how, by inducing the coloration reaction to occur rather than depolymerization to monomer, a material can be produced, without loss of volatile products, which is very much more stable than the parent polymer by virtue of its fused ring structure. But once again these structures which confer thermal stability are also responsible for destroying the useful physical properties of the parent material.

Recently Bresler, Koton, and their co-workers (138) have observed that the cyclic structures produced (eqs. 69 and 70) when methylamine and water are liberated thermally from poly(methyl methacrylamide) and poly(methacrylic acid), respectively, are also very much more thermally stable than the parent substances. The residues obtained (eq. 71)

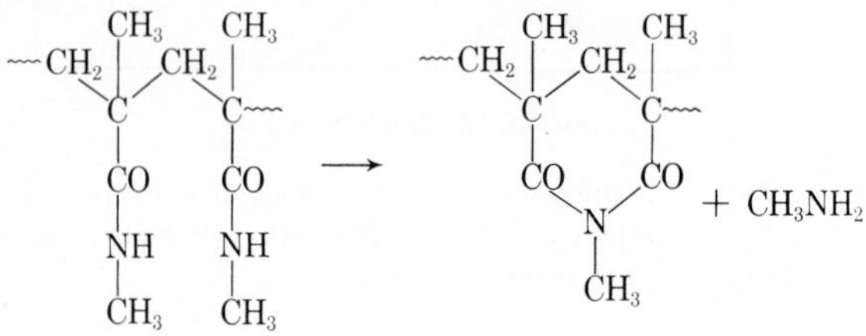

(69)

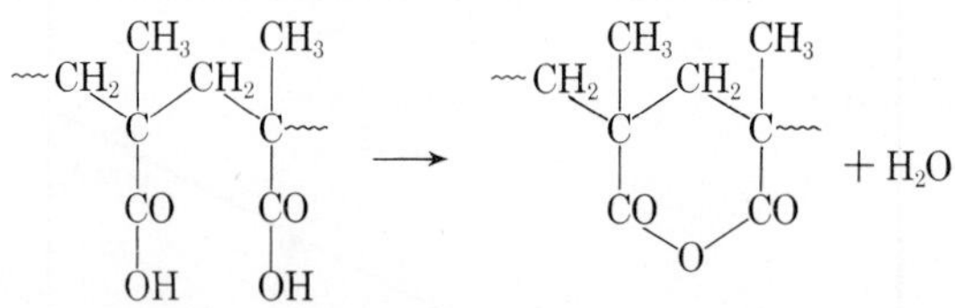

(70)

by elimination of water from methyl vinyl ketone and methyl isopropenyl ketone are presumably of a similar type.

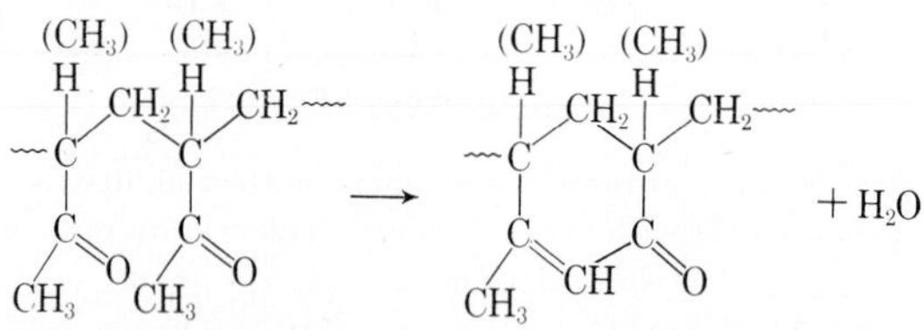

(71)

The decomposition of poly(methacrylic acid) has been studied by Grant and Grassie (83) in greater detail, however, since poly(methacrylic acid) is an intermediate product in the decomposition of certain polymethacrylates, a reaction which has been referred to above (see Part 2e) and which is discussed below in greater detail (see Part 3d 3). Water is the predominating volatile product of thermal degradation of poly(methacrylic acid) at 200°C. This water is always detectably acidic, however, and Grant and Grassie have shown that this is probably due to approximately 0.2% of methacrylic acid which is a genuine degradation product. Methacrylic acid, like polymethacrylonitrile and certain of the higher polymethacrylates (see Part 2e), is apparently capable of depolymerization to monomer but is effectively prevented from doing so by the predominating dehydration reaction.

It is convenient to follow Grant and Grassie (83) in referring to thermally degraded poly(methacrylic acid) as anhydropoly(methacrylic acid) in order to distinguish it from the material obtained by polymerization of methacrylic anhydride.

The infrared spectra of poly(methacrylic acid) and anhydropoly(methacrylic acid) are illustrated in Figure VIII-30. (*B*) can be recognized as

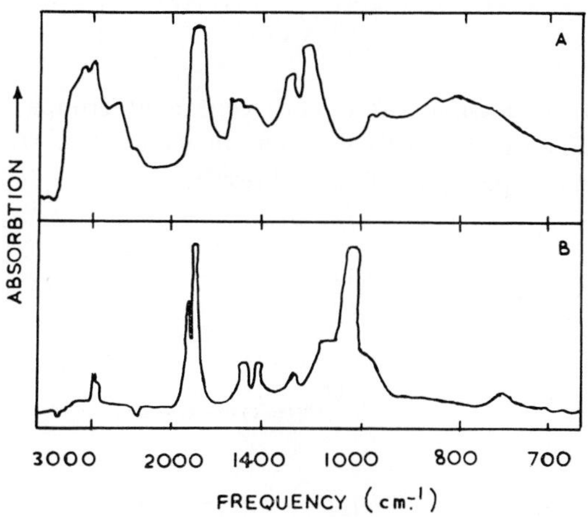

Fig. VIII-30. Infrared spectra of (*A*) poly(methacrylic acid) and (*B*) anhydropoly-(methacrylic acid). (Taken from ref. 83.)

the spectrum of an anhydride by the virtual disappearance of the broad "bonded" hydroxyl absorption (3600–2500 cm.$^{-1}$) characteristic of (*A*), the presence of twin carbonyl peaks (1795 and 1750 cm.$^{-1}$) and the intense C—O—C peaks at 1022 cm.$^{-1}$. Three anhydride structures are possible, however.

If poly(methacrylic acid) has a head-to-tail structure in common with other vinyl polymers, then anhydride formation between adjacent carboxyl groups would result in six-membered glutaric anhydride type rings

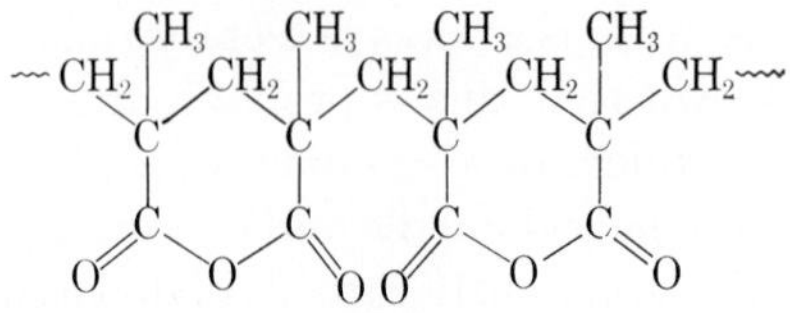

(XXV)

(XXV). Head-to-head, tail-to-tail structures, on the other hand, would give the succinic anhydride type of rings (XXVI)

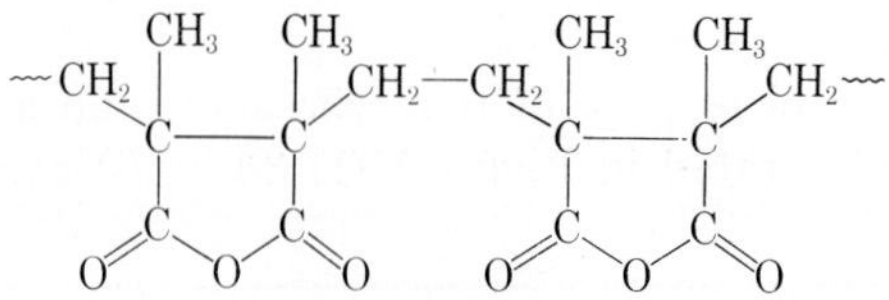

(XXVI)

It may also be possible for nonadjacent acid groups or acid groups attached to different chains to interact, in which case structures of isobutyric anhydride type (XXVII) would result.

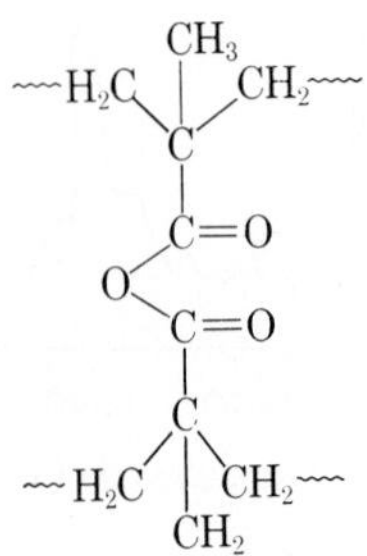

(XXVII)

It has been possible to decide among these three structures principally by considering three features of the twin carbonyl peaks of the anhydride spectrum, namely, frequencies, separation of frequencies, and relative intensities.

(1) Frequencies

Values for model compounds are compared with those for anhydropoly(methacrylic acid) in Table VIII-6.

TABLE VIII-6
Frequencies of Twin Carbonyl Peaks in Infrared Spectra of Anhydrides[a]

	Infrared frequency, cm.$^{-1}$	
	Found	Literature
Succinic anhydride	1855, 1776	1865, 1782
Glutaric anhydride	1802, 1756	1802, 1761
Isobutyric anhydride	1803, 1743	
Poly(methacrylic anhydride) / Anhydropoly(methacrylic acid)	1795, 1750	

[a] Taken from ref. 83.

The higher frequency of absorption of succinic anhydride is typical of strained-ring anhydrides, and the data show quite clearly that no appreciable proportion of succinic type anhydride rings can exist in the degraded polymer.

(2) Separation of Frequencies

The separation of carbonyl frequencies in anhydrides varies from 40 to 80 cm.$^{-1}$, and this has been correlated with structure. Those with six-membered rings usually have the least separation and the small separation (45 cm.$^{-1}$) in the case of anhydropoly(methacrylic acid) suggests that glutaric rather than isobutyric type units predominate.

(3) Relative Intensities

Examination of the infrared spectra of a variety of succinic and glutaric type ring anhydrides show the lower frequency absorption to be the more intense. Open chain compounds such as acetic anhydride, on the other hand, show a more intense higher frequency peak. Anhydropoly(methacrylic acid) has a more intense lower frequency peak, from which it is concluded that the predominant anhydride structure is of the glutaric type. The insolubility which develops during degradation has shown, however, that anhydropoly(methacrylic acid) must also possess a few cross-links of the isobutyric type.

Grassie and Grant (83) have proposed that the mechanism of formation of anhydropoly(methacrylic acid) may be analogous to that of an acid-catalyzed esterification (eq. 72), which is equivalent to proposing that the

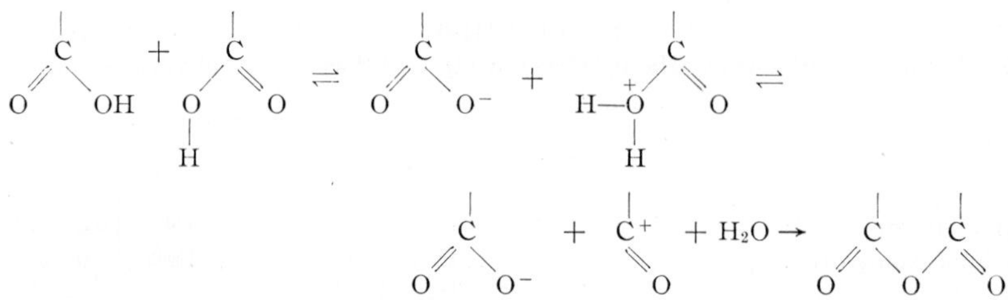

(72)

overall reaction passes through the transition state.

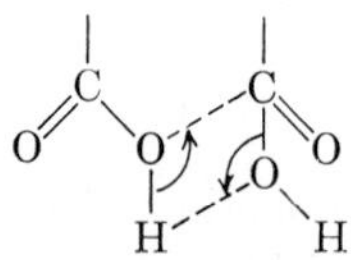

(XXVIII)

d. Ester Decomposition Reactions

A number of commercial polymers are esters and, like short chain esters, are found to decompose thermally to acid and olefin. Poly(vinyl acetate), for example, liberates acetic acid, leaving a residue deeply colored due to conjugated carbon–carbon structures and which can presumably be described as polyacetylene. The principal characteristics of this reaction can be satisfactorily explained in terms of the molecular mechanism by which fatty acid alkyl esters are believed to decompose, although certain new characteristics are impressed upon it by the fact of its occurring in the environment of a long chain polymer. While the thermal decomposition of poly(vinyl chloride) is superficially similar in the sense that the corresponding product, hydrogen chloride, is liberated, its mechanism appears to be quite different. Although a number of features remain to be explained, fundamentally it also appears to be similar to the corresponding reaction in its model compounds, namely the simple alkyl chlorides. The nitrile polymers, polyacrylonitrile, and polymethacrylonitrile are exceptional among polyvinyl compounds of this type. Thus while hydrogen cyanide has been reported as a minor decomposition product of the former, other reactions predominate.

In poly(vinyl chloride) and poly(vinyl acetate) the olefinic unsaturation which results, remains in the polymer chains and has a strong influence upon the course of the reaction. Among those acrylate esters which undergo decomposition to acid and olefin, however, the olefinic product is volatile. It is therefore convenient to consider poly(vinyl chloride), poly(vinyl acetate), and polyacrylates individually.

(1) Poly(vinyl Chloride)

Early in the life of poly(vinyl chloride) (PVC) as a commercial polymer it was recognized that its thermal discoloration is due to the development of carbon–carbon conjugation as a direct result of the loss of hydrogen chloride. Since this coloration is evident after only minute proportions of hydrogen chloride are lost, it is clear that the hydrogen chloride tends to be liberated from groups of adjacent units rather than at random. From this it was a short step to the conclusion that unsaturated centers must activate adjacent units, and that reaction thus moves along the chain from unit to unit.

A great deal of effort was devoted to the study of the degradation of PVC in the early 1950's and with some ill-defined stepwise mechanism for loss of hydrogen chloride usually in mind, attempts were made to discover the effects of the various variables on the overall reaction. A great deal of contradictory evidence was presented at this time, partly due to inadequate control of experimental conditions and partly to a lack of appreciation of the interplay of the various degradative agencies, principally heat, light, and oxidation. A good deal of the more convincing work carried out in this period is summarized in Circular 525 of the National Bureau of Standards (43) in four papers by Druesedow and Gibbs (139), by Kenyon (140), by Scarbrough, Kellner, and Rizzo (141), and by Havens (142).

The extent of the thermal reaction proved to be linear with time at low temperatures (130°C.), becoming autocatalytic at higher temperatures (142). But degradation at temperatures of this magnitude represents stability far less than one would expect if all the chlorine atoms in PVC were secondary (139). Hence, it was concluded that there must be "points of activation" which might be, for example, unsaturated structures, chain branches, points of oxidation, or catalyst residues. Thus the linear reaction at 130°C. possibly radiates from unsaturated structures, while the acceleration at higher temperatures may be due to initiation from less labile structures such as chain branches.

Similarly, in studying the photodegradation, Kenyon (140) showed that alkyl chlorides and therefore pure PVC should not be affected by radiation of wavelength greater than 2350 A. Light absorption and degradation do occur, however, and so it appears that initiation is the result of absorption at impurities. Infrared measurements show that carbonyl absorption increases during irradiation in air, and the presence of carbonyl compounds like acetone does increase the rate. But even in pure poly(vinyl chloride) some light absorption and degradation occur, and this was attributed by Kenyon to unsaturation resulting from minute loss of HCl during processing.

Exposure to light for even a short time also markedly accelerates degradation during subsequent heat aging. On the other hand, the color of heat-aged material rapidly fades during subsequent storage.

These results illustrate one of the greatest weaknesses of a good deal of the published work on PVC, namely, the fact that oxidative effects have often complicated the issue to an extent which may not have been appreciated and also is difficult to assess in the overall reaction.

Thus fading of thermally degraded material is clearly an oxidative reaction of the type to which conjugated structures are particularly susceptible. This is now known to proceed by a radical mechanism and results ultimately in the destruction of the conjugated sequences which cause the color.

The accelerating effect of light on subsequent heat aging is probably due to the fact that a small amount of unsaturation has been produced by the radiation which labilizes adjacent units.

A great deal of information of this type is contained in these four papers (139–142). It is of great interest and importance but it does not give any unequivocal evidence of the precise nature of the mechanism of loss of hydrogen chloride.

Nevertheless, the general effects of light, the photosensitizing action of ketonic structures, the fact that butyl groups appear in PVC irradiated in presence of dibutyltin diacetate and other evidence of this type did gradually focus attention on the possibility of a radical process being involved, and Arlman, who also showed that free radical catalysts promote decomposition, was the first to formulate a mechanism (143).

About this time a great deal of interest was focused upon the thermal decomposition of alkyl chlorides (45), and it became clear that provided the structural features of the chlorocompound did not preclude it, the decomposition could be described in terms of a chain mechanism exemplified here by 1,2-dichloroethane (eqs. 73–76).

Initiation:

$$\mathrm{Cl{-}CH_2{-}CH_2{-}Cl \rightarrow ClCH_2{-}CH_2\cdot + Cl\cdot} \tag{73}$$

Propagation:

$$\mathrm{Cl\cdot + ClCH_2{-}CH_2Cl \rightarrow HCl + ClCH_2{-}CHCl\cdot} \tag{74}$$

$$ClCH_2{-}CHCl\cdot \rightarrow CH_2{=}CHCl + Cl\cdot \quad (75)$$

Termination:

$$Cl\cdot + ClCH_2{-}CH_2\cdot \rightarrow HCl + CH_2{=}CHCl\cdot \quad (76)$$

On carrying this mechanism over to the thermal decomposition of poly(vinyl chloride) it is obvious that radicals may attack either the methylene or the tertiary hydrogen atoms. Only in the former case could the reaction be propagated as above since in the latter a radical results which has no chlorine atom in the α position which could be liberated as in the second propagation reaction. It has been shown by Fuchs and Louis (144), however, that when PVC is chlorinated, methylene groups disappear. The major portion of the resulting product does not have the structure of poly(vinylidene chloride), as was formerly believed, but one chlorine atom is attached to each carbon atom. This indicates that the major portion of free radical attack is on the methylene hydrogen atom (145). Once unsaturation is produced in this way, then the nearest methylene group to the liberated chlorine atom is also allylic, and so abstraction of its hydrogen atoms should be particularly highly favored. Even if some reaction did occur at the tertiary hydrogen atoms it is not likely to be of such a magnitude that "zips" are terminated by it before they attain the length necessary for color (6–8 units).

Stromberg, Straus, and Achhammer (146) have presented a kinetic treatment based on a mechanism of this sort. They suggest that initiation occurs by scission of a C—Cl bond. The weakest C—Cl bonds in the molecule will be those adjacent to unsaturated centers which are most likely to exist at the chain ends since double bonds will be formed as a result of disproportionation or transfer to monomer during polymerization. Talamini and Pezzin (147) have recently shown that the rate of decomposition of poly(vinyl chloride) is inversely proportional to the molecular weight of the polymer which is strong evidence for chain end initiation. Frye and Horst (148,149) have been able to show that stabilization of poly(vinyl chloride) by barium, cadmium, and zinc carboxylates is the result of exchange of these labile chlorine atoms by the more stable carboxylate groups. In their kinetic treatment, however, Stromberg and his colleagues denote the rate of initiation by k_1C, in which C is the fraction of undegraded monomer units. This implies that the initiation may equally probably occur at any monomer unit. Any assumption about preferential reaction at chain ends thus immediately invalidates their kinetic treatment.

They also suggest that termination is caused initially by combination of polymer radicals to produce crosslinking which explains the development of insolubility. As the chains become less mobile, however, the combination of chlorine atoms becomes more probable.

The mechanism has therefore been represented as shown in eqs. (77)–(80).

Initiation:

$$\sim\!\!\sim CHCl—CH_2—CHCl—CH_2\sim\!\!\sim \xrightarrow{k_1} \sim\!\!\sim CHCl—CH_2—\dot{C}H—CH_2\sim\!\!\sim + Cl\cdot \quad (77)$$

Propagation:

$$\sim\!\!\sim CH_2—CHCl—CH_2—CHCl\sim\!\!\sim + Cl\cdot \xrightarrow{k_2} \sim\!\!\sim CH_2—CHCl—\dot{C}H—CHCl\sim\!\!\sim + HCl \quad (78)$$

$$\sim\!\!\sim CH_2—CHCl—\dot{C}H—CHCl\sim\!\!\sim \xrightarrow{k_3} \sim\!\!\sim CH_2—CHCl—CH{=}CH—CH_2\sim\!\!\sim + Cl\cdot \quad (79)$$

Termination:

$$Cl\cdot + Cl\cdot \rightarrow Cl_2 \quad (80)$$

If C is the fraction of undegraded monomer units and R· represents a polymer radical, then in the stationary state,

$$d[Cl\cdot]/dt = k_1C - k_2[Cl\cdot]\,C + k_3\,[R\cdot] - k_4\,[Cl\cdot]^2 = 0 \quad (81)$$

and

$$d[R\cdot]/dt = k_2\,[Cl\cdot]\,C - k_3\,[R\cdot] = 0 \quad (82)$$

$$-dC/dt = k_1C + k_2\,[Cl\cdot]\,C \quad (83)$$

Combining eqs. (81) and (82) yields

$$[Cl\cdot] = (k_1C/k_4)^{1/2}$$

Neglecting the first term in eq. (83) as being negligible compared with the second term yields

$$-\,dC/dt = k_2\,(k_1/k_4)^{1/2}C^{3/2} \quad (84)$$

Experimental data are presented by these authors which indicate a close dependence of rate of degradation upon the three halves power of monomer unit concentration.

While the evidence is in favor of the propagation processes represented in the mechanism above (eqs. 77–80), this cannot be accepted as a final picture of the thermal degradation of poly(vinyl chloride) in view of the limitations, mentioned above, which this mechanism places upon the nature of initiation and also the fact that a good deal of additional evidence about initiation is now available.

In considering possible abnormal structures at which HCl loss might be initiated, Baum and Wartman (150) suggest unsaturated chain ends formed by monomer transfer but they also point out that up to 20 branches may exist per molecule as well as catalyst fragments and oxygenated structures. The effect of chlorination of the polymer is to reduce the rate of HCl loss presumably by saturation of labile unsaturated centers. Chlorination also results in a lower carbonyl content after ozonization—further proof that chlorination is removing double bonds. Ozonization and recovery of the formic acid formed showed that 60% of the molecules in their poly(vinyl chloride) sample had unsaturated ends, but the molecular weight does not decrease very much so there cannot be any appreciable number of double bonds in the body of the molecules.

Dehydrochlorination of chlorinated PVC must be initiated at branches, and ozonization followed by viscosity measurements shows that HCl is lost much less readily from branches than from chain ends.

The fact that oxygen increases the rate manyfold is probably due to the formation of labile structures by oxidation of conjugated sequences.

Baum and Wartman point out that unsaturated chain ends may be α- or β-chloro, depending upon whether they are formed by disproportionation of radicals or chain transfer to monomer. Experiments on model compounds were designed to provide evidence of the nature of the labile terminal structures in PVC. The evidence is in support of transfer ends.

The role of HCl in the degradation of poly(vinyl chloride) has caused a great deal of controversy. The progressive liberation of HCl coupled with the autocatalytic nature of the reaction led early investigators to believe that HCl catalyzed the reaction. This assumption was reinforced by the fact that HCl absorbers usually possess stabilizing properties. Arlman (151) presented the first really direct and convincing evidence proving fairly conclusively that there was no catalytic effect. Subsequent work has supported this, and it has been suggested by Winkler (145) that stabilizers which were believed to act by absorbing HCl probably function by interfering with the radical process. It is known, for example, that butyl groups appear in the polymer when PVC is irradiated in presence of the stabilizer dibutyltin diacetate (140). It seems feasible that stabilization may therefore involve termination of a radical process by reaction with a butyl radical from this compound.

Thus it is clear that most of the features of PVC degradation can be accounted for, qualitatively at least, in terms of a radical process. The present position may be summarized as follows. Thermal initiation consists of loss of a chlorine atom from a labile structural abnormality. In pure polymer this occurs most readily at unsaturated chain terminal structures produced by transfer during polymerization. In addition, and particularly at higher temperatures, chlorine atoms adjacent to chain branches may be liberated. The reaction can also be initiated by ultraviolet radiation which is absorbed at unsaturated structures resulting in liberation of adjacent chlorine atoms. In the presence of oxygen, both thermal and photo reactions are accelerated by reason of the labilizing effects of conjugated and particularly ketonic structures in the polymer chains.

Once the reaction has been initiated by some such process it can be propagated from unit to unit along the chain as represented in the mechanism above to result ultimately in conjugation of considerable length.

There are a number of possible termination processes of which the more likely appear to be combination of chlorine atoms or polymer radicals in pairs, the latter also accounting for the appearance of insolubility. Stabilization can be explained in terms of inhibition of the radical process.

Chain scission, bleaching, and associated phenomena which have been observed are a result of subsequent attack on the conjugated structures by oxygen and light.

(2) Poly(vinyl Acetate)

The decomposition of carboxylic acid esters into acid and olefin is a well established reaction (45). It proceeds by a molecular mechanism which is facilitated by the six-membered ring interaction which can clearly exist between the β-hydrogen atom of the alcohol residue and the carboxyl group.

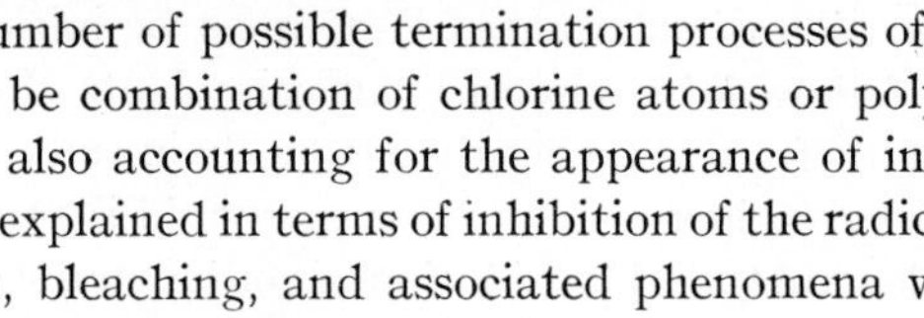

(85)

The tendency for the β-hydrogen atom to be attracted to the oxygen atom is enhanced by electron-attracting substituents in the positions R_2–R_5. Thus, the tendency in polymers like poly(vinyl acetate) for adjacent units to react to produce conjugation and color can be explained in terms of the electron attracting properties of the carbon–carbon double bond activating the adjacent methylene group (XXIX): Thus the liberation

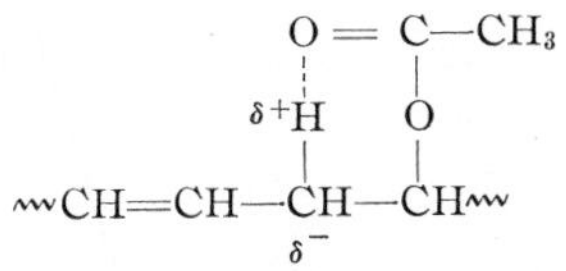

(XXIX)

of acetic acid from poly(vinyl acetate) and the accompanying coloration is a molecular chain reaction in which initiation consists of the loss of a molecule of acetic acid from a saturated chain. The double bond so formed facilitates loss of an adjacent acid molecule which is the propagation step.

Once the reaction is initiated, successive units decompose over a relatively long period of time so that the rate continues to increase as more and more reaction chains are initiated. The autocatalytic properties which result are illustrated in Figure VIII-31 (152). Grassie (153) has shown that initiation of this nonradical chain process occurs exclusively near the chain ends. The energies of activation for initiation and propagation are 33.2 ± 2 and 20.4 ± 2 kcal./mole, respectively. The former value compares unfavorably with 44–45 kcal./mole obtained for the decomposition of secondary acetates which are the closest models for which data are available, but this difference could be due to the fact that the energy distribution and transfer properties of small molecules in the gas phase are not strictly comparable with those in large molecules in a molten highly viscous state. The difference between the initiation and propagation values is a measure of the activating effect of the adjacent double bond.

While loss of the appropriate acid is the only significant reaction at temperatures up to 200–250°C. in both poly(vinyl chloride) and poly(vinyl acetate), it is interesting that at higher temperatures appreciable amounts of benzene and other aromatic hydrocarbons can be recovered from the volatile products (152,154). This is in marked contrast to the behavior of saturated hydrocarbon polymers such as polyethylene, from which linear small molecules are produced. This fundamental difference is presumably due to the fact that the aromatic stability in the products from the unsaturated hydrocarbon polymer reduces considerably the energy requirements for chain scission. No comparable stability exists in the corresponding alicyclic products which would result from the decomposition of saturated polymers.

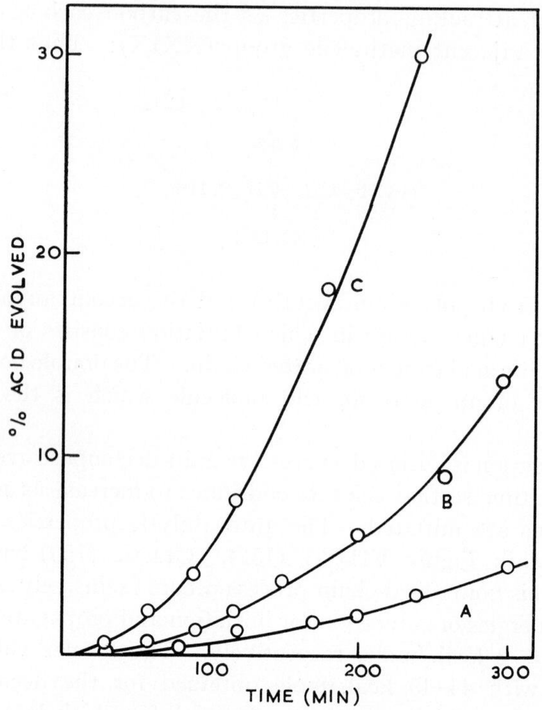

Fig. VIII-31. Evolution of acetic acid from poly(vinyl acetate): (*A*) at 213°C.; (*B*) at 224°C.; (*C*) at 235°C. (Taken from ref. 152.)

(3) Poly(*tert*-butyl Methacrylate)

It has already been shown (see Part 2e) that while depolymerization to monomer is typical of methacrylate esters, it is the exclusive reaction only in poly(methyl methacrylate) among those which have been studied. This polymer is the only one so far studied which does not have a β-hydrogen atom in the alcohol residue and which cannot therefore undergo the ester decomposition reaction which occurs to a greater or lesser extent in other polymethacrylates. Poly(*tert*-butyl methacrylate) represents the other extreme, in that ester decomposition occurs almost to the exclusion of depolymerization; it is thus the ideal material for study in order to clarify the nature of the ester decomposition process in this type of polymer.

Grant and Grassie (84) showed that on heating poly(*tert*-butyl methacrylate) to 200°C. and maintaining it at that temperature, the curve in Figure VIII-32, which exhibits three distinct and reproducible maxima,

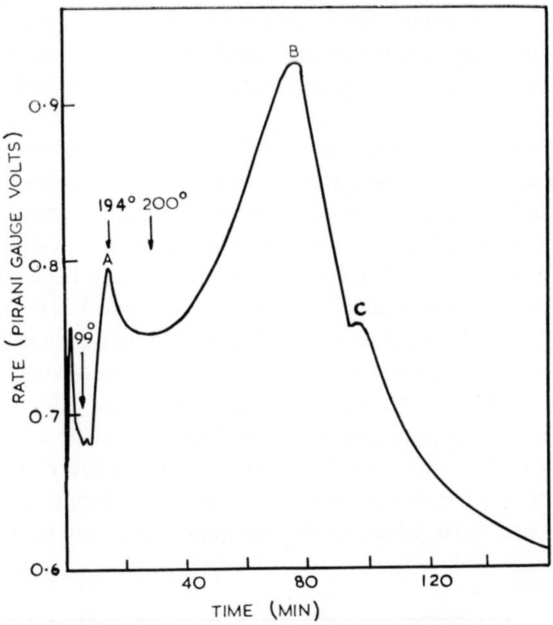

Fig. VIII 32. Decomposition of poly(*tert*-butyl methacrylate) heated to 200°C. and maintained at that temperature. (Taken from ref. 84.)

was obtained. The residue is poly(methacrylic anhydride) and is identical with the residue obtained by the thermal decomposition of poly(methacrylic acid) (see Part 3c).

By stopping the reaction after each maximum and analyzing the products, the results in Table VIII-7 were obtained. Monomer is clearly produced only in the early stages of reaction and must therefore be associated with peak A.

TABLE VIII-7
Product Yields Associated with Maxima A, B, and C[a]

	Percentage of products				
Maximum	Total	Single stage	Isobutene	Monomer	Water
A	10	10	6	3.4	0.6
B	35	25	22.3	0.1	2.6
C	47.4	12.4	6.5	0	5.5

[a] Taken from ref. 84.

Isobutene, the major component, occurs in all three stages but mainly in the second, which includes the largest peak, B. Water becomes relatively more important in the later stages, suggesting its association with peak C.

It appears, therefore, that the overall decomposition process consists of three principal and consecutive reactions, namely, depolymerization, which results in monomer, ester decomposition which eliminates isobutene, and anhydride formation by elimination of water from the methacrylic acid primarily formed. This reaction sequence has been confirmed by infrared spectral evidence which is illustrated in Figure VIII-33.

Grant and Grassie were able to show that the small proportion of monomer is produced in a radical depolymerization process strictly analogous to that which occurs in other polymethacrylates, and that its production ceases early in the reaction owing to the blocking effect of the anhydride structures ultimately produced. This is qualitatively identical with the behavior of other methacrylate polymers but different in degree owing to the great ease with which ester decomposition can occur in tertiary esters.

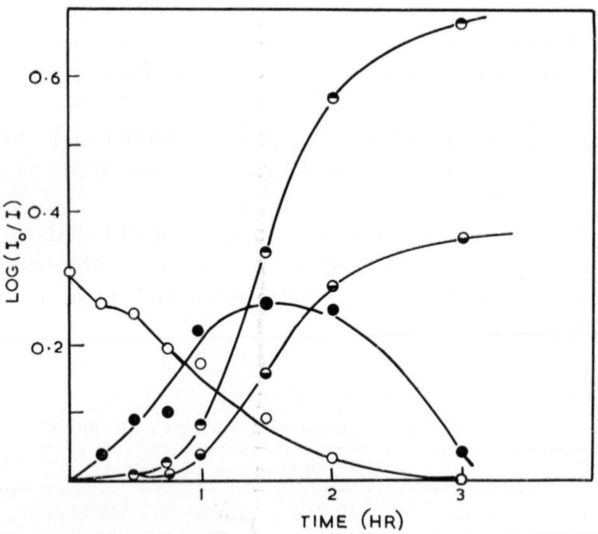

Fig. VIII-33. Changes in the infrared absorption spectrum of poly(*tert*-butyl methacrylate) during decomposition at 192.5°C.: (○) 848 cm.$^{-1}$ (ester); (●) 2580 cm.$^{-1}$ (acid) (multiplied by 10); (◐) and (◑) 1022 cm.$^{-1}$ and 1795 cm.$^{-1}$ (anhydride). (Taken from ref. 84.)

From the shape of peak B in Figure VIII-32 it is clear that the liberation of isobutene exhibits autocatalytic properties rather similar to those observed during the evolution of acetic acid from poly(vinyl acetate). By analogy with poly(vinyl acetate) (see Part 3d), therefore, it seems that the residues from units which have reacted, namely methacrylic acid units, can accelerate the decomposition of adjacent ester units.

In the case of poly(*tert*-butyl methacrylate) it is possible to formulate a modified transition state for olefin elimination involving an adjacent

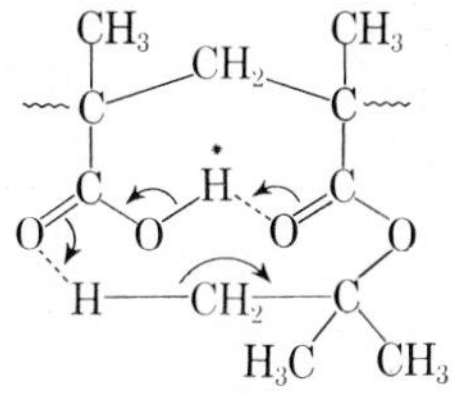

(XXX)

acid unit (XXX). Because of the ease with which H* tends to be liberated as a proton this might occur very much more readily than the reaction of single isolated units (XXXI). Thus the reaction will tend to be prop-

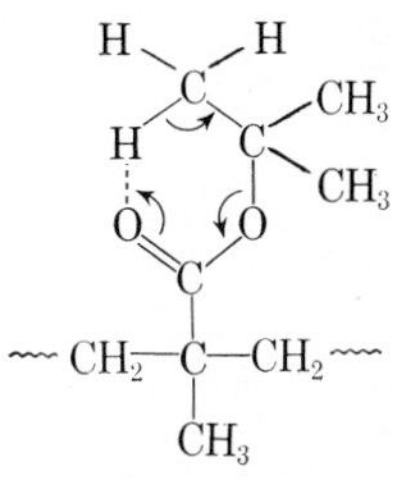

(XXXI)

agated from unit to unit along the polymer molecule in a molecular chain process.

If this "acid catalysis" mechanism is correct, it should not be necessary for the acid units to be built into the chains in order to accelerate the reaction, and Grassie and Grant were able to show that 3,5-dinitrobenzoic acid has a considerable catalytic effect.

There is also a purely physical, alternative explanation for acceleration by adjacent decomposed units. Thus there must be considerable steric interfernece between adjacent *tert*-butyl groups in the polymer chains which must inhibit to a large extent the free rotation about the bonds in these groups. Thus, in intact chains the β-hydrogen atoms may be effectively held out of contact with the carbonyl oxygen atoms with which they must interact in the transition state as in (XXXII). Liberation of an isobutene molecule might release this steric strain to such an extent that this interaction is facilitated. This would give rise to the autocatalytic effect observed.

C. RADIATION

A. R. Shultz

Minnesota Mining and Manufacturing Co.

1. Introduction

The interaction of radiant energy with polymers to produce chemical change has been of concern to man for a very long time. Until fairly recently the principal radiation of interest has been light. The role of light in biochemical polymer processes and in the aging or weathering of natural and synthetic polymers has in the past, and will in the future, command a considerable fraction of the efforts of chemical research. The use of light to modify properties of polymers under controlled conditions is becoming more prevalent. However, during the past decade the effects of high energy, ionizing radiations upon polymers have been subject to more intense scientific scrutiny than have the effects of light. The emergence of a massive nuclear technology and the development of more efficient electron and ion accelerators have provided stimulus. Of equal importance has been the response to the intellectual challenge presented by the complex array of chemical reaction possibilities afforded by high energy radiations. The simultaneous presence of electrons, ions, free radicals, and molecules in excited and thermalized states has evoked a multiplicity of hypotheses to explain observed radiation-chemical transformations. Experimental studies of increasing refinement are furnishing data for testing and altering these hypotheses. As will be seen in subsequent discussions no proposed mechanisms have been unambiguously demonstrated.

This section on polymer chain cleavage by radiation and a later section (Chapter IX-A) on polymer crosslinking by radiation will be restricted mainly to the consideration of ionizing radiation effects on synthetic polymers. Some naturally occurring polymers will be discussed, but not in the contexts of biological environment or function. Mention of the effects of ultraviolet light will be interjected from time to time for comparative purposes. These restrictions are regrettable, but they are necessary to allow concentration upon the more extensive chemical studies of radiation-induced changes in synthetic polymers. The interpretations of the experimental studies in this latter area will hopefully serve to clarify the effects produced in biological systems by radiation. The application of the experimental technivues and analytical methods developed in ionizing radiation research to the elucidation of effects of ultraviolet light on polymers is now, and will increasingly become, of great utility.

The purpose of the present writing is to give a unified discussion of published studies. A fairly extensive, but not exhaustive, reference to open literature on ionizing radiation effects on polymers will be presented in the discussion of given topics. Books specifically treating these effects on synthetic and natural polymers (155,156) have appeared. Radiation effects on biological and other polymeric systems (157–159) have been described in some detail. Reviews of the radiation chemistry of polymers and other organic compounds are available for literature guides (160–165). A recent book on the radiation chemistry of organic compounds is a useful collateral source (166). An indication of the expanding radiation-chemical technology of polymers is found in a partial survey of patent literature (167).

We will briefly view the types of ionizing radiations, the general nature of their interactions with organic polymers, and the units of the resultant energy absorption. The gross effects of "degradation" and crosslinking of polymer molecules will be mentioned and a correlation of the relative extent of these processes to the chemical structure of the polymer chains will be indicated. Following a survey of measurement methods employed to reveal radiation-induced changes in polymers we will study in some detail the changes observed in specific polymers and polymer families. The division of the subject according to chemical compound type rather than according to chemical reaction type (e.g., dehydrogenation, oxidation, decarboxylation, etc.) is desirable. Many different reactions can and do occur simultaneously in a polymer undergoing irradiation. The correlation of these reactions with the peculiar structures of the polymer can be more instructive than the creation of tenuous theoretical bridges for each reaction type. However, some general theories will be noted.

2. High Energy Radiations and Their Interactions with Polymers

High energy radiations may be classified as electromagnetic (nonparticulate) and particulate. Of the former, γ-radiations and x-radiations should be mentioned. The particulate radiations are electrically charged (α particles, β particles, protons, deuterons, high energy electrons, etc.) or electrically neutral (neutrons). Reasonably extensive descriptions of the nature of these radiations, their sources, and their interactions with polymers have been published (168,169). Considering the diversity of the radiation types, energies, intensities, energy transfer efficiencies, and sources, it is at first surprising that the effects produced in a pure polymer by the absorption of a given amount of energy per gram are usually independent of these factors. The reasons for this approximate independence are twofold.

First, each radiation transfers energy to a polymer principally by ionization (ejection of electrons from molecular orbitals) and by subionizing excitation of the orbital electrons. High energy neutrons and to some extent massive charged-particle radiations achieve this by secondary means through the dislodgement of charged atoms (e.g., protons) by inelastic collisions. Ionization and subionizing excitation are of comparable magnitude in the dissipation of radiant energy and total to an average of approximately 34.5 e.v. (electron volts) per ion pair produced. Most of the ion pair formation is accomplished by the initially ejected electrons which ionize and excite molecules along their paths before slowing down and being captured by positive ion sites. Since 1 e.v. per molecule is equivalent to 23.05 kcal./mole, it is obvious that at a neutralization site there is sufficient energy available to cleave many chemical bonds. A large part of this cleavage should be homolytic, thus yielding free radical species capable of undergoing their characteristic reactions. Due to the large amount of available energy, some nonradical, molecular detachment reactions are also possible.

The second reason for the approximate equality of chemical effects in bulk polymers undergoing irradiations of different types and intensities is the apparent short kinetic reaction chain length, or "caged" reaction, which exists. This depresses the effect of concentration of reactive species upon the reaction efficiency. Therefore, densely ionizing radiations (α particles, protons, deuterons) which have a high linear energy transfer (L.E.T.) in the polymers do not exhibit greatly diminished chemical reaction efficiency within their tracks. Similarly, variation by many orders of magnitude in the intensities of penetrating radiations (γ-rays and x-rays) does not appreciably change the reaction efficiency on the basis of energy absorbed. The interaction between reactive species in different ionization tracks within solid polymers is not usually evident. When dose rate and L.E.T. effects are observed they may yield evidence valuable in formulation of hypotheses for reaction mechanism.

The relative importance of ionic and free radical reactions in polymers during irradiation continues to be debated. The majority of investigators have proposed reaction mechanisms involving free radical species. However, the feasibility of ionic and ion-molecular reaction paths has been demonstrated in the very dilute medium of the mass-spectrometer ionization chamber, and it has been proposed to exist in solid polymers. These reaction paths will be discussed briefly in Chapter IX-A.

In mixtures of two or more compounds, a given compound may be affected directly by the interaction of radiation with it or indirectly by radiation activation of the other compound(s) with subsequent energy transfer to, or reactive species attack upon, the compound of interest. The response of a polymer to radiation must be examined carefully in the light of contaminant or diluent presence. Air, free-radical inhibitors or traps, and other inadvertent or intentional inclusions may alter the effect of radiation. The radiation response of a plasticized polymer or a polymer in solution can differ markedly from that of the pure polymer. The influences of foreign compounds upon the reactions of a polymer undergoing irradiation will be cited as evidence for or against proposed reaction mechanisms.

Several radiation units exist. Of particular applicability to the present topic is the *rad*. A rad is the quantity of radiation which deposits 100 ergs (6.24×10^{13} electron volts) of energy within a gram of the material irradiated. A million rad (1 megarad) dose constitutes 10^8 ergs, 6.24×10^{19} e.v., or 2.4 cal. of energy absorbed per gram. Another unit which has been used in the past is the *rep* (roentgen equivalent physical) which corresponds to approximately 93 ergs/g. energy deposition in organic polymers. Dosimetry is achieved by calorimetric, ionization chamber, or chemical oxidation measurements.

In describing the efficiencies of radiation-induced reactions a quantity G(event) is commonly used. G(cleavage), for instance, is the number of cleavages of polymer chains produced per 100 e.v. of radiant energy absorbed by the polymer. Other quantities, E_d and E_c, corresponding to election volts absorbed per chain cleavage or per crosslinked unit formed, respectively, will also be employed here.

Among the effects of radiation on polymer molecules chain cleavage (scission, "degradation") and intermolecular chemical bonding (crosslinking, "curing") produce the most obvious bulk property changes. Methods of measuring these and other structural and chemical effects will now be mentioned.

3. Methods of Measurement

Each polymer chain on cleavage produces one new polymer molecule plus possibly several smaller molecules. Measurement of the polymer's number-average molecular weight, $\bar{M}_n$, as a function of energy absorption allows calculation of the number of cleavages and hence G(cleavage) or E_d (170). With proper corrections for the effect of molecular weight distribution, weight-average molecular weight, $\bar{M}_w$, from light scattering may be used. Intrinsic viscosities $[\eta]$ from solution measurements are useful if molecular weight distribution and crosslink-branching influences are taken into account (171–177). Crosslinking concurrent with cleavage complicates the counting of cleavages in any evaluation. If crosslinking predominates, i.e., there is more than one crosslinked unit formed for every two chain cleavages, an estimate of the cleavage efficiency can be obtained from the curve relating weight fraction of insoluble polymer with radiation dose after gelation (178). Infrared spectroscopy on irradiated polymers and resulting gases produced can give chemical information. Mass spectrometry has been used to identify gaseous products. Electron spin resonance (ESR) absorption is increasingly employed to study the transient free radicals (and radical-ions?) which are present during and after irradiation (179). Bulk mechanical properties such as modulus, tensile strength, ultimate elongation, hardness, brittle point, etc., have been extensively studied from some of the earliest broad investigations of radiation effects (180,181) to the most recent studies. Although of great importance to polymer technology, the quantitative translation of these results into information on specific molecular structure is difficult. Some such translation is possible, and the use of changes in bulk properties as evidence of general sensitivity to radiation is obvious. Nuclear magnetic resonance spectroscopy and x-ray analyses are also used to observe molecular mobility and alterations in morphology.

4. Polymer Structure and Effect of Radiation

A polymer may be classified according to whether the predominant effect of radiation upon it is chain cleavage or crosslinking. In most polymers both processes occur, but one overrides the other. An early classification revealed that vinyl polymers having unit structures —CH_2 CHR— undergo predominant chain-to-chain crosslinking upon irradiation. On the other hand, vinyl polymers of unit structure —CH_2CRR'— undergo predominant chain cleavage if neither R nor R′ is hydrogen (180–182). This chain instability was tentatively attributed to lack of resonance stabilization of the initial radical assumed to be formed by loss of hydrogen (183). Cleavage of the main chain gave structures in which resonance between a double bond formed and a side group was achieved in one fragment. However, the resulting radical —$CRR'CH_2\cdot$ was not resonance-stabilized.

A positive correlation between low heats of polymerization, readiness to depolymerize at elevated temperatures, and chain cleavage by radiation was noted (184). Steric hindrance was suggested as a factor in all three phenomena. Also for α-methyl polymers —$CH_2CR(CH_3)$—, the possibility of a hydrogen atom being abstracted from the α-methyl group to give —$CH_2CR(\dot{C}H_2)CH_2CR(CH_3)$— followed by rearrangement with cleavage to —$CH_2CR({=}CH_2)$ and $\cdot CH_2CR(CH_3)$— was hypothesized (184).

$$2\text{—}CH_2\underset{\underset{CH_3}{|}}{C}R\text{—} \rightarrow \text{—}CH_2\underset{\underset{\cdot CH_2}{|}}{C}RCH_2\underset{\underset{CH_3}{|}}{C}R\text{—} \rightarrow \text{—}CH_2\underset{\underset{CH_2}{\|}}{C}R + \cdot CH_2\underset{\underset{CH_3}{|}}{C}R \qquad (86)$$

Simple disproportionation at homolytic main-chain cleavages with hydrogen atom transfer was an early proposal (185) for α-methyl polymers (eq. 87).

$$\text{—}\overset{\overset{R}{|}}{\underset{\underset{CH_3}{|}}{C}}CH_2\overset{\overset{R}{|}}{\underset{\underset{CH_3}{|}}{C}}CH_2\text{—} \rightarrow \text{—}\overset{\overset{R}{|}}{C}(CH_3)_2 + CH_2{=}\overset{\overset{R}{|}}{C}CH_2\text{—} \qquad (87)$$

One proposed mechanism (186) associates the main-chain cleavage with the simultaneous loss of side chain elements through a transient 1,4-diradical state (eq. 88). The 1,4-diradical should instantaneously rear-

$$\text{—}CH_2CRR'CH_2CRR'CH_2CRR'\text{—} \rightarrow CH_2\dot{C}RCH_2CRR'\dot{C}HCRR'\text{—} + R'H^* \qquad (88)$$

$$\text{—}CH_2\dot{C}RCH_2CRR'\dot{C}HCRR'\text{—} \rightarrow \text{—}CH_2\underset{\underset{CH_2}{\|}}{C}R + CRR'{=}CHCRR'\text{—} \qquad (89)$$

range by electronic shifts to the stable fragments —$CH_2CR({=}CH_2)$ and $CRR'{=}CHCRR'$—. If R or R′ is a methyl group, both of the vinylidene endgroups formed may be of the type —$CH_2CR({=}CH_2)$. Recently it has been proposed that the initial step in chain cleavage is the loss of a hydrogen atom from the sterically shielded methylenic groups in the chain (187–189). This would lead to the radical —$CRR'\dot{C}HCRR'$—. Subsequent rearrangement with cleavage similar to the decomposition proposed previously (184) might then follow. The various proposed cleavage mechanisms will be referred to in the specific radiation-degradation discussions whenever supporting evidence appears.

Aside from the fairly well established classification of —CH_2CHR— and —CH_2CRR'— polymers into the categories of predominant crosslinking or cleaving, respectively, very few further general groupings have become evident. Copolymers composed of two monomer units which lead to crosslinking or cleavage in their respective homopolymers exhibit an intermediate response to radiation. Polymers from diene monomers preferentially crosslink. Perhalogenated carbon-chain polymers predominantly cleave. Polymers containing aromatic groups are less efficiently crosslinked or cleaved than are their aliphatic counterparts. Linear condensation polymers having functional groups in the backbone such as polyesters, polyamides, polyethers, etc., lie principally in the crosslinking category. Polysulfide rubbers are borderline cases. The carbohydrates are quite susceptible to chain cleavage.

In the following sections we will correlate and analyze in some detail the studies on cleavage of polymers by radiation conducted during the past decade. An emphasis will be placed upon those results which yield information concerning cleavage efficiencies and chemical changes. Changes in bulk properties will be mentioned only insofar as they allow alteration in interpretation of molecular structure.

5. Polymethacrylates

The polymethacrylates and in particular poly(methyl methacrylate) have been the most thoroughly investigated of all the radiation-degraded polymers. This family will therefore serve well as an introduction to the radiation cleavage of polymeric chains.

a. Poly(methyl Methacrylate)

It was early established that poly(methyl methacrylate) (PMMA) underwent random chain cleavage when subjected to ionizing radiations (181,182,190–194). Analysis of decrease in molecular weight of the polymer as a function of radiation dose has revealed an energy absorption per chain cleavage for Co^{60} γ-irradiated PMMA of $E_d = 61$ e.v. (185) and 59 e.v. (195). $E_d = 59$ e.v. was calculated for PMMA irradiated with 1-M.e.v. peak electrons near room temperature (175). E_d values ranging from 50 to 81 e.v. were reported for γ-irradiated PMMA samples which had undergone prior heat treatment at 100°C. under vacuum (196). A recent study found $E_d = 83$ e.v. for PMMA irradiated *in vacuo* with γ-rays (188). Polonium α-particles are reported (197) to be very inefficient in PMMA chain cleavage with $E_d = 263$ e.v. Wasteful multiple cleavages within a short segment of a given polymer chain due to the high density of ionization sites in the α particle's path was proposed to explain this. Room temperature irradiations with 2 M.e.v. electrons and with γ-rays yielded $E_d = 55$ and 71 e.v., respectively (197). In summary, the experimental results show that PMMA irradiated *in vacuo* at room temperature by high energy electrons or gamma rays undergoes approximately one random chain cleavage for each 60 e.v. of radiant energy absorbed. Knowledge of this cleavage energy has allowed quantitative degradative analyses of the structure of crosslinked poly(methyl methacrylate) (198).

The efficiency of chain cleavage increases slightly with increasing temperature in the -196 to $+75$°C. range (185,197,199). The observed temperature dependence is definitely not exponential in $1/T$ and does not suggest possible thermally activated slow steps in the cleavage mechanism. Subtle changes in local mobility with temperature might account for the small temperature effect noted. However, we will find in later discussion of electron spin resonance data that the structure of the persistent free radical species is a function of temperature. The possible importance of this to cleavage stabilizations will be considered at that time.

Despite early indications to the contrary (185), it has been established that the presence of air during irradiation decreases the apparent radiation cleavage of PMMA chains (195,199). It has been variously postulated that this decrease is due to peroxide bridging of incipient chain breaks (199), to peroxide crosslinking independent of the scission sites (195), or to an electron-trapping action of oxygen molecules to give O_2^- and consequent decrease in electronic degradative processes (200). A somewhat similar electron trapping mechanism was suggested to explain oxygen competition with dye molecules in irradiated PMMA (201). The presence in PMMA irradiated in air of groups whose decomposition is accelerated by traces of *tert*-butyl catechol, hydroquinone, or dimethylaniline and whose presence initiates vinyl polymerization lends some support to the peroxide hypotheses (193,194,196,199). Admission of air to PMMA powder which has been irradiated *in vacuo* causes the superposition of an asymmetric electron spin resonance spectrum, attributed to a peroxy radical, upon the original symmetric five-line (plus four shoulders) ESR radical spectrum (202). The spectra of both the initial and the peroxy radical proceed to decay according to second-order kinetics. The course of reaction from the peroxy radicals to the postulated peroxide bridges is not known. The post-irradiation decrease of molecular weight with time in PMMA has been measured recently and several of the possible mechanisms were discussed (203).

The addition of compounds such as allylthiourea, aniline, benzoquinone, or 8-hydroxyquinoline decreases the chain cleavage of PMMA by radiation (185,204,205). The protective action was believed to be accomplished principally by direct action through energy transfer rather than by competition for free radicals. This energy transfer caused little chemical change in naphthalene, but contributed to the destruction of 8-hydroxyquinoline (206). No chemical "bridging" of chain cleavages by naphthalene was found by analysis of the irradiated PMMA chains for incorporated naphthalene. The protection was much less in dense ionization tracks (197). Incorporation of styrene as a comonomer in the polymer chain decreased PMMA degradation presumably by a similar energy transfer process (207). The intramolecular energy transfer may be more efficient, since the styrene units in a methyl methacrylate–styrene copolymer are less efficient in quenching the fluorescence of added terphenyl (208). Energy transport by both excited and ionized states has been proposed as the protective mechanism for PMMA with lead stearate or certain aromatic compounds as protectants (209). PMMA chains immersed in various solvent media during irradiation exhibited marked differences in cleavage efficiency (210,211). The protective effect of aromatic solvents may be chiefly through energy transfer, but the greatly enhanced chain cleavage in such solvents as carbon tetrachloride and chloroform must arise from free radical attack. Evidence of such attack was found in the attachment during irradiation of iodine and diphenylpicrylhydrazyl to the dissolved PMMA in numbers 10 to 70 times the number of chain scissions (210,212).

Gaseous decomposition products liberated from PMMA by irradiation have been analyzed by mass spectrometry (185,188,196,207). The principal gases are H_2, CO, CO_2, and CH_4. The composition of the mixture approximates the composition of the ester side groups $—CO_2CH_3$, or possibly HCO_2CH_3. Considerable differences are observed in the percentages reported although the overall agreement persists. Approximately the elements of one side chain group are liberated for each main chain cleavage counted (185,196). The yield may be slightly less than one for one (188), but the difference does not appear significant. Methyl formate was found to the extent of 5.5 mole-% (196) and 6.0 mole-% (188) of the evolved gas in the later studies. Heating the irradiated PMMA at 100°C. for 5 min. to assist gas diffusion from the sample increased the methyl formate percentage to 14.2, decreased the CO and CO_2 percentages, and made formaldehyde, methylal, and MMA monomer concentrations worthy of consideration (188). The heating was believed to liberate the true radiation-produced gaseous composition, although the possibility of thermal promotion of subsequent free radical reactions was discussed. Whether or not a side chain decomposition is directly associated with PMMA chain cleavage will now be considered in relation to proposed cleavage mechanisms.

As mentioned in the general discussion of polymer structure and radiation effect relationships, several mechanisms have been proposed for the chain cleavage of α-methyl polymers. Some of these do not assume correlation between side chain decomposition and backbone cleavage. Direct disproportionation of an excited chain section (eq. 90) was suggested (185).

$$-CH_2\underset{CH_3}{\overset{COOCH_3}{\underset{|}{\overset{|}{C}}}}- \rightarrow -CH_3 + \underset{CH_2}{\overset{COOCH_3}{\underset{\|}{\overset{|}{C}}}}- \qquad (90)$$

The loss of a hydrogen atom from the α-methyl group would lead to an unstabilized radical, $-CH_2C(\dot{C}H_2)(COOCH_3)-$, which might rearrange with cleavage (183) to give a new radical and a double bond in resonance with the ester group, $-\dot{C}H_2 + CH_2{=}C(COOCH_3)-$. The residual radical would have to be removed eventually by combination or disproportionation with another radical. These and other hypotheses (187,213) involving no side chain loss have been reviewed and criticized (214).

The one-to-one correspondence of chain cleavage and side chain decomposition has prompted three theories of cleavage that would lead to such correspondence. A rather violent instantaneous rupture of the main chain and nearby side chain groups with the formation of multiple radical sites has been proposed (214,215). The initial fragmentation and succeeding reactions produce the stabilized chain cleavage and the side chain products. A less complex concerted mechanism (186) with the simultaneous formation of an unstable 1,4-diradical intermediate and the elements of methyl formate

$$-CH_2\dot{C}(CH_3)CH_2C(\dot{C}H_2)(COOCH_3)CH_2- + HCOOCH_3$$

would seem more feasible. Electronic rearrangement of the diradical would give the stable chain cleavage

$$-CH_2C(CH_3)(=CH_2) + CH_2{=}C(COOCH_3)CH_2-$$

If the initial hydrogen atom removal in the concerted mechanism was from a methylenic group in the chain, this chain end would be CH_3C-

$(COOCH_3){=}CH{-}$. A recently postulated mechanism (188) starts with the loss of a hydrogen atom from a chain methylenic group,

$$-C(CH_3)(COOCH_3)\dot{C}HC(CH_3)(COOCH_3)CH_2-$$

which is followed by chain cleavage with a 1,3 hydrogen atom transfer to give an unsaturated end group and a chain radical,

$$-C(CH_3)(COOCH_3)CH{=}C(CH_3)(COOCH_3) + \cdot CH_2C(CH_3)(COOCH_3)-$$

The radical is then assumed to rearrange with formation of a double bond and expulsion of the side chain as a free radical, thus,

$$-C(CH_3)(COOCH_3)\dot{C}H_2 \rightarrow -C(CH_3)({=}CH_2) + \cdot COOCH_3 \qquad (91)$$

The reaction scheme is reasonable. It also leads to the same two unsaturated endgroups resulting from the 1,4-diradical mechanism. If these two endgroups are eventually verified experimentally the choice between the mechanisms may prove to be difficult. The connection of side chain decomposition to chain cleavage in PMMA and other α-methyl polymers is not proven, but at present it seems most likely.

Attempts to detect, identify, and measure intermediate radical species in irradiated polymers have markedly increased recently. Electrical property changes indicative of persistent "free electron" species are observed (216–218) in irradiated PMMA. A temporary optical polarization similar to the Kerr electrooptic effect is created in PMMA by electron irradiation (219). This may be the result of the primary beam or oriented space charges, but it is more likely due to transient secondary nonpaired electronic species. An early measurement (220) of electron paramagnetic resonance, ESR, in x-irradiated PMMA set the stage for extensive ESR spectral studies in recent years. An ESR spectrum consisting of a five-plus-four line fine structure is normally observed at room temperature and sometimes at low temperatures. This spectrum is ascribed (221) to the radical $-CH_2\dot{C}(CH_3)(COOCH_3)$ and is found to be independent of the radiation type (x-ray, γ-ray, ultraviolet light) and of the ester alkyl group. This is the normal propagating radical in polymerizing methyl methacrylate and it has been observed in high-conversion methyl methacrylate–ethylene dimethacrylate polymerizates (222). However, there is some evidence (223) that this radical may be formed in irradiated PMMA by the addition of traces of monomer to the originally produced radical species. Pure PMMA, especially at 77°K., may yield a broad-line ESR spectrum with poorly resolved fine structure. This could arise from a $\cdot COOCH_3$ radical (224) or from several unidentified radicals initially produced. A weak quintet spectrum was found (225) for PMMA γ-

irradiated at 77°K. A broad quintet was noted for poly(ethyl methacrylate) that had been irradiated and measured similarly. It was suggested that this might result from removal of hydrogen from the ethyl group, but, of course, a corresponding explanation of the PMMA quintet was not possible. Other references (226–230) describing ESR measurements on PMMA should be consulted to gain a perspective on the variation in results due to experimental conditions and, perhaps, to polymer purity. The presence of SO_2 during room temperature γ-irradiation of PMMA quenches persistent radical formation to the point that no ESR spectrum is measurable (231). Addition of the SO_2 to PMMA previously irradiated *in vacuo* gives reaction and a change of the original radical spectrum. The yield (radicals/100 e.v.) of measurable free radical species at room temperature in PMMA irradiated under vacuum conditions has been estimated as G(radical) = 2.5 (221), 0.16 (202), and ~0.02, as estimated (202) from earlier data (231a). The magnitude of these differences allows no direct correlation of chain cleavage efficiency, G(cleavage) = 1.66, with residual radical concentration. Indeed, the probability that these radicals originate in the cleavage process is questionable. Of the two or three radical species detected the one giving rise to the five-plus-four line spectrum could form by monomer addition to any initially formed radicals. Failure of methyl methacrylate to graft onto PMMA (232) by radiation suggests that these radicals are not attached to the PMMA chains. The monomer could be present in the original PMMA or be one of the radiation degradation products (188). The other radicals, a quintet and a singlet have not been satisfactorily identified. The decay rates of the long-lived radicals appear to be closely associated with the mobility of the chain segments (202,233).

b. Poly(methacrylic Acid)

Before proceeding to a discussion of radiation effects on polymethacrylates other than PMMA, a few remarks on the radiation degradation of the "parent" polymer, poly(methacrylic acid), are in order. The degradation of poly(methacrylic acid) (183) by radiation has been studied only slightly, and then principally in partially neutralized aqueous solutions (234–237). The main effect of radiation upon poly(methacrylic acid) in such solutions is most likely that of the indirect action of radiation-produced water fragments and active oxygenated species. Conceivable reactions have been reviewed (238) for this system. The G-

(cleavage) = 1.6 for the dissolved polymer happens to coincide well with the G(cleavage) = 1.66 for solid PMMA. In an ESR study of γ-irradiated solid poly(methacrylic acid) it has been suggested (225) that decarboxylation is the first step in chain cleavage. Some supporting evidence has appeared (224) for the production of $\cdot$COOH in poly(methacrylic acid) irradiated at 77°K.

c. *Other Polymethacrylates*

As one progresses up the series of poly(n-alkyl methacrylates) one observes an increase in the energy absorption, E_d, per apparent radiation-induced cleavage. Thus, the apparent E_d is 59 e.v. for PMMA (175), 75 e.v. for poly(ethyl methacrylate), and 146 e.v. for poly(n-butyl methacrylate) (186,195). The very long side chain polymers, poly(dodecyl methacrylate) and poly(octadecyl methacrylate), exhibit predominant crosslinking when irradiated and yield insoluble, infinite networks (186). In view of these observations a self-consistent theory of chain cleavage and crosslinking in polymethacrylates was postulated (195). It is assumed that the cleavage and crosslinking are independent of each other and each is proportional to the radiant energy absorbed. It is also assumed that the chain cleavage energy, E_d, of all the n-alkyl methacrylate polymers is a constant equal to 59 e.v. Then $1/E_d$(apparent) = (1/59) $[1-2(\alpha/\beta)]$, where $\alpha/\beta = E_d/E_c$ is the ratio of radiation-induced crosslinked units to radiation-induced chain cleavages. A linear plot was obtained for α/β versus $(n-1)$, the number of methylenic groups in the normal alkyl ester group. It was postulated that these methylenic groups provide the crosslinking sites. By interpolation and extrapolation of the relationship, E_d(apparent) values for poly(n-propyl methacrylate) and poly(n-pentyl methacrylate) should be 98 and 295 e.v., respectively. Poly(n-heptyl methacrylate) was predicted to exhibit predominant crosslinking and to yield gel. This has subsequently been proven experimentally (239). Poly(n-hexyl methacrylate), theoretically predicted to be "borderline" with respect to crosslinking predominance, was not gelled by a fairly large γ-radiation dose. Also *sec*-heptyl, *sec*-octyl, and *sec*-nonyl methacrylate polymers failed to gel at reasonable doses (239). This suggests that the crosslinking mechanism is not dependent only upon the number of methylenic groups in the side chain, but, as in the polyacrylate series (see Chapter IX-A), is inhibited by branching on the carbon attached to the ester oxygen. The influence of hydrogen atoms on this carbon was also demonstrated (240) in the aryl and alkaryl methacrylate polymers. Apparent E_d values of poly(benzyl methacrylate) and poly-(phenyl methacrylate) were found to be 711 and 228 e.v., respectively. A correlation exists between the ability of polymethacrylates to cross-link and to graft under irradiation (195,232). The failure of poly(methyl methacrylate) and poly(*tert*-butyl methacrylate) (E_d = 43 e.v.) (175) to serve as graft substrates is especially significant. It is reasonable to believe that the grafting sites and crosslinking sites are identical and reside in the side chains. Electron spin resonance spectra (225) at 77°K. of irradiated poly(ethyl methacrylate) and poly(*n*-butyl methacrylate) indicated a quintet and heptet line structure, respectively. These could correspond to the $—O\dot{C}HCH_3$ and $—OCH_2CH_2\dot{C}HCH_3$ radicals which would serve as crosslinking or grafting radicals. Irradiation of these polymers at room temperature gave no residual radical signals probably because the radicals coupled to yield crosslinks.

In summary, the self-consistent theory of competitive crosslinking and chain cleavage in polymethacrylates during irradiation appears to be well founded though not as yet proven.

Ultraviolet light also produces random chain cleavage in poly(methyl methacrylate). At elevated temperatures the cleavage initiates depolymerization (241). At room temperature stable cleavages result without appreciable depolymerization (209,242,243). Two of the studies gave comparable quantum yields for cleavage by 2537 A. light in air 0.017 (242) and 0.032 (209) while the third reported a much lower value of 0.0023 (243). Gases obtained (242) from the photolyzed PMMA film after heating at 110°C. were principally methyl methacrylate, methyl formate, and methanol with quantum yields 0.20, 0.145, and 0.483, respectively. When based on cleavage in the nonheated film this represents considerably more than one unit of chain decomposition per chain cleavage. The effect of post-heating may have been great. Gases analyzed without heating were chiefly methyl formate with lesser amounts of hydrogen, methane, carbon monoxide and carbon dioxide. This is very similar to the gas composition from ionizing radiation experiments except for less fragmentation of the methyl formate in the photolytic act. A very low gas yield, 0.23×10^{-3} molecules/quantum absorbed, has been reported (244) for PMMA irradiated with 3030–3130 A. wavelength light. There are as yet too few quantitative data on the photolysis of PMMA to permit formulation of a firm reaction mechanism. A continuing comparison of the effects of high energy radiation and ultraviolet light on this polymer will prove to be very advantageous.

6. Polymeric Hydrocarbons

a. Polyisobutylene

Polyisobutylene (PIB) and its partially unsaturated copolymer, butyl rubber, suffer degradation by random chain cleavage when subjected to ionizing radiations (180,182,245). This is in accord with the instability of polymers having quaternary carbon atoms in the main chain —CH_2-$C(CH_3)_2$— (183) and having low exothermal heats of polymerization accompanied by steric hindrances in the backbone (184). Under electron or γ-irradiation the absorbed energy per chain cleavage was found to be $E_d = 20$ e.v. at 20°C. A slight (nonexponential) temperature dependence of E_d was noted (246): −196°C., 45 e.v.; −80°C., 27 e.v.; 20°C., 20 e.v.; 70°C., 12 e.v.; 90°C., 10 e.v.

The presence of oxygen apparently has no effect on the efficiency of cleavage (246) and causes no readily detectable oxidation (247). Ultraviolet light absorption spectra of irradiated PIB have shown some indication of oxygenated species being formed independent of the cleavage process (205,246). Protection is afforded the isobutylene chain units by copolymerized styrene units (204,248). The protection is believed due to energy transfer, and some attempt has been made to estimate the effect of spatial separation upon the degree of protection afforded. PIB in solution in chloroform, carbon tetrachloride, carbon disulfide, or heptane was observed to undergo decomposition by direct radiation (249). The rate of chain cleavage was the same in these four solvents and corresponded to $E_d = 5.4$ e.v. If, indeed, free radical attack by the irradiated solvents does not cause chain cleavage, the greater cleavage rate must be ascribed to greater freedom of the chain to first form and then stabilize scission. This could be similar to the temperature effect in the bulk polymer. Dissolved oxygen, iodine, or diphenylpicrylhydrazyl (DPPH) did not affect the chain cleavage of PIB in the above solutions. In heptane, iodine and DPPH became chemically bonded to the PIB, indicating free radical reactivity of the polymer under γ-irradiation. The number of additive attachments was less than the number of chain cleavages. Benzene–heptane (1:1), disobutylene, and cyclohexene as solvents protected the PIB and increased its apparent E_d to 31, 40, and 56 e.v., respectively (249). Styrene monomer was found (250) to provide considerable protection for dissolved PIB, and the resultant radiation-induced polymerization indicated that both macroradicals and small radicals were created from the PIB.

Mass spectrometric analyses revealed methane, hydrogen, and isobutylene to be the only significant gases evolved during irradiation (246). The evolution of methane and hydrogen was proportional to the chain cleavage, but the rate of evolution of isobutylene increased with dose. The latter is assumed to arise from cleavages at original and radiation-produced chain ends. Infrared absorption corresponding to 1.87 vinylidene groups, $RR'C{=}CH_2$, per chain cleavage was observed (246).

Chain cleavage with disproportionation (eq. 92) was postulated as the

$$—CH_2C(CH_3)_2CH_2C(CH_3)_2— \rightarrow —CH_2C(CH_3)(=CH_2) + (CH_3)_3C— \quad (92)$$

mechanism for the radiation-induced decomposition (246). This would introduce one vinylidene group per scission. The remaining unsaturation was assumed to originate in side group cleavages and radical abstraction reactions not associated with the chain cleavage. Mechanisms (186, 188,214,215) associating the formation of gaseous products with the cleavage reaction seem more plausible to the present author. By the mechanism of concerted cleavage and expulsion of by-product gas (186) (eq. 93) two vinylidene groups and one methane molecule would result

$$—CH_2C(CH_3)_2CH_2C(CH_3)_2— \rightarrow$$
$$—CH_2C(CH_3)(=CH_2) + CH_4 + CH_2{=}C(CH_3)— \quad (93)$$

per scission. The possible source of hydrogen gas is not obvious in this mechanism (251). If it were formed from the excited CH_4 molecule leaving the 1,4-diradical site, other products such as ethylene and ethane would be expected. The observation of reactivity of PIB with radical species during irradiation (249) suggests that hydrogen atom losses and abstractions independent of the fundamental chain cleavage process may be occurring. On the other hand, an explanation of PIB free radical addition reactions in solution on the basis of partial macroradical formation, $—CH_2\dot{C}(CH_3)_2 + \cdot CH_2C(CH_3)_2—$, and partial molecular (disproportionation) cleavage, $—CH_2C(CH_3)(=CH_2) + (CH_3)_3(C—$, has been proposed (249). Although the mechanisms discussed usually consist of free radical reactions or molecular decompositions, ion-molecule reactions known to occur in hydrocarbons under special conditions (252–254) should not be completely overlooked. Such reactions will be inspected with regard to the response of polyethylene to radiation (Chapter IX-A).

The ESR absorption of PIB irradiated at −195°C. has been reported (189) to be a doublet which disappears completely upon warming to room temperature. This was logically interpreted to arise from the radical $—C(CH_3)_2\dot{C}HC(CH_3)_2—$. If this radical species is involved in the chain cleavage process the postulated mechanism (188) involving its decomposition has gained support. The appearance of such a radical, on the other hand, may be a clue to a hydrogen producing reaction which is independent of chain cleavage.

b. Poly-α-methylstyrene

Poly-α-methylstyrene is degraded by ionizing radiations (181,182). E_d values of 1660 and 770 e.v. (in air), respectively, were measured for γ-irradiated and 1-M.e.v. peak electron-irradiated poly-α-methylstyrene (255). A more extensive study (256) with Co^{60} γ-radiations at room temperature with various atmospheres has revealed the following E_d values: 400 e.v. (in vacuum); 417 e.v. (H_2, 1 atm.); 625 e.v. (air, 1 atm.); 1250 e.v. (O_2, 1 atm.).

Gas analysis together with monomer determination by bromine titration and infrared absorption, showed the principal low molecular weight degradation product to be monomeric α-methylstyrene (256). At room temperature under vacuum the monomer yield was 100 molecules per chain cleavage indicating extensive depropagation following initial chain rupture. A theory of random breaking of skeletal bonds with depropagation and chain transfer was formulated. If chain cleavage is associated with side chain decomposition in poly-α-methylstyrene, as it is proposed to be in PMMA and PIB, one would expect to find approximately one benzene molecule formed per cleavage. Whether this occurred and was not detected as a minor by-product is not known. Degradation and crosslinking of styrene–α-methylstyrene copolymers revealed additivity of these effects on a mole-fraction basis (257). No preferential protection was expected since the two units would presumably have similar abilities for energy dissipation.

Electron spin resonance spectra of γ-irradiated poly-α-methylstyrene (258) had a four-peak pattern which was ascribed to the normal chain-propagating species, $—CH_2\dot{C}(CH_3)(C_6H_5)$. The methyl group was thought to be relatively free to rotate, and no appreciable hyperfine interactions with the methylenic groups in the chain exist if the assignment is correct. G(radical) = 0.05 at 77°K. and G(radical) = 0.015 at 300°K. If it is assumed that the radical observed is associated with chain cleavage, the energy absorption 100/0.05 = 2000 e.v. per radical produced at 77°K. is not exorbitant if, even at such a low temperature, about $^2/_3$ of the radicals are not stabilized. However, the radical $—C(CH_3)(C_6H_5)\dot{C}H_2$ which would be the other radical expected from simple homolytic cleavage of the chain was not detected. As in the case of the polymethacrylates, whether the propagating radical observed is a primary scission product or is formed by monomer addition to initial radicals is difficult to ascertain.

Photolysis of poly-α-methylstyrene with near-ultraviolet light under vacuum (259) gave chain cleavage and slight depropagation. The quantum yield for photolysis at 27°C. was approximately 0.02. About seven monomer units were liberated per chain cleavage. This is much less than the one hundred monomer units liberated per chain scission in γ-induced radiolysis (256) and may suggest excess energy availability under the latter conditions to sustain the depropagation. Volatile products of photolysis at 115°C. in order of decreasing quantum yield were H_2, CO_2, CO, acetylene, ethylene, isobutene, methane, ethane, propene, butanes, and pentanes. It was postulated that the surprising presence of CO_2 and CO, whose sum of molecules approximately equalled the number of chain cleavages, might have been derived from photolytically labile units incorporated into the polymer chains. Further data will be necessary to determine if this is so, and to determine the similarities or differences existing between radiolytic (high energy) and photolytic degradation mechanisms of poly-α-methylstyrene.

7. Halogen-Containing Polymers

a. Polytetrafluoroethylene

Polytetrafluoroethylene (PTFE) was classified early in radiation studies as one of the most readily degraded polymers. A lack of simple methods for determining molecular weight changes in PTFE has forestalled quantitative measurement of E_d. Decreases in mechanical strength (181,260–264), decreases in melt viscosity and melt tensile failure (265–268) and increases in crystallinity (267,268) have been used to infer a low E_d, i.e., efficient chain cleavage, of PTFE by ionizing radiations. Nuclear magnetic resonance studies of deuteron-irradiated PTFE (269) revealed an appreciable increase relative to nonirradiated PTFE in the absorption line-width and second moment above −75°C. where segmental motional narrowing occurs. This might be due to new bond formation (cross-linking) or merely to increased crystallinity. Structure alteration in PTFE by radiation has been demonstrated by irreversible increases in the permeability and solubility of argon (270). Reversible permeability increases for gases in PTFE during irradiation are ascribed to an increase in gas diffusion coefficients rather than to an increase in solubility (271).

Permanent electrical insulating damage produced in PTFE by ionizing radiation has been reported to be considerable (272). However, after removal of 4 and 8 mil specimens from γ-irradiation to 5.7×10^7 rad the bulk resistivity has been reported to increase steadily toward its preirradiation value (273). Also the dielectric strengths of 3, 5, and 11 mil specimens were not significantly changed. Irradiation and test condition differences may be responsible for the disagreement. During irradiation the volume resistivity can readily be reduced by three orders of magnitude (273,274). The induced conductivity during irradiation has been found proportional to the 0.63 power (274) or to the 1.0 power (275) of the radiation intensity. In the latter study less temperature dependence of the induced conductivity was noted, and the charge carriers were believed to be electronic rather than ionic.

In spite of the high C—F bond strength, radiation apparently releases copious amounts of fluorine from PTFE (276–279). Fluorine, titrated as fluoride ion in dilute aqueous sodium hydroxide, was produced according to the relation, $X = 3.78 \times 10^{-7} Y^{1.151}$, where X is micrograms of fluorine per gram of PTFE and Y is the dose in roentgens (278). In a later study (279) a similar expression for fluorine evolution was obtained with the exponent of Y equal to 1.2. The increasing efficiency of C—F scission with increased dose is probably real, but increased permeability of the more highly irradiated samples (270) could account for greater accessibility of the evolved fluorine. Associated with fluorine evolution were infrared absorption band formations in the polymer at 1754 and 1538 cm.$^{-1}$ attributed to —CF═CF— and —CF═CF_2, respectively. Mass spectrometry and infrared spectroscopy of gases evolved from PTFE irradiated *in vacuo* with 4-M.e.v. electrons (276) and Co^{60} γ-rays (277) gave positive identification of CF_4, C_2F_6, C_3F_8, and SiF_4 (by attack of fluorine on the containing vessel) with other saturated fluorocarbon products up to C_6 compounds. The average G values up to 10^8 rad for C_1, C_2, C_3, and C_4 fluorocarbon gases were reported to be 0.12, 0.03, 0.002, and 0.004, respectively (277). The PTFE weight loss during pile irradiation was found proportional to the square of the radiation dose (262). This correlates neither with fluorine evolution nor with normal proportionality of polymer chain cleavage to the first power of the dose. The infrared absorption bands in irradiated PTFE previously reported (278) were not found, but two bands at 982 and 1350 cm.$^{-1}$ appeared (276). These bands were not assigned definitely, although the former was thought possibly due to a branch point vibration.

The mechanism of chain cleavage in PTFE remains obscure. Initial random formation of primary —$CF\dot{C}F_2$ and secondary —$CF_2\dot{C}FCF_2$— radicals by C—C and C—F bond scissions followed by addition of fluorine atoms has been suggested (276). Attack of fluorine atoms upon the polymer backbone to produce cleavage is another possibility (277). Steric interference and strains in PTFE chains may favor chain cleavage and discourage crosslinking (279a,280). Electron spin resonance studies (265,281–284) have revealed at least two persistent radicals in irradiated PTFE. The presence of a triplet due to $—CF_2\dot{C}F_2$ (283,285) and a double quintet due to $—CF_2\dot{C}FCF_2—$ (282) have been fairly well established. The triplet has also been attributed to $—CF_2CF_2O\cdot$ arising from traces of oxygen (286). Evidence for this radical species appeared in the formation of CF_2O gas when PTFE was irradiated in air (276). Some crosslinking or branching by reactions of $—CF_2\dot{C}FCF_2—$ radicals has been tentatively proposed (287), but this cannot be very prevalent. Crosslinking of PTFE to other polymers by the localized action of neutrons on lithium- or boron-containing interlayers has been reported (288).

The presence of oxygen greatly increases the radiation-cleavage of PTFE. Rigorous outgassing of PTFE prior to γ-irradiation gave samples which still retained 43% of their original tensile strength at a dose eight times that required to cause "zero" tensile when the irradiation was in the presence of air (265,287). Surface oxidation of PTFE during irradiation has been inferred from the lowering of contact angles of aqueous base droplets on the surface (289). The kinetics of the formation of peroxy radicals believed to be $—CF_2(CFOO\cdot)CF_2—$ and $—CF_2CF_2OO\cdot$ have been studied (286,290). The former peroxy radical was found to form and decompose reversibly. Similarly, with NO, ESR spectra indicated the reversible reaction

$$—CF_2\dot{C}FCF_2— + NO \rightleftharpoons —CF_2(CFNO\cdot)CF_2— \tag{94}$$

Following changes in the ESR spectra of irradiated PTFE has permitted evaluation of the kinetics of oxygen diffusion in the polymer and has yielded some rate constants and equilibrium constants for peroxide formation and decomposition (291,292).

Despite the difficulty of the initial fluorocarbon radicals to crosslink or recombine, such reactions seem to occur. The apparent rate constant and activation energy for disappearance of radicals by recombination were found to vary widely among samples (293). It was speculated that the variations were due to differences in crystallinity. Rather than a continuous increase in the rate of radical disappearance, two distinct temperature regions for radical decay have been reported (285). The lower temperature region, 70–100° C., corresponding to onset of appreciable segmental motion in the amorphous regions of PTFE provided about 60% decrease of the ESR signal. The second region, above about 180° C., was thought to represent radical decay in the crystalline regions (PTFE m.p. = 327° C.).

At present it appears that several reactions contribute to the chain cleavage of PTFE. The vigorous research now proceeding in this field may isolate the principal cleavage mechanism or mechanisms in the near future.

b. Other Halogen-Containing Polymers

In comparison to the numerous studies of radiation effects in PTFE the research on other radiation-degraded halogen-containing polymers has been slight.

Polychlorotrifluoroethylene having a unit structure —CF_2CFCl— quite similar to PTFE also undergoes chain cleavage by radiation (181,182). Its reduction in tensile strength to one-half its initial value required about eight times the dose necessary for a similar reduction in PTFE (181). This indicates somewhat less radiation sensitivity than that possessed by PTFE, but the efficiency of chain cleavage is still high. Chlorine and fluorine, analyzed as fluoride and chloride ions in aqueous base, were evolved in nearly equal amounts from γ-irradiated polychlorotrifluoroethylene (294). The C—Cl bond therefore appears to be approximately three times as labile as the C—F bond. The *G* value for total halogen produced was about 5, which is roughly three times the *G* value for fluorine from PTFE. Although the scatter of data was great, there was good indication that rate of evolution of halogen increased with dose. The radiation dose required to cause dielectric breakdown of the polymer under beta irradiation in air has been found to increase with the square root of the radiation intensity (295). The complexity introduced by air diffusion, chain cleavage, and mechanical changes in the film makes analysis of the results from dielectric breakdown difficult. It should further be considered that the efficiencies of formation of HF and HCl from the polymer fragmentation and hydrolysis may be diffusion controlled. The resultant conductive species can contribute strongly to dielectric breakdown.

Poly(vinylidene chloride) suffers predominant main chain cleavage under irradiation (182). Vinyl chloride–vinylidene chloride copolymers respond similarly with rapid degradation of mechanical properties (181,261). It is not known to what extent concurrent crosslinking occurs in the copolymer. Radiation-induced absorption of visible light (181,296) by the copolymer was noted. Increase in optical density at 2600 A. wavelength of 1 mil copolymer films irradiated in air has been suggested as a dosimetry method for Co^{60} γ-radiation (297). In the range 5×10^4–1×10^7 r the relation $r = 1.1 \times 10^7 \Delta^{4/3}$ was found, where r is the dose in roentgens and Δ is the increase in optical density at 2600 A. The increase in absorption appeared independent of dose rate, but the optical densities increased with time after exposure to saturation values at about 100 hr. The greater than first-power dependence of the chromophore on the radiation dose is reminiscent of the similar relation of halogen production in the perhalogenated polymers. Although the groups responsible for the ultraviolet light absorption were not identified (297), they are probably C=C bonds produced by chain cleavage and by dehydrochlorination. The expected byproduct of cleavage associated with "side-chain" decomposition would be HCl.

The random chain cleavage of trifluoronitrosomethane–tetrafluoroethylene copolymer, —$CF_2N(CF_3)OCF_2$—, by γ-radiation has been studied (298). The energy per chain cleavage is $E_d = 44$ e.v. Analyses of the gaseous degradation products revealed equimolar amounts of CF_2O and $CF_3N{=}CF_2$ evolved. These are the same gases that result from thermal degradation (248,299), and they are postulated to arise from the initial cleavage of the N—O bond followed by a short "depropagation" chain. Ultraviolet light (2537 A.) was found to cause similar cleavage and evolution of gas with a quantum yield for cleavage of 0.91×10^{-3} scissions/photon (298).

8. Cellulose and Related Polymers

The most important, as yet unmentioned, polymers which undergo predominant scission by ionizing radiations are cellulose and the other cellulosics (300,301). Early work revealed that cellulose was chiefly degraded by radiation (182,302–304). Chain cleavage was indicated to occur equally as efficiently in the crystalline portions as in the noncrystalline portions (304). An analysis of solution viscosity data yielded $E_d = 9$ e.v. for irradiated cellulose (305,306). This is the lowest reported energy per chain cleavage of any polymer. Approximately one glucosyl unit is destroyed per chain cleavage, and it has been postulated that scission of the 1,4-acetal bond is the most likely reaction of chain breaking (300). One carboxyl group formation per chain break has been reported (307–309). It is logical to assume, although as yet unproven, that the carboxyl group constitutes one of the chain ends resulting from cleavage. About twenty carbonyl groups are formed per chain cleavage (308). These obviously do not result from chain cleavage. Their formation most likely stems from glucosyl ring cleavages which, by internal disproportionation, can give $R_2C{=}O$ groups without chain rupture.

An atmosphere of oxygen as compared to nitrogen increases the chain cleavage, carboxyl group formation, and carbonyl group formation only slightly (308). Contradicting evidence (310) based upon heats of wetting cellulose fibers has led to the inference that "oxidative degradation" of the cellulose was greater for fibers γ-irradiated in air than for those irradiated in a vacuum. Comparison of dyeing characteristics has suggested (311) that γ-radiation gave only the effect of oxidation of cellulose while γ-radiation plus neutron radiation gave also the effect of hydrolysis of cellulose. In weighing such evidences as these based upon physical effects it is well to remember that morphological changes due to crystallinity alteration and changes in internal surface area can be very important. Direct chemical analyses and molecular weight assays are more readily correlated to the actual radiation-induced reactions. Further studies of changes in properties of cellulose as functions of ionizing radiation treatment under varied conditions are available (312–314).

Irradiated cellulose (231,315) and similar highly crystalline compounds (231,315–317) possess ESR spectra indicative of very persistent free radicals. These radicals are believed to be kept from reaction by the hydrogen-bonded crystal structures which prevent the penetration or contacting of possible reactants. The ESR absorptions decay rapidly near the melting points of the crystals or in the presence of water (315). These residual radicals are the most probable sources of post-irradiation degradation of cellulose and pectin (318,319), and of monomer grafting sites on irradiated cellulose (312,315).

Like the parent, cellulose, cellulose derivatives also exhibit chain cleavage by radiation (181,214,303,320,321). It has not been quantitatively ascertained if the various substituent groups produced specific protective, accelerative, or crosslinking effects. By means of the indirect action of water radiolysis, water-soluble, nonionic cellulose derivatives have been crosslinked (322,323). Sodium carboxymethylcellulose, on the other hand, degraded in aqueous solution (324). This may be due to ionic repulsions between the polymer chains preventing the close approach necessary to couple radicals which are produced on the chains. Irradiation of cellulose acetate plasticized with triallyl citrate produces a cellulose acetate–poly(allyl citrate) graft copolymer, presumably both by radical initiation from the cellulose acetate and by chain transfer to the cellulose acetate chains (325). The linking of cellulose acetate into a polymerizing system is not surprising since a polymerization chain reaction is a very efficient radiation-chemical process. However, the crosslinking to gelation of cellulose derivatives in aqueous solution by short radical chain reactions is remarkable considering the low E_d of the competing chain-cleavage process.

Dextran, principally a chain of α-1,6-glucosyl units with occasional branching at the 3-position, is degraded by ionizing radiations (326,327). The apparent energy per cleavage E_d = 130 e.v. calculated (328) from molecular weight by light scattering (326) on electron-irradiated dry dextran is much higher than that of cellulose (E_d = 9 e.v.). This suggested concurrent crosslinking of dextran by radiation (328). Simultaneous chain cleavage and crosslinking of dextran by γ-radiation has been reported recently, but a fairly low E_d = 19 e.v. was calculated (329). Highly branched original polymers were found to decrease in ramified structure, while initially lower branch-number polymers became more branched. Polymolecularity was reported to increase during degradation. This is surprising in light of the earlier study (326) and the fact that a polymer with an initially broad molecular weight distribution normally undergoes a narrowing of distribution if cleavage predominates over crosslinking.

The presence of air was found to increase degradation of dextran by radiation (326). Electron spin resonance spectra revealed very stable free radicals in irradiated dextran. A hypothesis for degradation was advanced assuming an initial radical ion formation followed by its dissociation into a positive ion and an alkoxy radical. The low molecular weight decomposition products of dextran in aqueous solution by γ-radiation include glucose, isomaltose, isomaltotriose, gluconic acid, glucoronic acid, glyoxal, erythrose, and glyceraldehyde, indicating complex breakdown of the chains (330). These analyses and similar analyses on radiation-degraded low molecular weight carbohydrates (331,332) may ultimately lead to establishing a mechanism or mechanisms of cleavage in aqueous media. Analyses of the decomposition products and transient species of the direct radiation effects on dry dextran will be needed for postulating modes of cleavage of the pure polymer.

9. Poly(vinyl Alcohol)

Poly(vinyl alcohol) (PVA) will be placed tentatively in the category of polymers undergoing predominant chain cleavage by radiation due to considerable recent evidence favoring this classification. The author is reluctant to do this since, if true, this is the only reported exception to the general rule that —CH_2CHR— polymers predominantly crosslink.

Either by irradiation in air or in a vacuum PVA was found to degrade, and carbonyl formation was observed (333). An apparent E_d = 110 e.v.

was found with γ-irradiation in air, and approximately one carbonyl and one carboxyl group were formed per molecule created (334). Oxygen played a partial role in these group formations. The γ-irradiation of PVA *in vacuo* yielded an apparent E_d = 100 e.v. and approximately 0.3 to 0.4 carbonyl and carboxyl groups, respectively, per chain cleavage (335). An inference from proton nuclear magnetic resonance data of some crosslinking in addition to chain cleavage in deuteron- and γ-irradiated PVA has been reported (336). These studies were extended to neutron radiation on PVA (337).

Crosslinking of PVA by radiation has been reported by others (338). Radiation-produced crosslinks in dry PVA were found susceptible to oxidative cleavage by periodic acid (339), suggesting coupling of $—CH_2\dot{C}(OH)CH_2—$ radicals to give the vicinal glycol structure $R_2C(OH)C(OH)R_2$. The crosslinking of PVA in aqueous solution is well established (338,340–345). Here the action of radiation is principally indirect. Contrary to crosslinks formed in PVA irradiated in the dry state, only part of those formed in PVA irradiated in water are oxidatively cleaved by periodic acid (339). This may indicate hydrogen atom abstraction (unlikely) to give $—\dot{C}HCH(OH)—$ radicals or loss of hydroxyl radical to give $—CH_2\dot{C}H—CH_2—$ radicals leading to crosslinking in aqueous solution. Special sensitivity to radiation of 1,2-glycol groups in the original PVA (either dry or in water) was also postulated (339). This is surprising since 1,2-glycol groups are the preferred stable products when low molecular weight alcohols are irradiated.

The classification of PVA according to predominant chain cleavage or crosslinking is still uncertain. If, indeed, PVA does predominantly degrade the hydrogen-bonded crystal structure which was postulated to stabilize radicals and possibly cleavages in cellulose may be a clue to its instability. The persistent stable free radicals in irradiated PVA have been studied (227, 231,346) by ESR. The disappearance of these radicals upon heating (346) may be a source of the post-irradiation thermal crosslinking of PVA (347) although the formation of ketal bonds was postulated as the principal mechanism in the latter study. It seems significant to the writer that PVA is the only vinyl polymer which upon depolymerization would not yield its monomer, $CH_2{=}CH(OH)$. The aldehyde-favored aldo-enol tautomerism may be a weakening factor in possible chain-stabilizing recombinations. The formation of water in the concerted mechanism for cleavage would be a reasonably strong thermodynamic driving force:

$$—CH_2CH(OH)CH_2CH(OH)CH_2CH(OH)— \rightarrow —CH_2CH{=}CH_2 + H_2O + O{=}CHCH_2CH(OH)— \quad (95)$$

By this mechanism one vinyl and one carbonyl group would form per cleavage. However, the observed carbonyls were believed to be ketonic (333). Carboxyl formation through hydroperoxide groups $-CH_2C(OH)(OOH)-CH_2-$, with subsequent cleavage and rearrangement, is conceivable in the case of available oxygen.

10. Miscellaneous Polymers

In addition to the above-discussed polymers there are a few other synthetic polymers which have been found to undergo predominant main chain cleavage by radiation. In many cases the evidence is nonconclusive. Degradation of mechanical properties is sometimes the only basis upon which classification is made. For reasonable completeness these polymers or polymer families will be mentioned.

Poly(methyl isopropenyl ketone) (PMIPK) is degraded by γ-radiation (348). An E_d of 84–94 e.v. was observed. This cleavage energy is somewhat higher than that of poly(methyl methacrylate). The $-CH_2C(CH_3)(COCH_3)-$ unit structure which contains the "quaternary" main chain carbon atom places this polymer in the expected classification. Ultraviolet light cleaves the polymer very efficiently (348) with a quantum yield for film in air of ϕ (2537 A.) = 0.22. Higher temperature photoinitiation of PMIPK depolymerization has also been described (349).

Polysulfide elastomers have been reported to degrade under irradiation (180,247,350). However, others have found them to be predominantly crosslinked (351) or only slowly both crosslinked and cleaved (352). It is likely that under stress and radiation, flow of crosslinked polysulfides would be observed due to chemical lability of the sulfide linkages. Although these polymers are mentioned here in the degrading category they certainly are borderline.

Judging from loss of mechanical strength poly(vinyl formal) and poly(vinyl butyral) predominantly undergo scission (181).

Thermosetting polymers, such as phenol–formaldehyde, urea–formaldehyde, and melamine–formaldehyde resins are classified as radiation-degraded based on deterioration of bulk properties (181). Aniline–formaldehyde resin, having the aromatic ring pendant on the crosslinked net, was found to be more resistant than the others (181,353). Epoxy coatings were observed to suffer radiation-degradation in air (354), but some crosslinking is also believed to occur (355). In categorizing the various thermoset families as predominantly radiation-degraded it must be remembered that the evidence is fragmentary. Numerous chemical structures, especially flexibilizing aliphatic chains, which can be incorporated into thermoset networks could readily lead to predominant crosslinking. Inclusion of thermosets *in toto* in the chain cleavage classification is done with reservation.

11. Conclusion

The amount of radiation research done on such polpmers as poly(methyl methacrylate), polyisobutylene, and polytetrafluoroethylene has been sufficient for some postulates of reaction mechanisms. None of the postulates have been completely verified although some would explain nearly all of the observed changes, e.g., chain cleavage, unsaturation production, and gaseous products. Hope for verifying present postulated mechanisms or postulating better mechanisms depends mainly on future work in three areas of research. First, more quantitative and thorough determinations of chain cleavages and ultimate products are necessary. Second, continued research on transient intermediate identifications and on their conversions to ultimate products is required. Finally, probing of the initial events transpiring in radiation interactions with organic molecules is of primary importance. Until it is made significantly clearer as to what primative processes initiate the reaction chains, hypotheses of reaction mechanisms will continue to lack firm bases.

The author wishes to acknowledge the encouragement of the Minnesota Mining and Manufacturing Company during the preparation of the above manuscript.

D. OZONIZATION

R. W. MURRAY and P. R. STORY

Bell Telephone Laboratories

1. The Ozonization Reaction

The greatest bulk of the literature concerning organic ozone chemistry consists of the reactions of ozone with unsaturated linkages, primarily the carbon–carbon double bond. Relatively little research has been reported on the reactions of ozone with saturated linkages. Bailey (356) has written an excellent review discussing both these general areas and covering the literature up to 1958. Consequently, only a brief sketch of the presently accepted mechanisms of ozone behavior, as they may influence our interpretations of ozone-polymer chemistry, will be presented here.

a. Cleavage of Unsaturated Linkages

Ozone reacts rapidly and usually quantitatively to cleave carbon–carbon double bonds and may produce ozonides, carbonyl compounds, and peroxides, depending on the reactant molecule and reaction conditions. The probable path of this reaction has been at least partially elucidated by Criegee and co-workers in a series of papers (357).

According to the Criegee mechanism, which is outlined in eq. (96), the first reaction intermediate is a primary ozonide (I) of uncertain structure but probably still retaining a carbon–carbon bond. A primary ozonide has never been isolated, but Criegee and Schröder (358) have recently demonstrated the presence of a primary ozonide in the ozonization of *trans*-di-*tert*-butylethylene. Indications are that a primary ozonide is not a necessary intermediate in every reaction. The primary ozonide (I) may then cleave to form the zwitterion (II) and the carbonyl moiety (III). Usually aldehydic carbonyl moieties will then recombine with the zwitterion to form the ordinary ozonide (IV). This path is not available to ketonic carbonyl moieties. If, however, a reactive solvent such as methanol is used, a methoxy hydroperoxide (V) may be formed. The zwitterion may also react with water in the same fashion. In most ozonolyses in inert solvents and particularly in the case of ketonic carbonyl moieties (III) dimeric (VI) or polymeric peroxides will be formed.

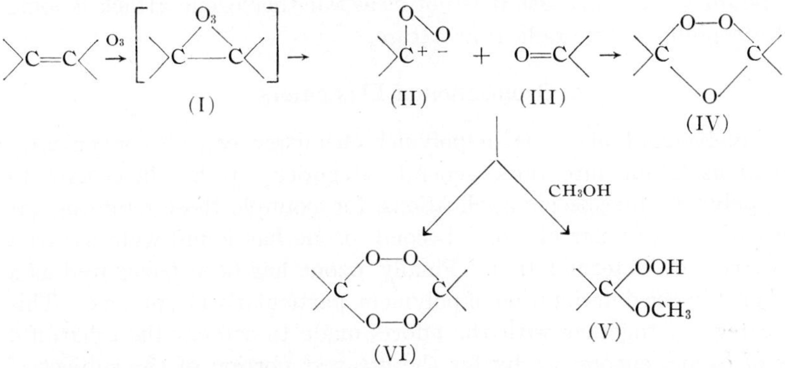

(96)

Early evidence indicated that ozone did not cleave carbon–nitrogen double bonds. Recently, however, Bailey (359) has shown that certain Schiff bases may be cleaved and that ozone appears to react as a nucleophile rather than as an electrophile as in reactions with the carbon–carbon double bond.

b. Reaction with Saturated Molecules

The reaction of ozone with saturated hydrocarbons, amines, alcohols, and sulfides has received comparatively little attention. Primary and secondary amines are decomposed by ozone, but the complex mixture of products obtained has made difficult the elucidation of the reaction mechanism and stoichiometry. Tertiary amines, on the other hand, are rapidly and nearly quantitatively converted to amine *N*-oxides by ozone (360). Both amines (361) and phosphites (362) have been used to reduce peroxy intermediates in the ozonization of carbon–carbon double bonds.

Ozone is less reactive toward saturated hydrocarbons, aldehydes, and ketones and appears to react by a different mechanism, possibly free radical. Briner (363) has shown that ozone is probably only an accelerating catalyst in the oxidation of aldehydes in the presence of oxygen. The mechanism of the catalysis is still unknown. However, in the reaction of ozone with methane, the prior decomposition of ozone to give highly reactive atomic oxygen is apparently ruled out (364). Ozone also serves to reduce or eliminate the induction period observed in many oxidations. For example, Hay, Eustance, and Blanchard (365) have initiated the cobalt-catalyzed oxidation of xylenes with ozone.

Barnard, McSweeney, and Smith (366) have demonstrated that ozone will decompose hydroperoxides to give the corresponding alcohol as the major product. In this case it is not clear whether ozone attack is ionic and electrophilic or free radical in nature.

2. Ozonization of Elastomers

The involvement of ozone in polymer chemistry can be conveniently looked at as falling into three general categories. It has been used to modify polymers for specific applications, for example those requiring the presence of surface polar groups. Second, ozone has found wide use as a tool in structure determination. Finally, ozone has been recognized as a prime agent in the deterioration of polymers, particularly elastomers. This latter category, together with the efforts made to combat these harmful effects of ozone, encompass by far the greatest portion of the subject of ozone in polymer chemistry. The discussion which follows covers the ozonization of elastomers. The ozonization of other polymers is considered in the succeeding section.

a. Determination of Structure

One of the earliest, most useful and important applications of ozone in the polymer field was its use by Harries (367,368) in 1904 to determine the structure of natural rubber. Harries found the major products of ozone cleavage of rubber to be levulinaldehyde and levulinic acid. On the basis of these results Harries proposed an eight-membered cyclic structure (VIII) for rubber. Harries' work was later repeated and confirmed by Pummerer (369,370).

```
CH3—C—CH2—CH2—CH
    ‖          ‖
   HC—CH2—CH2—C—CH3
```

(VIII)

The long chain polyisoprene model accepted today was suggested by Pickles (371) in 1910. The fact that only levulinaldehyde and levulinic acid were obtained from natural rubber indicated that it was regularly oriented. An irregular orientation would have produced some succinic aldehyde and acetonyl acetone in ozonolytic cleavage of the double bonds as shown in eqs. (97) and (98). In the original laboratory polymerizations of isoprene a

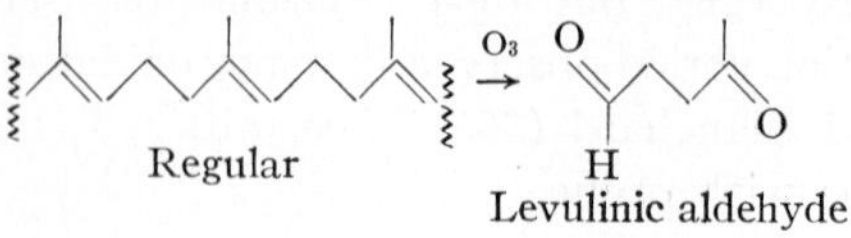

(97)

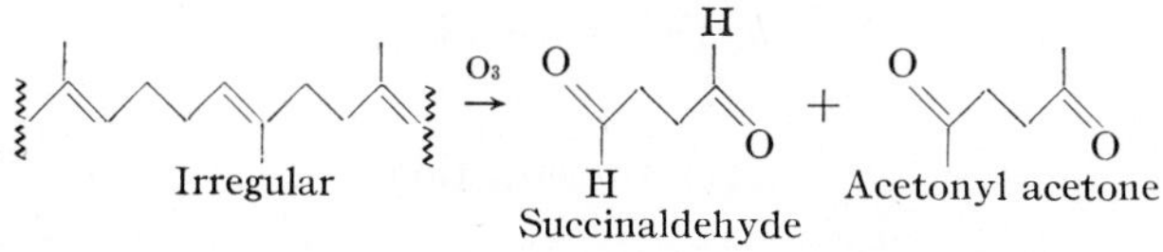

(98)

polyisoprene was obtained which was irregularly oriented and which gave succinic acid and acetonyl acetone as well as levulinic compounds when it was ozonized. Today, of course, we know that natural rubber has the *cis*-1,4-polyisoprene structure.

Harries' work was an isolated example of the use of ozone in the polymer field until relatively recent times. With the advent of numerous synthetic elastomers the usefulness of ozone as a tool in structure determination was again realized. Structural factors were thought to be correlated with the rubberlike properties of these synthetic materials, and hence structure determination received considerable attention. Ozonolysis of sodium-catalyzed butadiene polymer led Pummerer (372) to the conclusion that these polymers are formed with the occurrence of both 1,2 and 1,4 addition, with 1,2 addition predominating. Hill, Lewis, and Simonsen (373) used ozone to determine the structure of emulsion-polymerized polybutadiene and of butadiene–methyl methacrylate coplymer. This method of cleavage of double bonds with ozone was used by Alekseeva on butadiene–styrene (374) and butadiene–acrylonitrile copolymers (375) and by Klebanskii (376,377) on polychloroprene. Mochel and Nichols (378) used ozonolysis to determine the per cent 1,4 content of various polychloroprenes. Rabjohn and co-workers (379) used a similar technique to obtain structural information on styrene–butadiene copolymers. In a study of the copolymer of butadiene and *o*-chlorostyrene using the ozone cleavage technique, Marvel and Light (380) were able to determine that the styrene units are distributed randomly along the polymer chain. Rehner (381,382) has taken advantage of the ozone cleavage reaction to determine the degree of unsaturation in butyl rubbers. While these polymers are almost completely saturated, they contain a small amount of unsaturation which is essential for the vulcanization process. Rehner had previously shown (383) that this small degree of unsaturation could not be satisfactorily determined by conventional methods such as the addition of iodine monochloride. Yakubchik and co-workers (384,385) have used ozonolysis extensively to determine the structure of various butadiene rubbers. It was found, for example, that lithium-butadiene rubber has more 1,4 units than sodium-butadiene rubber. The lithium-butadiene type also showed better regularity of structure. Also the external double bonds of sodium-butadiene rubber ozonized more rapidly than the internal ones.

b. Ozone Cracking

(1) Introduction

The deterioration of rubber articles by atmospheric ozone is today a problem of major concern to the rubber industry. It has been known for many years that natural rubber under stress and exposed to the atmosphere develops cracks in a direction perpendicular to the direction of stress. Thompson (386) first reported that ozone generated in the laboratory could crack stretched vulcanized rubber. This type of cracking was originally thought by some to be due to oxygen or light or their combination. Williams (387) was the first to point out that this type of cracking is due to the action of ozone in the atmosphere. Haushalter (388) on the basis of his work on the effect of coronas on rubber, had earlier come to the conclusion that the cracking was caused by either the bombardment of gas ions or the action of ozone generated in the corona. It is now known that light and oxygen are involved only to the extent that light does convert a very small part of the atmospheric oxygen to ozone. Newton (389) carried out extensive work on the general problem of the factors essential in causing cracking. He concluded that ozone and strain in the sample are the only factors necessary to produce cracking.

In 1934, after completing a literature survey, Jackson (390) was convinced that light caused exposure cracking. Actually the results which led to this conclusion could be satisfactorily explained once it was realized that ozone was the real cause of cracking. Some workers (391,392) had found more severe cracking in tests conducted outdoors than in those conducted indoors. Here is an example where false conclusions with respect to the effects of light could be reached. Actually there were lower ozone concentrations in the indoor tests as well as reduced light intensity. Also ozone concentrations are normally higher in the spring and early summer than in the winter. Again this information could lead to erroneous conclusions as to the necessity of sunlight. Newton (389) also pointed out that a number of workers had erroneously concluded that light was essential for cracking to occur because they had experimental designs which excluded ozone as well as light. Newton was puzzled by some of his own results until he came to the realization that the cardboard boxes used in some of his experiments were absorbing ozone, as demonstrated by Ewell (393). Likewise Tener, Smith, and Holt (394) had concluded that sunlight was necessary in order to obtain cracking but they had used a black cloth to keep out the light and, at the same time, of course, had also excluded ozone. A similar misinterpretation was made by Asano (395) who concluded that ultraviolet light causes cracking because a sample which was covered with a piece of black paper did not crack. Reynolds (396) on the other hand, found that excluding light gave no change in the degree of cracking of rubber samples stretched in glass tubes through which air was drawn. Van Rossem and Talen (397) and Potter (398) found that samples exposed only at night cracked in the same manner as those exposed during daylight hours, thus clearly demonstrating that light is not essential to the cracking process.

Williams (387) had shown that light can actually decrease the extent of cracking by forming an oxidized layer on the rubber surface which protects the underlying material. In fact, the rate of skin formation could be increased by painting an oxidation catalyst on the surface of the rubber. The effect of this oxidized layer was also realized by Van Rossem and Talen (397), who found that more cracks were formed on the shaded side of a sample used for exposure testing. The sunny side presumably had formed a more complete protective layer and thus was less susceptible to cracking. The differences in cracking of rubbers with different colored pigments is also related to the existence of this protective surface skin. Shepard, Krall, and Morris (399) found that addition of small amounts of carbon black to white vulcanizates leads to more cracking. Turner (400) and Evans (392) made similar observations. These results were originally interpreted to indicate that white rubbers reflected the light and therefore did not crack. Dark or black rubbers, according to this view, absorbed the damaging light and so they cracked. Turner (400) provided an alternate interpretation of these facts, however. He reasoned that more light was actually present in the surface layer of light-colored rubbers because it passed through this layer once then was reflected back through again one or more times depending on whether there was any internal reflection. In a black rubber the light passes through once and then is absorbed. The net result of this process would be a thicker oxidized layer on the surface of light rubbers which would lead to a greater protection against cracking. However, the difference in dark and light rubbers could be explained on the grounds that the chromophores in dark rubbers act as a light screen and dissipate absorbed light energy by nondestructive paths. Turner demonstrated his explanation by exposing light and dark stretched rubbers with a half of each being shielded. In the light sample the shielded portion cracked and the light-exposed portion did not. In the black sample the degree of cracking was the same in both portions. It has also been suggested by Wurm (401), Ball and Bradley (402), Howard, and Boehmer (403), and Northam (404) that the ozone which causes this cracking is produced at the rubber surface by the action of ultraviolet light. This seems highly unlikely, since the wavelengths which can best produce ozone rarely reach the lower atmosphere.

For a time it was believed that atmospheric cracking was caused by oxygen. This view was expressed by Shepard, Krall, and Morris (399) and by Evans (392). Poor correlation between oxidation and aging in sunlight has been observed by Werkenthin et al. (405), however. Likewise, the possibility that heat causes cracking was also considered (399). Dawson and Scott (406) demonstrated, however, that stretched rubber does not crack when subjected to heat aging. This latter observation was also made by Kelly, Taylor, and Jones (407) and by Somerville, Ball, and Cope (408).

Some work has been done involving attempts to exclude ozone by filtering it out. Thus Reynolds (396) found that cracking could be prevented when the air used on his samples was first filtered through copper sulfate or chalk. Newton (389) found that filters of sawdust would absorb ozone, while filters of glass wool would decompose it at low flow rates.

In 1932 Dufraisse (409) offered an hypothesis to explain exposure cracking. According to this view particles of organic material in the air contain relatively volatile, reactive organic peroxides produced by irradiation from the sun. Dufraisse reasoned that when these particles settled on stretched rubber they would cause a peroxide attack similar to that caused by ozone. Dark reactions could be explained by assuming that the reactivity of the peroxides persisted for several hours. Newton (389) cites a number of reasons for rejecting the Dufraisse hypothesis, particularly the fact that cracking could not be induced by heating rubber surfaces with peroxides.

Many of the earlier workers failed to realize the small amount of ozone required to cause cracking or that these small amounts have a natural occurrence in the atmosphere. Duclaux (410), Merz (411), and Edgar and Paneth (412) all argued either that ozone does not exist in the atmosphere or that the small amount present is too small to cause the observed cracking. It is interesting, however, that in 1845 Schönbein (413), who discovered ozone, claimed that it was present in the normal atmosphere. The first clear demonstration that ozone actually existed in the atmosphere was not made until some 75 years after Schönbein's claim (414,415). The work of Williams (387) and Van Rossem and Talen (397) clearly established that atmospheric ozone was responsible for cracks in stretched rubber.

Ozone is constantly being produced in the stratosphere by the action of ultraviolet light on oxygen. Meetham has shown (416) that the ozone diffuses to the troposphere and then it is brought down to the earth's surface by winds. A balance is maintained between this transfer of ozone from the stratosphere and its destruction by organic matter, particularly gases. The dependence of the surface concentration of ozone upon the winds was shown by a number of workers, including Gluckauf and Paneth (417). Variations of atmospheric ozone concentrations with weather disturbances and the seasons has been studied by Dobson (418,419), Tonsberg and Chalonge (420), Gluckauf (421), and Wulf (422). Paetzold (423) has described a balloon ascent method which permits a more detailed analysis of the factors influencing ozone distribution. Generally speaking, the concentration of ozone in the atmosphere is from zero to 10 parts per hundred million. This is because ozone readily reacts with most organic materials such as wood and other types of vegetation so that its atmospheric concentration is reduced rapidly at the surface of the earth. Atmospheric ozone concentrations can be unusually high when atmospheric conditions cause direct downward air currents. Likewise, ozone concentrations may run high in coastal areas and at higher locations where normal deozonization is limited.

Ozone is also produced in electrical discharges, consequently it exists in higher concentrations around high voltage equipment. While the dependence of ozone concentration on discharge current and energy absorbed has been determined, the precise nature of the reaction producing the ozone is not well understood (424).

Normal atmospheric ozone concentrations vary greatly over the surface of the earth. In recent years, studies (425) have indicated that in some areas, particularly the Los Angeles area, ozone concentrations can run much higher than originally found. Concentrations of up to 12 parts per hundred million have been found in several cities (426). During periods of bad smog, Los Angeles was reported to have ozone concentrations of 50–90 parts per hundred million (427). Renzetti (428) has recently reviewed the work being done to determine atmospheric ozone concentrations in the Los Angeles area. These higher ozone concentrations have been linked to air pollution. The suggestion that the peroxide compounds, formed by the action of ozone on the unsaturated hydrocarbons contained in smog, are responsible for cracking has been refuted by Bartel and Temple (429). Peroxide fractions of Los Angeles smog, trapped by refrigeration, failed to induce cracking in rubber. Haagen-Smit (430, 431) has demonstrated that mixtures of low molecular weight hydrocarbons and nitrogen dioxide when present in low concentrations in air can generate ozone in photochemical reactions.

Today the unique deteriorating power of ozone is universally recognized. The fact that atmospheric concentrations of ozone are sufficient to explain the observed cracking is no longer questioned.

Some workers have assumed that ozone does not affect unstretched rubber. Considering the chemical nature of rubber this clearly cannot be the case. The fact that in some cases there are no obvious physical changes when unstretched rubber is exposed to ozone has undoubtedly led to erroneous conclusions. Kohman (432) found that when he exposed a sample of unstretched rubber to ozonized oxygen the rate of uptake of the ozonized oxygen was different from that for unozonized oxygen. The ozonized oxygen had an initially higher absorption and then fell to a lower absorption than that for pure oxygen. Also, the total uptake was less for the ozonized oxygen, leading Kohman to the conclusion that the reaction was not autocatalytic. The ozone seemed to be changing the surface of the rubber so that it was less susceptible to attack by oxygen. It was suggested that it might be possible to improve the aging of rubber by giving it a preliminary treatment with ozone.

Haushalter (433) and Haushalter, Jones, and Schade (434) have reported that the tensile strength of unstretched rubber does not decrease after prolonged exposure to high ozone concentrations. Also, Newton (389) exposed unstretched samples to ozone and found only very small absorptions of ozone. He concluded that a surface film of ozonide was formed which protected against further ozone attack. He felt that all of the unsaturation to a depth of 0.5 μ was destroyed by the ozone. Ozone can also attack saturated bonds, however, as shown by Briner et al. (435) and Durland and Adkins (436). Kendall and Mann (437), using a microscope technique, observed the formation of a white film on the surface of unstretched rubber exposed to ozone. This condition has been described as frosting (438). It is clear, therefore, that ozone does react with unstretched rubber although its affects are sometimes difficult to detect.

Care must be taken to distinguish between ozone-caused cracking which is characteristically perpendicular to the direction of strain and other types of cracking. These other types of cracking have been variously described as sun-checking, sun-cracking, light-oxidized cracking, alligatoring, crazing, and mud-cracking. In general these latter types are an irregular cracking whose exact cause is still a matter of dispute. This type of cracking usually forms in a resinous skin on the surface of the rubber instead of in the rubber itself. It can occur in both stretched and unstretched rubber. A summary of the differences between the two general types of cracking has been given by Morris et al. (439,440). Buist and Welding (441) have carefully distinguished between crazing and ozone cracking and have published photographs of the two phenomena occurring side by side in a tire. The essential differences between flex cracking and ozone cracking has been demonstrated by Thornley (442). Flex cracking and ozone cracking were found to depend in quite different ways on the stress–strain conditions set up when rubber is deformed.

Newton (389) has pointed out that when considering exposure cracking, three different phenomena must be carefully distinguished, namely, the rate of ozone attack, the rate of formation of cracks, and the rate of growth of cracks. He also suggested that the total phenomenon be called ozone cracking. Van Rossem and Talen (397) had earlier called the effect atmospheric cracking but Newton felt that this de-emphasized the role of the ozone.

While several days exposure to normal atmospheric concentrations are necessary to give visible cracks in stretched rubber, concentrations of approximately 0.1% of ozone will cause stretched rubber to crack and break almost immediately. Indeed, Albrecht (443) has called ozone the "chemical knife" because of the dramatic way that small concentrations of it can sever a stretched rubber band. The great importance of this undesirable cracking effect of ozone to commercial users of elastomers has prompted extensive research in this field in the last decade. Most of this effort has been devoted toward finding a means of combating the cracking phenomenon. To date the problem has not been completely eliminated, although means have been found to reduce the cracking effect of ozone. In some cases the success achieved has been quite rewarding. In general, the measures applied to eliminate or reduce ozone cracking are the use of waxes, the use of chemical antiozonants, and the use of combinations of waxes and antiozonants. In addition to these efforts manufacturers of articles containing elastomers have adopted design and production methods which tend to minimize the other element necessary to cause cracking, namely the presence of strain.

(2) Mechanism of Ozone Cracking

In recent years the fundamental nature of ozone cracking has received an increasing amount of attention by rubber research workers. Reviews of work in this field have been given by Biggs (444), Newton (389), and Crabtree and Kemp (445). Ozone cracks form randomly over the surface of an elastomer under stress, and Smith and Gough (446) have shown the growth of these cracks to be linear with time. Reduced to its simplest terms it seems almost certain that the phenomenon must involve cleavage of double bonds by ozone. The chain scission idea has been disputed by Tucker (447), however, who felt that because the entire rubber surface is under a uniform bombardment of ozone molecules, a directed chain scission process is unrealistic. Tucker explained cracking as being due to a change in the stress–strain characteristics of the reaction product with ozone as compared with the original rubber.

The research which has been carried out in this area has uncovered a number of facts which were not easily explained by the simple cleavage picture, however. For example, the fact that the ozone attack occurs at relatively few points was difficult to explain. Albrecht (443) has provided what seems to be a reasonable explanation for this observation. He suggests that once a crack is started at a point, the stress at that point is increased and further attack becomes concentrated there. Replica electron microscopy has been used to study the progressive reaction of ozone with surfaces of natural rubber (448). According to this work the surface degradation of unstrained rubber is at a rate which is consistent with diffusion of the ozone with simultaneous chemical reaction. This explanation says that this process of diffusion with reaction and the consequent formation of a degraded layer is the basic character of ozone attack on natural rubber surfaces. In a strained sample the greater rate of ozone penetration is attributed to the presence of stress-raising flaws which give rise to pits and fissures which penetrate into the rubber more rapidly than the diffusion boundary.

The fact that stressed elastomers crack whereas those in a relaxed state are almost completely unaffected must be related to the fundamental chemistry of the ozone–double bond reaction. Cuthbertson and Dunnom (449) suggested that rubber cleaves into radicals during the ozonization process and that in a strained rubber these radicals are prevented from recombining. Delman, Simms, and Ruff (450) have also attributed ozone degradation to a radical process except that they postulate a chain process which is initiated when an ozonide spontaneously decomposes to give radicals.

Crabtree and Biggs (451) have reported that certain free radicals produced in ultraviolet light irradiation of peroxides cause rubber to crack in a manner indistinguishable from ozone cracking. Biggs (444) points out that this latter observation does not mean that ozone is necessarily acting like a free radical but does suggest some similarity in mechanism. Later work indicates that free radicals themselves do not cause ozone-type cracking of a stressed rubber sample. The Crabtree and Biggs observation has been explained (451) by postulating the production of ozone from oxygen and free radicals produced by ultraviolet irradiation. This ozone would then be responsible for the observed cracking. This explanation was disputed by Layer (452).

Kearsley (453) explained cracking by saying that ozone formed a surface film which had little strength and would crack under strain. Van Rossem and Talen (397) disproved this by ozonizing strips of unstretched rubber and then stretching them without observing cracks. Tuley (454) explained cracking by assuming that the reaction product of ozone with rubber is a viscous liquid which would be weak and therefore would crack when strained. Smith and Gough (446), although primarily concerned with the mechanism of crack formation after the initial chemical act, agree that ozone attack at a double bond must cause scission. Also they agree with Newton (389) that normal recombination of the fragments produced in this scission is prevented when stress is applied, thus leading to the initiation of cracking. These latter workers devote considerable effort to developing a statistical theory of crack inception. The outlines of this theory had been laid down earlier by Powell and Gough (455). Smith and Gough postulated that a crack begins when a number of adjacent molecules are all strained and then attacked by ozone at the same time. The broken ends are then considered to be pulled too far apart for the usual recombination by kinetic motion so a crack forms. They further postulate that the highly strained extremities of the crack thus produced are pulled apart and so crack growth continues. Smith and Gough point out that this argument explains the reduced probability of new cracks since the mechanism suggested provides for stress release in the vicinity of already formed cracks. Newton (389) and Biggs (444) have suggested that ozonization involves a two-stage process with separation between fragments occurring between the two stages. In a strained rubber the second stage would be prevented from taking place and a crack develops. Newton (389) suggested that the two-stage process corresponded to the formation of an unstable ozonide followed by decomposition and rearrangement to a more stable product. Certainly the fact that an unstretched piece of rubber can absorb sufficient ozone to cause cracking if it were stretched and then, upon subsequent stretching, does not crack must be accounted for in the ultimate explanation for cracking. Story and Murray (456) have given a similar explanation which involves the Criegee (357) mechanism for the ozonization of a double bond. The Criegee mechanism, depicted in eq. (96), can explain the observed results if it is postulated that in a strained rubber the zwitterion (V) and carbonyl (VI) fragments are prevented from recombining to give the normal ozonide

(VII). This causes a break in the surface of the stretched rubber and exposes unsaturation in layers beneath the surface. Continuation of this process would lead to a visible crack.

(3) Evaluation of Cracking

(*a*) *General.* Attempts to evaluate the extent of cracking have led to the adoption of a number of experimental schemes. These schemes have been based on the number of cracks, the depth of the cracks or the volume of the cracks. Werkenthin (457), for example, measured the volume of cracks by rubbing a heavy powder into them and measuring the increase in weight. A similar scheme was used by Kalinsky and Werkenthin (458) using radioactive powder and counting the total activity. Cuthbertson and Dunnom (449) have inked a cracked sample and used it as a stamp to print the crack pattern on paper. This latter method, while providing a record of the cracks, does not really assess their extent. Rugg (459,460) has devised an evaluation technique which is somewhat quantitative. Using a twenty-power microscope equipped with a millimeter scale Rugg viewed a sample in cross section, measured the deepest cracks, and averaged their depths. Creed, Hill, and Breed (461) made use of observational standards to rate test samples. The standards were obtained by choosing samples of varying degrees of cracking and rating them from one to six in increasing severity of cracking. A similar scheme has been used by Edwards and Storey (462) with rating based on the number and depth of cracks. Shaw and Adams (463) used a technique whereby the loss in electrical conductivity of a stretched sample was measured. When cracking occurs there is a reduction in cross-sectional area, thus changing the conductivity and permitting the evaluation of the degree of cracking, particularly the depth. The principle of stress relaxation has been used to devise a number of different evaluation methods. Norton (464) evaluated cracking by hanging weights on rubber strips and measuring the time to fall of the weights. Thompson, Baker, and Brownlow (465) have used a similar method. Buckley and Robison (466) used a version in which increase in elongation at constant stress was measured during the test. Constant stress was obtained by holding the bottom of the sample rigid and attaching the top to a beam with a counterweight on its other end. Veith (467) has described a system using buckets containing lead shot to provide the elongation. The relaxation due to ozone exposure is then measured with a cathetometer. Eller and Stein (468) and Vodden and Wilson (469) have described an apparatus employing the principle of stress relaxation which permits quantitative measurement of the degradation of elastomers by ozone. Gable and Leeper (470) have studied the effect of antiozonants on the continuous creep of samples exposed to ozone.

Another general method of evaluation is based on determining the time required to detect the first cracks with a magnifying glass. A modification of this general method has been described in which the time for cracks to appear and time to failure is measured for several deformations, ozone concentrations, and over a range of temperature (471). This method requires considerable judgment and skill on the part of the observer. It has proved useful in actual operation over the years, however, and will probably continue to be used.

Buswell and Watts (472) have described an extensive investigation in which a number of factors affecting the static and dynamic ozone resistance of elastomers has been studied. These authors also discuss methods of evaluating ozone resistance. Ozone resistance was found to be a function of the type of polymer, the type and quantity of protective additive, the type and quantity of added filler, the type and degree of cure, the degree of aging, and finally the conditions of service.

Various kinds of samples have been used to study ozone cracking, but the ones most commonly used are modifications of dumbbell shapes. This type of sample was first used by Van Rossem and Talen (397) and permits a continual gradation of strain when the sample is stretched. Fielding (473) used long tapered strips and Edwards and Storey (462) used trapezoidal strips. These latter authors and Winkelmann (474) used samples which had been extruded with a triangular cross section. When these samples were bent in a loop, maximum strain was obtained at the apex of the triangle. In more recent work Cox (475) has reported on the results of extensive tests designed to measure ozone susceptibility as a function of sample geometry. As expected, shapes and geometries with large strains cracked faster.

Newton (476), Eccher (477), and Rainier and Gerke (478) have pointed out that ozone cracking has the same general appearance as that which occurs in the early stages of flex cracking. Newton (389) earlier had devised a quantitative way of assessing flex cracking by means of graded photographs, and these were adapted for use in the ozone cracking work. Another general method of evaluating cracks is by the use of various microscopic techniques. This method has been used by Van Rossem and Talen (397) and by Norton (464). The deteriorating effect of ozone can also be studied by following the change in a mechanical property, such as tensile strength. The application of this technique has been summarized by Werkenthin (405,479). This method does suffer from the disadvantage that a change in a mechanical property, which is related to total deterioration, may not be at all well correlated with surface cracking. In fact, Dawson and Scott (406) have shown that some samples of rubber with identical tensile strengths can be cracked or uncracked.

The resistance of the various kinds of rubber to cracking has been studied extensively (389). In the styrene–butadiene copolymers there does not seem to be a simple relationship between the butadiene content in the copolymer and resistance to cracking. Polyisoprene has been found to be more resistant than polybutadiene. When acrylonitrile is substituted for butadiene in the styrene copolymers the resistance to cracking shows a definite improvement. There are now available some commercial rubbers which are completely saturated and so almost completely resistant to ozone cracking. Among the unsaturated rubbers, resistance to ozone varies widely. Ossefort (480) has discussed a classification of rubbers based on ozone resistance. According to this classification rubbers can be divided into two large groups. The first group contains those rubbers which are inherently resistant to ozone. These are the saturated rubbers. The second group contains those rubbers whose resistance is a function of their compounding. This second group can be further divided into those which require a chemical antiozonant for ozone resistance and those which do not require this additive.

Neoprene gum stock which contains the same number of double bonds as natural rubber is quite ozone resistant, presumably because the reactivity of the double bond is reduced in the presence of the chlorine atom. In compounded neoprene containing plasticizers and pigments, however, this resistance is decreased somewhat (465,481). In butyl rubber the small amount of unsaturation present is reduced considerably during cure (482), so the finished product is quite ozone-resistant. The small amount of unsaturation remaining can be troublesome, however. Workers disagree on the exact ozone resistance of butyl rubbers (483,484), probably because of different conditions of cure.

The largest group of rubbers, the polybutadienes and polyisoprenes, are quite susceptible to ozone attack. Nitrile rubbers, which fall into this latter group, are generally considered to be quite susceptible to ozone attack although there is some disagreement on this point (485). The resistance of polyurethanes varies with their degree of unsaturation. The polysulfides, while not unsaturated, are susceptible to attack, presumably at the disulfide link. Hydropol, a hydrogenated polybutadiene (485), is quite ozone-resistant regardless of the amount of residual unsaturation it contains. This resistance has been explained in two ways. One explanation is that hydrogenation removes the most accessible double bonds, leaving only the inactive ones, so there can be no ozone attack. The second explanation suggests that the polymer may be the block variety, and ozone cleavage forms waxlike segments which then act to protect the surface from ozone. Adducts of mercaptans with elastomers vary widely in unsaturation and, hence, resistance to ozone attack. Pierson et al. (487) reported that mercaptan adduct rubbers that were only 69% saturated were as resistant as neoprene. Also Meyer, Naples, and Rice (488) reported that this type of rubber was actually superior to neoprene and butyl rubber when tested at high ozone concentrations.

Van Rossem and Talen (397) have shown that the influence of the degree of vulcanization on the formation of cracks could be attributed solely to mechanical properties, particularly the modulus. They found that the smaller the modulus the larger the cracks.

The formation of cracks and their manner of growth have received attention from a number of workers, including Norton (464), Powell and Gough (455), and Buist (489). Smith and Gough (446) gained some valuable information on the development of cracks by their use of time-lapse microphotography. By studying the motion picture produced from this technique these authors determined that cracks appear to form randomly over the surface of a strained sample. Some cracks were observed joining together and others disappearing. Also, crack formation continued up to a point after which no new cracks were formed. In fact, because of crack joining, the actual number of cracks actually decreased.

Although in most cases the cracks observed run in one direction, perpendicular to the direction of strain, there are a few reports of cracking of the mud crack or alligator type which should be attributed to ozone. Norton (464), for example, found that a rubber sheet stretched over a ball and exposed to ozone gave a cracking pattern of the mud crack type. Ossefort and Touhey (490) made a similar observation and concluded that when biaxial stresses are present ozone can cause a cracking which is difficult to distinguish from the mud crack type. Mud cracking is normally attributable to the effect of light, heat, or oxygen in outdoor weathering.

(*b*) *Influence of Strain.* The subject of the effect of stress on the degree of cracking has been examined by a number of workers, sometimes with conflicting results. Haushalter and co-workers (434) found that maximum loss of tensile strength occurs between 5 and 12% elongation, whereas the stresses needed to give the maximum losses of tensile strength were from 11 to 20 psi. Haushalter (433) had earlier found that the degree of cracking was more severe at 40 psi. Ball, Youmans, and Rausell (491) found that maximum cracking would occur at 15 or 50%, strain depending on the rubber used. Newton's work (389) showed that maximum cracking occurred between strains of 19 and 100% with stresses of 40–200 psi. depending on the particular compound used.

Most investigators who have studied ozone cracking are in agreement that the degree of cracking observed appears to be a function of strain. The general conclusion to be drawn is that maximum cracking occurs at some low value of strain and then decreases. Williams (387), for example, found maximum cracking to occur at 3 to 5% strain. Shepard, Krall, and Morris (399) found that, although there seemed to be a critical elongation to give maximum cracking, an increase in strain produced a large number of smaller cracks which were less visible than those produced at lower strains. Kearsley (453) made a similar observation, namely, that increasing the strain increased the number of cracks but decreased the size. Kearsley also showed that increasing the pigment loading of a rubber compound also increased the elongation necessary to give maximum cracking. Also, exposing stretched rubber test samples to air for several days before exposing them to ozone decreased the tendency to crack. Van Rossem and Talen (397) observed maximum cracking at between 10 and 20% strain. They also observed that above 20% strain the number of cracks increased while their size decreased. In this latter work 90–100% strain gave cracks so small that they could barely be detected with the naked eye. Newton (389) carried out extensive research into the effect of strain on cracking, using a microscope to assist in observing the cracks. He found that cracks occur more rapidly at higher strains, that is, above 75%. Newton was careful to distinguish between the rate of formation and the rate of growth of cracks. He found that the rate of formation of cracks was very low at strains below 30%. The rate of formation increases with strain until about 70% strain above which it is independent of strain. At the lower strains, however, the rate of crack growth is more rapid than the rate of formation.

Zuev and Pravednikova (492) have examined the concept of a critical elongation and found that the time required for cracks to appear in a number of rubbers decreases with increasing percentage elongation. At the same time, however, the rate of growth of cracks was found to increase at first with increasing elongation to pass through a maximum at a small percentage elongation, the critical elongation, and then to decrease for elongations up to 500%. Furthermore, for all the rubbers examined, the time required to rupture the sample at different per cent elongations passed through a minimum at the critical elongation.

A number of attempts have been made to explain these observations on the effect of strain on cracking. Prior to the time when ozone was identified as the factor responsible for cracking, Dawson (493) had suggested that the optimum strain feature was connected with the reduction of oxygen permeability at high strains. At that time oxygen was believed to be the agent responsible for cracking; thus a reduced permeability would lead to a lowered accessibility and less cracking. Proceeding on the basis that the rubber molecule was a spiral, Cotton (494) suggested that this molecule would be in its most unstable condition at about 10% elongation thus giving more cracking. The suggestion that the critical strain might be due to crystallization upon stretching was made by Van Rossem and Talen (397), although they realized that crystallization, as detected by x-ray diffraction, occurred only at much higher elongations. On the basis of work which indicated a sudden decrease in hardness at low strains, Haushalter, Jones, and Schade (434) concluded that the structure of the rubber becomes modified with strain and reaches a point at low strain where it is unusually susceptible to attack. Newton (389) devised a theory to explain the so-called critical elongation which was based on the geometry of the distribution of cracks. According to this view the smaller number of cracks which are produced in the critical elongation region, as compared to higher strains, cannot relieve the strain without opening up to a greater width, thus producing more severe cracks. His theory, based on the number of cracks available to relieve the applied strain, predicts the greatest crack size to occur at about 20% elongation.

Ball, Youmans, and Rausell (491) claim that the modulus of the material in question is the important consideration. Thus the elongation at which maximum cracking occurs would be lower for a high modulus material. These workers felt that samples should be compared at equal stress rather than at equal strain. On the other hand, Popp and Harbison (495) and van Pul (496–498) have found little correlation between modulus and cracking.

Some interesting aspects of the influence of strain, particularly in butyl rubbers, have been presented by Grossman and Bluestein (499). Ozone failure time was postulated to be dependent on stress only when reorientation of polymer chains is possible. Thus, in the case of butyl rubbers at elongations greater than 100–200% when the polymer chains are formed into an ordered pattern, the rubber is no longer able to accommodate chain scissions by readjustment, and ozone failure time becomes independent of elongation. Also, the second-order dependence upon ozone concentration in the cracking of butyl rubber suggested to the authors that a more complicated process than ozonolysis of double bonds is taking place. A mechanism involving simultaneous ozonolysis and oxidation was suggested. The fact that the ozone resistance of butyl rubber has a large temperature dependence was interpreted to indicate the presence of a free radical oxidation process.

In their study of antiozonant requirements versus strain, Edwards and Storey (500) found that more antiozonant was required to give protection as strain was increased. Cox (475) has also studied the effect of elongation on antiozonant requirements and found that increased strain raised the level of antiozonant required to give crack-free performance.

It has also been known for some time that a threshold strain must be reached before cracking occurs at all. Winkelmann (474) found that once this threshold strain was passed then increased strain led to faster cracking. In a comprehensive study of factors affecting crack formation and growth, Braden and Gent (501,502) found very definitely that a cut in the edge of a stretched piece of rubber would not grow in an ozone atmosphere unless the applied tensile stress exceeded a critical value. When the applied stress was reduced below the critical value the cut growth stopped. On the basis of critical stress values for a number of natural rubber vulcanizates, it was concluded that a constant stored elastic energy was required in order to have crack growth. This critical stored energy was found to be similar for a large number of elastomers. The growth in the cut was at a constant rate which was independent of applied stress once the critical stress was reached.

In general, then, it appears that ozone cracking is more serious at 5–10% elongations than at higher or lower elongations. Also the critical elongation for maximum cracking varies with the type of vulcanizate, but is certainly related to stress–strain characteristics. Since rubber is easily extended, most rubber articles, even when they are in a static condition, will have some points at the critical elongation. In fact most everyday uses of rubber require that it be in a stretched condition where it is most susceptible to ozone attack.

(*c*) *Accelerated Testing.* Since the establishment, by earlier workers, that the combination of ozone and strain are the factors responsible for cracking, the various groups working in this field have devised methods of evaluating these and other factors. The large number of important variables requires that ozone testing be conducted under carefully controlled conditions. Ozone concentration must be accurately known, and humidity and temperature must be controlled. Among these earlier workers, Kearsley (453) and Van Rossem and Talen (397) designed equipment suitable for ozone testing. Crabtree and Kemp (503) devised one of the better laboratory devices for studying the resistance of rubber samples to varying ozone concentrations. Their device made it possible to correlate indoor and outdoor testing. The success of the Crabtree-Kemp test chamber was due to the fact that it used ozone concentrations comparable to those found in the atmosphere. Prior to this time workers in the field were using ozone concentrations that were much too high. The Crabtree-Kemp chamber used a concentration of 25 parts per hundred million which, it was felt, constituted an accelerated test since extensive measurements had shown that the atmospheric ozone concentrations in the area of the tests (Murray Hill, New Jersey) varied from zero to six parts per hundred million. The test chamber itself was an aluminum cylinder through which the ozone moved by convection aided by a small fan. The ozone was generated by a small quartz mercury lamp with controlled voltage to regulate the ozone concentration. The chamber was also equipped with heaters to permit temperature control. This apparatus was eventually adopted as ASTM Test Method D1149-55T. This basic system has been used extensively by workers in this field, in some cases with modifications. Two later versions of the early test chamber using forced air circulation have become available commercially. Veith (467) has described a version which is larger, has a highly efficient circulating fan, and a revolving test rack for mounting samples. Buist (504) has described an apparatus which uses a silent discharge method of ozone generation. This method presumably overcomes the difficulty associated with a decreased output of ultraviolet light with aging of the lamp in devices using this method of ozone generation.

The use of test chambers for accelerated testing depends upon frequent ozone analysis in order to control the ozone concentrations. Most of the methods used are based on iodimetry. Automatic devices based on this method have been described by Crabtree and Kemp (503), Veith (467), and Bowen and Regener (505). The rate of cracking of rubber has been used as the underlying principle in another method of ozone analysis. This method has been used successfully by Bradley and Haagen-Smit (506) and by Crabtree and Erickson (507). The Goodrich ozonometer, devised by Beatty and June (508) uses the decrease of stress of rubber when exposed to ozone. An ultraviolet light absorption method has also been used.

While the Crabtree-Kemp chamber or one of its modifications was suitable for static testing of samples, many users of rubber, tire manufacturers, for example, were interested in dynamic tests which more closely approximated actual in-service conditions. Consequently a number of chambers were devised which permitted continuous or periodic flexing of the sample. Fielding (473) used an apparatus which permitted the periodic flexing of a large number of rubber strips. Ford and Cooper (509,510) describe a machine which, besides permitting flexing, also has provisions for controlling temperature, humidity, strain and ozone concentration. Shaw, Ossefort, and Touhey (511) at the Rock Island Arsenal, have designed a simpler machine which has been used in an extensive program. Other test machines have been described by Creed, Hill, and Breed (461), Meyer and Sommer (512), Carlson (513), Eccher (477), and Thornley and Watts (514). These dynamic tests have been especially useful for testing protective agents for tires. Smith and Tuley (515) have reported on an extensive test comparing protective agents in laboratory and outdoor tests using both static and dynamic tests.

There have been a number of reports on the effect of wind on cracking rate in outdoor tests. Cracks appear to form more rapidly on windy days. In some cases this has been attributed to higher ozone concentrations. Cheetham and Gurney (516) have shown, however, that fewer cracks form on calmer days at constant ozone concentrations. These workers investigated this phenomenon and demonstrated that the velocity of the ozone-containing air does affect the extent of cracking. This led to the concept of an effective ozone concentration which would take account of velocity, a factor which the authors point out has long been neglected. It is likely that failure to take account of effective ozone concentrations has led to the apparent discrepancies between various test stations and, in some cases, between outdoor and accelerated tests.

Accelerated testing has proven valuable in assessing various rubbers and protective additives because they give information faster. In some cases, such as in the testing of antiozonants, there is not always good correlation between outdoor and laboratory testing. Thorough outdoor testing still seems to be the most valuable method if information on in-service performance is desired. Laboratory testing can be useful in more basic studies on protective agents, however.

(4) Protection Against Cracking

(*a*) *Methods of Protection.* Modern protectants against ozone attack fall into two general categories. These are waxes, which have been used for many years, and chemical antiozonants, which constitute a relatively new method. The combined use of antiozonants and waxes has also proven especially useful in some cases. In recent years the term antiozonant has become as well known as accelerator or antioxidant to the rubber compounder. Particular care must be taken, however, to distinguish between the terms antiozonant and antioxidant.

Some protective measures have been known for a long time. Williams (387) had found that oxidized rubber was less susceptible to ozone attack than fresh rubber. He even suggested that one way of protecting the rubber would be to treat the surface with copper chloride. The use of continuous coatings of materials inert to ozone was advocated by a number of workers. Norton (464) suggested alkyd resins as a coating, while Newton (517) and Buist (489) used a polyurethane as a protective coating. Harvey (518) has a patent on a method involving hydrogenation of the surface of rubber to protect against ozone. Patents have also been issued on a method using phenol–formaldehyde resin as a surface covering (519) and on the addition of hydrogen sulfide adducts (520). Rinne and Kvet (521) have reported the use of poly(vinyl chloride) paints to obtain protection from ozone, while Haushalter (433) found that a complete film of cellulose would provide protection. The modification of acrylonitrile–butadiene polymers with poly(vinyl chloride) resins to give vulcanizates with improved ozone resistance has been reported by a number of workers (522–525).

Crabtree and Kemp (445) in discussing means of protecting against ozone attack suggest a number of ways of removing the surface unsaturation. Thus, exposure to light and air, hydrogen peroxide, bromine, nitrogen peroxide, and bomb ageing all will remove some or all surface unsaturation. Unfortunately, the resultant surface is often quite brittle and suffers stress cracking. The idea of adding highly unsaturated substances which would have a sacrificial role in reacting with ozone to protect the rubber surface was also considered. Materials such as unsaturated drying oils and sorbic acid, among others tried, proved useless as protective additives, however. Most of the methods described above were specific remedies for a particular problem, however, and did not have general application.

Waxes have had wide application as protective agents. The relative abilities of the various types of waxes in providing protection have been studied by a number of workers (474,496,497,526–528). As early as 1881 (529) it was known that the addition of a wax to a rubber compound would inhibit deterioration, although the fact that the wax was effective against atmospheric ozone obviously was not realized. The microcrystalline waxes, in particular, are claimed to provide good protection. It is generally agreed that waxes protect by migrating to the surface and there form a coating which keeps the ozone away from the rubber. Waxes have to be used in the proper amount, however. Too much wax can lead to cracking of the wax coat, while too little wax can lead to concentration of ozone attack at a few unprotected points with the resultant production of severe cracks. Garvey and Emmet (530) found that, although refined paraffin wax provided protection at low ozone concentrations, no protection was obtained at high ozone concentrations. If it is assumed that the ability of wax to protect is dependent upon its migration to the surface, then those factors which affect its migratory ability are obviously important to its usefulness. These factors include solubility of the wax in the rubber, molecular weight, and possible interference from other additives such as fillers or pigments. Those rubbers which have inherent good resistance to ozone can be almost completely protected for long periods with the use of waxes (526). Paraffin wax itself is not effective in accelerated ozone tests because it flakes off, particularly when the test sample is flexed. Bennet (531) has summarized the characteristics of the two general classes of waxes used, namely, the paraffin and microcrystalline waxes. In practice, blends of microcrystalline and paraffin waxes are used, the paraffin wax being added to aid in migration so that sufficient surface bloom will be realized (472).

There is some disagreement as to the success achieved in correlating protective ability of waxes and their physical properties. Ferris et al. (532) claim that it is not possible to make such a correlation, while van Pul (496) found a reasonable correlation between protective power and physical properties. Baker (533) on the other hand, recommends a wax with a distinct melting point range as the optimum one to use for protection. The superiority of linear chain waxes as opposed to the branched chain type was observed by Winkelmann (474).

Crabtree and Kemp (503) found that the performance of waxes was quite dependent on temperature. Poorer protection was observed at higher temperatures. These authors suggest that the surface wax can be resorbed at higher temperatures thus decreasing protection. They also point out that at lower temperatures, such as those occurring in the winter months, the wax film becomes brittle, cracks, and again protection is reduced. Whether or not wax is useful for both dynamic and static service seems to be a matter of debate. Some workers advise against its use in dynamic service, (473,496,532–534), while others claim that microcrystalline wax can provide protection even in dynamic service (500,527,528,535).

The other broad class of materials used to combat ozone cracking are chemical additives, called antiozonants. These materials are distinguished from antioxidants by their function. In a few cases some materials used as antioxidants are effective as antiozonants and vice versa. In general, however, the two types of materials are distinct and should be treated accordingly. The search which led to the use of antiozonants was initiated largely by the obvious shortcomings of waxes as protective agents for some rubbers, mostly butadiene and isoprene rubbers, and particularly when these materials are used in dynamic service. As early as 1939 Tuley (536) had found that certain chemical additives were effective in preserving the surface of rubber. Tuley studied a number of materials and found that most antioxidants were ineffective for this purpose while some materials such as aldehyde-amines and ketone-amines were slighly effective. His most significant finding, however, was that one class of chemicals, the primary diamines, specifically, *p*-phenylenediamine, benzidene, and 4,4′-diaminodiphenylmethane, were more effective than all other materials tried. Today these materials and their derivatives are still the best antiozonants available. Another class of materials, the pyrroles, appeared to give early promise as antiozonants. Barton (537) received a patent for the use of 1-(*p*-aminophenyl)-2,5-dimethylpyrrole as a protective additive in 1943. These materials have not proven as useful as the aryl diamines, however. Pinazzi and Billuart (538) have reported that nickel dibutyldithiocarbamate is useful as an antiozonant, particularly when used with wax. The adaptation of existing antioxidants as antiozonants was investigated by several groups. Gaughan (534) found that some antioxidants gave ozone protection but felt that this was purely accidental. Thompson et al., (465) on the other hand, carried out an extensive study of antioxidants as antiozonants and divided them into three classes; that is, some were good, some ineffective, and some were even found to be harmful. Van Pul (496–498) found similar behavior of antioxidants. Some of the more useful antioxidants were amines which served to lead investigators into this area in their search for antiozonants. This search proved successful for Creed, Hill, and Breed (461) who found that 6-ethoxy-1,2-dihydro-2,2,4-trimethylquinoline performed well as an antiozonant. In the meantime, other groups were continuing the investigation of *p*-phenylenediamine derivatives, particularly at the Rock Island Arsenal. In 1954 Shaw, Ossefort, and Touhey (511) published a paper describing the results of an extensive investigation of various amines as potential antiozonants. This study indicated the best antiozonants to be *N*,*N*′-dialkyl-*p*-phenylenediamines. These workers also found that the efficiency of an antiozonant is greater when it is used with a wax. In general, samples used outdoors lasted correspondingly longer than those in the accelerated tests. If one assumes that the antiozonant must diffuse to the surface to be effective, as some authors do, then the explanation given for this last observation is that the longer times and lower ozone concentrations encountered in the outdoor tests permit diffusion of adequate antiozonant to the rubber surface. Van Pul (496–498) and Bergstrom (539) found the best antiozonant to be *N*-phenyl-*N*′-cyclohexyl-*p*-phenylenediamine. The results that accumulated led some workers to believe that the hydrogen on the nitrogen in the secondary *p*-phenylenediamine derivatives was necessary in order to observe good antiozonant action. However, Bruce et al. (540) have found that some tetrasubstituted *p*-phenylenediamines also serve as excellent antiozonants, indicating that the presence of the hydrogen is not a necessary requisite. Studies on variations of the fundamental structure of successful antiozonants by placing other groups between the two amino groups in place of phenylene have produced the following order of decreasing ozone resistance, phenylene, diphenylene, methylenediphenylene, and aminodiphenylene.

The use of a particular material as an antiozonant is dependent upon a large number of variables. The amount and type of antiozonant used depends largely upon the ultimate use of the material in question. In addition, questions of toxicity, volatility and the possible pro-oxidant activity of some antiozonants must be considered. Cox (475) has given a summary of the factors to be considered in choosing an antiozonant as well as a good description of the relative effectiveness of existing antiozonants.

Possible interactions between the antiozonant and the curing system used must also be considered in choosing an antiozonant. Thus, Ossefort (480) found that amine-type antiozonants were incompatible with the dicumyl peroxide cure system, apparently due to a reaction between the amine and the peroxide. In these cases some protection can be achieved by applying the antiozonant directly on the surface of the vulcanizate (480).

(*b*) *Mechanism of Antiozonant Action.* While continued research in the field of antiozonants has led to the successful use of a number of chemicals to give protection against ozone cracking, the mechanism by which these materials afford protection is still rather obscure. It has been only in very recent years that this aspect of the antiozonant problem has received more than casual attention. A number of research groups are now devoting major efforts toward determining the mechanism of antiozonant action so that more effective agents can be developed on a solid foundation. It seems clear, as has been expressed by Delman et al. (541), among others, that antiozonants act by a mechanism different from that for the antioxidants. One group has found that the best antiozonants were the least active as antioxidants. Likewise, the best antioxidants were the least active as antiozonants (542). This again suggests that these two additives function by completely different mechanisms. However, the inverse correlation does suggest a possible relationship.

A number of mechanisms of antiozonant action have been proposed on the basis of the existing data. Perhaps the most widely held view is that antiozonants are effective by diffusing to the surface of the rubber and there scavenge ozone before it has an opportunity to attack the rubber (444, 543–545). If this were the case then those materials which would be expected to be the best scavengers, i.e., which react more rapidly with ozone, should be the best antiozonants. In practice, however, this has not been found to be the case. Today's successful antiozonants are, generally speaking, a single specific class of materials, namely the *p*-phenylenediamines. While it is true that other materials have proven effective in some instances, the phenylenediamines are by far the most common antiozonants. Although the phenylenediamines do react faster with ozone, though not dramatically so, the fact that other materials which react more rapidly with ozone, are not effective as antiozonants (546) suggests that the effectiveness of the successful antiozonants must be due to some other inherent quality. The scavenging mechanism would seem to be lacking in several other fundamental ways. This mechanism requires a stoichiometric relationship between the antiozonant and ozone which is not confirmed by the extended periods of protection provided by a number of materials (444, 480). This objection has been raised by Story and Murray (456) and by Braden and Barnard (547). Also the scavenger mechanism requires some rather unrealistic diffusion rates for the antiozonant. Recently, Braden (548) has shown that the diffusion rate of one phenylenediamine derivative is too slow to be consistent with a scavenger mechanism of protection. Proceeding on the basis that diffusion of the antiozonant to the surface was beneficial for effective antiozonant action van Pul (498) added small amounts of paraffin wax to assist this diffusion and found no improvement in ozone protection. However, van Pul did not prove that the paraffin wax had actually increased diffusion rates. Also arguing against the scavenger mechanism is the observation (498,547), that in some cases, concentrations of antiozonant greater than about 1% resulted in no additional protection. In fact, in one case (549), an optimum concentration of antiozonant was found above which less protection was achieved. Braden and Gent (546), in a recent publication, have concluded, after extensive work with phenylenediamine derivatives, that the scavenging mechanism is not applicable to this class of antiozonants. On the other hand, Hodgkinson and Kendall (550) have found a correlation between protection against ozone cracking and the ability of antiozonants to bloom to the surface. The effectiveness of a phenylenediamine antiozonant was found to be greatly influenced by the presence of waxes and liquid or semiliquid blooming agents. Certain polyethylene glycol derivatives, for example, gave greatly enhanced protection. This work led to the concept of an "antiozonant carrier," that is, a blooming agent which is also a good solvent for the antiozonant. It would seem, then, that the scavenger mechanism still has some attraction, at least in some cases.

Part of the difficulty in finding a reasonable mechanism for antiozonant action is that most of the data collected are not strictly comparable. Many workers (475,551) have compared antiozonants on a parts per hundred of rubber basis, rather than an equivalent weight basis. Compounding on the former basis is still the practice in the rubber industry. The use of these data to compare the relative effectiveness of antiozonants and to postulate theories concerning the mechanism of protection can lead to erroneous conclusions, however. In some cases apparent differences in effectiveness are completely voided when molecular weights of the subject compounds are taken into consideration.

Another mechanism which has been proposed to explain the effectiveness of antiozonants is that they form a protective film over the surface of the rubber (475,552,553). Buist (489) has referred to the sweating of diamine antiozonants to the surface where they presumably form a physical barrier to ozone. Likewise, Ossefort (480) depicts a mechanism in which the reaction product of ozone and the diamine antiozonant forms an inert barrier on the surface. Story and Murray (456) have argued against both the scavenger and protective film explanations partly on the basis of some data collected by Erickson et al. (553). It has been found, in the case of one vulcanizate, that the rate of ozone absorption with antiozonant present, although initially much higher than the same vulcanizate without antiozonant, dropped to a much lower level in a matter of 40 min. Story and Murray argue that if a scavenger mechanism were operating, then the protected sample should have a higher rate of absorption until all of the antiozonant were used up and then should show a decline to the same final rate as the unprotected sample. They also argue against the lower final rate of the protected sample being due to the formation of a protective film, since one would have to argue that this film was formed in a matter of 40 min., which would call for some unlikely diffusion rates for the antiozonant.

Lorenz and Parks (554) have recently sought to determine the mechanism of antiozonant action by studying some of the basic chemistry involved. The consumption of different phenylenediamines in rubber vulcanizates was studied as a function of the exposure time in ozone. The antiozonants were found to react rapidly with ozone initially with a subsequent slowing down of the reaction rate. The authors have interpreted their results as indicating the formation of a protective layer by the ozonized antiozonant on the surface of the rubber. The layer also makes it more difficult for ozone to react with additional antiozonant. The individual ability of an antiozonant to protect was found to be dependent on the physical state of the ozonized antiozonant. Those giving tarry ozonization products provided the best protection. This study also indicated that some of the antiozonant becomes attached to the rubber network presumably because of reactions between the antiozonants and rubber ozonization products. In an additional study (555), these same workers examined the ozonization of a model compound and the effect of added antiozonants on this ozonization process as well as on the products of the ozonization. The authors conclude that the antiozonants react in three distinct ways, namely, direct reaction with ozone, reduction of peroxy compounds to the corresponding carbonyl compounds, and reaction with aldehydes. They also find a relinking reaction of *p*-phenylenediamines with aldehydes which, in some cases, could be the mechanism by which antiozonants afford protection.

Kilbourne et al. (556), after an extensive program designed to determine the effect of substituents on antiozonant activity of several materials, concluded that antiozonant activity was related to the stopping of ozone-induced free radical chain reactions in the rubber. However, if ozone cracking were due to an ozone-induced chain reaction then one would not expect strain to be essential for its occurrence.

None of the mechanisms discussed to this point offers a completely satisfactory explanation for the effectiveness of antiozonants. There seems to be a feeling today that there is probably more than one mechanism operating. Braden and Gent (546,557), who have conducted an intensive investigation of the physical factors involved in the ozone cracking problem, divide antiozonants into two general classes. The first class contains those which are affective because they reduce the rate of crack formation and includes 6-ethoxy-2,2,4-trimethyl-1,2-dihydroquinoline. The second class, which is made up of the dialkyl-substituted *p*-phenylenediamines, is effective by increasing the critical energy required for crack growth to occur. Bloomfield et al. (558) have made a similar twofold classification. Story, Murray, and Bebbington have also suggested that antiozonants may function in different ways. These latter authors have suggested that some antiozonants are effective because they can be involved in a reaction sequence which leads to the removal of surface unsaturation (456,559). According to this explanation the amine antiozonants can react with peroxy type linkages formed during the cleavage of double bonds by ozone, as described earlier in this section. In this cleavage materials with nitrogen–oxygen bonds would be formed which would be expected to undergo facile homolysis to generate free radicals. These radicals are then postulated to initiate a short length crosslinking chain reaction with the consequent removal of unsaturation in the immediate vicinity. The net result of this process, then, would be a saturated surface several molecular layers thick, which would be impregnable to ozone. According to this view the difference in effectiveness of the various antiozonants is related to their nucleophilicity since this is what determines their ability to cleave the peroxy bond. Thus, phenylenediamines as a class are effective because of the presence of the two conjugated nitrogen atoms. One of these nitrogen atoms is made more able to conduct a nucleophilic attack by the presence of the other. Substituents influence effectiveness as they influence nucleophilicity. Thus alkyl substituents would be expected to give more effective antiozonants than aryl substituents which reduce nucleophilicity. Important to this view is the apparent inability of ozone to penetrate very deeply into the surface of elastomers (559). Delman et al. (551), on the other hand, have related the relative effectiveness of the various antiozonants to the comparative stability of their free radicals.

To substantiate their view Story and Murray (456) have referred to the use of ozone as a crosslinking agent in various saturated polymers. Landler and Lebel (560,561) had found that the temperatures required to produce crosslinking in ozonized polymers could be materially reduced by adding dimethylaniline. In addition, Story, Murray, and Bebbington have found that samples of polyisoprene containing antiozonant increase in viscosity with increasing exposure in an ozone chamber (559). These latter authors have also suggested that some antiozonants, the difunctional amines, for example, could be effective by bridging the gap in the early stages of crack growth, possibly by connecting two zwitterions (see eq. 96). Braden and Gent (546) have suggested that the antiozonant combines with the ozonized rubber to give a stable material and have also noted that this may be attributable to the difunctionality of the antiozonant. These authors have also suggested the possibility of *N,N'*-dioctyl-*p*-phenylenediamine relinking the ozone-severed rubber molecules to prevent cracking (562). This study revealed the critical condition for crack growth to be similar for all the polymers examined and to be largely independent of the conditions of exposure. The energy requirements for crack growth was found to be 40 ergs/cm.^{2} for the newly formed surface.

A completely different type of mechanism of antiozonant action has been suggested by Barnhart and Newby (563). This proposal, which is based on the work of Michaelis and co-workers (563a) makes use of the hydroquinone, semiquinone, quinone equilibrium of the phenylenediamines. Michaelis found that *p*-phenylenediamine derivatives which are effective antiozonants all have stable semiquinone forms whereas those which do not function as antiozonants have unstable semiquinone forms. Barnhart and Newby suggest that ozone could react with an antiozonant to give the stable semiquinone form which would then react with the rubber peroxide or isozonide to give the quinone form and presumably prevent chain splitting. Under this proposal antiozonant activity would cease when all of the hydroquinone and semiquinone forms of the antiozonant were depleted.

At present, therefore, the precise mechanism by which antiozonants confer protection remains obscure, although the research efforts of recent years have brought us closer to a total understanding of the fundamental chemistry involved. It seems likely that more than one mechanism may be involved depending on the chemical nature of the antiozonant. The search for better antiozonants will undoubtedly demand that efforts to understand mechanisms of protection be given continued attention by research workers.

3. Ozonization of Nonelastomers

As indicated earlier, saturated hydrocarbons such as polyethylene are relatively inert to ozone. This is especially true at ordinary atmospheric concentrations of ozone (564). It has not been established that ozone will directly attack either a carbon–carbon single bond or a carbon–hydrogen bond. It is well established, however, that ozone serves as an initiator and catalyst in the oxidation of polymers. Thus any degradative effect of ozone on a saturated polymer is similar to that caused by oxygen except that it occurs at a faster rate and usually without an induction period.

It is not surprising, then, that this area of ozone-polymer chemistry has received relatively little attention, and, indeed, much of the fundamental work has been accomplished with model systems. For the most part, the treatment of nonelastomers with ozone has been directed toward graft polymerization (565,566) and, more recently, toward crosslinking of the polymer (561,567). Both of these areas, however, lie outside the domain of this chapter.

One of the earliest investigations into the action of ozone on a nonelastomeric polymer was that of Staudinger et al. (568), who ozonized polystyrene in carbon tetrachloride. The viscosity of these solutions first decreased then increased with eventual formation of gel. This sequence could be caused by initial chain cleavage followed by formation of polymeric peroxides which would result in a crosslinked polymer. More recently, Cameron and Grassie (569) have used ozone to determine the nature of the "weak links" which occur in polystyrene to the extent of about 0.1% of the styrene units. These investigators found no change in molecular weight in the initial stages of ozonization. Subsequently, however, the molecular weight rose to eventually give insoluble material. If aliquots of ozonized solution were treated with zinc–acetic acid, the molecular weight began to drop immediately, passed through a minimum, and then rose as before to give insoluble material. The authors drew the very reasonable conclusion that the weak links were due to quinoid structures formed by chain propagation through the benzene ring. The eventual gel formation even after zinc–acetic acid reduction is difficult to understand unless one assumes that only ozonides are being reduced or that there is insufficient reducing agent present in the latter stages of ozonization.

Beachell and Nemphos (570) have followed the ozonization of various deuterated polystyrenes by observing the 5.7 μ absorption in the infrared spectrum of the product. These workers concluded that the principal point of attack was the tertiary hydrogen α to the benzene ring. The source of the 5.7 μ absorption was not identified, however, and in fact is more likely to arise from ozonization of the benzene ring to yield aldehydes rather than from oxidation of the tertiary chain hydrogen. Lebel (571) has pointed out that the polymer chain is protected somewhat by preferential attack of ozone on the phenyl substituents.

Cooper and Prober (572) have compared the effects of oxygen corona and ozone on polyethylene. Samples placed directly in the corona discharge rapidly lost weight due to formation of volatile products, e.g., carbon dioxide and water. Samples exposed to ozone generated by the discharge evidenced rapid carbonyl formation but gained slightly in weight. The carbonyl groups were attributed to ketones and acids produced by cleavage of the double bonds present. Chain cleavage to yield carbonyl-containing functional groups could also have arisen by ozone-catalyzed oxidation of the saturated chain, however.

Alter (573) has studied the metal-catalyzed oxidation of polyethylene using Cr, Mn, Fe, Co, and others. It was found that ozonized oxygen reduced the polymer completely to low molecular weight products, whereas oxygen alone, under the same conditions, gave only a 5–10% yield of low molecular weight materials. Beachell and Nemphos (570), using infrared spectral analysis, have also ozonized polyethylene and obtained results identical to those found in the oxidation reaction, except that the ozone-catalyzed reaction was faster.

Lazar et al. (574), have ozonized atactic polypropylene and found, curiously enough, that the polymer was degraded less than in pure oxygen.

The extent of degradation was found to be dependent on the concentration of the accumulated peroxide groups. This apparent anomaly is resolved if it is recalled that Barnard (366) found that ozone decomposed hydroperoxides to the corresponding alcohols. Thus a build-up of hydroperoxides would be prevented. Lazar also found that the rate of oxidation depended on $[O_3]^{0.5}$.

Ozone is used widely in structure determination of polymers, perhaps with too much faith, considering the number of possible side reactions and that relatively little is known about the reaction mechanism. Roberts and Day (575) have used ozone to elucidate the structures of the polymers obtained from α- and β-pinene. More recently Yakubchik and Spasskova (576) used ozone to find that butadiene homopolymer contained 23% unsaturated side chains. Ozone cleavage has also been used to follow loss of HCl from poly(vinyl chloride). Baum and Wartman (577) were able to establish that reactive allylic chloride at unsaturated chain ends was responsible for HCl elimination and resultant degradation of the polymer.

References

A. Hydrolysis

1. Freudenberg, K., W. Kuhn, W. Dürr, F. Bolz, and G. Steinbrunn, *Ber.*, **63**, 1510 (1930).
2. Nickerson, R. F., and J. A. Habrle, *Ind. Eng. Chem.*, **39**, 1507 (1947).
3. Sharples, A., *Trans. Faraday Soc.*, **54**, 913 (1958); *Chem. Abstr.*, **53**, 3687c (1959).
4. Gibbons, G. C., *J. Textile Inst.*, **43**, T25 (1952); *Chem. Abstr.*, **46**, 3838i (1952)
5. Grassie, N., *Chemistry of High Polymer Degradation Processes*, Butterworths, London, 1956, pp. 118–129.
6. Kuhn, W., *Ber.*, **63**, 1503 (1930).
7. Montroll, E. W., and R. Simha, *J. Chem. Phys.*, **8**, 721 (1940).
8. Montroll, E. W., *J. Am. Chem. Soc.*, **63**, 1215 (1941).
9. Farrow, G., and D. Preston, *Brit. J. Appl. Phys.*, **11**, 353 (1960); *Chem. Abstr.*, **55**, 4969d (1961).
10. Matthews, J. L., H. J. Peiser, and R. B. Richards, *Acta Cryst.*, **2**, 85 (1949); *Chem. Abstr.*, **43**, 6485h (1949).
11. Cobbs, W. H., Jr., and R. L. Burton, *J. Polymer Sci.*, **10**, 275 (1953).
12. Miller, R. G. J., and H. A. Willis, *J. Polymer Sci.*, **19**, 485 (1956).
13. Daubeny, R. de P., C. W. Bunn, and C. J. Brown, *Proc. Roy. Soc.* (*London*), A**226**, 531 (1954); *Chem. Abstr.*, **49**, 2147f (1955).
14. Farrow, G., and I. M. Ward, *Polymer*, **1**, 330 (1960).
15. Bunn, C. W., in *Fibre Science*, J. M. Preston, ed., 2nd ed., The Textile Institute, Manchester, 1953, p. 192.
16. Patterson, D., and I. M. Ward, *Trans. Faraday Soc.*, **53**, 1516 (1957); *Chem. Abstr.*, **52**, 12517h (1958).
17. Conix, A., *Makromol. Chem.*, **26**, 226 (1958).

18. Marshall, I., and A. Todd, *Trans. Faraday Soc.*, **49,** 67 (1953); *Chem. Abstr.*, **47,** 2871e (1953).
19. Ward, I. M., *Nature,* **180,** 141 (1957).
20. Ravens, D. A. S., and I. M. Ward, *Trans. Faraday Soc.*, **57,** 150 (1961); *Chem. Abstr.*, **55,** 16469f (1961).
21. Goodman, I., and B. F. Nesbitt, *Polymer,* **1,** 384 (1960).
22. Furrer, E., *Eidgnöss Materialprufungs-u. Versuchsanstalt Ind. Bauw. u. Gewerbe, Zurich/St. Gallen,* No. **187** (1956); through *Chem. Abstr.*, **51,** 15137 (1957).
23. McMahon, W., H. A. Birdsall, G. R. Johnson, and C. T. Camilli, *J. Chem. Eng. Data,* **4,** 57 (1959).
24. Golike, R. C., and S. W. Lasoski, *J. Phys. Chem.*, **64,** 895 (1960).
25. Davies, T., P. L. Goldsmith, D. A. S. Ravens, and I. M. Ward, *J. Phys. Chem.*, **66,** 175 (1962).
26. Small, K. W., and M. Freeman, private communication.
27. Ward, I. M., private communication.
28. Hammett, L. P., *Physical Organic Chemistry,* 1st ed., McGraw-Hill, New York, 1940, p. 267.
29. Frost, A. A., and R. G. Pearson, *Kinetics and Mechanism,* 1st ed., Wiley, New York, 1953, p. 267.
30. Ravens, D. A. S., *Polymer,* **1,** 375 (1960).
31. Reddish, W., private communication.
32. Thompson, A. B., and D. W. Woods, *Trans. Faraday Soc.*, **52,** 1383 (1956); *Chem. Abstr.*, **51,** 6209i (1957).
33. Waters, E., *J. Soc. Dyers Colourists,* **66,** 609 (1950); *Chem. Abstr.*, **45,** 2211i (1951).
34. Myagkov, V. A., and A. B. Pakshver, *Kolloidn. Zh.*, **14,** 172 (1952); *Chem. Abstr.*, **46,** 8484 (1952).
35. Heikens, D., *J. Polymer Sci.*, **35,** 277 (1959).
36. Heikens, D., P. H. Hermans, and H. A. Veldhoven, *Makromol. Chem.*, **30,** 154 (1959).
37. Matthes, A., *J. Prakt. Chem.*, **162,** 245 (1943); *Chem. Abstr.*, **38,** 2546 (1944).
38. Hoshino, K., and M. Watanabe, *J. Am. Chem. Soc.*, **73,** 4816 (1951).
39. Liquori, A. M., and A. Mele, *Gazz. Chim. Ital.*, **82,** 828 (1952); *Chem. Abstr.*, **47,** 11918 (1953).
40. Pakshver, A. B., and E. Mankash, *Kolloidn. Zh.*, **14,** 112 (1952); *Chem. Abstr.*, **46,** 7774 (1952).
41. Rotinyan, A., and B. Drozdov, *Zh. Obshch. Khim.*, **19,** 1843 (1949); *Chem. Abstr.*, **44,** 416 (1950).
42. Petitpas, T., and M. Mathieu, *Bull. Soc. Chim. France,* **1949,** D43; *Chem. Abstr.*, **48,** 6061 (1949).

B. Thermal Degradation

43. *Polymer Degradation Mechanisms,* Circular 525, National Bureau of Standards, Washington, D. C., 1953.
44. Jellinek, H. H. G., *Degradation of Vinyl Polymers,* Academic Press, New York, 1955.
45. Grassie, N., *The Chemistry of High Polymer Degradation Processes,* Butterworths London, 1956.

46. *Thermal Degradation of Polymers,* Society of Chemical Industry, Monograph No. 13, London, 1961.
47. Simha, R., L. A. Wall, and P. J. Blatz, *J. Polymer Sci.*, **5,** 615 (1950).
48. Simha, R., and L. A. Wall, *J. Phys. Chem.*, **56,** 707 (1952).
49. Simha, R., and L. A. Wall, *J. Polymer Sci.*, **6,** 39 (1951).
50. Simha, R., *Trans. N. Y. Acad. Sci.*, **14,** 151 (1952); *Chem. Abstr.*, **46,** 7857f (1952).
51. Grassie, N., and H. W. Melville, *Proc. Roy. Soc.*, (*London*), **A199,** 1, 14, 24, 39 (1949); *Chem. Abstr.*, **44,** 2342h (1950).
52. Wall, L. A., S. L. Madorsky, D. W. Brown, S. Straus, and R. Simha, *J. Am. Chem. Soc.*, **76,** 3430 (1954).
53. Wall, L. A., Ref. 46, p. 146.
54. Wall, L. A., and S. Straus, *J. Polymer Sci.*, **44,** 313 (1960).
55. Gordon, M., Ref. 46, p. 163.
56. Madorsky, S. L., *J. Polymer Sci.*, **9,** 133 (1952).
57. Madorsky, S. L., *J. Polymer Sci.*, **11,** 491 (1953).
58. Straus, S., and S. L. Madorsky, *J. Res. Natl. Bur. Std.*, **50,** 165 (1953); *Chem. Abstr.*, **47,** 9050h (1953).
59. Madorsky, S. L. and S. Straus, *J. Res. Natl. Bur. Std.*, **40,** 417 (1948); *Chem. Abstr.*, **42,** 6156c (1948).
60. Madorsky, S. L., S. Straus, D. Thompson, and L. Williamson, *J. Res. Natl. Bur. Std.*, **42,** 499 (1949); *J. Polymer Sci.*, **4,** 639 (1949).
61. Madorsky, S. L., V. E. Hart, S. Straus, and V. A. Sedlak, *J. Res. Natl. Bur. Std.*, **51,** 327 (1953); *Chem. Abstr.*, **48,** 4945*f* (1954).
62. Madorsky, S. L., and S. Straus, *J. Res. Natl. Bur. Std.*, **53,** 361 (1954); *Chem. Abstr.*, **49,** 7344b (1955).
63. Wall, L. A., D. W. Brown, and V. E. Hart, *J. Polymer Sci.*, **15,** 157 (1955).
64. Madorsky, S. L., and S. Straus, *J. Res. Natl. Bur. Std.*, **55,** 223 (1955); *Chem. Abstr.*, **50,** 12905g (1956).
65. Wall, L. A., and R. E. Florin, *J. Res. Natl. Bur. Std.*, **60,** 451 (1958); *Chem. Abstr.*, **52,** 19366e (1958).
66. Straus, S., and S. L. Madorsky, *J. Res. Natl. Bur. Std.*, **61,** 77 (1958); *Chem. Abstr.*, **53,** 23065c (1959).
67. Madorsky, S. L., *J. Res. Natl. Bur. Std.*, **62,** 219 (1959); *Chem. Abstr.*, **53,** 18537f (1959).
68. Madorsky, S. L., and S. Straus, *J. Polymer Sci.*, **36,** 183 (1959).
69. Madorsky, S. L., and S. Straus, *J. Res. Natl. Bur. Std.*, **63A,** 261 (1959); *Chem. Abstr.*, **54,** 10384h, (1960).
70. Wall, L. A., and S. Straus, *J. Polymer Sci.*, **44,** 313 (1960).
71. Madorsky, S. L., and S. Straus, Ref. 46, p. 60.
72. Madorsky, S. L., and S. Straus, *J. Res. Natl. Bur. Std.*, **40,** 417 (1948); *Chem. Abstr.*, **42,** 6156c (1948).
73. Cameron, G. G., and N. Grassie, *Polymer*, **2,** 367 (1961).
74. Jellinek, H. H. G., *J. Polymer Sci.*, **3,** 850 (1948).
75. Jellinek, H. H. G., *J. Polymer Sci.*, **4,** 1 (1949).
76. Jellinek, H. H. G., *J. Polymer Sci.*, **4,** 13 (1949).
77. Barlow, A. R. S. Lehrle, and J. C. Robb, *Polymer*, **2,** 27 (1961).
78. Grassie, N., and E. Vance, *Trans. Faraday Soc.*, **49,** 184 (1953); *Chem. Abstr.*, **47,** 8487i (1953).

79. Cowley, P. R. E. J., and H. W. Melville, *Proc. Roy. Soc. (London)*, **A210**, 461 (1952); *Chem. Abstr.*, **46**, 11765e (1952).
80. Cowley, P. R. E. J., and H. W. Melville, *Proc. Roy. Soc. (London)*, **A211**, 320 (1952); *Chem. Abstr.*, **46**, 11765f (1952).
81. Bywater, S., *J. Phys. Chem.*, **57**, 879 (1953).
82. Crawford, J. W. C., *J. Soc. Chem. Ind.*, **68**, 201 (1949).
83. Grant, D. H., and N. Grassie, *Polymer*, **1**, 125 (1960).
84. Grant, D. H., and N. Grassie, *Polymer*, **1**, 445 (1960).
85. Grassie, N., and J. R. MacCallum, *J. Polymer Sci.*, **A2**, 983 (1964).
86. Grassie, N., *Plastics Inst. (London) Trans. J.*, **28**, 233 (1960).
87. Brown, D. W., and L. A. Wall, *J. Phys. Chem.*, **62**, 848 (1958).
88. Grant, D. H., E. Vance, and S. Bywater, *Trans. Faraday Soc.*, **56**, 1697 (1960); *Chem. Abstr.*, **55**, 13010i (1961).
89. Cowie, J. M. G., and S. Bywater, *J. Polymer Sci.*, **54**, 221 (1961).
90. Bradt, P., V. H. Dibeler, and F. L. Mohler, *J. Res. Natl. Bur. Std.*, **50**, 201 (1953); *Chem. Abstr.*, **47**, 10993f (1953).
91. Jellinek, H. H. G., and L. B. Spencer, *J. Polymer Sci.*, **8**, 573 (1952).
92. Grassie, N., and W. W. Kerr, *Trans. Faraday Soc.*, **53**, 234 (1957); *Chem. Abstr.*, **51**, 12611d (1957).
93. Wall, L. A., and D. W. Brown, *J. Polymer Sci.*, **14**, 513 (1954).
94. Grassie, N., and W. W. Kerr, *Trans. Faraday Soc.*, **55**, 1050 (1959); *Chem. Abstr.* **54**, 6266d (1960).
95. Cameron, G. G., and N. Grassie, *Makromol. Chem.*, **51**, 130 (1962).
96. Cameron, G. G., and N. Grassie, *Makromol. Chem.*, **53**, 72 (1962).
97. Hurd, C. D., and F. M. Blunck, *J. Am. Chem. Soc.*, **60**, 2419 (1938).
98. Blades, T., *Can. J. Chem.*, **31**, 418 (1953).
99. Oakes, W. G., and R. B. Richards, *J. Chem. Soc.*, **1949**, 2929.
100. Van Schooten, J. W., and P. W. O. Wijga, Ref. 46, p. 432.
101. Simha, R., *J. Chem. Phys.*, **24**, 796 (1956).
102. Grassie, N., and I. C. McNeill, *J. Chem. Soc.*, **1956**, 3929.
103. Grassie, N., and I. C. McNeill, *J. Polymer Sci.*, **27**, 207 (1958).
104. Grassie, N., and I. C. McNeill, *J. Polymer Sci.*, **30**, 37 (1958).
105. Grassie, N., and I. C. McNeill, *J. Polymer Sci.*, **33**, 171 (1958).
106. Grassie, N., and I. C. McNeill, *J. Polymer Sci.*, **39**, 211 (1959).
107. Talât-Erben, M., and S. Bywater, Intern. Symp. Macromol. Chem. (IUPAC), Milan-Turin, 1954 [Published as *Ricerca Sci.*, **25A**, 11 (1955)].
108. Talât-Erben, M., and S. Bywater, *J. Am. Chem. Soc.*, **77**, 3710 (1955).
109. Talât-Erben, M., and S. Bywater, *J. Am. Chem. Soc.*, **77**, 3712 (1955).
110. Talât-Erben, M., and A. N. Isfendiyarŏglu, *Can. J. Chem.*, **36**, 1156 (1958).
111. Canale, A. J., W. E. Goode, J. B. Kinsinger, J. R. Panchak, R. L. Kelso, and R. K. Graham, *J. Appl. Polymer Sci.*, **4**, 231 (1960).
112. Gilbert, M., F. F. Miller, S. J. Averill, R. F. Schmidt, F. D. Stewart, and H. L. Trumbull, *J. Am. Chem. Soc.*, **76**, 1074 (1954).
113. Grant, E., and N. Grassie, unpublished work.
114. Lewis, E. E., and M. A. Naylor, *J. Am. Chem. Soc.*, **69**, 1968 (1947).
115. Florin, R. E., L. A. Wall, D. W. Brown, L. A. Hymo, and J. D. Michaelsen, *J. Res. Natl. Bur. Std.*, **53**, 121 (1954); *Chem. Abstr.*, **49**, 4326a (1955).

116. Wall, L. A., and J. D. Michaelsen, *J. Res. Natl. Bur Std.*, **56**, 27 (1956); *Chem. Abstr.*, **50**, 13500i (1956).
117. Michaelsen, J. D., and L. A. Wall, *J. Res. Natl. Bur. Std.*, **58**, 327 (1957); *Chem. Abstr.*, **51**, 13535*b* (1957).
118. Koton, M. M., *J. Polymer Sci.*, **52**, 97 (1961).
119. Vansheidt, A. A., E. P. Mel'nikova, M. G. Krakovyak, L. V. Kukhareva, and G. A. Gladkovskĭi, *J. Polymer Sci.*, **52**, 179 (1961).
120. Szwarc, M., *J. Chem. Phys.*, **16**, 128 (1948).
121. Schaefgen, J. R., *J. Polymer Sci.*, **41**, 133 (1959).
122. Errede, L. A., and M. Szwarc, *Quart. Rev.* (*London*), **12**, 301 (1958).
123. Horrex, C., and S. E. Miles, *Discussions Faraday Soc.*, **10**, 187 (1951); *Chem. Abstr.*, **46**, 3378a (1952).
124. Goodings, E. P., Ref. 46, p. 211.
125. Ritchie, P. D., Ref. 46, p. 106.
126. Straus, S., and L. A. Wall, *J. Res. Natl. Bur. Std.*, **60**, 39 (1958); *Chem. Abst.* **52**, 7764e (1958).
127. Rafikov, S. R., and R. A. Sorokina, *Vysokomolekul. Soedin.*, **1**, 549 (1959); *Polymer Sci. USSR*, (*English Transl.*), **1**, 189 (1960); *Chem. Abstr.*, **54**, 14763c (1960).
128. Kamerbeek, B., G. H. Kroes, and W. Grolle, Ref. 46, p. 357.
129. Burlant, W. J., and J. L. Parsons, *J. Polymer Sci.*, **22**, 249 (1956).
130. Kennedy, J. P., and C. M. Fontana, *J. Polymer Sci.*, **39**, 501 (1959).
131. Strause, S. F., and E. Dyer, *J. Am. Chem. Soc.*, **78**, 136 (1956).
132. Skoda, W., and J. Schurz, *Makromol. Chem.*, **29**, 156 (1959).
133. Grassie, N., and I. C. McNeill, *J. Polymer Sci.*, **34**, 120 (1959).
134. McCartney, J. R., Ref. 43, p. 123.
135. Grassie, N., and J. N. Hay, *J. Polymer Sci.*, **56**, 189 (1962).
136. Grassie, N., and J. N. Hay, Ref. 46, p. 184.
137. Skoda, W., J. Schurz, and H. Bayzer, *Z. Physik. Chem.* (*Leipzig*), **210**, 35 (1959); *Chem. Abstr.*, **53**, 10828i (1959).
138. Bresler, S. E., M. M. Koton, A. T. Os'minskaia, A. G. Popov, and M. N. Savitskaia, *Vysokomolekul. Soedin.*, **1**, 1070 (1959); *Polymer Sci. USSR* (*English Transl.*) **1**, 393 (1960); *Chem. Abstr.*, **54**, 15998c (1960).
139. Druesedow, D., and C. F. Gibbs, Ref. 43, p. 69.
140. Kenyon, A. S., Ref. 43, p. 107.
141. Scarbrough, A. L., W. L. Kellner, and P. W. Rizzo, Ref. 43, p. 95.
142. Havens, C. B., Ref. 43, p. 107.
143. Arlman, E. J., *J. Polymer Sci.*, **12**, 547 (1954).
144. Fuchs, W., and D. Louis, *Makromol. Chem.*, **22**, 1 (1957).
145. Winkler, D. E., *J. Polymer Sci.*, **35**, 3 (1959).
146. Stromberg, R. R., S. Straus, and B. G. Achhammer, *J. Polymer Sci.*, **35**, 355 (1959).
147. Talamini, G., and G. Pezzin, *Makromol. Chem.*, **39**, 26 (1960).
148. Frye, A. H., and R. W. Horst, *J. Polymer Sci.*, **40**, 419 (1959).
149. Frye, A. H., and R. W. Horst, *J. Polymer Sci.*, **45**, 1 (1960).
150. Baum, B., and L. H. Wartman, *J. Polymer Sci.*, **28**, 537 (1958).
151. Arlman, E. J., *J. Polymer Sci.*, **12**, 543 (1954).
152. Grassie, N., *Trans. Faraday Soc.*, **48**, 379 (1952); *Chem. Abstr.*, **47**, 6343d (1953).
153. Grassie, N., *Trans. Faraday Soc.*, **49**, 835 (1953); *Chem. Abstr.*, **48**, 3123h (1954).
154. Bradt, P., and F. L. Mohler, *J. Res. Natl. Bur. Std.*, **55**, 323 (1955).

C. Radiation

155. Bovey, F. A., *The Effects of Ionizing Radiation on Natural and Synthetic High Polymers*, Polymer Reviews Series, Vol. I, Interscience, New York, 1958.
156. Charlesby, A., *Atomic Radiation and Polymers*, Pergamon Press, New York, 1960.
157. Bacq, Z. M., and P. Alexander, *Fundamentals of Radiobiology*, Academic Press, New York, and Butterworths, London, 1955.
158. Haissinsky, M., *Actions Chimiques et Biologiques des Radiations*, Series 1, Masson, Paris, 1955.
159. Lea, D. E., *Actions of Radiations on Living Cells*, 2nd ed., University Press, Cambridge, 1955.
160a. Charlesby, A., and A. J. Swallow, in *Annual Review of Physical Chem.*, H. Eyring, C. J. Christensen, and H. D. Johnston, eds., Vol. 10, Annual Reviews, Inc., Palo Alto, Calif., 1959, pp. 289–330.
160b. Carrol, J. G., and R. O. Bolt, *Nucleonics*, **18** (9), 78 (1960); *Chem. Abstr.*, **55,** 85d (1961).
161. Collinson, E., and A. J. Swallow, *Quart. Rev. (London)*, **9,** 311 (1955).
162. Dainton, F. S., in *Annual Review of Nuclear Science*, J. G. Beckerly, M. D. Kamen, L. I. Schiff, eds., Vol. 5, Annual Reviews, Inc., Stanford, Calif., 1955, pp. 213–240.
163. Gehman, S. D., and T. C. Gregson, *Rubber Chem. Technol.*, **33,** 1375 (1960).
164. Hamill, W. H., in *Annual Review of Physical Chem.*, H. Eyring, C. J. Christensen, and H. D. Johnston, eds., Vol. 11, Annual Reviews, Palo Alto, Calif., 1960, pp. 87–106.
165. Sun, K. H., and F. A. Pecjak, *Mod. Plastics*, **32** (1), 141 (1954).
166. Swallow, A. J., *Radiation Chemistry of Organic Compounds*, Pergamon Press, New York, 1960.
167. Pinner, S. H., *Brit. Plastics*, **34,** 30, 76 (1961).
168. Bovey, F. A., Ref. 155, pp. 1–47.
169. Charlesby, A., Ref. 156, pp. 1–111.
170. Charlesby, A., *Proc. Roy. Soc. (London)*, **A224,** 120 (1954); *Chem. Abstr.*, **49,** 37d (1955).
171. Inokuchi, M., *J. Phys. Soc. Japan*, **14,** 79 (1959); *Chem. Abstr.*, **53,** 13734c (1959).
172. Inokuchi, M., and K. Katsuura, *J. Phys. Soc. Japan*, **14,** 1379 (1959); *Chem. Abstr.*, **54,** 7290 (1960).
173. Katsuura, K., *J. Phys. Soc. Japan*, **15,** 2310 (1960); *Chem. Abstr.*, **56,** 10365e (1962).
174. Kilb, R. W., *J. Phys. Chem.*, **63,** 1838 (1959).
175. Shultz, A. R., P. I. Roth, and G. B. Rathmann, *J. Polymer Sci.*, **22,** 495 (1956).
176. Stockmayer, W. H., and M. Fixman, *Ann. N. Y. Acad. Sci.*, **57,** 334 (1953); *Chem. Abstr.*, **48,** 4287f (1954).
177. Zimm, B. H., and R. W. Kilb, *J. Polymer Sci.*, **37,** 19 (1959).
178. Charlesby, A., Ref. 156, pp. 170–181.
179. Ingram, D. J. E., *Free Radicals as Studied by Electron Spin Resonance*, Butterworths, London, 1958.
180. Bopp, C. D., and O. Sisman, U. S. At. Energy Comm. Rep. ORNL-1373, July, 1953.

181. Sisman, O., and C. D. Bopp, U. S. At. Energy Comm. Rep. ORNL-928, June, 1951.
182. Lawton, E. J., A. M. Bueche, and J. S. Balwit, *Nature,* **172,** 76 (1953).
183. Miller, A. A., E. J. Lawton, and J. S. Balwit, *J. Polymer Sci.*, **14,** 503 (1954).
184. Wall, L. A., *J. Polymer Sci.*, **17,** 141 (1955).
185. Alexander, P., A. Charlesby, and M. Ross, *Proc. Roy. Soc.* (*London*), **A223,** 392 (1954); *Chem. Abstr.*, **48,** 8079f (1954).
186. Shultz, A. R., *J. Polymer Sci.*, **35,** 369 (1959).
187. Slovokhotova, N. A., and V. L. Karpov, *Sb. Rabotpo Radiatsionnoi Khim. Akad. Nauk SSSR,* **1955,** 196; *Chem. Abstr.*, **50,** 4649h (1956).
188. Todd, A., *J. Polymer Sci.*, **42,** 223 (1960).
189. Tsvetkov, Yu. D., Yu. N. Molin, and V. V. Voevodskii, *Vysokomolekul. Soedin.*, **1,** 1805 (1959); *Polymer Sci.* (*USSR*) (*English Transl.*) **2,** 165 (1961); *Chem. Abstr.*, **54,** 19171f (1960).
190. Charlesby, A., *Nature,* **171,** 167 (1953).
191. Charlesby, A., and M. Ross, *Nature,* **171,** 1153 (1953).
192. Ross, M., and A. Charlesby, *Atomics* (*London*), **4,** 189 (1953).
193. Wall, L. A., and M. Magat, *J. Chim. Phys.*, **50,** 308 (1953); *Chem. Abstr.*, **47,** 9812c (1953).
194. Wall, L. A., and M. Magat, *Mod. Plastics,* **30** (11), 111 (1953).
195. Shultz, A. R., P. I. Roth, and J. M. Berge, paper presented at the 135th National Meeting of the American Chemical Society, Boston, Mass., Apr. 5–10, 1959. Submitted to J. Polymer Sci. for publication.
196. Wall, L. A., and D. W. Brown, *J. Res. Natl. Bur. Std.*, **57,** 131 (1956); *Chem. Abstr.*, **51,** 5571a (1957).
197. Itzhaki, R. F., and P. Alexander, *Radiation Res.*, **15,** 553 (1961); *Chem. Abstr.* **58,** 8054b (1963).
198. Shultz, A. R., *J. Am. Chem. Soc.*, **80,** 1854 (1958).
199. Wall, L. A., and D. W. Brown, *J. Phys. Chem.*, **61,** 129 (1957).
200. Weiss, J., *J. Polymer Sci.*, **29,** 425 (1958).
201. Day, M. J., and G. Stein, *Nature,* **168,** 644 (1951).
202. Ohnishi, S.-I., and I. Nitta, *J. Polymer Sci.*, **38,** 451 (1959).
203. Parkinson, W. W., and D. Binder, *Materials in Nuclear Applications, ASTM Special Technical Publication No. 276*, ASTM, Philadelphia, 1960, pp. 224–32.
204. Alexander, P., and A. Charlesby, *Nature,* **173,** 578 (1954).
205. Alexander, P., and A. Charlesby, in *Radiobiology Symposium,* Z. M. Bacq and P. Alexander, eds., Academic Press, New York, 1955, pp. 49–59; *Chem. Abstr.*, **49,** 12986a (1955).
206. Alexander, P., and D. J. Toms, *Radiation Res.*, **9,** 509 (1958); *Chem. Abstr.*, **53,** 4803a (1959).
207. Burlant, W., D. Green, and C. Taylor, *J. Appl. Polymer Sci.*, **1,** 296 (1959).
208. Okamura, A., T. Manabe, T. Higashimura, Y. Oishi, and S. Futami, *Large Radiation Sources Ind., Vol. 1, Proc. Conf. Warsaw, 8-12 Sept., 1959,* International Atomic Energy Agency, Vienna, 1960, pp. 391–405.
209. Gardner, D. G., and L. M. Epstein, *J. Chem. Phys.*, **34,** 1653 (1961).
210. Henglein, A., M. Boysen, and W. Schnabel, *Z. Physik. Chem.* (*Frankfurt*), **10,** 137 (1957); *Chem. Abstr.*, **51,** 6360d (1957).

211. Henglein, A., C. Schneider, and W. Schnabel, *Z. Physik. Chem. (Frankfurt)*, **12**, 339 (1957); *Chem. Abstr.*, **51**, 17469g (1957).
212. Henglein, A., and M. Boysen, *Makromol. Chem.*, **20**, 83 (1956).
213. Bevington, J. C., and A. Charlesby, Intern. Symp. Macromol. Chem., Milan-Turin, 1954 [published as; *Ric. Sci. Suppl.*, **25A**, 408 (1955)]; *Chem. Zentr.*, **1957**, 7948.
214. Chapiro, A., *J. Chim. Phys.*, **53**, 295 (1956); *Chem. Abstr.*, **50**, 8336c (1956).
215. Chapiro, A., *J. Chim. Phys.*, **53**, 306 (1956); *Chem. Abstr.*, **50**, 8336f (1956).
216. Fowler, J. F., and F. T. Farmer, *Nature*, **175**, 516 (1955).
217. Inuishi, Y., H. Sumitomo, and K. Hayata, *Technol. Rept. Osaka Univ.*, **8**, 243 (1958); *Chem. Abstr.*, **53**, 16623 (1959).
218. Munick, R. J., *Bull. Am. Phys. Soc.*, [2], **1**, 321 (1956).
219. Vanhuyse, V. J., G. J. Vanpraet, and J. F. van Landuyt, *Nature*, **191**, 595 (1961).
220. Schneider, E. E., M. J. Day, and G. Stein, *Nature*, **168**, 645 (1951).
221. Abraham, R. J., H. W. Melville, D. W. Ovenall, and D. H. Whiffen, *Trans. Faraday Soc.*, **54**, 1133 (1958); *Chem. Abstr.*, **53**, 12002a (1959).
222. Atherton, N. M., H. W. Melville, and D. H. Whiffen, *Trans. Faraday Soc.*, **54**, 1300 (1958); *Chem. Abstr.*, **53**, 11999g (1959).
223. Ungar, I. S., W. B. Gager, and R. I. Leininger, *J. Polymer Sci.*, **44**, 295 (1960).
224. Bamford, C. H., and J. C. Ward, *Polymer*, **2**, 277 (1961).
225. Ovenall, D. W., *J. Polymer Sci.*, **41**, 199 (1959).
226. Hukada, K., *Mem. Fac. Sci. Kyushu Univ.*, **B3**, (1) 41 (1960).
227. Ohnishi, S.-I., Y. Ikeda, M. Kashiwagi, and I. Nitta, *Polymer*, **2**, 119 (1961).
228. Tsvetkov, Yu. D., N. N. Bubnov, M. A. Makul'skii, Yu. S. Lazurkin, and V. V. Voevodskii, *Dokl. Akad. Nauk SSSR*, **122**, 1053 (1958); *Chem. Abstr.*. **54**, 23786c (1960).
229. Uebersfeld, J., *Compt. Rend.*, **239**, 240 (1954); *Chem. Abstr.*, **49**, 717b (1955).
230. Uebersfeld, J., *Ann. Phys. (Paris)*, **1**, 395 (1956); *Chem. Abstr.*, **50**, 11108a (1956).
231. Kuri, Z., and H. Ueda, *J. Polymer Sci.*, **50**, 349 (1961).
231a. Schneider, E. E., *Discussions Faraday Soc.*, **19**, 158 (1955); *Chem. Abstr.*, **50**, 9869c (1956).
232. Graham, R. K., M. S. Gluckman, and M. J. Kampf, *J. Polymer Sci.*, **38**, 417 (1959).
233. Higuchi, J., S. Shida, R. Kusaka, and T. Miyamae, *Bull. Chem. Soc. Japan*, **33**, 1232 (1960); *Chem. Abstr.*, **55**, 6912c (1961).
234. Alexander, P., and M. Fox, *Nature*, **169**, 572 (1952).
235. Alexander, P., and M. Fox, *Nature*, **170**, 1022 (1952).
236. Alexander, P., and M. Fox, *J. Chim. Phys.*, **50**, 415 (1953); *Chem. Abstr.*, **48**, 2448b (1954).
237. Alexander, P., and M. Fox, *Trans. Faraday Soc.*, **50**, 605 (1954); *Chem. Abstr.*, **49**, 1361g (1955).
238. Bovey, F. A., Ref. 155, pp. 143–145.
239. Graham, R. K., *J. Polymer Sci.*, **38**, 209 (1959).
240. Graham, R. K., *J. Polymer Sci.*, **37**, 441 (1959).
241. Grassie, N., and H. W. Melville, *Proc. Roy. Soc. (London)*, **A199**, 14, 24 (1949); *Chem. Abstr.*, **44**, 2342h (1950).
242. Fox, R. B., and L. G. Isaacs, NRL Report 5720, Dec. 14, 1961.

243. Shultz, A. R., *J. Phys. Chem.*, **65**, 967 (1961).
244. Frolova, M. I., and A. V. Riabov, *Vysokomolekul. Soedin.*, **1**, 1453 (1959); *Polymer Sci. (USSR) (English Transl.)*, **2**, 1 (1961); *Chem. Abstr.*, **54**, 13716f (1960).
245. Davidson, W. L., and I. G. Geib, *J. Appl. Phys.*, **19**, 427 (1948).
246. Alexander, P., R. M. Black, and A. Charlesby, *Proc. Roy. Soc. (London)*, **A232**, 31 (1955); *Chem. Abstr.*, **50**, 682d (1956).
247. Gehman, S. D., and L. M. Hobbs, *Rubber World*, **130**, 643 (1954).
248. Alexander, P., and A. Charlesby, *Proc. Roy. Soc. (London)*, **A230**, 136 (1955); *Chem. Abstr.*, **49**, 15282c (1955).
249. Henglein, A., and C. Schneider, *Z. Physik. Chem. (Frankfurt)*, **19**, 367 (1959); *Chem. Abstr.*, **54**, 2900f (1960).
250. Sebban-Danon, J., *J. Chim. Phys.*, **57**, 1123 (1960); *Chem. Abstr.*, **55**, 13021f (1961).
251. Bovey, F. A., Ref. 155, p. 119.
252. Libby, W. F., *J. Chem. Phys.*, **35**, 1714 (1961).
253. Schissler, D. O., and D. P. Stevenson, *J. Chem. Phys.*, **24**, 926 (1956).
254. Williams, T. F., *Trans. Faraday Soc.*, **57**, 755 (1961); *Chem. Abstr.*, **55**, 25439c (1961).
255. Roth, P. I. and A. R. Shultz, paper presented at the 134th Meeting of the American Chemical Society, Chicago, Ill., Sept. 7–12, 1958.
256. Kotliar, A. M., *J. Appl. Polymer Sci.*, **2**, 134 (1959).
257. Kotliar, A. M., *J. Polymer Sci.*, **55**, 71 (1961).
258. Florin, R. E., L. A. Wall, and D. W. Brown, *Trans. Faraday Soc.*, **56**, 1304 (1960); *Chem. Abstr.*, **55**, 6022d (1961).
259. Stokes, S., and R. B. Fox, NRL Report 5591, Feb. 20, 1961.
260. Bopp, C. D., and O. Sisman, *Nucleonics*, **13**, (10), 51 (1955); *Chem. Abstr.*, **50**, 7618i (1956).
261. Burr, J. G., and W. M. Garrison, U. S. At. Energy Comm., AECD-2078 (1950).
262. Charlesby, A., At. Energy Res. Estab. (G. Brit.) Rept. M/R-978 (1952).
263. Charlesby, A., *Plastics (London)*, **18**, 142 (1953).
264. Charlesby, A., *Nucleonics*, **12**, (6), 18 (1954).
265. Florin, R. E., and L. A. Wall, *J. Res. Natl. Bur. Std.*, **65A**, 375 (1961); *Chem. Abstr.*, **56**, 4935h (1962).
266. Matsumae, K., M. Watanabe, A. Nishioka, and T. Ichimiya, *J. Polymer Sci.*, **28**, 653 (1958).
267. Nishioka, A., K. Matsumae, M. Watanabe, M. Tajima, and M. Owaki, *J. Appl. Polymer Sci.*, **2**, 114 (1959).
268. Nishioka, A., M. Tajima, and M. Owaki, *J. Polymer Sci.*, **28**, 617 (1958).
269. Kusumoto, H., *J. Phys. Soc. Japan*, **15**, 867 (1960); *Chem. Abstr.*, **55**, 8046g (1961).
270. Tikhomirova, N. S., Yu. M. Malinskii, and V. L. Karpov, *Vysokomolekul. Soedin.*, **2**, 1335 (1960); *Chem. Abstr.*, **55**, 19312a (1961).
271. Tikhomirova, N. S., Yu. M. Malinskii, and V. L. Karpov, *Vysokomoleukl Soedin.*, **2**, 1349 (1960); *Chem. Abstr.*, **55**, 19312c (1961).
272. Linnenbom, V. J., *Insulation*, **6** (3), 11 (1960).
273. Loy, W. E., Jr., *Materials in Nuclear Applications, ASTM Special Technical Publication No. 276*, ASTM, Philadelphia, 1960, pp. 68–78.
274. Fowler, J. F., and F. T. Farmer, *Nature*, **174**, 136 (1954).

275. Meyer, R. A., F. L. Bouquet, and R. S. Alger, *J. Appl. Phys.*, **27,** 1012 (1956).
276. Golden, J. H., *J. Polymer Sci.*, **45,** 534 (1960).
277. Hornbeck, R., Report ER-10317, *Nucl. Sci. Abstr.*, **14:** 3528 (1960).
278. Ryan, J. W., *Mod. Plastics*, **31** (2), 152 (1953).
279. Worrall, R., At. Energy Res. Estab. (G. Brit.), Rept. M/R-2159, HX-2606, Jan. 1957.
279a. Bovey, F. A., Ref. 155, pp. 153–154.
280. Charlesby, A., Ref. 156, pp. 355–356.
281. Ard, W. B., H. Shields, and W. Gordy, *J. Chem. Phys.*, **23,** 1727 (1955).
282. Rexroad, H. N., and W. Gordy, *J. Chem. Phys.*, **30,** 399 (1959).
283. Schneider, E. E., *J. Chem. Phys.*, **23,** 978 (1955).
284. Wall, L. A., *ASTM Special Technical Publication No. 276*, ASTM, Philadelphia 1960, pp. 208–23.
285. Tamura, N., *J. Phys. Soc. Japan*, **15,** 943 (1960); *Chem. Abstr.*, **54,** 18023e (1960).
286. Matsugashita, T., and K. Shinohara, *J. Chem. Phys.*, **35,** 1652 (1961).
287. Wall, L. A., and R. E. Florin, *J. Appl. Polymer Sci.*, **2,** 251 (1959).
288. Barkalov, I. M., V. I. Gol'danskii, B. G. Dzantiev, and E. V. Egorov, *Vysokomolekul. Soedin.*, **2,** 1801 (1960); *J. Polymer Sci.*, **55,** S10 (1961).
289. Ehrenberg, L., and K. G. Zimmer, *Acta Chem. Scand.*, **10,** 874 (1956); *Chem. Abstr.*, **52,** 19229 (1958).
290. Matsugashita, T., and K. Shinohara, *J. Chem. Phys.*, **32,** 954 (1960).
291. Tsvetkov, Yu. D., Ya. S. Lebedev, and V. V. Voevodskii, *Vysokomolekul. Soedin.*, **1,** 1519 (1959); *Polymer Sci. (USSR) (English Transl.)* **2,** 45 (1960).
292. Tsvetkov, Yu. D., Ya. S. Lebedev, and V. V. Voevodskii, *Vysokomolekul. Soedin.*, **1,** 1634 (1959); *Polymer Sci. (USSR) (English Transl.)* **2,** 85 (1961).
293. Lebedev, Ya. S., Yu. D. Tsvetkov, and V. V. Voevodskii, *Kinetika i Kataliz*, **1,** 496 (1960); *Nucl. Sci. Abstr.*, **15:** 10998T (1961); *Chem. Abstr.*, **55,** 20584g (1961).
294. Byrne, J., T. W. Costikyan, C. B. Hanford, D. L. Johnson, and W. L. Mann, *Ind. Eng. Chem.*, **45,** 2549 (1953).
295. Goodman, J., and J. H. Coleman, *J. Polymer Sci.*, **25,** 253, 502 (1957).
296. Proctor, B. E., and M. Karel, *Mod. Packaging*, **28,** (6), 137 (1955).
297. Harris, K. K., and W. E. Price, *Intern. J. Appl. Radiation Isotopes*, **11,** 114 (1961). *Chem. Abstr.*, **56,** 3093a (1962).
298. Shultz, A. R., N. Knoll, and G. A. Morneau, *J. Polymer Sci.*, **62,** 211 (1962).
299. Barr, D. A., and R. N. Haszeldine, *J. Chem. Soc.*, **1955,** 1881.
300. Bovey, F. A., Ref. 155, pp. 190–196.
301. Charlesby, A., Ref. 156, pp. 359–367.
302. Lawton, E. J., W. D. Bellamy, R. E. Hungate, M. P. Bryant, and E. Hull, *Science*, **113,** 380 (1951).
303. Little, K., *Nature*, **170,** 1075 (1952).
304. Saeman, J. F., M. A. Millett, and E. J. Lawton, *Ind. Eng. Chem.*, **44,** 2848 (1952).
305. Charlesby, A., At. Energy Res. Estab. (G. Brit.) M/R-1342 (1954). *Mod. Plastics*, **31** (12), 148 (1954).
306. Charlesby, A., *J. Polymer Sci.*, **15,** 263 (1955).
307. Arthur, J. C., Jr., *Textile Res. J.*, **28,** 204 (1958).
308. Blouin, F. A., and J. C. Arthur, Jr., *Textile Res. J.*, **28,** 198 (1958).

309. Demint, R. J., and J. C. Arthur, Jr., *Textile Res. J.*, **29**, 276 (1959).
310. Usmanov, Kh. U., E. I. Kalabanovskaya, and R. B. Damovskii, *Vysokomolekul. Soedin.*, **3**, 223 (1961); *Chem. Abstr.*, **56**, 2607 (1962).
311. Teszler, O., H. Wiehart, and H. A. Rutherford, *Textile Res. J.*, **28**, 131 (1958).
312. Pan, H.-P., B. E. Proctor, S. A. Goldblith, H. M. Morgan, and R. Z. Naar, *Textile Res. J.*, **29**, 415, 422 (1959).
313. Pan, H.-P., B. E. Proctor, and S. A. Goldblith, *Textile Res. J.*, **29**, 425 (1959).
314. Sobue, H., and Y. Saito, *Bull. Chem. Soc. Japan*, **34**, 1343 (1961); *Chem. Abstr.*, **56**, 3053c (1962).
315. Kuri, Z., Y. Fugiwara, H. Ueda, and S. Shida, *J. Chem. Phys.*, **33**, 1884 (1960).
316. Bailey, A. J., S. A. Barker, J. S. Brimacombe, D. Pooley, and D. H. Spence, *Nature*, **190**, 259 (1961).
317. Williams, D., B. Schmidt, M. L. Wolfrom. A. Michelakis, and L. J. McCabe, *Proc. Natl. Acad. Sci. U. S.*, **45**, 1744 (1959); *Chem. Abstr.*, **54**, 12785f (1960).
318. Glegg, R. E., and Z. I. Kertesz, *Science*, **124**, 893 (1956).
319. Kertesz, Z. I., B. H. Morgan, L. W. Tuttle, and M. Lavin, *Radiation Res.*, **5**, 372 (1956); *Chem. Abstr.*, **51**, 7464h (1957).
320. Karel, M., and B. E. Proctor, *Mod. Packaging*, **30**, (5), 141 (1957).
321. Winogradoff, N. N., *Nature*, **165**, 72, 123 (1950).
322. Leavitt, F. C., *J. Polymer Sci.*, **45**, 536 (1960).
323. Leavitt, F. C., *J. Polymer Sci.*, **51**, 349 (1961).
324. Sugai, S., M. Ishikawa, and J. Furuichi, *J. Phys. Soc. Japan*, **14**, 544 (1959); *Chem. Abstr.*, **53**, 18606b (1959).
325. Pinner, S. H., T. T. Greenwood, and D. G. Lloyd, *Nature*, **184**, 1303 (1959).
326. Price, F. P., W. D. Bellamy, and E. J. Lawton, *J. Phys. Chem.*, **58**, 821 (1954).
327. Ricketts, C. R., and C. E. Rowe, *Chem. Ind. (London)*, **1954**, 189; *Chem. Abstr.*, **48**, 5670g (1954).
328. Bovey, F. A., Ref. 155, pp. 199–201.
329. Granath, K. A., and P.-O. Kinell, *Acta Chem. Scand.*, **15**, 141 (1961); *Chem. Abstr.*, **55**, 19432g (1961).
330. Phillips, G. O., and G. J. Moody, *J. Chem. Soc.*, **1958**, 3534.
331. Phillips, G. O., and W. J. Criddle, *J. Chem. Soc.*, **1961**, 3756.
332. Phillips, G. O., G. J. Moody, and G. L. Mattok, *J. Chem. Soc.*, **1958**, 3522.
333. Danno, A., *J. Phys. Soc. Japan*, **13**, 609 (1958); *Chem. Abstr.*, **52**, 15267f (1958).
334. Sakurada, I., and S. Matsuzawa, *Kobunshi Kagaku*, **17**, 689 (1960); *Nucl. Sci. Abstr.*, **15**: 11000(T) (1961); *Chem. Abstr.*, **55**, 25728c (1961).
335. Sakurada, I., and S. Matsuzawa, *Kobunshi Kagaku*, **17**, 693 (1960); *Nucl. Sci. Abstr.*, **15**: 11000(T) (1961); *Chem. Abstr.*, **55**, 25728d (1961).
336. Fujiwara, S., *J. Polymer Sci.*, **44**, 93 (1960).
337. Fujiwara, S., *J. Polymer Sci.*, **51**, S15, S18 (1961).
338. Berkowitch, J., A. Charlesby, and V. Desreux, *J. Polymer Sci.*, **25**, 490 (1957).
339. Hirano, Y., and A. Amemiya, *Bull. Chem. Soc. Japan*, **34**, 292 (1961); *Nucl. Sci. Abstr.*, **15**: 18097 (1961); *Chem. Abstr.*, **55**, 14026i (1961).
340. Danno, A., *J. Phys. Soc. Japan*, **13**, 722 (1958); *Chem. Abstr.*, **52**, 17786c (1958).
341. Dieu, H., and V. Desreux, *Large Radiation Sources Ind., Vol. 1, Proc. Conf., Warsaw, 8-12 Sept. 1959*, International Atomic Energy Agency, Vienna, 1960, pp. 341–6.

342. Matsumoto, M., and A. Danno, *Large Radiation Sources Ind., Vol. 1, Proc. Conf., Warsaw, 8–12 Sept. 1959*, International Atomic Energy Agency, Vienna, 1960, pp. 331–9.
343. Saito, O., *J. Phys. Soc. Japan*, **14,** 792 (1959); *Chem. Abstr.*, **53,** 23053c (1959).
344. Sakurada, I., and Y. Ikeda, *Bull. Inst. Chem. Res. Kyoto Univ.*, **39,** 99 (1961); *Nucl. Sci. Abstr.*, **15:** 19953 (1961).
345. Sakurada, I., A. Nakajima, and H. Aoki, *Battelle Tech. Rev.*, **8,** 484a (1959).
346. Ogawa, S., *J. Phys. Soc. Japan*, **16,** 1488 (1961); *Chem. Abstr.*, **56,** 2094f (1962).
347. Danno, A., *J. Phys. Soc. Japan*, **13,** 614 (1958); *Chem. Abstr.*, **52,** 15267g (1958).
348. Shultz, A. R., *J. Polymer Sci.*, **47,** 267 (1960).
349. Wissbrun, K. F., *J. Am. Chem. Soc.*, **81,** 58 (1959).
350. Jackson, W. W., and D. Hale, *Rubber Age (N. Y.)*, **77,** 865 (1955).
351. Charlesby, A., and D. Grove, *Proc. Rubber Technol. Conf. 3rd London*, **1954,** T. H. Messenger, ed., Institute of the Rubber Industry, London, p. 317.
352. Ryan, J. W., *Nucleonics*, **11** (8), 13 (1953); *Chem. Abstr.*, **48,** 4244g (1954).
353. Bovey, F. A., Ref. 155, p. 178.
354. Horrocks, L. A., *Mater. Design Eng.*, **47,** (1), 120 (1958); *Chem. Abstr.*, **52,** 4999d (1958).
355. Aitken, I. D., and K. Ralph, At. Energy Res. Estab. (G. Brit.), Rept. 3085 (1960).

D. Ozonization

356. Bailey, P. S., *Chem. Rev.*, **58,** 925 (1958).
357. For a summary see: Criegee, R., *Record Chem. Progr.* (Kresge-Hooker Sci. Lib.), **18,** 111 (1957).
358. Criegee, R., and G. Schröder, *Chem. Ber.*, **93,** 689 (1960).
359. Riebel, A. H., R. E. Ecískson, C. J. Abshire, and P. S. Bailey, *J. Am. Chem. Soc.*, **82,** 1801 (1960).
360. Maggiolo, A., and S. J. Niegowski, in *Ozone Chemistry and Technology*, Advances in Chemistry Series, No. 21, American Chemical Society, Washington, D. C., 1959, p. 202.
361. Slomp, G., and J. L. Johnson, Ref. 360, p. 162.
362. Knowles, W. S., and Q. E. Thompson, *J. Org. Chem.*, **25,** 1031 (1960).
363. Briner, E., Ref. 360, p. 184.
364. Dillemuth, F. J., D. R. Skidmore, and C. C. Schubert, *J. Phys. Chem.*, **64,** 1496 (1960).
365. Hay, A. S., J. W. Eustance, and H. S. Blanchard, *J. Org. Chem.*, **25,** 616 (1960).
366. Barnard, D., G. P. McSweeney, and J. F. Smith, *Tetrahedron Letters*, **1960,** (14), 1.
367. Harries, C., *Ber.*, **37,** 2708 (1904).
368. Harries, C., *Ber.*, **38,** 1195 (1905).
369. Pummerer, R., G. Ebermayer, and K. Gerlach, *Ber.*, **64,** 804, 809 (1931).
370. Pummerer, R., and H. Richtzenhain, *Ann. Chem.*, **529,** 33 (1937).
371. Pickles, S. S., *J. Chem. Soc.*, **97,** 1085 (1910).
372. Pummerer, R., *Kautschuk Gummi*, **10,** 149 (1934); *Chem. Abstr.*, **29,** 4209 (1935).
373. Hill, R., J. R. Lewis, and J. L. Simonsen, *Trans. Faraday Soc.*, **35,** 1067, 1073 (1939); *Chem. Abstr.*, **34,** 77[4] (1940).
374. Alekseeva, E. N., and R. M. Belitskaya, *Zh. Obshch. Khim.*, **11,** 358 (1941); *Rubber Chem. Technol.*, **15,** 693 (1942).

375. Alekseeva, E. N., *Zh. Obshich. Khim.*, **11,** 353 (1941); *Rubber Chem. Technol.*, **15,** 698 (1942).
376. Klebanskii, A., and V. G. Vasileva, *J. Prakt. Chem.*, **144,** 251 (1936); *Rubber Chem. Technol.*, **10,** 126 (1937); *Chem. Abstr.*, **30,** 4357[8] (1936).
377. Klebanskii, A., and K. Chevychalova, *Zh. Obshch. Khim.*, **17,** 941 (1947); *Rubber Chem. Technol.*, **21,** 605 (1948).
378. Mochel, W. E., and J. B. Nichols, *Ind. Eng. Chem.*, **43,** 154 (1951).
379. Rabjohn, N., C. E. Bryan, G. E. Inskeep, H. W. Johnson, and J. K. Lawson, *J. Am. Chem. Soc.*, **69,** 314 (1947).
380. Marvel, C. S., and R. E. Light, Jr., *J. Am. Chem. Soc.*, **72,** 3887 (1950).
381. Rehner, J., Jr., and P. Gray, *Ind. Eng. Chem., Anal. Ed.*, **17,** 367 (1945).
382. Rehner, J., Jr., *Ind. Eng. Chem.*, **36,** 46 (1944).
383. Rehner, J., Jr., *Ind. Eng. Chem.*, **36,** 118 (1944).
384. Yakubchik, A. I., A. I. Spasskova, A. G. Zak, and I. D. Shotatskaya, *Zh. Obshch. Khim.*, **28,** 3090 (1958); *Chem. Abstr.*, **53,** 7645 (1959).
385. Yakubchik, A. I., N. G. Kasatkina, and T. E. Pavlovskaya, *Zh. Obshch. Khim.*, **27,** 1487 (1957); *J. Gen. Chem. USSR (English Transl.)*, **27,** 1561 (1957); *Rubber Chem. Technol.*, **32,** 284 (1959).
386. Thompson, W., *J. Soc. Chem. Ind.*, **4,** 710 (1885).
387. Williams, I., *Ind. Eng. Chem.*, **18,** 367 (1926).
388. Haushalter, F. L., *Electron. World*, **86,** 267 (1925).
389. Newton, R. G., *J. Rubber Res. Inst. Malaya*, **14,** 27, 41 (1945); *Chem. Abstr.*, **39,** 2901[2] (1945).
390. Jackson, H., *Trans. Inst. Rubber Ind.*, **10,** 292 (1934); *Chem. Abstr.*, **29,** 3871 (1935).
391. McKee, R. H., and H. A. Depew, *Ind. Eng. Chem.*, **20,** 484 (1928).
392. Evans, B. B., *Trans. Inst. Rubber Ind.*, **5,** 442 (1930); *Chem. Abstr.*, **24,** 4664 (1930).
393. Ewell, A. W., *J. Appl. Phys.*, **13,** 759 (1942).
394. Tener, R. F., W. H. Smith, and W. L. Holt, *J. Res. Natl. Bur. Std.*, **A21,** 353 (1927); *Chem. Abstr.*, **21,** 4095 (1927).
395. Asano, K., *India Rubber J.*, **70,** 307, 347, 389 (1925); *Chem. Abstr.*, **19,** 3616 (1925).
396. Reynolds, W. C., *J. Soc. Chem. Ind.*, **49,** 168 (1930); *Chem. Abstr.*, **24,** 3584 (1930).
397. Van Rossem, A., and H. W. Talen, *Kautschuk*, **7,** 79, 115 (1931); *Rubber Chem. Technol.*, **4,** 490 (1931); *Chem. Abstr.*, **25,** 5795 (1931).
398. Potter, W. J., *India Rubber World*, **103,** 41 (1940).
399. Shepard, N. A., S. Krall, and H. L. Morris, *Ind. Eng. Chem.*, **18,** 615 (1926).
400. Turner, H., *Trans. Inst. Rubber Ind.*, **10,** 21 (1934); *Rubber Chem. Technol.*, **8,** 58 (1935).
401. Wurm, E., *Kautschuk Gummi*, **8,** 21 (1932); *Chem. Abstr.*, **26,** 2619 (1932).
402. Ball, J. M., and C. E. Bradley, *Rubber Age (N. Y.)*, **50,** 425 (1942); *Rubber Chem. Technol.*, **15,** 647 (1942).
403. Howard, J. C., and H. C. Boehmer, through Ref. 402.
404. Northam, A. J., E. I. duPont de Nemours and Co., Inc., Elastomers Dept., Report No. 38-2 (1938).

405. Werkenthin, T. A., D. Richardson, R. F. Thornley, and R. E. Morris, *Rubber Age (N. Y.)*, **50,** 103, 199 (1941); *Chem. Abstr.*, **36,** 3065[8] (1942).
406. Dawson, T. R., and J. R. Scott, *Trans. Inst. Rubber Ind.*, **16,** 198 (1940); *Rubber Chem. Technol.*, **14,** 673 (1941).
407. Kelly, A., B. S. Taylor, and W. N. Jones, *Ind. Eng. Chem.*, **20,** 296 (1928); *Rubber Chem. Technol.*, **1,** 106 (1928).
408. Somerville, A. A., J. M. Ball, and W. H. Cope, *Ind. Eng. Chem.*, **21,** 1183 (1929).
409. Dufraisse, C., *Rev. Gen. Caoutchouc*, **9,** (85), 4–10; (86), 3–21 (1932); *Rubber Chem. Technol.*, **6,** 157 (1933).
410. Duclaux, J., *J. Phys. Radium*, **6,** 401 (1935); *Chem. Zentr.*, **1936,** II, 586.
411. Merz, O., *Kautschuk Gummi*, **8,** 73 (1932); *Chem. Abstr.*, **26,** 4503 (1932).
412. Edgar, J. L., and F. A. Paneth, *J. Chem. Soc.*, **1941,** 519.
413. Schönbein, C. F., *Ann. Phys.*, **65,** 69, 161 (1845).
414. Fabry, C., and H. Buisson, *J. Phys. Radium*, **2,** 197 (1921).
415. Fowler, A., and R. G. Strutt, *Proc. Roy. Soc. (London)*, **A93,** 577 (1917); *Chem. Abstr.*, **12,** 450 (1918).
416. Meetham, A. R., *Quart. J. Roy. Meteorol. Soc.*, **70,** 20 (1944).
417. Paneth, F. A., and E. Gluckauf, *Nature*, **147,** 614 (1941).
418. Dobson, G. M. B., *Quart. J. Roy. Meteorol. Soc.*, **62,** 52 (1936).
419. Dobson, G. M. B., *Endeavour*, **11,** 215 (1952); *Chem. Abstr.*, **47,** 6197h (1953).
420. Tonsberg, E., and D. Chalonge, *Quart. J. Roy. Meteorol. Soc.*, **62,** 55 (1936).
421. Gluckauf, E., *Quart. J. Roy. Meteorol. Soc.*, **70,** 13 (1941).
422. Wulf, O. R., *Proc. Am. Sci. Congr. 8th, Washington, D. C.*, **7,** 439 (1940); *Chem. Abstr.*, **37,** 5290 (1943).
423. Paetzold, H. K., Ref. 360, p. 209.
424. Lunt, R. W., Ref. 360, p. 286.
425. Nellen, A. H., W. B. Dunlap, Jr., C. J. Glaser, Jr., and R. A. Landes, *Rubber Age (N. Y.)*, **66,** 659 (1950).
426. Kettering Lab., Univ. of Cincinnati, "Concentrations of Oxidizing Substances in the Atmosphere of a Number of American Cities," Sept., 1954.
427. Air Pollution Foundation, 704 South Spring Street, Los Angeles, California, "An Aerometric Survey of the Los Angeles Basin," July 1, 1955.
428. Renzetti, N. A., Ref. 360. p. 230.
429. Bartel, A. W., and J. W. Temple, *Rubber Age (N. Y.)*, **69,** 326 (1951).
430. Haagen-Smit, A. J., C. E. Bradley, and M. M. Fox, *Ind. Eng. Chem.*, **45,** 2086 (1953).
431. Haagen-Smit, A. J., *Ind. Eng. Chem.*, **44,** 1342 (1952).
432. Kohman, G. T., *J. Phys. Chem.*, **33,** 226 (1929).
433. Haushalter, F. L., *India Rubber J.*, **70,** 897 (1925); *Chem. Abstr.*, **20,** 678 (1926).
434. Haushalter, F. L., W. N. Jones, and J. W. Schade, *Ind. Eng. Chem.*, **20,** 300 (1928); *Rubber Chem. Technol.*, **1,** 120 (1928).
435. Briner, E., C. El-Djabri, and H. Paillard, *Helv. Chim. Acta*, **21,** 95 (1938); *Chem. Abstr.*, **32,** 4058[9] (1938).
436. Durland, J. R., and H. Adkins, *J. Am. Chem. Soc.*, **61,** 429 (1939).
437. Kendall, F. H., and J. Mann, *J. Polymer Sci.*, **19,** 503 (1956).
438. Beaudry, J. T., *Rubber Age (N. Y.)*, **69,** 429 (1951).
439. Morris, R. E., R. R. James, and T. A. Werkenthin, *Rubber Age (N. Y.)*, **51,** 205 (1942); *Rubber Chem. Technol.*, **16,** 209 (1943).

440. Morris, R. E., J. W. Hollister, A. E. Barrett, and T. A. Werkenthin, *Rubber Age (N. Y.)*, **55**, 45 (1944).
441. Buist, J. M., and G. N. Welding, *Trans. Inst. Rubber Ind.*, **21**, 49 (1945); *Chem. Abstr.*, **40**, 2022[8] (1946).
442. Thornley, E. R., in *Proceedings of the Rubber Technology Conference, 5th*, T. H. Messenger, ed., Institution of the Rubber Industry, 1962.
443. Albrecht, H. O., *J. Chem. Phys.*, **21**, 1421 (1953).
444. Biggs, B. S., *Rubber Chem. Technol.*, **31**, 1015 (1958).
445. Crabtree, J., and A. R. Kemp, *Ind. Eng. Chem.*, **38**, 278 (1946).
446. Smith, D. M., and V. E. Gough, *Trans. Inst. Rubber Ind.*, **29**, 219 (1953); *Chem. Abstr.*, **48**, 3055c (1954).
447. Tucker, H., *Am. Soc. Testing Mater. Spec. Tech. Publ. No. 229*, ASTM, Philadelphia, 1958, p. 30.
448. Andrews, E. H., and M. Braden, *J. Polymer Sci.*, **55**, 787 (1961).
449. Cuthbertson, G. R., and D. D. Dunnom, *Ind. Eng. Chem.*, **44**, 834 (1952).
450. Delman, A. D., B. B. Simms, and A. E. Ruff, *J. Polymer Sci.*, **45**, 415 (1960).
451. Crabtree, J., and B. S. Biggs, *J. Polymer Sci.*, **11**, 280 (1953).
452. Layer, R. W., *J. Polymer Sci.*, **37**, 545 (1959).
453. Kearsley, E. P. W., *Rubber Age (N. Y.)*, **27**, 649 (1930), *Rubber Chem. Technol.*, **4**, 13 (1930); *Chem. Abstr.*, **25**, 232 (1931).
454. Tuley, W. F., *Ind. Eng. Chem.*, **31**, 714 (1939).
455. Powell, E. F., and V. E. Gough, *Trans. Inst. Rubber Ind.*, **21**, 102 (1945); *Chem. Abstr.*, **40**, 2023[8] (1946).
456. Murray, R. W., and P. R. Story, Paper presented at the 139th Meeting of the American Chemical Society, St. Louis, Missouri, Mar. 21–30, 1961.
457. Werkenthin, T. A., *Rubber Age (N. Y.)*, **59**, 697 (1946).
458. Kalinsky, J. L., and T. A. Werkenthin, *Rubber Age (N. Y.)*, **75**, 375 (1954).
459. Rugg, J. S., *Anal. Chem.*, **24**, 818 (1952).
460. Rugg, J. S., *Rubber Age (N. Y.)*, **69**, 326 (1951).
461. Creed, K. E., R. B. Hill, and J. W. Breed, *Anal. Chem.*, **25**, 241 (1953).
462. Edwards, D. C., and E. B. Storey, *Trans. Inst. Rubber Ind.*, **31**, 45 (1955); *Chem. Abstr.*, **49**, 13682e (1955).
463. Shaw, R. F., and S. R. Adams, *Anal. Chem.*, **23**, 1649 (1951).
464. Norton, F. J., *Rubber Age (N. Y.)*, **47**, 87 (1940); *Rubber Chem. Technol.*, **13**, 576 (1940); *Chem. Abstr.*, **34**, 6475[9] (1940).
465. Thompson, D. C., R. H. Baker, and R. W. Brownlow, *Ind. Eng. Chem.*, **44**, 850 (1952).
466. Buckley, D. J., and S. B. Robison, *J. Polymer Sci.*, **19**, 145 (1956).
467. Veith, A. G., Ref. 447, p. 97.
468. Eller, S. A., and A. A. Stein, *Rubber Age (N. Y.)*, **89**, 972 (1961).
469. Vodden, H. A., and M. A. A. Wilson, *Trans. Inst. Rubber Ind.*, **35**, 82 (1959); *Chem. Abstr.*, **53**, 23032a (1959).
470. Leeper, H. M., and C. L. Gable, *Rubber World*, **134**, 703 (1956).
471. Zuev, Yu. S., and S. I. Pravednikova, *Kauchuk i Rezina*, **20**, (1), 30 (1961); *Soviet Rubber Technol. (English Transl.)*, **20**, 17 (1961); *Chem. Abstr.*, **55**, 24070h (1961).
472. Buswell, A. G., and J. T. Watts, *Trans. Inst. Rubber Ind.*, **37**, 175 (1961); *Rubber Chem. Technol.*, **35**, 421 (1962).

473. Fielding, J. H., *India Rubber World*, **115**, 802 (1947).
474. Winkelmann, H. A., *Ind. Eng. Chem.*, **44**, 841 (1952).
475. Cox, W. L., Ref. 447, p. 57.
476. Newton, R. G., *Trans. Inst. Rubber Ind.*, **15**, 172 (1939); *Chem. Abstr.*, **34**, 5697[7] (1940).
477. Eccher, S., *Gomma*, **4** (1), 1 (1940), *Rubber Chem. Technol.*, **13**, 566 (1940).
478. Rainier, E. T., and R. H. Gerke, *Ind. Eng. Chem. Anal. Ed.*, **7**, 368 (1935).
479. Werkenthin, T. A., D. Richardson, R. F. Thornley, and R. E. Morris, *India Rubber World*, **105**, 143, 264 (1941); *Rubber Chem. Technol.*, **15**, 358 (1942).
480. Ossefort, Z. T., Ref. 447, p. 39.
481. Hartman, A., and F. Glander, *Kautschuk Gummi*, **8**, WT35 (1955); *Rubber Chem. Technol.*, **29**, 166 (1956).
482. Zapp, R. L., R. H. Decker, M. S. Dyroff, and H. A. Rayner, *J. Polymer Sci.*, **6**, 331 (1951).
483. Neu, R. F., paper presented at Fort Wayne Rubber and Plastics Group April 11, 1957; cf. *Rubber World*, **137**, 398 (1957).
484. Dunkel, W. L., and R. R. Phelan, *Rubber Age* (*N. Y.*), **83**, 281 (1958).
485. Elliot, R., and R. G. Newton, *J. Rubber Res. Inst. Malaya*, **17**, 17 (1948); *Chem. Abstr.*, **42**, 3611a (1948).
486. Jones, R. V., C. W. Moberly, and W. B. Reynolds, *Ind. Eng. Chem.*, **45**, 1117 (1953).
487. Pierson, R. M., W. E. Gibbs, G. E. Meyer, F. J. Naples, W. M. Saltman, R. W. Shrock, L. B. Tewksbury, and G. S. Trick, *Rubber Plastics Age*, **38**, 592, 708 (1957)
488. Meyer, G. E., F. J. Naples, and H. M. Rice, paper presented at 134th meeting of The American Chemical Society, Chicago, Ill., Sept. 7–12, 1958.
489. Buist, J. M., *Rev. Gen. Caoutchouc*, **31**, 479 (1954); *Rubber Chem. Technol.*, **28**, 230 (1955).
490. Ossefort, Z. T., and W. J. Touhey, *Rubber World*, **132**, 62 (1955).
491. Ball, J. M., R. A. Youmans, and A. F. Rausell, *Rubber Age* (*N. Y.*), **55**, 481 (1944).
492. Zuev, Yu. S., and S. I. Pravednikova, *Dokl. Akad. Nauk SSSR*, **116**, 813 (1957); *Proc. Acad. Sci. USSR, Phys. Chem. Sect.* (*English Transl.*), **116**, 641 (1957); *Rubber Chem. Technol.*, **32**, 278 (1959).
493. Dawson, T. R., *Trans. Inst. Rubber Ind.*, **3**, 451 (1928).
494. Cotton, F. H., *Trans. Inst. Rubber Ind.*, **6**, 165 (1930); *Chem. Abstr.*, **25**, 3517 (1931).
495. Popp, G. E., and L. Harbison, *Ind. Eng. Chem.*, **44**, 837 (1952).
496. van Pul, B. I. C. F., *Trans. Inst. Rubber Ind.*, **34**, 28 (1958); *Rubber Chem. Technol.*, **31**, 866 (1958); *Chem. Abstr.*, **52**, 10627c (1958).
497. van Pul, B. I. C. F., *Trans. Inst. Rubber Ind.*, **34**, 37 (1958); *Rubber Chem. Technol.*, **31**, 874 (1958); *Chem. Abstr.*, **52**, 19218h (1958).
498. van Pul, B. I. C. F., *Trans. Inst. Rubber Ind.*, **34**, 86 (1958); *Rubber Chem. Technol.*, **31**, 882 (1958); *Chem. Abstr.*, **52**, 19219a (1958).
499. Grossman, R. F., and A. C. Bluestein, *Rubber Age* (*N. Y.*), **84**, 440 (1958).
500. Edwards, D. C., and E. B. Storey, *Rubber Age* (*N. Y.*), **79**, 787 (1956).
501. Braden, M., and A. N. Gent, *J. Appl. Polymer Sci.*, **3**, 90 (1960).
502. Braden, M., and A. N. Gent, *J. Appl. Polymer Sci.*, **3**, 100 (1960).
503. Crabtree, J., and A. R. Kemp, *Ind. Eng. Chem. Anal. Ed.*, **18**, 769 (1946).

504. Buist, J. M., *Trans. Inst. Rubber Ind.*, **33**, 102 (1957); *Chem. Abstr.*, **52**, 16632e (1958).
505. Bowen, G., and V. H. Regener, *J. Geophys. Res.*, **56**, 307 (1951).
506. Bradley, C. E., and A. J. Haagen-Smit, *Rubber Chem. Technol.*, **24**, 750 (1951).
507. Crabtree, J., and R. H. Erickson, *India Rubber World*, **125**, 719 (1952).
508. Beatty, J. R., and A. E. Juve, *Rubber World*, **131**, 232 (1954).
509. Ford, E. W., and L. V. Cooper, *India Rubber World*, **124**, 696 (1951).
510. Ford, E. W., and L. V. Cooper, *India Rubber World*, **125**, 55 (1951).
511. Shaw, R. F., Z. T. Ossefort, and W. J. Touhey, *Rubber World*, **130**, 636 (1954).
512. Meyer, D. A., and J. G. Sommer, Dayton Rubber Co., Final Report to Detroit Arsenal, June 30, 1957.
513. Carlson, L. E., and R. S. Havenhill, paper presented at Meeting of Rubber Division of the American Chemical Society, Cincinnati, Ohio, May 14–16, 1958.
514. Thornley, E. R., and J. T. Watts, *Proc. Intern. Rubber Conf. Preprint Papers*, Washington, D. C., 1959, p. 190.
515. Smith, F. B., and W. F. Tuley, paper presented at the 134th Meeting of The American Chemical Society, Chicago, Ill., Sept. 7–12, 1958.
516. Cheetham, I. C., and W. A. Gurney, *Trans. Inst. Rubber Ind.*, **37**, 35 (1961); *Chem. Abstr.*, **55**, 24065 (1961).
517. Newton, R. G., *India Rubber J.*, **121**, 257 (1951).
518. Harvey, M., U. S. Patent 2,678,892 (to Harvel Research Corp.), May 8, 1954; *Chem. Abstr.*, **48**, 10371e (1954).
519. Shinkle, S. D., U. S. Patent 2,648,613 (to United States Rubber Co.), Aug. 11, 1953; *Chem. Abstr.*, **47**, 11795d (1953).
520. McMillan, F. M., U. S. Patent 2,514,661 (to Shell Development Co.), July 11, 1950; *Chem. Abstr.*, **44**, 9184d (1950).
521. Rinne, W. W., and E. J. Kvet, paper presented at Army Conf. on Elastomers, Ft. Belvoir, Virginia, April, 1957.
522. Wilson, W. A., *Rubber Age* (*N. Y.*), **90**, 85 (1961).
523. Young, D. W., D. J. Buckley, R. G. Newberg, and L. B. Turner, *Ind. Eng. Chem.*, **41**, 401 (1949).
524. Emmet, R. A., *Ind. Eng. Chem.*, **36**, 730 (1944).
525. Winkelmann, H. A., *India Rubber World*, **113**, 801 (1947).
526. Lundberg, C. V., G. N. Vacca, and B. S. Biggs, *Rubber World*, **135**, 699 (1957).
527. Sharpe, P. D., *Rubber Age* (*N. Y.*), **77**, 884 (1955).
528. Best, L. L., and R. C. W. Moakes, *Trans. Inst. Rubber Ind.*, **27**, 103 (1951); *Chem. Abstr.*, **45**, 6411e (1951).
529. Kreusler and Budde, German Patent 18,740 Aug. 26, 1881.
530. Garvey, B. S., and R. A. Emmet, *Ind. Eng. Chem.*, **36**, 209 (1944).
531. Bennett, H., ed., *Commercial Waxes*, 2nd ed., Chemical Publishing Co., New York, 1956.
532. Ferris, S. W., S. S. Kurtz, Jr., and J. S. Sweely, Ref. 447, p. 72.
533. Baker, D. E., *Rubber Age* (*N. Y.*), **77**, 58 (1955).
534. Gaughan, J. E., *Rubber World*, **133**, 803 (1956).
535. Cutting, I. E., *Rubber Age* (*N. Y.*), **77**, 707 (1955).
536. Tuley, W. F., *Ind. Eng. Chem.*, **31**, 714 (1939).
537. Barton, B. C., U. S. Patent 2,324,056 (to United States Rubber Co.), July 13, 1943; *Chem. Abstr.*, **38**, 280[3] (1944).

538. Pinazzi, C. P., and M. Billuart, *Rev. Gen. Caoutchouc*, **31,** 123 (1954); *Rubber Chem. Technol.*, **28,** 438 (1955).
539. Bergstrom, E. W., Rock Island Arsenal Laboratory Report No. 58-105 (1958).
540. Bruce, F. C., R. E. Isley and B. Hunt, Ordinance Corp. Project No. TT1-718, Report No. 57, Burke Research Co., Oct. 1, 1957.
541. Delman, A. D., B. B. Simms, and A. R. Allison, *Anal. Chem.*, **26,** 1589 (1954).
542. Thelin, J. H., and A. R. Davis, *Rubber Age (N. Y.)*, **86,** 81 (1959).
543. Lowman, M. M., and H. P. Miller, *Proc. Intern. Rubber Conf. Preprint Papers*, Washington, D. C., 1959, p. 212.
544. Sullivan, F. A. V., and A. R. Davis, *Rubber World*, **141,** 240 (1959); *Rubber Chem. Technol.*, **33,** 899 (1960).
545. England, W. D., J. A. Krimian, and R. H. Heinrich, *Rubber Chem. Technol.*, **32,** 1143 (1959).
546. Braden, M., and A. N. Gent, *J. Appl. Polymer Sci.*, **6,** 449 (1962).
547. Braden, M., and D. Barnard, Summaries of Papers, Natural Rubber Producers Research Association Symposium, July, 1960, Brit. Rubber Div., Pub. 13, p. 13, 1960.
548. Braden, M., *J. Appl. Polymer Sci.*, **6,** S6 (1962).
549. Bebbington, G. H., Bell Telephone Laboratories, Inc., unpublished results.
550. Hodgkinson, G. T., and C. E. Kendall, in *Proceedings of the Rubber Technology Conference, 5th,* T. H. Messenger, ed., Institution of the Rubber Industry, 1962.
551. Delman, A. D., A. E. Ruff, B. B. Simms, and A. R. Allison, Ref. 360, p. 176.
552. Murray, R. M., *Rubber Chem. Technol.*, **32,** 1117 (1959).
553. Erickson, E. R., R. A. Berntsen, E. L. Hill, and P. Kusy, Ref. 447, p. 11.
554. Lorenz, O., and C. R. Parks, *Rubber Chem. Technol.*, **36,** 194 (1963).
555. Lorenz, O., and C. R. Parks, *Rubber Chem. Technol.*, **36,** 201 (1963).
556. Kilbourne, H. W., G. R. Wilder, J. E. van Verth, J. O. Harris, and C. C. Tung, *Rubber Chem. Technol.*, **32,** 1155 (1959).
557. Braden, M., and A. N. Gent, *Rubber Age (N. Y.)*, **89,** 753 (1961).
558. Bloomfield, G. F., M. Braden, J. R. Dunn, S. G. Fogg, and M. W. Philpott, *Rubber Age (N. Y.)*, **89,** 805 (1961).
559. Story, P. R., R. W. Murray and G. H. Bebbington, Paper presented at the 81st Meeting of the Rubber Div. of the American Chemical Society, Boston, Mass., Apr. 25–27, 1962. G. H. Bebbington, Bell Telephone Laboratories, Inc., unpublished results, has shown that ozone does not penetrate elastomer films of ca. 0.5 mil thickness.
560. Polyplastic, French Patent 1,166,607-8, June 23, 1958.
561. Polyplastic, French Patent 1,166,652-3 Nov. 13, 1958; *Chem. Abstr.*, **54,** 26004d (1960).
562. Braden, M., and A. N. Gent, *Kautschuk Gummi*, **14,** WT157 (1961); *Rubber Chem. Technol.*, **35,** 200 (1962).
563. Barnhart, R. R., and T. H. Newby in *Introduction to Rubber Technology*, M. Morton, ed., Reinhold, New York, 1959, p. 140.
563a. Michaelis, L., *Biol. Antioxidants, Trans. 3rd Conf.*, **1948,** 11; *Chem. Abstr.*, **44,** 4053d (1950).
564. Biggs, B. S., *Bell System Tech. J.*, **30,** 1078 (1951); *Chem. Abstr.*, **46,** 11761f (1952).

565. Polyplastic, French Patent 1,176,772 (by I. Landler and P. Lebel), Apr. 15, 1959; *Chem. Abstr.*, **54,** 25970a (1960).
566. Koslov, P. V., M. M. Iovleva, and N. A. Plate, *Vysokomolekul. Soedin.*, **1,** 1100 (1959); *Chem. Abstr.*, **55,** 4034 (1961).
567. Polyplastic, French Patent, 1,186,992 Sept. 4, 1959; *Chem. Abstr.*, **54,** 25974e (1960).
568. Staudinger, H., K. Frey, P. Garbsch, and S. Wehrli, *Chem. Ber.*, **62,** 2912 (1929).
569. Cameron, G. G., and N. Grassie, *Makromol. Chem.*, **53,** 72 (1962).
570. Beachell, H. C., and S. P. Nemphos, Ref. 360, p. 168.
571. Lebel, P., *J. Polymer Sci.*, **34,** 697 (1959).
572. Cooper, G. D., and M. Prober, *J. Polymer Sci.*, **44,** 397 (1960).
573. Alter, H., *Am. Chem. Soc. Div. Paint Plastics Printing Ink Chem. Preprints*, **19,** 74 (1959); *Chem. Abstr.*, **57,** 4866 (1962).
574. Lazar, M., J. Pavlinec, Z. Manasek, M. Micko, and D. Berek, *Vysokomolekul. Soedin.*, **3,** 943 (1961); *Rubber Chem. Technol.*, **36,** 527 (1963).
575. Roberts, W. J., and A. R. Day, *J. Am. Chem. Soc.*, **72,** 1226 (1950).
576. Yakubchik, A. I., and A. I. Spasskova, *Zh. Obshch. Khim.*, **26,** 1629 (1956); *Chem. Abstr.*, **51,** 1897 (1957).
577. Baum, B., and L. H. Wartman, *J. Polymer Sci.*, **28,** 537 (1958).

Chapter IX

INTERMOLECULAR REACTIONS

A. CROSSLINKING BY RADIATION

A. R. Shultz

Minnesota Mining & Manufacturing Co.

1. Introduction

The crosslinking of polymers by high energy, ionizing radiations has received more scientific attention than has cleavage of polymer chains (Chapter VIII-C) by these radiations. This is the natural result of the fact that there are more synthetic polymers in common supply which predominantly crosslink during irradiation. Also, the more constructive nature of crosslinking has encouraged attempts to understand the radiation-chemical processes which can lead to improvements in polymer physical properties. This has been especially true of the crosslinking of polyethylene by radiation. Prior to the discovery of this method no simple manner of achieving this effect was known. Subsequently developed chemical crosslinking methods for polyethylene have somewhat offset the initial unique advantages of the radiation process. However, the original impetus provided by practical considerations has been extended by the hope of fathoming the radiation-crosslinking steps occurring in a polymer of "simple" structure.

The general nature of the interaction of radiation with polymers and the experimental methods used in evaluating the changes produced were described in Chapter VIII-C. Polymers which predominantly crosslink form infinite networks which are amenable to study by equilibrium and dynamic viscoelastic methods. The degrees of solubility and swelling of the networks also allow counting of crosslinks and chain cleavages. The extension of earlier statistical theories of random crosslinking of polymer chains (1–3) to radiation-induced crosslinking (4–6) provides a framework for relating observed network properties to the efficiency of crosslink formation. Specialization and refinement of the theories continue (7,8). Aspects of network formation relevant to radiation effect evaluation have been summarized and discussed (9,10). The normal crosslink under consideration is one consisting of a tetrafunctional branch point created by the chemical bonding together of two adjacent polymer chains. One crosslink (two crosslinked polymer chain units) is thereby formed from which four polymeric chain arms emanate. Quantities expressing the efficiency of tetrafunctional crosslinking are G(crosslink), the number of crosslinks formed per 100 electron volts (e.v.) energy absorption, and $E_c = 100/2G$(crosslink), the energy (e.v.) absorbed per crosslinked chain unit formed. A trifunctional branch point can conceivably form by the attack of a reactive polymer chain fragment end upon the backbone of an adjacent chain with attachment thereto (11–14). The extent of such "endlinking" in polymers under irradiation is not known. In most radiation crosslinking studies the formation of tetrafunctional branch-point crosslinks has been assumed.

We will first examine some theories of radiation-induced crosslinking and then proceed to inspect the observed crosslinking characteristics of specific polymer types.

2. Theories of Crosslinking by Radiation

The postulated modes of crosslinking in polymers due to ionizing radiation fall into two main categories. These are crosslinking by means of free radicals which are secondary products of the interactions and crosslinking by means of ionic species which are primary products of the interactions.

The presence of free radicals in irradiated polymers has been amply demonstrated by reactions involving free radical scavengers, by the initiation of free radical polymerizations, and by electron spin resonance absorptions. An early study (15) found that a considerable amount of hydrogen was liberated from polyethylene during irradiation. It was proposed that this was an initial step in formation of crosslinks. The later suggestion (16) that a polymeric free radical formed by hydrogen loss might attack an adjacent chain to form a crosslink with release of a second hydrogen atom (eq. 1) is questionable in the light of energy considerations.

$$\begin{gathered} RCH_2R' \rightarrow R\dot{C}HR' + H\cdot \\ R\dot{C}HR' + R''CH_2R''' \rightarrow RR'CHCHR''R''' + H\cdot \end{gathered} \qquad (1)$$

The formation of a crosslink by the coupling of radicals created on adjacent chains by hydrogen atom loss and abstraction (eqs. 2–4) was

$$-CH_2\underset{\underset{R}{|}}{CH}- \rightarrow -CH_2\underset{\underset{R}{|}}{\dot{C}}- + H\cdot \qquad (2)$$

$$H + \text{—}CH_2\underset{\displaystyle R}{\underset{|}{C}}H\text{—} \rightarrow \text{—}CH_2\underset{\displaystyle R}{\underset{|}{\dot{C}}}\text{—} + H_2 \tag{3}$$

$$\text{—}CH_2\underset{\displaystyle R}{\underset{|}{\dot{C}}}\text{—} + \text{—}CH_2\underset{\displaystyle R}{\underset{|}{\dot{C}}}\text{—} \rightarrow \text{—}CH_2\underset{\displaystyle R}{\underset{|}{\overset{|}{C}}}\underset{\displaystyle R}{\underset{|}{\overset{|}{C}}}CH_2\text{—} \tag{4}$$

postulated (17). The presence of atoms which are readily transferable under free radical attack would favor this mechanism (18). The hydrogen atoms in the backbone α to the side group in vinyl polymers have appreciable lability toward radical attack. The side group is often capable of stabilizing by resonance the radical produced by abstraction. The concept of production of hydrogen in a caged reaction between neighboring chains is appealing, in that it provides the necessary proximal radical sites for crosslinking. Invocation of polymeric radical migration through the irradiated polymer is then not needed. Indication that active sites, either excited energy states or free radicals, do possess some migratory ability has been deduced (19–22).

The participation of unsaturated groups in crosslinking by radical mechanisms must be considered a possibility (23). However, the fact that highly unsaturated polymers such as natural rubber and polybutadiene crosslink with E_c values comparable to that of polyethylene argues against exceptional crosslinkability due to the unsaturation. Admittedly the yield of free radicals is lower in the unsaturated polymers, thus tending to depress any gains in crosslinking efficiency. Kinetic analyses of free radical processes which might lead to crosslinks and other observed changes in polymers during irradiation have been published (24,25). Although such analyses become fairly complex even under simplifying assumptions, extension of the methods as more definitive chemical evidences of mechanism are accrued should be profitable.

Despite the obvious formation and reactions of free radicals in polymers during irradiation the possibility exists that reactions of organic ion radicals and ions can provide the mechanism for crosslink formations. Arguments supporting ionic mechanisms have been advanced and summarized recently (26). The energetics of various ion-molecule reactions appear to correlate qualitatively with the observed influence of structure on the relative probabilities of crosslinking and cleavage of polymeric hydrocarbons (27). Ion-molecule reactions of (28) the type of eqs. (5) and (6)

$$\begin{array}{l} \text{—}CH_2\overset{+}{C}H_2CH_2\text{—} \\ \text{—}CH_2CH_2CH_2\text{—} \end{array} \rightarrow \begin{array}{l} \text{—}CH_2\overset{+}{C}HCH_2\text{—} \\ \qquad\;\; | \\ \text{—}CH_2CHCH_2\text{—} \end{array} + H_2 \tag{5}$$

$$\begin{matrix} -CH_2\overset{+}{C}H_2CH_2- \\ -CH_2CH_2CH_2 \end{matrix} \rightarrow \begin{matrix} -CH_2CHCH_2- \\ | \\ -CH_2CHCH_2- \end{matrix} + H_2^+ \qquad (6)$$

would eliminate the necessity for migrations of reactive sites in the process. For other observed phenomena in which migration of reactive sites or energy transfer are required, hole transport in a pseudo-lattice band mode has been proposed (29).

Mechanisms postulated for the radiation crosslinking of various polymers in the following discussions are couched principally in free radical terminology. This arises both from the preponderance of literature treating the reactions in this manner and from the present writer's disposition in favor of such a viewpoint. Proofs of the relative importance of free radical and ionic reactions in polymer crosslinking by ionizing radiations may emerge slowly in the future.

3. Polymeric Hydrocarbons

Crosslinking of polyethylene by irradiation occurs readily with only slight associated cleavage. Polypropylene is more difficult to crosslink and suffers relatively greater fractures of the chain. Polystyrene exhibits a much lower crosslinking efficiency presumably due to the energy-wasting capability of the phenyl groups. The unsaturated hydrocarbon polymers, natural rubber and polybutadiene, do not show greatly enhanced radiation crosslinkability relative to the saturated aliphatic polymers. All of these hydrocarbon polymers yield hydrogen as the principal gaseous product. Crosslinking appears to result chiefly from the coupling of free radical sites left on the polymer chains by removal of hydrogen atoms. Various interrelations of evolution of hydrogen, formation of free radicals, crosslinking, changes in unsaturation, and competitive side reactions will be observed in the following discussions of the responses of specific polymeric hydrocarbons to radiation.

a. Polyethylene

Radiation studies on polyethylene (PE) have been more numerous than those on any other polymer or polymer family. The general agreement on chemical and physical changes induced in PE by radiation has been remarkably good considering the broad ranges in short- and long-chain branching, crystallinity, and impurity content of the samples, and in conditions of irradiation. Four principal chemical changes are evident in polyethylene undergoing ionizing irradiation *in vacuo*. These are cross-linking, evolution of hydrogen, formation of *trans*-vinylene unsaturation, and disappearance of vinylidene and vinyl unsaturation.

Predominant crosslinking of PE by irradiation in an atomic reactor (15,30,31) and bombardment by high energy electrons (32) was reported early. The crosslink yield, G(crosslink) in crosslinks/100 e.v. absorbed energy, near room temperature has been reported to be: 1.25 (33) and 1.9 (34), x-rays; 1.6–1.65 (35) and 2.5 (at 0°C.) (36), 2 M.e.v. electrons; 2.5–3.0 (37), γ-rays; 4.2 (5), atomic reactor; 3.4–4.6 (38–40), 800 kvp electrons. Two methods used to deduce the formation of a crosslinked network are observation of changes in bulk properties (38,39,41–43) and measurement of partial insolubilization and the swelling of the resultant gel (5,15,38). The rather broad range in G(crosslink) values appears to derive principally from different methods of measuring and calculating the number of crosslinks. G(crosslink) = 3.1 for saturated aliphatic hydrocarbons (atomic reactor irradiation) (44) and G(crosslink) = 2.8 for octacosane (800 kvp electron irradiation) (40) support a value of G(crosslink) $\simeq$ 3.0, this $E_c \simeq$ 17 e.v./crosslinked unit, for PE at room temperature. The present writer believes this to be the best available estimate. A lower value G(crosslink) = 1.8 for hexadecane (45) may be attributable to its liquid state, but this was not noted to be a factor in a previous study (5). A G(crosslink) value of 0.5 calculated from incipient gelation and initial light-scattering molecular weights of 2 M.e.v. electron-irradiated PE points up the fact that the crosslinking efficiency is still under debate (46). The G(crosslink) in electron-irradiated low density PE was found to be independent of the dose, of the dose rate in the 6–2070 Mrad/min. range, and of the energy of the bombarding electrons (47). Similarly, below a dose of 100 Mrad development of *trans*-vinylene unsaturation in high density PE appeared independent of dose rate in the 0.017–20 Mrad/min. range (48). Variations above 100 Mrad suggested possible rate dependency of crosslinking, assuming it to be competitive with *trans*-vinylene formation. PE crosslinking by α-particles which have high linear energy transfer (L.E.T.) is reported to be more efficient than that by low L.E.T. γ-radiation (49). With respect to local concentrations of reactive species this may be considered to be a dose rate effect. The G(crosslink) for γ-irradiated (37) and electron-irradiated (36) PE increases from about 1 to 5 with temperature increase from −100 to +150°C. Very slight decrease in G(crosslink) occurs in going from −100 to −196°C. Since evolution of hydrogen $G(H_2) \simeq$ 3.1, and *trans*-vinylene production, G(—CH=CH—) $\simeq$ 1.3, are essentially constant over the −196 to +100°C. range, the simplest relation $G(H_2) = G(\text{crosslink}) + G(\text{—CH=CH—})$ does not hold well. This causes difficulty in postulating satisfactory crosslinking mechanisms.

Some changes in bulk properties in crosslinked PE have been studied recently by low frequency, forced oscillations (50) and plastic deformations (51). At high radiation doses in an atomic reactor PE samples can be made "rubberlike" at room temperature (52). Electrical conductivity induced in PE during irradiation has been reported proportional to the 0.75 power (γ-rays) (53), the 0.7–0.8 power (γ-rays) (54), the 0.8 ± 0.05 power (x-rays) (55), and the 1.0 power (γ-rays on PE preirradiated with electrons) (54) of the radiation intensity. An ionic, possibly protonic, conduction was suggested for the PE under γ-irradiation (53). The induced conductivity is more likely due to holes or electrons. Radiation-produced *trans*-vinylene bonds may serve as shallow traps for the conductive species (56). The electric strength of PE crosslinked with 4 M.e.v. electrons did not decrease with increasing temperature to the extent predicted by a theory of intrinsic electric strength (57). It appeared to be sustained and stabilized by the crosslinked network. Radiation crosslinking decreases the permeability of PE to O_2, N_2, CO_2, and CH_3Br (58). The decreases are believed due to lowered diffusion coefficients. The diffusion coefficient of water vapor in PE is lowered by irradiation crosslinking, but the permeability is greatly increased due to increased solubility (59). Irradiation has been found to increase the permeability and solubility coefficients in PE of several organic solvents at low temperatures and decrease these parameters at high temperatures (60). The low-temperature effect may arise from crystallinity disruption (cf. seq.) while the decreases at high temperatures reflect impedance to diffusion caused by the constricting network.

Chain scission relative to crosslinking in PE under atomic reactor irradiation was estimated by ultimate gel content to be $\beta/\alpha = 0.35$ chain scissions per crosslinked unit (5). A somewhat lower value, $\beta/\alpha = 0.18$–0.20, was calculated for electron-irradiated PE by partial solubilization of highly crosslinked PE (43). Electron-irradiated liquid *n*-alkanes also show carbon–carbon cleavage by the presence of lower hydrocarbon fractions and hydrocarbons lying between the original alkanes and their dimers (45). Small hydrocarbon molecules formed during x-irradiation were found to be approximately six times as abundant in high pressure (branched) PE as in low pressure PE (33). Carbon–carbon cleavages at branch points in irradiated poly-1-pentene were considered precursors to *trans*-vinylene groups (61). Statistically, two out of three such cleavages would yield chain cleavages. However, the efficiency of *trans*-vinylene production in linear PE was calculated to be nearly the same as in poly-1-pentene. A peculiar efficacy of branch points as chain-cleavage sites is doubtful. Stabilized carbon–carbon bond cleavages in side chains have been estimated to be more probable than those in the main chain (20).

The relation of decay of vinyl and vinylidene groups and of formation of *trans*-vinylene groups to production of crosslinks in PE during irradiation has been a source of much controversy. Crosslinking by losses of hydrogen atoms from neighboring chains with subsequent coupling of the polymeric radicals requires no correlation between crosslinking and unsaturation changes (17). What appears to be a very constant G(crosslink) from low to high doses in PE and other aliphatic hydrocarbons favors the lack of interplay between unsaturation and crosslinking. Terminal unsaturation was found to yield slightly enhanced radiation crosslinking efficiency in low molecular weight hydrocarbons (44). Under atomic reactor irradiation E_c (per crosslinked unit) equalled ~16 e.v. for saturated hydrocarbons, ~9.7 e.v. for 1-decene and 1-octadecene, and ~6.5 e.v. for 1-acetylenes. Unsaturation not located at the chain ends had little effect upon crosslinkability. Small amounts of vinyl (40) and vinylidene (19,20,40) unsaturation initially present in polyethylenes disappear rapidly during early stages of irradiation. An initial G(vinyl) = 9.6 was calculated for a linear PE (62). In a low density PE G(vinylidene) = 3.7 was found. These are very high values, since the initial unsaturation concentration is low and the energy absorption is based on the total polymer. It has been proposed (22,62–65) that vinyl disappearance occurs through an endlinking process. This could involve (65) irradiation decoupling of the π-electrons followed by attack of the excited biradical upon an adjacent saturated chain (eq. 7). Similar reaction of a vinylidene group would yield a cross-

$$\text{—CH}{=}\text{CH}_2 \rightarrow \text{—}\dot{\text{C}}\text{H}\dot{\text{C}}\text{H}_2,\ \text{—}\dot{\text{C}}\text{H}\dot{\text{C}}\text{H}_2 + \overset{|}{\underset{|}{\text{C}}}\text{H}_2 \rightarrow \text{—CH}_2\text{CH}_2\overset{|}{\underset{|}{\text{C}}}\text{H} \text{ or —CH(CH}_3)\overset{|}{\underset{|}{\text{C}}}\text{H} \tag{7}$$

link (tetrafunctional). Endlinking through vinyl groups or vinylidene groups near chain ends was believed especially effective in inhibiting PE crystallization (65). Free radical attack upon vinylidene and vinylene groups has also been suggested as a crosslinking mechanism (43), while such attack upon vinyl groups would give endlinking as in eqs. (8)–(10)

$$\text{R}\cdot + \text{CH}_2{=}\overset{|}{\underset{|}{\text{C}}} \rightarrow \text{RCH}_2\overset{|}{\underset{|}{\text{C}}}\cdot \tag{8}$$

$$\text{R}\cdot + \text{—CH}{=}\text{CH—} \rightarrow \text{—CHR}\dot{\text{C}}\text{H—} \tag{9}$$

$$\text{R}\cdot + \text{CH}_2{=}\text{CH—} \rightarrow \text{RCH}_2\dot{\text{C}}\text{H—} \tag{10}$$

where R· is $—CH_2\dot{C}HCH_2—$. The resulting free radicals are assumed to abstract hydrogen atoms. By repetitions of this process a chain reaction leading to crosslinking would result, but no indication of such has been reported.

The *trans*-vinylene groups are produced in PE by radiation with an efficiency G(—CH=CH—) variously reported as 1.25 (33), 1.2–1.5 (36), 1.5–2.2 (62), 2.2 (40), and 3.4 (66). G(—CH=CH—) values of 1.9 for liquid hexadecane (45) and of 1.9 for solid octacosane (40) are in general agreement with the values in PE and suggest negligible dependence of G (—CH=CH—) upon the molecular weight or physical state of the hydrocarbon. Negligible temperature dependence in the room temperature to −196°C. range was found (36). Vinylene groups are generally assumed to arise from loss of hydrogen by molecular detachment (36,40):

$$—CH_2—CH_2— \rightarrow —CH{=}CH— + H_2 \tag{11}$$

by detachment and abstraction of atomic hydrogen (67):

$$—CH_2—CH_2— \rightarrow —CH_2—\dot{C}H— + H\cdot \tag{12}$$

$$—CH_2—\dot{C}H— + \cdot H \rightarrow —CH{=}CH— + H_2 \tag{13}$$

or by disproportionation of chain radicals:

$$—CH_2—\dot{C}H— + —CH_2—\dot{C}H— \rightarrow —CH{=}CH— + —CH_2—CH_2— \tag{14}$$

The molecular or "instantaneous" hydrogen molecule loss mechanism is supported by constant $G(H_2)$ and G(—CH=CH—) values reported to very low temperature (−196°C.). A considerable increase in $G(H_2)$ between room temperature and 142°C. has been reported, however (68). The *trans*-vinylene groups are also removed during irradiation by hydrogen addition, crosslinking, or other reactions. A steady-state concentration of unsaturation appears to be approached at high doses (62). An apparent "equilibrium" ratio of one double bond per 20 carbon atoms was found in irradiated paraffins (66). Mixing of *trans*-1,4-polybutadiene (5%) into PE decreases $G(H_2)$ and G(vinyl) markedly in the liquid state (+142°C.), but has little effect in the solid state (64). The protection was attributed to energy and/or ion transfer. Very efficient vinylene decay, −G(—CH=CH—) as high as 50.6 initially, was observed in the liquid mixtures (68). Intramolecular ring formation in the polybutadiene through an allylic radical intermediate was postulated as a possible decay mechanism. This follows somewhat the suggestion that $—\dot{C}HCH{=}CH—$ radicals are crosslinking intermediates in PE under irradiation (69). Intermolecular coupling of such radicals would give crosslinking, but no vinylene loss. The participation of vinylene groups directly in crosslinking does not seem essential considering the lack of sensitivity of G(crosslink) to vinylene content.

The melting point of PE irradiated at room temperature is not appreciably lowered (70–72), but melting and recrystallization lead to a lower degree of crystallinity (63,73). Radiation crosslinking of PE above its melting point substantially lowers the melting point, per cent crystallinity, crystallite and spherulite sizes, and crystallization rate upon cooling (68,72,74–76). Radiation crosslinking of oriented PE fibers (77,78) and of nonoriented spherulitic PE films (72,74,79) encourages maintenance of original long-range order during subsequent fusion and resolidification. Irradiated "single-crystal" PE exhibits a longer induction period and slower crystallization rate than its nonirradiated control in crystallizing from solution (80). Partial crystallite destruction and crosslink buildup by irradiation have been observed by dilatometry (42,81), specific heat measurement (70), x-ray diffraction (41,42,82,83), audiofrequency modulus and loss alterations (84–86), and proton magnetic resonance spectroscopy (83,87–89). All of these observations suggest that crosslinking is produced by radiation in both the crystalline and amorphous regions of PE. Melt index determinations on irradiated high and low density PE failed to clarify the relative ease of crosslinking in these regions because of the compensating effects of differing initial molecular weight (90). Crosslinking by electron irradiation of high and low density PE having various degrees of branching and crystallinity gave essentially identical crosslinking efficiencies measured by swelling and elastic modulus (35,91). Contrary to these findings, crosslinking mainly in the amorphous regions during irradiation has been reported (92,93). Depressed crosslinking in crystalline regions was attributed to free radical trapping, i.e., partial immobilization (68,92,93). Allowing oxygen to react with the trapped radicals, especially in high density PE, prevented their eventually forming crosslinks. Preferential crosslinking in amorphous regions has also been inferred from the control of per cent crystallinity and crystallite sizes in irradiated PE (75). The present writer feels that a preponderance of data supports belief in the near equivalence of crosslinking in the crystalline and amorphous regions of PE if competition with oxidation is avoided.

Oxidation of PE exposed in air to atomic reactor, high energy electron, or γ-radiations was noted early in radiation studies (15,31,94). The oxidation was greatest in the surface regions and in the amorphous regions where greater oxygen concentrations were maintained. Tesla coil and corona discharges at atmospheric pressure and glow discharges at low pressure produce unsaturated and oxidized PE film surfaces wettable by polar liquids

(95,96). A correlation of one oxygenated product, oxalic acid, with the theoretical electron penetration depth in a corona discharge supports an electron bombardment mechanism for the process (96). Oxygen was first thought to promote chain cleavage rather than to inhibit crosslinking in PE (97). Subsequent studies have shown fairly conclusively that oxygen inhibits crosslinking by competing for the reactive intermediates (67,98–100). With liquid *n*-hexane a G(dimer) = 2.0 under electron irradiation was reduced to essentially zero when oxygen at 10 atm. was present (101). Hexanone-2 and hexanone-3 were the principal products. In PE the carbonyl group and hydroperoxides formed during irradiation were found to depress both crosslinking and *trans*-vinylene formation (100). The ratio of carbonyl to *trans*-vinylene appears to increase with decreasing linear energy transfer (L.E.T.) of the radiation employed (67,94). This implies that a high concentration of reactive intermediates favors *trans*-vinylene group formation (and probably also crosslinking) relative to oxidation. A chemical-kinetic study of linear PE oxidation under γ-radiation has shown the consumed oxygen to be converted to carbonyl (25%), H_2O (14%), CO_2 (6%), CO (5%), and peroxides and alcohols (by difference, 50%) (99). Possible free radical mechanisms for the oxidation were discussed. Gases have been reported to depress crosslinking in PE by γ-radiation in the order of decreasing effectiveness: $NO_2 >> O_2 > NH_3 \geq SO_2 \geq Cl_2$ (102). Carbon monoxide and hydrogen had no effect, while nitrous oxide appeared to increase the crosslinking slightly. Irradiated PE is readily susceptible to post-irradiation oxidation (33,92,93,103). This oxidation is especially evident in high density PE (33) and, as mentioned above, may arise principally from residual free radicals trapped in the crystalline regions of the polymer (92,93).

Residual free radicals in irradiated PE have been studied by electron spin resonance (ESR) spectroscopy. Since these radicals may also be the crosslinking intermediates, their nature is of special interest. In a liquid hydrocarbon possibly 60% of the hydrogen evolution occurs by extremely rapid, perhaps molecular, processes to yield crosslinks or *trans*-vinylene unsaturation (101). The remaining 40%, or more in solid hydrocarbons such as PE, of hydrogen evolution yields free radicals having longevities determined by their reactivities and mobilities. An early study at room temperature found radicals in irradiated low density PE but not in high density PE (104). Irradiated PE has been reported to contain radicals having hyperfine ESR structures of six and seven lines (105–107) and of six, five, and single lines (93,108). The six-line spectrum, stable for extended periods only at low temperatures, has been assigned to the alkyl radical,

—$CH_2\dot{C}HCH_2$—(105–109). This radical is more persistent in highly crystalline PE (106,109–111). The more stable seven-line ESR absorption most likely arises from allyl radicals, —$CH_2\dot{C}HCH{=}CHCH_2$— (106,107, 111). The reported five-line spectrum may be this seven-line species. Anisotropic ESR spectra in irradiated, oriented PE have been observed (109,112,113). Kinetics of formation of the allyl radical have been interpreted to indicate a considerable ability for migration of the initial radical sites (106,111), although the rapid disappearance of initial radicals has also been interpreted to arise from nonrandom locations of radical formation (114). The singlet ESR spectrum which exists at higher radiation doses and longer times is ascribed to a radical site trapped within a conjugated sequence by resonance (108):

$$—CH{=}CH\overset{\longleftarrow\cdot\longrightarrow}{CHCHCH}{=}CHCH{=}CH—$$

Since free radical production in PE by radiation is readily demonstrable and the disappearance of some of these free radicals can be associated with crosslinking, a free radical mechanism of crosslinking is most probable. The radicals, giving rise to crosslinking by coupling, may be formed in proximity to each other by nearly instantaneous hydrogen atom expulsion and abstraction, or they may migrate considerable distances. Annealing of PE *in vacuo* after irradiation aids polymer radical site migration and favors crosslinking relative to free radical disappearance by reaction with oxygen or other mobile scavengers. Vinyl and vinylidene consumption in early stages of irradiation may result in endlink or crosslink reactions. Equilibration and *trans*-vinylene formation have not been shown to affect appreciably the crosslinking process.

b. Polypropylene

The nature and efficiency of radiation crosslinking in polypropylene (PP), $\text{+}CH_2CH(CH_3)\text{+}$, demand much further study for satisfactory definition. Under 2 M.e.v. electron irradiation *in vacuo* at room temperature, PP ($\bar{M}_n \simeq 90{,}000$) prepared by a Ziegler process exhibited $E_c \simeq 33$ e.v. and $\beta/\alpha \simeq 0.8$–1.0 (115,116). These quantities are based on gel content/dose relations assuming tetrafunctional crosslinking of a polymer having initially a most probable molecular weight distribution. Analysis of swelling and elasticity data on two PP samples irradiated to 100 Mrad with 4 M.e.v. electrons yielded $E_c \simeq 39$–83 e.v. (117). A much higher $E_c = 500$ e.v. (with $\beta/\alpha = 0.8$) has been reported for PP γ-irradiated *in vacuo* at 25°C.

(118). In the latter study, post-irradiation annealing at 180°C. lowered E_c to 310 e.v. (with $\beta/\alpha = 0.7$), while irradiation at 180°C. gave no gelation.

An apparent preferential crosslinking in the amorphous regions of neutron-irradiated PP has been inferred from proton magnetic resonance absorption line-width versus temperature observations (119). This would support the findings of increased crosslink yield with elevated temperature annealing. However, the magnetic resonance data are not unambiguous and could be interpreted as disruption of crystalline regions by crosslinks at the lower doses.

Hydrogen is practically the only gas evolved from irradiated PP (120). γ-Irradiation at room temperature yielded gas compositions of 97.2% H_2, 2.5% CH_4 from isotactic PP and 95.7% H_2, 3.9% CH_4 from atactic PP (121). The lack of appreciable amounts of C_2–C_6 gaseous hydrocarbon which were found in irradiated branched polyethylene was reasonably interpreted to show negligible short-chain branching (i.e., groups larger than methyl) in either of the PP types. The tertiary hydrogen atom may be the principal source of the evolved hydrogen. An eight-peak ESR spectrum found for PP γ-irradiated at 77°K. (122) and at 123°K. (123) has been tentatively assigned to the $—CH_2\dot{C}(CH_3)CH_2—$ radical. The radical adds and loses sulfur dioxide reversibly at and above room temperature (122,124). In addition to the eight-peak spectrum a singlet, seven-peak spectrum and possibly a six-peak spectrum have been reported for electron-irradiated PP (107). High frequency electric discharges in hydrogen at low pressure over PP produce radicals having complex ESR hyperfine structure (125). They may in part be $—CH_2\dot{C}(CH_3)CH_2—$ and $—CH_2\dot{C}HCH_2—$ radicals. Low temperature γ-irradiation of isobutane also gives a complex ESR spectrum (105). Radiolyses of liquid and gaseous isobutane reveal that most of the hydrogen gas is produced by radical processes rather than molecular processes (126). Considering the high mobility of hydrogen atoms this should also be true in radiolysis of PP.

As mentioned above the steps in the radiation crosslinking of PP are obscure. In the pre-gelation region the intrinsic viscosities have been observed to decrease initially with irradiation. Rather than direct proportionality of chain cleavage and crosslinking to the radiation dose a proportionality of each to the square of the dose has been reported (116). Chain fractures stabilized by disproportionation

$$—\underset{\displaystyle CH_3}{\underset{|}{CH}}\dot{C}H_2 + \underset{\displaystyle CH_3}{\underset{|}{\dot{C}H}}CH_2— \rightarrow —\underset{\displaystyle CH_3}{\underset{|}{C}}{=}CH_2 + CH_3CH_2CH_2— \qquad (15)$$

are assumed to produce the observed vinylidene unsaturation. An end-linking mechanism (11,13) is then postulated in which polymer radicals attach to these preformed vinylidene structures (116,127). The suggested enhancement of crosslinking by a small number of vinylidene groups is large. If nonproportionality between crosslinking, chain cleavage, and dose exists, and trifunctional branch points do form, then the evaluations of crosslinking efficiencies and β/α values in the first paragraph above do not have exact meaning. Judgement of the mode of crosslink formation must be held in abeyance at present.

c. *Natural Rubber*

Radiation studies of natural rubber, *cis*-polyisoprene, $\text{+}CH_2C(CH_3){=}CHCH_2\text{+}$, have progressed fairly rapidly due to the commercial importance of this elastomer. A large share of the research has been upon complex mixtures of rubber and additives. This has made theoretical interpretations difficult in many cases.

Early observations of degradation of rubber in solution by electric discharges (128) probably resulted from the presence of oxygen and the formation of ozone. Some initial increases in the molecular weight and solution viscosity of polyisoprene were noted (129). Later experiments with the use of electric discharge found predominant crosslinking in both natural rubber and polyisoprene (130). Crosslinking was revealed by increases in modulus and hardness and by decreases in ultimate elongation and solubility of rubber specimens irradiated in atomic reactors (131–133), in spent fuel element storage canals (134,135) and in Co^{60} γ-radiation facilities (135, 136).

Calculated efficiencies for the radiation crosslinking of natural rubber have ranged from $E_c = 13$ e.v. for extracted rubber γ-irradiated in air (137) to $E_c = 67$ e.v. for purified specimens irradiated *in vacuo* with 4 M.e.v. electrons (138). The latter value was obtained by an attempted correction of apparent crosslinks measured by network swelling to chemical crosslinks (138,139). E_c values determined by various methods under diverse radiation conditions are 29–50 e.v. (with 42 e.v. deemed best) (140), 48 e.v. (141,142), 60 e.v. (143,144), and 31 e.v. (145). A value of $E_c =$ 40–50 e.v. now appears most reasonable for natural rubber. There is general agreement that a low $\beta/\alpha = 0.03$–0.11 exists in rubber irradiated under nonoxidizing conditions (133,142–144, 146).

Oxygen has been found to increase the scission rate and to decrease the crosslinking efficiency in irradiated rubber (147,148). Carbonyl groups are formed, giving rise to a broad absorption band in the 5.8 μ region (137); also some hydroxyl absorption appears around 2.8 μ. The interference with crosslinking and contribution to chain scission probably arise from competition by oxygen for radiation-produced radicals on the polymer chains. Crystalline, oriented racked rubber has been found to be crosslinked twice as effectively as amorphous rubber by γ-radiation (149). Invocation of special polymer unit orientation and proximity effects might be made to explain this. However, such postulates may be premature. No appreciable effect upon crosslinking and scission efficiencies due to general crystallinity was noted in an irradiation study of rubber over a wide temperature range (144). Low apparent activation energies for radiation crosslinking of 0.76 and 0.26 kcal./mole were calculated above and below the glass transition, respectively. Irradiation of stretched rubber samples at 75°C. causes stress relaxation and decreased crystallinity (150–151). The stress apparently helps promote scission by preventing radical recombinations at sites of chain scission. The retention of anisotropic mechanical properties of natural rubber that has been radiation-crosslinked in oriented configurations has been demonstrated (141,149).

The effects of additives upon the radiation crosslinking of natural rubber support a free radical mechanism. Compounds most effective in "protecting" rubber are those having the ability to donate hydrogen atoms and which, after loss of hydrogen, form relatively inactive radicals (147,148, 152). The most efficient "antirads" are aromatic amines, quinones, aromatic hydroxyl compounds, and various aromatic nitrogen and sulfur compounds. A close correlation of their protective efficiency with radical-stopping ability has been pointed out (147,148,153). At high concentrations of the additives about two-thirds of the crosslink formations can be prevented. In addition to decreasing the crosslinking many of the antirads serve to diminish oxidative chain scission during irradiation.

The addition of certain halogenated compounds enhances the radiation crosslinking efficiency in natural rubber by increasing the yield of free radicals (153–156). The presence of water in latex also appears to increase the crosslink yield (154–159) on radiation. Compounding of the usual chemical vulcanizing agents, including sulfur, into rubber prior to irradiation was found not to alter appreciably the radiation crosslinking efficiency (160). Sulfur is attached to rubber by irradiation at 25°C. (161) and slightly decreases the crosslinking. Some fillers enhance the radiation cure, possibly by attachment of the rubber chains to the filler particles. Irradiation initiates graft polymerization of styrene onto rubber in a free radical process with G(initiating radicals on rubber chains) = 0.26 (162). Either the radicals formed are less efficient in initiating polymerization than in crosslinking or, more likely, the presence of styrene decreases radical formation.

Hydrogen, evolved in direct proportion to the radiation dose, is practically the only gaseous product of irradiation (133,145). $G(H_2)$, having a value of 0.64, is just slightly over one half of the G(crosslink) yield. Reported decreases in unsaturation in rubber during irradiation have been ascribed to addition of hydrogen to double bonds (140) and to cyclization within the rubber chains (163). An observed decrease in unsaturation of 44% in deproteinized natural rubber crepe neutron-irradiated in benzene (0.5 g. rubber/100 ml. benzene which is 0.02M in triphenylmethane) approximates the theoretical value for complete cyclization within the chains (164). Unsaturation decreases of 50% (163) and 80% (140) have been reported for irradiated bulk rubber. Surprisingly other studies have found very slight reduction of unsaturation in irradiated rubber (143,144, 165) and in irradiated squalene (hexaisoprene) (145). Rationalization of these apparently contradictory findings has not been achieved. A slight amount of *trans*-vinylene formation due to isomerization or to double bond shifts has been noted (143,144,165).

The radiation crosslinking of natural rubber appears to be accomplished through the formation of allylic free radicals by hydrogen atom expulsions and abstractions followed by coupling of these radicals. Peroxide-cured rubber should possess the same carbon–carbon crosslinks and display similar post-cure chemical behavior (166). There are six possible allylic radical structures (I–VI) derived from hydrogen loss to be considered (139,165).

$$\underset{\text{(I)}}{\text{—CH}_2\text{C(CH}_3\text{)=CH}\dot{\text{C}}\text{H—}} \leftrightarrow \underset{\text{(IV)}}{\text{—CH}_2\dot{\text{C}}\text{(CH}_3\text{)CH=CH—}}$$

$$\underset{\text{(II)}}{\text{—}\dot{\text{C}}\text{HC(CH}_3\text{)=CHCH}_2\text{—}} \leftrightarrow \underset{\text{(V)}}{\text{—CH=C(CH}_3\text{)}\dot{\text{C}}\text{HCH}_2\text{—}}$$

$$\underset{\text{(III)}}{\text{—CH}_2\text{C(}\dot{\text{C}}\text{H}_2\text{)=CHCH}_2\text{—}} \leftrightarrow \underset{\text{(VI)}}{\text{—CH}_2\text{C(=CH}_2\text{)}\dot{\text{C}}\text{HCH}_2\text{—}}$$

Coupling of such radicals on adjacent chains will lead to crosslinks. Disproportionation of structures I or II would lead to triene groups, as would also molecular loss of H_2 (eq. 16). Disproportionation of structures IV, V,

$$\text{—}\underset{\text{CH}_3}{\text{C}}\text{=CHCH}_2\text{CH}_2\underset{\text{CH}_3}{\text{C}}\text{=CH—} \rightarrow \text{—}\underset{\text{CH}_3}{\text{C}}\text{=CHCH=CH}\underset{\text{CH}_3}{\text{C}}\text{=CH—} + \text{H}_2 \qquad (16)$$

or VI would give conjugated diene groups. A study of changes in the ultraviolet and infrared absorption spectra of irradiated rubber has shown the sum of these unsaturation-producing reactions to be less than 15% of the crosslinking, coupling reactions (165).

d. Polybutadiene and Butadiene Copolymers

Polybutadiene (PBD) chains consist mainly of *cis*- and *trans*-$\{CH_2CH=CHCH_2\}$ units formed by 1,4 additions of monomer during polymerization. Pendant double bonds also occur due to 1,2 additions which yield $\{CH_2CH(CH=CH_2)\}$ units. The composition of a PBD sample depends upon the polymerization conditions employed. Radiation-induced *cis–trans* isomerization of PBD has been discussed in Chapter II-A (167).

The consumption of double bonds during γ-irradiation was studied by acid ozonolysis followed by product chromatography of irradiated PBD samples of known 1,2 and 1,4 content (168). The reduction in chromatogram peak heights allowed calculation of the double bond consumptions in 1,4–1,4, 1,4–1,2–1,4, and 1,4–1,2–1,2–1,4, sequences. Sodium 1,4-butadiene rubber and sodium 1,2-butadiene rubber exhibited similar reductions in unsaturation (about 40–50% reduction in 4 Mrad). A Ziegler catalyst-initiated 1,4-butadiene rubber showed less efficient double bond removal initially, but then exceeded the sodium rubber efficiencies at 3 Mrad. However, 1,2-butadiene rubber made in the presence of a Ziegler catalyst underwent 80% reduction in unsaturation at less than 1 Mrad exposure. Utilization of pendant vinyl groups in crosslink formation by the mechanism (169) of eq. (17) was suggested. Considering the extremely high

$$\text{—}\dot{C}H\text{—} + CH_2{=}CH\underset{}{\overset{|}{C}}H\text{—} \rightarrow \text{—}\overset{|}{C}HCH_2\overset{|}{\dot{C}}H\overset{|}{C}H\text{—} \qquad (17)$$

efficiency reported for the unsaturation removal, internal cyclization leading to structures like VII, may be postulated.

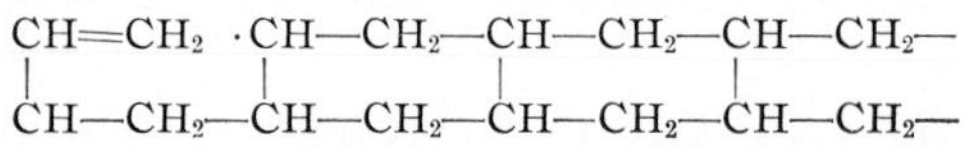

(VII)

An infrared study of x-irradiated sodium butadiene rubber (170) revealed marked reductions in unsaturation, the appearance of chain branching, and the formation of oxidation products (when irradiated in air). Also, essentially complete disappearance of unsaturation in an acetone-extracted butadiene–styrene copolymer, SKS-30, sample irradiated to 55 Mrad was observed by infrared absorption changes (137).

An early attempt to determine the E_c for PBD was thwarted by a gel network in the original polymer (171). γ-Irradiation from a Co^{60} source crosslinks PBD with an efficiency represented by E_c = 14 e.v. (172) or 12.5 e.v. (173). In the latter study fractionation of the irradiated PBD before gelation led to the belief that several molecules were linked together by a short chain reaction following the primary formation of a radical. This would conform to an intermolecular polymerization disappearance of double bonds similar to the intramolecular polymerization suggested above. However, the E_c values calculated are not low enough to suggest intermolecular polymerization chains of appreciable length. Adducts of PBD with methyl mercaptan $\text{+}CH_2CH(SCH_3)CH_2CH_2\text{+}$, are quite resistant to ozone, heat, and radiation relative to the rather highly reactive PBD (174).

The crosslinking of butadiene–styrene copolymers has received more attention than has that of the butadiene homopolymers (171,175–178). The styrene comonomer reduces the crosslinking efficiency so that E_c = 17–18.5 e.v. for a γ-irradiated copolymer containing 23% styrene (179). The E_c elevation due to styrene is slightly greater than would be calculated by mole fraction additivity of styrene unit, [G(crosslink) = 0.045–0.060] and butadiene unit [G(crosslink) = 3.6–4.0] crosslinking probabilities (172). This had been credited to energy transfer within the polymer chains to the resistant styrene units. A low $\beta/\alpha \simeq 0.07$ was found (179) to be enhanced by incorporating methyl methacrylate for sites of cleavage (172). An inexplicably low E_c of about 3 e.v. has been reported for a γ-irradiated butadiene–styrene rubber (180). Terpolymerization of methacrylic acid into SBR rubbers gives increased crosslinking (180–182). At low dosages (0–20 Mrad) the G(crosslink) value increases linearly with the carboxyl content of the original polymer, and the crosslinking correlates closely with decarboxylation (180,182). It was proposed that the principal initiation of crosslinking involves decarboxylation with subsequent attack of the polymeric radical formed thereby upon double bonds in adjacent chains. Isolated methacrylic acid units thus appear to foster crosslinking, while methyl methacrylate units, possibly in pairs, triads, etc., cause chain scission.

Compounding of SBR copolymers with carbon black or silica fillers increases apparent crosslinking as measured by swelling and stress relaxation (179). Finely divided heavy metals as fillers increase crosslinking by giving higher yields of secondary electrons to the surrounding rubber. Aromatic oil plasticizers increase chain scission and decrease crosslinking by radiation (183). Antirads (already discussed) decrease radiation crosslinking in the absence of aromatic oils and decrease both radiation induced crosslinking and scission in the presence of aromatic oils (183). Air promoted some chain cleavage as judged by a slightly diminished net crosslinking. In neutron fields inclusion of boron nitride or lithium methoxide increases the yield of crosslinks by furthering ionization through n,α reactions (184). A SBR copolymer in dilute solution in toluene appeared to cleave randomly under γ-irradiation with $E_d = 300$ e.v. (185). This correlates fairly well with $E_d = E_c/(\beta/\alpha) = 18.5/0.07 = 260$ e.v. for bulk polymer and may indicate little difference in energy exchange with the surroundings during chain cleavage in the two media. Radiation gelation of the copolymer in chloroform occurred rapidly, $E_c = 0.33$ e.v., showing attack upon the chains by free radicals produced in the solvent to be of prime importance (185). Radiation cleavage of the chains was not similarly accelerated by chloroform. The pendant vinyl groups were attacked more rapidly than were interior double bonds. Free radical mechanisms involving allylic radical formations, intermolecular radical transfers, and cleavage of carbon–carbon bonds β to the double bonds in the chain were postulated (185).

Butadiene–acrylonitrile (BD–AN) copolymers crosslink less readily than SBR during irradiation (171). Compounding with additives and fillers can extend the dose range over which these rubbers possess useful physical properties, but high doses of radiation lead to low ultimate elongations, compression set, and embrittlement (186,187). A selective decomposition of a softener, triethyl phosphate, was noted in a BD–AN rubber irradiated by spent reactor fuel elements (134). The mode of radiation crosslinking of BD–AN copolymers has not been clarified. Copolymers containing 20–50% acrylonitrile were found by swelling measurements to crosslink in direct proportion to absorbed γ-radiation (188). On the other hand, using similar conditions of irradiation and methods of measurement others found a protective influence of the acrylonitrile units up to about 3×10^7–5×10^7 r followed by loss of protection and possibly enhanced crosslinking due to the acrylonitrile content (175). The mechanisms of such structure-accumulated dose interactions are not understood

e. Polystyrene

Polystyrene (PS), $+CH_2CH(C_6H_5)+$, is crosslinked by ionizing radiations (4,32,189,190) with an E_c of about 855 e.v. (191). This high value of E_c is generally ascribed to the energy-wasting capability of the aromatic rings. In the absence of air the cleavage of the main chain is slight with $\beta/\alpha \simeq 0.2$ (4). Changes in mechanical properties (132,192–194) support the observation of predominant crosslinking, but the changes are appreciable in the glassy polymer only at very high doses. The solubility and swelling characteristics of radiation-crosslinked PS have been instructive in establishing the applicability of such analytical methods and in studying molecular weight distributions (4,190,195). The crosslinking is believed to be proportional to the energy absorbed and independent of the type and intensity of radiation. However, greater crosslinking efficiency by reactor irradiation compared with γ-irradiation has been reported (196).

Permanent increases in electrical conductivity of PS films result from large electron radiation doses (197). These increases are due principally to dehydrogenation of the polymer producing double bonds in the backbone which conjugate with each other and with the pendant phenyl groups. At lower doses transient conductivity by radiation-induced carriers has been found proportional to the 0.6 power of x-radiation intensity with an apparent thermal activation energy of 0.44 e.v. (198). On the other hand β-irradiation was found to induce conductivity proportional to the radiation-produced ions which disappeared by bimolecular reaction (199).

The γ-irradiation of PS dissolved in chloroform revealed that some protection against a decrease in viscosity was provided by added compounds containing labile hydrogen atoms (e.g., phenols, β-naphthol, and some amines) or by derivatives of thiourea, derivatives of thiuram, and dithiocarbamates (200). The latter group of additives inhibited the post-irradiation degradation usually found. An apparent "equilibrium" between polymerization and degradation of styrene–PS in chloroform under γ-irradiation has been reported (201). This seems to the present writer to demand critical evaluation, since the reactions of cleavage by radiation and addition of monomer do not necessarily represent reversible paths in the same chemical process. PS has been shown preferentially to crosslink in ethyl acetate and dioxane, predominantly to cleave in chloroform and benzene, and to remain border-line in butanone and toluene during γ-irradiation (202,203). At high concentrations of polymer crosslinking was favored and gelation was possible. PS in benzene irradiated by γ-rays exhibited both crosslink branching and chain cleavage (204). Tracer studies indicated recombinations of polymeric radicals even in dilute solution.

The sites of crosslinking are not firmly established. Electron spin resonance spectra of γ-irradiated PS and substituted polystyrenes at 77°K. are triplets possibly compatible with $—CH_2\dot{C}(C_6H_5)—$ as the persistent radical structure (104,205). Bombardment of PS "fluffs" with hydrogen atoms gives a similar ESR spectrum, presumably due to α-hydrogen abstractions (206). On the other hand the ESR triplet in irradiated PS has also been tentatively interpreted as a free electron residing in the phenyl group (123). Coupling of $—CH_2\dot{C}(C_6H_5)—$radicals may be the major method of production of crosslinks. Radicals of this type would also form the carbonyl compounds observed in PS irradiated with ultraviolet light (207) and in post-oxidation of γ-irradiated PS (208). Unsaturation produced by the irradiation (209) might also be sites for subsequent oxidation. The presence of oxygen during irradiation can change the response of PS from essentially pure crosslinking in a vacuum through increasing β/α values to predominant scission during slow irradiation in air (4,97,191,199). The contribution of oxygen to the chain cleavage of PS is perhaps even more striking on irradiating PS in solution (210–213). Residual oxygenated species (peroxy radicals, peroxides, hydroperoxides) are available for post-irradiation reactions. It is surprising, if the —$CH_2\dot{C}(C_6H_5)$— radical participates both in crosslinking and in oxidation, that the presence of oxygen does not inhibit crosslinking but simply encourages chain cleavage (97). This appears to be true in several radiation studies.

Reactions of the pendant phenyl groups may contribute to crosslinking. Differences in the ESR spectra of hydrogen atom- and deuterium atom-bombarded PS support atom additions to the aromatic rings (206). Tetrafunctional crosslinks could form by the coupling of cyclohexadienyl radicals to neighboring radicals (214). This idea has been extended to explain the exceptionally low radiation yield of reaction in PS by assuming that the cyclohexadienyl radicals also disproportionate with backbone radicals to restore the original polymer molecules (215).

4. Silicones

Polydimethylsiloxane (PDMS), having a unit structure $\text{+}Si(CH_3)_2O\text{+}$ has been found to crosslink under varied ionizing radiation conditions (32,132,135,136, 216–219). The crosslinking is very efficient. Radiation studies on PDMS and its low molecular weight oligomers have yielded energies per crosslinked unit, E_c, values of 13–17 e.v. (220), 11 or 21 e.v. (221), 18–21 e.v. (219), 20–23 e.v. (222), 20 e.v. (223), and 17 e.v. (224, 225). Considering the variety of methods of measurement, types of radiation, conditions, and types of compounds the agreement is remarkably good. An E_c value of 17–20 e.v., i.e., G(crosslinks) = 2.5–3.0, has thus been well established. A low cleavage-to-crosslinked unit ratio, $\beta/\alpha \leq 0.1$, has been inferred from the shape of the insolubilization versus radiation dose curves (220), from an analysis of pregelation solution viscosities (226), and from the determination of Si—O cleavages by donation of hydrogen from mercaptans during irradiation (227). A somewhat higher value $\beta/\alpha = 0.27$, has been reported for PDMS irradiated in solution in its low molecular weight oligomers (225).

The depression of solution viscosities by branching in irradiated PDMS was demonstrated (228). Although the viscosities increase with irradiation they do not rise as fast as is suggested by the increase in the molecular weight (191,226). The increase in bulk viscosity of the polymer can be used satisfactorily to estimate the gelation point from pregelation measurements (217,229). Changes in several bulk properties of pure and compounded silicone elastomers have been described by others (132,230–235). The dielectric constant and dielectric strength remained unchanged, and the resistivity and electrical loss tangent increased slightly in several silicones after ca. 5 Mrad. γ-exposure at 25 and 150°C. (236).

The nature of the crosslinks in irradiated PDMS is probably better known than that of any other irradiated polymer. Of the three possibilities Si—CH_2—Si, Si—Si, and Si—CH_2—CH_2—Si, the first two were determined by infrared spectroscopy to be present in the ratio 2:1 and the third was not detected (237). The observation of Si—H formation at a rate 1/20 that of crosslinked unit formation (221) may relate to H· additions to sites of chain cleavage or of Si—C rupture. With the use of electron-irradiated hexamethyldisiloxane as a model it has been inferred that Si—CH_2—Si, Si—Si, and Si—CH_2—CH_2—Si crosslinks in the ratio 2:1:0.6 are formed in irradiated PDMS (238). This agrees with the Si—CH_2—Si to Si—Si ratio of the earlier study, but shows a very appreciable amount of Si—CH_2—CH_2—Si crosslinking. The latter finding is supported by similar data in which approximate ratios of 2:1.2:0.55 were reported for the three types of crosslinks in PDMS electron-irradiated at 25°C. (224).

The number of gas molecules liberated from PDMS by radiation should equal the number of crosslinks since production of unsaturation is not feasible. Methane, hydrogen, and ethane were found in proportions of 47, 41, and 12 vol.-%, respectively, from atomic reactor-irradiated PDMS (220), and 60.4, 34.1, and 4.6 vol.-%, respectively, from γ-irradiated octamethylcyclotetrasiloxane (219). These three gases constitute essentially the total yield of gas. In a more recent study of PDMS electron-irradiated at 25°C. at a dose rate of 13.8 Mrad/min. (224), the CH_4, H_2, and C_2H_6 percentages were 34.7, 40.6 and 24.6 mole-%, with $G(CH_4) = 1.07$, $G(H_2) = 1.25$, and $G(C_2H_6) = 0.76$. This represents a reversal in the relative amounts of hydrogen and methane and a larger proportion of ethane. At 25°C. at a dose rate of 0.138 Mrad/min. the methane predominated and the ethane diminished giving $G(CH_4) = 1.80$, $G(H_2) = 1.34$, and $G(C_2H_6) = 0.54$. Both yields of gas and crosslinks increased with temperature over the range -180 to $+100$°C. These increases with increasing temperature or decreasing radiation intensity are attributed to the favoring of abstraction of hydrogen by H· and ·CH_3 relative to their combinations (224). The correspondence between moles of gas evolved and moles of crosslinks formed is reasonably good.

The electron spin resonance spectrum of hexamethyldisiloxane γ-irradiated at 77°K. consists of a symmetrical triplet, possibly $-\dot{C}H_2$, and a central singlet, possibly $-\overset{|}{\underset{|}{Si}}\cdot$ or —O· (239). The radical yields were estimated as G(triplet) = 1.7 and G(singlet) = 0.05. Other radical species which must also be produced initially were not detected. The observed radicals were stable up to about −120°C., above which they disappeared rapidly to no residual signal at −60°C.

Evidence of radical reactions in PDMS under irradiation is furnished by additive studies. A dimethylsiloxane rubber and a polymethylphenylsiloxane liquid have been chlorinated at 0°C. under γ-irradiation (240). In the latter the aromatic ring was the point of initial chlorine attack. Accelerated crosslinking and cleavage by γ-rays of PDMS in cyclohexane are best explained by free radical reactions (225). The $G(-I_2)$ = 1.25 in a γ-irradiated silicone fluid corresponding to G(radical) = 2.5 and also a G(−anthracene) = 2.5 at high concentration in an irradiated silicone are compatible with a free radical mechanism (241). However, the kinetics do not support a mechanism of competition between radical–radical and radical–anthracene reactions. We might also note that the number of radicals counted is only about one fourth the number of polymeric plus small radicals required for observed crosslinking in PDMS if initial Si—C and C—H cleavages were the only radical-forming steps. With the assumption of Si—C and C—H cleavages with subsequent abstractions of hydrogen atoms leading to polymeric radicals which crosslink by combination, just one half the number of required radicals were counted by the disappearance of the iodine and anthracene.

Oxygen depresses the crosslinking yield in silicones (174,223,241,242). Electron irradiation of hexamethyldisiloxane under 10 atm. of oxygen diminishes the yield of products as compared to vacuum radiation. The compounds produced are believed to be a carboxylic acid, $(CH_3)_3SiOSi(CH_3)_2COOH$, and two peroxides, $(CH_3)_3SiOSi(CH_3)_2OOSi(CH_3)_3$ and $(CH_3)_3SiOSi(CH_3)_2OOCH_3$ (223). Oxygen decreases the electron radiation crosslinking of PDMS from G(crosslinks) = 3 (O_2 pressure = 0) to G(crosslinks) = 1 (O_2 pressure > ca. 150 psi) (227). Because of thermal stability and stability toward bromine in carbon tetrachloride the residual crosslinks at the high oxygen pressures are believed to be neither peroxide nor Si—Si bonds. Elevated temperatures and high dose rates are reported (242) to increase greatly the crosslinking efficiency of polysiloxanes, presumably in part due to suppression of interference by oxygen and in part due to an increase in abstraction relative to radical combinations, as discussed above.

Phenyl groups markedly decrease radiation crosslinking in siloxane polymers (219,229,231,239,242–245). Silicone polymers γ-irradiated in the presence of air exhibited G(crosslinking) values of 1.60, 1.12, and 0.06 for PDMS, poly(dimethyl–diphenyl) siloxane (95:5), and poly(dimethyl–diphenyl) siloxane (75:25), respectively (229). The protective effect of the phenyl groups was estimated to extend over five or six neighboring dimethylsiloxane units. A study of low molecular weight siloxanes of known structure containing methyl and phenyl groups has revealed (239) a quantitative relation between the yield of gases non-condensable at 77°K. and the electron fraction, ϵ (methyl), of methyl electrons in the compounds:

$$\log G(\text{noncondensable}) = 5.65\ \epsilon\ (\text{methyl}) + \log 0.006$$

Also Si—H bonds in tetramethyldisiloxane were calculated to be about 30 times as sensitive to radiation as C—H and Si—C bonds.

The numerous recent studies and continuing research bode well for improvement in our understanding of the radiation-chemical reactions of polysiloxanes.

5. Polyacrylates

Compounded rubbers of poly(ethyl acrylate) (132) and of ethyl acrylate–acrylonitrile–vinylethoxysilane terpolymer (135) were found to crosslink under exposure to ionizing radiation. Changes in hardness, tensile strength, and ultimate elongation were observed. Polyacrylic esters as a group were classified as radiation-crosslinked polymers in an early survey (32). The observation helped to suggest the concept of polymers having $\text{+}CH_2CHR\text{+}$ unit structures (17) being susceptible to crosslinking by radiation.

A systematic study was conducted to determine the effects of structure of side chains upon crosslinking of poly(alkyl acrylates) by electron irradiation (246). Insolubilization of the polyacrylates due to formation of networks was the experimental method employed. The polymers studied and their energy absorptions, E_c, per crosslinked unit formed were: poly(methyl acrylate), 87–103 e.v.; poly(*n*-butyl acrylate), 80 e.v.; poly(isobutyl acrylate), 80 e.v.; poly(*sec*-butyl acrylate), 107 e.v.; poly(*tert*-butyl acrylate), 282–335 e.v.; poly(neopentyl acrylate), 87 e.v.; poly(1,1-dihydroperfluorobutyl acrylate), 37–82 e.v. All of these polyacrylates exhibited an energy absorption per chain cleavage, E_d, of approximately 530 ± 100 e.v. with no trend attributable to variation in structure of the side chain. The obviously exceptional polymer among the alkyl acrylate polymers studied is poly(*tert*-butyl acrylate) which requires three to four times the energy required by the others per crosslinked unit formed. Poly(*sec*-butyl acrylate) shows a slight increase in energy requirement over the *n*- and isobutyl polymers. It was postulated (246) that crosslinking in the poly(alkyl acrylates) is facilitated by hydrogen atoms on the carbinol carbon. A part of the crosslink formation was believed to involve the carbinol carbon. This concept has some support in observed formation of vicinal glycol, RCH(OH)CH(OH)R, in ion-bombarded alcohols (247) and in the ESR spectrum of x-irradiated propanol at 77°K. tentatively assigned to the CH_3-$CH_2\dot{C}HOH$ radical (248). The extrapolation of the radiation behavior of hydrogen atoms on carbinol carbons in alcohols to their behavior in esters is, of course, open to serious criticism. Poly(benzyl acrylate) and poly(β-phenylethyl acrylate) are readily crosslinked by γ-radiation while poly(phenyl acrylate) crosslinks to a network only at high radiation dose (249). This again appears to support the idea that hydrogen atoms on the carbinol carbon atom play a role in the crosslinking.

Electron spin resonance studies on polyacrylates seem to be lacking. The ESR spectrum of poly(acrylic acid) γ-irradiated at room temperature indicated a *G*(radical) value of 2.5, surprisingly high for persistant radicals in a crosslinking polymer (104). The fine structure of the spectrum was mainly a 1:2:1 triplet, but weak shoulders were present and an assignment of radical structure(s) was not attempted. Although radiation crosslinking is the predominant reaction of poly(acrylic acid) in bulk, indirect radiation effects on sodium polyacrylate in aqueous solution cause degradation (250). Similarly, poly(ethyl acrylate) irradiated in dilute solution (e.g., in carbon tetrachloride or benzene) in the presence of oxygen undergoes degradation by indirect action (251). In concentrated solutions of poly(ethyl acrylate), some competition between chain cleavage and crosslinking is noted. In the solid state, crosslinking with some concurrent chain cleavage occurs in the presence or absence of oxygen (251).

Gases liberated from γ-irradiated poly(methyl acrylate) were reported to be chiefly CH_4, CO, CO_2, $HCOOCH_3$, H_2, and CH_3OH (252). The gas mixture was qualitatively similar to that evolved from poly(methyl methacrylate) by sidechain decompositions, but it was considerably less in quantity. A reported decrease in the efficiency of gas evolution with increasing dose and an increase in efficiency due to copolymerized styrene units do not appear amenable to logical interpretation at present.

Ultraviolet light (2537 A.) used to irradiate films of poly(ethyl acrylate) in a vacuum at room temperature produced crosslinking and gelation (253). An analysis of the gel content versus exposure time revealed a chain cleavage-to crosslinked unit ratio of $\beta/\alpha = 0.50$. Correction for film thickness (254) would lower this calculated value considerably. Mass spectrometric analyses of the evolved gases after exposures of 4 and 16 hr. gave CH_4 (33.9, 44.7%), CO (59.2, 45.6%), CO_2 (6.2, 8.9%), and H_2 (0.7, 0.8%). The presence of methane and absence of ethane cannot be readily explained. Otherwise, loss and decomposition of side chains would seem to be a principal photolysis step. It was postulated (255) that the crosslinking might arise principally by the steps:

$$\text{—}CH_2CH(COOC_2H_5)\text{—} \rightarrow \text{—}CH_2\dot{C}H\text{—} + \cdot COOC_2H_5 \tag{18}$$

$$\text{—}CH_2\dot{C}H\text{—} + \text{—}CH_2\dot{C}H\text{—} \rightarrow \text{—}CH_2\overset{|}{C}H\overset{|}{C}HCH_2\text{—} \tag{19}$$

A disproportionation leading to chain cleavage was envisioned as:

$$\text{—}CH_2\dot{C}HCH_2CH(COOC_2H_5)\text{—} \rightarrow \text{—}CH_2CH{=}CH_2 + \cdot CH(COOC_2H_5)\text{—} \tag{20}$$

Crosslinking efficiency decreased as the temperature decreased from +26 to −20°C; no insolubilization of the poly(ethyl acrylate) (PEA) was found at −20°C. even with a fairly long exposure to ultraviolet radiation. Since the glass transition temperature of PEA is −17°C., the inhibition of crosslinking was ascribed to a lack of mobility of the radicals presumably necessary for crosslinking.

The mechanism of crosslinking of polyacrylates by high energy radiation is by no means well characterized. The invocation of carbinol hydrogens as active agents in the crosslinking of poly(methyl acrylate) is in apparent contradiction to the noncrosslinkability of poly(methyl methacrylate) by the same route. Also the absence of increase in ability to crosslink of the poly(n-butyl acrylate) compared to poly(methyl acrylate) is not in accord with the results in the polymethacrylate series. The possibility of side chain crosslinking with backbones is of course more feasible in polyacrylates. Side chain-to-side chain or side chain-to-backbone links in irradiated polyacrylates should be subject to cleavage by vigorous alkaline saponification. No data have appeared concerning this in high energy radiation studies, but a brief mention was made of absence of cleavage of crosslinks by alkali in poly(ethyl acrylate) crosslinked by ultraviolet light (255). Backbone-to-backbone crosslinks of the type suggested above and also those resulting from the combination of radicals produced by abstraction from the backbone of α-hydrogen would be nonsaponifiable. The reactions under high energy radiations and ultraviolet light may differ owing to the greater amount of excitation energy available in the former.

A correlation of decomposition of side chains with crosslinking in irradiated polyacrylates may or may not exist. Quantitative simultaneous studies of these two events are needed. The question of the effect of local mobility of the polymer chains upon the crosslinking ability of polyacrylates and polymethacrylates subjected to ionizing radiation needs study. In the poly(butyl acrylates) the difference, $T(\text{room}) - T_g$, between room temperature and the glass transition temperature T_g, should increase in the order *tert*-$<$*sec*-$<$iso-$<$*n*-alkyl. This is in opposite order to their crosslinking efficiencies at room temperature. Similarly in the poly(*n*-alkyl methacrylates), crossover from predominant cleavage to predominant crosslinking during irradiation at room temperature occurs approximately, though not exactly, in the region of passage from glassy to nonglassy state (256). One must remember, however, that the rigid, partially crystalline poly(octadecyl methacrylate) predominantly crosslinks despite severe restrictions on mobility (257). Apparent correlations between local mobility and the ability of polymers to crosslink may often be coincidental, but they deserve continued investigation.

6. Poly(vinyl Chloride)

Crosslinking, chain cleavage and dehydrochlorination are the principal changes induced in poly(vinyl chloride) (PVC) by high energy radiations. Early data (30,132,136,258,259) on physical properties in PVC and vinyl chloride copolymers changed by irradiation suggested in some cases predominant crosslinking and in other cases predominant cleavage (260). Although PVC was tentatively classified (32) as a radiation-degraded polymer, subsequent studies have established that in the absence of air PVC is predominantly crosslinked by radiation (261). $G(\text{crosslinks}) = 2.15$, i.e., $E_c = 23$ e.v., is the best available estimate of the crosslinking efficiency (262, 263). Elevating the temperature or introducing a swelling agent after irradiation in vacuum and prior to contact with air facilitates crosslinking (264). The competition of chain cleavage is evident in the decrease in intrinsic viscosity of PVC during early stages of the approach to gelation by irradiation (263,265). If the cleavage reactions were not so efficient under normal radiation conditions, the curing by radiation of pure PVC would be generally practicable. However, for greater efficiency, graft polymerization of tetrafunctional monomers incorporated as plasticizers in PVC (266–270) was used to produce crosslinking by radiation.

Dehydrochlorination with an approximate $G(\mathrm{HCl}) = 7$ was found for γ-irradiated shavings of PVC (259). Electron irradiation liberates HCl with an efficiency ranging from $G(\mathrm{HCl}) = 5.6$ when the irradiation is at -90°C. or lower to $G(\mathrm{HCl}) = 23$ when the irradiation is at $+70$°C. (271). The liberated HCl has observable effects upon the electrical properties of PVC (272,273). Additives which decrease the thermal dehydrochlorination of PVC also depress this loss in electrical properties. The process appears to be a chain reaction (cf. seq.) which creates extended polyene systems, —CH=CH—CH=CH—CH= etc. These polyene systems, their conjugated allylic radical precursors, and oxidation products are logical sources of visible coloration in irradiated PVC (261,274–279). The γ-irradiation of PVC even at room temperature produces persistent free radicals with an approximate value $G(\text{radical}) = 1.7$ (104). Irradiation of alkyl halides at 77°K. yields the alkyl radical as the principal trapped species (280). Electron spin resonance spectra of PVC irradiated at 77°K. reveal the formation of two or more radical species (279,281–284). Two of the radicals were assigned structures —CHCl$\dot{\mathrm{C}}$HCHCl— and —$CH_2\dot{C}ClCH_2$— (281). The formation of hydrogen $G(H_2) = 0.4$ supports the formation of such radicals (282). The total radical yield (282) was $G(\text{radical}) = 2.1$, and it was deduced that $G(\mathrm{HCl}) = G(\text{—}CH_2\dot{C}HCH_2\text{—}) = 0.5$, $G(\text{—CH=CH}\dot{\mathrm{C}}\text{HCHCl—}) = 0.14$, and $G(\text{potential crosslinking radicals}) = 0.97$. The —$CH_2\dot{C}HCH_2$— discussed here and in a previous work (274) was not detected in another study (277). Successive dehydrochlorination proceeding from radicals of the —CH=CH$\dot{\mathrm{C}}$HCHCl— type could build the polyene structure to a series of about 11 conjugated double bonds believed to be the asymptotic limit (285). The decay rates of radical species in irradiated PVC and their reactivities, e.g., with oxygen and other gases, vary with radical type and the temperatures of formation and observation (282,284,286–289). The length of the polyene chain in resonance with the unpaired electron is one likely source of differences in reactivity. Peroxy radicals, possibly of the form —CH(OO·)—, have been observed (261,277). Their formation appears to be controlled by diffusion of oxygen; their first-order decay has been interpreted as an autoxidation process which delocalizes the unpaired electron (288).

Irradiation of PVC in morpholine produces some attachment of the solvent to the polymer and leads to crosslinking (290). Irradiation of PVC in tetrahydrofuran produces both intramolecular and intermolecular crosslinking (291,292). Above 5% PVC concentration the intrinsic viscosity increases steadily and gelation occurs. In cyclohexanone PVC was found not to crosslink, and much less evolution of gas was observed (292). This is not at present understood. Certain plasticizers and thermal stabilizers have been found to diminish the chemical action of radiation upon PVC to a considerable extent (293–296).

7. Polyesters

Definitive data concerning crosslinking and chain cleavage of polyesters by radiation are very limited. Arguing from structural comparison with polyacrylates and polymethacrylates, the aliphatic polyesters, $\text{+OC(CH}_2)_x\text{-COO(CH}_2)_y\text{O+}$ or $\text{+O(CH}_2)_x\text{CO+}$, should have $\beta/\alpha < 2$ and exhibit predominant crosslinking (297). With the ester linkage RCH_2COOR' rather than $RR'CHCOOR''$ or $RR'R''CCOOR'''$ the amount of chain cleavage probably becomes even less than predicted by the comparison. Experimentally several γ-irradiated linear, aliphatic polyesters have been found to undergo predominant crosslinking (298). As would be anticipated, the crosslinking is favored by longer paraffinic chains between the ester linkages.

The most intensively studied polyester has been poly(ethylene terephthalate) (PET), $\text{+OCC}_6\text{H}_4\text{COOCH}_2\text{CH}_2\text{O+}$. The aromatic ring in the chain increases the energy requirements for both crosslinking and chain cleavage. Also, merely two methylene groups per unit are available for crosslinking in the aliphatic chain. Both predominant crosslinking (299) and predominant chain cleavage (31,300,301) have been claimed for irradiated PET. The former claim was based upon partial insolubilization of PET while the latter, involving more detailed studies, was based upon no insolubles detected, a steady decrease in intrinsic viscosity with increasing dose, and physical and mechanical evidences of chain cleavage. Despite a lack of conclusive proof the present author tentatively places PET in the predominantly radiation-crosslinked category.

In mechanical property changes PET is fairly resistant to moderate doses of radiation. The tensile strength and ultimate elongation begin to decrease appreciably above 50 Mrad and deteriorate rapidly in the 100–500 Mrad range during atomic pile irradiation (30,302–304). Irradiation has been reported to increase (304), decrease (305), or leave essentially unchanged (300) the amount of crystallinity in PET as revealed by x-ray analyses. A lowering of the glass transition temperature by reactor radiations exceeding 1000 Mrad (306) probably results from the lowering of the polymer $\bar{M}_n$ by chain cleavage and from plasticization by the low molecular weight fragments formed.

The only chemical change data reported are observations of terminal carboxyl groups produced in PET irradiated *in vacuo*, and hydroxyl and carbonyl (as in an aromatic aldehyde or ketone) groups produced in PET irradiated in air (300). This appears to indicate different mechanisms of reaction predominant in the two cases. Dependence of ultraviolet light transmission on dose rate and thickness in irradiated PET films probably reflects the difference in groups produced depending upon accessibility of oxygen (307). Despite these effects the use of such films as radiation dosimeters was deemed feasible.

Post-curing of styrene-modified polyester resins by 10 Mrad of γ-radiation has been reported to increase their tensile strengths and elastic moduli (308). Considering the low dose applied the mechanical improvement must arise through furtherance of the polymerization reaction rather than crosslinking as treated in this section.

Random chain scission of poly(ethylene terephthalate) by ultraviolet light has been deduced from the lowering of intrinsic viscosity (309,310). Possible concurrent crosslinking was not detected in these measurements.

8. Polyamides

Polyamides, e.g., nylon 66 $\text{+OC(CH}_2)_4\text{CONH(CH}_2)_6\text{NH+}$, and nylon 6 $\text{+OC(CH}_2)_5\text{NH+}$, are crosslinked by radiation (32,299). G(apparent crosslink) = 0.35 was found for electron-irradiated nylon 6 at room temperature by the dose-to-gelation method (311). If the G(amine group) = 0.6 (311) represents the total chain cleavage reaction we may calculate from G(apparent crosslink) = G(crosslink) − $^1/_4G$(chain cleavage) that G(crosslink) = 0.5 or E_c = 100 e.v., and β/α = 0.6. An analysis of data on nylon 66 irradiated with electrons at 25°C. suggests a similar G(crosslink), but a higher β/α and an increase in G(crosslink) with increasing dose was calculated (312). The assumptions used in the analysis may have led to the dose dependency of G(crosslink) as an artifact. The initial decreases in intrinsic viscosity with increasing radiation dose reflect a sizeable β/α which, however, may have been constant throughout the approach to gelation.

Agreement that polyamides are predominantly crosslinked has not been unanimous. Some early work fostered the conclusion that nylon 66 may have preferentially degraded under atomic pile irradiation (31,300). It was pointed out at that time that the presence of air increased the relative amount of chain cleavage and caused a considerable increase in terminal carbonyl groups. The effect of air has been demonstrated for γ-irradiated fibers of nylon 6. In vacuum, crosslinking is dominant, but in air degradation predominates (313). This is a possible explanation of an observed fragmentation of two polyamide samples by low intensity γ-irradiation as judged by proton magnetic resonance line narrowing (314). An inhibition of crosslinking has been studied in 2 M.e.v. electron-irradiated nylon 66 and nylon 610 by observing the disappearance of colored radicals during infusion of oxygen and observing the influence of thickness of sample on solution viscosity (312). Approximate diffusion coefficients were calculated for oxygen in the polyamide films.

Most physical properties of irradiated polyamides have indicated crosslinking with varying degrees of accompanying chain cleavage. Nylon 66 irradiated in a nuclear reactor exhibits rubberlike characteristics at temperatures above its melting point (315,316). The changes in dynamic modulus at lower temperatures also suggest a crosslinked structure. Decrease in ultimate elongation and tensile strength in reactor-irradiated nylon 610 fibers, both drawn and undrawn, reflected a decrease in crystallinity (317). The extent of crosslinking and scission could not be estimated. At γ-radiation doses up to 250 Mrad no changes in x-ray patterns for nylon 6 and nylon 66 were observed (318). Their melting points decreased with increasing dose, and a 250 Mrad sample was crosslinked to a coherent network state upon heating. Earlier work (300) also showed no difference in x-ray pattern in nylon 66 irradiated in a reactor to a high dose level. It appears that x-ray patterns are not very sensitive to crosslinking and cleavage in these polymers. Reductions in crystallinity sufficient to markedly decrease tensile strength are not detected by x-ray analysis. An infrared study revealed decreases in intermolecular hydrogen bridging (β-form) and increases in intramolecular bridging (α-form) (319). This may be responsible for much of the loss in strength. An observed decrease in infrared absorptions due to —CH_2— deformation vibrations is compatible with crosslinking (319). Dielectric loss measurements indicate that crosslinking to the extent of one chain unit in 15 in nylon 66 greatly limits the dipole orientation-mode contribution to loss (320). Other thermomechanical evidences of radiation crosslinking and chain cleavage in polyamides have been reported (321,322).

Some information on the nature of the crosslinking species in polyamides is available. Hydrogen gas is evolved during the irradiation of nylon 66, thereby creating potential crosslinking sites (300). A low molecular weight amide, caproamide, irradiated at −80°C. with 2 M.e.v. electrons has a five-peak electron spin resonance spectrum having relative intensities 1:2:2:2:1 (323). This was interpreted to arise from the radical $CH_3(CH_2)_3$-$\dot{C}HCONH_2$ with the unpaired electron density distributed at the β,β,α protons in the ratios 1:1:2. Deuteration of the nitrogen did not alter the spectrum. In the same study irradiated ε-caprolactam gave an ESR spectrum which was not amenable to interpretation. A five-peak ESR spectrum in γ-irradiated nylon 6 (324) might arise from a radical similar to that in irradiated caproamide. However, residence of the radical in the amine portion of polyamides is more probable. The free radicals produced in low molecular weight amides and in polyamides absorb in the visible and near-ultraviolet light regions (312,325,326). From a study of several different irradiated amides and polyamides it was concluded that free radicals formed are most likely $RCONH\dot{C}HR'$ (325). The radicals terminate in a diffusion-controlled reaction in the absence of oxygen and are bleached by oxygen. By means of iodine as a scavenger G (radical) = 5.8 was estimated for nylon 66 irradiated with 2 M.e.v. electrons at −78°C. (325). The calculation assumed equal production of radicals in the crystalline and amorphous regions with iodine reacting with radicals only in the latter. It was postulated that all the crosslinking in irradiated nylon 66 occurs in the amorphous region and that the radicals formed in the crystalline regions "migrate" slowly by abstraction of hydrogen and terminate by disproportionation (325). This would explain many of the data presented, but without considerable corroborative evidence acceptance of such a scheme is not easy. The crosslinking yield is increased by raising the temperature of irradiation, by heating after irradiation, by the presence of water as a plasticizer, and by lower degrees of crystallinity (325). All of these factors seem to indicate the importance of mobility to the crosslinking reaction.

No direct experimental proof of the crosslink structure in irradiated polyamides has been published. If radicals of the $RCONH\dot{C}HR'$ type couple, the resultant crosslink should have good stability. A proposed disproportionation reaction for such radicals would lead to the group $RCON{=}CHR'$ by the loss of hydrogen (312). This is presumably a weak unit which may undergo cleavage at a later time.

Probable crosslinking and chain cleavage reactions for polyamides during exposure to high energy radiation may be inferred from studies with ultraviolet light. Cleavage of the C—N bond of amides by light has been demonstrated (327–329). The production of hydrogen by ionizing (300) and ultraviolet (330) irradiations indicates initial C—H bond cleavages. These and other possible reactions are summarized in eqs. (21)–(26) (330).

$$\text{—}CH_2CH_2CONHCH_2CH_2\text{—} \xrightarrow{h\nu} \text{—}CH_2CH_2CONH\dot{C}HCH_2\text{—} + H\cdot \qquad (21)$$

$$\text{—}CH_2CH_2CONHCH_2CH_2\text{—} + H\cdot \rightarrow \text{—}CH_2CH_2CONH\dot{C}HCH_2\text{—} + H_2 \qquad (22)$$

$$—CH_2CH_2CONHCH_2CH_2— \xrightarrow{h\nu} —CH_2CH_2\dot{C}O + \cdot NHCH_2CH_2— \quad (23)$$

$$\downarrow$$

$$—CH_2\dot{C}H_2 + CO$$

$$—CH_2\dot{C}H_2 + —NHCH_2CH_2— \rightarrow —CH_2CH_3 + —NH\dot{C}HCH_2— \quad (24)$$

$$—CH_2CH_2\dot{N}H + —CONHCH_2CH_2— \rightarrow —CH_2CH_3NH_2 + —CONH\dot{C}HCH_2— \quad (25)$$

$$2 —CH_2CH_2CONH\dot{C}HCH_2— \rightarrow \begin{array}{c} —CH_2CH_2CONHCHCH_2— \\ | \\ —CH_2CH_2CONHCHCH_2— \end{array} \quad (26)$$

The initial hydrogen atom removal (eq. 21) and the hydrogen abstractions (eqs. 22, 24, and 25) are represented as creating the $—NH\dot{C}HCH_2—$ radical which has been observed experimentally. The initial C—H bond breaks may be more random and subsequent hydrogen abstraction and migration leads to the $—NH\dot{C}HCH_2—$ radical. This radical has been found to be the site of attachment of oxygen in the photooxidation of *N*-alkyl amides (331). The peroxy radical $—NHCH(—OO\cdot)CH_2—$ is the probable source of an absorption band centered around 2900 A. in nylon irradiated in air (332,333). The greater yields of hydrogen than of carbon monoxide (330) must indicate very appreciable reaction as in eq. (21), even with ultraviolet light, although aldehyde formation by abstraction,

$$—CH_2\dot{C}O + —CH_2— \rightarrow —CH_2CHO + —\dot{C}H—$$

and cyclic ketone formations (329) may depress the CO yield. The crosslink formation shown in reaction (26) is the most logical one at present under either ultraviolet light or high energy radiation.

9. Miscellaneous Polymers

In addition to the polymers discussed above several other polymers have been found to be crosslinked by ionizing radiations. Such polymers having $C[H_2CH(R)]$ unit structure are polyacrylonitrile (334), polyacrylamide (335), polyvinylpyrrolidone (335), poly(vinyl alkyl ethers) (17), poly(vinyl methyl ether) (336), and poly(vinyl acetate) (337). Poly(vinyl alcohol) is the only reported possible exception to the rule that $[CH_2CH(R)]$ type polymers are crosslinked by radiation (cf. Chapter VIII-C). Poly(ethylene oxide) crosslinks (217,338,339) as do some polysulfide elastomers (134,171). Polychloroprene is readily crosslinked by ionizing radiations (32,134–136,171,340). Its response is therefore in accord with that of natural rubber. The highly halogenated copolymers, chlorotrifluoroethylene-vinylidene fluoride (135) and hexafluoropropylene-vinylidene fluoride, (341) undergo predominant crosslinking during irradiation. This is remarkable, since polychlorotrifluoroethylene is predominantly cleaved; polyhexafluoropropene would be expected to respond similarly, and poly-(vinylidene fluoride), by analogy with poly(vinylidene chloride), should degrade. Either the flexibilizing influence of the $—CH_2—$ group or its specific chemical nature when surrounded by the electronegative fluorinated structures must give rise to the radiation crosslinkability observed.

10. Conclusion

As in the examination of polymer chain cleavage by radiation (Chapter VIII-C), polymer crosslinking by radiation requires extensive future studies involving quantitative measurements of the intermediate and ultimate chemical species formed. Only upon a base of reliable chemical and kinetic analysis can postulated mechanisms of crosslinking be tested and modified. The relating of changes in molecular and macroscopic physical properties of irradiated polymers to the random crosslinking and cleavage within them has resulted in considerable progress toward reaction mechanism elucidation. With increasing sophistication in both physical and chemical methods of attack the paths of radiation-chemical events in polymer systems must eventually yield to scientific inquiry.

The author wishes to acknowledge the encouragement of the Minnesota Mining and Manufacturing Company during the preparation of the above manuscript.

B. CROSSLINKING BY MONOMER

W. G. Carson

Rohm and Haas Co.

1. Types of Systems

A polymer capable of being crosslinked by reaction with a monomer must, in general, possess unsaturated groups with which the monomer can polymerize. However, crosslinking does not necessarily result from such a polymerization. Unless the polymer chains are connected through linkages formed by the polymerizing monomer only branching or grafting results. When the polymer chains contain two or more unsaturated groups they are capable of being crosslinked by polymerization with suitable monomers to form a network which is three dimensional or infinitely complex on a molecular scale. Several general classes of unsaturated polymers can be distinguished and some of the more important polymer–monomer systems within these classes will be discussed below. In addition, several types of saturated polymers which have been crosslinked by reaction with monomers will also be considered.

a. Unsaturated Condensation Polymers

Perhaps the most important class of unsaturated polymers are those formed from unsaturated molecules containing two or more functional groups through which they can be joined to form a polymer chain usually by a condensation reaction. The most widely known polymers of this class are the unsaturated polyesters. These polyesters are formed by the condensation of glycols and dibasic acids, with part or all of either the acidic or glycol component being unsaturated. Dibasic acids such as maleic, itaconic, and citraconic or glycols such as 2-butenediol-1,4 have been used to make these polyesters.

Early studies (342) of these unsaturated polyesters were concerned principally with their drying characteristics in coatings applications, where it was recognized that they could be converted by heat into insoluble thermoset products. It was also recognized that oxygen and certain catalysts accelerated this process and that an average of two unsaturated groups per polyester molecule was required before gelation could occur (343). It was then demonstrated that these polyesters could be copolymerized with vinyl monomers under the influence of heat and peroxide initiators to form a variety of thermoset plastics (344,345). Liquid resins formed by the solution of unsaturated polyesters in a vinyl monomer now constitute an important segment of the plastics market.

Most of the commercial unsaturated polyester resins are made with maleic anhydride as the unsaturated component. During the polyesterification reaction a large majority of the maleic groups isomerize to the fumaric form and it is actually these fumarate units which copolymerize readily with monomers (346,347). The concentration of fumarate groups in the polyester (348) and the type of saturated dibasic acid and glycol used all have an important influence on the physical properties of the final product. For example, the use of chlorendic acid (Diels-Alder adduct of hexachlorocyclopentadiene and maleic anhydride) promotes flame resistance (349) and glycols derived from bisphenol A [2,2-bis(4′-hydroxyphenyl)-propane] contribute chemical resistance (350).

Many different vinyl monomers have been used to crosslink unsaturated polyesters. The monomer used most widely in commercial resins is styrene because of its low cost and its ability to copolymerize readily with fumarate unsaturation. Other monomers used in commercial polyester resins include various allyl types, such as diallyl phthalate and diallyl maleate, which are used because of their lower volatility and because they contribute to rigidity at elevated temperatures (351). Methyl methacrylate is used to improve outdoor durability (352). Triallyl cyanurate is used for outstanding stability at elevated temperature (353). Numerous other vinyl monomers have been reported as crosslinking agents for unsaturated polyesters, and these together with other compositional variations associated with polyester resin systems are described in more comprehensive references on unsaturated polyester resins (354,355).

b. Unsaturated Vinyl Polymers

Another large class of unsaturated polymers are those formed by the polymerization of di- or polyvinyl monomers. In many cases such monomers can be polymerized through one of their vinyl groups so that the remaining vinyl group, which may be located in the chain or pendant to the chain, is then free to polymerize in a separate reaction with another monomer. Generally, however, chain growth and crosslinking occur simultaneously during the polymerization of a divinyl monomer. This latter situation will not be treated here specifically, since it is felt to be somewhat beyond the scope of reactions involving polymers. However, only secondary differences exist in both reaction and structure between this case and that of second-stage crosslinking by a monomer (356).

Alfrey, Bohrer, and Mark (357) point out that the type of polymerization which occurs with a divinyl monomer depends chiefly on its symmetry or the similarity of its unsaturated groups and the degree of interdependence in the reactivity of these groups. These authors have classified the various types of divinyl monomers with respect to these characteristics; Table IX-1 lists examples.

TABLE IX-1
Classification of Divinyl Monomers[a]

Group	Symmetrical	Unsymmetrical
Independent vinyl groups	Ethylene glycol dimethacrylate	Allyl acrylate
Intermediate	Divinylbenzene	*p*-Isopropenylstyrene
Interdependent	Butadiene	Chloroprene

[a] Taken from ref. 357.

A symmetrical molecule with vinyl groups which polymerize independently of each other cannot be homopolymerized (or copolymerized with moderate amounts of monovinyl monomer) to a very high degree of conversion without the formation of a large number of crosslinks and the rapid development of an infinite network. Polymer chains of even low molecular weight containing unreacted pendant vinyl groups would be difficult to prepare from ethylene glycol dimethacrylate, for example. In contrast, butadiene can be converted to a relatively high molecular weight polymer containing an unsaturated group in each structural unit. The two vinyl groups in this molecule are highly interdependent, and after the first one reacts the second one becomes less than 1/150 as reactive as either group was in the monomeric state (357). Despite this, crosslinking and gelation do occur at high degrees of conversion (358). The second-stage crosslinking or vulcanization of rubbers formed from such butadiene polymers or butadiene–styrene copolymers is normally accomplished by reaction with sulfur and is described elsewhere. However, these polymers can also be crosslinked by reaction with monomers, and their reaction with vinyl monomers to form graft copolymers is well known (359).

It is possible to form unsaturated polymer chains of significant molecular weight from unsymmetrical divinyl monomers even when the two vinyl groups react in a completely independent manner, since relative reactivities of the two groups may be sufficiently different to permit a nearly complete reaction of one group and no reaction of the other. An interesting example of this type of reaction is described by Butler and Nash (360), who reacted vinyl β-chloroethyl ether with various alkenoxides to form vinyl ethers with different unsaturated groupings. The vinyl ether portion was then polymerized with BF_3 at $-70°C.$, leaving the second unsaturated group undisturbed and available for second-stage crosslinking with another monomer. It can thus be seen that unsaturated polymers capable of being crosslinked by reaction with a monomer can probably be prepared from any divinyl monomer which does not possess structurally identical and independently reacting vinyl groups.

Several unsaturated polymers prepared from divinyl monomers have been offered commercially, usually as reactive resin solutions in a monomeric component. These materials are then polymerized at a later stage by the application of heat and a free radical initiator to form a highly crosslinked product. An important resin of this type consists of partially polymerized diallyl phthalate, which can be dissolved in different monomers, frequently its own, and copolymerized with them to form a thermoset product (361). Similar prepolymers of diethylene glycol bis(allyl carbonate) are available under the tradename CR-39 from the Pittsburgh Plate Glass Co. Another resin of this general type is made from a butadiene–styrene copolymer of low molecular weight (8,000–10,000) and high unsaturation (iodine number of 300). This polymer is dissolved in styrene or other monomers and crosslinked in a second-stage reaction (362). Another polymer consisting of an unsaturated polyolefin which is partly epoxidized is available commercially and this may be crosslinked by reaction with both monomers and epoxy crosslinkers (363).

c. *Unsaturated Derivatives of Saturated Polymers*

A third class of unsaturated polymers is prepared essentially by the modification of an existing saturated polymer. No instances are known of such polymers being crosslinked in a second-stage reaction with a monomer, but Smets (364) refers to several cases where this type of polymer has been grafted by polymerization with a monomer. Examples of such polymers are a polystyrene containing nonaromatic unsaturation formed by dehydrohalogenation of a brominated styrene polymer (365) and a cellulose polymer containing methacrylate groups formed by the reaction of cellulose with methacrylyl chloride (366).

d. Saturated Polymers

Several cases have been reported where saturated polymers have been crosslinked by reaction with a monomer. For example, certain functional groups found on polymers can be reacted with a monomer through an ionic mechanism. Kovacic (367) has reported the crosslinking of polymers containing amino groups by reaction of these groups with the unsaturated groups in dimaleimides. A second possibility for the crosslinking of a saturated polymer by a monomer exists in the case of polymers containing peroxide groups (368,369). Here the polymer acts as a polyfunctional initiator for the monomer and crosslinking can occur when growing chains terminate by combination. A third case involves the possibility of crosslinkages developing in polymerization reactions where extensive chain transfer occurs between growing chains and dead polymers. Ordinarily this situation causes branching, but under certain circumstances the formation of a network structure is possible (370).

2. Crosslinking Reactions

The general crosslinking reaction which occurs during polymerization involving components with a functionality greater than two has been studied extensively. The statistical analysis of molecular distributions in such reactions is due primarily to Flory (371). The statistics of the crosslinking or vulcanization of polymer chains have been derived from Flory's work by Alfrey, Bohrer, and Mark (357) for the three cases of a polymer which is (*a*) monodisperse in degree of polymerization, (*b*) polydisperse in degree of polymerization, and (*c*) polydisperse in polymerization degree and in chemical composition.

In the specific case of crosslinking of unsaturated polymer chains by polymerization with monomers the reaction can, in general, be considered to occur in three stages (372). The first stage is essentially equivalent to a linear copolymerization reaction but proceeds only to a rather low degree of conversion. The composition is controlled by the reactivity ratios associated with the two types of unsaturated groups which are reacting and the rate by factors normally operative in linear copolymerizations. The second stage is characterized by the formation of a gel structure and by an exponential increase in the rate of reaction resulting from diffusion control of the termination step (Trommsdorf-Norrish acceleration) due to the increase in viscosity. In the third step, propagation, transfer, and even initiation rates become diffusion-controlled as the gel structure becomes increasingly dense.

a. Pregelation Reaction

The initial stage of a copolymerization between polymer unsaturation and a crosslinking monomer has been studied in detail by Gordon, Grieveson, and McMillan (373). The system studied was the copolymerization between methyl methacrylate (MMA) and poly(ethylene fumarate) (PEF). From this work they were able to determine reactivity ratios for the two reactants. This is the first pair of ratios reported where one of the reactants is a polyfunctional monomer.

Two major difficulties were encountered in this work which are not present in the study of conventional copolymerizations. First, it was necessary to characterize carefully the unsaturated polyester, and second, much care had to be exercised in separating unattached polyester from the crosslinked copolymer. Polymerizations of various proportions of reactants were carried to the gel point and unreacted components were extracted from the copolymer. Analysis of the copolymer permitted a determination of the weight fraction of total fumarate units in the copolymer which in turn permitted a calculation of the fraction ρ' of polymerized bonds which were

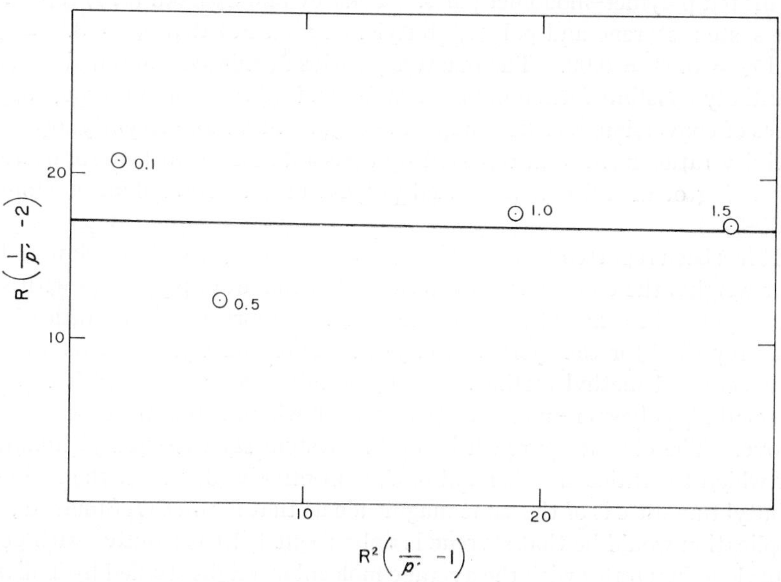

Fig. IX-1. Evaluation of monomer reactivity ratios for methyl methacrylate–poly(ethylene fumarate). The points describe results for four resins with the designated methyl methacrylate/poly(ethylene fumarate) feed ratios. (Taken from ref. 373.)

fumarate rather than methacrylate. This factor was related to the reactivity ratios r_1 and r_2 for methacrylate and fumarate, respectively, in a modification of the copolymerization equation (eq. 27), where R is the feed ratio of moles of fumarate to moles of methacrylate.

$$r_2R^2[(1/\rho') - 1] + R[(1/\rho') - 2] = r_1 \tag{27}$$

This expression assumes a linear noncrosslinked copolymer and will apply at the gel point to a close approximation since at this point only an average of one of the several fumarate chains in the copolymer will have reacted through a second bond. Figure IX-1 shows $R[(1/\rho') - 2]$ plotted against $R^2[(1/\rho') - 1]$ for different designated R values from which the values for r_1 and r_2 were determined as the slope and intercept. From this figure, the intercept, r_1, is found to equal 17 and the slope, $-r_2$, is found to equal zero. The scatter in the data reflects the experimental difficulties. However, despite the inaccuracies the authors were able through a consideration of the possible errors involved to select with some confidence the following ranges for the reactivity ratios: $10 < r_1 < 25$ and $0 < r_2 < 0.7$.

More recently several other reactivity ratios have been reported for unsaturated polymer–monomer pairs. Tokarev and Spasskiĭ (374) report for the system styrene and poly(1,3-butylene fumarate) that $r_1 = 3.0 \pm 0.4$ and $r_2 = 0.03 \pm 0.03$. The reactivity ratios in this system remained substantially constant for a number of different feed ratios and for various degrees of conversion over the range of 9–35%. Still more recently, other reactivity ratios have been reported by Spasskiĭ and co-workers for systems consisting of modified unsaturated polyesters and crosslinking monomers (375–377).

It has been reported by Spasskiĭ and Molchanova (378) that at low molecular weights the coreactivity of unsaturated fumarate polyesters with styrene approaches that of fumarate diesters. Unfortunately no ratios have been reported for the system dibutyl fumarate and styrene or for diethyl fumarate and methyl methacrylate to permit a comparison with the corresponding polyester–monomer systems for which ratios have been given above. The closest approach is for the system styrene–diethyl fumarate for which the ratios are 0.30 and 0.07, respectively (379). If the ratio for dibutyl fumarate is of the same magnitude as that for diethyl fumarate, the implication would be that styrene is only about 1/10 as reactive with poly(butylene fumarate) with the average molecular weight studied by Tokarev and Spasskiĭ (374) as it is with dibutyl fumarate. If it is assumed that all the fumarate groups in a polyester are equally reactive, as was done by Gordon and co-workers (373), then it would appear that each group in the polyester is less reactive on the average than the fumarate in a diester. Steric factors make this a reasonable possibility.

b. Reaction near Gel Point

The second stage of the monomer crosslinking reaction is dominated by the formation of an infinite network which is characterized by the manifestation of a gel structure. The necessary and sufficient condition for the formation of an infinite network occurs when the expected number of polymer chains united through crosslinks formed by the monomer to a given chain selected at random exceeds two (371). Expressed quantitatively, following Flory (356), the expectancy ϵ of additional crosslinked units to be found in a polymer chain previously linked to another chain (assuming a random crosslinking process with all units equally reactive and no cyclization) is given by the expression

$$\epsilon = \rho(y - 1) \tag{28}$$

where ρ equals the probability that any one unit of the chain is crosslinked and $y - 1$ is the total number of chain units capable of being crosslinked. If $\epsilon < 1$ the possibility of an indefinite continuation of the structure is impossible. Only if $\epsilon > 1$ may an indefinite continuation sometimes occur. Therefore, the critical condition for the formation of infinite structures is $\epsilon_c = 1$ or

$$\rho_c = 1/(y - 1) \cong 1/y \tag{29}$$

A more general expression which holds regardless of primary molecular weight distribution is

$$\rho_c = 1/(\bar{y}_w - 1) \cong 1/\bar{y}_w \tag{30}$$

where $\bar{y}_w$ is the weight-average degree of polymerization of the primary molecules. This expression, which is applicable to all types of polymer crosslinking, has been extended to apply in the case of vinyl–divinyl copolymerization where all groups are equally reactive by Stockmayer (380) who derived the following expression from Flory's more general analysis (371).

$$\theta_c = 1/\rho_0(\bar{y}_w - 1) \tag{31}$$

In this case θ_c is the critical fractional conversion of double bonds at the gel point and ρ_0 is the fraction of double bonds in the divinyl units. This equation is accurate only for low divinyl monomer concentrations and gives

θ_c as a lower limit, since intramolecular reactions are not considered in the derivation.

A further extension of this expression to the case of unsaturated polymer chains crosslinked by reaction with a monomer has been made by Gordon, Grieveson, and McMillan (381), who derived the following expressions:

$$\varphi_c = 1/\rho'(\bar{y}_w - 1)\ (DP_{wc} - 1) \tag{32}$$

$$\theta_c = R'/(R' + 1)\rho'^2(\bar{y}_w - 1)\ (DP_{wc} - 1) \tag{33}$$

Here φ_c is the critical fractional conversion of chain unsaturation and θ_c is the critical fractional conversion of all unsaturation at the gel point. DP_{wc} is the number of double bonds in the initial weight-average polymer chain, R' is the ratio of unreacted fumarate unsaturation to unreacted methacrylate unsaturation, and ρ' has been defined above for eq. (27). The term $\bar{y}_w$ in this case is the weight-average length of the chain radical formed by the monomer. Two basic assumptions made in the derivation of these expressions are equal reactivity of all unsaturated groups in the chain and the absence of cyclization.

It can be seen that eq. (32) reduces to eq. (31) for the case of vinyl–divinyl polymerization, where $DP_{wc} = 2$. Also the above expressions clearly indicate that as the degree of unsaturation in the polymer chains increases the critical degree of conversion at gelation decreases.

Gordon, Grieveson, and McMillan (381) extended their analysis of the gelation phenomenon to derive an expression for the gel time. It was observed through shrinkage measurements that the rate $d\theta/dt$ of the reaction for the system MMA–PEF was constant up to the gel point and then suddenly increased. An expression was derived for the rate in terms of the individual rate constants for the propagation and termination steps. The following equation for the gel time, t_c, was then derived from the relation $\theta_c = (d\theta/dt)t_c$, the expression for the rate, and eq. (33):

$$t_c = k_t r_1^2/[1.5k_p^2(\mathrm{R}'r_2 + 1)^2(DP_{wc} - 1)F] \tag{34}$$

The term k_t/k_p^2 which relates the termination and propagation rate constants for MMA is known from independent studies of the homopolymerization of MMA. Thus (34) expresses a linear relation between t_c and $1/F$, where F is the concentration of unreacted fumarate. Figure IX-2 shows the relation between experimentally determined values for t_c and $1/F$ for two polyester samples having different DP_{wc} values. Good agreement with these values was obtained with eq. (34) when the values of 31 and 0.25

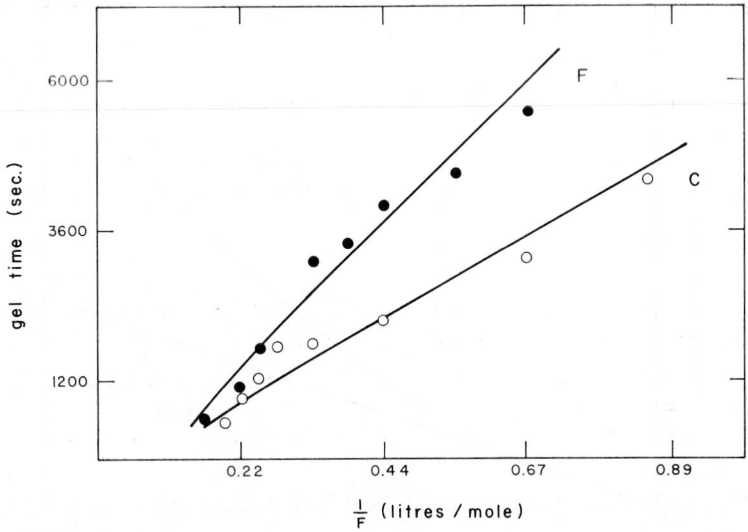

Fig. IX-2. Gel time as a function of the reciprocal of the unreacted fumarate concentration from eq. (34) in the copolymerization of methyl methacrylate and poly(ethylene fumarate) for polyesters with average double bond contents of (F) 5.56 and (C) 9.46. (Taken from ref. 381.)

were used, respectively, for r_1 and r_2. These values compare favorably with those given above for the same system.

These authors also consider the influence of temperature on the gel time, and from an Arrhenius plot of log t_c versus $1/T$ they determined a mean overall energy of activation of gelation for several MMA–PEF resins of 14.8 ± 0.8 kcal./mole. The effects of catalyst type and concentration on the gel point were also studied. According to eq. (34), t_c should be independent of the concentration and nature of catalyst. Although this equation was derived only for isothermal conditions which are not usually encountered in practice, t_c was found to be constant for a range of concentrations with methyl ethyl ketone peroxide as the catalyst. Also the rate of conversion with this catalyst varied as would be expected with the square root of the concentration up to the gel point. With other catalysts, t_c was less constant since the gelling system is critically affected by side reactions.

In another paper (372), Gordon and McMillan compare the system poly(propylene fumarate–phthalate) (PPFP) and styrene with the PEF–MMA system described above. In order to do this they described results

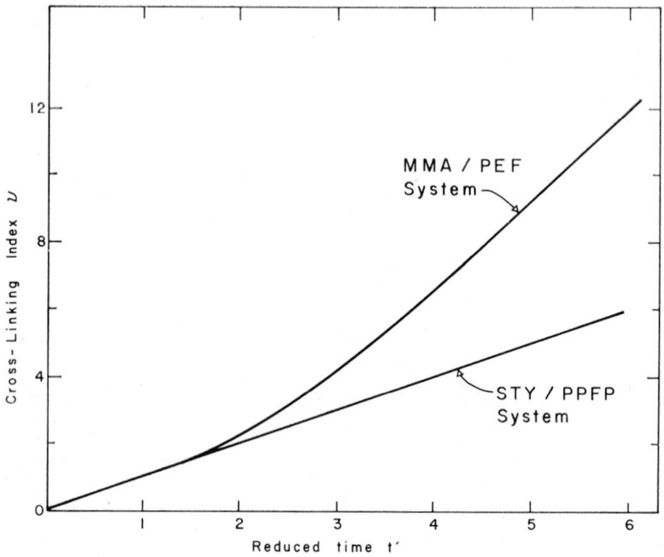

Fig. IX-3. Reduced rate curves for the copolymerization of methyl methacrylate–poly(ethylene fumarate) and styrene–poly(propylene phthalate–fumarate). (Taken from ref. 372.)

by a reduced rate curve of crosslinking index versus reduced time. The crosslinking index ν, defined as the number of crosslinks per weight-average primary polymerization chain, is unity at the gel point. If the fractional conversion θ of the unsaturation is known, ν can be determined at all stages of the reaction, since θ is proportional to ν and the gel point fixes the proportionality constant. All θ scales can be transformed to ν scales by the relation $\nu = \theta/\theta_c$. Likewise, the time scale can be transformed by the relation $t' = t/t_c$, so that all initial rates can be brought into coincidence. Curves for the MMA–PEF system over a 70-fold rate range could be superposed, and the combined curve is shown in Figure IX-3.

An increase in rate is seen at the gel point for the MMA–PEF sample. The system styrene–PPFP, however, fails to show such an increase in rate at the gel point or even up to $t' = 4$. The authors point out that shorter primary chain lengths are attained by styrene than by MMA, and this minimizes diffusion control so that a rate increase does not occur at the gel point. It can be shown from eq. (33) that the polyaddition chains $\bar{y}_w$ formed in the styrene system are about 1/100 as long as those formed in the MMA system. The authors express the view that this ratio of lengths seems plausible when the chain lengths formed by homopolymerization of the pure monomers are considered.

c. *Post-Gelation Reaction*

The study of polymerization which occurs in a monomer crosslinking reaction beyond the gel point (frequently termed "curing") presents the investigator with perhaps even more experimental difficulties than the first two stages. When high conversions are reached the rate (at least in bulk polymerizations) normally decreases because of restrictions on diffusion. This situation generally places a limit on the degree of conversion which can be obtained. Loshaek and Fox (382), in a study of MMA–dimethacrylate systems, concluded that crosslinking efficiency is limited by restrictions on the motion of pendant vinyl groups and by the passage of the system from a rubbery or fluid state to the glassy state. Starkweather and Eirich (383) reached the same conclusion in a study of diallyl polymerization where maximum conversions of about 70% were obtained because of diffusion restrictions on reactive groups.

Studies of the latter stages of polymerization of the system MMA–PEF were made by Gordon and McMillan (372) and Gordon and Grieveson (384). In these studies the degree of polymerization was determined from shrinkage measurements and from energy absorption determinations made by measuring the rebound of a steel ball after impact with the resin surface, a process which is dependent upon relaxation characteristics of the resin and hence on the degree of crosslinking. Samples of resin were polymerized isothermally at 62°C. to a pseudoequilibrium point indicated by a decay of the shrinkage rate to zero. The samples were then subjected to a so-called isoelastic cure in which the temperature was raised at a rate sufficient to maintain a constant ball rebound height. The results indicated a linear increase in the second-order transition temperature up to a certain level at which an equilibrium was reached. Analysis of density and weight changes, however, indicated that the observed results were due to loss of residual MMA as well as to further polymerization.

Gordon and McMillan (372) point out that the degree of cure in the latter stages of a crosslinking polymerization is a function of three parameters representing (*a*) the degree of resinification or crosslinking, (*b*) plasticization by residual free polymer chains, and (*c*) plasticization by free residual monomer. The last two parameters detract from hardness, rigidity, or other indications of cure. Shrinkage measurements on MMA–PEF samples cured isothermally at 62°C. indicated the relative magnitude of these parameters. Calculations showed that only about 10% of the fumarate groups polymerized. Thus, in the third stage of the crosslinking reaction, the copolymerization equation, which was seen to predict composition fairly well in the first two stages, overestimates the amount of reacted polymer chain unsaturation which is more strongly diffusion controlled than the monomeric component.

The degree of crosslinking which takes place in the final curing reaction has also been studied by measuring changes in electrical resistance at different temperatures as a function of time. Fineman and Puddington (385) have studied resistivity changes in crosslinked unsaturated polyester systems, and Warfield and Petree (386) have examined changes in polymerizing diallyl phthalate. The resistance increases linearly with time to a certain point and then levels off. The rate at which the resistance changes increases with temperature. It is suggested that conductivity in these systems is due to small amounts of ionized impurities and the increased crosslinking which takes place in the curing reaction restricts their mobility.

Another means of determining the extent of reaction in monomer-crosslinked polymer systems, which is independent of changes in mechanical and electrical properties, has been examined by Murphy and co-workers (387). In this study a differential thermal analysis was made of triallyl cyanurate-crosslinked polyester samples which had been subjected to different curing cycles. From these analyses it was possible to determine the exothermic heat given off by polymerization which took place in incompletely cured samples as the temperature was raised to the point where further reaction could occur. In this way the relative degree of reaction resulting from the initial curing conditions could be determined from the magnitude of the exothermic curves.

3. Structure and Properties

In order to obtain an idea of the structure of crosslinked polymer systems it will be of interest to consider the following factors: (*a*) the degree to which copolymerization has occurred between the monomer and polymer as opposed to the homopolymerization of each component, (*b*) the amount of residual unsaturation, (*c*) the crosslinking density or the amount of crosslinking as opposed to branching, and (*d*) the length of the average crosslink. Considerable information has been obtained concerning these factors by direct physical and chemical analysis of cured, crosslinked materials.

a. Structure from Reactivity Ratios

An approximate indication of the structure can be gained from a consideration of the monomer reactivity ratios. The ratio $(1 - \rho')/\rho'$ which specifies the number of units in the crosslinking chain per reacted unsaturated unit in the original polymer chain is found from eq. (27) to equal $(r_1 + R)/R(r_2R + 1)$. With Gordon's (373) values of $r_1 = 17$ and $r_2 = 0$ for MMA and PEF it can be seen that for a feed ratio of unity there is, on the average, a chain of 18 MMA units between two linked polyester chains. Tokarev and Spasskiĭ's (374) values of $r_1 = 3.0$ and $r_2 = 0.03$ for styrene and poly(1,3-butylene fumarate) indicate that with a feed value of unity the average styrene chain linking two polyester chains contains about 4 units. Similar calculations for crosslinked polyester systems have been made by Wycherley (388) and by Robertson and Shepherd (389) using reactivity ratios for dialkyl fumarates rather than for the polyesters. With this approach a copolymer of styrene and diethyl fumarate is found to contain an average of 1.2 styrene units for every diethyl fumarate unit at a molar feed ratio of unity. It should be recognized from what has preceded that all calculations of this type have limited validity because of diffusion-controlled restrictions on the polymerizability of the components during the latter stages of the reaction.

b. Structure from Changes in Volume and Refractivity

An indication of structure has been obtained by Spasskiĭ and co-workers (390) from specific volume and specific refractivity measurements of poly(diethylene fumarate) crosslinked with MMA and with styrene. Specific volumes and refractivities were determined for the copolymers and for the polyester and monomers. These together with the feed ratios and specific shrinkage or refractivity change were used to calculate the weight fraction of reacted fumarate groups. Results indicated that only about 11% of the fumarate groups in a 6/94 weight ratio of styrene/polyester reacted, and about 28% of the fumarate groups in a 60/40 weight ratio of MMA/polyester reacted. By assuming that all the monomer has reacted and copolymerized, it is possible from these results to obtain an estimate of the average length of the monomer-derived crosslinks. This, of course, presupposes that crosslinking occurs rather than branching. The tendency for one or the other of these reactions to occur is dependent, in part, on whether the principal mode of termination for the crosslinking chains is combination or disproportionation.

c. Structure from Chemical Decomposition

Several investigators have broken down polyester resins crosslinked with styrene by hydrolysis of the ester groups and determined the relative amounts of the various hydrolysis products. The expected products of a hydrolytic breakdown of a styrene-crosslinked polyester are free acid and glycol, the copolymer of fumaric acid and styrene, and possibly styrene and fumarate homopolymer. Hayes, Read, and Vaughan (391) studied styrene-crosslinked poly(propylene fumarate) and poly(propylene phthalate–fumarate). It was shown that the length of styrene crosslinks (number of styrene molecules per reacted fumarate bond assuming no styrene homopolymer) in copolymers with poly(propylene fumarate) dropped suddenly when the styrene content was raised to about 40 wt.-%. A marked increase in the number of reacted fumarate double bonds also occurred at this point. An increase in the styrene content beyond this point gave only a slight increase in crosslinking density. Results obtained on a series of styrene–poly(propylene fumarate) resins with varying styrene/polyester ratios are listed in Table IX-2, together with data obtained on the same resins by a spectroscopic method in which the infrared absorption of cured and uncured resin was compared to indicate extent of reaction of the fumarate groups.

TABLE IX-2
Reduction of Double Bond Content in Styrene–Poly(propylene Fumarate) Copolymers With Increasing Styrene Concentration in Initial Resin[a]

Styrene in resin, %	No. of styrene molecules per reacted fumarate group	Reduction of polyester bond content during cure, %	
		Hydrolytic method	Spectroscopic method
20.0	1.31	27.4	31.0
35.5	2.48	35.5	41.6
39.4	1.57	62.1	58.8
45.9	2.00	63.5	68.6
50.0	2.27	66.2	64.9

[a] Taken from ref. 391.

The authors point out that the ratio where the sharp increase in crosslinking density occurred corresponded to an equimolar ratio of polyester and styrene. An examination of the styrene–fumaric copolymer obtained by hydrolysis showed that the average styrene crosslinking chain joined 6–10 polyester chains. This indicates that crosslinking rather than branch-

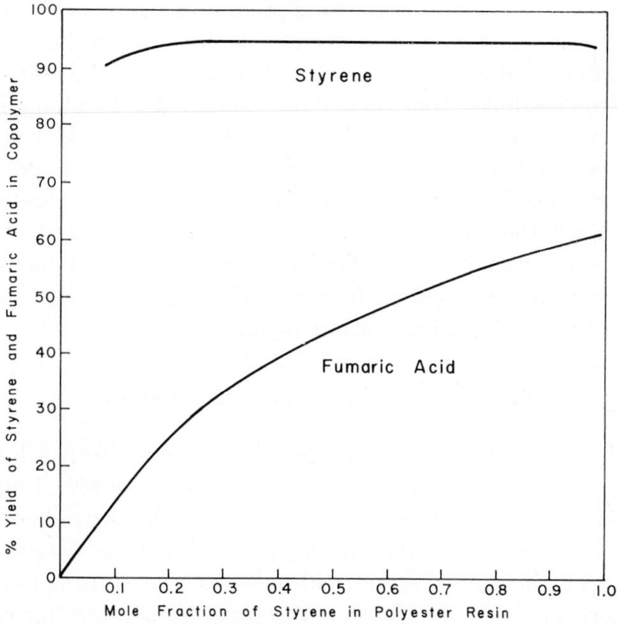

Fig. IX-4. Yield of polymerized styrene and fumarate units in styrene–poly(butylene fumarate) copolymer as a function of the mole fraction of styrene in the resin. (Taken from ref. 392.)

ing is the principal type of reaction. Similar results were obtained with the styrene-crosslinked poly(propylene phthalate–fumarate)system. The average length of the styrene crosslinks between fumarate units for both polyesters was 1–3 units over a 20–50% range in styrene concentration. The value of 1.6 styrene units per crosslink for styrene–poly(propylene fumarate) at a molar feed ratio of unity thus compares rather closely with Wycherley's (388) value of 1.2 units calculated from the copolymerization equation using the reactivity ratios for styrene and diethyl fumarate.

Hamann, Funke, and co-workers (392,393) have studied the structure of styrene-crosslinked poly(butylene fumarate) by chemical degradation of the cured resin. It was found that the mole ratio of styrene to fumarate was always greater in the hydrolysis product than in the original mixture. No appreciable amounts of polystyrene were formed in resins containing up to 90 mole-% styrene. In these results, however, there was no marked increase in the amount of reacted fumarate at the point where equal molar amounts of styrene and polyester were reacted. The fraction of reacted styrene and fumarate found in the final product is shown in Figure IX-4 as a function of the mole fraction of styrene in the initial resin.

These authors estimated the average distance along the polyester chain between two crosslinks from their data. There are 10 atoms in a poly-(butylene fumarate) chain between double bonds. At a 91/9 polyester/styrene feed ratio (by weight) the average distance between crosslinks was 59.9 atoms; i.e., only about every sixth fumarate unit was reacted. When the feed ratio was reduced to 50/50 about every other fumarate group was reacted. Similar results were obtained by Ghanem (394) for the same system from measurements made by tracer techniques by using C^{14}-tagged maleic anhydride.

4. Influence of Structure on Properties

Physical properties of crosslinked polymer systems are to a large degree dependent on the structural features discussed above. Properties of systems which are basically copolymers, however, also depend upon average composition. Short crosslinks and high crosslinking densities can be expected to result in harder, more rigid and less heat-deformable products. Fox and Loshaek (395) showed that the glass temperature for crosslinked systems is directly proportional to the degree of crosslinking for low degrees of crosslinking. Bockstahler and co-workers (348) described the influence of temperature on the modulus of elasticity of a series of poly(diethylene succinate–fumarate) polyesters crosslinked with different concentrations of styrene. Because of the similarity between succinate and fumarate groups it was possible to vary the number of potential crosslinking sites without otherwise changing the structure of the polyester. Figure IX-5 illustrates how the moduli of elasticity for two of these polyesters, one with a 70/30 fumaric/succinic ratio and the other with a 20/80 ratio, vary with temperature. Each polyester was crosslinked with four different concentrations of styrene. It can be seen that the more highly crosslinked 70/30 fumaric/succinic polyester remained more rigid with increasing temperature than the 20/80 polyester. The styrene/polyester ratio had a relatively minor effect on the modulus–temperature relationship, and there was no pronounced change in behavior at the 1/1 styrene/polyester molar ratio.

Structural influences on mechanical properties were also noted by Robertson and Shepherd (389), who showed that a polyester crosslinked with vinyl acetate or styrene was much tougher than when crosslinked with MMA or acrylonitrile. Results were given to indicate that the two former monomers formed much shorter crosslinks than the latter at approxi-

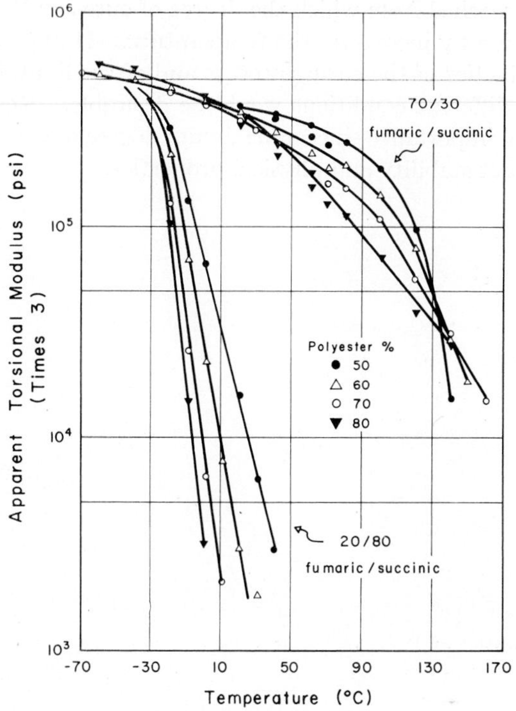

Fig. IX-5. Temperature dependence of the rigidity of styrene–poly(diethylene succinate–fumarate) copolymers as influenced by polyester unsaturation. (Taken from ref. 348.)

mately the same monomer/polyester ratio. Here, of course, compositional differences as well as structural factors influenced results somewhat. Studies (396) of the thermomechanical properties of similar polyesters with the same two pairs of monomers showed that resins crosslinked with vinyl acetate and styrene underwent deformation at higher temperatures than those crosslinked with MMA and acrylonitrile.

Changes in the mechanical and electrical properties of crosslinked systems which result from structural changes in the final curing reaction have been previously cited.

From what has been discussed it is apparent that the typical monomer crosslinked polymer system contains an appreciable concentration of unreacted primary chain unsaturation. The degree of conversion seems to be highly dependent on reaction conditions (372,384). Frequently a pseudoequilibrium is reached from which the degree of cure can be advanced to a limiting condition by increasing the temperature. It appears that further study of the kinetics of the curing process and of the limiting state of cure obtained with different conditions would be desirable. Results should be of technological importance since a maximum degree of cure would provide optimum product stability and physical properties.

C. CROSSLINKING OF ELASTOMERS

David Craig

B. F. Goodrich Research Center

1. Introduction

Crosslinking in high polymer systems usually is classified as pertaining to one of two types of chemical processes. In one, crosslinks form concurrently with coupling or extension of the main chain as an adjunct to a polymerization; in the other, crosslinks are inserted between two units of different preformed molecular chains or between units of the same chain, restricting to some degree, slippage of chains. Where crosslinking is under study it is usually necessary to consider scission and extension as possible complicating factors.

This chapter will be concerned mostly with the crosslinking by sulfur of elastomers. Those which have been studied most frequently are natural rubber (NR), butyl (IIR), styrene–butadiene rubber (SBR), nitrile–butadiene rubber (NBR), and neoprene (CR). At present, the crosslinking of polybutadiene rubber (BR) and "synthetic natural" (SN) is under study in many laboratories. Thiokol [poly(ethylene polysulfide)], the first commercial synthetic rubber (397), is of some chemical interest, mostly in the study of interchange, both in crosslinks and in the main chain, and also because of the possibility of main chain extension. A relatively new elastomeric system, the polyurethane, has been used for the study of rubbery behavior with findings of direct application to sulfur crosslinking even in this system.

During about the last 20 years considerable agreement as to the general nature of high polymers has been reached, particularly of elastomers. Many people consider regarding the sulfur crosslinking of rubber (398) that "a more intractable system for study could hardly be imagined". This remark, here taken out of context, was originally applied to vulcanization by sulfur, which is a complex process including crosslinking as the main step following an induction (scorch) period and preceding a final stage called reversion. The important reactions involving the elastomeric chain in scorch and reversion result in degradation by chain scission. When suitable allowances are made for these subtle effects, crosslinking behavior may appear more understandable. The mechanisms often are controversial, mostly because they are so poorly understood. Much of the information on crosslinking remains empirical in nature.

The discussion for this chapter conveniently could include a classical or theoretical approach as recommended by Flory for the general study of polymers, starting with some of the simpler results of the kinetic theory of elasticity applied to any substance having the requirements necessary for elastomeric behavior. However, on account of the predominantly empirical features which will be emphasized, it seems better to examine first the origin and use of the term crosslink and then return to the kinetic theory.

2. Historical Development

Weber (399) in 1894 believed the reaction of sulfur monochloride with rubber

$$C_{10}H_{16} + S_2Cl_2 \rightarrow C_{10}H_{16}S_2Cl_2 \qquad (35)$$

as shown in reaction (35) to be related to the sulfur–rubber reaction and so to be useful as a model for the study of vulcanization. The product from equivalent amounts of reactants calculated on the basis of this reaction was saturated toward addition of bromine. $C_{10}H_{16}$ and $C_{10}H_{16}S_2Cl_2$ were considered as empirical formulas. Weber believed rubber molecules to be multiples of $C_{10}H_{16}$ (actually multiples of C_5H_8) and to be large, although the values he assigned are relatively small by present standards. He observed that the reaction with the sulfur monochloride gave a product which was insoluble in rubber solvents, even when only small amounts had reacted to form, as he proposed, $S_2(C_{120}H_{192}Cl)_2$. Later workers (400,401) made the claim that insoluble sulfur, which was later shown to consist of linear chains of high molecular weight, was formed in vulcanization by sulfur monochloride. This claim has been refuted (402).

The mechanism of the Levinstein mustard gas synthesis, frequently used as a model for vulcanization by sulfur monochloride, has rather recently been studied in detail by Fuson and co-workers (403). The results have important implications for crosslinking of high molecular weight olefins by the same reactant. The crude product from the reaction with excess ethylene at 35°C. consists of 70% bis(2-chloroethyl) sulfide and 30% of the polysulfide $(ClCH_2CH_2)_2S_x$, where usually $x = 7$. It is noteworthy that the disulfide $(ClCH_2CH_2)_2S_2$ is nearly absent, as is also free sulfur. The disulfide is formed as an early intermediate as in reaction (36) and subsequently is rapidly cleaved by reaction with the sulfur monochloride as in reaction (37) to yield a sulfenyl chloride and trisulfur dichloride.

$$2C_2H_4 + S_2Cl_2 \rightarrow ClC_2H_4SSC_2H_4Cl \tag{36}$$

$$ClC_2H_4SSC_2H_4Cl + 3S_2Cl_2 \rightarrow 2ClC_2H_4SCl + 2S_3Cl_2 \tag{37}$$

The 2-chloroethyl sulfenyl chloride reacts with ethylene to form mustard gas, i.e., the monosulfide, and the S_3Cl_2 reacts with ethylene to form a trisulfide. The trisulfide is cleaved and sulfurated further in an analogous way, and extension of the reaction sequence leads to still higher sulfides.

Pickles (404) in 1910 was able to understand the structure of rubber more fully than Weber owing to the ozonolysis results of Harries (405). He considered rubber to be composed of linearly connected 1,4 head-to-tail isoprene units, but the truly macromolecular nature of rubber and many other polymers was proposed by Staudinger in the 1920's. Staudinger also contributed to the nature of crosslinking, but not until 1935, by studying the copolymerization of styrene with small amounts of divinylbenzene. Very small amounts of the divinyl comonomer were found to lead to a swellable but insoluble and, therefore, three-dimensional network.

The idea of chemical crosslinking, however, seems to have originated prior to 1894 with Weber (399,406). He referred to the coupling or joining of two polyisoprene molecules by disulfur bonds not as crosslinking, but rather as copulation or conjugation when it results from the reaction with sulfur monochloride. He also considered vulcanization to be a crosslinking reaction, but by 1903 when his book *The Chemistry of India Rubber* appeared, he may have modified his views somewhat to include colloidal concepts, which were beginning to appear although considered misguided by some authors. The 1903–1906 editions of Weber's book (406) (pages 82–115) are especially interesting, as are the corresponding parts of the revision of the fifth edition (1906) by Lothar Weber published in 1926.

The development of chain or threadlike molecular structures and their chemistry naturally required the term crosslink as applied to the 1894 concept of Weber, yet the exact origin of it is somewhat obscure. In 1928, Meyer and Mark (400) also considered the cold vulcanization of rubber to involve the joining of molecules (and also micelles) by the reaction of sulfur monochloride. Their views differed from those of Weber in that, on account of Staudinger's researches, they were aware of the great length of rubber molecules whereas Weber was not. Apparently, they also differed from Weber in that they considered rubber to exist as a spherocolloid.

They thought that the sulfur link connected the micelles as well as the rubber molecules inside the micelles.

In 1931 Carothers (407,408) used the term crosslinking, as we use it today, to denote the essential step in vulcanization. He illustrated his concept with a diagram of the three-dimensional polychloroprene network and evidently saw no need to retain the older spherocolloid concept.

3. Concept of Crosslinking

Crosslink is not used as a main entry in the subject index of *Chemical Abstracts* (*CA*). References are found, for example, under *Bonds, cross-linkage; Rubber, crosslinked; Rubber from ethylene and propene, cross-linkage;* and *Ethylene polymers, crosslinking of. Coupling reactions* in the *CA* index is in connection with entries on dye chemistry. Coupling, meaning crosslinking, is rarely used (409). The term vulcanization is usually limited to the rubber field, but crosslinking, crosslink, crossbond, bridgebond and sometimes other variants, are used in proteins, plastics, resins, and high polymers generally.

In the rubber industry, cure or curing often is a synonym for vulcanization. Cure sometimes signifies the period, temperature, and other conditions of heating or treatment for effecting the chemical process of vulcanization. Thus, we might say, "the 30-min., 300°F., hot-water cure failed to vulcanize." The term cure and its variants are much more common in nonrubber fields than the synonym vulcanization. *CA* does not index the term cure, but occasionally does index curing agents. Molding and curing are often of similar meanings and frequently involve crosslinking as the important chemical change. In rubber technology it is common usage to say "the stock molded 30 min. at 300°F. came out tightly cured," meaning (to some people, but perhaps not all) that the vulcanizate possessed a high concentration of crosslinks. Molding and related word forms are extensively indexed in *CA*.

In translations of Russian language literature on crosslinking, the word *structurization* often appears where an increase in crosslink density is meant or, where, e.g., an increase in viscosity, not involving chemical crosslinks, is meant. Here the context may be important, since structurization as well as an increase in crosslink density can occur in different ways. Likewise, the French word *reticulation* usually means crosslinking but may mean structurization and usually is not the equivalent of the English word reticulation.

In the physics and chemistry of crosslinking processes, as applied to solutions of high polymers, incipient gelling and the concept of gel point are important. By gel point is meant the instant when an increase in crosslink concentration will cause gel formation. In effect, gel point thus represents a crosslink concentration and usually is interpreted as that concentration at which all primary polymer molecules on the average are attached at only one point to the network. This implies adequate stability of primary polymer chains. When such stability does not exist, any observed gel point must have a meaning, probably connected with the nonexistence of long primary molecules.

4. Elastomeric Behavior

The requirements for rubberlike behavior were stated by Busse (410) prior to 1932 but were published in that year. By his treatment a substance is found to be rubbery (or elastomeric by a more recent term) if it has the following characteristics: (*1*) composition of long molecules, the main chain bonds of which are freely rotatable so that the chains are flexible; (*2*) weak interaction between the long molecules so that they can slip by one another; (*3*) a crosslink concentration sufficient to give a three-dimensional network. These properties, taken together, imply that long range elasticity results from the kinetic motions, not of whole rubber molecules, but of segments. Any segment contributing to elasticity is said to be elastically effective or active. Such a segment has the average molecular weight between crosslinks, M_c. When from 0.1 to one crosslink or more per hundred monomer units are present in a specimen, it appears to be vulcanized. The size of the kinetic or statistical unit actually is much smaller than M_c, and for natural rubber amounts in size to about one to five isoprene units. The kinetic motions of segments resemble those of gas or liquid molecules, but since they are immobilized at the ends (i.e., to each other and at the crosslinks) their kinetic activity is somewhat limited.

The importance of crosslinking as part of the kinetic theory is commonly recognized. Thus, according to Scanlan and Watson (411), the elastic properties of vulcanized rubber depend on both the primary molecular weight and the degree of crosslinking. When this degree increases excessively elastomeric properties decline and a hard rubber stage is finally reached.

The physics of rubber elasticity has been treated at length by Treloar (412) and the principles of polymer chemistry by Flory (413). Works such as theirs give the historical and theoretical background of the kinetic theory as well as much of the usable present-day knowledge.

5. Measurement of Crosslinks

a. Retraction Force

The kinetic theory relates the force of retraction f of a strip of rubber of original cross section A in simple extension to the extention ratio α by the expression:

$$f = (\rho RT/M_c)[\alpha - (1/\alpha^2)]A \tag{38}$$

where ρ is density, R the gas constant, T absolute temperature, and M_c the average molecular weight between crosslinks. An equivalent expression is:

$$f = NkTA[\alpha - (1/\alpha^2)] \tag{39}$$

where N is the number of chain segments in an ideal network and k is Boltzmann's constant. These equations do not take into account network defects such as free chain ends resulting from those ends of the primary polymer molecules or polymer segments not joined at all to the network or to defects caused by chain entanglements. Mullins (414) studied the equation of Rivlin

$$f = 2A(\alpha - 1/\alpha^2)(C_1 + C_2/\alpha) \tag{40}$$

and identified the elastic constant, C_1, as $^1/_2\rho RT/M_c$. An empirical relation between physical and chemical crosslinks including a correction for flaws due to chain ends is given by eq. (41). M_c(physical) is the number-average

$$C_1 = {}^1/_2\rho RTM_c^{-1}(\text{physical})[1\text{–}2.3M_c(\text{chemical})/M] \tag{41}$$

molecular weight of the elastically effective chain segments and includes the contributions of all crosslinks, both real and virtual, such as entanglements. M_c(chemical) is the molecular weight between chemical crosslinks, and M the molecular weight before crosslinking.

The kinetic or statistical theory is improved from time to time as illustrated by the work of Mullins just cited. Allowing for loose chain ends attached to the network, an early modification by Flory led to the equation:

$$f = (RTA/M_c)(1 - 2M_c/M)(\alpha - 1/\alpha^2) \tag{42}$$

Mullins modified this equation to give eq. (43), which then led to eq. (41).

$$f = (RTA/M_c)(1 - 2.3M_c/M)(\alpha - 1/\alpha^2) \tag{43}$$

The question of crosslinking and network formation as part of the statistical theory has been reviewed recently by Scanlan and Watson (411).

Crosslinks can be regarded, they state, as tetrafunctional with four branches emanating from a single branch point but their main theme is that allowance must be made for network flaws, free ends, molecular entanglements, etc. They state that more accurate data on crosslinking are needed. In a later article, Scanlan (415) deals with the question of three function branch points. Functionalities of 0, 1, 2, 3, and 4 are considered by Mullins and Thomas (416).

b. Equilibrium Swelling

The equilibrium swelling of cured rubber often is used for measuring crosslinking. Here the Flory-Rehner equation (eq. 44) may be used. In

$$-\ln (1 - v_r) - v_r - \mu v_r^2 = \rho(V_0/M_c)v_r^{1/3} \tag{44}$$

it v_r is the volume fraction of rubber in the swollen system, ρ is the density of the unswollen rubber, M_c is the molecular weight between crosslinks, V_0 is the molar volume of the solvent, μ is the polymer–solvent interaction coefficient (now considered to be about 0.42 for natural rubber in benzene). The Flory-Rehner equation in the form given in eq. (45) has been applied to filled stocks by Kraus (417); here ν is used instead of $1/M_c$, V_s instead of V_0, and f denotes the crosslink functionality. ν is the number of effective chains per volume of rubber.

$$\nu = -\frac{1}{V_s}\left[\frac{\ln (1 - v_r) + v_r + \mu v_r^2}{v_r^{1/3} - (2v_r/f)}\right] \tag{45}$$

In a recent important review of the kinetics of vulcanization Scheele (418) has stated that the Flory-Rehner concept may not be applied with certainty to sulfur vulcanizates. For the purpose of following rates he prefers reciprocal swelling as a measure of relative degree of crosslinking.

c. Freezing of Swollen Elastomer

The work of Kuhn, Peterli, and Majer (419,420) on the freezing of vulcanizates swollen in benzene has provided a new approach to the nature of crosslinking. They found, for example, that the state of cure in sulfur-cured vulcanizates can be gauged by the freezing point of the imbibed benzene. This freezing point may be 20°C. lower than the freezing point of the pure solvent. They consider a frozen swollen vulcanizate to consist of crystallites of solvent (specifically benzene) isolated from each other by the elements of the network. The freezing point of such crystallites, on account of the small size, would be lower than that of ordinary macro-

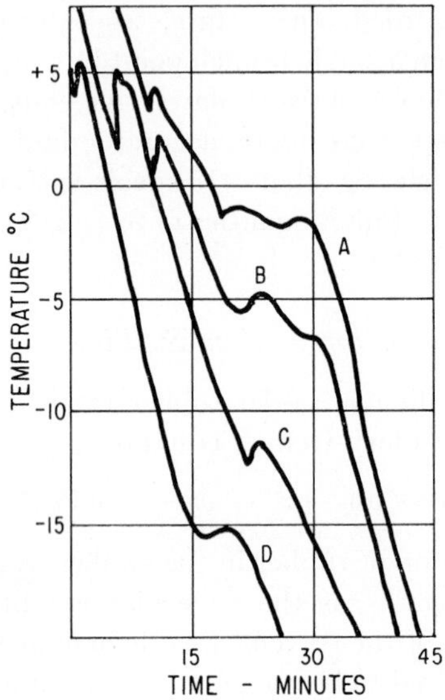

Fig. IX-6. Freezing curves for swelled rubber samples of different degrees of vulcanization. (Taken from ref. 420.)

crystals, and the authors consider that the difference, δT, can be estimated by the expression

$$\delta T = 4 \times 10^3 E_m \sigma / \rho R T_0 \alpha \quad (46)$$

where T_0 is the melting point of benzene (278.5°K.) E_m is the molal freezing point constant of benzene (5.12°C.), σ is the interfacial tension between liquid and solid benzene, ρ is the density of solid benzene, R is the gas constant (8.3×10^7 ergs/degree mole) and α is the edge length of a cubic microcrystal of benzene; and further it is assumed that $\delta T = -3.5 \times 10^{-6}\ \xi/\alpha$, where ξ is a dimensionless quantity of about 1, which allows for existing uncertainty in estimation of σ and, as well, any deviation from cubical in the shape of microcrystallites of benzene. From considerations based on Kuhn's theory of elasticity, δT may be computed from

$$\delta T = 4.73 \times 10^{-3} (E_q^{1/3}/q^{1/6}) \quad (47)$$

where E_q is the elastic modulus and q is the degree of swelling. Some data given by Kuhn and co-workers for four samples of natural rubber cured with different amounts of sulfur are given in Table IX-3. In this table, a is the average length between crosslink ends, and μ is the vulcanization points per cubic centimeter of gel.

The cooling curves for these specimens are reproduced in Figure IX-6. The cooling for the specimens was provided by solid carbon dioxide acting through an annular air space around the benzene–rubber system and was quite rapid. The "macrocrystalline" part of the cooling curve usually involved several degrees of supercooling. For the "microcrystalline" region it involved about one degree or less. The time for microcrystallization varied from about 1.5 min. for the tightest cure to about 5 min. for the least cured sample.

TABLE IX-3
Effect of Crosslinking on Modulus and Degree of Swelling[a]

Sample	E_q, $\times 10^{-6}$	q	δT Calculated	δT Found	a, cm., $\times 10^{-7}$	μ, cc.$^{-1}$, $\times 10^{-18}$
A	4.00	4.65	7.3	6.4	17.0	5.94
B	10.16	4.01	10.7	11.0	10.5	16.6
C	18.45	3.07	16.8	17.0	7.45	25.3
D	26.5	2.58	20.8	20.9	5.99	58.1

[a] Taken from ref. 420.

TABLE IX-4
Molecular Weights Calculated from Freezing Point Depression

Sample	q	δT	Molecular weight
A	4.65	6.4	170
B	4.01	11.0	115
C	3.07	17.0	97
D	2.58	20.9	95

The freezing point depression data of Kuhn and co-workers may be inserted in the usual cryoscopic molecular weight equation, and when this is done for the same samples, the computed values are as in Table IX-4. These values seem unrelatable to any sort of actual unit in the rubber system, such as cryoscopic, kinetic, or the molecular weight between crosslinks, real, or virtual. Indeed, they seem to be in part the result of benzene after its syneresis from the network. Since 100% syneresis is unlikely even by lowering the temperature as much as 20°C., the fraction of benzene still in contact with the network is unknown. Another interpretation of the various peaks and plateaus of the cooling curve may be needed, especially in systems containing only moderate proportions of benzene.

In unpublished work carried out with larger samples of uncured natural rubber (25 g.) which were swollen for about 7 days with benzene (140% on the rubber), the cooling curve displayed a well defined plateau at +1.0°C., with no supercooling or plateau near the melting point of benzene. Syneresis thus was not apparent. The freezing point depression = 5.4°C. − 1.0°C. = 4.4°C. should be corrected for benzene-soluble impurities. Assuming these impurities to have a molecular weight of 256 (as for palmitic acid) and to amount to 2% of the rubber, the corrected T is still 4.12°C., a rather large value. The molecular weight indicated is (1000 × 100/140)/4.12/5.08 = 880 and may be referred to as the cryoscopic molecular weight, M_{cryo}. This particular sample of pale crepe was only about 97% soluble in benzene and so contained a few actual crosslinks. M_{cryo} includes the effects of those entanglements, associative interactions, and other virtual crosslinks, which together effectively limit the segment action by the polymer on the activity of the solvent at 140% swell. Here the polymer is acting as a stationary solute.

The 880 value for linear polyisoprene should be compared with M_{cryo} values of other linear polymers having more methyl groups attached to the main chain as well as to linear polybutadiene which has none. This has been done with some preliminary results as follows:

Butyl rubber (212°F., ML 4 min. = 75) at 140% swell in benzene was found to have a poorly reproducible value for ΔT of 2.75°C. corresponding to an M_{cryo} of 1420. For each four carbon atoms in the main chain (two isobutylene units) butyl has four methyl group appendages and a formula weight of 56 × 2 = 112. Relative to polyisoprene, the calculated M_{cryo} = (112/68) 880 = 1450 is in good agreement with the found value of 1420.

All-*cis* (98%) 1,4-polybutadiene has a formula weight of 54 for four carbon atoms in the main chain. The calculated value relative to polyisoprene at 140% swell is (54/68) 880 = 700. The value found for a high molecular weight sample was 700.

Trivisonno (421) has computed the molecular weight (i.e., the segment weight) of natural rubber based on the vapor pressure lowering data of Gee and Treloar for benzene solutions. The value at 140% swell is 1280, in fair agreement with M_{cryo} of 880.

It can be argued since benzene is a good solvent for *cis*-polybutadiene but a poor solvent for butyl that this should affect the M_{cryo} value for butyl. A more complete study may yet reveal that the M_{cryo} values of butyl in benzene tend to be high as compared to those of butyl in a good solvent such as cyclohexane.

6. Noncovalent Crosslinks

a. Virtual Crosslinks

The term virtual crosslinking is commonly applied to any noncovalent crosslinking process such as molecular interaction between long molecules which is physical in nature, or to crosslinking not fully chemical as, for example, crosslinking due to hydrogen bonding. It is involved in ordinary sulfur crosslinking as a second order effect but for the polymeric polysulfides and elastic sulfur is of prime importance. Thus, with Thiokol, a certain polymer which is soluble and which is millable may have reactive chain ends. Condensation of these ends with or without the incorporation of moieties from the condensing agent (zinc oxide, diisocyanate, etc.) extends the polymer chains. The change in properties such as modulus reveals the polymer to be cured (422). Since there is no obvious possibility of covalent crosslinking, it is presumed that the increase in linear molecular weight has made possible virtual crosslinking through cumulative intermolecular action that is not possible with short molecules. Similar effects as well as hydrogen bonding may be invoked to account for the virtual crosslinking of polyurethanes (423).

b. Crystallites

Effective crosslinking results also by the formation from polymer chains of solid crystallites of about the same dimensions as carbon black particles. The intermolecular connections established in such cases are called giant crosslinks. In the case of crystallites which form during the deformation of those elastomers which crystallize, this type of crosslinking is transient, reversible, and may depend on a summation of crystallization rate, melting rate and deformation frequency effects. Giant crosslinking is polyfunctional, i.e., it involves more than five chains extending from a single network junction and can arise in some polymers as a result of the colonizing or clumping of tetra- or trifunctional crosslinks. Usually, it and crosslinking by sulfur occur cooperatively with one superimposed over the other.

c. Reinforcing Fillers

The many studies of reinforcement in uncured rubber–filler mixtures have revealed that such mixtures consist of individual filler particles and aggregates of filler particles enclosed in a matrix of partially crosslinked rubber. The attachment of the rubber to the filler surface is incompletely understood and may be physical or chemical or both. The crosslinking of the polymer which occurs during mixing is a mechanochemical reaction caused by the high shear rate breaking of polymer chains to give reactive ends. These reactive ends may link with the surface of the filler or with the middle portions of other chains to form trifunctional crosslinks. No doubt, some interchange of segments and tetrafunctional crosslinking also occurs, as well as the formation of unbound polymer of low molecular weight. This unbound polymer can be extracted with solvents, but once removed cannot be reswelled into the network. An important recent finding is that of Westlinning, Butenuth, and Leineweber (424), who showed that bound rubber in the case of NR–carbon black mixes is partially crystalline and so resembles stark rubber. The crosslink density appears highest near the filler surface. This was evident from a previous study by Westlinning and Butenuth (425), who applied the Kuhn method of studying crosslinking by thermal (cooling) analysis of swollen black-filled specimens. According to these authors this produces in the cured stocks regions of high crosslink density in contact with regions of low crosslink density. It certainly appears that the curing of filled stocks must involve the superposition of one network derived from sulfur crosslinking over others derived from mechanochemical crosslinking during mixing. Giant crosslinking by the black filler surface may occur by the attachment of rubber chains, but our knowledge here is scant, and if it does occur it may be incidental to the main reinforcement effects.

7. Effectiveness of Types of Crosslinks

Cluff and Gladding (426) made a comparison of crosslinking with sulfur and with diisocyanates. A polyurethane of molecular weight 54,000 ($\bar{M}_n$) was synthesized with the structure I.

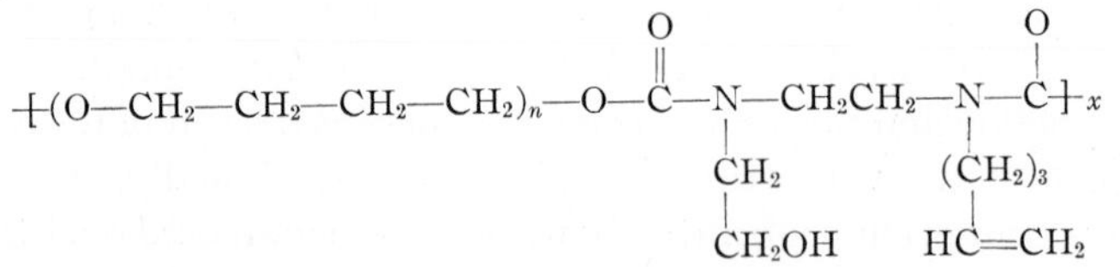

(I)

The purpose of introducing pendant hydroxy and vinyl groups was to provide an equal number of sites for crosslinking by diisocyanate and by sulfur. The pairs of such sites were separated by segments of about 1200 in molecular weight. The rather unusual accelerated sulfur recipe contained in parts per hundred parts of rubber: sulfur 1.0, mercaptobenzothiazyl disulfide 4.0, mercaptobenzothiazole 2.0, zinc chloride complex of mercaptobenzothiazyl disulfide 0.7, and cadmium stearate 1.0. The diisocyanate used for curing was 3,3′-dimethoxy-4,4′-biphenylene diisocyanate derived from dianisidine. By using different amounts of the two curing systems, different numbers of crosslinks could be conveniently inserted and properties compared at equal concentrations of effective network chains. The authors computed the effective network chains per cubic centimeter of polymer, ν/V, from the expression:

$$\nu/V = FV_r^{1/3}/ART(\alpha - \alpha^{-2}) \tag{48}$$

where V_r is the volume fraction of polymer (always kept less than 0.25) swollen in toluene, F is the force in grams required for an extension ratio α of the swollen sample, A is the cross section of the unswollen sample, and T is the absolute temperature. The modulus measurements on swollen samples revealed no difference between the ν/V values for the two curing systems, and so no difference was indicated between the effectiveness of crosslinking by sulfur and by diisocyanate.

A long chain diisocyanate was also used by Cluff and Gladding to give a crosslink about 19 times longer than the low molecular weight diisocyanate and comparable to the length of the network chains, according to the authors. The crosslinks in this case were trifunctional, whereas they were tetrafunctional with the short urethane crosslinks. It may be assumed that the chemical reaction of the long chain diisocyanate as well as the short chain one is quantitative and that enough of the long chain diisocyanate was added for less than 40% of the hydroxyls to react, as was stated to be the case for the short chain diisocyanate. Though not especially emphasized by the authors, the trifunctional crosslinks turned out to be as effective as the tetrafunctional, of course allowing for the fact that a trifunctional crosslink holds three active chains compared to four in the tetrafunctional case.

The finding that vulcanizate properties (resilience, modulus, and hardness) at equivalent concentrations of effective network chains were the same for all three types of crosslinking appears to be significant. Although no explanation for this was offered, the principle of virtual crosslinking advanced by Schollenberger and co-workers (423) appears to provide one.

The Schollenberger group prepared a linear polyurethane of molecular weight 36,000 ($\bar{M}_n$) from diphenylmethane-4,4′-diisocyanate, adipic acid, and 1,4-butanediol. The elastomeric properties of this polyurethane at room temperature are listed in Table IX-5. The stress–strain data reported were obtained on a Scott tester at a jaw separation speed of 20 in./min,

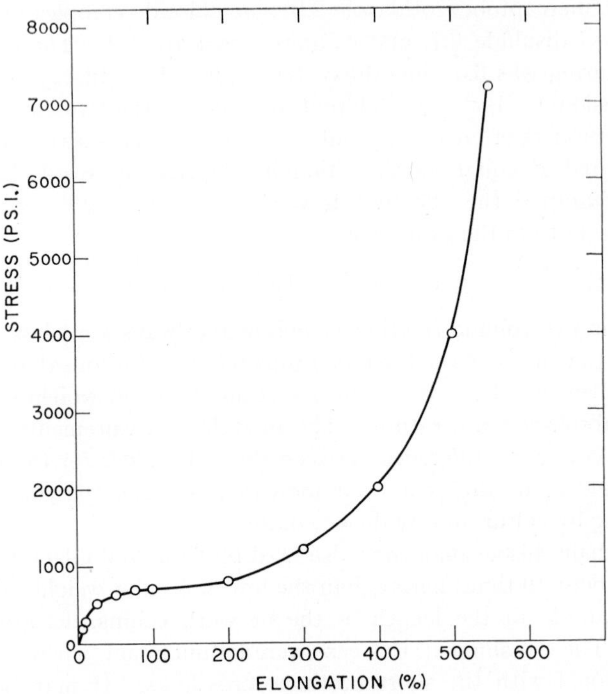

Fig. IX-7. Stress–strain relationship in VC polyurethane at 75°F. (Taken from ref. 423.)

Figure IX-7 shows the full stress–strain curve for the VC polyurethane. The portion of the curve below 100% extension was determined on a Tate-Emery tester, also at a jaw separation rate of 20 in./min. The shape of the curve is typical of the stress–strain curve for cured natural rubber. The high tensile strength following a high extension range at low modulus indicates extensive chain interaction resulting from the orienting effect of deformation. The polymer is soluble in suitable solvents, which demonstrates the substantial absence of covalent crosslinks, and so the conclusion is justified that the chain interaction effect is sufficient to crosslink the bulk polymer in the total absence of covalent crosslinks. When this effect of virtual crosslinking is superimposed over the effects of covalent crosslinks, as in the networks of Cluff and Gladding, it would be expected that the resilience, hardness, and modulus at equivalent effective network chain concentration would be the same. This they found to be true.

TABLE IX-5
Rubberlike Properties of Polyurethane VC[a]

25% modulus, psi	500
200% modulus, psi	600
Ultimate strain, %	550
Tensile strength, psi	7,200
Yerzley resilience, %	78
Compression set (ASTM D 395-53T) at 25°C., %	39
Shore A hardness	85
DeMattia flex life (to index 1)	639,000

[a] Taken from ref. 423.

The superposition of a covalent network over the virtually crosslinked network often leads to enhanced elastomeric properties which may transcend those of rubber itself, and even those of stereoregular polybutadiene vulcanizates. Thus, the ultimate tensile strength of some polyurethane elastomers may reach values as high as 14,000 psi.

One feature of the polyurethane network which may need emphasis is that the primary molecular weight before curing can be low and still have, or lead to, good properties when the system is later crosslinked by covalent bonds. This undoubtedly is due to virtual chain extension so that the system is more or less devoid of chain ends. The system then behaves as though the primary molecular weight were very high indeed.

A very strong natural rubber vulcanizate was prepared by Busse (410). A latex sheet 0.005 in. thick was stretched to 1200% and in this crystalline state cured with gaseous sulfur monochloride at 0°C. for 15 min. The vulcanizate displayed an ultimate tensile strength of 17,000 psi at 25% extension. The unusual strength was probably due to several networks superimposed over one another. The crosslinks are so numerous as to be indistinguishable from main links except on an arbitrary basis. Crystallite (giant) crosslinks are present as well as entanglements (virtual crosslinks). Presumably, chain end flaws are present in small number only.

8. Chemical Structure of Crosslinks

a. Sulfur

The study of the nature of crosslinking in both gum and filled stocks actually has been under study for some time by Studebaker and Nabors (427). One of their techniques involves the microtoming of chloroform-extracted, ether–HCl-treated, cured specimens imbedded in paraffin. The microtomed specimens are swollen in *n*-hexane and then are in a suitable state for reaction with solutions of lithium aluminum hydride in tetrahydrofuran. Under conditions applied this reagent was found to effect, after subsequent hydrolysis, the reactions shown in eqs. (49)–(51).

$$\text{R—S—R} \rightarrow \text{No reaction} \tag{49}$$

$$\text{R—SS—R} \rightarrow \text{2RSH} \tag{50}$$

$$\text{R—S—S}_x\text{—S—R} \rightarrow \text{2RSH} + x\text{S} \tag{51}$$

The RSH and sulfide ions are determined by potentiometric titration. Total crosslinks are determined by the swelling method of Kraus (417). This approach is attractive for the study of many features of vulcanization. Thus, for vulcanization by tetramethylthiuram disulfide of NR or Cis-4, their data show that monosulfide crosslinks are present to the substantial exclusion of any other type except possibly for a few carbon-carbon crosslinks.

It might be expected that disulfide crosslinks would be present in sulfur cured rubber, but the studies by Studebaker (428) have yielded no data in support of this expectation. They show that mono- and polysulfide crosslinks are present in amounts depending on the time and temperature of cure, the type of rubber, the type of accelerator and the presence of carbon black. The filler tends to increase the proportion of monosulfide bonds. The absence of disulfidic groups in vulcanizates is somewhat analogous to their absence previously referred to in mustard gas. Diphenylguanidine as the accelerator tends to form polysulfide links, especially tetrasulfides. In natural rubber in the early stages of cure polysulfide links are formed. These change during continued cure to links containing fewer sulfur atoms. Cures with mercaptobenzothiazole contain many monosulfide crosslinks except during the early stages. In Cis-4 rubber, unlike in NR, polysulfide formation is low during the early stages but increases steadily during continued cure. Further results with this approach, it is hoped, will lead to extended and much more precise knowledge of vulcanization. The approach seems to emphasize the importance of monosulfide crosslinks.

Even after accepting Studebaker's evidence and that of other investigators (429,430) that tetramethylthiuram disulfide (TMTD) and similar curing agents insert monosulfur crosslinks, there is the problem of the structure of the network adjacent to the crosslinks. Gregg (431) has approached this problem by following the rate of reaction of suitable vulcanizates and model sulfides with methyl iodide and methyl bromide.

His vulcanizates are prepared with small amounts of cadmium oxide and stearic acid as activators and 2-benzothiazyl-4-morpholyl disulfide (BMD)

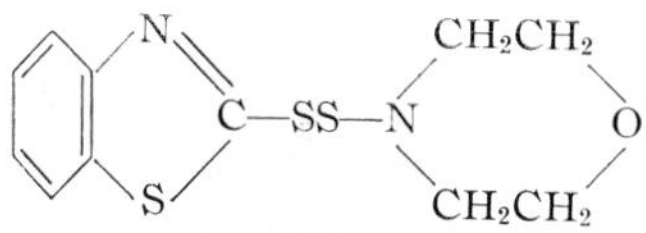

BMD

as the curing agent. The cured stocks are remarkably free of reversion. Gregg's findings are summarized as follows.

The reaction of methyl halides with organic sulfur compounds has been known for years, and methyl iodide, in particular, has been used frequently for attacking the sulfur bonds in cured rubber. Undoubtedly, the most extensive recorded use of this reagent to study vulcanizates was by Selker and Kemp (432–436). One clear result from their series of papers is the realization of the multiplicity of possible chemical structures involved in the crosslinked network. In an effort to reduce the number of initial variables, Gregg's work is confined to vulcanizates containing a high proportion of monosulfide crosslinks. A further reduction in complexity is achieved by the use of the recently available *cis*-1,4-polybutadiene as the elastomer instead of NR. Thus, the model vulcanizate chosen for initial study is a gum vulcanizate of *cis*-1,4-polybutadiene containing monosulfidic crosslinks. The presence of monosulfide crosslinks and the absence of other types is well established for TMTD vulcanizates by the extensive work of Studebaker already discussed. Vulcanizates with a similar type of curing agent (BMD) were prepared; it is assumed that they also contain no crosslinks other than the monosulfidic type. Moore (429) reported that 3.6 moles of TMTD were required to insert one crosslink in hevea; it now appears that 2.7 moles of BMD are required in *cis*-1,4-polybutadiene and 2.9 moles in hevea for the insertion of one crosslink.

The basis of the measurement of chemical structure of the crosslink is the interpretation of the first order kinetics of crosslink scission by methyl halides following standardization of the cleavage reaction applied to sulfides of known structure. This scission rate may be measured by means of the variation of volume swelling of the vulcanizates and is correlated to the crosslink density. The correlation follows comprehensive work reported in a series of papers by Moore, Watson, and Mullins (438).

The reactions of methyl iodide with dialkyl monosulfides, according to Scheele and Triebel (439), are given in eqs. (52)–(56).

$$R—S—R + CH_3I \rightleftharpoons R—\overset{\overset{\Large CH_3}{|}}{\underset{\underset{\Large I}{|}}{S}}—R \qquad (52)$$

$$R—\overset{\overset{\Large CH_3}{|}}{\underset{\underset{\Large I}{|}}{S}}—R \xrightarrow{k_1} R—S—CH_3 + RI \qquad (53)$$

$$R—S—CH_3 + CH_3I \rightleftharpoons R—\overset{\overset{\Large CH_3}{|}}{\underset{\underset{\Large I}{|}}{S}}—CH_3 \qquad (54)$$

$$R—\overset{\overset{\Large CH_3}{|}}{\underset{\underset{\Large I}{|}}{S}}—CH_3 \xrightarrow{k_3} CH_3—S—CH_3 + RI \qquad (55)$$

$$CH_3—S—CH_3 + CH_3I \rightleftharpoons CH_3—\overset{\overset{\Large CH_3}{|}}{\underset{\underset{\Large I}{|}}{S}}—CH_3 \qquad (56)$$

The crosslink scission reaction is involved only in eq. (53) so that it is the rate of this reaction (k_1) which must be measured on the model compounds for suitable correlation with the rate of reaction of the vulcanizate.

Polarographic measurement on model compounds formed from the reaction of methyl iodide with dialkyl monosulfides of varying structures permit the measurement of k_1. These values given in Table IX-6 vary widely according to the structure of the dialkyl monosulfide.

TABLE IX-6
Influence of Dialkyl Monosulfide Structures on Reactivity

Model structure	k_1 at 42°C. in CH_3I, $hr.^{-1} \times 10^3$
$R—CH_2—S—CH_2R$	130
$R—CH_2—S—CH\begin{matrix} R \\ R \end{matrix}$	30
$\begin{matrix} R \\ R \end{matrix}CH—S—CH\begin{matrix} R \\ R \end{matrix}$	5.5

Because the allylic monosulfides react so rapidly with methyl iodide and the resulting secondary allylic iodides are somewhat unstable, some of the measurements were made with methyl bromide at 42°C. for comparison with the methyl iodide reactions carried out at the same temperature. Results are shown in Table IX-7.

TABLE IX-7
Influence of Allylic Monosulfide Structure on Reactivity

Model structure	k_1 at 42°C. in CH_3Br, hr.$^{-1}$ $\times 10^3$
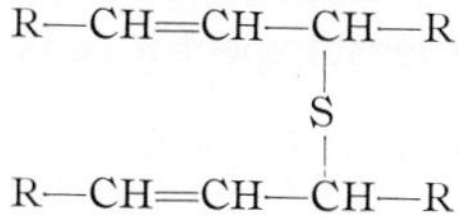	100
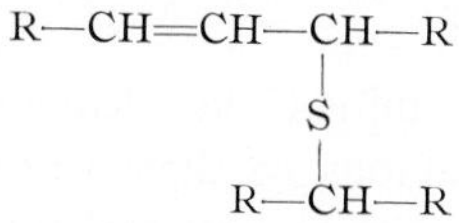	50
$R—CH_2—S—CH_2—R$	40
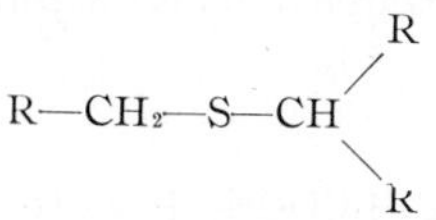	11
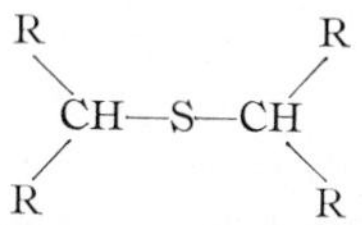	ca. 2

At present the monosulfide crosslink structure of a vulcanizate of *cis*-1,4-polybutadiene has been measured in both methyl iodide and methyl bromide. Both reagents show the presence of a minor amount of allylic sulfide. The predominant crosslink structure seems to be composed of saturated sulfides as in structures II and III. While both reagents show

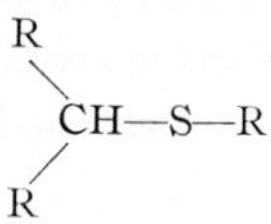

Trifunctional crosslink (II)

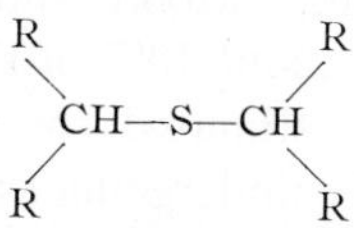

Tetrafunctional crosslink (III)

agreement as to structure of crosslink, they do not show agreement as to the quantitative amounts of each. The ratio of tetrafunctional to trifunctional crosslinks is 35/65 based on the rate with methyl iodide, but 67/33 based on methyl bromide.

Currently much attention is paid to the induction or "scorch" period in vulcanization as set forth in recent reviews by Scheele (418) and by Dogadkin and Shershnev (440). An earlier review (402) proposed that chain scission could account for a substantial part of the "delayed action" effects. It was emphasized that fundamentally scission is first-order, while crosslinking is second-order (more concentration dependent). Glazer and Cotton (409) have reported that the crosslink in natural rubber cured with sulfur monochloride is disulfidic but, by analogy with the synthesis of mustard gas already discussed, we would at least expect it to be polysulfidic and monosulfidic as well.

b. *Peroxide*

Moore and Scanlan (437) carefully examined the cleavage action of dicumyl peroxide on natural rubber. Previous to their study the crosslinking action of this reagent had been considered quantitative following the reactions shown in eqs. (57)–(59). In these equations R· signifies a rubber

$$C_6H_5\underset{CH_3}{\overset{CH_3}{C}}OO\underset{CH_3}{\overset{CH_3}{C}}C_6H_5 \rightarrow 2C_6H_5\underset{CH_3}{\overset{CH_3}{C}}O\cdot \rightarrow 2C_6H_5COCH_3 + 2CH_3\cdot \qquad (57)$$

$$\underset{\substack{\text{or}\\ CH_3\cdot}}{C_6H_5\underset{CH_3}{\overset{CH_3}{C}}O\cdot} + RH \rightarrow \underset{\substack{\text{or}\\ CH_4}}{C_6H_5\underset{CH_3}{\overset{CH_3}{C}}\text{—}OH} + R\cdot \qquad (58)$$

$$2R\cdot \rightarrow R\text{—}R \qquad (59)$$

radical, R—R crosslinked rubber, and the bond between the R groups a C—C crosslink. Moore and Scanlan found the effects of scission to be equivalent to about 10% of the new elastically effective crosslinks formed. Scission was estimated by stress relaxation of a stretched vulcanizate simultaneously undergoing further cure.

The significance of Moore and Scanlan's findings rests on the reliability of physical and chemical theory of networks and on the assumed mechanism of formation. Parks and Lorenz (441) have investigated the reaction of dicumyl peroxide with 2,6-dimethylocta-2-*trans*-6-diene. The products were determined by gas-phase chromatography. At molar ratios of 40/1 of peroxide to diene the product was almost exclusively composed of isomeric dehydro dimers as though the peroxide reacted exclusively by hydrogen abstraction followed by dimerization of the resulting radicals. Reactions (57)–(59) were thus substantiated.

Moore and Scanlan pointed out the difficulty of deducing the reactions of macromolecules by the use of model compounds. Scission in polyisoprene would be much more a factor than it is in 2,6-dimethylocta-2,6-diene. Even if primary molecular weight is not a factor in determining the number of scissions per 1,5-diene unit, the occurrence of even minute amounts of cleavage causes an induction period in crosslinking. Evidence for an induction period is of two kinds. First, the change in viscosity with time at curing temperatures for rubber–dicumyl peroxide mixes has a shape characteristic of delayed action and the physical properties show that slight degradation occurs before crosslinking sets in. Second, when butyl rubber, which has a low concentration of isoprene units, is heated with dicumyl peroxide, the predominant effect is cleavage. Clearly, R·, in the case of butyl cannot dimerize on account of the low concentration, but the cleavage reactions usually postulated are first-order and will occur irrespective of concentration.

It is not entirely clear that the dimerization shown in eq. (59) is very probable in polyisoprene. Since dicumyl peroxide is the most efficient of the common curing agents, and since it reacts in α-methylenic polymers exclusively by hydrogen abstraction, reactions other than simple dimerization should be considered for the fate of the R· radical. Indeed Moore and Scanlan mentioned the cleavage reaction (eq. 60) followed by radical combination (eq. 61). The product R′—R is a branched molecule. Since branches are crosslinks this process constitutes a route to an infinite network. It would not be an efficient process unless the loose ends R″ could react to enhance network formation. The probability of this recombination should be no greater than the dimerization shown in eq. (61).

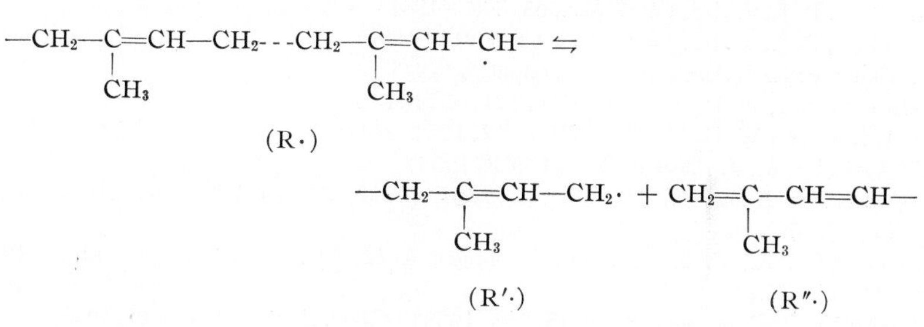

(60)

$$R'\cdot + R\cdot \rightarrow R'{-}R \qquad (61)$$

An alternative reaction to simple dimerization is shown by eq. (62), in which radical R· adds to the double bond in an adjacent chain, RH, to

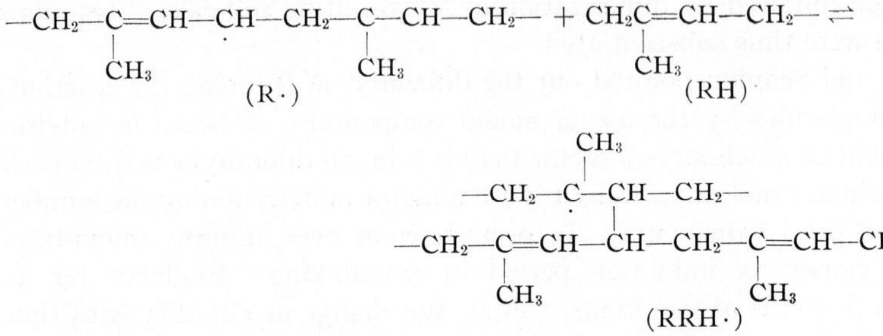

(62)

form RRH·. This radical is tertiary and should have a relatively long life. It should show a strong tendency to dissociate into R· and RH and should have only a slight tendency to abstract hydrogen. On the contrary, it should readily give up a hydrogen atom by reaction (63) with dicumyl

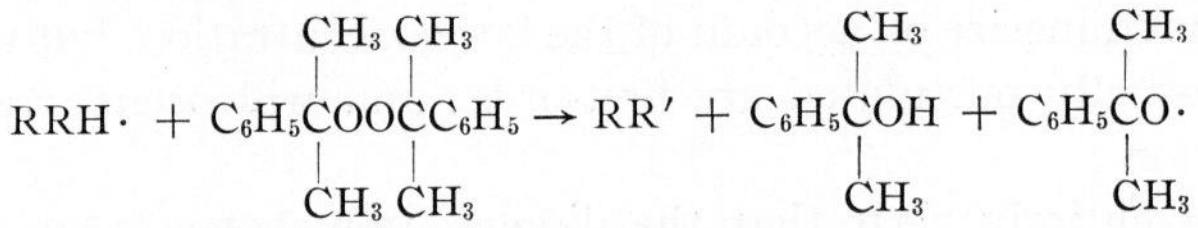

(63)

peroxide to form dimethylbenzyl alcohol, one or more stable branched dehydro dimers, and a dicumyl peroxy radical.

The crosslinking process (eqs. 58, 62, and 63) should give the same overall yield of crosslinks from dicumyl peroxide as from eqs. (58) and (59). The structures of the crosslinks by the two processes are not identical but probably would be equivalent with respect to network properties.

References

A. Crosslinking by Radiation

1a. Flory, P. J., *J. Am. Chem. Soc.*, **63**, 3083 (1941).

1b. Flory, P. J., *J. Am. Chem. Soc.*, **63**, 3091 (1941).

1c. Flory, P. J., *J. Am. Chem. Soc.*, **63**, 3096 (1941).

2. Stockmayer, W. H., *J. Chem. Phys.*, **11**, 45 (1943).

3. Stockmayer, W. H., *J. Chem. Phys.*, **12**, 125 (1944).

4. Charlesby, A., *J. Polymer Sci.*, **11**, 513 (1953).

5. Charlesby, A., *Proc. Roy. Soc. (London)*, **A222**, 60 (1954); *Chem. Abstr.*, **48**, 6290a (1954).

6. Charlesby, A., *Proc. Roy. Soc. (London)*, **A222**, 542 (1954); *Chem. Abstr.*, **48**, 6202a (1954).

7. Saito, O., *J. Phys. Soc. Japan*, **13**, 198 (1958); *Chem. Abstr.*, **52**, 11462f (1958).

8. Inokuti, M., *J. Chem. Phys.*, **33**, 1607 (1960).

9. Bovey, F. A., *The Effects of Ionizing Radiation on Natural and Synthetic High Polymers*, Polymer Reviews Series, Vol. I, Interscience, New York, 1958, pp. 61–65, 73–90.
10. Charlesby, A., *Atomic Radiation and Polymers*, Pergamon Press, New York, 1960, pp. 134–158, 170–173, 532–536.
11. Charlesby, A., *Proc. Roy. Soc.* (*London*), **A231,** 521 (1955); *Chem. Abstr.*, **50,** 651g (1956).
12. Bovey, F. A., ref. 9, pp. 90–96.
13. Charlesby, A., Ref. 10, pp. 174–177.
14. Saito, O., *J. Phys. Soc. Japan*, **13,** 1451 (1958); *Chem. Abstr.*, **53,** 12023e (1959).
15. Charlesby, A., *Proc. Roy. Soc.* (*London*), **A215,** 187 (1952); *Chem. Abstr.*, **47,** 4759a (1953).
16. Charlesby, A., Ref. 10, p. 470.
17. Miller, A. A., E. J. Lawton, and J. S. Balwit, *J. Polymer Sci.*, **14,** 503 (1954).
18. Wall, L. A., *J. Polymer Sci.*, **17,** 141 (1955).
19. Dole, M., and C. D. Keeling, *J. Am. Chem. Soc.*, **75,** 6082 (1953).
20. Dole, M., C. D. Keeling, and D. G. Rose, *J. Am. Chem. Soc.*, **76,** 4304 (1954).
21. Dole, M., and F. Cracco, *J. Am. Chem. Soc.*, **83,** 2584 (1961).
22. Arvia, A. J., M. Dole, and T. F. Williams, *Anales Asoc. Quim. Arg.*, **46,** 265 (1958); *J. Appl. Chem.* (*London*), **9,** ii-627 (1959).
23. Pearson, R. W., *J. Polymer Sci.*, **25,** 189 (1957).
24. Okamoto, H., and A. Isihara, *J. Polymer Sci.*, **20,** 115 (1956).
25. Simha, R., and L. A. Wall, *J. Phys. Chem.*, **61,** 425 (1957).
26. Libby, W. F., *J. Chem. Phys.*, **35,** 1714 (1961).
27. Williams, T. F., *Trans. Faraday Soc.*, **57,** 755 (1961); *Chem. Abstr.*, **55,** 25439c (1961).
28. Collyns, B. G., J. F. Fowler, and J. Weiss, *Chem. Ind.* (*London*), **1957,** 74.
29. Weiss, J., *J. Polymer Sci.*, **29,** 425 (1958).
30. Sisman, O., and C. D. Bopp, U. S. At. Energy Comm. Rept. ORNL-928, 1951.
31. Little, K., *Nature*, **170,** 1075 (1952).
32. Lawton, E. J., A. M. Bueche, and J. S. Balwit, *Nature*, **172,** 76 (1953).
33. Schumacher, K., *Kolloid-Z.*, **157,** 16 (1958); *Chem. Abstr.*, **52,** 9647h (1958).
34. Chapiro, A., *J. Chim. Phys.*, **52,** 246 (1955); *Chem. Abstr.*, **49,** 11427c (1955).
35. Charlesby, A., E. von Arnim, and L. Callaghan, *Intern. J. Appl. Radiation Isotopes*, **3,** 226 (1958); *Chem. Abstr.*, **53,** 899e (1959).
36. Charlesby, A., and W. H. T. Davison, *Chem. Ind.* (*London*), **1957,** 232.
37. Black, R. M., *Nature*, **178,** 305 (1956).
38. Lawton, E. J., J. S. Balwit, and A. M. Bueche, *Ind. Eng. Chem.*, **46,** 1703 (1954).
39. Lawton, E. J., P. D. Zemany, and J. S. Balwit, *J. Am. Chem. Soc.*, **76,** 3437 (1954).
40. Miller, A. A., E. J. Lawton, and J. S. Balwit, *J. Phys. Chem.*, **60,** 599 (1956).
41. Charlesby, A., and N. H. Hancock, *Proc. Roy. Soc.* (*London*), **A218,** 245 (1953); *Chem. Abstr.*, **47,** 9664f (1953).
42. Charlesby, A., and M. Ross, *Proc. Roy. Soc.* (*London*), **A217,** 122 (1953); *Chem. Abstr.*, **47,** 7861g (1953).
43. Baskett, A. C., and C. W. Miller, *Nature*, **174,** 364 (1954).
44. Charlesby, A., *Radiation Res.*, **2,** 96 (1955); *Chem. Abstr.*, **49,** 8711e (1955).
45. Dewhurst, H. A., *J. Phys. Chem.*, **61,** 1466 (1957).
46. Busse, W. F., and G. H. Bowers, *J. Polymer Sci.*, **31,** 252 (1958).

47. Atchison, G. J., *J. Polymer Sci.*, **35,** 557 (1959).
48. Fydelor, P. J., and R. W. Pearson, *J. Appl. Polymer Sci.*, **5,** 171 (1961).
49. Itzhaki, R. F., and P. Alexander, *Radiation Res.*, **15,** 553 (1961).
50. Fukada, E., R. W. B. Stephens, and A. Charlesby, *Phys. Chem. Solids*, **16,** 53 (1961); *Chem. Abstr.*, **55,** 14031c (1961).
51. Cornish, E. H., and D. M. Cutting, *Nature*, **183,** 1804 (1959).
52. Rady, A. A., *J. Appl. Polymer Sci.*, **1,** 129 (1959).
53. Mayburg, S., and W. L. Lawrence, *J. Appl. Phys.*, **23,** 1006 (1952).
54. Wintle, H. J., *Brit. J. Radiol.*, **33,** 706 (1960); *Intern. J. Appl. Radiation Isotopes*, **8,** 132 (1960); *Chem. Abstr.*, **55,** 11910i (1961).
55. Fowler, J. F., and F. T. Farmer, *Nature*, **171,** 1020 (1953); **173,** 317 (1954).
56. Wintle, H. J., *Polymer*, **2,** 444 (1961).
57. Stark, K. H., and C. G. Garton, *Nature*, **176,** 1225 (1955).
58. Sobolev, I., J. A. Meyer, V. Stannett, and M. Szwarc, *J. Polymer Sci.*, **17,** 417 (1955).
59. Chmutov, K. V., and E. E. Finkel, *Russ. J. Phys. Chem.* (*English Transl.*), **33,** 93 (1959); *Zh. Fiz. Khim.*, **33,** 1648 (1959); *Chem. Abstr.*, **54,** 9443g (1960).
60. Bent, H. A., *J. Polymer Sci.*, **24,** 387 (1957).
61. Cooper, G. D., and A. R. Gilbert, *J. Polymer Sci.*, **38,** 275 (1959).
62. Dole, M., D. C. Milner, and T. F. Williams, *J. Am. Chem. Soc.*, **80,** 1580 (1958).
63. Williams, T. F., H. Matsuo, and M. Dole, *J. Am. Chem. Soc.*, **80,** 2595 (1958).
64. Dole, M., and T. F. Williams, *Discussions Faraday Soc.*, **27,** 74 (1959); *Chem. Abstr.*, **54,** 14928g (1960).
65. Dole, M., T. J. Stolki, and T. F. Williams, *J. Polymer Sci.*, **48,** 61 (1960); *Intern. Symp. Macromol. Chem. Vol. III* (IUPAC) Moscow, 1960, pp. 269–279.
66. Black, R. M., *J. Appl. Chem.* (*London*), **8,** 159 (1958).
67. Shinohara, K., A. Amemiya, and A. Danno, *J. Phys. Soc. Japan*, **13,** 604 (1958); *Chem. Abstr.*, **52,** 16010h (1958).
68. Williams, T. F., and M. Dole, *J. Am. Chem. Soc.*, **81,** 2919 (1959).
69. Snow, A. I., and H. C. Moyer, *J. Chem. Phys.*, **27,** 1222 (1957).
70. Dole, M., and W. H. Howard, *J. Phys. Chem.*, **61,** 137 (1957).
71. Marker, L., R. Early, and S. L. Aggarwal, *J. Polymer Sci.*, **38,** 369 (1959).
72. Ushakov, G. P., Yu. A. Guscho, Yu. S. Lazurkin, and V. S. Kazakov, *Vysokomolekul. Soedin.*, **2,** 1513 (1960); *Chem. Abstr.*, **55,** 19316a (1961).
73. Zarauz, Y. de, *Compt. Rend.*, **249,** 1348 (1959); *Chem. Abstr.*, **54,** 14766f (1960).
74. Mandelkern, L., D. E. Roberts, J. C. Halpin, and F. P. Price, *J. Am. Chem. Soc.*, **82,** 46 (1960).
75. Levy, B., *J. Appl. Polymer Sci.*, **5,** 408 (1961); *Trans. Am. Nucl. Soc.*, **4,** 124 (1961).
76. Price, F. P., *J. Phys. Chem.*, **64,** 169 (1960).
77. Mandelkern, L., D. E. Roberts, and A. F. Diorio, *J. Am. Chem. Soc.*, **80,** 500 (1958).
78. Mandelkern, L., D. E. Roberts, A. F. Diorio, and A. S. Posner, *J. Am. Chem. Soc.*, **81,** 4148 (1959).
79. Hammer, C. F., W. W. Brandt, and W. L. Peticolas, *J. Polymer Sci.*, **24,** 291 (1957).
80. Salovey, R., *J. Polymer Sci.*, **51,** S1 (1961).

81. Charlesby, A., and L. Callaghan, *Phys. Chem. Solids*, **4**, 306 (1958); *Chem. Abstr.*, **52**, 19235e (1958).
82. Charlesby, A., *J. Polymer Sci.*, **10**, 201 (1953).
83. Slichter, W. P., and E. R. Mandell, *J. Phys. Chem.*, **62**, 334 (1958).
84. Butta, E., and A. Charlesby, *J. Polymer Sci.*, **33**, 119 (1958).
85. Deeley, C. W., J. A. Sauer, and A. E. Woodward, *J. Appl. Phys.*, **29**, 1415 (1958).
86. Deeley, C. W., D. E. Kline, J. A. Sauer, and A. E. Woodward, *J. Polymer Sci.*, **28**, 109 (1958).
87. Fuschillo, N., and J. A. Sauer, *J. Appl. Phys.*, **28**, 1073 (1957).
88. Fujiwara, S., A. Amamiya, and K. Shinohara, *J. Chem. Phys.*, **26**, 1343 (1957).
89. Glick, R. E., R. P. Gupta, J. A. Sauer, and A. E. Woodward, *Polymer*, **1**, 340 (1960).
90. Harper, B. G., *J. Appl. Polymer Sci.*, **2**, 363 (1959).
90a. Harper, B. G., *J. Appl. Polymer Sci.*, **5**, 601 (1961).
91. Epstein, L. M., *J. Polymer Sci.*, **26**, 399 (1957).
92. Lawton, E. J., J. S. Balwit, and R. S. Powell, *J. Polymer Sci.*, **32**, 257 (1958).
93. Lawton, E. J., R. S. Powell, and J. S. Balwit, *J. Polymer Sci.*, **32**, 277 (1958).
94. Ballantine, D. S., G. J. Dienes, and B. Manowitz, Report BNL-1677, Dec. 18, 1953; *Nucl. Sci. Abstr.*, **8**, 1840 (1954).
95. Rossmann, K., *J. Polymer Sci.*, **19**, 141 (1956).
96. Grossman, R. F., and W. A. Beasley, *J. Appl. Polymer Sci.*, **2**, 163 (1959).
97. Alexander, P., and D. Toms, *J. Polymer Sci.*, **22**, 343 (1956).
98. St. Pierre, L. E., and H. A. Dewhurst, *J. Chem. Phys.*, **29**, 241 (1958).
99. Matsuo, H., and M. Dole, *J. Phys. Chem.*, **63**, 837 (1959).
100. Black, R. M., and A. Charlesby, *Intern. J. Appl. Radiation Isotopes*, **7**, 126 (1959); *Chem. Abstr.*, **54**, 6268h (1960).
101. Dewhurst, H. A., *J. Phys. Chem.*, **62**, 15 (1958).
102. Okada, Y., and A. Amemiya, *J. Polymer Sci.*, **50**, S22 (1961).
103. Black, R. M., and A. Charlesby, *Intern. J. Appl. Radiation Isotopes*, **7**, 134 (1959); *Chem. Abstr.*, **54**, 6269a (1960).
104. Abraham, R. J., and D. H. Whiffen, *Trans. Faraday Soc.*, **54**, 1291 (1958); *Chem. Abstr.*, **53**, 12001h (1959).
105. Smaller, B., and M. S. Matheson, *J. Chem. Phys.*, **28**, 1169 (1958).
106. Koritskii, A. T., Yu. N. Molin, V. N. Shamshev, N. Ya. Buben, and V. V. Voevodskii, *Vysokomolekul. Soedin.*, **1**, 1182 (1959); *Polymer Sci. (USSR) (English Transl.)* **1**, 458 (1960).
107. Ohnishi, S.-I. Y. Ikeda, M. Kashiwagi, and I. Nitta, *Polymer*, **2**, 119 (1961).
108. Lawton, E. J., J. S. Balwit, and R. S. Powell, *J. Chem. Phys.*, **33**, 405 (1960).
109. Libby, D., M. G. Ormerod, and A. Charlesby, *Polymer*, **1**, 212 (1960).
110. Kashiwabara, H., and K. Shinohara, *J. Phys. Soc. Japan*, **15**, 1129 (1960); *Chem. Abstr.*, **55**, 20494g (1961).
111. Charlesby, A., D. Libby, and M. G. Ormerod, *Proc. Roy. Soc. (London)*, **A262**, 207 (1961); *Chem. Abstr.*, **55**, 21651i (1961).
112. Kiselev, A. G., M. A. Mokulskii, and Yu. S. Lazurkin, *Vysokomolekul. Soedin.*, **2**, 1678 (1960); *Chem. Abstr.*, **56**, 2556c (1961).
113. Libby, D., and M. G. Ormerod, *Phys. Chem. Solids*, **18**, 316 (1961).
114. Loy, B. R., *J. Polymer Sci.*, **44**, 341 (1960).
115. Black, R. M., and B. J. Lyons, *Nature*, **180**, 1346 (1957).

116. Black, R. M., and B. J. Lyons, *Proc. Roy. Soc. (London)*, **A253,** 322 (1959); *Chem. Abstr.*, **54,** 16908g (1960).
117. Waddington, F. B., *J. Polymer Sci.*, **31,** 221 (1958).
118. Sobue, H., and Y. Tazima, *Nature*, **188,** 315 (1960).
119. Gupta, R. P., *Kolloid-Z.*, **174,** 74 (1961).
120. Hornbeck, R. F., and W. W. Parkinson, U. S. At. Energy Comm. Rept.-ORNL-2413, Aug., 1957.
121. Dole, M., and W. Schnabel, *J. Polymer Sci.*, **54,** S29 (1961).
122. Ayscough, P. B., K. J. Ivin, and J. H. O'Donnell, *Proc. Chem. Soc.*, **1961,** 71.
123. Tsvetkov, Yu. D., Yu. N. Molin, and V. V. Voevodskii, *Vysokomolekul. Soedin.*, **1,** 1805 (1959); *Polymer Sci. (USSR) (English Transl.)* **2,** 165 (1961); *Chem. Abstr.*, **54,** 19171f (1960).
124. Kuri, Z., and H. Ueda, *J. Polymer Sci.*, **50,** 349 (1961).
125. Bamford, C. H., and J. C. Ward, *Polymer*, **2,** 277 (1961).
126. Kivel, J., and A. F. Voigt, *Intern. J. Appl. Radiation Isotopes*, **10,** 181 (1961); *Chem. Abstr.*, **55,** 21902e (1961).
127. Williams, T. F., *Nature*, **186,** 544 (1960).
128. Fromandi, G., *Kolloidchem. Beih.*, **27,** 189 (1928); *Chem. Abstr.*, **23,** 1009 (1929).
129. Fromandi, G., *Kautschuk*, **4,** 185-9 (1928); *Rubber Chem. Technol.*, **2,** 161 (1929).
130. Hock, L., and H. Leber, *Kolloid-Z.*, **90,** 65 (1940); *Rubber Chem. Technol.*, **13,** 831 (1940).
131. Davidson, W. L., and I. G. Geib, *J. Appl. Phys.*, **19,** 427 (1948).
132. Bopp, C. D., and O. Sisman, U. S. At. Energy Comm. Rept. ORNL-1373, July 1953.
133. Charlesby, A., *Atomics Atomic Technol.*, **5,** (1) 12 (1954); *Chem. Abstr.*, **48,** 4999b (1954); *Rubber Chem. Technol.*, **28,** 1 (1955).
134. Ryan, J. W., *Nucleonics*, **11,** (8), 13 (1953); *Chem. Abstr.*, **48,** 4244g (1954).
135. Jackson, W. A., and D. Hale, *Rubber Age (N. Y.)*, **77,** 865 (1955); *U. S. Govt. Research Repts.*, **24,** 69 (1955); *Chem. Abstr.*, **49,** 16495a (1955).
136. Gehman, S. D., and L. M. Hobbs, *Rubber World*, **130,** 643 (1954).
137. Dogadkin, B. A., Z. N. Tarasova, M. Ya. Kaplunov, V. L. Karpov, and N. A. Klauzen, *Kolloidn. Zh.*, **20,** 260 (1958); *Colloid J. (USSR) (English Transl.)* PB 141064T-1, Paper No. 2; *Chem. Abstr.*, **52,** 21203i (1958).
138. Turner, D. T., *J. Polymer Sci.*, **35,** 541 (1959).
139. Moore, C. G., and W. F. Watson, *J. Polymer Sci.*, **19,** 237 (1956).
140. Charlesby, A., Ref. 10, pp. 264–65.
141. Charlesby, A., and E. von Arnim, *J. Polymer Sci.*, **25,** 151 (1957).
142. Mullins, L., and D. T. Turner, *J. Polymer Sci.*, **43,** 35 (1960).
143. Hayden, P., *Nature*, **184,** 1865 (1959).
144. Hayden, P., *Intern. J. Appl. Radiation Isotopes*, **8,** 65 (1960); *Chem. Abstr.*, **55,** 8909b (1961).
145. Turner, D. T., *Polymer*, **1,** 27 (1960).
146. Mullins, L., and D. T. Turner, *Nature*, **183,** 1547 (1959).
147. Bauman, R. G., and J. W. Born, *J. Appl. Polymer Sci.*, **1,** 351 (1959).
148. Bauman, R. G., *J. Appl. Polymer Sci.*, **2,** 328 (1959).
149. Roberts, D. E., and L. Mandelkern, *J. Am. Chem. Soc.*, **80,** 1289 (1958).
150. Shelberg, W. E., and L. H. Gevantman, *Rubber Age (N. Y.)*, **87,** 263 (1960): *Rubber Chem. Technol.*, **34,** 250 (1961).

151. Shelberg, W. E., and L. H. Gevantman, *Nature*, **183**, 456 (1959).
152. Born, J. W., Symposium on Preservation for Mobilization Requirements, U. S. Naval Civil Eng. Res. and Evaluation Lab., Port Hueneme, Calif., Oct. 23–26, 1956.
153. Turner, D. T., *J. Polymer Sci.*, **27**, 503 (1958); *Rubber Chem. Technol.*, **31**, 737 (1958).
154. Lamm, G., A. Lamm, and H. Madelaine, *Rapp. Cent. El. nucl. Saclay* No. 1375, *1959; J. Appl. Chem. (London)*, **11**, Feb., i-189 (1961).
155. Lamm, G., A. Lamm, and H. Madelaine, *Rev. Gen. Caoutchouc*, **36**, 1163 (1959); *Kautschuk Gummi*, **13**, WT 80 (1960); *Chem. Abstr.*, **54**, 17934i (1960).
156. Minoura, Y., and M. Asao, *J. Appl. Polymer Sci.*, **5**, 401 (1961).
157. Lamm, A., and G. Lamm, German Rubber Congress, Abstract, Berlin, Oct. 4–8, 1960.
158. Gregson, T. C., T. H. Rogers, L. B. Bangs, and D. W. Peabody, *Rubber Age (N. Y.)*, **89**, 81 (1961).
159. Minoura, Y., and M. Asao, *J. Appl. Polymer Sci.*, **5**, 233 (1961).
160. Gehman, S. D., and I. Auerbach, *Intern. J. Appl. Radiation Isotopes*, **1**, 102 (1956); *Rubber Chem. Technol.*, **30**, 380 (1957).
161. Tarasova, Z. N., M. Ya. Kaplunov, V. T. Kozlov, N. A. Klauzen, and B. A. Dogadkin, *Vysokmolekul. Soedin.*, **2**, 1201 (1960); *Chem. Abstr.*, **55**, 24067g (1961).
162. Turner, D. T., *J. Polymer Sci.*, **35**, 17 (1959).
163. Kuzminskii, A. S., T. S. Nikitina, E. V. Zhuravskaya, L. A. Oksentevich, L. L. Sunitsa, and N. I. Vitushkin, *Proc. Second Intern. Conf. on the Peaceful Uses of Atomic Energy*, United Nations, Geneva, 1958, A/Conf. 15/P/2085.
164. Nicolau, Cl. S., *Z. Physik. Chem. (Leipzig)*, **212**, 1 (1959); *Nucl. Sci. Abstr.*, **14**, 4590 (1960); *Chem. Abstr.*, **54**, 2797b (1960).
165. Evans, M. B., G. M. C. Higgins, and D. T. Turner, *J. Appl. Polymer Sci.*, **2**, 340 (1959).
166. Dunn, J. R., *Kautschuk Gummi*, **14**, WT114 (1961); *Rubber Chem. Technol.*, **34**, 910 (1961).
167a. Golub, M. A., *J. Am. Chem. Soc.*, **80**, 1794 (1958).
167b. Golub, M. A., *J. Am. Chem. Soc.*, **81**, 54 (1959).
167c. Golub, M. A., *J. Am. Chem. Soc.*, **82**, 5093 (1960).
168. Yakubchik, A. I., and V. A. Filatova, *J. Appl. Chem. USSR (English Transl.)*, **33**, 1166 (1960).
169. Chapiro, A., *Ind. Plastiques Mod. (Paris)*, **9**, (1), 41 (1957); *Chem. Abstr.*, **51**, 4809*a* (1957).
170. Salimov, M. A., E. V. Zhuravskaya, and A. S. Kuzminskii, *Vestnik Moskov. Univ. Ser. Mat. Mekhan. Astron. Fiz. i Khim.*, **3**, (3), 177 (1959); *Nuc. Sci. Abstr.*, **14**: 16057 (1960); *Chem. Abstr.*, **54**, 10370f (1960).
171. Charlesby, A., and D. Groves, in *Proc. Rubber Technol. Conf. 3rd London 1954*, T. H. Messenger, ed., Institute of the Rubber Industry, London, p. 317; *Rubber Chem. Technol.*, **30**, 27 (1957).
172. Witt, E., *J. Polymer Sci.*, **41**, 507 (1959).
173. Vaughan, G., D. E. Eaves, and W. Cooper, *Polymer*, **2**, 235 (1961).
174. Meyer, G. E., W. E. Gibbs, F. J. Naples, R. M. Pierson, W. M. Saltman, R. W. Schrock, L. B. Tewksbury, and G. S. Trick, *Rubber World*, **136**, 529, 695 (1959).

175. Bauman, R., and J. Glantz, *J. Polymer Sci.*, **26,** 397 (1957).
176. Harrington, R., *Rubber Age (N. Y.)*, **82,** 1003 (1958).
177. Tarasova, Z. N., M. Ya. Kaplunov, B. A. Dogadkin, V. L. Karpov, and A. Kh. Breger, *Kauchuk i Rezina*, **17,** No. 5, 14 (1958); *Nucl. Sci. Abstr.*, **15:** 8831, NP-tr-549 (1961).
178a. Harmon, D. J., *Rubber Age (N. Y.)*, **83,** 659 (1958).
178b. Harmon, D. J., *Rubber Age (N. Y.)*, **86,** 251 (1959).
179. Arnold, P. M., G. Kraus, and H. R. Anderson, Jr., *Kautschuk Gummi*, **12,** WT27 (1959); *Rubber Chem. Technol.*, **34,** 265 (1961).
180. Dogadkin, B. A., I. Mladenov, and I. A. Tutorskii, *Vysokomolekul. Soedin.*, **2,** 259 (1960); *Polymer Sci. USSR (English Transl.)*, **2,** 240 (1961).
181. Harrington, R., *Rubber Age (N. Y.)*, **88,** 475 (1960).
182. Mladenov, I., I. A. Tutorskii, and B. A. Dogadkin, *Intern. Symp. Macromol. Chem. Vol. III*, (IUPAC) Moscow, 1960, pp. 293–301.
183. Anderson, H. R., Jr., *J. Appl. Polymer Sci.*, **3,** 316 (1960); *Rubber Chem. Technol.*, **34,** 228 (1961).
184. Anderson, H. R., Jr., *J. Polymer Sci.*, **43,** 59 (1960).
185. Delman, A. D., B. B. Simms, I. J. Stanley, A. E. Ruff, and E. Goldberg, *J. Appl. Polymer Sci.*, **5,** 501 (1961).
186a. Harrington, R., *Rubber Age (N. Y.)*, **85,** 963 (1959).
186b. Harrington, R., *Rubber Age (N. Y.)*, **90,** 265 (1961).
187. Morris, R. E., R. R. James, and F. Caggegi, *Rubber Age*, **85,** 243 (1959); *J. Appl. Chem.*, **9,** ii-392 (1959).
188. Parker, J. A., and E. A. Peterson, paper presented at the 132nd Meeting of the American Chemical Society, New York, N. Y., Sept. 8–13, 1957.
189. Charlesby, A., At. Energy Res. Estab. (Gr. Brit.) Rept. M/R-1051, Nov., 1952.
190. Charlesby, A., *J. Polymer Sci.*, **11,** 521 (1953).
191. Shultz, A. R., P. I. Roth, and G. B. Rathmann, *J. Polymer Sci.*, **22,** 495 (1956).
192. Bopp, C. D., and O. Sisman, *Nucleonics*, **14,** (3), 52 (1956).
193. Baccaredda, M., P. G. Bordoni, E. Butta, and A. Charlesby, *Chim. Ind. (Milan)*, **28,** 561 (1956); *Chem. Abstr.*, **51,** 754d (1957).
194. Kline, D. E., *J. Appl. Polymer Sci.*, **5,** 191 (1961).
195. Graessley, W. W., Doctoral Thesis, Univ. of Michigan, 1960; *Dissertation Abstr.*, **21,** 324 (1960).
196. Parkinson, W. W., D. Binder et al., U. S. At. Energy Comm. Rept. ORNL-3017, 101 (1960); *Nucl. Sci. Abstr.*, **15:** 5066 (1961).
197. Brockes, A., *Z. Physik*, **149,** 353 (1957); *Chem. Abstr.*, **53,** 8832i (1959).
198. Fowler, J. F., and F. T. Farmer, *Nature*, **174,** 800 (1954).
199. Feng, P. Y., and J. W. Kennedy, *J. Am. Chem. Soc.*, **77,** 847 (1955).
200. Fox, M., *Compt. Rend.*, **237,** 1682 (1953); *Chem. Abstr.*, **48,** 5000a (1954).
201. Rossi, C., and U. Bianchi, *J. Polymer Sci.*, **53,** 187 (1961).
202. Henglein, A. et al., *International Conf. on the Peaceful Uses of Atomic Energy*, United Nations, Geneva, Sept., 1958, Paper 962.
203. Henglein, A., *J. Phys. Chem.*, **63,** 1852 (1959).
204. Soboleva, I. G., N. V. Makletsova, and S. S. Medvedev, *Kolloidn. Zh.*, **21,** 625 (1959); *Nucl. Sci. Abstr.*, **14:** 4586 (1960); *Chem. Abstr.*, **55,** 5098d (1961).
205. Florin, R. E., L. A. Wall, and D. W. Brown, *Trans. Faraday Soc.*, **56,** 1304 (1960); *Chem. Abstr.*, **55,** 6022d (1961).

206. Ingalls, R. B., and L. A. Wall, *J. Chem. Phys.*, **35**, 370 (1960).
207. Reiney, M. J., M. Tryon, and B. G. Achhammer, *J. Res. Natl. Bur. Std.*, **51**, 155 (1953); *Chem. Abstr.*, **48**, 4878e (1954).
208. Sears, W. C., and W. W. Parkinson, Jr., *J. Polymer Sci.*, **21**, 325 (1956).
209. Slovokhotova, N. A., Z. F. Ilicheva, and V. A. Kargin, *Vysokomolekul. Soedin.*, **3**, 191 (1961); *Chem. Abstr.*, **55**, 26514e (1961).
210. Wall, L. A., and M. Magat, *J. Chim. Phys.*, **50**, 308 (1953); *Chem. Abstr.*, **47**, 9812c (1953).
211. Wall, L. A., and M. Magat, *Mod. Plastics*, **30**, (11), 111 (1953).
212. Durup, J., *J. Polymer Sci.*, **30**, 533 (1958).
213. Durup, J., *J. Chim. Phys.*, **56**, 873 (1959); *Chem. Abstr.*, **54**, 23936c (1960).
214. Wall, L. A., and D. W. Brown, *J. Phys. Chem.*, **61**, 129 (1957).
215. Pravednikov, A. N., and I. Shen-Kan (S. K. Ying), *J. Polymer Sci.*, **53**, 61 (1961); *Intern. Symp. Macromol. Chem., Vol. III*, (IUPAC), Moscow, 1960, pp. 433–439.
216. Charlesby, A., *Nucleonics*, **12**, (6), 18 (1954); *Chem. Abstr.*, **48**, 11937c (1954).
217. Charlesby, A., *Nature*, **173**, 679 (1954).
218. Osthoff, R. C., A. M. Bueche, and W. T. Grubb, *J. Am. Chem. Soc.*, **76**, 4659 (1954).
219. Warrick, E. L., *Ind. Eng. Chem.*, **47**, 2388 (1955).
220. Charlesby, A., *Proc. Roy. Soc. (London)*, **A230**, 120 (1955); *Chem. Abstr.*, **49**, 15277b (1955).
221. Bueche, A. M., *J. Polymer Sci.*, **19**, 297 (1956).
222. Barnes, W., H. A. Dewhurst, R. W. Kilb, and L. E. St. Pierre, *J. Polymer Sci.*, **36**, 525 (1959).
223. St. Pierre, L. E., and H. A. Dewhurst, *J. Phys. Chem.*, **64**, 1060 (1960).
224. Miller, A. A., *J. Am. Chem. Soc.*, **82**, 3519 (1960).
225. Schnabel, W., and A. Henglein, *Makromol. Chem.*, **44/46**, 611 (1961).
226. Kilb, R. W., *J. Phys. Chem.*, **63**, 1838 (1959).
227. Miller, A. A., *J. Am. Chem. Soc.*, **83**, 31 (1961).
228. Charlesby, A., *J. Polymer Sci.*, **17**, 379 (1955).
229. Koike, M., and A. Danno, *J. Phys. Soc. Japan*, **15**, 1501 (1960); *Chem. Abstr.*, **55**, 6905d (1961).
230. Harrington, R., *Nucleonics*, **14**, (9), 70 (1956); *Chem. Abstr.*, **51**, 17511g (1957).
231. Krause, K. H., *Kunststoffe*, **48**, 564 (1958); *Chem. Abstr.*, **53**, 5720a (1959).
232. Kuzminskii, A. S., T. S. Nikitina, and L. A. Oksentevich, *Large Radiation Sources Ind. Vol. 1. Proc. Conf. Warsaw, 8–12 Sept. 1959*, International Atomic Energy Agency, Vienna, 1960, pp. 347–358.; *Nucl. Sci. Abstr.*, **14**: 21530 (1960).
233. Oksentevich, L. A., T. S. Nikitina, and A. S. Kuzminskii, *Kauchuk i Rezina*, **18**, (5), 21 (1959); *Chem. Abstr.*, **54**, 7206i (1960).
234. Poddubnyi, I. Ya. et al., *Kauchuk i Rezina*, **19**, (9), 5 (1960); *Nucl. Sci. Abstr.*, **15**: 20762 (1961).
235. Poddubnyi, I. Ya., S. V. Aver'yanova, and L. A. Aver'yanova, *Dokl. Akad. Nauk SSSR*, **139**, 651 (1961); *Nucl. Sci. Abstr.*, **15**: 29233 (1961). *Chem. Abstr.*, **56**, 7479a (1962).
236. Currin, C. G., *Materials in Nuclear Applications. ASTM Special Technical Publication No. 276.*, ASTM, Philadelphia, 1960, pp. 233–243.
237. Kantor, S. W., quoted by A. M. Bueche, *J. Polymer Sci.*, **19**, 297 (1956).
238. Dewhurst, H. A., and L. E. St. Pierre, *J. Phys. Chem.*, **64**, 1063 (1960).

239. Zack, J. F., E. L. Warrick, and G. Knoll, *J. Chem. Eng. Data,* **6,** 279 (1961).
240. Dzhagatspanyan, R. V., V. I. Zetkin, G. V. Motsarev, and M. T. Filippov, *Vysokomolekul. Soedin.,* **3,** 607 (1961); *Chem. Abstr.,* **55,** 26503d (1961).
241. Charlesby, A., and D. G. Lloyd, *Proc. Roy. Soc. (London),* **A254,** 343 (1960); *Chem. Abstr.,* **54,** 18036f (1960).
242. Fischer, D. J., and V. Flegel, *Rubber Age (N. Y.),* **88,** 816 (1961).
243. Fischer, D. J., R. G. Chaffee, and V. Flegel, *Rubber Age (N. Y.),* **87,** 59 (1960).
244. Fischer, D. J., R. G. Chaffee, and E. L. Warrick, *Rubber Age (N. Y.),* **88,** 77 (1960).
245. Fischer, D. J., J. F. Zack, and E. L. Warrick, *Lubrication Eng.,* **15,** 407 (1959).
246. Shultz, A. R., and F. A. Bovey, *J. Polymer Sci.,* **22,** 485 (1956).
247. McDonell, W. R., and A. S. Newton, *J. Am. Chem. Soc.,* **76,** 4651 (1954).
248. Alger, R. S., T. H. Anderson, and L. A. Webb, *J. Chem. Phys.,* **35,** 49 (1961).
249. Graham, R. K., *J. Polymer Sci.,* **37,** 441 (1959).
250. Sugai, S., *J. Phys. Soc. Japan,* **14,** 1573 (1959); *Chem. Abstr.,* **54,** 11642h (1960).
251. Heyns, H., and V. Desreux, *Large Radiation Sources Ind. Vol. 1. Proc. Conf. Warsaw, Sept. 8–12, 1959,* International Atomic Energy Agency, Vienna, 1960, pp. 257–62.
252. Burlant, W., D. Green, and C. Taylor, *J. Appl. Polymer Sci.,* **1,** 296 (1959).
253. Jacobs, H., and R. Steele, *J. Appl. Polymer Sci.,* **3,** 239 (1960).
254. Shultz, A. R., *J. Chem. Phys.,* **29,** 200 (1958).
255. Jacobs, H., and R. Steele, *J. Appl. Polymer Sci.,* **3,** 245 (1960).
256. Shultz, A. R., P. I. Roth, and J. M. Berge, *J. Polymer Sci.,* to be published; presented in part at the 135th National Meeting of the American Chemical Society, Boston, Mass., Apr. 5–10, 1959.
257. Shultz, A. R., *J. Polymer Sci.,* **35,** 369 (1959).
258. Burr, J. G., and W. M. Garrison, U. S. At. Energy Comm. Rept., AECD-2078, 1948.
259. Byrne, J., T. W. Costikyan, C. B. Hanford, D. L. Johnson, and W. L. Mann, *Ind. Eng. Chem.,* **45,** 2549 (1953).
260. Bovey, F. A., ref. 9, pp. 150–151.
261. Chapiro, A., *J. Chim. Phys.,* **53,** 895 (1956); *Chem. Abstr.,* **51,** 9334g (1957).
262. Wippler, C., IUPAC Polymer Symposium, Prague, 1957, Paper No. 7.
263. Wippler, C., *J. Polymer Sci.,* **29,** 585 (1958).
264. Kuri, Z., H. Ueda, S. Shida, and K. Shinohara, *J. Polymer Sci.,* **43,** 570 (1960).
265. Takayanagi, M., T. Aramaki, and T. Konomi, *Sen-i Gakkaishi,* **15,** (2), 124 (1959); *Nucl. Sci. Abstr.,* **14:** 13036 (1960); *Chem. Abstr.,* **53,** 7602c (1959).
266. Miller, A. A., *Ind. Eng. Chem.,* **51,** 1271 (1959).
267. Miller, A. A., *J. Appl. Polymer Sci.,* **5,** 388 (1961).
268. Pinner, S. H., *Nature,* **183,** 1108 (1959).
269. Pinner, S. H., *Large Radiation Sources Ind., Vol. 1. Proc., Conf. Warsaw, 8–12 Sept. 1959,* International Atomic Energy Agency, Vienna, 1960, pp. 273–89.
270. Pinner, S. H., *Plastics,* **25,** 1960, 35.
271. Miller, A. A., *J. Phys. Chem.,* **63,** 1755 (1959).
272. Nachtigall, D., *Naturwissenschaften,* **46,** 530 (1959); *Chem. Abstr.,* **54,** 5212e (1960).
273. Kiessling, D., *Kolloid-Z.,* **176,** 119 (1961); *Chem. Abstr.,* **55,** 26515c (1961).
274. Miller, A. A., *J. Phys. Chem.,* **63,** 1755 (1959).

275. Okada, Y., T. Ito, and A. Amemiya, *J. Phys. Soc. Japan*, **15**, 938 (1960); *Chem. Abstr.*, **54**, 20473i (1960).
276. Wuckel, L., *Naturwissenschaften*, **47**, 109 (1960); *Chem. Abstr.*, **55**, 15082d (1961).
277. Yegorova, Z. S., Yu. M. Malinskii, V. L. Karpov, A. E. Kalmanson, and L. A. Blyumenfeld, *Vysokomolekul. Soedin.*, **2**, 891 (1960); *Polymer Sci. (USSR) (English Transl.)* **2**, 448 (1961).
278. Atchison, G. J., *J. Polymer Sci.*, **49**, 385 (1961).
279. Loy, B. R., *J. Polymer Sci.*, **50**, 245 (1961).
280. Ayscough, P. B., and C. Thomson, *Proc. Chem. Soc.*, **1961**, 247.
281. Tsvetkov, Yu. D., N. N. Bubnov, M. A. Makul'skii, Yu. S. Lazurkin, and V. V. Voevodskii, *Dokl. Akad. Nauk SSSR*, **122**, 1053 (1958). *Chem. Abstr.*, **54**, 23786c (1960).
282. Lawton, E. J., and J. S. Balwit, *J. Phys. Chem.*, **65**, 815 (1961).
283. Gautron, R., J. Roch, and C. Wippler, *J. Chim. Phys.*, **58**, 159 (1961); *Chem. Abstr.*, **55**, 17233a (1961).
284. Gautron, R., J. Roch, M. Ptak, and C. Wippler, *J. Chim. Phys.*, **58**, 649 (1961); *Chem. Abstr.*, **55**, 24242b (1961).
285. Ohnishi, S.-I., Y. Ikeda, S.-I. Sugimoto, and I. Nitta, *J. Polymer Sci.*, **47**, 503 (1960).
286. Fukuda, K., J. Ishii, and Z. Miduno, *J. Phys. Soc. Japan*, **14**, 1643 (1959); *Chem. Abstr.*, **54**, 11658c (1960).
287. Kuri, Z., H. Ueda, and S. Shida, *J. Chem. Phys.*, **32**, 371 (1960).
288. Loy, B. R., *J. Phys. Chem.*, **65**, 58 (1961).
289. Ueda, H., Z. Kuri, and S. Shida, *J. Appl. Polymer Sci.*, **5**, 478 (1961).
290. Nakamura, Y., *Kobunshi Kagaku*, **17**, 721 (1960); *Nucl. Sci. Abstr.*, **15**: 11002T (1961).
291. Rougee, H. M., and C. Wippler, *IUPAC Symposium*, Wiesbaden, Oct., 1959, Section IV, Paper No. IV C 12.
292. Wippler, C., *Nucleonics*, **18**, (8), 68 (1960); *Chem. Abstr.*, **55**, 85i (1961).
293. Wells, H., and I. Williamson, *Brit. Plastics*, **31**, 311 (1958).
294. Wippler, C., *Rev. Gen. Caoutchouc*, **36**, 369 (1959); *Chem. Abstr.*, **55**, 15993a (1961).
295. Wells, H., and I. Williamson, *Chem. Process Eng.*, **41**, 191 (1960).
296. Yanova, L. P., M. S. Monastyrskaya, S. A. Pavlov, and T. T. Gorbateva, *Izv. Vysshikh Uchebn. Zavedenii Tekhnol. Legkoi Prom.*, 1960 (4), 46; *Nucl. Sci. Abstr.*, **15**: 18093 (1961); *Chem. Abstr.*, **55**, 11914c (1961).
297. Bovey, F. A., ref. 9, pp. 173–174.
298. D'Alelio, G. F., and R. Haberli, *IUPAC Polymer Symposium*, Wiesbaden, Oct., 1959, Section IV, Paper No. IV C 6.
299. Charlesby, A., *Nature*, **171**, 167 (1953).
300. Little, K., *Nature*, **173**, 680 (1954).
301. Todd, A., *Nature*, **174**, 613 (1954).
302. Bopp, C. D., and O. Sisman, *Nucleonics*, **13**, (10), 51 (1955); *Chem. Abstr.*, **50**, 7618i (1956).
303. Haynes, A., and C. C. Hsiao, *J. Appl. Phys.*, **31**, 1871 (1960).
304. Hsiao, C. C., and S. T. Chow, *J. Appl. Phys.*, **31**, 1869 (1960).
305. Slovokhotova, N. A., G. K. Sadovskaya, and V. A. Kargin, *Vysokomolekul. Soedin.*, **4**, 515 (1961); *Chem. Abstr.*, **55**, 26514e (1961).

306. Kline, D. E., and J. A. Sauer, *Polymer*, **2**, 401 (1961).
307. Ritz, V. H., *Radiation Res.*, **15**, 460 (1961); *Chem. Abstr.*, **57**, 6835c (1962).
308. Colichman, E. L., and J. M. Scarborough, *J. Appl. Chem. (London)*, **8**, 219 (1958).
309. Osborne, K. R., *J. Polymer Sci.*, **38**, 357 (1959).
310. Shultz, A. R., and S. M. Leahy, *J. Appl. Polymer Sci.*, **5**, 64 (1961).
311. Majury, T. G., and S. H. Pinner, *J. Appl. Chem. (London)*, **8**, 168 (1958).
312. Zimmerman, J., *J. Polymer Sci.*, **46**, 151 (1960).
313. Koshimo, A., *Kobunshi Kagaku*, **17**, 552 (1960); *Nucl. Sci. Abstr.*, **15**: 10999 (1961); *Chem. Abstr.*, **55**, 22838c (1961).
314. Lösche, A., *Maxwell-Ampere Conference, Londres, Apr. 1–3*, **1959**, Geneva, July, 1959, p. 205.
315. Deeley, C. W., Ph.D. Thesis, Pennsylvania State Univ.; *Dissertation Abstr.*, **18**, 259 (1958).
316. Deeley, C. W., A. E. Woodward, and J. A. Sauer, *J. Appl. Phys.*, **28**, 1124 (1957).
317. Hsiao, C. C., Y. C. Das, and A. Haynes, *Brit. J. Appl. Phys.*, **11**, 277 (1960).
318. Juilfs, J., and H. Busch, *Kolloid-Z.*, **178**, 173 (1961). *Chem. Abstr.*, **56**, 7531g (1962).
319. Slovokhotova, N. A., *Dokl. Akad. Nauk SSSR.*, **127**, 831 (1959); Rept. Acad. Sci. USSSR, PB 141015T-44, Paper No. 29. OTS. *Chem. Abstr.*, **55**, 20585d (1961).
320. Boyd, R. H., *J. Chem. Phys.*, **30**, 1276 (1959).
321. Tsetlin, B. L., and S. R. Rafikov, *Izv. Akad. Nauk SSSR Otd. Khim. Nauk*, **1957**, 1411; *Bull. Acad. Sci. USSR Div. Chem. Sci. (English Transl.)*, **1957**, 1435; *Chem. Abstr.*, **52**, 5028f (1958).
322. Pavlova, S. A., S. R. Rafikov, and B. L. Tsetlin, *Dokl. Akad. Nauk SSSR*, **123**, 127 (1958); *Chem. Abstr.*, **55**, 1149c (1961).
323. Bennett, R. G., R. L. McCarthy, B. Nolin, and J. Zimmerman, *J. Chem. Phys.*, **29**, 249 (1958).
324. Ballantine, D. S., and Y. Shinohara, *Trans. N. Y. Acad. Sci.*, **23**, 433 (1961).
325. Zimmerman, J., *J. Appl. Polymer Sci.*, **2**, 181 (1959).
326. Zimmerman, J., *J. Polymer Sci.*, **43**, 193 (1960).
327. Rideal, E. K., and J. S. Mitchell, *Proc. Roy. Soc. (London)*, **A159**, 206 (1937); *Chem. Abstr.*, **31**, 7760[2] (1937).
328. Carpenter, D. C., *J. Am. Chem. Soc.*, **62**, 289 (1940).
329. Achhammer, B. G., F. W. Reinhart, and G. M. Kline, *J. Res. Natl. Bur. Std.*, **46**, 391 (1951); *Chem. Abstr.*, **45**, 10662g (1951).
330. Rafikov, S. R., and T. P. Hsu, *Vysokomolekul. Soedin.*, **3**, 56 (1961); *Chem. Abstr.*, **55**, 25330g (1961).
331. Sharkey, W. H., and W. E. Mochel, *J. Am. Chem. Soc.*, **81**, 3000 (1959).
332. Ford, R. A., *Nature*, **176**, 1023 (1955).
333. Edgerton, G. S., and S. L. Fitton, *Nature*, **178**, 41 (1956).
334. Burlant, W. J., and C. R. Taylor, *J. Phys. Chem.*, **62**, 247 (1958).
335. Alexander, P., and A. Charlesby, *J. Chim. Phys.*, **52**, 694 (1955).
336. Duffey, D., *Ind. Eng. Chem.*, **50**, 1267 (1958).
337. Charlesby, A., *Plastics Inst. (London) Trans. J.*, **23**, 133 (1955); *Chem. Abstr.*, **49**, 9319e (1955).
338. Okamura, S. et al., *Proc. Second Int. Conf. on Peaceful Uses of Atomic Energy. Vol.* **29**, United Nations, Geneva, 1958, p. 176.

339. Pearson, R. W., *First UNESCO Conf. on Radioisotopes in Scientific Research, Paris, 1957 Vol. 1,* Pergamon Press, New York, 1958, p. 151.
340. Bopp, C. D., and O. Sisman, *Nucleonics,* **13,** (7), 28 (1955); *Chem. Abstr.,* **50,** 9781g (1956).
341. Dixon, S., D. R. Rexford, and J. S. Rugg, *Ind. Eng. Chem.,* **49,** 1687 (1957).

B. Crosslinking by Monomer

342. Carothers, W. H., and J. A. Arvin, *J. Am. Chem. Soc.,* **51,** 2560 (1929).
343. Bradley, T. F., E. L. Kropa, and W. B. Johnston, *Ind. Eng. Chem.,* **29,** 1270 (1937).
344. Kropa, E. L., and T. F. Bradley, *Ind. Eng. Chem.,* **31,** 1512 (1939).
345. Ellis, C., U. S. Patent 2,255,313 (to Ellis-Foster Co.), Sept. 9, 1941; *Chem. Abstr.,* **36,** 192[7] (1942).
346. Feuer, S. S., T. E. Bockstahler, C. A. Brown, and I. Rosenthal, *Ind. Eng. Chem.,* **46,** 1643 (1954).
347. Vansco-Szmercsanyi, I., K. Maros-Greger, and E. Makay-Bodi, *J. Polymer Sci.,* **53,** 241 (1961).
348. Bockstahler, T. E., G. E. Forsyth, J. J. Gouza, F. R. Shirak, and E. M. Beavers, *Ind. Eng. Chem.,* **46,** 1639 (1954).
349. Robitschek, P., and C. T. Bean, *Ind. Eng. Chem.,* **46,** 1628 (1954).
350. Kass, P., U. S. Patent 2,634,251 (to Atlas Powder Co.), April 27, 1953; *Chem. Abstr.,* **47,** 8414i (1953).
351. Hoppens, H. A., U. S. 2,532,498 (to Libbey-Owens-Ford Glass Co.), Dec. 5, 1950; *Chem. Abstr.,* **45,** 1814f (1951).
352. Smith, A. L., and J. R. Lowry, *Mod. Plastics,* **35,** (7), 134 (1958).
353. Elliott, P. M., *Mod. Plastics,* **29,** (11), 113 (1952).
354. Schildknecht, C. E., *Vinyl and Related Polymers,* Wiley, New York, 1952.
355. Bjorksten Research Laboratories, *Polyesters and Their Application,* Reinhold, New York, 1956.
356. Flory, P. J., *Principles of Polymer Chemistry,* Cornell Univ. Press, Ithaca, New York, 1953.
357. Alfrey, T., J. J. Bohrer, and H. Mark, *Copolymerization,* High Polymer Series, Vol. VIII, Interscience, New York, 1952.
358. Flory, P. J., *J. Am. Chem. Soc.,* **69,** 2893 (1947).
359. Burlant, W. J., and A. S. Hoffman, *Block and Graft Polymers,* Reinhold, New York, 1960.
360. Butler, G. B., and J. L. Nash, Jr., *J. Am. Chem. Soc.,* **73,** 2538 (1951).
361. Raech, H., Jr., and J. L. Thomas, *Mod. Plastics,* **38** (10), 143 (1961).
362. Clark, H., and B. M. Vanderbilt, Proceedings 14th Ann. Conf. of Soc. Plastics Industry, Reinforced Plastics Div., Feb. 1959.
363. Johnston, C. W., and F. P. Greenspan, *Mod. Plastics,* **38,** (8), 135 (1961).
364. Smets, G., and R. Hart, *Fortschr. Hochpolymer. Forsch.,* **2,** 173 (1960/1961).
365. Saigusa, T., and R. Oda, *Bull. Inst. Chem. Res. Kyoto Univ.,* **33,** 126 (1955); *Chem. Abstr.,* **50,** 1357 (1956).
366. Berlin, A. A., and T. A. Makarova, *Zh. Obshch. Khim.,* **21,** 1267 (1951); *Chem. Abstr.,* **46,** 1996d (1952).
367. Kovacic, P., and R. W. Hein, *J. Am. Chem. Soc.,* **81,** 1187 (1959).
368. Metz, D. J., and R. B. Mesrobian, *J. Polymer Sci.,* **16,** 345 (1955).

369. Lazar, M., R. Rado, and J. Pavlinec, *J. Polymer Sci.*, **53,** 163 (1961).
370. Fox, T. G, and S. Gratch, *Ann. N. Y. Acad. Sci.*, **57,** 367 (1953); *Chem. Abstr.*, **48,** 4286c (1954).
371. Flory, P. J., *J. Am. Chem. Soc.*, **63,** 3083, 3091, 3096 (1941).
372. Gordon, M., and I. D. McMillan, *Makromol. Chem.*, **23,** 188 (1957).
373. Gordon, M., B. M. Grieveson, and I. D. McMillan, *J. Polymer Sci.*, **18,** 497 (1955).
374. Tokarev, A. V., and S. S. Spasskiĭ, *Zh. Fiz. Khim.*, **33,** 554 (1959); *Resins, Rubbers and Plastics*, **13,** 1001 (1959); *Chem. Abstr.*, **53,** 20900i (1959).
375. Matkova, M. E., and S. S. Spasskiĭ, *Vysokomolekul. Soedin.*, **2,** 879 (1960); *Chem. Abstr.*, **55,** 7898h (1961).
376. Butalov, M. A., and S. S. Spasskiĭ, *Vysokomolekul. Soedin.*, **2,** 658 (1960); *Chem. Abstr.*, **55,** 7899a (1960).
377. Spasskiĭ, S. S., and M. E. Matkova, *Zh. Obshch. Khim.*, **29,** 3438 (1959); *Chem. Abstr.*, **54,** 15234c (1960).
378. Spasskiĭ, S. S., and T. V. Molchanova, *Vysokomolekul. Soedin.*, **2,** 1481 (1960); *J. Polymer Sci.*, **51,** S103 (1961).
379. Lewis, F. M., C. Walling, W. Cummings, E. R. Briggs, and F. R. Mayo, *J. Am. Chem. Soc.*, **70,** 1519 (1948).
380. Stockmayer, W. H., *J. Chem. Phys.*, **12,** 125 (1944).
381. Gordon, M., B. M. Grieveson, and I. D. McMillan, *Trans. Faraday Soc.*, **52,** 1012 (1956); *Chem. Abstr.*, **51,** 6277d (1957).
382. Loshaek, S., and T. G Fox, *J. Am. Chem. Soc.*, **75,** 3544 (1953).
383. Starkweather, H. W., Jr., and F. R. Eirich, *Ind. Eng. Chem.*, **47,** 2452 (1955).
384. Gordon, M., and B. M. Grieveson, *J. Polymer Sci.*, **29,** 9 (1958).
385. Fineman, M. N., and I. E. Puddington, *Can. J. Research*, **25B,** 101 (1947).
386. Warfield, R. W., and M. C. Petree, *J. Polymer Sci.*, **37,** 305 (1959).
387. Murphy, C. B., J. A. Palm, C. D. Doyle, and E. M. Curtiss, *J. Polymer Sci.*, **28,** 447 (1958).
388. Wycherley, V., *Chem. Ind. (London)*, **1957,** 431.
389. Robertson, W. G. P., and D. J. Shepherd, *Chem. Ind. (London)*, **1958,** 126.
390. Spasskiĭ, S. S., A. I. Tarasov, and A. V. Tokarev, *Zh. Fiz. Khim.*, **33,** 249 (1959); *Resins, Rubbers, Plastics*, **13,** 999 (1959); *Chem. Abstr.*, **53,** 20900h (1959).
391. Hayes, B. T., W. J. Read, and L. H. Vaughan, *Chem. Ind. (London)*, **1957,** 1162.
392. Funke, W., W. Gebhardt, H. Roth, and K. Hamann, *Makromol. Chem.*, **28,** 17 (1958); *Resins, Rubbers, Plastics*, **13,** 319 (1959).
393. Hamann, K., W. Funke, and H. Gilch, *Angew. Chem.*, **71,** 596 (1959); *Resins, Rubbers, Plastics*, **14,** 629 (1960); *Chem. Abstr.*, **54,** 7224c (1960).
394. Ghanem, N. A., *Makromol. Chem.*, **36,** 109 (1960).
395. Fox, T. G, and S. Loshaek, *J. Polymer Sci.*, **15,** 371 (1955).
396. Spasskiĭ, S. S., M. E. Matkova, and A. V. Tokarev, *Vysokomolekul. Soedin.*, **2,** 1297 (1960); *J. Polymer Sci.*, **51,** S91 (1961).

C. Crosslinking of Elastomers

397. Fettes, E. M., *Organic Sulfur Compounds*, N. Kharasch, ed., Vol. 1, Pergamon Press, New York, 1961, p. 266.
398. Walling, C., *Free Radicals in Solution*, Wiley, New York, 1957, p. 335.

399. Weber, C. O., *J. Soc. Chem. Ind. (London)*, **13,** 11 (1894).
400. Meyer, K. H., and H. Mark, *Chem. Ber.*, **61B,** 1939 (1928); *Chem. Abstr.*, **23,** 1524 (1929).
401. Meyer, K. H., and W. Hohenemser, *Helv. Chim. Acta*, **18,** 1061 (1935); *Rubber Chem. Technol.*, **9,** 201 (1936); *Chem. Abstr.*, **30,** 4047[1] (1936).
402. Craig, D., *Rubber Chem. Technol.*, **30,** 1291 (1957).
403. Fuson, R. C., R. E. Foster, and R. D. Lipscomb, *J. Org. Chem.*, **11,** 504 (1946).
404. Pickles, S. S., *J. Chem. Soc.*, **97,** 1085 (1910); *Chem. Abstr.*, **4,** 2936 (1910).
405. For review of work of C. D. Harries, see G. S. Whitby, *Rubber Chem. Technol.*, **34,** (4) xiii (1961).
406. Weber, C. O., *The Chemistry of India Rubber*, Charles Griffin & Co., Ltd., London, 1903 to 1906 editions, pp. 56, 82–119, and especially pages 56, 92, and 97.
407. Carothers, W. H., *J. Am. Chem. Soc.*, **53,** 4203 (1931).
408. Carothers, W. H., *Chem. Rev.*, **8,** 353 (1931).
409. Glazer, J., and F. H. Cotton, in *The Applied Science of Rubber*, W. J. S. Naunton, ed., Edward Arnold, Ltd., London, 1961, pp. 992, 1050.
410. Busse, W. F., *J. Phys. Chem.*, **36,** 2862 (1932); *Rubber Chem. Technol.*, **7,** 273 (1934).
411. Scanlan, J., and W. F. Watson, *Rubber Chem. Technol.*, **33,** 1201 (1960).
412. Treloar, L. R. G., *The Physics of Rubber Elasticity*, Oxford University Press, New York, 1958.
413. Flory, P. J., *Principles of Polymer Chemistry*, Cornell University Press, Ithaca, New York, 1953.
414. Mullins, L., *J. Appl. Polymer Sci.*, **2,** 257 (1959); *Rubber Chem. Technol.*, **34,** 290 (1961).
415. Scanlan, J., *J. Polymer Sci.*, **43,** 501 (1960).
416. Mullins, L., and A. G. Thomas, *J. Polymer Sci.*, **43,** 13 (1960).
417. Kraus, G., *Rubber World*, **135,** 67, 254 (1956); *Rubber Chem. Technol.*, **30,** 928 (1957).
418. Scheele, W., *Rubber Chem. Technol.*, **34,** 1306 (1961).
419. Kuhn, W., E. Peterli, and H. Majer, *J. Polymer Sci.*, **16,** 539 (1955).
420. Kuhn, W., E. Peterli, and H. Majer, *Z. Elektrochem.*, **62,** 296 (1958); *Rubber Chem. Technol.*, **33,** 245 (1960).
421a. Trivissono, N. M., private communication; for data from G. Gee and L. R. G. Treloar, *Trans. Faraday Soc.*, **38,** 147 (1942).
421b. Trivissano, N. M., and D. Craig, *J. Polymer* Sci., **B1,** 253 (1963).
422. Fettes, E. M., J. S. Jorczak, and J. R. Panek. *Ind. Eng. Chem.*, **46,** 1539 (1954); *Rubber Chem. Technol.*, **28,** 139 (1955).
423. Schollenberger, C. S., H. Scott, and G. R. Moore, *Rubber World*, **137,** 549 (1958); *Rubber Chem. Technol.*, **35,** 742 (1962).
424. Westlinning, H., G. Butenuth, and G. Leineweber, *Makromol. Chem.*, **50,** 253 (1961).
425. Westlinning, H., and G. Butenuth, *Makromol. Chem.*, **47,** 215 (1961); *Rubber Chem. Technol.*, **35,** 274 (1962).
426. Cluff, E. F., and E. K. Gladding, *J. Appl. Polymer Sci.*, **3,** 290 (1960); *Rubber Chem. Technol.*, **34,** 629 (1961).
427. Studebaker, M. L., and L. G. Nabors, *Rubber Chem. Technol.*, **32,** 941 (1959).
428. Studebaker, M. L., private communication.

429. Moore, C. G., *J. Polymer Sci.*, **32**, 503 (1958); *Rubber Chem. Technol.*, **33**, 394 (1960).
430. Bevilacqua, E. M., *J. Polymer Sci.*, **28**, 651 (1958).
431. Gregg, E. C., Jr., private communication.
432. Selker, M. L., and A. R. Kemp, *Ind. Eng. Chem.*, **36**, 16 (1944).
433. Selker, M. L., and A. R. Kemp, *Ind. Eng. Chem.*, **36**, 20 (1944).
434. Selker, M. L., and A. R. Kemp, *Ind. Eng. Chem.*, **39**, 895 (1947).
435. Selker, M. L., *Ind. Eng. Chem.*, **40**, 1467 (1948).
436. Selker, M. L., and A. R. Kemp, *Ind. Eng. Chem.*, **40**, 1470 (1948); *Rubber Chem. Technol.*, **22**, 8 (1949).
437. Moore, C. G., and J. Scanlan, *J. Polymer Sci.*, **43**, 23 (1960); *Rubber Chem. Technol.*, **34**, 309 (1961).
438. Bibliography in reference 437.
439. Scheele, W., and W. Triebel, *Kautschuk Gummi*, **11**, WT127 (1958).
440. Dogadkin, B. A., and V. A. Shershnev, *Usp. Khim.*, **30**, 1013 (1961); *Rubber Chem. Technol.*, **35**, 1 (1962).
441. Parks, C. R., and O. Lorenz, *J. Polymer Sci.*, **50**, 287 (1961).

Chapter X

BRANCHING REACTIONS

A. SELF-BRANCHING IN POLYMERIZATION

MAURICE MORTON

Institute of Rubber Research, University of Akron

1. General Introduction

The concept of branching during polymerization probably arose simultaneously with the development of the first understanding of polymerization reactions. This becomes obvious from a consideration of the effect of functionality on polymer structure. Thus, in polycondensation, the presence of more than two reacting groups in the monomer leads to branching chains. Similarly, in addition polymerization, the presence of more than one double bond in the monomer has the same effect. Such branching reactions during polymerization were the first to be considered, since they were found to lead to the formation of gels, defined as "three-dimensional" networks. Although this phenomenon was known for a long time, it was only relatively recently that a quantitative treatment of network formation was developed, mainly due to the statistical approach suggested by Flory (1) and Stockmayer (2).

A more subtle form of branching came under consideration when evidence became available that chain transfer reactions (3) can occur in addition polymerization, especially by the free radical mechanism. Thus two types of chain transfer reactions can be suggested as leading to the formation of branched chains, i.e., transfer to monomer and transfer to polymer. In the first case, the growing chain radical transfers its activity to a monomer unit, either by abstracting from it or donating to it a hydrogen (or other labile) atom. In this way a polymer chain is formed having a terminal double bond, the latter presumably being capable of attack by growing radicals, thus leading to branched chains. In the second case, the growing chain radical transfers its activity to a polymer molecule by abstracting a suitable atom from the latter, thus permitting the polymer chain to grow a branch.

Although the vinyl polymers were assumed to possess varying degrees of branching, because of the above transfer reactions, no appropriate means were available for a long time for the quantitative estimation of such branching. Actually it was only during the past decade that refinements in various techniques made it possible to achieve this goal. The methods so used include infrared spectroscopic analysis of polymer chain structure, measurement of molecular weights and solution properties of the polymers, observations of the physical behavior of the polymers, and kinetic studies. Using a combination of these methods provides an even more powerful tool for the quantitative determination of branching.

2. Branching in Polyethylene

The branching reaction in addition polymerization has been studied most extensively in the case of polyethylene. This is probably due to the fact that it occurs to such a large extent in this polymer that its detection and quantitative estimation is easier than for other polymers. Hence it is not surprising that a large body of evidence has been amassed for the extent of branching in polyethylene, based on the various experimental approaches mentioned above.

a. Infrared Spectroscopy of Polyethylene

Since any branching occurring in polyethylene by a chain transfer between polymer chains leads to formation of methyl groups, it is not surprising that the earliest attempts were directed toward detection of these groups in the polymer. Naturally, the polyethylene referred to is of the high pressure, free radical-polymerized variety. Perhaps the first reported results were those of Fox and Martin (3) who used infrared spectroscopy and assigned the absorption at 3.38 μ to the presence of methyl groups, and that at 3.502 μ to methylene groups (—CH_2—). Later workers (4,5) assigned the additional frequency of 7.25 μ to methyl groups. From the intensities of these absorptions and a knowledge of the molecular weight of the polymer, it becomes possible to calculate the number of branches per chain, assuming two methyl endgroups per linear chain.

In this way, Rugg (6) found that the number of branches per 100 carbon atoms depended on the chain length, ranging from 6 branches (per 100 carbons) at a (number-average) molecular weight of 1000, to 1 branch (per

100 carbons) at a molecular weight of 10,000. He used ebulliometry for the determination of the molecular weights. Bryant and Voter (7) also calculated the branching frequency, using the 7.25 μ absorption for methyl groups. They also found a variation in the methyl groups per 100 carbons, ranging from 0.2 to 4.6. In addition, however, they used the absorption at 11.2 μ for estimation of ethyl groups, and found that these corresponded very well with the total number of methyl groups. Hence they concluded that none of the branches could consist of methyl groups alone, but must contain *at least* two carbon atoms.

From all the above experimental evidence, it becomes apparent that high pressure polyethylene is characterized by the presence of frequent "short-chain" branching. This unexpected result was probably first explained by Roedel (8), who proposed an intramolecular chain-transfer mechanism, as shown in eq. (1). Although the formation of the butyl branches was not based on direct evidence (other than the fact that these branches contained at least two carbon atoms), it was proposed on the basis of the known stability of a five-membered ring

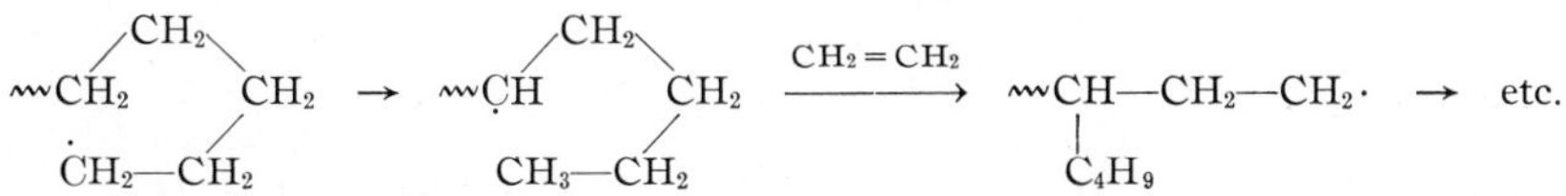

(1)

conformation. Such an *intramolecular* transfer mechanism was, of course, required in order to account for the presence of the large number of methyl groups, or branches, per chain. However, this does not vitiate the possibility for the existence of some long-chain branches, perhaps caused by *intermolecular* chain transfer.

More recently, Slowinski, Walter, and Miller (9) rechecked the methyl content of polyethylene, using the absorption peak in the 7–7.5 μ region but a different calibration standard. They used the high molecular weight n-octapentacontane ($C_{58}H_{118}$), which they synthesized from n-nonacosyl alcohol ($C_{29}H_{59}OH$) and n-nonacosyl iodide ($C_{29}H_{59}I$). By using such a long-chain hydrocarbon, instead of the usual C_{16} or C_{18} compounds, they hoped to obtain a more accurate calibration. By this means they found that polyethylene contains up to 3% methyl groups, compared with the 4% methyl content of their standard. They also used this determination to correlate some of the physical properties of the polymer with short-chain branching, e.g., a decrease in density at higher branching, as well as a drop in shear modulus.

Varga (10) has also recently suggested improved techniques for determination of methyl group content in polyethylene by infrared spectroscopy, using pressed films.

In a recent, careful study of polyethylene structure by infrared spectroscopy, Willbourn (11) used linear and branched polymethylenes of known structure to calibrate his measurements. He also used irradiation degradation to determine the amount of ethane and butane arising from ethyl and butyl branches, respectively, and thus found twice as many ethyl as butyl groups. On the basis of his findings, he proposed the intramolecular chain transfer mechanism shown in eq. (2) modifying Roedel's (8) original mechanism as shown in eq. (1). Hence two ethyl groups and one butyl group are presumably formed for each initial chain transfer step, due to the two possibilities shown for the second transfer step.

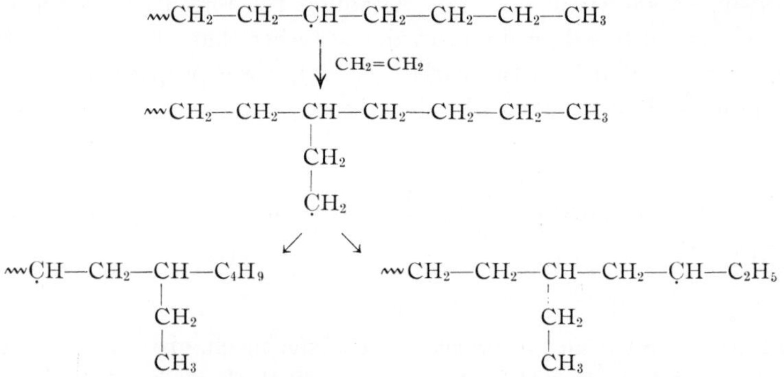

(2)

b. Molecular Weight Distribution in Polyethylene

Molecular weight measurements on polyethylene have been used extensively, not only to provide general information, but also to characterize the extent of branching. It is obvious, from kinetic considerations, that the molecular weight distribution would be greatly affected only by intermolecular chain transfer reactions, and not by the intramolecular reaction discussed above. The intermolecular transfer reaction is considered to lead to long-chain branching, which is not easily detected by methyl group content analysis, but shows up in a broadening of the molecular weight distribution.

Beasley (12) treated the kinetics of intermolecular chain transfer and developed an expression for predicting the effect of this reaction on the molecular weight distribution, as shown in eq. (3).

$$\frac{\bar{P}_w}{\bar{P}_n} = \frac{2}{1 - (k_b/k_p)\,(\bar{P}_n)\,[p]/[M]} \tag{3}$$

where $\bar{P}_w$, $\bar{P}_n$ are weight-average and number-average degrees of polymerization, respectively, k_b, K_p are rate constants for intermolecular chain transfer, and propagation, respectively, $[P]$ is polymer concentration (moles of combined monomer per unit volume), and $[M]$ is monomer concentration (moles per unit volume). He pointed out that such transfer reaction should broaden the molecular weight distribution, leading to a long "tail" at high molecular weights as well as a very broad distribution in the number of branches per chain, a large fraction of the polymer chains remaining unbranched. Subsequently Nicolas (13) also developed a kinetic treatment of intermolecular chain transfer, in which he predicted an increase in branching with molecular weight.

Billmeyer (14) determined the $\bar{M}_w/\bar{M}_n$ ratio of polyethylene, using light scattering and osmometry, and found values as high as 20/1, indicating extensive long-chain branching. On the other hand, Nicolas (15) obtained an $\bar{M}_w//\bar{M}_n$ ratio of only 3.70 and considered this as sufficient proof of the existence of long-chain branching. Mussa (16) actually used the $\bar{M}_w/\bar{M}_n$ ratios for polyethylene to calculate Beasley's β parameter. He found it to vary from 0.05 at an $\bar{M}_n$ of 15,000 to 0.4 at an $\bar{M}_n$ of 40,000. Here β is as defined by Beasley (12), i.e.,

$$\beta = \frac{(k_b/k_p)\ ([P]/[M])\bar{P}_n}{1 + (k_b/k_p)\ ([P]/[M])\bar{P}_n} \tag{4}$$

and

$$\bar{P}_w/\bar{P}_n = 2(1-\beta)/(1-2\beta) \tag{5}$$

Hence Mussa's $\bar{P}_w/\bar{P}_n$ ratios varied from about 2 to 6.

Trementozzi (17) fractionated high pressure polyethylene into 19 fractions and the Ziegler (low pressure) type into 12 fractions, and determined their molecular weight distributions. He also measured the molecular weight of the unfractionated polymer by light scattering and osmometry. He found the $\bar{M}_w/\bar{M}_n$ ratio for the Ziegler type to be about 2, indicating the absence of long-chain branching. However, the high pressure polymer showed an $\bar{M}_w/\bar{M}_n$ ratio of from 7 to 100, indicating excessive branching. He also used his data to prove that the second virial coefficient is lower for the branched polymer. On the other hand, Muus and Billmeyer (18) determined the molecular weights of *unfractionated* polyethylene (high pressure) using an ultracentrifuge, light scattering, and osmometry. They found $\bar{M}_w/\bar{M}_n$ ratios of 11 to 18, showing a considerable extent of long-chain branching.

It is also interesting to note that, in this work, the above authors found that some microgel was present in their polyethylene solutions, and had to be removed by high temperature centrifugation prior to light scattering measurements. Subsequently, Nicolas (19) also pointed out that the presence of microgel (i.e., highly branched species due to long-range branching) in polyethylene can complicate light scattering measurements on polyethylene solutions.

c. Branching and Physical Properties of Polyethylene

The effect of molecular size and structure on the physical properties and mechanical behavior of polyethylene has offered a very fruitful field of study. In such studies, the effect of branching has, of course, played a major role. Actually, however, these studies have been a two-way street, since they made it possible, in turn, to determine the extent and type of branching from the physical characteristics of the polymers.

The solution properties of polyethylene have been used extensively to characterize the extent of branching, mainly by determining the dimensions of the coiled chain in solution. Such measurements should yield information on *long-chain branching*. Thus Billmeyer (14) compared the intrinsic viscosity and $\bar{M}_w$ values (by light scattering) of branched and unbranched (polymethylene) polymers. From these data he was able to calculate the value of n, i.e., the weight-average number of branch points per chain, using the Zimm and Stockmayer (20) treatment. He found that these n values varied from 4 to 34, rising with molecular weight.

Using a similar approach, Trementozzi (21) measured the relation of intrinsic viscosity to molecular weight on fractions of both high pressure and low pressure polyethylene and used the Zimm-Stockmayer (20) and Zimm-Thurmond (22) treatment to calculate n values, assuming the low pressure polymer to be linear. He found these to range from zero at a molecular weight of 10,000 up to 3–8 at a molecular weight of 200,000. This led to a downward concavity in the logarithmic plot of intrinsic viscosity versus molecular weight. Moore and co-workers (23) used a combination of ultracentrifuge and solution viscosity measurements to evaluate the degree of long-chain branching in linear and branched polyethylene, using the Zimm-Stockmayer (20) method to calculate the extent of branching. They found that, for a branched polymer, the fractions showed an increase in branching with molecular weight, going from 2 branches per chain to as many as 25 at high molecular weights. Furthermore, they found that polymers which showed a broader molecular weight distribution also showed a higher degree of branching, showing that long-chain branching is a phenomenon related to intermolecular chain transfer.

Richards (24) was probably the first to show the effect of short-chain branching on the extent of crystallinity in polyethylene, and how this affects the physical behavior of the polymer. He showed that, although the molecular weight and its distribution has only a slight effect on crystallinity (shorter chains showing lower crystalline content), branching has a large effect in destroying crystallinity. He then went on to show that short-chain branching, by influencing the crystallinity, can markedly affect such physical properties as Young's modulus in tension, bending modulus, yield point and surface hardness, all of which are sensitive to crystalline content of the polymer. On the other hand, he showed that the tensile strength, tear resistance, and low temperature properties are more dependent on the molecular weight and very little on crystallinity.

Roedel (8) was able to distinguish between the effects of short-chain and long-chain branching on physical properties by studying polyethylenes prepared at different conversions and temperatures. Thus the high conversion polymers, which can be considered as high in long-chain branching, due to intermolecular transfer, exhibited such physical properties as highly elastic melts and greater insolubility. On the other hand, higher polymerization temperatures, which can be expected to increase short-chain branching (at low conversions), were found to decrease the crystallinity and thus also the density.

Sperati, Franta, and Starkweather (25) carried out a definitive study on the effects of short-chain and long-chain branching on the physical properties of polyethylene. They used infrared spectroscopy data (7) to characterize the short-chain branching, and molecular weight data (14) for the long-chain branching. They thus concluded that short-chain branching affects the crystallinity, density, stiffness, yield point, melting point, and sorption of solvents. They also found that both the density and the molecular weight ($\bar{M}_n$, from melt viscosity) affect the hardness and ultimate elongation. On the other hand, they concluded that the molecular weight ($\bar{M}_n$) and long-chain branching both affect the viscoelastic properties of the molten polymer, as well as the tensile strength.

The effect of short-chain branching in disrupting polymer crystallinity was also found (26) to affect the refractive index, which increases with greater crystallinity, but is independent of molecular weight. Charlesby and Callaghan (27) studied the melting behavior of high and low density polyethylene. They deduced the presence of much smaller crystals in the high pressure (branched) polymer, due to interference by the side branches.

Other workers (28) also showed that the short side branches disrupted crystallinity. Gubler and Kovacs (29) actually measured volume–temperature relations for high and low pressure polyethylenes and were able to relate the melting temperature directly to the length of the linear segments in the polymer. Their calculated value for short-chain branching agreed quite well with infrared data. Majer and Osecky (30) subsequently confirmed these dilatometric results.

Hawkins and Smith (31) fractioned linear and branched polyethylene and studied the effects of molecular weight and branching on various physical properties. They found that the solubility of polyethylene is a function of both the short-chain branching and the molecular weight. Thus a branched polymer is more soluble than a linear one, since it is less crystalline, as well as having more chain ends to increase the solubility. By the same token, higher molecular weights lead to lower solubility. They also stated that the physical properties of the linear polyethylene are largely due to the linearity rather than to the presence of high molecular weight polymer.

The melt viscosity of polyethylene has been the topic of many investigations. Thus Peticolas and Watkins (32) found that both the linear and the branched polymers followed the Flory-Fox relation, i.e.,

$$\eta = K\bar{M}_w^{3.4}$$

where η is flow time, $\bar{M}_w$ is weight-average molecular weight, and K is a constant, provided the branched polymers are corrected for short-chain branching, since the latter will increase the free volume and hence decrease the viscosity. On the other hand, long-chain branching apparently had no effect of the melt viscosity. At the same time, other workers (33) determined the number-average molecular weights of polyethylene in the range of 5000 to 50,000 by cryoscopy and osmometry, and found no relation between their molecular weights and melt viscosities (or solution viscosities).

Moore (34), however, took issue with these views concerning the effect of short-chain branching on the free volume and hence on the melt viscosity. He pointed out that the density of molten polyethylene, as opposed to the solid, crystalline polymer, is very little affected by branching (35). Hence there should be no significant difference between the free volume of branched and linear polymers. Instead he ascribed the difference in melt viscosity to differences in long-chain branching, which are related, in most polyethylenes, to short-chain branching. Thus long-chain branching decreases the melt viscosity by decreasing the entanglements, since the more "compact" chain would have a higher value of M_e, the molecular weight between entanglements.

Finally, one additional property of polyethylene has been related to branching, viz., thermal stability. Although this is not a physical property, it still throws interesting light on the differences between branched and linear polymers. Thus Oakes and Richards (36) showed that, since tertiary hydrogen atoms are most easily abstracted by free radicals, the branch points in polyethylene are most readily attacked. Hence branched polymers degrade more rapidly than linear, and degraded polymer is more linear than the original polymer.

3. Branching in Vinyl Polymers

Self-branching in the polymerization of vinyl monomers has been studied for only a few monomers and to varying extents. The most extensively investigated monomer has been vinyl acetate, presumably due to its marked proclivity for branching, as compared to the other vinyl monomers. As for the case of polyethylene, many of the methods used for detection of branching have been based on measurements of molecular weight and solution viscosities. Spectroscopic analysis of chain structure has not been fruitful for these polymers, since they do not exhibit the intensive transfer reactions of polyethylene. On the other hand, kinetic studies have been very useful in these cases, since they can be sensitive to small extents of chain transfer.

a. Vinyl Acetate

The vinyl acetate system represents an especially interesting case, since branching by radical chain transfer, either to monomer or to polymer, can occur in two ways. These can be illustrated, in the case of monomer transfer, as shown in eq. (7). It is obvious at once that species I can lead to a

$$R\cdot + CH_2{=}CHOCOCH_3 \longrightarrow \begin{cases} RH + CH_2{=}CHOCO\dot{C}H_2 \quad \text{(I)} \\ RH + CH_2{=}\dot{C}OCOCH_3 \quad \text{(II)} \end{cases} \tag{7}$$

branched chain in which the branch is hydrolyzable, while this is not the case for species II. This monomer presents a rather unique case, since the methyl group is especially susceptible to radical attack by virtue of the fact that the adjacent carbonyl group can provide some resonance stabilization of the resulting free radical. This is not the case for the acrylate esters.

Furthermore, the poly(vinyl acetate) radical, not being resonance stabilized, has a high reactivity and should presumably participate in frequent transfer reactions.

Wheeler and co-workers (37) studied the molecular weights of poly(vinyl acetate) prepared to various conversions, and noted the effect of hydrolysis and reacetylation on the chain length. In this way they were able to establish that about half of the branches were hydrolyzable, and that the branches occurred with greater frequency at higher conversions. Thus the chain length per branch was found to be about 12,000 monomer units at 20% conversion, but only 1100 monomer units at 95% conversion. This increase in branching with conversion is to be expected if branching occurs as a result of intermolecular chain transfer between a growing chain and a polymer molecule.

Ukida and co-workers (38) used another method for studying the effect of polymerization conditions on branching of poly(vinyl acetate). They examined the poly(vinyl alcohol) obtained by hydrolysis of the acetate and found that it was less crystalline and more easily swollen by solvents when the parent polymer was prepared at higher temperature. Hence they concluded that branching was increasing with polymerization temperature. Another group of Japanese investigators (39) studied the structure of poly(vinyl acetate) formed in the initial stages of polymerization. They compared the molecular weight of the acetate and the corresponding poly(vinyl alcohol) obtained by hydrolysis, and concluded that no branches were initiated on the acetyl group, at least. This is perhaps not surprising since any branching by intermolecular chain transfer would tend to be negligible at the start of the polymerization.

Patat and Potchinkov (40) also measured the extent of branching at the acetyl group, by saponification and reacetylation. They used photodecomposition of azobisisobutyronitrile to initiate the polymerization, and determined the effect of temperature, conversion and initiator concentration on branching. Elias and Patat (41) prepared fractions of poly(vinyl acetate) ranging in molecular weight from 17,000 to 1,200,000 and found no difference in their intrinsic viscosity–molecular weight relation or in their thermodynamic parameters, indicating no change in branching (if any) with molecular weight.

On the other hand, Okamura et al. (42) studied the molecular weight of poly(vinyl acetate) prepared by x-rays, γ-radiation, or by thermal initiation and found that these molecular weights rose sharply with conversion, indicating increased branching by polymeric chain transfer. They also found the same phenomenon to occur with poly(methyl acrylate) but not with poly(methyl methacrylate). The monomer transfer constants did not change with conversion.

To prove the presence of branching at the acetyl group, Imoto, Ukida, and Kominami (43) polymerized vinyl trimethylacetate in presence of poly(vinyl acetate). They saponified the graft copolymer and deduced that most of the branching occurred at the acetyl group and only very little at the secondary carbon atom in the chain. The same group of workers (44) measured the monomer transfer constant of vinyl acetate by determining the double bond content of the polymer. They obtained values of 0.02–0.04 mole-% double bond, leading to a monomer transfer (C_M) of 2.5×10^{-4}. They also obtained an activation energy difference between monomer transfer and propagation ($E_{trM} - E_p$) of 3.3 kcal. Since they found no double bond content in the poly(vinyl alcohol) obtained from the acetate, they concluded that monomer transfer occurs largely at the acetyl group.

Clarke (45) recalculated Wheeler's data (37) and concluded that most of the branches in poly(vinyl acetate) are saponifiable. Melville and Sewell (46) carried out an interesting study along the same lines by hydrolyzing and reacetylating a series of poly(vinyl acetate) fractions. They found a decrease in molecular weight, indicating a molecular weight between ester branch points of about 300,000 (compared to about 400,000 from Wheeler's data at 60% conversion). However, some of their fractions appeared to be linear, as evidenced by the linear relation between their intrinsic viscosity and molecular weight (on a logarithmic plot), and by a constant value of the Huggins parameter, k'. Hence these authors suggested the possibility of long-chain *intramolecular* chain transfer as shown in eq. (8).

$$\sim\!\!\sim CH_2\text{—}\underset{\substack{|\\ OCOCH_3}}{CH}\text{—}CH_2\text{—}\underset{\substack{|\\ OCOCH_3}}{\dot{C}H} \rightarrow \sim\!\!\sim CH_2\text{—}\underset{\substack{|\\ OCO\dot{C}H_2}}{CH}\text{—}CH_2\text{—}CH_2OCOH_3 \qquad (8)$$

This reaction would lead to a hydrolyzable link in the main chain, without any long-chain branches. In a very high molecular weight fraction, however, the above authors did find evidence of some long-chain branching.

By polymerizing vinyl acetate in the presence of C^{14}-poly(vinyl acetate) and analyzing the product, Bevington, Guzman, and Melville (47) were able to calculate the actual intermolecular transfer constant leading to branching. They obtained a value of $C_T = k_{trP}/k_p = 3.1 \times 10^{-3}$ at 40°C., where k_{trP} is the rate constant for the transfer reaction between the chain radical and the polymer, and k_p is the propagation rate constant. They also obtained an activation energy difference ($E_{trP} - E_p$) of 5.0 kcal./mole.

More recently, Morton and Piirma (48) determined the value of the intermolecular polymer transfer constant for poly(vinyl acetate) by carrying out polymerizations of vinyl acetate in presence of oligo(vinyl acetate). Their values of k_{trP}/k_p were 3.2×10^{-3} at 40°C. and 4.8×10^{-3} at 60°C., leading to a value of $E_{trP} - E_p$ of 4.0 kcal./mole. These values are in rather good agreement with those of the previously mentioned authors.

b. Styrene

Because styrene has been the subject of many polymerization studies, it is not surprising that some attention has been given to the question of branching in this system. One of the earliest of such studies was that of Walker and Winkler (49), who measured the Huggins parameter k' by the usual method based on the concentration dependency of dilute solution viscosity. They found that polystyrene fractions of various molecular weights, and prepared by different methods and at different temperatures, all showed a constant value of k', indicating a negligible amount of branching. Wall and Brown (50) polymerized both α- and β-deuterostyrene and showed that the resulting polymers had the same relation between intrinsic viscosity and molecular weight as normal polystyrene. Hence they concluded that the absence of any isotope effect precluded any possibility of a transfer reaction between the chain radical and the α or β hydrogen. As a control, they used *S*-deuterobutyl mercaptan as a chain transfer agent, and observed an isotope effect factor of 4.

Schulz, Henrici, and Olivé (51) carried out kinetic measurements of the branching reaction in free radical styrene polymerization, by polymerizing styrene in presence of oligostyrene. By noting the effect of the low molecular weight oligomer on the chain length of the polystyrene, they were able to calculate the transfer constant involved. Their value for k_{trP}/k_p was 1.3×10^{-3} at 50°C., which appears rather high, in view of all the other evidence for negligible branching in this polymer. In a later work, Henrici-Olivé and Olivé (52) studied the Trommsdorff effect in styrene polymerization, and showed that the molecular weight increase was greater than could be accounted for by the rate increase, indicating possible branching. Furthermore, by studying the molecular weights of the polymer formed in solution to high conversion, thus avoiding the Trommsdorff effect, they were able to show a similar molecular weight rise which they ascribed to branching.

On the other hand, Morton and Piirma (53) also carried out a kinetic study of the polymerization of styrene in presence of oligostyrene (M.W. 1000–4000) in order to determine the polymer transfer constant. Their technique differed from that of Schulz et al. (51) in that they carried out actual separations of the oligomer and polymer, prior to determining the intrinsic viscosity of the polymer, whereas the former corrected for the presence of the oligostyrene in the polymer solution. As a result they were not able to detect any chain transfer between the chain radicals and the oligostyrene. Hence any transfer reaction which may occur would have to have a transfer constant less than 5×10^{-4}, a limit imposed by the kinetic chain length. This result is in better agreement with the generally accepted low degree of branching (if any) assumed for free radical polystyrene.

In this connection, it is interesting to note that Henrici-Olivé, Olivé, and Schulz (54), in a later work, obtained a new and different value for the polymer transfer constant of polystyrene than stated previously (51). This new value was 1.9×10^{-4} at 50°C., which is smaller than the original value by a whole order of magnitude, and is within the limits set by the work quoted above (53).

Meyerhoff and Cantow (55) used the viscosity versus molecular weight relation to determine the existence of branching in three types of polystyrene, viz., isotactic polystyrene (prepared by the Ziegler catalyst), atactic (thermal free radical), and anionic (sodium naphthalene catalyst). They also used the Zimm-Stockmayer treatment (20) to estimate the degree of branching from these data. They found no evidence for branching in the isotactic polymer or in the anionic, although the latter was limited to the lower molecular weight range. There was also an unexplained lower viscosity in the case of the anionic polymer, for a given molecular weight. The thermal (free radical)polymer, prepared at 60°C., showed no branching up to a molecular weight of 500,000 (5×10^3 units), and then showed an increasing number of branches with increase in molecular weight. This was noted by a fall off in the intrinsic viscosity values as the molecular weight increased beyond 10^6. The frequency of branching agrees quite well with the previously quoted kinetic data.

Cantow, Meyerhoff, and Schulz (56) prepared polystyrene by free radical initiation at 60°C. and examined low conversion (7.8%) and high conversion (77–85%) samples. The former were assumed to be linear, and indeed showed no change in linearity of the logarithmic plot of intrinsic viscosity versus molecular weight for a series of fractions. On the other hand, the high conversion polystyrene showed a definite decrease in this relationship as the molecular weight increased above 10^5. From these data, using the Zimm-Stockmayer relation (20), the authors deduced a value for the polymeric transfer constant at 60°C. of $1.9 \pm 0.5 \times 10^{-4}$, which agrees very well with the values quoted above (53,54).

Bevington, Guzman, and Melville (57) had previously used a radioactive tracer technique to determine the kinetics of polymeric chain transfer in styrene polymerization. They polymerized C^{14}-styrene in the presence of normal polystyrene and measured the extent of transfer. They found a negligible amount of transfer, except at very high conversion. Their value for the transfer constant k_{trP}/k_p was 1.8×10^{-4} at 129°C., which is somewhat lower than the other kinetic values discussed (53,56). They point out, however, that their value is very similar to the transfer constant for ethylbenzene.

c. *Acrylic Esters*

Relatively little work has been done on the extent of branching in the acrylate polymers. Schulz and co-workers (51,58) determined the transfer constant of methyl methacrylate with its own polymer, by carrying out polymerizations in presence of oligomers and noting the effect on the molecular weight of the polymer. They obtained a value of 1.5×10^{-4} for the transfer constant of the "interior" units in the chain at 50°C., and 3.5×10^{-2} for the endgroups of their oligomer. The latter value is, of course, not too important, since the endgroups are much less prevalent in a normal polymer than in the oligomer and are also dependent on the termination mechanism.

The above value can be compared with the transfer constant of 2.1×10^{-4} obtained at 60°C. for this polymer by Morton and Piirma (53). The latter also found an activation energy difference, $E_{trP} - E_p$ of 1.9 kcal./mole, indicating that this reaction has a relatively low activation energy (~8 kcal./mole) and a very high steric factor ($A = 3 \times 10^4$), presumably due to interference caused by the presence of methyl groups on both the attacking radical and on the polymer chain.

As stated previously, Okamura et al. (42) had found that the molecular weight of poly(methyl acrylate) increased considerably with conversion during polymerization induced by heat or radiation, whereas that of poly(methyl methacrylate) and poly(vinyl acetate) showed no such rise. This he attributed to the occurrence of branching in the case of the methyl acrylate, presumably because of the presence of the tertiary hydrogen.

d. *Vinyl Chloride*

The study of branching in poly(vinyl chloride) has also been of very limited scope, perhaps due especially to the unusual insolubility of this polymer. Bengough and Norrish (59) observed an autocatalytic effect in the polymerization of this monomer which they ascribed to possible branching. Cotman (60) carried out some extensive studies in the use of infrared spectroscopy to detect branching in the polymer. He pointed out the difficulties involved in attempting to evaluate the infrared spectrum of this polymer, and attempted instead to convert the poly(vinyl chloride) to a polyethylene type by reductive hydrogenation, with chlorine removal. This process converts the chlorine substituted chain carbons into methylene groups, while at the same time changing any terminal chloromethyl groups into methyl groups. Endgroups of the chloromethyl type can be expected to form either through chain termination by disproportionation or through chain transfer (hydrogen abstraction). A maximum of one chloromethyl endgroup for every two chains can be expected in the absence of branching, hence any excess of such end groups can be ascribed to branching.

Cotman (60) actually found that poly(vinyl chloride), after reductive hydrogenation, showed a methyl group content ranging from 4×10^{-3} CH_3 groups per CH_2 group, up to a value of 11×10^{-3} for the ratio, depending on the molecular weight. This corresponds to 9–20 branches per chain, with the higher molecular weights obviously containing the greater number of branches. From these results, the molecular weight per branch point falls in the range of 3000–7600, i.e., a branch for every 40–100 chain units.

Bier and Krämer (61) attempted to use another approach in determining the extent of branching. They examined the relations between intrinsic viscosity and molecular weight of fractions of poly(vinyl chloride) prepared in an emulsion system to different conversions, but found that the high conversion polymers showed a higher viscosity for a given molecular weight, instead of lower, as would be expected from a branched polymer. They ascribed these anomalous results to the difficulties involved in fractionation of this polymer. These authors (62) also attempted to confirm Cotman's results, by reducing the polymer with lithium aluminum hydride and measuring the methyl group content. They obtained a value of about 8 branches per 1000 monomer units, which is somewhat lower than the lowest value quoted by Cotman.

e. *Acrylonitrile*

Very little information is available concerning the extent of branching in polyacrylonitrile, undoubtedly due to the well-known insolubility and intractability of the polymer. For example, kinetic studies in this case are very difficult, since the polymer is insoluble in its own monomer.

Shibukawa and Nakaguchi (63) studied the molecular weight distribution of the polymer formed in the aqueous solution and bulk polymerization of acrylonitrile. They also measured the Huggins constant k' of this polymer. However, their conclusions concerning any branching are rather indefinite.

Bensasson and Bernas (64) carried out the polymerization of this monomer by Co^{60} irradiation and noted an after-effect. The polymer obtained during this after-effect showed a lower intrinsic viscosity for a given molecular weight, and also a higher value for the Huggins constant k' which was taken to indicate the occurrence of branching. However, no quantitative estimation of its extent was given.

Peebles (65) probably carried out the most comprehensive study on the structure of polyacrylonitrile. He measured the molecular weight of this polymer in dimethylformamide solution, using intrinsic viscosity, osmotic pressure, light-scattering, and ultracentrifuge methods. He also included some acrylonitrile–vinyl acetate copolymers, containing less than 10% vinyl acetate. In this work, he found that the logarithmic plot of intrinsic viscosity against molecular weight was linear up to an $[\eta]$ value of 3.0 but showed a downward curvature beyond that point, indicating the existence of branched polymer at the higher molecular weights. He also found the presence of some microgel, which could not be considered as possible microcrystals, since it could be broken up by vigorous solution methods and did not reform on cooling. The occurrence of branching and possibly cross-linking in this polymer was postulated as taking place by polymerization through the nitrile groups. It was pointed out by the author that, for the polymer in question, the reaction of one nitrile group in 700 would be sufficient to form gel.

4. Branching in 1,3-Dienes

Unlike the monovinyl monomers, the 1,3-dienes are "bifunctional," i.e., they offer two separate possibilities of addition polymerization. Whether the primary polymerization reaction leads to a 1,4 or a 1,2 addition, the resulting polymer chain still has one double bond in each chain unit, presumably capable of being further attacked by a growing polymer chain. Hence these monomers possess the special feature of being capable of forming three-dimensional networks or gel polymers. This can, of course, be considered as a form of branching, prior to the actual formation of the infinite network, although the kinetic analysis of these systems tells us that no chains can become highly branched, due to the rapid nature of formation of networks. The main effect is a distortion of the molecular weight distribution toward higher molecular weight (66).

Aside from this "bifunctional" polymerization, however, there is still the possibility of the usual polymer transfer reaction, especially due to the expected reactivity of the allylic hydrogen in the polymer chain. This should lead to the same type ot branching found in the vinyl monomers.

However, it becomes obvious that it would be difficult if not impossible to distinguish between the branching caused by the two different reactions possible for the polydienes.

Actually, Flory (67) was the first to suggest a simple kinetic treatment for the reaction of growing chains with polymer double bonds in the free radical polymerization of the dienes. In this treatment, the system is considered to involve a "copolymerization" of polymer and monomer double bonds, and the density of crosslinks (formed by attack on polymer double bonds) is then related to the gel point by the well-known statistics of network formation (2). On the basis of this treatment, Flory arrived at the following relation between the frequency of crosslinks and the extent of polymerization:

$$\rho = -2K[1 + \ln(1 - \alpha)/\alpha] \tag{9}$$

where ρ is the fraction of crosslinked units in the polymer, α is the degree of conversion of monomer to polymer, K is the relative crosslinking rate constant ($= k_x/k_p$, where k_x and k_p are the rate constants for crosslink formation and propagation, respectively).

The experimental application of this treatment was carried out by Morton and Salatiello (68), who modified eq. (9) in order to apply it to the case of emulsion polymerization, and developed the following relation:

$$\rho = 2K/m \tag{10}$$

where m is the monomer/polymer ratio (weight) in latex particles.

Using this approach, they obtained values for ρ (at the gel point) in the case of butadiene (68,69) at various temperatures, as follows: at 50°C., $\rho = 3 \times 10^{-4}$; at 0°C., $\rho = 5 \times 10^{-5}$.

In other words, at 50°C., the polybutadiene would have about one branch for every 3000 units, at incipient gelation.

From this work it was also possible to calculate the value of K, the relative crosslinking rate constant, i.e., the relative rate of attack on polymer double bonds versus monomer double bonds. Thus, at 50°C. the K value for butadiene turns out to be about 1.3×10^{-4} and the activation energy difference $E_x - E_p$ is about 7.5 kcal./mole.

In later work by Morton and Piirma (70) and Morton and Gibbs (71), similar values were obtained for two other dienes, viz., isoprene and 2,3-dimethylbutadiene (DMBD). All the values are listed for comparison in Table X-1. Thus it can be seen that the double bonds in polyisoprene and polydimethylbutadiene are much less reactive than in polybutadiene, which is perhaps not surprising in view of the presence of the methyl substituents. The consistency of these data, which are based on a crosslinking reaction of the polymer double bonds, and ignore any branching caused by a transfer reaction with the polymer, indicates that the latter is much less important than the former.

In addition to the above kinetic approach, various other attempts have been made to determine the extent of branching, all of these being restricted to butadiene polymers. Thus Johnson and Wolfangel (72) determined the relation between intrinsic viscosity and molecular weight for polybutadienes

TABLE X-1
Crosslinking Data for 1,3-Dienes[a]

Monomer	Temp., °C.	ρ (at gel point) $\times 10^4$	$K \times 10^4$
Butadiene	40	2.4	1.0
	60	4.6	2.0
Isoprene	60	0.69	0.34
	70	0.93	0.43
DMBD	70	0.29	0.12
	80	0.37	0.15

[a] Taken from refs. 68, 70, and 71.

prepared by emulsion polymerization at various temperatures. They found that the exponent a in this equation decreased with increasing polymerization temperature, which they ascribed to increased branching at the higher temperatures. Cragg and Fern (73) determined the Huggins constant k' from solution viscosities on fractions of butadiene–styrene copolymers prepared at different temperatures, and showed that these k' values increased with polymerization temperature, indicating a greater degree of branching.

None of the above two methods yielded any quantitative data on the actual extent of branching. Hayes (74) attempted to measure the extent of transfer between growing chains and polymer in the emulsion polymerization of butadiene. He actually determined the amount of new polybutadiene grafted onto an insoluble, crosslinked polybutadiene (in latex). He also determined the length of such "branches" by measuring the intrinsic viscosity of the soluble polybutadiene formed, assuming that the average size of the branches and the soluble chains would be equal. The polymer transfer constant thus obtained was 1.1×10^{-3} at 50°C., or one branch for every 800 units. However, this relatively high value is subject to considerable doubt, since it is based exclusively on a transfer reaction of the polymer, and entirely ignores the possibility of a direct, crosslinking attack on the polymer double bonds. It is obvious that such a reaction would markedly affect these measurements, since it does not lead to formation of any soluble polymer, whereas the transfer reaction presumably should.

Drysdale and Marvel (75) generally confirmed the results of Morton and Salatiello (68) on polybutadiene. They carried out the emulsion polymerization in presence of various model compounds like biallyl, hexane, 3-methyl-1-butene, and isopentane, in order to note any possible chain transfer with active allylic hydrogen in these compounds. Since they found no measurable transfer occurred, they assumed that similar structures in the polymer would also be inactive. They also measured the effect of varying the amount and type of initiator on the crosslinking reaction and found that this was not a factor, i.e., direct attack on the polymer by the initiator is unimportant.

Pollock, Elyash, and DeWitt (76) attempted to determine the extent of branching in emulsion polybutadiene by measuring the unperturbed chain dimensions in solution, and applying the Zimm-Stockmayer (20) treatment. As expected, they found a falling off in the $[\eta]$ values at the higher molecular weights, indicating branching. Their calculations, based on a tetrafunctional branch point (such as would be formed from a crosslinking attack on the polymer), yielded ρ values (fraction of branched units in the polymer) of 1.5×10^{-4} at 50°C. and 1.0×10^{-4} at 5°C. Considering the difference in methods used, these values are in remarkably good agreement with the kinetic values of Morton and Salatiello (68). They certainly tend to corroborate the view that the main cause of branching in polybutadiene is a crosslinking reaction rather than transfer to polymer.

Finally, Cleland (77) applied the Zimm-Stockmayer approach to the study of the structure of Alfin polybutadiene. He measured the molecular weight of the polymer by light scattering, obtaining values for the unfractionated polymer varying from 5 to 20 million, and determined the relation between intrinsic viscosity and molecular weight of polymer fractions. Assuming tetrafunctional branch points, he obtained ρ values (fraction of branched units in the chain) varying from 10^{-5} to 10^{-4}, with the lower values applying to polymers made at higher conversions. Hence it is obvious that this type of polybutadiene is considerably less crosslinked than the emulsion polymer and thus can attain remarkably high molecular weight without forming insoluble networks.

5. Summary

For the sake of convenience, all the available transfer constants for reactions involving radical chains and their own polymers are listed in Table X-2. This provides some idea of the extent of branching that may be expected in vinyl polymers. The relative crosslinking rate constants for the dienes, which also provide a measure of the branching frequency, have already been listed in Table X-1.

TABLE X-2
Polymeric Transfer Constants

Polymer	Transfer constant $k_{trP}/k_p \times 10^4$	$E_{trP} - E_p$, kcal./mole	Reference
Poly(vinyl acetate)	31 (40°C.)	5.0	47
	32 (40°C.)	4.0	48
Polystyrene	13 (50°C.)	—	51
	<5 (130°C.)	—	53
	1.9 (50°C.)	—	54
	1.9 ± 0.5 (60°C.)	—	56
	1.8 (129°C.)	—	57
Poly(methyl methacrylate)	1.5 (50°C.)	—	51,58
	2.1 (60°C.)	1.9	53

The author wishes to express his appreciation to Dr. I. Piirma for her kind assistance in carrying out much of the literature survey for this section.

B. GRAFT COPOLYMERIZATION

NORMAN G. GAYLORD and FRANK S. ANG

Gaylord Associates, Inc.

The chemical structure of the side chain which results from self-branching in polymerization is limited by the nature of the monomers in the polymerization charge. Thus, both addition and condensation polymerization yield branches which are similar in nature to the main chain, e.g., polystyrene branches on a polystyrene backbone or polyester branches on an alkyd resin.

The technique of graft copolymerization permits tailor-making of the polymer structure so that branches may be entirely different from the backbone. The typical graft copolymer is represented as

```
  B    B         B
  .    .         .
  .    .         .
  .    .         .
  .    .         .
  .    .         .
  B    B         B
  |    |         |
—A.....A.....A.....A.....A—
```

where the macromolecule consists of a backbone or trunk of poly-A with branches of poly-B. The backbone may be either an addition or a condensation polymer, as may the branches. Thus, polyethylene branches (from addition polymerization) or poly(ethylene oxide) branches (from ring-opening polymerization) may be affixed to a poly(vinyl acetate) addition polymer backbone, or to a poly(hexamethylene adipamide) condensation polymer backbone.

The typical graft copolymer represented above is actually a segmented polymer containing sequences of repeating units of varying length. An isomeric segmented structure is the so-called block copolymer in which the segments occur in an overall linear structure in contrast to the branch structure obtained in graft copolymerization. The typical block copolymer structure is represented as

A........AB........BA........A

In this type of structure the length of the uninterrupted stretches may range from a few to more than 100 monomeric units. Where very large blocks are present, the properties may be similar to a mechanical mixture of the homopolymers poly-A and poly-B.

It has become customary for block and graft polymers to be grouped together; in fact, a number of recent reviews and books on the subject have been so titled (78–81). This is due to the fact that both types of polymers are generally prepared from preformed polymeric structures even though in many cases the method of synthesis will vary. In this discussion both areas, i.e., block and graft copolymers, will be considered. Although block copolymerization yielding its linear structure is obviously not a branching technique, it is a chain extending technique and very loosely can then be considered to yield an appendage upon the original structure; in this case the appendage continues in the same direction. A great number of the reactions discussed in other chapters in this volume lead to block and graft copolymers. Consequently such reactions will not be discussed in detail but will only be mentioned in context.

Since graft copolymerization involves the polymerization of monomers onto a polymer backbone, the various methods of accomplishing polymerization reactions can be utilized for the synthesis of graft copolymers. Thus, addition polymerization reactions of vinyl monomers initiated by free radical or ionic means and condensation or ring-opening polymerization reactions of compounds containing reactive functional groups are suitable tools.

1. Free Radical-Initiated Graft Copolymerization of Vinyl Monomers

Two general methods have been utilized for the preparation of graft copolymers from vinyl monomers: (*a*) polymerization of a monomer in the presence of a polymer so that the growth of branches is initiated by chain transfer, and (*b*) polymerization of a monomer in the presence of a polymer containing reactive groups or positions which are capable of being activated to initiate the growth of side chains.

a. Initiation by Chain Transfer

The process of chain transfer wherein a free radical, such as in a growing chain or arising from the decomposition of a polymerization catalyst, abstracts an atom such as hydrogen from a polymer chain to yield a free radical site for the growth of branches, is a fairly well recognized phenomenon. This reaction is considered to be responsible for the production of branched polymers in the polymerization of monomers such as ethylene, vinyl acetate, vinyl chloride, and acrylic esters, as discussed in the previous section.

(11)

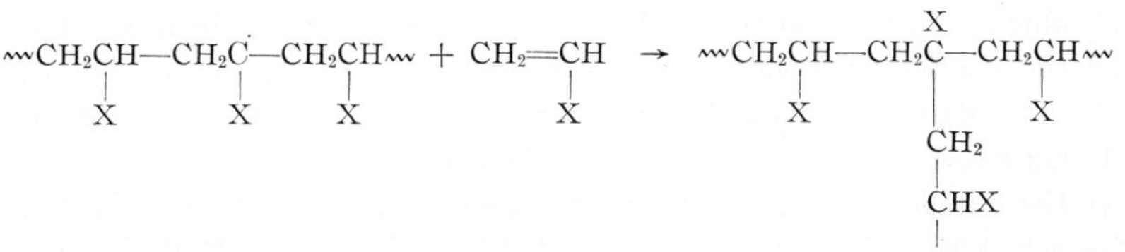

(12)

The occurrence of a reaction between a monomer and a dead polymer chain has been confirmed by the use of radioactive tracer techniques. Thus, monomeric styrene labeled with carbon-14 has been polymerized in the presence of inactive polystyrene to yield polystyrene containing branches derived from the active monomer. Similarly, unlabeled vinyl acetate monomer has been polymerized in the presence of labeled poly(vinyl acetate) to yield an active polymer in which the sidechains are inactive (82).

In order to produce a graft copolymer by the chain transfer mechanism it is obviously necessary to have three components present in the system, i.e., a polymerizable monomer, a polymer chain upon which it is desired to graft this monomer as a branch, and a free radical source or catalyst which is capable of abstracting an atom from the polymer to initiate the chain reaction. The success of the chain transfer method in producing graft copolymers is directly dependent upon the structures of the monomer, the polymer, and the catalyst.

The nature of the catalyst is important in that it serves two functions. On the one hand, it may initiate the polymerization of the polymerizable monomer to yield a radical species which is now capable of attacking the original polymer to produce a site for grafting, i.e., to produce a free radical attached to the trunk. Alternatively, the initiator may yield a radical which is directly responsible for graft copolymerization in that the radical derived from this initiator, in lieu of polymerizing monomer, directly attacks the backbone of the original polymer which is present in the system, and abstracts the hydrogen or other atom to produce the site for a grafting reaction.

Regardless of the origin of the site on the backbone of the polymer, the ability of this site to participate in a grafting reaction is dependent upon its reactivity. Whether the radical is highly stabilized and as such has little tendency to add monomer from the reaction system or whether it is highly reactive and hence will readily add such monomer is very important. Therefore, the structure of the original polymer is very significant in leading to successful graft copolymerization by the chain transfer mechanism.

The nature of the monomer in the system becomes important due to the problem of relative reactivity ratios in a copolymerization system. The radical which is formed on the backbone of the polymer may be unreactive toward the particular monomer which is present in the system. Consequently, not all monomers can be grafted on all polymeric backbones nor can all polymeric backbones necessarily be grafted with the same monomer.

Since the amount of catalyst normally added to a polymerization system is extremely low and is on the order of 1–5%, it is obvious that if this is the sole source for the initiation of radical sites on the backbone of the polymer by way of the chain transfer reaction, very few branches can be expected to be produced. For the attachment of many branches to the polymer backbone by graft copolymerization, it is necessary that growing polymer chains abstract the hydrogen atoms to produce the new sites. The growing chain which is appended to the original polymer must abstract a hydrogen from another backbone so that while the branch is terminated, it is at the same time initiating a branch site on the second polymeric backbone. The success of the chain transfer method to produce graft copolymers, therefore, depends upon the frequency of the chain transfer step as compared with the normal propagation step. This will of course vary from monomer to monomer and from polymeric backbone to polymeric backbone.

Attempts to prepare graft copolymers by the chain transfer method, where the monomer to be grafted is different from the monomer in the polymeric backbone, generally result in the formation of a heterogeneous mixture consisting of pure poly-B, resulting from homopolymerization of the second monomer, pure poly-A, from the original polymer which was not attacked by free radicals and therefore did not participate in the grafting reaction, and the graft copolymer containing branches of poly-B growing out of the backbone of poly-A. The mixture of polymers can generally be separated into the individual components by solvent extraction due to the different solubilities of the homopolymers and the graft copolymer. However, a clean fractionation and purification of the graft copolymer is not always possible.

The relative amounts of homopolymers and graft copolymer are, as indicated earlier, dependent upon the nature of the polymer, monomer and catalyst. Although some polymerizing systems are sensitive to the nature of the initiator, other systems may be insensitive (83). Thus, it has been shown that the polymerization of methyl methacrylate in the presence of polystyrene yields appreciable amounts of graft copolymer if the reaction is initiated with benzoyl peroxide while the use of azobisisobutyronitrile or di-*tert*-butyl peroxide yields significantly less graft copolymer. A similar result has been noted in the grafting reactions on rubber wherein benzoyl peroxide has been found to be an effective graft initiator while the azo compound fails to yield any graft copolymer (84). In contrast, the polymerization of vinyl acetate in the presence of poly(methyl methacrylate) gives appreciable quantities of pure graft copolymer independent of the nature of the initiator (83). Thus, the relative reactivities of the primary radicals, that is, the radicals which are produced from the initiator, for transfer and propagation reactions may differ considerably as a function of their origin.

The site of the growth of a branch will vary with the point of attack of the free radical on the polymer chain. This is illustrated by the results obtained in grafting side chains of polyethylene onto a backbone of poly-(vinyl acetate) (85). The polymerization of ethylene in the presence of poly(vinyl acetate), with diethyl peroxide as the catalyst in solution in benzene, gave a modified poly(vinyl acetate) which after alkaline methanolysis yielded mixtures of long-chain fatty acids and ethylene-modified poly(vinyl alcohol). The hydrolysis to long-chain fatty acids shows that chain transfer occurs on the acetoxy group of poly(vinyl acetate) to initiate the growth of polyethylene chains. The formation of ethylene-modified poly(vinyl alcohol) shows that chain transfer, and subsequent growth of polyethylene chains, occurs on the backbone carbon of poly(vinyl acetate). These reactions are summarized in eq. (13).

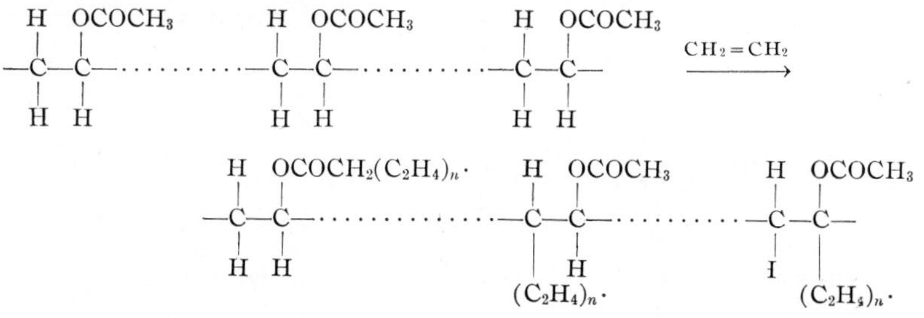

(13)

In addition to hydrogen atoms, chlorine atoms may be used as the chain transfer points. Thus, vinyl acetate (VAc) has been polymerized in the presence of a styrene–vinylidene chloride copolymer to yield a copolymer with poly(vinyl acetate) as branches, as shown in eq. (14). Similarly,

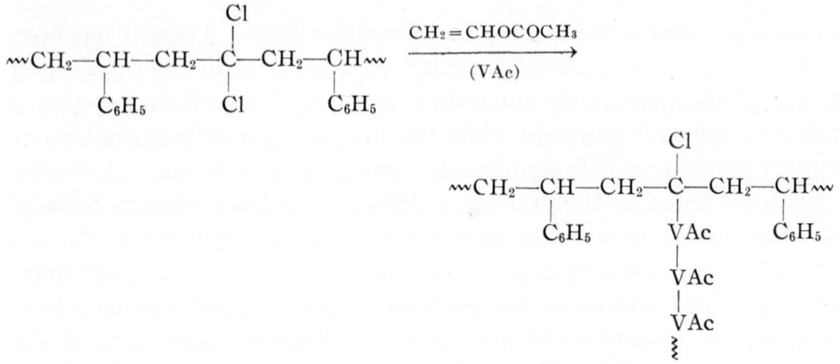

(14)

styrene has been polymerized in the presence of a copolymer of a maleic ester and vinyl trichloroacetate to give a copolymer with side chains of polystyrene (86).

The polymerization of vinyl benzoate is characterized by the formation of branched polymers arising from chain transfer reactions on the aromatic nucleus. This nuclear reactivity has been used in the grafting copolymerization of methyl methacrylate and vinyl acetate on the aromatic nuclei of poly(vinyl benzoate) by heating the monomer and poly(vinyl benzoate) in the presence of benzoyl peroxide (87), as shown in eq. (15).

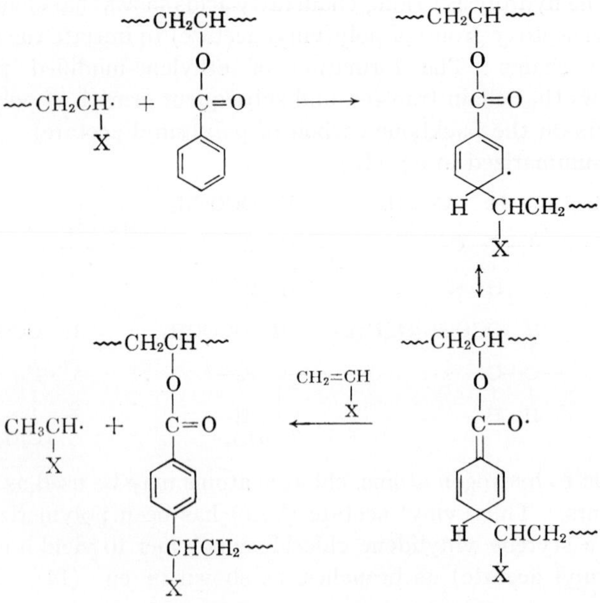

(15)

Sites which are particularly susceptible to chain transfer may be introduced into the structure of the polymeric backbone either during the synthesis or by post reaction. The polyester prepared by condensation of pentaerythritol dibromide and adipic acid is a polymer containing abstractable bromine atoms. Polymerization of styrene in the presence of this polyester yields a graft copolymer by chain transfer, as indicated in eq. (16). Analytical data suggest that the graft contains one polystyrene

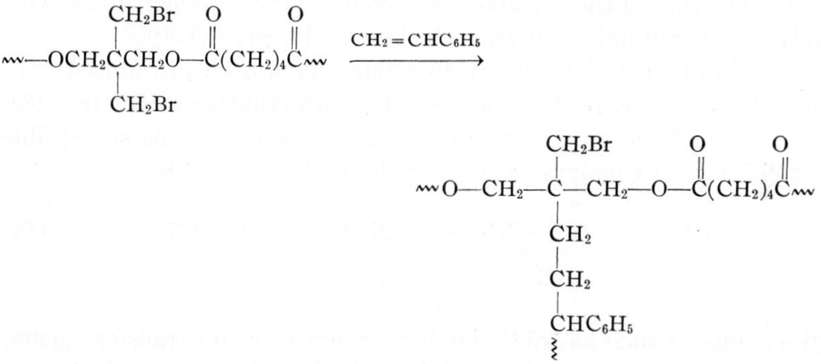

(16)

chain of DP 600 for every 23,000 ester units (88).

Treatment of cellulose with a mixture of acetic and 11-bromoundecanoic acids yields a mixed cellulose ester containing bromine atoms on the side chain. The polymerization of styrene in the presence of this ester yields a graft copolymer due to the abstraction of the bromine atom and the growth of polystyrene on the resultant free radical.

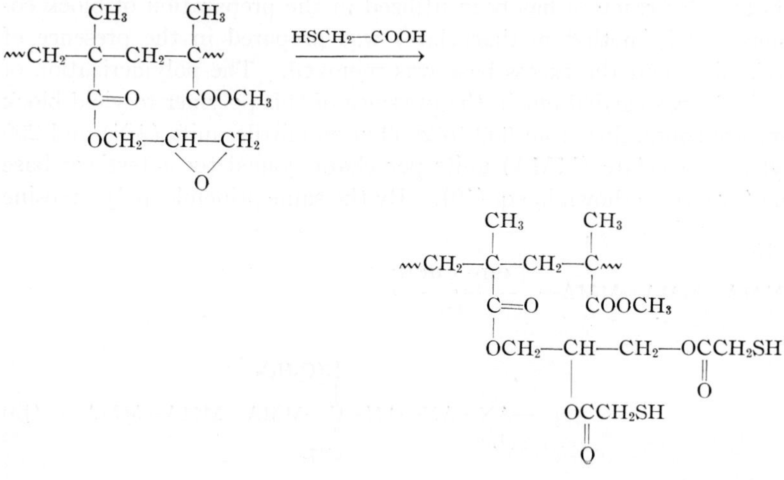

(17)

The highly susceptible mercaptan group has been utilized in the synthesis of graft copolymers via the post reaction technique. Thus, copolymerization of methyl methacrylate with a few mole-% of glycidyl methacrylate yields a copolymer containing pendant epoxy groups. Reaction of this polymer with thioglycolic acid or hydrogen sulfide yields a polymer containing pendant mercapto groups (eq. 17). The free radical polymerization of a monomer such as styrene or an acrylic or methacrylic ester in the presence of this backbone results in graft copolymerization with relatively minor contamination from the homopolymers (89,90).

In an analogous reaction, mercapto groups have been introduced onto a cellulose backbone by reaction of the latter with ethylene sulfide (eq. 18). Polymerization of the vinyl monomer in the presence of this susceptible polymer yields graft copolymers on the cellulose backbone (91).

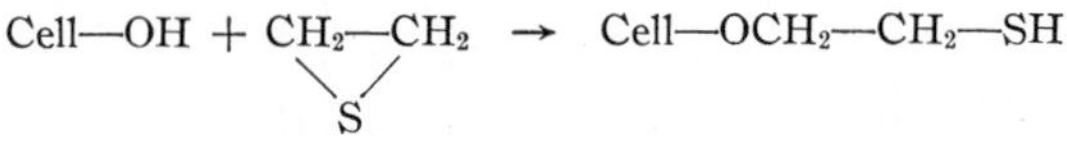
(18)

Tertiary amines such as triethylamine are active chain transfer agents, the transfer reaction apparently involving a hydrogen atom attached to an α carbon atom. The resultant radical is capable of reacting with a monomer to yield a polymer containing a basic residue. When a polymerization is carried out in the presence of a sufficiently high concentration of tertiary base, each polymer chain carries the terminal base residue. By virtue of this residue the polymer can act as a transfer agent in a second polymerization.

This transfer reaction has been utilized in the preparation of block copolymers. Poly(methyl methacrylate) was prepared in the presence of triethylamine, and the excess base was removed. The polymerization of acrylonitrile was carried out in the presence of this polymer to yield block copolymers containing from 600 to 2000 acrylonitrile units (AN) and 200 methyl methacrylate (MMA) units per chain, joined by a tertiary base residue (92,93), as shown in eq. (19). By the same principle, polysarcosine

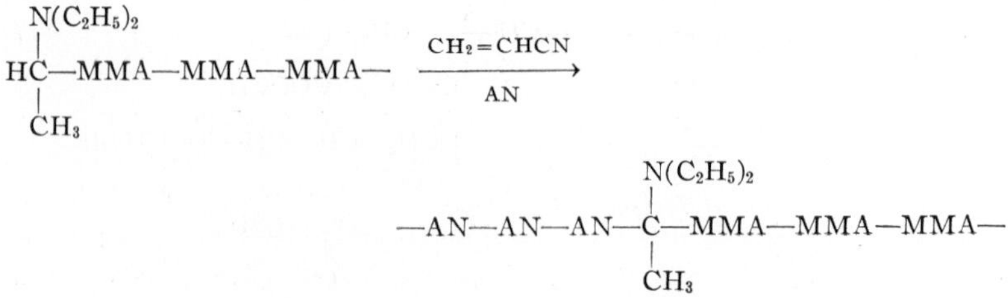

(19)

dimethylamide was used as the backbone in the preparation of block copolymers with acrylonitrile (94).

Although a polymer containing double bonds, e.g., rubber or a butadiene copolymer, possesses hydrogen or other atoms capable of being abstracted by a free radical to produce, by chain transfer, a free radical located on the polymeric chain, the double bond presents also a site for addition copolymerization. Thus, in addition to the grafting of branches initiated from the highly susceptible allylic position or any other carbon atom on the chain, branches can grow by the addition of a free radical across the double bond followed by reaction with monomeric material. Therefore, grafting on an unsaturated backbone polymer is more complex than simple initiation by chain transfer and will be discussed separately in a later section.

Graft copolymerization has been carried out in bulk, i.e., by dissolving the polymer and catalyst in the monomer, in solution, and in emulsion. Grafting in either bulk or solution has been carried out with benzoyl peroxide, azobisisobutyronitrile, or heat as the catalyst. By this method the following graft copolymers have been prepared: *p*-chlorostyrene on poly(methyl acrylate); methyl methacrylate, styrene, vinyl acetate, and vinyl chloride on poly(methyl methacrylate); and methyl methacrylate on polystyrene. Attempts to graft vinyl acetate on polystyrene and methyl methacrylate on poly(vinyl acetate) or poly(vinyl chloride) have been unsuccessful by this method. These results have been interpreted as indicating that after the formation of a macroradical by chain transfer, the addition of monomer depends upon the reactivity and polarity of the monomer and consequently upon the stability of the derived radical.

Grafted acrylonitrile copolymers have been prepared by polymerizing acrylonitrile in solution in water or acetonitrile or in emulsion in the presence of preformed polymers containing amide groups, e.g., acrylamides, itaconamides, maleamides, maleamates, fumaramates, and citraconamates. Various water-soluble polymers have been used as the backbone for acrylonitrile grafting, e.g., partially hydrolyzed poly(vinyl acetate), polymethacrylamide, poly(acrylic acid), polyvinylpyrrolidone, poly(ethylene oxide), gelatin, starch, starch methyl ether, and cellulose methyl ether.

In the preparation of graft copolymers by emulsion polymerization, the monomer and the catalyst, generally potassium persulfate, are added without additional emulsifier to a latex containing the polymeric backbone. The omission of additional emulsifier is a critical factor since emulsifier would favor the homopolymerization of the monomer rather than the graft copolymerization. Although the patent literature contains numerous reports of the preparation of graft copolymers by the emulsion technique, the addition of emulsifier along with the second monomer in many of these cases indicates that a mixture of the original latex polymer and a homopolymer from the second monomer was probably formed.

A quantitative study of emulsion graft copolymerization has shown that whereas effective grafting occurs with vinyl acetate on poly(vinyl chloride) and polyacrylonitrile, very little grafting occurs with vinyl acetate or vinyl chloride on polystyrene, vinyl chloride or styrene on poly(vinyl acetate), and styrene on poly(vinyl chloride). The efficiency of grafting decreases with the addition of dodecyl mercaptan or a decrease in the temperature of polymerization. This supports a transfer mechanism, since a strong transfer agent competes with the polymer for the free radicals and a decrease in temperature reduces the tendency for chain transfer. The efficiency of grafting increases with an increase in persulfate concentration, indicating that the transfer reaction with the polymer may proceed more rapidly with the free radical derived from the catalyst than with the growing polymeric chain. However, a very sharp decrease in efficiency occurs when a persulfate–bisulfite catalyst–activator system is used in place of persulfate alone. Retardation occurs in polymerizations involving vinyl acetate and vinyl chloride with polystyrene (95).

Styrene–butadiene graft copolymers have been prepared by polymerizing styrene in aqueous emulsion until at least 90% of the styrene was converted to polystyrene, then adding butadiene and completing the polymerization.

Suspension polymerization of vinyl acetate is generally carried out with poly(vinyl alcohol) as a suspension stabilizer. Considerable grafting of vinyl acetate upon poly(vinyl alcohol) occurs in this process.

b. Initiation by Growing Chain Radicals

Block copolymers of butyl acrylate–styrene and acrylonitrile–styrene have been prepared in a flow system. Butyl acrylate monomer, containing 1-azo-bis-1-cyanocyclohexane as a photosensitive initiator, was subjected to very intense ultraviolet radiation while streaming rapidly through a capillary. The monomer issuing from the capillary contained a high concentration of free radicals and on entering a large excess of styrene monomer initiated its polymerization. Thus, blocks of polystyrene were added on the poly(butyl acrylate). Similarly, acrylonitrile monomer was irradiated in a capillary and made to flow into styrene monomer to produce polyacrylonitrile containing blocks of polystyrene (96).

The tendency for long-lived radicals to form in the vapor-phase polymerization of both methyl methacrylate and chloroprene has been utilized in the preparation of what has been referred to as a multilayer polymer sandwich but which was probably a block copolymer (97,98). A layer of poly-(methyl methacrylate) was laid down on the walls of a reaction vessel. The system was freed of methyl methacrylate vapor and filled with chloroprene. The latter polymerized spontaneously, presumably over the original layer. By repeated alternation of monomers a macromolecular sandwich was formed. Methyl isopropenyl ketone was copolymerized with poly(methyl methacrylate) by the same technique.

Block copolymers have been prepared *in situ* by using a mixture of a water-soluble and an oil-soluble monomer (99,100). Acrylic acid or methacrylic acid was dissolved in water, and styrene was emulsified in the water phase. With a persulfate catalyst or a hydrogen peroxide–ferrous sulfate mixture, polymerization of the acid occurred in the water phase until the growing chain diffused into a micelle containing styrene monomer, whereby styrene units grew on the poly(acrylic acid) chains to form a block copolymer.

The trapped radicals remaining on polymer particles when an emulsion polymerization is taken to completion have been used to initiate the growth of a block of polymer derived from an added monomer. Thus, a block of polyacrylonitrile has been grown on poly(vinyl chloride), poly(vinylidene chloride), and their copolymers by adding monomeric acrylonitrile to a just completed emulsion polymerization of these monomers (101). Similarly, blocks of poly(methyl methacrylate) have been grown on emulsion-polymerized poly(vinyl acetate) (102).

c. *Addition Copolymerization and/or Chain Transfer to Unsaturated Polymer*

An unsaturated polymer presents two separate sites for the growth of a branch or graft. The carbon atoms alpha to the double bond are particularly reactive and susceptible to attack by a free radical and by chain transfer to yield sites for grafting. In addition, the double bond can copolymerize with a vinyl monomer and thus serve as the site for growth of branches. Crosslinking and gelation result from the incorporation of more than one double bond in a given branch. Crosslinking may also occur by the coupling of two branches, on different macromolecular backbones, particularly in the case of styrene monomer whose polymerization terminates by combination.

A soluble polymer containing residual double bonds on the sidechain has been obtained by copolymerizing methyl methacrylate with ethylidene dimethacrylate in solution in a 200:1 molar ratio, and carrying the reaction to less than 40% conversion. By polymerizing ethyl acrylate and styrene in the presence of this unsaturated methyl methacrylate copolymer, graft copolymers were obtained by addition copolymerization (103), as shown in eq. (20).

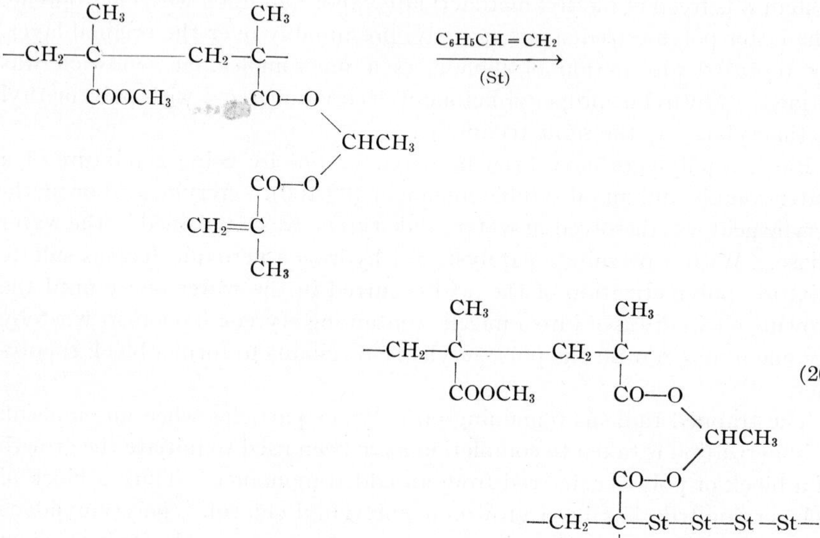

(20)

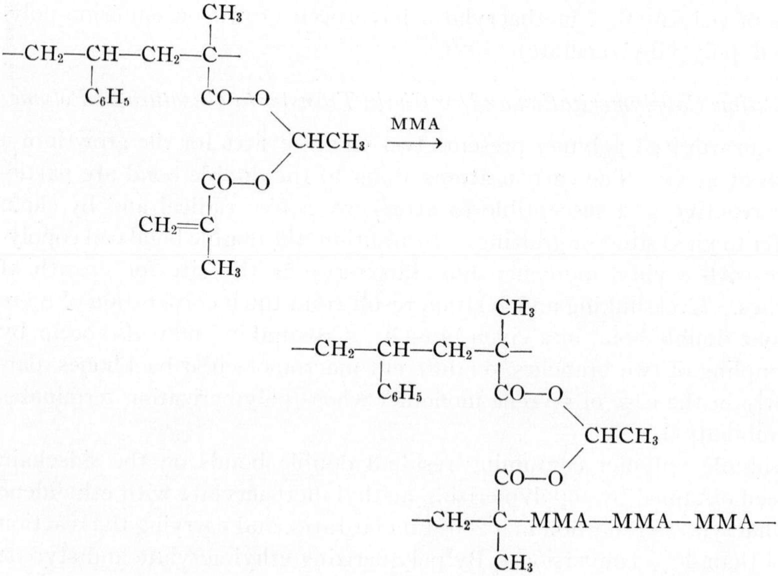

(21)

In a similar manner a soluble polymer has been prepared by the copolymerization of styrene and ethylidene dimethacrylate in a 200:1 molar ratio. A graft copolymer was prepared by the polymerization of methyl methacrylate in the presence of this unsaturated polymer, as shown in eq. (21).

The bromination of polystyrene with *N*-bromosuccinimide in the presence of benzoyl peroxide has given a polymer in which 61% of the styrene units were brominated on the backbone carbon chain. Treatment of a solution in benzene of the brominated polymer with sodium butylate gave a debrominated polystyrene containing structural units I, II, and III.

		Br
		|
—CH=C—	$—CH_2CH—$	$—CH_2C—$
|	|	|
C_6H_5	C_6H_5	C_6H_5
49.1%	39.1%	11.8%
(I)	(II)	(III)

Other proportions of these structures were obtained by decreasing the amount of bromination and varying the concentration of sodium butylate and the reaction temperature.

Vinyl acetate was grafted on the backbone of the debrominated polystyrene by refluxing a benzene solution of the monomer and polymer in the presence of benzoyl peroxide. In view of the previously mentioned unsuccessful attempts to graft vinyl acetate on polystyrene, it is probable that the successful grafting in this case was not due to the abstraction of bromine or hydrogen in structure II and III, respectively, but resulted from copolymerization of vinyl acetate and the double bond in the unsaturated polymer (104).

Grafting on various natural polymers has been carried out by incorporating unsaturated groups on the polymer. The reaction of starch with allyl chloride in the presence of alkali yields the unsaturated ether, allyl starch. The copolymerization of allyl starch with styrene in the presence of cumene hydroperoxide yields the graft copolymer, styrenated allyl starch. In order to reduce crosslinking only a few allyl groups are built onto the starch molecule.

Graft copolymers have been prepared in an analogous manner on a cellulosic backbone. Treatment of ethylcellulose with ethylene oxide followed by dehydration of the resultant hydroxyethyl derivative yields ethyl/vinylcellulose. Reaction of this unsaturated polymer with a maleic ester yields a graft copolymer. Ethyl/allylcellulose, prepared by reaction of ethylcellulose with an allylic halide, and the methacrylic and crotonic esters of cellulose can also be used as the polymeric backbone for the grafting operation.

Styrenated polyesters and alkyds and analogous products based on other vinyl monomers are representative of graft copolymers with commercial application. The polymeric backbones are prepared by the condensation of unsaturated dibasic acids and saturated glycols or saturated dibasic acids and unsaturated glycols. Among the unsaturated acids used as such or in the form of their anhydrides are maleic, fumaric, itaconic, mesaconic, and *cis*-3,6-endomethylene-Δ^4-tetrahydrophthalic acids (the adduct of cyclopentadiene and maleic anhydride). 1,4-Butenediol has been used as the unsaturated glycol. In addition to styrene, vinyl acetate, acrylic and methacrylic esters, vinyl toluene and allyl compounds have been used in this application. Mixtures of monomers such as styrene and methyl methacrylate have been used as well as various difunctional monomers such as divinylbenzene and diallyl phthalate. The most commonly used system involves the styrenation of a maleic polyester.

The reaction of styrene with a polyester can yield a linear polymer by addition of styrene to the terminal maleate groups, a crosslinked graft copolymer by the addition of styrene to internal maleate groups, and polystyrene by homopolymerization of monomeric styrene. The styrenated polyester undoubtedly contains a mixture of all these components.

The crosslinked graft copolymer results from the incorporation of a number of maleate groups in the styrene chain, as shown in IV. A crosslinked

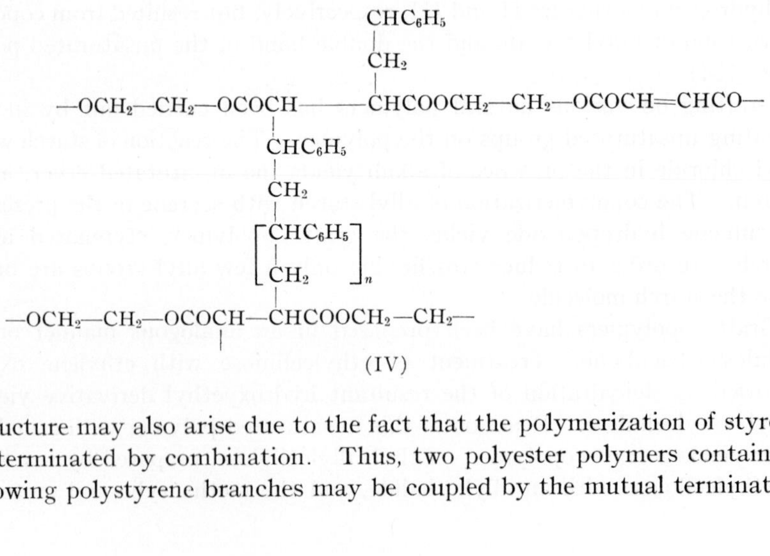

(IV)

structure may also arise due to the fact that the polymerization of styrene is terminated by combination. Thus, two polyester polymers containing growing polystyrene branches may be coupled by the mutual termination of the growing chains. Where methyl methacrylate is used as the vinyl monomer in the preparation of these resins, crosslinking results from the copolymerization of the methacrylate with the maleate groups. Since methyl methacrylate polymers are terminated by disproportionation rather than combination, the polyester–methacrylate copolymer probably contains numerous poly(methyl methacrylate) branches and corresponds to a true graft copolymer.

The use of a triol such as glycerol or trimethylolpropane in the preparation of a polyester permits the incorporation of sidechains in the polymer structure. In the presence of unsaturated monobasic acids derived from dehydrated castor oil, tung oil, linseed oil, soya oil, or cottonseed oil, the polyester contains unsaturated sidechains. The reaction of an unsaturated polyester or alkyd and a vinyl monomer such as styrene is analogous to the reaction of the maleic polyester to yield a crosslinked graft copolymer.

An epoxy or ethoxyline resin, prepared by the reaction of a bisphenol such as 2,2′-bis(*p*-hydroxyphenyl)propane and epichlorohydrin in the presence of a base, can be reacted with drying oil acids to yield polymers with unsaturated sidechains. The copolymerization of the ethoxyline resin esters with a vinyl monomer yields a crosslinked graft copolymer.

An interesting type of graft copolymer has been prepared by the emulsion polymerization of sulfur dioxide and an olefin, such as 1-butene, 2-butene, or 1-octene, in the presence of a liquid polybutadiene of low molecular weight with lithium nitrate as catalyst, as shown by V (105).

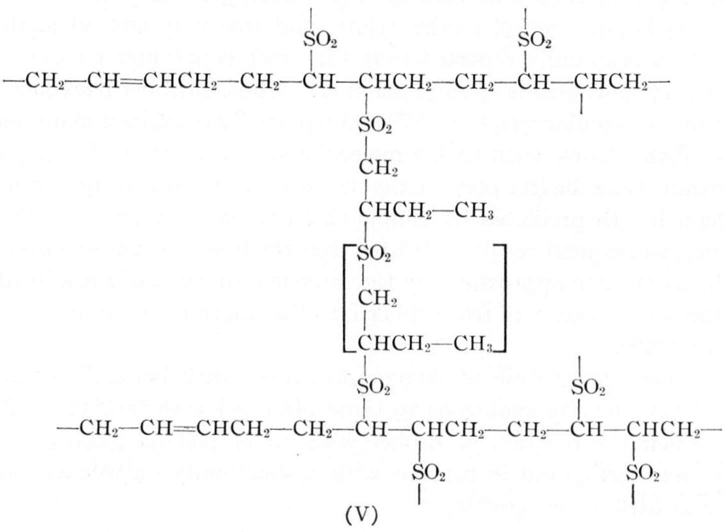

(V)

In the case of an unsaturated polymer such as rubber, polybutadiene, or a butadiene copolymer, graft copolymerization is not restricted to either initiation by chain transfer or addition across the double bond but apparently involves a combination of the two initiation sites or a hitherto uncharacterized mechanism.

Graft copolymerization on natural rubber has been carried out in bulk, for example, on a rubber mill, in solution, and in the latex (106,107).

Some of the earliest work on the reaction of a vinyl monomer and rubber involved maleic anhydride. Since the latter is capable of copolymerization but not homopolymerization, it is not possible to add more than one monomer unit for each site of attack on the rubber molecule. The product is therefore not a true graft copolymer wherein branches grow on the polymeric backbone but is more allied, at least at higher contents of maleic anhydride, to a block copolymer with the anhydride acting as a bridging unit between rubber molecules.

In the case of a vinyl monomer which is capable of homopolymerization, the configurations are somewhat more complex. The bridges between molecules of rubber can be of different lengths and the grafts may be true branches rather than bridges.

A quantitative study of the polymerization of methyl methacrylate and styrene in the presence of rubber has been carried out in benzene with benzoyl peroxide and azobisisobutyronitrile as catalysts (108). With peroxide catalysis, the total product in the case of methyl methacrylate consisted of a mixture of unmodified free rubber, graft polymer, i.e., rubber containing bound methyl methacrylate, and free poly(methyl methacrylate). It was initially reported that the graft copolymer contained numerous very short chains of vinyl polymer. Thus, a rubber backbone polymer with a molecular weight of 270,000 reportedly contained many methyl methacrylate chains, each with a molecular weight of approximately 5000. At the same time the free poly(methyl methacrylate) grew to approximately the chain length predicted by simple chain transfer theory, i.e., 185,000. However, subsequent results indicated that the free and grafted vinyl polymer chains grow to approximately the same length, the early results arising from the solubilization of free rubber into the fraction containing the graft polymer (109).

Graft copolymerization of styrene on rubber with benzoyl peroxide in benzene gave results analogous to those obtained with methyl methacrylate. When the reaction of rubber with either methyl methacrylate or styrene was carried out in benzene with azobisisobutyronitrile as catalyst, there was little or no grafting.

The literature contains numerous references to the polymerization of various vinyl monomers dispersed in natural rubber latex. In order that a reaction should take place between the monomer and rubber, a low proportion of surface-active stabilizer was used, and adequate time was allowed for diffusion of monomer into the rubber so that most of the polymerization occurred within the swollen rubber particles. In the presence of a large amount of dispersing agent much of the monomer polymerized independently of the rubber.

Persulfates, perborates, hydrogen peroxide, alkyl hydroperoxides, benzoyl peroxide, reduction-activated organic hydroperoxides, diazoaminobenzene, diazothioethers, and diazonium salts have been used to initiate polymerization of vinyl monomers in natural rubber latex. Reduction-activated hydroperoxides and hydroperoxides activated by polyethylene polyamine were especially suitable since they did not require deammoniation of the latex nor were they particularly sensitive to inhibition by oxygen.

For specific monomers certain initiators were more effective than others in promoting polymerization and/or grafting. Thus, the preferred initiator for the preparation of graft polymers from styrene or methyl methacrylate was a polyamine-activated hydroperoxide. A dihydroxyacetone–ferrous ion–*tert*-butyl hydroperoxide system was effective with acrylonitrile and vinylidene chloride (110).

Attempts to graft vinyl acetate on rubber have been unsuccessful due to the severe retardation of polymerization and the low reactivity of allyl radicals derived from the rubber toward this monomer. The presence of high proportions of emulsifying agent has permitted the polymerization of vinyl acetate in rubber latex to give a mixed product indistinguishable from that obtained by blending a rubber latex and a poly(vinyl acetate) emulsion.

Graft copolymers of styrene and methyl methacrylate with rubber can be readily compounded to give light-colored articles of high tensile strength. The rubber–methyl methacrylate polymer shows reduced hysteresis and outstanding resistance to flex cracking and fatigue. Higher methacrylates give less reinforcement as the size of the ester group is increased. Acrylates behave similarly to methacrylates in giving good yields of graft copolymers in the presence of rubber, but the products are different in that snappy, insoluble materials are obtained which appear to be quite heavily cross-linked.

When a divinyl monomer is added to the styrene or methyl methacrylate used in grafting, the modified polymers are hard and possess more tear resistance than the unmodified graft polymers.

Styrene, ethyl acrylate, methyl methacrylate, and various other vinyl monomers have been polymerized in the presence of gel-free butadiene polymers and copolymers in latex form to produce graft copolymers. If the homopolymers of the vinyl monomer were hard and resinous, e.g., styrene and methyl methacrylate, the grafts stiffened the polymers, and if the homopolymers were soft and elastic, e.g., ethyl acrylate, the grafts had little stiffening action. Methyl methacrylate grafted on a butadiene polymer or copolymer produced a greater degree of reinforcement than an equal weight of styrene, which in turn produced more reinforcement than either mono- or dichlorostyrene. An interesting aspect of the grafting process in this case is that there is little tendency to crosslink the primary chains; the graft polymer can be prepared free from gel.

Butadiene–styrene graft copolymers have been prepared by first polymerizing butadiene in emulsion and then adding styrene or a butadiene–styrene mixture and polymerizing in the same emulsion. Similarly butadiene has been grafted on a butadiene–styrene copolymer. Butadiene–acrylonitrile graft copolymers have been prepared in an analogous manner.

Divinylbenzene has been copolymerized with a liquid polybutadiene to yield a solid thermosetting resin. Polybutadiene, prepared by emulsion polymerization, has been hydrogenated to reduce residual unsaturation and treated with acrylonitrile in the presence of benzoyl peroxide to yield a graft copolymer.

Proliferous or "popcorn" polymerization is a special case of graft polymerization wherein a vinyl monomer polymerizes in the presence of a crosslinked, insoluble polymer containing double bonds. Chains of the vinyl polymer become grafted onto the pre-existing polymer.

The formation of popcorn or "cauliflower" polymer from vinyl monomers requires the presence in them of a crosslinking, i.e., bifunctional, monomer. The copolymerization of the vinyl monomer with a small amount of the bifunctional monomer, e.g., the copolymerization of styrene with 0.2–2% of divinylbenzene, may yield an insoluble polymer which occupies about three times the volume of the original liquid. Initially a few specks of solid polymer, containing residual unsaturation, appear. These specks of insoluble polymer imbibe styrene monomer which polymerizes so rapidly that substantially all of the monomer is consumed by the growth process before there is time for any appreciable quantity of normal polymer to form in the free liquid phase. The erratic expansion or "popping" of the insoluble polymer probably arises from the fact that the rate of formation of new insoluble polymer exceeds the rate at which it can attain swelling equilibrium with remaining monomer.

The product of a popcorn polymerization will grow and produce more popcorn polymer if it is placed in a monomer, not necessarily containing any crosslinking agent. The extent of this growth is determined by the amount of unsaturation in the seed polymer.

A variety of monomers in addition to styrene can be grafted onto the popcorn seed polymer. Different monomers can be grafted onto the same seed, provided that at the conclusion of each step sufficient unsaturation is left in the seed for more growth. Thus, popcorn polyisoprene has been grown in methyl methacrylate monomer and the resultant polymer grown in styrene.

d. Initiation by Rupture of Polymer Chains

Under the influence of applied shear polymer chains can be ruptured to produce free radicals at the ruptured ends of the chains. Block copolymers have been prepared by utilizing the radicals from chain rupture to initiate the polymerization of a monomer present in the polymer being subjected to the shearing forces. When a mixture of two polymers is subjected to applied shear, block copolymers are produced by the coupling of the free radicals at the ends of segments derived from the different polymers. In practice, the products are actually mixtures of block and graft copolymers, since chain transfer in some instances results in the location of the free radical in a nonterminal position on the polymer chain. Further, since styrene is the only monomer whose polymerization has been shown, to date, to terminate by combination, the termination of two radical-containing fragments should be by disproportionation to yield one polymer chain terminated by a double bond. The copolymerization of the latter with a free radical-containing fragment would yield a graft copolymer.

The shearing forces utilized in this degradation to produce free radicals include intensive shaking, high speed stirring, milling, kneading, grinding, pumping through gear and piston pumps, passage through filters and capillaries, and exposure to ultrasonic irradiation. Among the polymers which have been subjected to such degradation are addition polymers such as poly(vinyl chloride), polybutadiene, polystyrene, poly(methacrylic acid), and polyacrylamide, as well as cellulose esters and ethers, linear phenol–formaldehyde condensation products, and linear phthalic acid–glycol polyesters.

Mechanical agitation of the types described above has been used to prepare copolymers by the degradation of various synthetic and natural high polymers in the presence of monomers. The operability of this method has been shown by the increase in molecular weight when polystyrene, polymethacrylonitrile, and poly(methyl methacrylate) are agitated in this manner in the absence of air, in the presence of their respective monomers.

Numerous block copolymers prepared in this manner from vinyl polymers and monomers are given in Table X-3. In addition, mechanical treatment of ethyl cellulose in the presence of methyl methacrylate and of the polyamide, hexamethylene trimethyladipamide, in the presence of acrylonitrile, has yielded the corresponding block copolymers (111).

TABLE X-3
Various Block Copolymers Prepared by Mechanical Rupture of Polymer Chains in Presence of Monomers

Polymer unit	Monomer
Acrylamide	Acrylonitrile
Isobutylene	Acrylonitrile
	Styrene
	Vinylidene chloride
Methyl acrylate	Vinyl chloride
	Vinylidene chloride
Methacrylonitrile	Acrylonitrile
Methacrylonitrile-*co*-vinyl chloride	Methyl methacrylate
Methyl methacrylate	Methacrylonitrile
	Styrene
	Vinyl chloride
	Vinylidene chloride
	Acrylonitrile-*co*-vinylidene chloride
Methyl methacrylate-*co*-methacrylonitrile	Styrene
Styrene	Methyl methacrylate
	Vinylidene chloride
Vinyl acetate	Vinyl chloride
Vinyl chloride	Methyl vinyl ketone

Irradiation with ultrasonic waves results in the degradation of polymers and the production of free radicals. Thus, poly(methyl methacrylate), polystyrene, poly(methacrylic acid), and polyacrylamide have been shown to yield free radicals under the influence of ultrasonic waves.

The ultrasonic degradation of a polymer in the presence of a monomer has been used in the preparation of block copolymers. Although initial attempts to polymerize methyl methacrylate, styrene, and vinyl acetate in the presence of degrading poly(methyl methacrylate) were inconclusive, block and graft copolymers have been successfully prepared from polyacrylamide–acrylonitrile (112) and polymethacrylonitrile–acrylonitrile (111).

The simultaneous degradation of two different suitable polymers results in the formation of block copolymers by the cross-termination of the resultant radicals. Ultrasonic degradation of a mixture of polystyrene and poly(methyl methacrylate) has resulted in the preparation of a block copolymer which is probably of a sandwich type, since any copolymer formed can undergo further degradation (113).

When rubber is masticated on a mill, the applied shear ruptures the rubber molecules into free radicals. The radicals from chain rupture have been utilized to initiate the polymerization of a vinyl monomer present in the rubber being masticated, in the absence of oxygen (114,115).

Methyl methacrylate and styrene have been polymerized during cold mastication of natural rubber sheet to yield interpolymers which were soluble up to complete polymerization. Benzoyl peroxide and azobisisobutyronitrile did not increase the rate of polymerization except during the induction period.

Chloroprene, acrylic acid, methacrylic acid, methyl and ethyl acrylate, acrylonitrile, acrylamide, and divinylbenzene all polymerized on mastication with natural rubber to yield insoluble interpolymers. Vinyl acetate, which has been unsuccessfully utilized in the attempted preparation of graft copolymers on natural rubber by the chain transfer technique, has been unreactive in the mastication procedure.

The composition of the block copolymer formed by the mastication of rubber in the presence of a mixture of monomers is controlled by the monomer reactivity ratios. The approximately equal reactivity ratios in the methyl methacrylate–styrene system results in the formation of a block copolymer whose composition is approximately that of the initial monomer mixture. The large difference in monomer reactivity ratios in the chloroprene–methyl methacrylate system results in the separate polymerization of the two monomers.

The mastication of rubber in the presence of vinyl monomers actually produces a mixture of graft and block copolymers. The shear rupture of a rubber molecule would produce primary radicals and break the backbone chain. The reaction of these radicals with the vinyl monomer would produce block copolymers, as indicated in eq. (22). However, these primary radicals can be terminated partly by abstraction of α-methylenic hydrogen atoms from rubber molecules, as in eq. (23). The resultant radicals can react with monomer to form graft copolymers, as illustrated in eq. (24).

$$-\overset{\overset{\displaystyle CH_3}{|}}{C}=CH-CH_2\cdot + CH_2=CHX \rightarrow -\overset{\overset{\displaystyle CH_3}{|}}{C}=CH-CH_2-(CH_2CHX)_n- \quad (22)$$

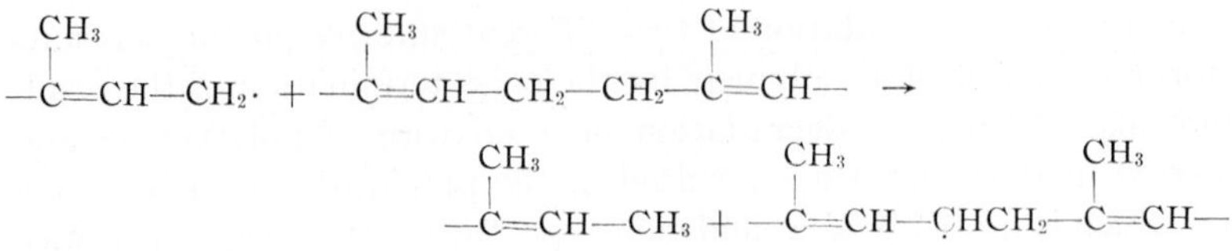

(23)

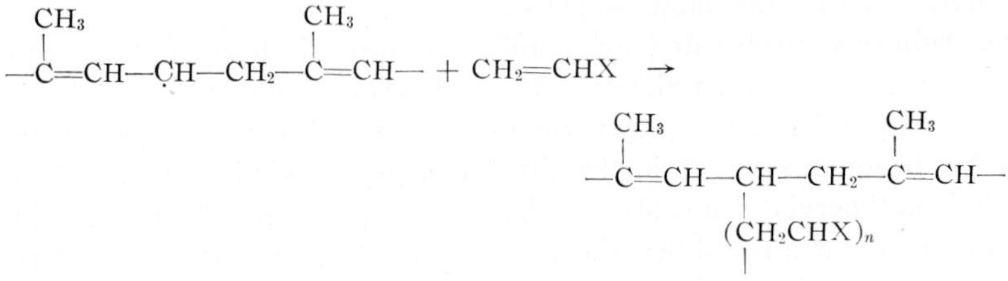

(24)

The synthetic rubbers, e.g. polychloroprene, poly(butadiene-*co*-styrene), poly(butadiene-*co*-acrylonitrile), polyisobutylene, butyl rubber, and polyurethane rubber, as commercially available, did not polymerize monomers on mastication but merely underwent degradation. However, after precipitation to remove antioxidant and a low molecular weight fraction, polymerization readily occurred on mastication with vinyl monomers, such as methyl methacrylate, styrene, chloroprene, methacrylic acid, and acrylonitrile. As in the case of solution and latex copolymerization, vinyl acetate did not polymerize in masticating rubber.

Propeller or paddle-type agitation has been used to produce the shearing force in the preparation of homogeneous, substantially linear, block copolymers from monomeric styrene derivatives and a natural or synthetic rubber. Monomers such as styrene and *o*-chlorostyrene, alone or in combination with other polymerizable monomers such as acrylonitrile or methyl isopropenyl ketone, have been copolymerized in this manner with natural rubber, polybutadiene, and copolymers of butadiene–styrene and butadiene–acrylonitrile.

Block and graft copolymers have been prepared by cold milling and masticating mixtures of various elastomers. Natural rubber, poly(butadiene-*co*-styrene), polychloroprene, and poly(butadiene-*co*-acrylonitrile) have been cold-milled in pairs to effect block copolymerization (116). Cold milling of polychloroprene under nitrogen produces gel, whereas natural rubber can be milled without gel formation. However, milling of mixtures of polychloroprene and natural rubber has produced gels containing the latter. Polychloroprene–natural rubber mixtures have been crosslinked by magnesium oxide with rubber bound into the vulcanizate, after, but not before, cold milling.

A Banbury mixer or a rubber mill has been used to produce block copolymers from blends of polystyrene, high styrene–low butadiene resinous copolymers, and high butadiene–low styrene rubbery copolymers. The products are tough plastic materials of excellent impact resistance.

Polyethylene and butyl rubber have been worked in a Banbury mixer at a temperature above the melting point of the polyethylene to produce a material which forms nongelling solutions in organic solvents and can be used as a major component of an adhesive for polyethylene surfaces.

A combined screw and scroll continuous "masticator-modifier" has been used to produce graft copolymers by polymer–polymer interaction (117,118). Graft copolymers of poly(vinyl chloride) and of poly(butadiene-*co*-acrylonitrile) with phenol–xylene–formaldehyde resins have been prepared in this manner.

Vibro-milling of blends of two or more polymers or of a polymer in the presence of a polymerizable monomer has yielded block copolymers (119).

The mechanical degradation of polymer chains during the freezing and thawing of aqueous solutions and emulsions has been utilized to prepare block copolymers of starch and polystyrene (120) and starch and polyacrylonitrile (121).

The swelling of a polymer in the vapors of a monomer, e.g., the swelling of poly(methyl methacrylate) by acrylonitrile and styrene, of cellulose acetate by acrylonitrile and of polyethylene by methyl methacrylate and styrene, results in the rupture of polymer chains to produce polymeric radicals and resultant block copolymer formation (80,122). Vapor-phase swelling may play a role in popcorn polymerization.

When solutions of polymers in monomer–solvent mixtures are subjected to high voltage spark discharges, block copolymerization is initiated by the macroradicals produced by mechanical degradation. Block copolymers of methyl methacrylate with polytrifluoroethylene and poly(vinyl chloride) have been prepared by this method (123,124).

e. Initiation by Activation

Active centers can be generated on a polymer by photochemical or radiochemical methods, i.e., by low or high energy radiation, or chemically. If this process is carried out in the presence of a polymerizable monomer, graft or block copolymerization can be induced.

(1) Low Energy Irradiation

Polymers containing appropriate labile groups may be irradiated directly to produce grafting sites.

Polystyrene in carbon tetrachloride has been photochemically brominated at room temperature until the bromine content rose to 5–10%. Under these conditions the bromine atoms replace essentially the tertiary hydrogen atoms on the backbone of the polymer. The brominated polymer was dissolved in styrene, and the solution irradiated with ultraviolet light of such a wavelength that the bromine atoms were removed, leaving radical sites on the backbone of the polymer which initiated the polymerization of the monomeric styrene to form branches (125), as shown in eq. (25). Poly(methyl methacrylate) branches were grafted on the polystyrene backbone by irradiating the brominated polymer in monomeric methyl methacrylate (126).

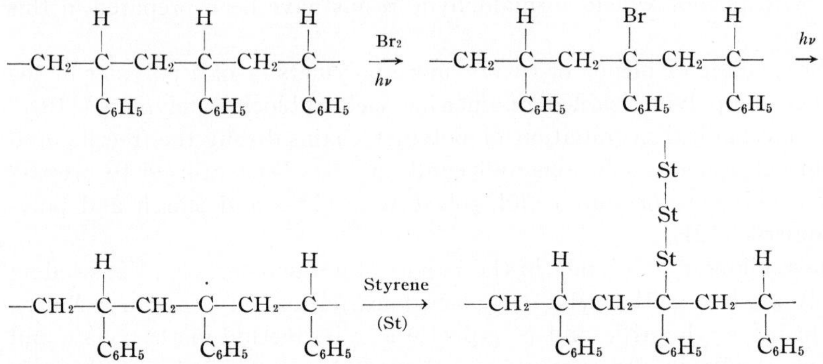

(25)

When the labile atoms are endgroups, block copolymerization occurs. Styrene was polymerized in the presence of carbon tetrabromide or trichlorobromomethane to yield polystyrene containing a bromine atom at one end and either a tribromo or a trichloro group at the other end. When this polystyrene was dissolved in methyl methacrylate and irradiated with ultraviolet light, cleavage of the carbon–bromine bond resulted in the formation of terminal free radicals which initiated polymerization of the methacrylate to form a block copolymer, as shown in eq. (26). The bromine free radical liberated by the scission of the terminal carbon–bromine bond initiated the polymerization of the monomer to yield poly(methyl methacrylate) (127).

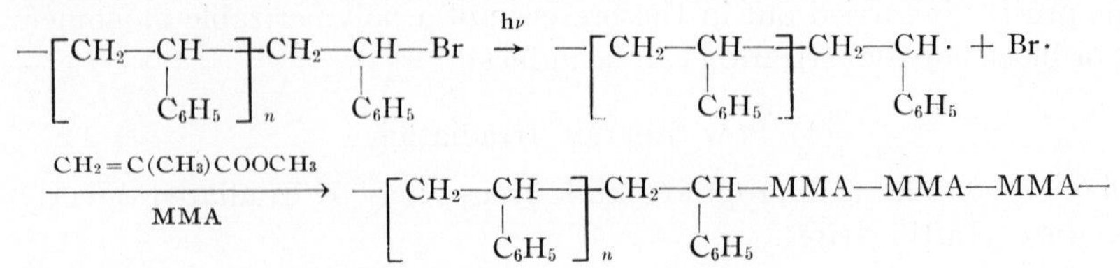

(26)

Ultraviolet irradiation has also been used in the graft copolymerization of acrylonitrile with poly(methyl vinyl ketone) (128). The polymer was dissolved in the monomer and irradiated to yield a polymer containing 54% acrylonitrile. In the absence of poly(methyl vinyl ketone), monomeric acrylonitrile was not polymerized on irradiation. Based on the known behavior of aliphatic ketones on photolysis, the initiation of polymerization of acrylonitrile can be attributed to two different radical sites, as in eq. (27). Methyl methacrylate and vinyl acetate have also been grafted on poly-(methyl vinyl ketone). By using copolymers containing relatively few ketone groups it is possible to synthesize graft copolymers with a wide range of chemical compositions.

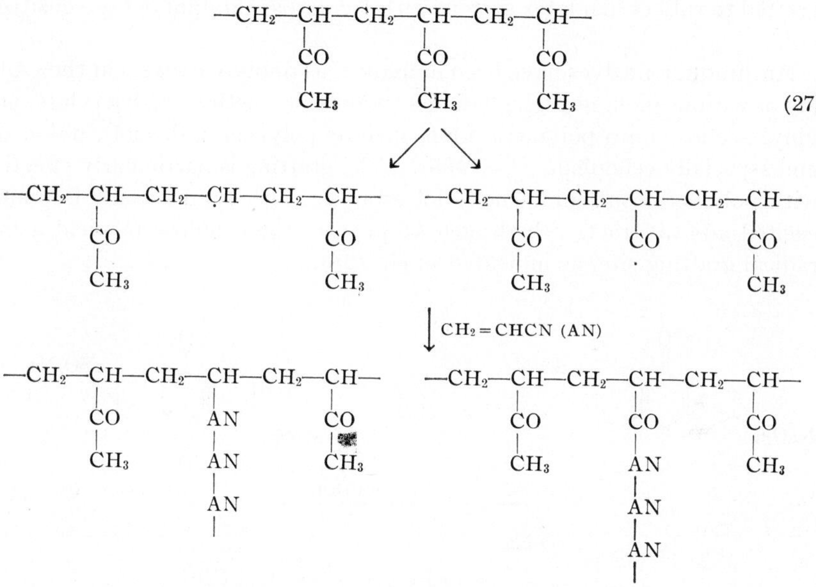

(27)

Copolymers containing a few per cent of α-chloroacrylonitrile have been photolyzed in the presence of a polymerizable monomer to yield graft co-polymers (129).

Photoactive endgroups have been located on the ends of a polystyrene chain by polymerizing styrene in the presence of tetraethylthiuram di-

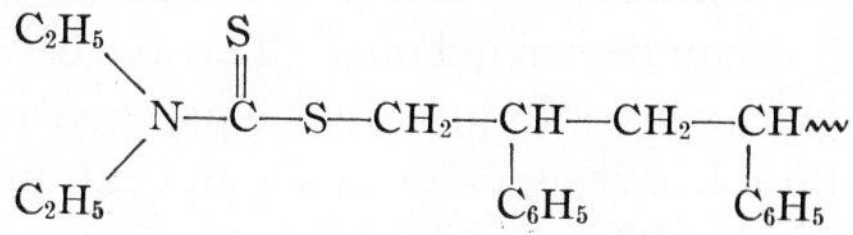

(VI)

sulfide, as in VI. The same groupings were introduced randomly along the polystyrene chain by refluxing polystyrene in benzene with the disulfide. Photolysis of these polymers in the presence of methyl methacrylate and vinyl acetate gave block copolymers from the active endgroups of the polymer and graft copolymers from the backbone-substituted polymer (130).

Irradiation of a polymer–monomer mixture in the presence of a photosensitizer yields graft copolymers, as a result of the formation of free radicals on the backbone of the polymer due to attack by free radicals derived from the photosensitizer. Acrylamide has been grafted on natural rubber containing benzophenone by irradiation (131). Methyl methacrylate was grafted to rubber in a latex system with 1-chloroanthraquinone as sensitizer (132).

Anthraquinone dyes have been employed as photosensitizers in the grafting of various monomers, including acrylonitrile, methyl methacrylate, and vinyl acetate, onto polymeric films such as poly(vinyl alcohol), nylon 66, and especially cellophane (133–135). The grafting is particularly effective with polymers containing methylol groups. The dye molecule is photoexcited and abstracts a hydrogen atom from the cellulose to yield a free radical grafting site, as indicated in eq. (28).

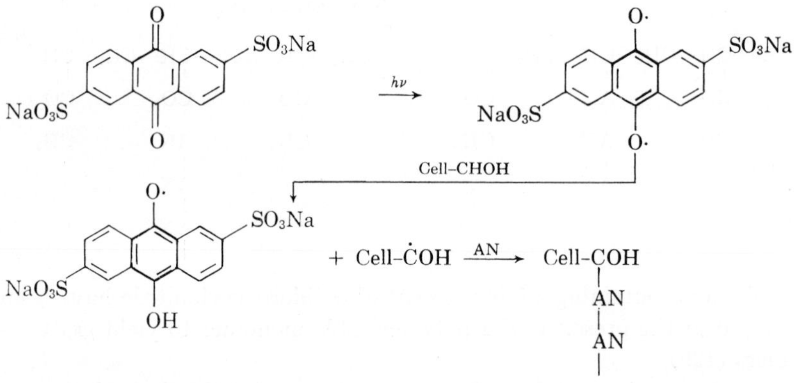

(28)

By incorporation of various dyes into polymer molecules, photosensitized graft copolymerization can be carried out. The dye becomes the site of the grafting reaction when exposed to light in the presence of a reducing agent-oxygen system. Suitable dyes include eosin and safranine. The reaction sequence is outlined in eq. (29).

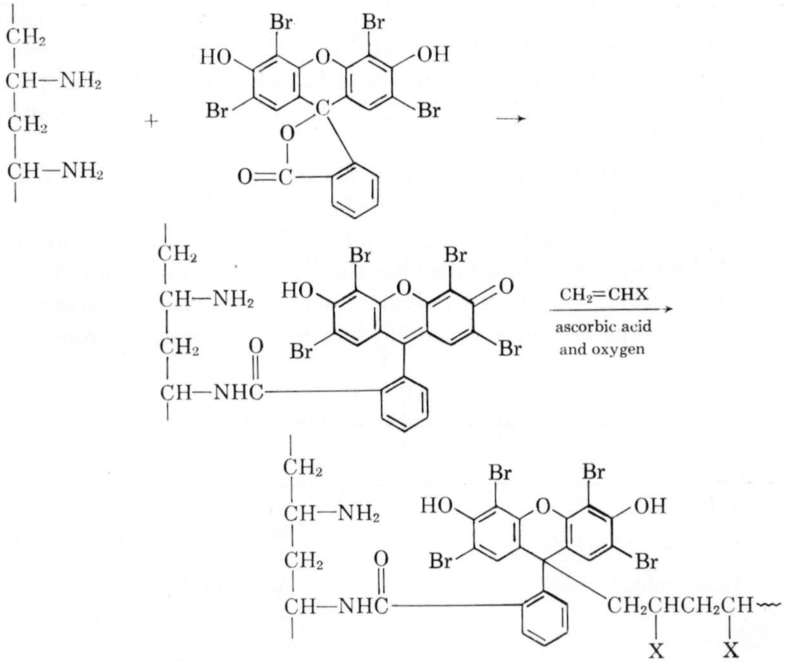

(29)

Oxidation-reduction reaction of the ascorbic acid–oxygen system under the influence of photoenergy transfers a hydrogen atom to the quinone oxygen of the dye and this generates the active free radical at the junction carbon for grafting. Monomers such as acrylamide, acrylic acid, acrylonitrile, and styrene have been grafted on this polymer (136).

The combination of hydrazine and cupric ions photosensitizes the ultraviolet grafting of methyl methacrylate in a latex of natural rubber (137).

(2) High Energy Irradiation

γ-Radiation from a Co^{60} source, high energy electrons from linear accelerators, and high energy x-rays have been used to create active sites on polymers for graft copolymerization (138–140).

The effect of γ-radiation on a polymer is to cleave a hydrogen from the polymer or to break a carbon–carbon bond; in either case, to produce a radical site. If the irradiation is carried out in the presence of a monomer, i.e., if a polymer swollen with monomer is irradiated, polymerization of the monomer is initiated at the active site on the polymer to yield a homogeneous graft or block copolymer. If the polymer is immersed in the monomer and is insoluble, or if insufficient time for swelling is allowed, heterogeneous surface grafting occurs. The experimental variables in the mutual irradiation of a monomer–polymer mixture include radiation dose, dose rate, polymer thickness, temperature, and the nature of the monomer–polymer solution.

Homopolymerization of the vinyl monomer and crosslinking of the polymer backbone occur simultaneously with the grafting reaction.

Homogeneous and/or surface grafting can be effected by utilizing solvents as well as in bulk systems. The latter has the disadvantage of high viscosity and heat generation. A swollen polymer–monomer mixture possesses an interior in which the monomer is present in a highly viscous environment.

TABLE X-4
Representative Mutual Irradiation Systems

Polymer	Monomer
Cellulose	Acrylonitrile
	Methyl methacrylate
	Styrene
Hevea rubber	Acrylonitrile
	Methyl methacrylate
	Styrene
Polychlorotrifluoroethylene	Acrylic acid
	Acrylonitrile
	Styrene
	Vinyl acetate
Polytetrafluoroethylene	Acrylic acid
	Acrylonitrile
	N-Vinylpyrrolidone
Poly(ethylene terephthalate)	Styrene
Poly(hexamethylene adipamide)	Styrene
Polydimethylsiloxane	Acrylonitrile
	Methyl methacrylate
Polyethylene	Acrylic acid
	Acrylonitrile
	Styrene
	Vinyl carbazole
	Vinylidene chloride
	4-Vinylpyridine
Polypropylene	Vinyl acetate
Poly(vinyl alcohol)	Acrylamide
	Acrylonitrile
	Methyl methacrylate
	Styrene
	Vinyl acetate

Due to the Trommsdorff-Norrish effect the molecular weight of the graft copolymer produced in the interior may be greater than that produced near the surface. Emulsion polymers do not become viscous at high conversions and therefore latices are attractive grafting media.

Graft copolymerization of a polymer-monomer mixture in the absence of air is termed the mutual irradiation technique. Some typical polymer-monomer systems are shown in Table X-4.

As a result of the irradiation-induced grafting on polyethylene various property changes occur. Acrylonitrile greatly reduces the swelling in and permeability to aromatic hydrocarbons while raising the softening range from 110 to 160°C. and providing for excellent adhesion to many polar materials. Vinyl carbazole maintains superior electrical properties while stiffening the polyethylene and raising the softening point to 215°C. Acrylic esters, even in quantities as small as 2–3%, after hydrolysis produce a permanent surface conductivity and prevent the accumulation of static charges, while providing for good adhesion to substances such as cellulose, glass, and metals. Styrene increases the melt viscosity although it decreases the tensile strength and elongation of the polyethylene. The styrene-grafted polyethylene can be sulfonated to yield a cation-exchange membrane.

Styrene grafted on polytetrafluoroethylene and polychlorotrifluoroethylene improves adhesion, prevents plastic flow, and increases the ultimate strength.

Styrene–unsaturated polyester mixtures can be cured by ionizing radiation to a highly crosslinked network with properties similar to those produced by chemical curing.

Graft copolymers may be produced by a preirradiation technique as well as by the mutual irradiation procedure. The solid polymer may be irradiated in the absence of air and monomer to produce trapped radicals. Subsequent treatment of the irradiated polymer with a vinyl monomer with or without the application of heat gives graft or block copolymers depending upon the mode of degradation of the polymer during the preirradiation. The trapped radical technique is capable of yielding a homogeneous product, free of homopolymer of the polymerizing monomer (141). Surface grafting can be obtained by the preirradiation technique by exposing the pretreated polymer, generally in the form of a fiber or film, to a vinyl monomer in the vapor state (142).

Preirradiation of a solid polymer in the presence of oxygen or air results in the formation of peroxide and hydroperoxide linkages as shown in eqs. (30)–(32). The resultant polymers thus contain catalytic species which

$$\sim CH_2{-}CH_2{-}CH_2\sim \;\rightarrow\; \sim CH_2{-}\dot{C}HCH_2\sim \;\xrightarrow{O_2}\; \sim CH_2{-}\underset{\substack{|\\ OO\cdot}}{C}HCH_2\sim \qquad (30)$$

$$\sim CH_2{-}\underset{\substack{|\\ OO\cdot}}{C}HCH_2\sim + \sim CH_2{-}CH_2{-}CH_2\sim \;\rightarrow$$
$$\sim CH_2{-}\underset{\substack{|\\ OOH}}{C}HCH_2\sim + \sim CH_2{-}\dot{C}HCH_2\sim \qquad (31)$$

$$\sim CH_2{-}\underset{\substack{|\\ OO\cdot}}{C}HCH_2\sim + \sim CH_2{-}\dot{C}HCH_2\sim \;\rightarrow\; \begin{matrix} \sim CH_2{-}CHCH_2\sim \\ | \\ O \\ | \\ O \\ | \\ \sim CH_2{-}CHCH_2\sim \end{matrix} \qquad (32)$$

may be decomposed thermally at about 60–70°C. in the presence of monomer to yield graft copolymers.

The polymeric peroxides and hydroperoxides produced by air irradiation are particularly useful for the modification of the surface of a fiber or film. Acrylonitrile, styrene and methyl methacrylate have been grafted to air-irradiated polyethylene, and polypropylene (141,143). The air preirradiation technique has been applied to poly(vinyl chloride), cotton, nylon, poly(ethylene terephthalate), cellulose acetate, and polyacrylonitrile. The polymerizable monomer can be contacted with the polymer from bulk, solution or aqueous systems, or from the vapor state.

High energy electrons from a van de Graaff generator or other linear electron accelerator as well as high energy x-rays are suitable for graft copolymerization reactions. The techniques of mutual irradiation and preirradiation in the absence or presence of air can be utilized with these high energy sources.

An interesting variation of the preirradiation technique involves introducing free radicals on a polymeric backbone by irradiating the latter in the presence of a "free radical former" such as benzoyl peroxide, aqueous hydrogen peroxide, or azobisisobutyronitrile. The polymer, immediately after irradiation, is immersed in a vinyl monomer to initiate graft copolymerization. Coatings of numerous vinyl monomers have been applied in this manner to polyethylene, poly(ethylene terephthalate), nylon, and poly(vinyl fluoride) (144). Although the reported reactions were carried out with high energy electrons, this technique should be equally effective with gamma or other high energy radiation.

(3) Chemical and Thermal Activation

The active site for radical-initiated graft copolymerization can be produced chemically and thermally as well as by irradiation.

Ceric salts are capable of oxidizing alcohols and produce free radicals which may initiate polymerization. When the alcohol is a polymer, a graft copolymer is produced (145). The reaction apparently proceeds by the formation of a ceric–alcohol complex which produces radicals by the reaction in eq. (33). It is not certain whether the hydrogen is abstracted from a

$$Ce^{4+} + R^{H}_{OH} \rightarrow Ce^{3+} + H^{+} + \dot{R}_{OH} \quad (33)$$

carbon or from the oxygen atom. At any rate, radicals are produced on the polymer and monomers can be grafted thereon. This method of grafting has been extremely effective with poly(vinyl alcohol), partially hydrolyzed poly(vinyl acetate), cellulose, and starch as polymeric backbones for grafts from acrylonitrile and acrylamide. Since the initiating sites are on the polymeric backbone, homopolymerization is reduced.

Cellulose adsorbs ferrous ions from a solution of a ferrous salt. Reaction of this cellulose with hydrogen peroxide and a monomer yields a graft copolymer (146). Since ferrous ions react with hydrogen peroxide to yield hydroxyl radials (eq. 34), the latter probably abstract hydrogen from cellulose (eq. 35) to yield grafting sites. This is essentially a chain transfer-

$$Fe^{2+} + H_2O_2 \rightarrow Fe^{3+} + OH^{-} + \cdot OH \quad (34)$$

$$\text{Cell—CHOH} + \cdot OH \rightarrow \text{Cell—}\dot{C}\text{OH} + H_2O \quad (35)$$

initiated graft copolymerization, as discussed in an earlier part of this section, and can be carried out on fibers or films. Since the radicals are produced within the cellulose the concentration of the latter is so high that it can compete with the monomer for hydroxyl radicals and keep the homopolymerization to a reasonable level.

An analogous technique for grafting vinyl monomers on cellulosics involves the use of ion-exchange-bonded metallic and nonmetallic catalysts or initiator components as reaction sites (147). This method is adaptable also to other natural or synthetic polymeric materials with functional groups capable of ion exchange reactions, e.g., proteins, starches, and nylons. In cellulosics, for example, the functional groups have weakly acidic properties and can be converted by an ion exchange reaction into catalyst cations. The second component of the catalytic system is generally an oxidant which, together with the monomer, diffuses to the site of the bound cation. As a result of a redox reaction, free radicals are formed and initiate polymerization of the monomer.

TABLE X-5
Systems of Cation-Oxidant for Ion-Exchange Grafting

Cation source	Oxidant
$FeSO_4 \cdot (NH_4)_2SO_4$	H_2O_2, benzoyl peroxide
$AgNO_3$	H_2O_2, persulfate
$SnCl_2$	H_2O_2
Cu(II)-ammonia	H_2O_2
Hydrazine hydrate	H_2O_2, *tert*-butyl hydroperoxide
Triethanolamine	Persulfate
$UO_2(NO_3)_2$	Light

Representative cation sources and oxidants used are listed in Table X-5. The monomers successfully utilized include acrylic esters, acrylonitrile, styrene, vinyl chloride, vinylidene chloride, and butadiene. Although the author characterizes the reaction as a cellulosic cation-catalyzed polymerization, the nature of the catalyst components and the polymerizable monomers indicate that this is a free radical initiated polymerization. However, it is probable that with all of the catalyst systems some, if not all, of the polymer is deposited or entrapped in the cellulosic matrix rather than grafted.

Another interesting grafting procedure involves chemically induced cleavage of polymer. In the presence of an Fe^{2+}–H_2O_2 redox system, wool may be grafted by cleavage of its disulfide bonds. The resulting RS· radicals can initiate the polymerization of acrylonitrile to form branch chains (148).

The thermal depolymerization of polytetrafluoroethylene proceeds by a free radical mechanism. Since thermal decomposition in a poor conductor can be localized on the surface by a rapid heating process, a high concentration of free radicals in the surface layer can be formed with little decomposition in the bulk. This method has been utilized to produce graft copolymers of styrene on polytetrafluoroethylene. The surface of a block of the polymer was heated *in vacuo* by means of radiant heat from a platinum filament close to the surface, and then immersed in styrene to yield a layer of polystyrene grafted on the surface of the polytetrafluoroethylene.

f. Initiation from Reactive Functional Groups

The synthesis of polymers containing reactive groups which can be thermally or chemically activated to yield free radicals permits the initiation of grafting at the site of these groups. An essential feature of this type of grafting is that the initiation of polymerization occurs only at these reactive sites, eliminating the formation of polymer from the second monomer, i.e., no pure poly-B is formed, and the product contains branches of B out of the backbone of poly-A.

The perester of poly(methyl acrylate) has been synthesized by treating the polymer with phosphorus pentachloride in benzene to form 25–26% of the acid chloride, followed by treatment with *tert*-butyl hydroperoxide in the presence of base, as shown in eq. (36). The resultant poly(methyl acrylate) contained about 5% of the perester. The polyacrylic ester was used as the polymerization catalyst for styrene, vinyl acetate, methyl acrylate, and acrylonitrile to produce graft copolymers of these monomers on the poly(methyl acrylate) (149).

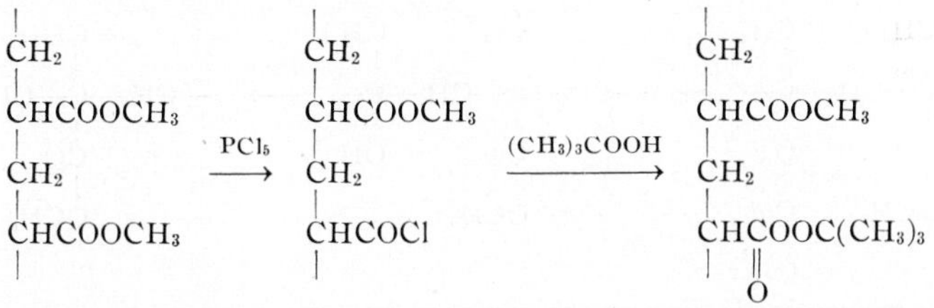

(36)

An analogous reaction has been carried out by treating poly(acrylyl chloride) with *tert*-butyl hydroperoxide. In this case the polymeric acid chloride was prepared by polymerization of monomeric acrylyl chloride. The polyacrylic-*tert*-butyl perester was used as an initiator in the graft polymerization of methyl methacrylate (150), as shown in eq. (37).

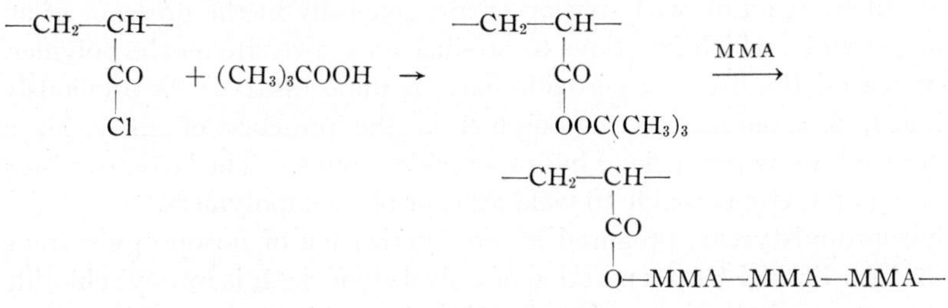

(37)

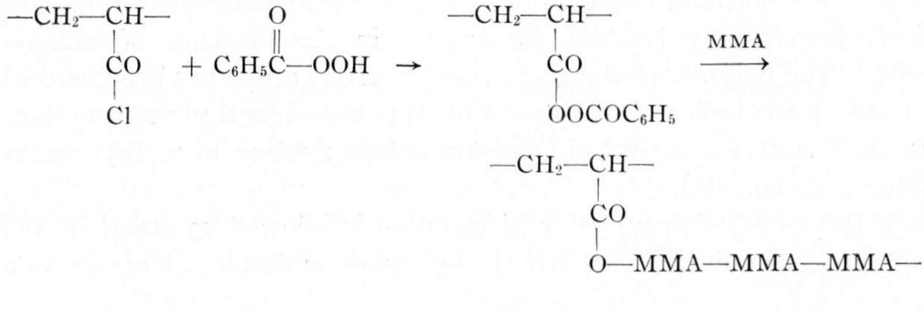

(38)

Polyacrylyl–benzoyl peroxide, prepared from polyacrylyl chloride and perbenzoic acid, has also been used in the graft polymerization of methyl methacrylate, as in eq. (38).

A copolymer of methyl methacrylate and isopropenyl hydroperoxide and a copolymer of styrene and monopermaleic acid have also been used to initiate sidechain copolymerization of methyl methacrylate (151). The former initiator was prepared by copolymerization of methyl methacrylate and isopropenyl acetate, followed by hydrolysis and treatment with hydrogen peroxide (eq. 39). The styrene–monopermaleic acid copolymer was prepared by treatment of the styrene–maleic anhydride copolymer with hydrogen peroxide (eq. 40).

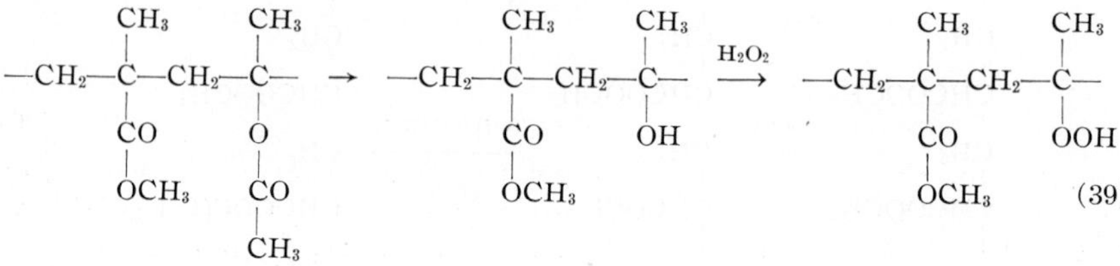
(39)

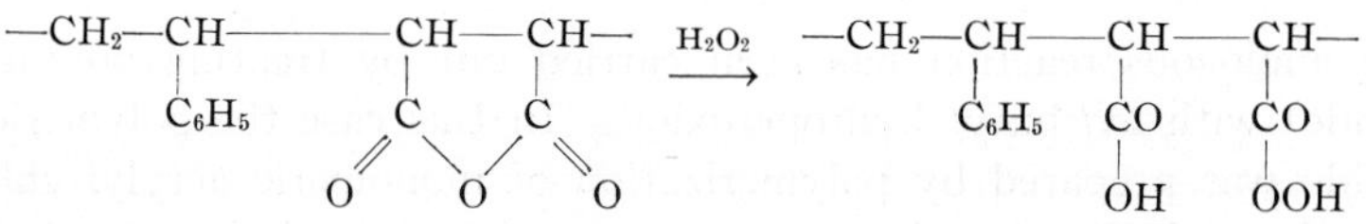
(40)

Peroxidation of a polymer to produce a polyfunctional initiator can be carried out by reaction with oxygen or air, generally in the presence of an organic peroxide, which functions to produce an active site on the polymer. In some cases, the use of a peroxide may be unnecessary. As previously mentioned, preirradiation of a polymer in the presence of air yields a polymer containing peroxide or hydroperoxide groups. The latter can then serve as a polymeric peroxide to yield graft or block copolymers.

Polyisopropylstyrene, prepared by polymerization of *p*-isopropylstyrene (152) or by a Friedel-Crafts reaction of polystyrene with isopropyl chloride in the presence of aluminum choride (150), is readily converted in part to the hydroperoxide by bubbling in oxygen in the presence of benzoyl peroxide. The polymer containing hydroperoxide groups has been used as an initiator in the bulk polymerization of styrene and methyl methacrylate and in the ferrous ion-activated emulsion polymerization of methyl methacrylate, as in eq. (41).

When the *o*-chlorobenzyl ester of cellulose is allowed to stand in air, peroxide groups are introduced into the polymeric molecule. The peroxide

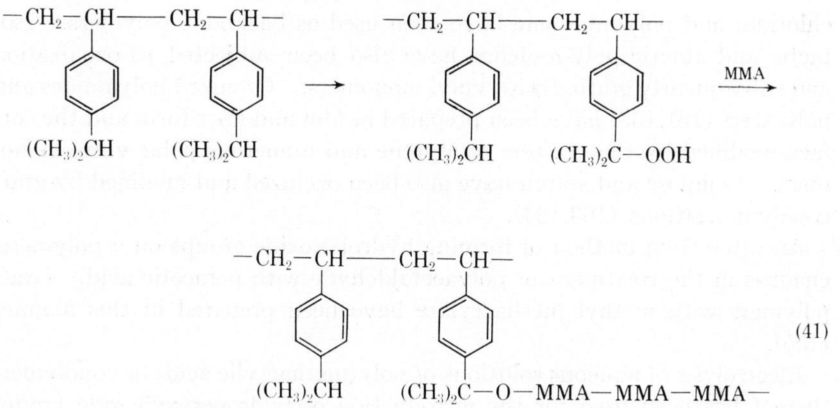
(41)

groups can serve as the site for the initiation of styrene polymerization to yield graft copolymers (153).

The air oxidation technique of peroxidation and subsequent utilization of the peroxidized polymer in graft copolymerization has been applied to styrene-*co*-4-vinyl-1-cyclohexene polymers (154), natural rubber latex (155), as well as partially hydrolyzed methyl methacrylate–isopropenyl acetate copolymers which contain tertiary hydroxyl groups (156).

Natta (157,158) studied the peroxidation of poly-α-olefins and found that surface peroxidation could be carried out at 70–80°C. with isotactic polypropylene and poly-1-butene, while atactic polymers gave more homogeneous results. Styrene, methyl methacrylate, and vinyl chloride were subsequently grafted to the peroxidized poly-α-olefins.

Ozonization is a more effective technique for producting active sites on a polymeric backbone than air oxidation, and has been applied to extremely varied polymer–monomer graft copolymer systems. In the earliest applications of the technique (159,160) acrylonitrile was grafted to ozonized polytetrafluoroethylene and polystyrene. In the latter case ozonization occurs in the aromatic ring of the polystyrene to give two grafting sites per ozonide structure as shown in eq. (42). The ozonized polymers are heated in the presence of the monomer to initiate graft copolymerization.

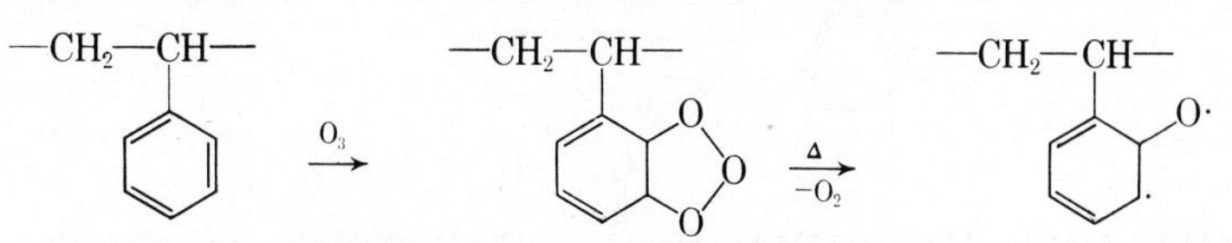
(42)

The polymer may be in the form of a fiber or film to give surface grafting or may be ozonized in solution. In addition to polyethylene, poly(vinyl chloride) and polybutadiene have been used as backbone polymers. Isotactic and atactic poly-α-olefins have also been subjected to ozonization and subsequently grafted with vinyl monomers. Ozonized polyamides and polyesters (161,162) have been prepared in film and fiber form and the surface modified by the grafting of styrene and numerous polar vinyl monomers. Cellulose and starch have also been ozonized and modified by graft copolymerizations (163,164).

An interesting method of forming hydroperoxide groups on a polymeric chain is in the treatment of polyacetaldehyde with peracetic acid. Graft polymers with methyl methacrylate have been prepared in this manner (165).

Electrolysis of aqueous solutions of poly(methacrylic acid) or copolymers thereof has been used for the introduction of hydroperoxide side groups (166). Some of the carboxyl groups undergo decarboxylation and, on addition of oxygen, yield hydroperoxides. The oxygen is generated by the electrolysis of the water. Acrylonitrile and acrylamide have been grafted on these electrolyzed polymers.

Although the polymerization of a vinyl monomer in the presence of a polyfunctional initiator such as polymeric phthaloyl peroxide, butyl disulfide, and ascaridole has been shown to result in monoradical rather than diradical initiation, polymeric phthaloyl peroxide has been utilized in the preparation of block copolymers.

When the polymerization of styrene with polymeric phthaloyl peroxide was stopped at a comparatively early stage, and the resulting polymer was

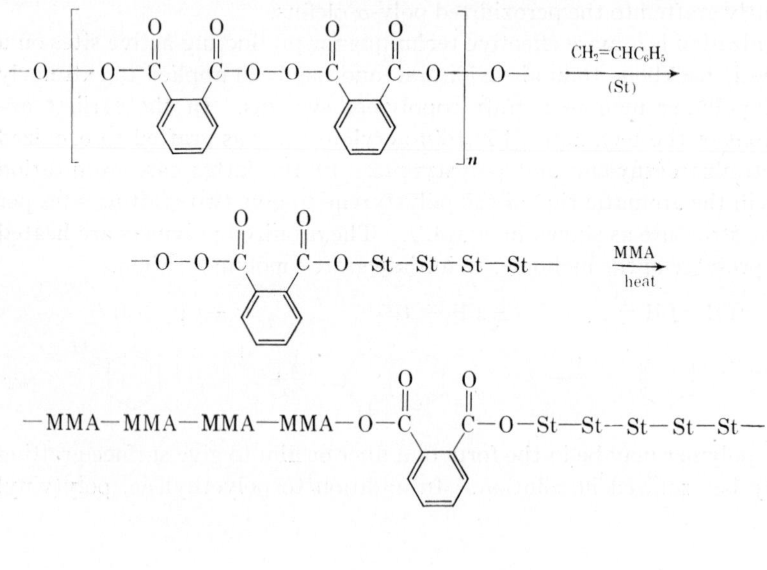

(43)

dissolved in a benzene solution of methyl methacrylate, terminal or internal peroxide groups decomposed into free radicals and initiated the polymerization of the second monomer to form block copolymers (167,168) as shown in eq. (43). By this method block copolymers containing 20–30% styrene have been prepared. Analogously, poly(vinyl acetate) was prepared with phthaloyl peroxide, and the polymer then heated with styrene to yield a block copolymer containing 40% vinyl acetate. On the other hand, the styrene–phthaloyl peroxide polymer was unable to initiate polymerization of vinyl acetate or vinyl pyrrolidone.

Poly(methyl methacrylate) has been found to initiate the polymerization of monomeric methyl methacrylate. This has been attributed to the presence of peroxide linkages which have been incorporated into the poly(methyl methacrylate) during its preparation. Methyl methacrylate and oxygen form a copolymer which has a peroxidic structure. When poly(methyl methacrylate) is heated in the presence of its monomer, the peroxide linkages cleave to form free radicals which initiate polymerization. The polymerization of styrene in the presence of the poly(methyl methacrylate) results in the formation of what is probably a block copolymer (169).

In a modification of this technique, monomers such as methyl methacrylate, styrene and vinyl acetate were bulk polymerized in the presence of oxygen to give polymers containing peroxidic linkages. The polymers were swollen with either acrylonitrile, styrene, vinyl acetate, or vinylidene chloride and then heated to 70°C. or above to degrade peroxidic linkages and initiate block copolymerization (170).

The polymerization of styrene with *m*-di(hydroperoxyisopropyl)benzene as an initiator results in the formation of polystyrene containing hydroperoxy end groups. Emulsification of a solution of this polymer in methyl methacrylate with a soap solution, followed by the addition of ferrous ion to decompose the hydroperoxy groups, results in the preparation of a block copolymer (171).

In addition to peroxides, hydroperoxides, and ozonides, diazonium functions can be introduced into polymer chains and later decomposed in the presence of a vinyl monomer to yield grafted copolymers.

Reduction of nitrated polystyrene to poly-*p*-aminostyrene, followed by diazotization yields a polymer containing diazonium groups. Decomposi-

$$\underset{\substack{| \\ C_6H_5}}{-CH_2-CH-} \rightarrow \underset{\substack{| \\ C_6H_4NO_2}}{-CH_2-CH-} \rightarrow \underset{\substack{| \\ C_6H_4NH_2}}{-CH_2-CH-} \rightarrow$$

$$\underset{\substack{| \\ C_6H_4N_2^+}}{-CH_2-CH-} \xrightarrow[-N_2]{Fe^{2+}} \underset{\substack{| \\ C_6H_4\cdot}}{-CH_2-CH-} \qquad (44)$$

tion of the polymeric diazonium salt in the presence of a ferrous salt yields radical grafting sites (172). This sequence of reactions is shown in eq. (44). This method has been used for the preparation of a graft copolymer of poly-*p*-aminostyrene and acrylamide.

Nitrosation of the acetylamino derivative of poly-*p*-aminostyrene yields a polymeric *N*-nitroso compound which decomposes to give active radical sites for graft copolymerization (173).

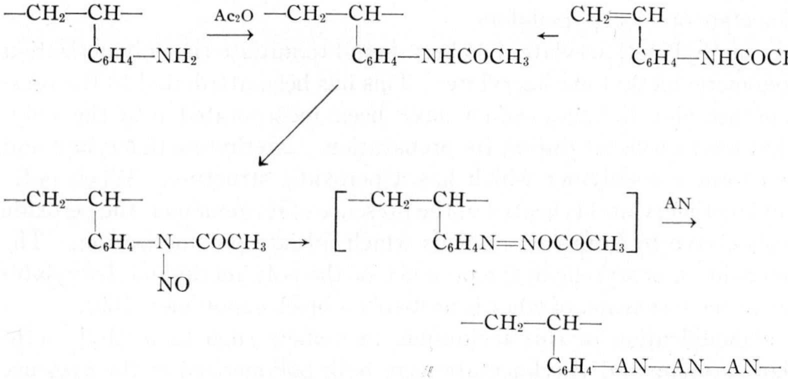

(45)

The diazonium derivatives of the *p*-aminophenacyl ether of cellulose and of the *p*-aminophenacyl ester of carboxymethylcellulose have been used with ferrous salts to initiate the graft copolymerization of acrylonitrile (174). Grafting experiments with vinyl acetate and styrene were not successful.

2. Ionic Initiation with Vinyl Monomers

a. Initiation by Carbonium Ions

Graft copolymerization by a cationic mechanism is obviously restricted to those monomers which are polymerizable by such a mechanism.

The ionic chain transfer reaction between a polystyrene carbonium ion and poly-*p*-methoxystyrene shown in eq. (46) has given a graft copolymer (175,176). Alkyl vinyl ethers, isobutylene, and *N*-vinylpyrrolidone could not be grafted on polystyrene, polyvinyltoluene, or poly-*p*-methoxystyrene by this technique.

Chloromethylated polystyrene in carbon disulfide solution in the presence of aluminum tribromide has been used as ionic carbonium initiator for the polymerization of isobutylene (177) as shown in eq. (47).

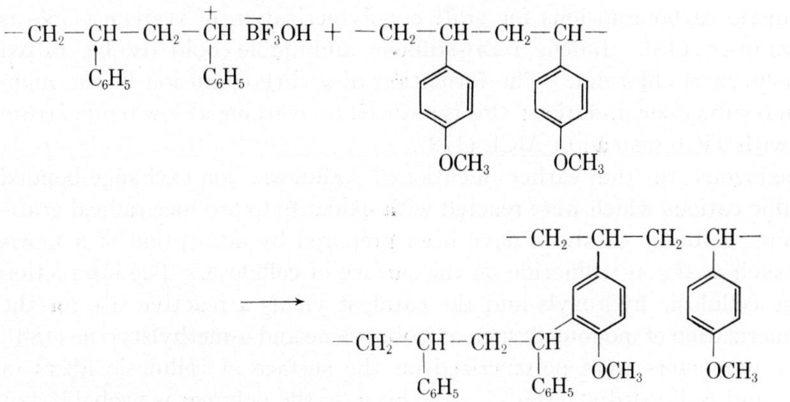

(46)

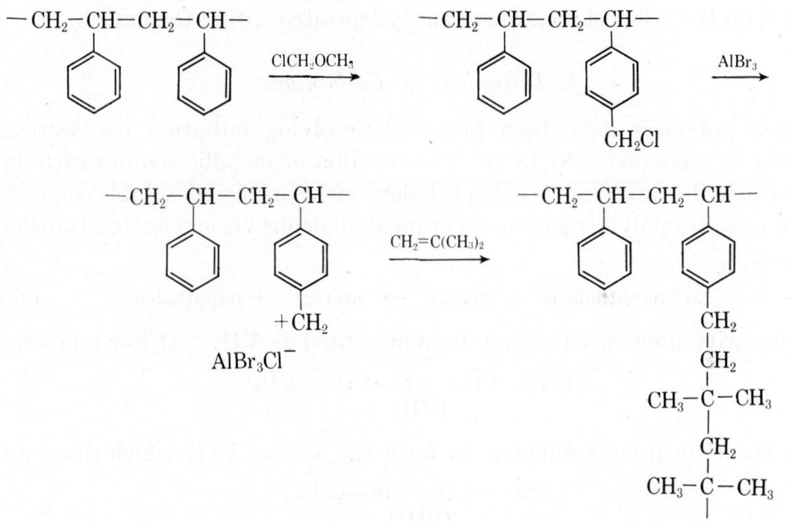

(47)

Treatment of poly(vinyl chloride) and poly(vinyl chloride-*co*-vinylidene chloride) with titanium tetrachloride or aluminum trichloride produced

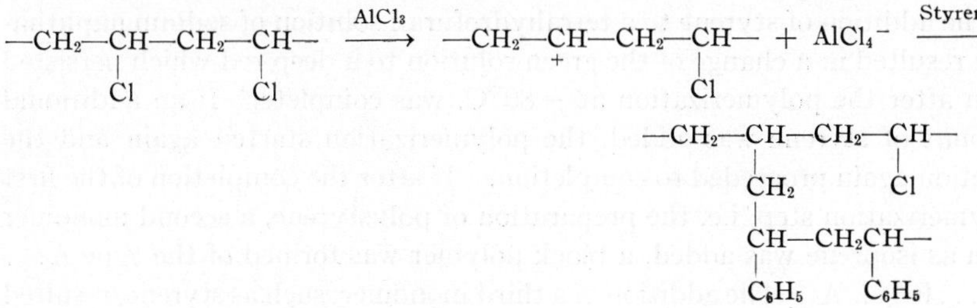

(48)

polymeric carbonium ions for graft copolymerization of styrene (178) as shown in eq. (48). Indene, *trans*-stilbene, and indole could also be grafted on poly(vinyl chloride). The formation of a carbonium ion in the main chain results in degradation; this is reduced by working at low temperature and with $TiCl_4$ instead of $AlCl_3$ (179).

Analogous to the earlier mentioned cellulosic ion-exchange-bonded metallic cations which were reacted with oxidants to produce radical grafting sites, cationic catalysts have been prepared by adsorption of a Lewis acid such as boron trifluoride on the surface of cellulose. The interaction of the cellulosic hydroxyls and the catalyst yields a reactive site for the polymerization of monomers such as isobutylene and α-methylstyrene (180). These monomers were polymerized on the surface of cellulosic fibers in paper and wallboard at −80°C. In this case the polymer is probably not grafted on the cellulosic backbone but is deposited within the matrix.

b. *Initiation by Carbanions*

Block polymers have been prepared involving initiation by electron transfer to monomer (181,182). The reaction of metallic sodium with an aromatic hydrocarbon such as naphthalene yields a colored, soluble complex which initiates polymerization of conjugated olefins via an electron transfer process:

$$Na^+ \text{naphthalene}^- + \text{styrene} \rightarrow \text{styrene}^- + \text{naphthalene} \qquad (49)$$

The negative monomer ion may be represented as VII. At low tempera-

$$^-{:}CHX{-}CH_2{\cdot} \quad \text{or} \quad {\cdot}CHX{-}CH_2{:}^-$$

(VII)

tures the radical ends dimerize to form the species VIII which does not

$$^-{:}CHX{-}CH_2{-}CH_2{-}CHX{:}^-$$

(VIII)

terminate but consumes all the monomer to produce a "living" polymer, via a carbanion polymerization mechanism.

The addition of styrene to a tetrahydrofuran solution of sodium naphthalene resulted in a change of the green solution to a deep red which persisted even after the polymerization at −80°C. was complete. If an additional amount of styrene was added, the polymerization started again and the reaction again proceeded to completion. If after the completion of the first polymerization step, i.e. the preparation of polystyrene, a second monomer such as isoprene was added, a block polymer was formed of the type A... AB...BA...A. The addition of a third monomer, such as styrene, resulted in the formation of a block copolymer of the type BABAB containing another block on each end.

If methyl methacrylate or acrylonitrile is added to "living" polystyryl dicarbanions, a block copolymer is formed. However, in this case, no third monomer can be added since the polymerization of these monomers is self-terminating. If methyl methacrylate is initially polymerized by the sodium naphthalene catalyst, no further polymerization occurs on addition of styrene or methyl methacrylate.

This termination reaction, which apparently involves the reaction of a carbanion endgroup with the ester group of the methacrylate, has been useful in the formation of graft copolymers. Thus, poly(methyl methacrylate) in tetrahydrofuran has been added to polystyrene anions formed by polymerization of styrene with benzylsodium or phenylisopropylpotassium as catalysts. The polystyrene monocarbanion reacts with the ester groups to yield a graft copolymer in which poly(methyl methacrylate) forms the main chain and polystyrene the branches (183).

Block copolymers are produced in the lithium-initiated copolymerization of equimolar mixtures of styrene and methyl methacrylate in tetrahydrofuran or heptane. The proposed mechanism invokes electron exchange initiation and ion-radical propagation but, in contrast to the situation in the "living" polymer type of reaction, the anionic end only adds methyl methacrylate while the free radical end forms a block of random styrene–methyl methacrylate copolymer (184,185).

The metalation of polymers yields polymeric polyanions capable of initiating the graft polymerization of anionic polymerizable monomers such as acrylonitrile, methyl methacrylate, styrene, and 4-vinylpyridine.

Treatment of poly-*p*-chlorostyrene or its copolymers with sodium naphthalene in tetrahydrofuran gives the sodium derivative (eq. 50), which is an effective initiator of graft copolymerization (186). Analogously, poly-*p*-dimethylchloromethylsilylstyrene and its copolymers with styrene can be converted into polymeric anionic initiators (eq. 51). The anionic grafting sites in these cases are "living," so that different monomers can be added to produce branches which are block copolymers.

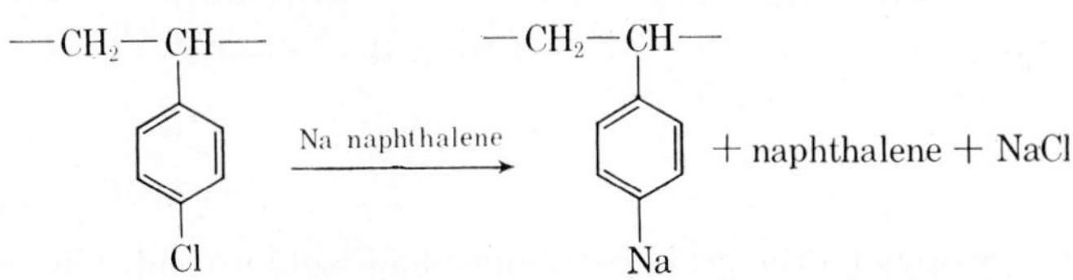

(50)

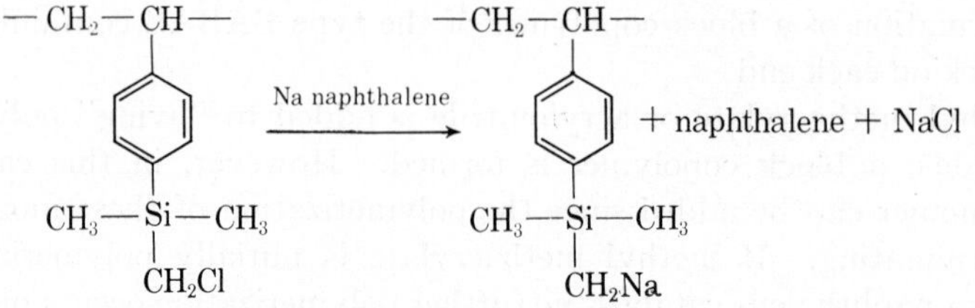

(51)

Polyvinylbenzophenone copolymers with styrene in the form of the sodium ketyl, are also effective anionic grafting initiators (188,187).

By reaction of dimethylsilylmethylmagnesium chloride with styrene–acrylonitrile copolymers, polymeric initiators are obtained which permit the low temperature graft polymerization of 4-vinylpyridine, acrylonitrile, and methyl methacrylate (188,189) as shown in eq. (52). The reaction of

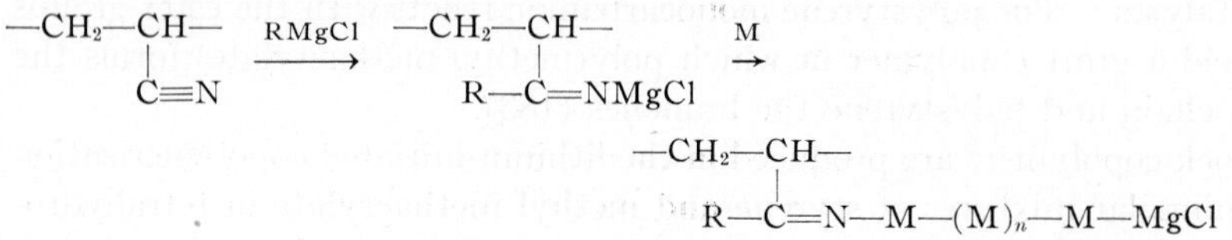

(52)

acrylonitrile copolymers with alkyllithium compounds analogously forms polymers with —C=N—Li groups which are polymerization initiators (188).

c. Initiation by Ionic Coordination

Polymers containing terminal double bonds can be converted to polymeric organoaluminum compounds by reaction with diethylaluminum hydride. Thus, addition of the alkylaluminum hydride to the vinyl double bonds of styrene–butadiene copolymers yields organoaluminum compounds which, with transition metal compounds, e.g., $TiCl_4$ and $TiCl_3$, form polymeric Ziegler-Natta type catalysts which permit graft polymerization of ethylene, propylene or styrene (188,190) as given in reaction (53).

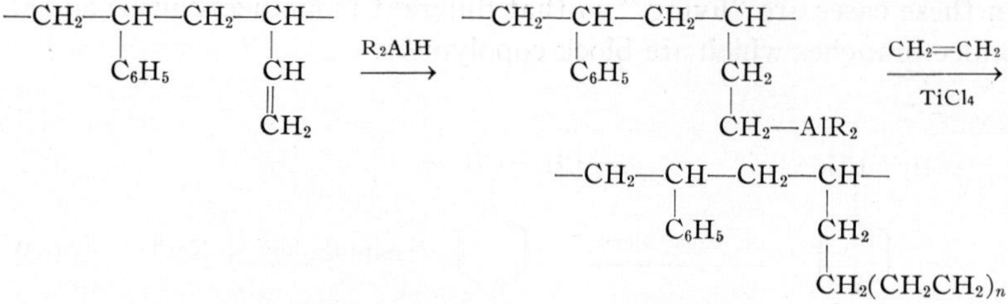

(53)

In the case of propylene the graft copolymer had isotactic side chains.

This reaction has been applied to the preparation of block copolymers with α,ω-dienes as the central block (190). Block copolymers of polyethylene and diallylpolysilmethylene were prepared by the reaction sequence in eq. (54).

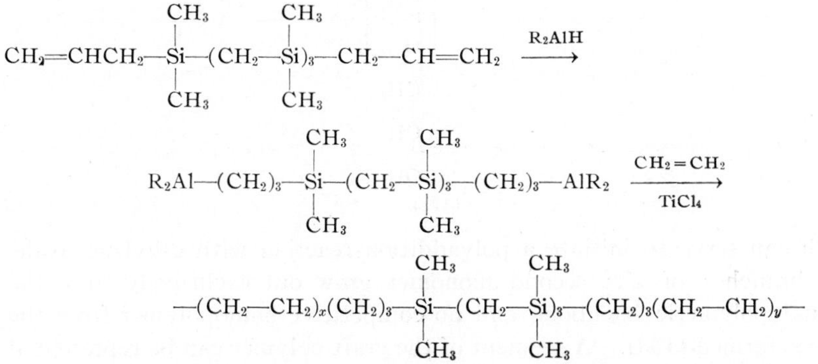

(54)

An interesting procedure which has recently been commercialized involves reaction of cellulosic hydroxyl groups with an aluminum alkyl to form an alkylaluminum alkoxide attached to cellulose, Cell-OAlR$_2$. On addition of a transition metal compound, ethylene, propylene, and styrene are polymerized onto the cellulosic fibers (191). The fibers are encapsulated by the vinyl polymer, and no actual chemical bond may be formed between the cellulose and the vinyl polymer.

The long lifetime of the chain ends in a polymerization catalyzed by a Ziegler-Natta type catalyst permits the formation of block copolymers. An α-olefin or diene may be polymerized to a soluble polymer with a still active chain end; subsequent addition of a second monomer initiates block copolymerization. Aluminum alkyl-titanium tetrachloride catalysts have been used to polymerize 1-pentene, 1-octene, cyclohexene, butadiene, or isoprene, followed by polymerization of allyl bromide, allyl chloride, isoprene, butadiene, styrene, 1-butene, or chloroprene (192). Ethylene-propylene block copolymers have been prepared in a similar manner.

3. Cyclic Monomers

The opening of an ethylene oxide ring by an active hydrogen such as in a hydroxyl or amide group permits the grafting of $(CH_2CH_2O)_n$ chains on a suitably substituted polymer.

The copolymerization of styrene with 1–2 mole-% of vinyl acetate results in the formation of a polystyrene containing widely separated acetate groups. Hydrolysis of the acetate produces widely spaced hydroxyl groups

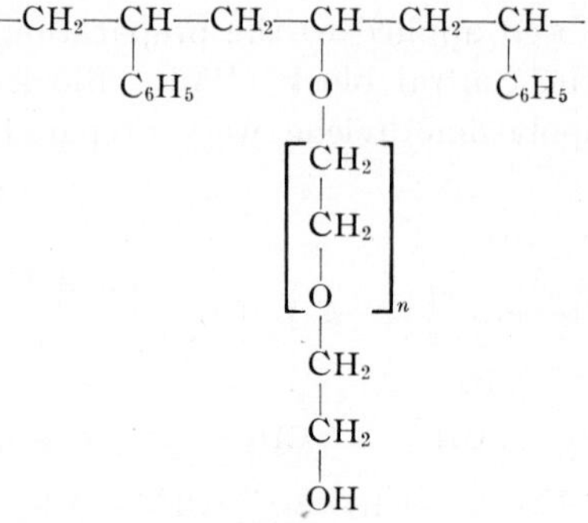

(IX)

which can serve to initiate a polyaddition reaction with ethylene oxide. The branches of the second monomer grow out exclusively from the original polymeric backbone and no competitive homopolymer from the oxide is formed (193). A segment of the graft polymer can be represented as in structure IX. A polymer of this type exhibits typical surface-active behavior. The macromolecule possesses water-soluble and oil-soluble segments. The segments derived from ethylene oxide are strongly solvated in water and keep the insoluble part of the polymer in stable suspension. If benzene is added to such a system it is accommodated in the oil-compatible polystyrene areas of the dispersed polymer molecules and we observe, as in the case of a detergent, solubilization of benzene in water. If the graft copolymer is placed in benzene, the oil-soluble segments of polystyrene keep the macromolecule in solution and water can be solubilized in the hydrocarbon phase.

Copolymers of styrene and dimethyl maleate have been converted to the copolymeric ethanolamide (eq. 55), and copolymers of styrene and allyl acetate have been hydrolyzed to the copolymeric alcohol (194) as in eq. (56). The hydroxyl groups in these copolymers initiate the graft copolymerization of ethylene oxide.

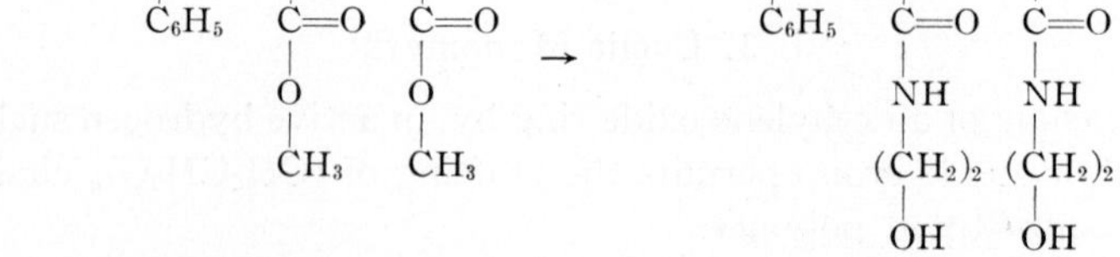

(55)

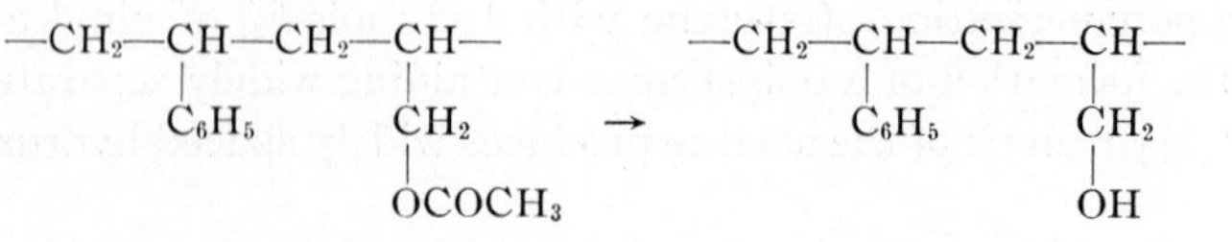

(56)

The reaction of cellulose (195) and poly(vinyl alcohol) (196) with ethylene oxide results in the addition of relatively short branches and therefore these are not truly graft copolymers.

The polymerization of propylene oxide initiated with propylene glycol yields macromolecules containing hydroxyl endgroups. If the reaction is continued with ethylene oxide, growth occurs at both ends of the center block, as shown in eq. (57). The product is a block copolymer with a center block of poly(propylene oxide) and two end blocks of poly(ethylene oxide). The Pluronics are commercially available nonionic surface-active agents of this type where the center block contains 20 to 40 propylene oxide units and the end blocks are of various lengths. Since these copolymers contain hydroxyl endgroups, poly(propylene oxide) blocks can again be grown on each end.

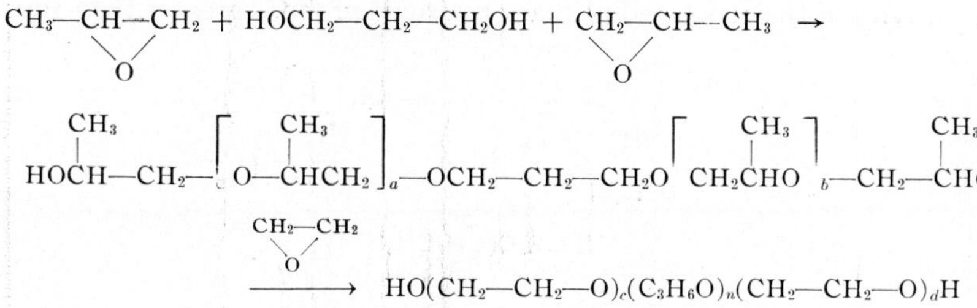
(57)

In an analogous manner, ethylenediamine can initiate the ring opening of propylene oxide to produce a tetraol with terminal hydroxyl groups capable of adding ethylene oxide to form a block copolymer.

Similar linear block copolymers can be obtained by polymerizing an α-amino-*N*-carboxyanhydride (Leuchs' anhydride) with a bifunctional initiator, as in eq. (58). The polymerization of ethylene oxide or another α-amino-*N*-carboxyanhydride can then be initiated by the reactive end groups of this polymer to form a block copolymer, as in eq. (59).

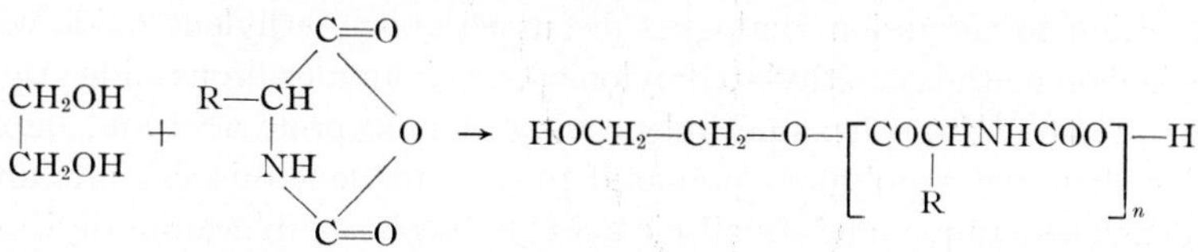
(58)

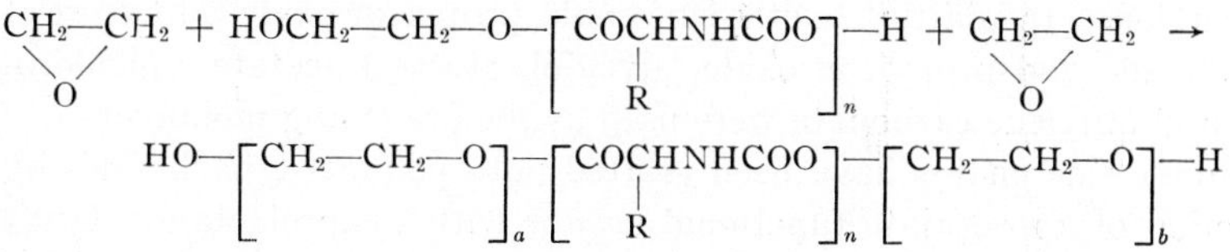
(59)

Ethylene oxide has been grafted on various superpolyamides and other amide-containing condensation polymers to produce a variety of "hydroxyethyl nylons" and related products (197). Nylon 66 prepared from hexamethylenediamine and adipic acid, nylon 6 prepared from caprolactam, and a 6, 66, 610 interpolymer prepared from caprolactam, hexamethylenediamine, adipic acid, and sebacic acid, were treated with excess ethylene oxide in a stainless steel bomb. In some cases a diluent such as toluene or dioxane was used.

Up to 55% ethylene oxide was grafted on the various derivatives, and in the case of the interpolymer more than 60% ethylene oxide was introduced. In all of the hydroxyethylated nylonlike materials, limited substitution of the backbone occurred, and a fairly high average length for the branches of polyethylene glycol was obtained (X). This was attributed to the fact that the reactivity of the generated primary hydroxyl group is greater than that

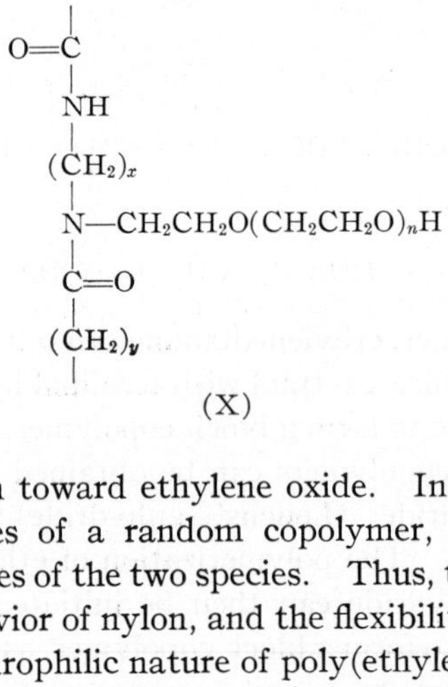

(X)

of the amide hydrogen toward ethylene oxide. Instead of possessing the intermediate properties of a random copolymer, these materials retain the individual properties of the two species. Thus, they have the solubility and high melting behavior of nylon, and the flexibility, second-order transition behavior, and hydrophilic nature of poly(ethylene oxides).

In addition to the nylon analogues discussed above, ethylene oxide was also grafted on methoxymethylated nylon 66, a polyamidesulfonamide interpolymer prepared from hexamethylene bis-ε-aminocaproic acid and hexamethylenediamine, a polyurea prepared from *m*-tolylene diisocyanate and hexamethylenediamine, and an adipic acid/diglycolic acid/hexamethylenediamine nylon. In addition to ethylene oxide, propylene oxide, a mixture of ethylene oxide and propylene oxide, glycidol, glycidol acetate, epichlorohydrin, and ethylene carbonate were used as the branching monomer.

Polyamide side chains have been grafted onto polymeric backbones by the reaction of appropriate functional groups with ε-caprolactam. Graft copolymers have been prepared from the lactam and a butadiene-styrene-methacrylic acid copolymer (198), styrene copolymers with acrylic acid, methyl acrylate, or maleic anhydride (199), and a styrene–*N*-methacryloylcaprolactam copolymer (200). For the most part the graft copolymers have been crosslinked.

The reaction of cotton with β-propiolactone yields graft polymers as a result of etherification and polyesterification (201). The polymers are mixed ethers and esters of cellulose due to the further reaction of the initial products with the lactone, as shown in eq. (60). The ether linkages are

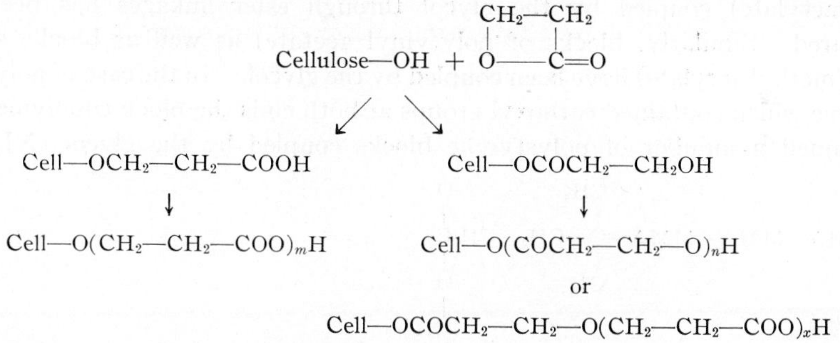

(60)

stable to saponification, while the ester linkages are broken. Therefore, saponification removes all but the carboxyethyl groups attached directly to the cellulose molecule. Dehydration of the β-propiolactone-treated cotton by azeotropically removing water with xylene (eq. 61) results in the production of unsaturated groups in the hydracrylic acid ester groups attached to the cellulose molecule. These are sites for copolymerization with vinyl monomers.

$$\text{Cell—OCOCH}_2\text{CH}_2\text{OH} \rightarrow \text{Cell—OCOCH{=}CH}_2 + \text{H}_2\text{O} \qquad (61)$$

4. Coupling Reactions

It is apparent that the existence of reactive functional groups on polymers permits the synthesis of block copolymers by the reaction of terminal groups, or the synthesis of graft copolymers by the reaction of terminal groups with side chain groups.

Addition polymers containing reactive endgroups have been prepared by polymerization of vinyl monomers initiated by specific catalysts. This subject is discussed extensively in Chapter IV.

The polymerization of styrene with 4,4′-azo-(4-cyano-*n*-valeric acid) as initiator has yielded polystyrene containing a carboxyl endgroup. Since termination in the case of styrene occurs by combination, the polystyrene contained a carboxyl group at each end. The polymerization of methyl methacrylate with this initiator yielded poly(methyl methacrylate) containing a carboxyl group at one end, since termination in this case is by disproportionation. In the case of vinyl acetate and methyl acrylate polymerization the polymers also contained one carboxyl endgroup. The carboxyl groups in these polymers were converted to the corresponding acid chlorides by treatment with thionyl chloride. Coupling was carried out by reaction with 1,6-hexanediol or 1,10-decanediol (202).

By this method a block copolymer containing two blocks of poly(methyl methacrylate) coupled by the glycol through ester linkages has been prepared. Similarly, blocks of poly(vinyl acetate) as well as blocks of poly(methyl acrylate) have been coupled by the glycol. In the case of polystyrene which contained carboxyl groups at both ends the block copolymer contained a number of polystyrene blocks coupled by the glycol (XI).

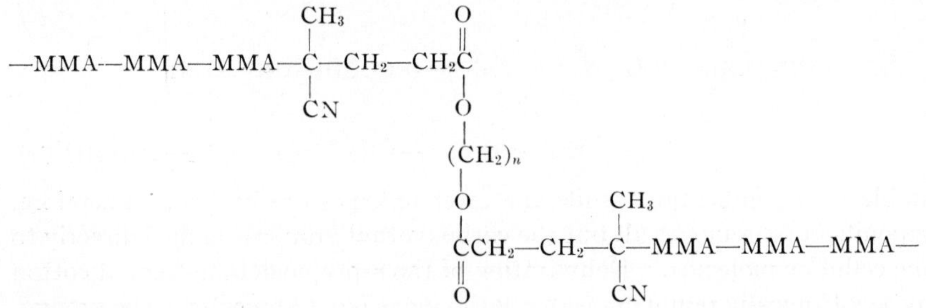

(XI)

A block copolymer of styrene and methyl methacrylate, in which one block of about 100 units of styrene was located between two blocks of methyl methacrylate each of approximately 120 units, has been prepared in an analogous manner.

The polymerization of styrene in the presence of hydrogen peroxide and ferrous sulfate at a low temperature yields polystyrene containing terminal hydroxyl groups (203,204). Similarly polymerization in solution with a *p*-bromobenzoyl peroxide–ferrous ion–benzoin initiating system gives a polystyrene with terminal hydroxyl groups. Reaction of the hydroxyl-

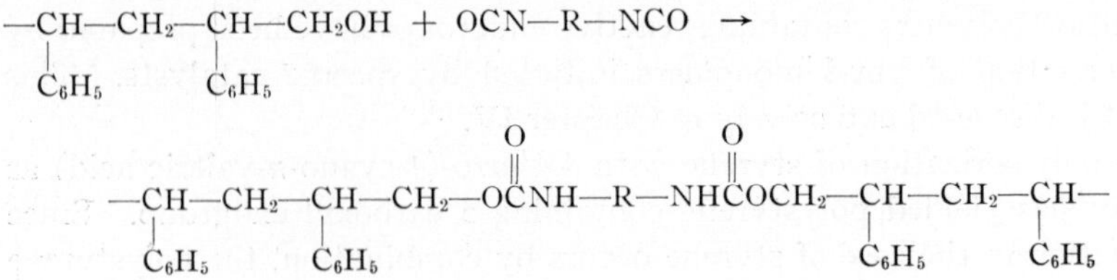

(62)

containing polymer with a diisocyanate yields a block copolymer shown in eq. (62).

Amine-terminated polystyrene has been prepared with sodium amide in liquid ammonia as initiator (205). The polystyrene contains one terminal amine group. A copolymer of methyl methacrylate, acrylonitrile, or styrene with a small amount of β-isocyanatoethyl methacrylate could be coupled with the amine-terminated polystyrene to give a grafted block copolymer. The amine-terminated polystyrene can also be coupled with a diisocyanate.

The reaction of polyethylene with sulfuryl chloride or a mixture of chlorine and sulfur dioxide yields chlorosulfonated polyethylene which contains $-SO_2Cl$ side chains. Reaction of the chlorosulfonated polymer with a hydroxyl-containing compound in the presence of an acid acceptor such as an organic or inorganic base gives the corresponding ester, as shown in eq. (63). Where the alcohol is polyfunctional, e.g., ethylene glycol or glycerol, a crosslinked block polymer is formed.

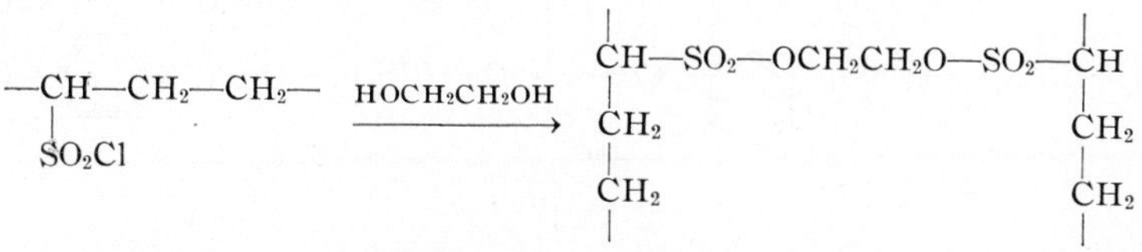

(63)

Where the alcohol is monofunctional, the resultant ester can be crosslinked to a block polymer by means of a dioxime, such as *p*-quinone dioxime or succinaldehyde dioxime, or compounds containing more than one hydroxyl, mercapto, amino, or amido group such as benzidine, as shown in eq. (64).

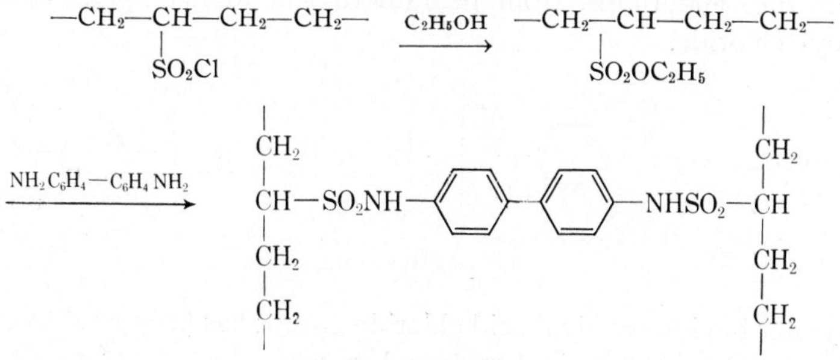

(64)

Block copolymers have been prepared from condensation polymers by a stepwise procedure wherein the blocks are prepared separately and then coupled through terminal reactive groups. If two polymer blocks contain different terminal groups which are capable of reaction, block copolymers are formed as a result of such reaction. If the two polymer blocks contain the same or similar terminal groups, a bifunctional coupling agent capable of reacting with such groups is used to prepare block copolymers. A few examples will illustrate the great number of variations possible by coupling condensation polymers.

Polyesters containing reactive terminal groups have been prepared and coupled to yield block copolyesters. Thus, poly(decamethylene isophthalate) with acid chloride endgroups is prepared by reacting decamethylene glycol with a slight excess of isophthaloyl chloride and carrying the reaction to substantial completion. Poly(decamethylene terephthalate) with hydroxyl end groups is prepared by reacting excess decamethylene glycol with terephthaloyl chloride. The reaction of substantially equivalent proportions of the two initial polyesters yields a block copolymer. A block copolyester of tetramethylene terephthalate and tetramethylene isophthalate (XII) is prepared in an analogous manner.

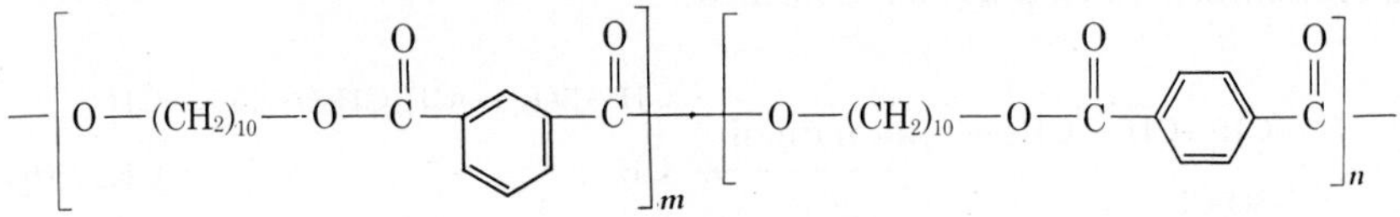

(XII)

A block copolyester of tetramethylene terephthalate and pentamethylene dithioterephthalate (XIII) is prepared by reacting poly(tetramethylene terephthalate) with acid chloride endgroups, from tetramethylene glycol and terephthaloyl chloride, with poly(pentamethylene dithioterephthalate) with mercapto endgroups, from pentamethylene dimercaptan and terephthaloyl chloride.

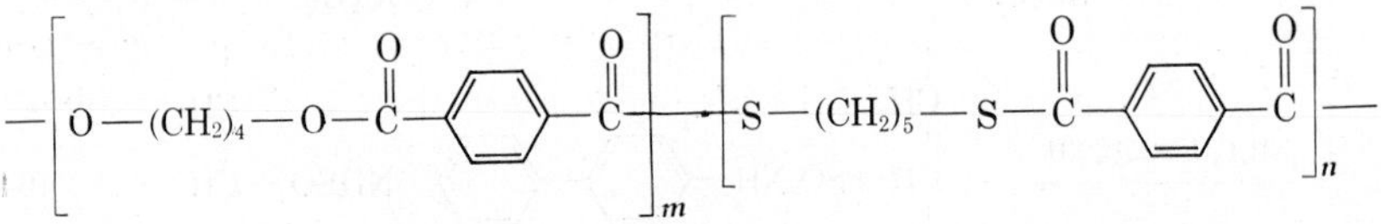

(XIII)

A polyester having terminal acid chloride groups has been used to couple two polyesters having terminal hydroxyl groups.

An interesting method of graft polymerization involves building the branch before the main chain (206). The monomer unit containing the branch has been prepared by the sequence of reactions shown in eq. (65). This ω-methylpolyoxyethylene 2-oxyterephthalate was heated with dimethyl terephthalate and ethylene glycol (with a trace of lead oxide as catalyst) to form the copolymer with poly(ethylene terephthalate) possessing the structure XIV.

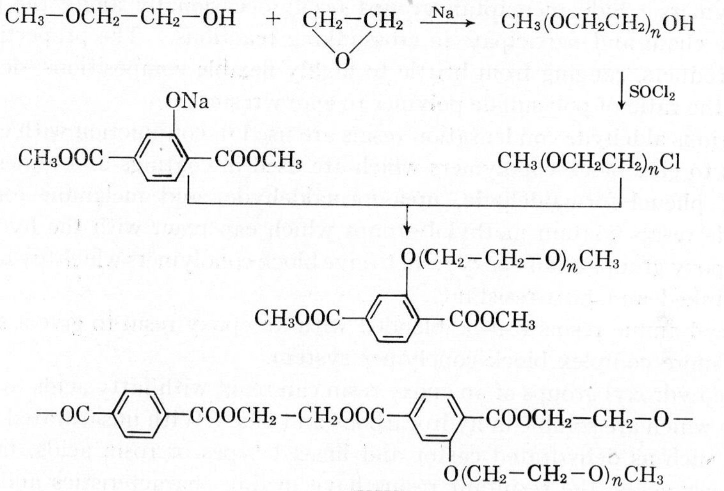

(65)

(XIV)

A number of commercially important block copolymers are based on the reaction of alkyd resins with polymers containing reactive groups to give useful coating compositions.

The so-called alkyd-amine resins are generally crosslinked block copolymers resulting from the interaction of an alkyd resin and a urea- or melamine-formaldehyde resin. The alkyd resin contains hydroxyl and carboxyl groups which react with the methylol or butoxymethyl groups of the anine-formaldehyde resin.

The alkyd-silicone resins result from the reaction of the hydroxyl and carboxyl groups of the alkyd resin with the hydroxyl groups of the silicone resin.

Epoxy resins, prepared by the condensation of epichlorohydrin with a polyhydroxy compound such as 2,2′-bis(*p*-hydroxyphenyl)propane or glycerol, contain secondary hydroxy groups and terminal epoxy groups which are capable of reacting with functional groups in polymers to form linear or crosslinked block copolymers.

Polyamides containing terminal primary amine groups and internal secondary amine groups are used to cure epoxy resins and give block copolymers ranging from rubbery, resilient solids to hard, tough, shock-resistant masses, depending upon the molecular weight and structure of the polyamide and the ratio of polyamide resin to epoxy resin.

Polysulfide liquid polymers are mercaptan-terminated chains which are capable of reacting with the epoxy groups of the epoxy resins to give block copolymers. Side mercaptan groups occur occasionally along the polysulfide chain and participate in crosslinking reactions. The properties of the products, ranging from brittle to highly flexible compositions, depend upon the ratio of polysulfide polymer to epoxy resin.

Various aldehyde condensation resins are used in conjunction with epoxy resins to give block copolymers which are used in coatings and adhesives. Thus, phenol–formaldehyde, urea–formaldehyde, and melamine–formaldehyde resins contain methylol groups which can react with the hydroxy and epoxy groups of an epoxy resin to give block copolymers which are highly crosslinked and heat-resistant.

Alkyd-amine resins can be blended with an epoxy resin to give a somewhat more complex block copolymer system.

The hydroxyl groups of an epoxy resin can react with fatty acids to form esters which are soluble in hydrocarbons and oils. With unsaturated fatty acids such as dehydrated castor and linseed types or rosin acids, tall oil or dimer acids, the resultant resins have drying characteristics and give cured block copolymers.

The epoxy resin esters based on unsaturated fatty acids can be copolymerized with vinyl monomers such as styrene or acrylic esters to give complex block copolymers containing units based on addition polymerization and others based on condensation polymerization.

Hydroxyl-containing addition polymers such as partially hydrolyzed vinyl chloride–vinyl acetate copolymers can react with an epoxy resin to give block copolymers.

Various nonpolymeric bifunctional compounds have been used to couple polymers containing reactive groups.

Poly(decamethylene isophthalate) and poly(decamethylene terephthalate), each having terminal hydroxyl groups, have been coupled by condensation with a diacyl chloride such as terephthaloyl chloride. Two polyesters, each having terminal acid chloride groups, can be coupled by means of a glycol or a dimercaptan.

The reaction of an epoxy resin with a diamine results in ring opening. Since the epoxy resin contains epoxide groups at both ends the product contains blocks of epoxy resin separated by the diamine. Generally polyalkylene polyamines such as triethylenediamine or tetraethylenepentamine are used and result in crosslinking due to reaction of both internal and terminal amino groups.

Acid anhydrides of dibasic acids such as phthalic, maleic, and succinic acids react with the hydroxyl groups of an epoxy resin to form crosslinked block copolymers. The half ester formed by the reaction of the anhydride and one hydroxyl group contains a carboxyl group which can react with the terminal epoxy groups of the epoxy resin.

Polyurethanes are prepared by the reaction between diisocyanates and polyesters or polyethers containing terminal hydroxyl groups. The reaction product is a block copolymer which has terminal isocyanate groups (XV), if the reaction is carried out with excess diisocyanate. Water, glycols, and diamines can be used for further reaction with the isocyanate terminated polymers.

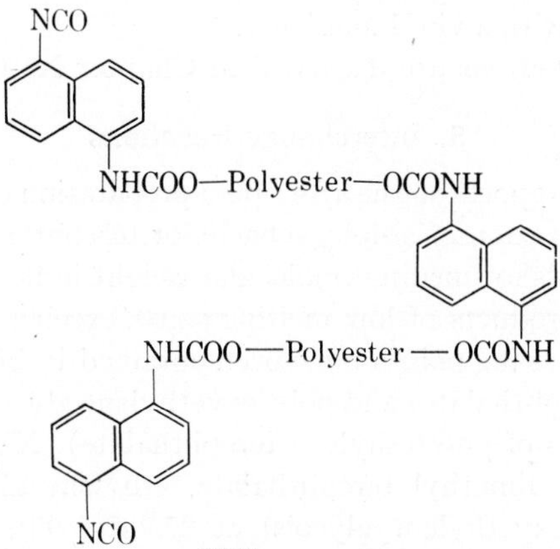

(XV)

Diisocyanates have been used to link together two different polyesters having terminal hydroxyl or carboxyl groups so that the two repeating units occur in blocks. When various amounts of poly(ethylene sebacate) and poly(ethylene adipate) are coupled with hexamethylene diisocyanate, copolymers containing up to 40% of the adipate have the same melting point as that of poly(ethylene sebacate). Further increase in the adipate content results in a rapid drop in melting point until the melting point of poly(ethylene adipate) is reached. In this series no great difference is found in impact strength between random and block copolymers. If, however, the crystalline poly(ethylene adipate) is replaced by the noncrystalline poly(propylene adipate), then block copolymers containing 15–30% of the latter have outstanding impact strength (207).

Block copolymers of a polyester and an epoxy resin have been prepared by means of coupling with a diisocyanate.

Crosslinked block copolymers have been prepared by coupling a saturated polyester with an unsaturated polyester by means of a diisocyanate and then copolymerizing the resultant unsaturated addition product with a vinyl monomer. Thus, poly(ethylene adipate) containing terminal hydroxyl groups is reacted with excess hexamethylene diisocyanate to yield a polymer containing terminal isocyanate groups. Reaction of this polymer with bis(diethylene glycol) maleate yields an unsaturated block polyester which is copolymerized with styrene in the presence of benzoyl peroxide. The unsaturated block polyester may also be prepared by reacting two moles of the diisocyanate with butenediol followed by reaction with a saturated polyester. The resultant unsaturated polyester can then be copolymerized with a vinyl monomer.

Diisocyanate reactions are discussed in Chapter XI-C.

5. Interchange Reactions

Although initial reports on the attempted preparation of block copolymers by the copolymerization of adipic, sebacic, or terephthalic acid with poly(oxyethylene glycols) of medium molecular weight indicated that the polymers were waxy products of low melting point, excellent mechanical properties and high melting points have been obtained in block copolymers of poly(ethylene terephthalate) and poly(oxyethylene glycols) (206).

The copolyesters of poly(ethylene terephthalate) (XVI) have been prepared by heating dimethyl terephthalate, ethylene glycol, and varying amounts of poly(oxyethylene glycols) at 275°C. The block copolymers consisted of amorphous poly(ethylene oxide) blocks interspersed among the crystalline poly(ethylene terephthalate) blocks. As much as 30% of the amorphous component did not lower the melting point appreciably, while the block copolymer retained the tenacity and extensibility of unmodified poly(ethylene terephthalate). The dyeability, moisture regain, and flexibility were all materially increased.

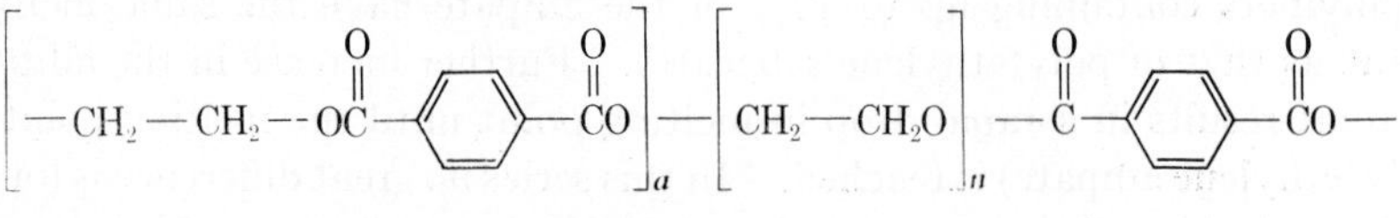

(XVI)

Analogous copolyesters of poly(ethylene terephthalate) have been prepared in which the secondary blocks were derived from poly(oxydecamethylene glycol) as well as the reaction products of 2,2′-bis(*p*-hydroxyphenyl)propane and ethylene oxide.

The fact that the products of these reactions are copolymers and not melt blends of poly(ethylene terephthalate) and poly(oxyethylene glycol) was shown by the incompatible mixture obtained by heating the two components together for 8 hr. at 275°C.

When a mixture of nylon 66, poly(hexamethylene adipamide), and nylon 610, poly(hexamethylene sebacamide), was heated under nitrogen at 290°C., amide interchange occurred. During the heating the interchange reaction results in the formation of block copolymers containing blocks of nylon 66 linked to blocks of nylon 610. At the end of 2 hr., equilibration resulted in what was either a block copolymer of uniform composition or a true random copolymer.

Transesterification between poly(methyl methacrylate) and various polyesters has been utilized in the grafting of side chains from the polyesters onto the vinyl polymer backbone (208). The structure and properties of the graft copolymers depend not only on the ratio of the initial substances and their nature but also on the duration of the transesterification reaction. When polyesters able to form ordered structures are grafted on poly(methyl methacrylate), the graft copolymers formed also have an ordered structure. Ordered structures are also found in graft copolymers formed by the reaction of isotactic poly(methyl methacrylate) with poly(ethylene azelate) (209).

The appendage of side chains or branches to various natural or synthetic high polymers results in the formation of a composite macromolecule whose properties generally differ from those of the individual components. The preparation of a graft or block copolymer represents a method of tailor-making a polymeric molecule in order to incorporate desired characteristics. It yields a new tool to be used in the task of controlling and molding molecular structure.

References

A. Self-Branching in Polymerization

1. Flory, P. J., *J. Am. Chem. Soc.*, **63,** 3083 (1941).
2. Stockmayer, W. H., *J. Chem. Phys.*, **12,** 125 (1944).
3. Fox, J. J., and A. E. Martin, *Proc. Roy. Soc.* (*London*) **A175,** 208 (1940); *Chem. Abstr.*, **34,** 4989[6] (1940).
4. Thompson, H. W., and P. Torkington, *Proc. Roy. Soc.* (*London*) **A184,** 3 (1945); *Chem. Abstr.*, **40,** 276[8] (1946).
5. Cross, L. H., R. B. Richards, and H. A. Willis, *Discussions Faraday Soc.*, **9,** 235 (1950); *Chem. Abstr.*, **46,** 3404i (1952).
6. Rugg, F. M., J. J. Smith, and L. H. Wartman, *Ann. N. Y. Acad. Sci.*, **57,** 398 (1953); *Chem. Abstr.*, **48,** 4288e (1954).

7. Bryant, W. M. D., and R. C. Voter, *J. Am. Chem. Soc.*, **75,** 6113 (1953).
8. Roedel, M. J., *J. Am. Chem. Soc.*, **75,** 6110 (1953).
9. Slowinski, E. J., Jr., H. Walter, and R. L. Miller, *J. Polymer Sci.*, **19,** 353 (1956).
10. Varga, S., *Chem. Zvesti*, **13,** 272 (1959); *Chem. Abstr.*, **53,** 20898i (1959).
11. Willbourn, A. H., *J. Polymer Sci.*, **34,** 569 (1959).
12. Beasley, J. K., *J. Am. Chem. Soc.*, **75,** 6123 (1953).
13. Nicolas, L., *Mem. Serv. Chim. Etat (Paris)*, **41,** 7 (1956); *Chem. Abstr.*, **52,** 16011a (1958); *J. Chim. Phys.*, **55,** 177, 185 (1958).
14. Billmeyer, F. W., Jr., *J. Am. Chem. Soc.*, **75,** 6118 (1953).
15. Nicolas, L., *Compt. Rend.*, **242,** 2720 (1956); *Chem. Abstr.*, **50,** 13500g (1956).
16. Mussa, C., *J. Polymer Sci.*, **20,** 223 (1956); **23,** 877 (1957).
17. Trementozzi, Q. A., *J. Polymer Sci.*, **23,** 887 (1957).
18. Muus, L. T., and F. W. Billmeyer, Jr., *J. Am. Chem. Soc.*, **79,** 5079 (1957).
19. Nicolas, L., *J. Polymer Sci.*, **29,** 191 (1958).
20. Zimm, B. H., and W. H. Stockmayer, *J. Chem. Phys.*, **17,** 1301 (1949).
21. Trementozzi, Q. A., *J. Polymer Sci.*, **22,** 187 (1956).
22. Thurmond, C. D., and B. H. Zimm, *J. Polymer Sci.*, **8,** 477 (1952).
23. Moore, L. D., Jr., G. R. Greear, and J. O. Sharp, *J. Polymer Sci.*, **59,** 339 (1962).
24. Richards, R. B., *J. Appl. Chem. (London)*, **1,** 370 (1951).
25. Sperati, C. A., W. A. Franta, and H. W. Starkweather, Jr., *J. Am. Chem. Soc.*, **75,** 6127 (1953).
26. Baccaredda, M., and G. Schiavinato, *J. Polymer Sci.*, **12,** 155 (1954).
27. Charlesby, A., and L. Callaghan, *Phys. Chem. Solids*, **4,** 227 (1958); *Chem. Abstr.*, **52,** 15955b (1958).
28. Sella, C., and J. J. Trillat, *Compt. Rend.*, **248,** 410 (1959); *Chem. Abstr.*, **53,** 12785h (1959).
29. Gubler, M. G., and A. J. Kovacs, *J. Polymer Sci.*, **34,** 551 (1959).
30. Majer, J., and P. Osecky, *Collection Czech. Chem. Commun.*, **25,** 2751 (1960); *Chem. Abstr.*, **55,** 5015c (1961).
31. Hawkins, S. W., and H. Smith, *J. Polymer Sci.*, **28,** 341 (1958).
32. Peticolas, W. L., and J. M. Watkins, *J. Am. Chem. Soc.*, **79,** 5083 (1957).
33. Ashby, C. E., J. S. Reitenour, and C. F. Hammer, *J. Am. Chem. Soc.*, **79,** 5086 (1957).
34. Moore, L. D., Jr., *J. Polymer Sci.*, **36,** 155 (1959).
35. Nielsen, L. E., *J. Appl. Phys.*, **25,** 1209 (1954).
36. Oakes, W. G., and R. B. Richards, *J. Chem. Soc.*, **1949,** 2929.
37. Wheeler, O. L., *Ann. N. Y. Acad. Sci.*, **57,** 360 (1953); *Chem. Abstr.*, **48,** 4249g (1954).
38. Ukida, J., R. Naito, and T. Kominami, *Kogyo Kagaku Zasshi*, **58,** 128 (1955); *Chem. Abstr.*, **49,** 13686g (1955).
39. Matsumoto, M., K. Imai, M. Maeda, Y. Oyanagi, and T. Saito, *Kobunshi Kagaku*, **12,** 398 (1955); *Chem. Abstr.*, **51,** 1695b (1957).
40. Patat, F., and J. A. Potchinkov, *Makromol. Chem.*, **23,** 54 (1957).
41. Elias, H. G., and F. Patat, *Makromol. Chem.*, **25,** 13 (1957).
42. Okamura, S., T. Yamashita, and T. Higashimura, *Bull. Chem. Soc. Japan*, **29,** 647 (1956); *Chem. Abstr.*, **51,** 18688i (1957).
43. Imoto, S., J. Ukida, and T. Kominami, *Kobunshi Kagaku*, **14,** 101, 127, 214 (1957); *Chem. Abstr.*, **52,** 1669h (1958).

44. Imoto, S., J. Ukida, and T. Kominami, *Kobunshi Kagaku,* **14,** 380 (1957); *Chem. Abstr.*, **52,** 5024b (1958).
45. Clarke, J. T., *Kunststoff-Plastics*, **3,** 151 (1956); *Chem. Abstr.*, **52,** 9646e (1958).
46. Melville, H. W., and P. R. Sewell, *Makromol. Chem.*, **32,** 139 (1959).
47. Bevington, J. C., G. M. Guzman, and H. W. Melville, *Proc. Roy. Soc.* (*London*), **A221,** 437 (1954); *Chem. Abstr.*, **48,** 6202f (1954).
48. Morton, M., and I. Piirma, *J. Polymer Sci.*, to be published.
49. Walker, O. J., Jr., and C. A. Winkler, *Can. J. Research,* **28B,** 298 (1950); *Chem. Abstr.*, **44,** 11162f (1950).
50. Wall, L. A., and D. W. Brown, *J. Polymer Sci.*, **14,** 513 (1954).
51. Schulz, G. V., G. Henrici, and S. Olivé, *Z. Elektrochem.*, **60,** 296 (1956); *Chem. Abstr.*, **50,** 11771f (1956).
52. Henrici-Olivé, G., and S. Olivé, *Kunststoffe-Plastics,* **5,** 315 (1958); *Chem. Abstr.*, **53,** 16580h (1959).
53. Morton, M., and I. Piirma, *J. Am. Chem. Soc.*, **80,** 5596 (1958).
54. Henrici-Olivé, G., S. Olivé, and G. V. Schulz, *Z. Physik. Chem.* (*Frankfurt*), **20,** 176 (1959); *Chem. Abstr.*, **54,** 1994b (1960).
55. Meyerhoff, G., and M. Cantow, *J. Polymer Sci.*, **34,** 503 (1959).
56. Cantow, M., G. Meyerhoff, and G. V. Schulz, *Makromol. Chem.*, **49,** 1 (1961).
57. Bevington, J. C., G. M. Guzman, and H. W. Melville, *Proc. Roy. Soc.* (*London*), **A221,** 453 (1954); *Chem. Abstr.*, **48,** 6158d (1954).
58. Schulz, G. V., G. Henrici, and S. Olivé, *J. Polymer Sci.*, **17,** 45 (1955).
59. Bengough, W. I., and R. G. W. Norrish, *Nature,* **163,** 325 (1949); *Proc. Roy. Soc.* (*London*) **A200,** 301 (1950); *Chem. Abstr.*, **45,** 4962i (1951).
60. Cotman, J. D., Jr., *Ann. N. Y. Acad. Sci.*, **57,** 417 (1953). *Chem. Abstr.*, **48,** 4288b (1954).
61. Bier, G., and H. Krämer, *Makromol. Chem.*, **18/19,** 151 (1956).
62. Bier, G., and H. Krämer, *Kunststoffe,* **46,** 498 (1956); *Chem. Abstr.*, **51,** 2320d (1957).
63. Shibukawa, T., and K. Nakaguchi, *Kobunshi Kagaku,* **14,** 353 (1957); *Chem. Abstr.*, **52,** 5027a (1958).
64. Bensasson, R., and A. Bernas, *J. Polymer Sci.*, **30,** 163 (1958).
65. Peebles, L. H., Jr., *J. Am. Chem. Soc.*, **80,** 5603 (1958).
66. Flory, P. J., *Principles of Polymer Chemistry,* Cornell University Press, Ithaca, New York, 1953, p. 384.
67. Flory, P. J., *J. Am. Chem. Soc.*, **69,** 2893 (1947).
68. Morton, M., and P. P. Salatiello, *J. Polymer Sci.*, **6,** 225 (1951).
69. Morton, M., *Ann. N. Y. Acad. Sci.*, **57,** 432 (1953); *Chem. Abstr.*, **48,** 4287d (1954).
70. Morton, M., J. A. Cala, and I. Piirma, *J. Polymer Sci.*, **15,** 167 (1955).
71. Morton, M., and W. E. Gibbs, *J. Polymer Sci.*, to be published.
72. Johnson, B. L., and R. D. Wolfangel, *Ind. Eng. Chem.*, **44,** 752 (1952).
73. Cragg, L. H., and G. R. H. Fern, *J. Polymer Sci.*, **10,** 185 (1953).
74. Hayes, R. A., *J. Polymer Sci.*, **13,** 583 (1954).
75. Drysdale, J. J., and C. S. Marvel, *J. Polymer Sci.*, **13,** 513 (1954).
76. Pollock, D. J., L. J. Elyash and T. W. DeWitt, *J. Polymer Sci.*, **15,** 335 (1955).
77. Cleland, R. L., *J. Polymer Sci.*, **27,** 349 (1958).

B. Graft Copolymerization

78. Smets, G., and R. Hart, *Fortschr. Hochpolymer. Forsch.*, **2**, 173 (1960).
79. Burlant, W. J., and A. S. Hoffman, *Block and Graft Polymers*, Reinhold, New York, 1960.
80. Ceresa, R. J., *Block and Graft Copolymers*, Butterworths, Washington, D. C., 1962.
81. Kolesnikov, G. S., and H. M. Ts'eng, *Usp. Khim.*, **31**, 1025 (1962); *Russ. Chem. Rev.* (*English Transl.*), **31**, 485 (1962); *Chem. Abstr.*, **58**, 577a (1963).
82. Bevington, J. C., G. M. Guzman, and H. W. Melville, *Nature*, **170**, 1026 (1952).
83. Smets, G., and M. Claeson, *J. Polymer Sci.*, **8**, 289 (1952).
84a. Allen, P. W., and F. M. Merrett, *J. Polymer Sci.*, **22**, 193 (1956).
84b. Allen, P. W., G. Ayrey, C. G. Moore, and J. Scanlan, *J. Polymer Sci.*, **36**, 55 (1959).
85. Roland, J. R., and L. M. Richards, *J. Polymer Sci.*, **9**, 61 (1952).
86. Alfrey, T., J. Bohrer, and H. Mark, *Copolymerization*, High Polymer Series, Vol. VIII, Interscience, New York, 1952, p. 159.
87. Smets, G., and A. Hertoghe, *Makromol. Chem.*, **17**, 189 (1956).
88. Schonfeld, E., and I. Waltcher, *J. Polymer Sci.*, **35**, 536 (1959).
89. Fox, T. G., M. S. Gluckman, F. Gornick, R. K. Graham, and S. Gratch, *J. Polymer Sci.*, **37**, 397 (1959).
90. Gluckman, M. S., M. J. Kampf, J. L. O'Brien, T. G Fox, and R. K. Graham, *J. Polymer Sci.*, **37**, 411 (1959).
91. Chaudhuri, D. K. R., and J. J. Hermans, *J. Polymer Sci.*, **51**, 373 (1961).
92. Bamford, C. H., and E. F. T. White, *Trans Faraday Soc.*, **52**, 716 (1956).
93. Bamford, C. H., and E. F. T. White, *Trans Faraday Soc.*, **54**, 268, 278 (1958).
94. Bamford, C. H., A. D. Jenkins, and E. F. T. White, *J. Polymer Sci.*, **34**, 271 (1959).
95. Hayes, R. A., *J. Polymer Sci.*, **11**, 531 (1953).
96a. Hicks, J. A., and H. W. Melville, *Nature*, **171**, 300 (1953); *J. Polymer Sci.*, **12**, 461 (1954).
96b. Hicks, J. A., and H. W. Melville, *Proc. Roy. Soc.* (*London*), **A226**, 314 (1954); *Chem. Abstr.*, **49**, 2774d (1955).
97. Bolland, J. L., and H. W. Melville, in *Proc. Rubber Technol. Conf., 1st, London, 1938*, T. R. Dawson and J. R. Scott, eds., Institution of the Rubber Industry, London, p. 239.
98. Melville, H. W., *J. Chem. Soc.*, **1941**, 414.
99. Dunn, A. S., and H. W. Melville, *Nature*, **169**, 699 (1952).
100. Hart, R., and A. de Pauw, Intern. Symp. Macromol. Chem. (IUPAC), Milan-Turin, 1954 [Published as *Ric. Sci. Suppl.*, **25**, 265 (1955)].
101. Coover, H. W., Jr., and J. B. Dickey, U. S. Patent 2,763,631 (to Eastman Kodak Co.), Sept. 18, 1956; *Chem. Abstr.*, **51**, 2304f (1957).
102. Allen, P. E. M., J. M. Downer, G. W. Hastings, H. W. Melville, P. Molyneux, and J. R. Urwin, *Nature*, **177**, 910 (1956).
103. Schmets, J., and G. Smets, *Bull. Soc. Chim. Belges*, **63**, 59 (1954); *Chem. Abstr.*, **48**, 10376d (1954).
104. Saigusa, T., and R. Oda, *Bull. Inst. Chem. Res., Kyoto Univ.*, **33**, 126 (1955); *Chem. Abstr.*, **50**, 1357h (1956).

105. Lynch, C. S., U. S. Patent 2,625,525 (to Phillips Petroleum Co.), Jan. 13, 1953; *Chem. Abstr.*, **47**, 4643a (1953).
106. Compagnon, P., and J. Le Bras, *Compt. Rend.*, **212**, 616 (1941); *Chem. Abstr.*, **38**, 1905[6] (1944).
107a. Le Bras, J., and P. Compagnon, *Bull. Soc. Chim. France*, **11**, 553 (1944); *Rubber Chem. Technol.*, **20**, 938 (1947); *Chem. Abstr.*, **40**, 1340[9] (1946).
107b. Le Bras, J., and P. Compagnon, *Rev. Gen. Caoutchouc*, **24**, 241, 281 (1947); *Chem. Abstr.*, **41**, 7795f (1947).
108. Merrett, F. M., *Trans. Faraday Soc.*, **50**, 759 (1954); *Chem. Abstr.*, **49**, 2108h (1955).
109. Merrett, F. M., and R. I. Wood, *Proc. Inst. Rubber Ind.*, **3**, 27 (1956); *Rubber Chem. Technol.*, **29**, 706 (1956).
110. Bloomfield, G. F., and P. M. Swift, *J. Appl. Chem. (London)*, **5**, 609 (1955).
111. N. V. de Bataafsche Petroleum Maatschappij, British Patent 679,562 (by K. Nozaki), Sept. 17, 1952; *Chem. Abstr.*, **47**, 7825c (1953).
112. Henglein, A., *Makromol. Chem.*, **14**, 128 (1955).
113. Henglein, A., *Makromol. Chem.*, **18/19**, 37 (1956).
114. Angier, D. J., and W. F. Watson, *J. Polymer Sci.*, **20**, 235 (1956).
115. Angier, D. J., R. J. Ceresa, and W. F. Watson, *J. Polymer Sci.*, **34**, 699 (1959).
116. Angier, D. J., and W. F. Watson, *J. Polymer Sci.*, **18**, 129 (1955).
117. Kargin, V. A., B. M. Kovarskaya, L. I. Golubenkova, M. S. Akutin, and G. L. Slonimskii, *Dokl. Akad. Nauk. S.S.S.R.*, **112**, 485 (1957); *Chem. Abstr.*, **52**, 7763f (1958).
118. Kovarskaya, B. M., L. I. Golubenkova, M. S. Akutin, and I. I. Levantovskaya, *Vysokomolekul. Soedin.*, **1**, 1042 (1959); *Chem. Abstr.*, **54**, 15998d (1960).
119. Grohn, H., and K. Bischof, *Chem. Tech. (Berlin)*, **11**, 384 (1959); *Chem. Abstr.*, **54**, 959b (1960).
120. Berlin, A. A., E. A. Penskaya, and G. I. Volkova, *J. Polymer Sci.*, **56**, 477 (1962).
121. Ceresa, R. J., *Polymer*, **2**, 213 (1961).
122. Ceresa, R. J., *Polymer*, **1**, 488 (1960).
123. Akutin, M. S., *Plastics Inst. (London) Trans. J.*, **28**, 216 (1960).
124. Akutin, M. S., N. Y. Parlaschkevitch, I. N. Kogan, V. V. Rubynshtein, and R. M. Grybkova, *Plasticheskie Massy*, **1960**, (6) 2; *Chem. Abstr.*, **55**, 7962b (1961).
125. Jones, M. H., H. W. Melville, and W. G. P. Robertson, *Nature*, **174**, 78 (1954).
126. Jones, M., *Can. J. Chem.*, **34**, 948 (1956).
127. Dunn, A. S., B. D. Stead, and H. W. Melville, *Trans. Faraday Soc.*, **50**, 279 (1954).
128. Guillet, J. E., and R. G. W. Norrish, *Nature*, **173**, 625 (1954).
129. Miller, M. L., *Can. J. Chem.*, **36**, 303, 306 (1958).
130a. Otsu, T., *J. Polymer Sci.*, **26**, 236 (1957).
130b. Imoto, M., T. Otsu, and J. Yonezawa, *Makromol. Chem.*, **36**, 93 (1960).
131. Oster, G., and O. Shibata, *J. Polymer Sci.*, **26**, 233 (1957).
132a. Cooper, W., and M. Fielden, *J. Polymer Sci.*, **28**, 442 (1958).
132b. Cooper, W., G. Vaughan, S. Miller, and M. Fielden, *J. Polymer Sci.*, **34**, 651 (1959).
133. Geacintov, N., V. Stannett, and E. W. Abrahamson, *Makromol. Chem.*, **36**, 52 (1959).

134. Geacintov, N., V. Stannett, E. W. Abrahamson and J. J. Hermans, *J. Appl. Polymer Sci.*, **3,** 54 (1960).
135. Schwab, E., V. Stannett, and J. J. Hermans, *Tappi*, **44,** 251 (1961).
136. Smets, G., W. de Winter, and G. Delzenne, *J. Polymer Sci.*, **55,** 767 (1961).
137. Menon, C. C., and S. L. Kapur, *J. Appl. Polymer Sci.*, **1,** 372 (1959).
138. Ballantine, D. S., *Mod. Plastics*, **35,** (1), 171 (1957).
139. Chen, W. K. W., R. B. Mesrobian, D. S. Ballantine, D. J. Metz, and A. Glines, *J. Polymer Sci.*, **23,** 903 (1957).
140. Restaino, A. J., *Effects of Radiation on Materials*, Reinhold, New York, 1958, chap. 11.
141. Ballantine, D. S., A. Glines, G. Adler, and D. J. Metz, *J. Polymer Sci.*, **34,** 419 (1959).
142. Bevington, J. C., and D. E. Eaves, *Nature*, **178,** 1112 (1956).
143. Chapiro, A., *J. Polymer Sci.*, **29,** 321 (1958); **34,** 439 (1959).
144. Gaylord, N. G., U. S. Patent 2,907,675 (to E. I. du Pont de Nemours & Co.), Oct. 6, 1959; *Chem. Abstr.*, **55,** 24102a (1961).
145a. Mino, G., and S. Kaizerman, *J. Polymer Sci.*, **31,** 242 (1959).
145b. Mino, G., S. Kaizerman, and E. Rasmussen, *J. Polymer Sci.*, **38,** 393 (1959).
146. Richards, G. N., *J. Appl. Polymer Sci.*, **5,** 539 (1961).
147. Bridgeford, D. J., *Ind. Eng. Chem., Prod. Res. Develop.*, **1,** 45 (1962).
148. Valentine, L., *J. Textile Inst.*, **46,** T270 (1955); *Chem. Abstr.*, **49,** 8604f (1955).
149. Oda, R., and T. Saigusa, *Bull. Inst. Chem. Res. Kyoto Univ.*, **32,** 32 (1954).
150. Hahn, W., and H. Lechtenböhmer, *Makromol. Chem.*, **16,** 50 (1955).
151. Saigusa, T., T. Nozaki, and R. Oda, *Kogyo Kagaku Zasshi*, **57,** 233, 243 (1954); *Chem. Abstr.*, **49,** 2773d (1955).
152. Metz, D. J., and R. B. Mesrobian, *J. Polymer Sci.*, **16,** 345 (1955).
153. Morrison, E. D., E. H. Gleason, and V. Stannett, *J. Polymer Sci.*, **36,** 267 (1959).
154. Manson, J. A., and L. H. Cragg, *Can. J. Chem.*, **36,** 858 (1958).
155. Sekhar, B. C., *Rubber Chem. Technol.*, **31,** 3430 (1958).
156. Hahn, W., and A. Fischer, *Makromol. Chem.*, **16,** 36 (1955).
157. Natta, G., *J. Polymer Sci.*, **34,** 531 (1959).
158. Natta, G., E. Beati, and F. Severini, *J. Polymer Sci.*, **34,** 685 (1959).
159. Landler, Y., and P. Lebel, *Intern. Symp. Macromol. Chem.* (IUPAC), Wiesbaden, 1959; Preprints, Section IV, A2.
160. Lebel, P., Ph.D. Thesis, University of Paris, 1957.
161. Korshak, V. V., and K. K. Mozgova, *Izv. Akad. Nauk. SSSR, Otd. Khim. Nauk.*, **1958,** 651; *Chem. Abstr.*, **52,** 19924f (1958).
162a. Korshak, V. V., K. K. Mozgova, and M. A. Shkolina, *Dokl. Akad. Nauk, SSSR*, **122,** 609 (1958).
162b. Korshak, V. V., K. K. Mozgova, and M. A. Shkolina, *Vysokomolekul. Soedin.*, **1,** 1364, 1573, 1604 (1959); *Chem. Abstr.*, **54,** 17956b, 4755c, 14755f (1960).
163. Kargin, V. A., P. V. Kozlov, N. A. Plate, and I. I. Konoreva, *Vysokomolekul. Soedin.*, **1,** 114 (1959); *Chem. Abstr.*, **53,** 17565i (1959).
164. Kargin, V. A., Kh. U. Usmanov, and B. I. Aikhodzhaev, *Vysokomolekul. Soedin.*, **1,** 149 (1959); *Chem. Abstr.*, **53,** 18476h (1959).
165a. Delzenne, G., and G. Smets, *Makromol. Chem.*, **18/19,** 82 (1956).
165b. Delzenne, G., and G. Smets, *Makromol Chem.*, **23,** 16 (1957).
166. Smets, G., A. Poot, M. Mullier, and J. P. Bex, *J. Polymer Sci.*, **34,** 287 (1959).

167. Smets, G., and A. E. Woodward, *J. Polymer Sci.*, **14**, 126 (1954).
168. Woodward, A. E., and G. Smets, *J. Polymer Sci.*, **17**, 51 (1955).
169. Melville, H. W., and W. F. Watson, *J. Polymer Sci.*, **11**, 299 (1953).
170. Ceresa, R. J., *Polymer*, **1**, 397 (1960).
171a. Orr, R. J., and H. L. Williams, *J. Am. Chem. Soc.*, **78**, 3273 (1956).
171b. Orr, R. J., and H. L. Williams, *J. Am. Chem. Soc.*, **79**, 3137 (1957).
172. Valentine, L., and B. Chapman. *Intern. Symp. Macromol. Chem.* (IUPAC), Milan-Turin, 1954 [Publ. as *Ric. Sci. Suppl.*, **25**, 278 (1955)].
173. Hahn, W., and A. Fischer, *Makromol. Chem.*, **21**, 77 (1956).
174. Richards, G. N., paper presented at the 138th Meeting of the American Chemical Society, New York, N. Y. Sept. 11–16, 1960.
175. Haas, H. C., P. M. Kamath, and N. W. Schuler, *J. Polymer Sci.*, **24**, 85 (1957).
176. Kamath, P. M., and H. C. Haas, *J. Polymer Sci.*, **24**, 143 (1957).
177. Kockelbergh, G., and G. Smets, *J. Polymer Sci.*, **33**, 227 (1958).
178. Plesch, P. H., *Chem. Ind. (London)*, **1958**, 954.
179. Teyssié, P., and G. Smets, *J. Polymer Sci.*, **20**, 351 (1956).
180. Rausing, G., and S. Sunner, *Tappi*, **45**, (1), 203A (1962).
181. Szwarc, M., *Nature*, **178**, 1168 (1956).
182. Szwarc, M., M. Levy, and R. Milkovich, *J. Am. Chem. Soc.*, **78**, 2656 (1956).
183. P. Rempp, V. I. Volkov, J. Parrod, and C. Sadron, *Vysokomolekul. Soedin.*, **2**, 1521 (1960).
184. O'Driscoll, K. F., R. J. Boudreau, and A. V. Tobolsky, *J. Polymer Sci.*, **31**, 115 (1958).
185a. O'Driscoll, K. F., and A. V. Tobolsky, *J. Polymer Sci.*, **31**, 123 (1958).
185b. O'Driscoll, K. F., and A. V. Tobolsky, *J. Polymer Sci.*, **37**, 363 (1959).
186. Greber, G., and J. Tölle, *Makromol. Chem.*, **53**, 208 (1962).
187. Greber, G., and G. Egle, *Makromol. Chem.*, **54**, 136 (1962).
188. Greber, G., and G. Egle, *Makromol. Chem.*, **53**, 206 (1962).
189. Greber, G., and G. Egle, *Makromol. Chem.*, **62**, 196 (1963).
190. Greber, G., and G. Egle, *Makromol. Chem.*, **64**, 68 (1963).
191. Orsino, J. A., D. F. Herman, and J. J. Brancato, Belgian Patent 575,559, Feb. 10, 1959.
192. Goodrich-Gulf Chemicals Inc., Belgian Patent 553,720, Dec. 27, 1956.
193. Mark, H., *Textile Res. J.*, **23**, 294 (1954).
194. Weiss, P., J. F. Gerecht and I. J. Krems, *J. Polymer Sci.*, **35**, 343 (1959).
195. Cohen, S. G., and H. C. Haas, *J. Am. Chem. Soc.*, **72**, 3954 (1950).
196. Cohen, S. G., H. C. Haas, and H. Slotnick, *J. Polymer Sci.*, **11**, 193 (1953).
197. Haas, H. C., S. G. Cohen, A. C. Oglesby, and E. R. Karlin, *J. Polymer Sci.*, **15**, 427 (1955).
198. Tutorskii, J. A., Z. I. Smelyi, and B. A. Dogadkin, *Vysokomolekul. Soedin.*, **1**, 1652 (1959); *Chem. Abstr.*, **54**, 20269d (1960).
199. Chapman, C. B., and L. Valentine, *J. Polymer Sci.*, **34**, 319 (1959).
200. Wichterle, O., and V. Gregor, *J. Polymer Sci.*, **34**, 309 (1959).
201a. Daul, G. C., R. M. Reinhardt, and J. D. Reid, *Textile Res. J.*, **24**, 738 (1954); *Chem. Abstr.*, **48**, 11796a (1954).
201b. Daul, G. C., R. M. Reinhardt, and J. D. Reid, *Textile Res. J.*, **25**, 330 (1955); *Chem. Abstr.*, **49**, 7860e (1955).
202. Bamford, C. H., and A. D. Jenkins, *Nature*, **176**, 78 (1955).

203. Baxendale, J. H., S. Bywater, and M. G. Evans, *J. Polymer Sci.*, **1,** 237 (1946).
204. Evans, M. G., *J. Chem. Soc.*, **1947,** 266.
205. Graham, R. K., *J. Polymer Sci.*, **24,** 367 (1957).
206. Coleman, D., *J. Polymer Sci.*, **14,** 15 (1954).
207. Coffey, R., and J. Meyrick, in *Proc. Rubber Technol. Conf., 3rd, London, 1954,* T. H. Messenger, ed., Institution of the Rubber Industry, London, p. 170.
208. Kolesnikov, G. S., and H. M. Ts'eng, *Vysokomolekul. Soedin.*, **2,** 1717 (1960); *Chem. Abstr.*, **55,** 25350c (1961).
209. Kolesnikov, G. S., and H. M. Ts'eng, *Vysokomolekul. Soedin.*, **1,** 1733 (1959); *Chem. Abstr.*, **54,** 17941a (1960).

Chapter XI

COUPLING REACTIONS

A. POLYSULFIDES

M. B. BERENBAUM

Thiokol Chemical Corp.

1. General Introduction

The polysulfide polymers are prepared by condensation of organic dihalides with aqueous sodium polysulfide solutions. The terminals of the polymers formed in the initial polymerization have been shown by Fettes, Jorczak, and Panek (1) to be predominantly hydroxylic in character.

$$\text{ClRCl} + \text{Na}_2\text{S}_2 \xrightarrow{\text{H}_2\text{O}} \text{HORS}\!\left(\text{SRS}\right)_n\text{SROH} \qquad (1)$$

Cure of these materials may be accomplished by reaction with metal oxides in the presence of activators. However, the resulting ionic bonds present in the vulcanized product render the polymer susceptible to chemorheologic flow as described in Chapter VII-C. In addition, in order to improve processing, most formulations for the vulcanization of these crudes include a base together with sulfur-containing accelerators such as mercaptobenzothiazole. These serve to facilitate processing by redistribution with the disulfides in the polymer backbone as well as by solubilizing the metal oxide used for chain extension. Again, these fragments promote chain interchange and consequent poor resistance to creep flow.

The outstanding solvent resistance of these products had led to a number of specialty applications of limited volume. However, the difficulty in handling these materials and poor compression set characteristics narrowly restricted their use. The breakthrough in technology which resulted in the rapid growth of the polysulfide polymers was the development by Patrick and Ferguson (2) of a technique for reducing these high molecular weight polymers to thiol-terminated liquids; these newer products will be the principal subjects in this section.

The reduction process is carried out on the polymer latex by treatment with sodium hydrosulfide and sodium sulfite followed by acidification to neutralize the sodium salts of the reduced polymer.

$$ClRCl + Na_2S_2 \rightarrow \sim SRSSRS\sim \quad (2)$$

$$\sim SRSSRS\sim + NaSH + Na_2SO_3 \rightarrow \sim SRSH + NaSRS\sim + Na_2S_2O_3 \quad (3)$$

$$\downarrow H+$$

$$\sim SRSH + HSRS\sim$$

The sodium sulfite is used to remove the labile sulfur in the thiomercaptide terminals formed as intermediates by reaction to form thiosulfate. At the same time, any trisulfide or higher rank polysulfide bonds are stripped down to the more stable disulfide structure.

The dihalide monomer used in most of the commercially available liquid polymers is bis(2-chloroethyl) formal, $ClCH_2CH_2OCH_2OCH_2CH_2Cl$. This intermediate yields polymers with fairly good physical properties and low odor in the cured state. The major limitation of this monomer is the susceptibility of the formal bond to hydrolytic breakdown in the presence of acids. Obviously, the resistance to oxidation is less than that of a saturated hydrocarbon but this is not as serious as the attack by acids.

In order to provide compression set resistance by formation of a crosslinked network, a trifunctional halide, trichloropropane, is incorporated into the polymerization system. More recently the need for improved low temperature performance has led to the development of polymers based on

TABLE XI-1
Physical Properties of Various Liquid Polymers

Polymer	Structure	Viscosity at 25°C., poises	Average molecular weight
LP-2	$-[SCH_2CH_2OCH_2OCH_2CH_2S]_n-$	350–450	4000
LP-3	"	7–12	1000
LP-8	"	2.5–4.0	600
LP-31	"	800–1400	7500
LP-32	"	350–450	4000
LP-33	"	14–16.5	1000
LP-205	$-[S(CH_2)_4OCH_2O(CH_2)_4S]_n-$	12–17	1200
LP-370	$-[S(CH_2)_4O(CH_2)_4S]_n-$	11.5–14.5	1200

dihalides with a higher proportion of hydrocarbon content. The polymers derived from bis(4-chlorobutyl) formal and bis(4-chlorobutyl) ether have outstanding low temperature properties although this is obtained at some sacrifice in solvent resistance.

Table XI-1 lists the various polysulfide liquid polymers now commercially available.

The thiol-terminated liquid polymers are amenable to a wide variety of cures and have proven to be very versatile, finding uses in many diverse applications. When properly formulated, cured compounds possess outstanding resistance to fuels, solvents, and many chemicals; excellent resistance to oxidation, ozone, and weathering; low permeability to gases and vapors; and good electrical insulation properties.

The lower molecular weight, lower viscosity polymers are used as casting and potting compounds, in adhesives and coatings, as binders for solid rocket propellants, as impregnants for leather and other porous materials, and as modifiers for epoxide and phenolic resins. Where higher viscosities can be tolerated, the intermediate molecular weight products (LP-2, LP-32) can be used for many of these applications. However, the major outlets for the 4000–8000 molecular weight polymers are in sealants and adhesives.

The cocure or coreaction of thiol-terminated polysulfide polymers of low molecular weight is an elegant technique for the preparation of block copolymers. The availability of the low molecular weight flexible polymer chains has led to a number of applications for these materials in which block copolymers are formed with relatively brittle resins. Incorporation of the flexible polysulfide moiety imparts impact strength and flexibility to epoxy resins, phenolic, and urea–formaldehyde resins.

The reduction technique has been successfully applied to the conversion of the relatively intractable high molecular weight polymer from bis(2-chloroethyl) formal to a processable crude elastomer, Thiokol polysulfide polymer, Type ST. This finds use in mechanical molded goods like gaskets, seals and O-rings.

Because of the success of these curable liquid products, a number of variations have been prepared experimentally (3,4) in which the thiol terminal is replaced by other functional groups including hydroxyl, allyl, carboxyl or epoxy. All but the last mentioned structure can be incorporated by any of the techniques represented in eqs. (4)–(6). Generally, use of the first

$$n\text{ClRCl} + 2\text{ClR'X} + \text{Na}_2\text{S}_2 \rightarrow \text{XR'S}(\text{SRS})_n\text{SR'X} \quad (4)$$

$$n\text{HSRSH} + 2\ \text{HSR'X} \xrightarrow{[\text{O}]} \text{XR'S}(\text{SRS})_n\text{SR'X} \quad (5)$$

$$\text{-(SRS)-}_m + n\text{XR'SSR'X} \xrightarrow{\text{Base}} \text{XR'S-(SRS)-}_n\text{SR'X} \quad (n \ll m) \qquad (6)$$

procedure involving cocondensation of the dihalide with the monofunctional halide carrying the desired structure is preferred. These intermediates are more readily available and the process is somewhat less expensive since it circumvents the various steps required for polymerization and reduction to the thiol terminal. The redistribution technique (see Chapter VII-C) may be useful, since the disulfides are fairly easy to prepare.

The epoxide terminal is introduced by procedures analogous to those used for the preparation of epoxy resins. The thiol-terminated liquid polymer is reacted with epichlorohydrin, and the resulting intermediate is treated with base to form the desired product (5).

Despite a great deal of work with the various modifications available, only the thiol-terminated polymers are sold in commercial quantities. The hydroxyl-terminated products are available in development quantities but have not yet found extensive markets. They are used primarily as epoxy modifiers and in special solvent resistant bases for lubricants.

The reaction of the thiol terminal can be used in chain extension processes which can be broken down into four categories: (*1*) mercaptide salt formation; (*2*) oxidation of the thiol terminals to disulfides; (*3*) addition reactions; (*4*) condensation reactions. A good cure must meet a rather extensive number of requirements. Chain extension should take place efficiently and completely to form the high molecular weight product by end-to-end chain extension which leads to the maximum in physical properties. Branching and free ends have been shown to detract from tear strength and tensile strength. The cure process should be free from side reactions which would bring about chain scission or undesired crosslinking either during cure or on aging. Sufficient working life for the formulated mixture is necessary while at the same time rapid and controllable conversion on application is desirable. Compatibility with conventional fillers, adhesive additives and other compounding ingredients is important. The curing agent should be easily incorporated into the liquid polymer by conventional methods. Last, but not least, the final cure formulation should be reasonable in cost.

2. Mercaptide Salt Formation

The thiol terminals readily form salts with polyvalent inorganic oxides which convert the commercial liquid polymers to high molecular weight elastomeric solids. For example, zinc oxide will react with LP-2 at 70°C. in 48 hr. to form an elastomer with good physical properties. Similar results can be had with lead oxide, antimony oxide, arsenic oxide and cadmium oxide. However, all of these salt cures suffer from a serious drawback, in that aging at 100–125°C. results in substantial weight losses, as much as 30% in 2 weeks at 125°C. This is due to a cyclodepolymerization reaction initiated at the mercaptide terminals:

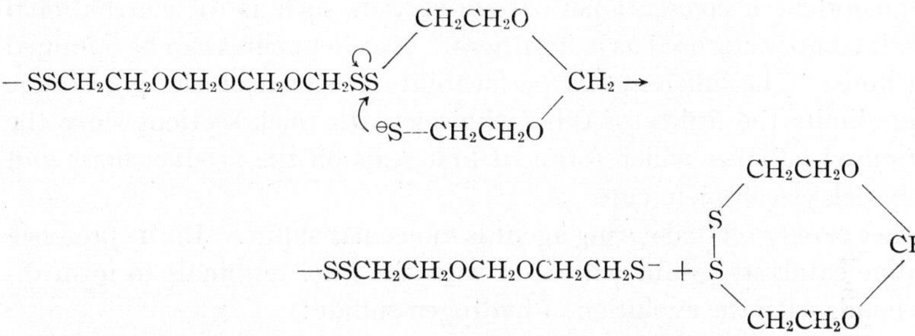
(7)

As indicated in the introduction, similar cures are possible with hydroxyl-terminated polymers. This method of vulcanization is used only with crude rubbers, not the liquid polymers. The thermoplasticity arising from interchange at the salt bonds restricts these formulations to applications such as inner-liner in composite hose where the outstanding solvent resistance of these polymers is needed or in printing rolls where service requirements are not such as to be handicapped by the flow properties and where solvent resistance is again essential.

3. Oxidative Cures: Inorganic Agents

An exceedingly wide variety of oxidizing agents have been used successfully to cure the thiol-terminated polysulfide liquid polymers, particularly in the intermediate molecular weight range. The lower molecular weight polymers, 500–1000 molecular weight, present difficulties because of the rather substantial weight proportions of oxidizer usually needed to bring about cure. Another problem is the magnitude of the exotherm during cure which can drive the oxidation of the thiol past the disulfide. The stronger oxidative curing agents can cleave the disulfide to form the relatively unstable thiolsulfonate or even the sulfonic acid. However, by proper selection of curing agents, it is possible to control the conversion of all of the liquid polymers to useful products at room temperature or at elevated temperatures depending on the service requirement. Since oxidation reactions, even in polymers, follow the rules of organic chemistry, chain extension is not accomplished at 100% yield. As a consequence, the lower the molecular weight of the liquid polymer, the poorer the physical properties upon cure. The various side reactions which can occur in all of the cures result in disruption of the product structure sufficient to cause reduction in tensile strength, elongation and tear strength.

The simplest curing agent is the oxygen present in air. Cures can be readily accomplished in the presence of alkaline activators such as diphenylguanidine or conventional oxygen carriers such as the conventional metal salt compounds used as paint driers. Excellent cures can be obtained in thin films. The inherent low permeability to gases of the polysulfide polymers limits the utility of this technique with thick sections since the skin of cured polymer which forms at first seals off the product mass and seriously delays complete cure.

Another closely related curing agent is molecular sulfur. In the presence of alkaline catalysts, sulfur will react with the thiol terminals to form disulfide bonds with the evolution of hydrogen sulfide:

$$HSRSH + S \rightarrow (SRS)_n + H_2S \quad (8)$$

This technique is limited to films since H_2S is evolved and must be permitted to escape before the cure is completed. Secondly, the excess sulfur normally used to insure completion of the cure is incorporated into the polymer chain to form higher rank polysulfide links. The trisulfide and higher alkyl polysulfide structures have a lower order of thermal stability than the disulfide bonds which make up the main product backbone. In addition, these high rank bonds are susceptible to chemorheological flow and cause poor compression set properties. However, sulfur is frequently used as an agent to accelerate many of the other oxidative cures.

The most widely used reagent is lead dioxide. With the intermediate molecular weight LP-2 polymers, this reagent yields excellent cures. Because of the need to disperse the finely divided inorganic oxide thoroughly, it is generally used as a 50% paste in a plasticizer such as dibutyl phthalate. Ball milling or paint milling in the inert vehicle serves to disperse the curing agent. Direct incorporation of the powdered reagent into the polymer may result in localized cure in which the polymer initially formed seals over the curing agent and prevents further reaction. The cure reaction may be controlled by a number of reagents. Bases will accelerate the vulcanization while weak organic acids serve as retarders. Stronger acids cannot be used, since they attack the formal link present in most of the commercially available products and bring about degradation of the polymer (eq. 9).

$$—SCH_2CH_2OCH_2OCH_2CH_2S— + H_2O \xrightarrow{H^+} —SCH_2CH_2OH + CH_2O + HOCH_2CH_2S— \quad (9)$$

Generally, an excess of the curing agent is used to insure complete conversion of the thiol terminals. Even under these circumstances, however, a few undesirable lead mercaptide bonds are incorporated into the polymer chain from the reaction of the lead monoxide formed in the oxidative cure process. This can be eliminated or minimized by incorporation of small amounts of sulfur where room temperature cures are desired since the sulfur serves to oxidize the mercaptide structures with formation of inert lead sulfide. At elevated temperatures, the lead mercaptide bonds break down to form a monosulfide structure and lead sulfide.

$$\text{HSRSH} + \text{PbO}_2 \rightarrow \text{-(S—R—S)-}_n + \text{PbO} + \text{H}_2\text{O} \quad (10)$$

$$\sim\text{RSH} + \text{PbO} \rightarrow \sim\text{RSPbSR}\sim + \text{H}_2\text{O} \quad (11)$$

$$\sim\text{RSPbSR}\sim + \text{S} \rightarrow \sim\text{RSSR}\sim + \text{PbS} \quad (12)$$

$$\sim\text{RSPbSR}\sim \xrightarrow{\Delta} \sim\text{RSR}\sim + \text{PbS} \quad (13)$$

All of the cures based on inorganic oxidizing agents appear to require at least a trace of moisture to initiate the cure reaction. For example, elimination of the 0.05–0.1% of water normally present in the liquid polymer will greatly retard the lead peroxide cure. This has been used on occasion as a technique to slow down vulcanization based on this system. However, the high reactivity of lead peroxide is such that stable one-package systems which can be triggered by absorption of moisture cannot be successfully prepared. Once the cure has started and water is generated in the oxidation reaction, then autoacceleration takes over to bring about fairly rapid complete conversion.

The alkaline earth peroxides are another useful family of agents for the LP-2 class of polymers. These compounds are also effective at room temperature, although some form of activation is needed. This can be accomplished by addition of trace amounts of water and bases such as calcium hydroxide.

These agents have provided a useful approach to one-package curing systems since in the absence of moisture, the intermediate molecular weight liquid polymers are stable in combination with barium and calcium peroxides for periods of three to six months. Absorption of moisture from the air triggers the cure. To facilitate cure throughout the polymer mass in thicker sections, hygroscopic salts or other agents can be added. This technique is particularly useful for sealant applications, although the problem of variable cure arising from humidity variation has been the subject of considerable research.

Zinc peroxide behaves similarly to the above agents but is somewhat more sluggish in its action. Acceleration with inorganic carbonates or amines is essential to obtain room temperature conversion to useful products.

Chromate salts in the presence of solubilizing agents yield excellent room temperature cures with the intermediate molecular weight liquid polymers (6,7). Water is frequently used but fairly substantial proportions are needed for optimum cure and this may adversely affect aging performance. Dimethylformamide, dimethyl sulfoxide, or other potent solvents for inorganic salts have proven to be effective activators.

These systems have shown outstanding high temperature performance for the polysulfide polymers. High temperature instability has been a serious limitation of the polysulfide polymers. Conventional cures based on lead peroxide are useful for intermittent service to about 250°F. A properly compounded chromate cure will give similar performance at 275–300°F. The improvement is probably due to the lower reactivity of the excess chromate at these temperatures to the susceptible disulfide and formal linkages in the polymer.

Anhydrous chromate salts have also been used successfully as the basis for one package sealants since the oxidation process in this system is particularly dependent on moisture.

Tellurium dioxide and manganese dioxide are relatively new curing agents which have proven to be quite versatile. Both can be used with the full range of liquid polymers to give products with good physical properties and excellent high temperature performance. Tellurium dioxide and manganese dioxide are generally used with dinitrobenzene to give better properties since the nitro compounds are useful curing agents in their own right. Not all sources of manganese dioxide are effective. Battery grade material can be used, particularly if activated by treatment with alkali. The most effective form is that prepared in the presence of caustic.

4. Oxidative Cures: Organic Agents

Suitable organic curing agents include the hydroperoxides and aliphatic peroxides, dioximes, and aromatic polynitro compounds. The organic curing agents are not as widely used as inorganic compounds because of the undesirable characteristics of many of the by-products of the oxidation process, and the poorer physical properties usually observed.

Organic peroxides are limited to use with the intermediate to higher molecular weight polymers. Their action is difficult to control with the lower molecular weight products. At elevated temperatures, most peroxides will attack the disulfide bonds. This results in poor high temperature properties since all cures are carried out with some excess over stoichiometry.

Cumene hydroperoxide is the most commonly used agent. However, contamination with by-product cumyl alcohol results in plasticization of the product. Use of an alkaline environment promotes room temperature cures. Organic amines are commonly added. Tris(dimethylaminomethyl) phenol or aliphatic amines are preferred since their action is less affected by humidity than the diphenylguanidine used in older formulations.

A novel activating system has been developed in which a small amount of iodine or iodine donor is coupled with cumene hydroperoxide (8). Iodine is an excellent, clean-cut oxidizing agent for the thiol group but the iodide formed is very corrosive. Here, the essentially catalytic amount of iodine is continually regenerated by reaction with the peroxide which is substantially less reactive to the thiol in the absence of a base. By suitably balancing the proportions of the curing agent, it is possible to control the working life and cure time within fairly broad limits.

Aliphatic peroxides like di*tertiary* butyl peroxide are relatively sluggish and require fairly high temperature cures which can be more easily accomplished by other methods. The acyl peroxides cannot be used since they usually yield some acid residue as a by-product. These acids will catalyze the breakdown of the formal bonds of the polymer, particularly on being heated, yielding products with poor aging performance. Attempts to incorporate buffers or other acid absorbers have been generally unsuccessful, and this relatively convenient and available type of peroxide is not used.

Organic oximes, particularly *p*-quinonedioxime, are another type of compound which can convert the full gamut of liquid polymers. These are mild agents requiring heat to drive the reaction. Addition of organic bases like diphenylguanidine is essential. Frequently, sulfur is added to complete the cure and give better compression set characteristics. The oximes are reduced to aromatic amines in cure. and the resulting susceptibility to staining of the product and of materials in contact with the product is a serious drawback. The activity of the amines at elevated temperature results in chain scission.

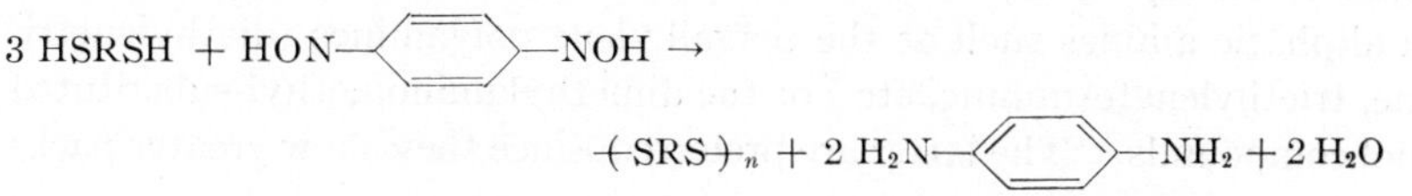

(14)

Aromatic polynitro compounds such as trinitrotoluene, dinitrobenzene, etc. are useful as cocuring agents with other systems. They are a bit too unreactive to be used as a primary vulcanizing agent. However, in combination with other systems such as manganese dioxide or tellurium dioxide, excellent cures can be obtained. This has been of advantage in the low molecular weight liquid polymer series where very considerable weights of these inorganic oxidizing agents would be needed to provide the necessary stoichiometry and would be present in sufficient proportion to modify physical properties. By combination with dinitrobenzene, it is possible to keep the hardness and modulus of the product under control.

$$8HSRSH + C_6H_4(NO_2)_2 \rightarrow (SRS)_n + C_6H_4(NH_2)_2 + 4H_2O \qquad (15)$$

5. Addition Reactions

The use of addition reactions to bring about chain extension of the polysulfide polymers has been exploited extensively in recent years. The most important of the addition reactions are those with epoxy resins and with isocyanates. A very limited amount of work has been done with polyunsaturated systems.

The reaction of hydroxyl- or thiol-terminated liquid polymers with the bisphenol epoxy resins in the presence of bases to form a new type of block copolymer was reported in 1951. With the advent in recent years of a wide variety of different types of epoxy resins and increasing markets for these materials, the use of the thiol-terminated liquid polymers in this field has increased substantially. A number of commercial applications have been found for these block copolymers in castings, encapsulation, coatings, adhesives and sealants. Incorporation of the flexible polysulfide chain segment into the relatively brittle epoxy resin brings about substantial improvement in impact strength and flexibility over the conventional epoxy systems (9–11).

Under base-catalyzed conditions, the thiol-terminated polymers react quite readily and are essentially completely incorporated into the cured product. The mercaptide groups react preferentially with the epoxide structure in competition with the amines. This is indicated by the absence of any free thiol polymer on extraction tests from a sample which has been allowed to cure properly. Room temperature cures are readily obtained with aliphatic amines such as the polyalkylene polyamines (diethylenetriamine, triethylenetetramine, etc.) or the dimethylaminomethyl-substituted phenol compounds. The latter are preferred, since they show greater package compatibility with the commercially available liquid polymers. Aromatic amines like *m*-phenylenediamine require heat for proper conversion.

Acid activation of the LP-epoxy cures is not too widely used. The Lewis acid family of catalysts generally affect the electrical properties adversely and at the same time promote poor heat aging performance since they catalyze the hydrolytic attack of the formal structure in the polysulfide moiety. Anhydride cures have been used successfully. However, normally these systems are designed to give high temperature performance, and while the introduction of the polysulfide structure does improve impact strength, it always does this at some sacrifice in the heat distortion temperature.

A relatively recent development has been the use of polyisocyanates as curing agents or an intermediates in the preparation of isocyanate-terminated liquid prepolymers (12,13). It is quite difficult to prepare stable prepolymers from the thiol-terminated polysulfide products. Apparently, trace impurities catalyze secondary crosslinking reactions which result in premature gelation. This can be avoided by rigorous purification. However, hydroxyl-terminated polymers can be converted to stable prepolymer systems and current activity is centered in this area.

The hydroxyl-terminated polysulfide crude rubbers can be cured under standard vulcanization conditions with polyaryl polyisocyanate (PAPI) to a product with fairly good compression set properties. This is one of the few techniques by which a hydroxyl-terminated polymer can be cured to a product resistant to chemorheologic flow.

The thiol-terminated polymers can also be converted to low density urethane foams with moisture and amine catalyst. These products have excellent oil and solvent resistance but rather poor physical properties compared with the polyester or polyether foams.

$$\text{HSRSH} + \text{OCN—R'—NCO} \rightarrow \text{OCN(R'NH}\overset{\text{O}}{\overset{\|}{\text{C}}}\text{SRS}\overset{\text{O}}{\overset{\|}{\text{C}}}\text{NR)}_n\text{R'NCO} \qquad (16)$$

$$\text{—R'NCO} + \text{H}_2\text{O} \rightarrow \text{—R'NHCONHR'—} + \text{CO}_2 \qquad (17)$$

Unsaturated polyester resins have been modified by addition of the thiol-terminated liquid polymers. Impact strength and shrinkage properties can be improved but the physical properties are adversely affected. The highly branched nature of these resins does not seem to lend itself too well to modification but the block copolymer approach and the needed flexibilization can be more readily achieved by suitable final monomer selection.

Phenolic resins, particularly for coating applications, have been successfully modified with the polysulfide polymers (14). Studies have shown that the thiol terminals will react readily with methylol phenols under acidic conditions to produce thioether (15). In the alkali-catalyzed phenolic resin synthesis, the mercaptide ion presumably reacts through the quinoid structure postulated as an intermediate. The degree of flexibilization is proportional to the polysulfide polymer content. The product properties are quite satisfactory but commercialization has been held up because of the relatively high cost of the polysulfide polymers in the amounts needed.

B. EPOXIDES

MARCO WISMER

Pittsburgh Plate Glass Co.

1. Preparation and Structure of Epoxy Resins

Epoxy resins are one of the more important thermosetting resins available today. They are being used on an increasing scale for a diversity of applications in the electrical, chemical, and engineering industries.

The common characteristic of epoxy resins is that they contain two or more oxirane groups. The epoxy resins which account for the major part of the commercial production are obtained by the reaction of polyphenols with epichlorohydrin. Other newer types of epoxy resins are obtained by the epoxidation of unsaturated compounds with peracetic acid. Epoxy resins produced by the reaction of an aliphatic polyol with epichlorohydrin represent only a small fraction of the market.

a. From Polyphenols and Epichlorohydrin

(1) 2,2-Bis(4-hydroxyphenyl)propane (Bisphenol A) (I)

The reactions leading to the formation of these resins take place above 50°C. in the presence of an alkaline catalyst. The primary reaction shown in eq. (18) involves the opening of the epoxide group by the phenolic hydroxyl groups (II). This reaction is followed by the dehydrochlorination to regenerate terminal epoxy groups, as shown by structure III in eq. (19).

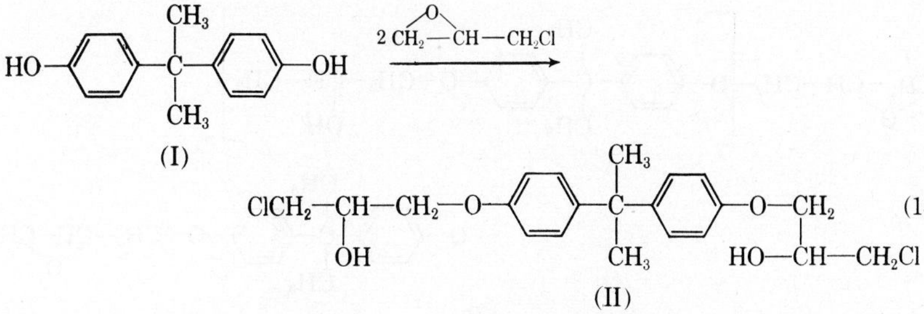

(18)

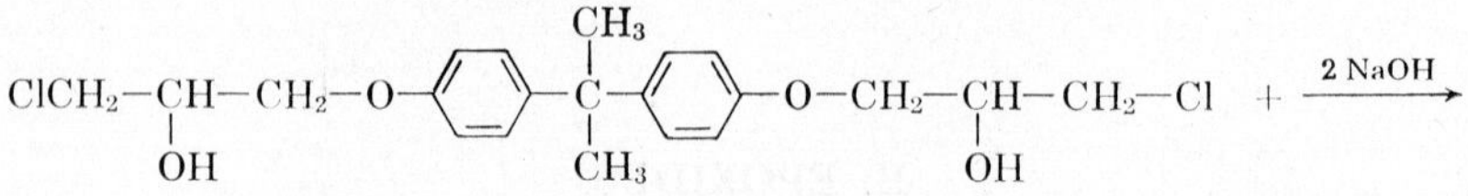

(19)

(II)

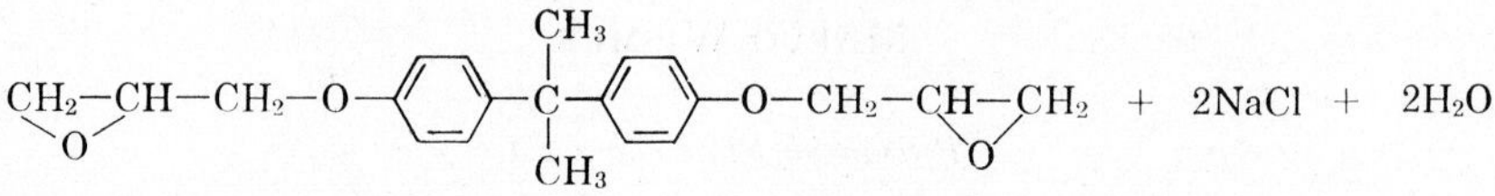

(III)

The condensation may proceed further by the reaction of the phenolic hydroxyl groups with the epoxy groups of the resin (IV) as shown in eq. (20).

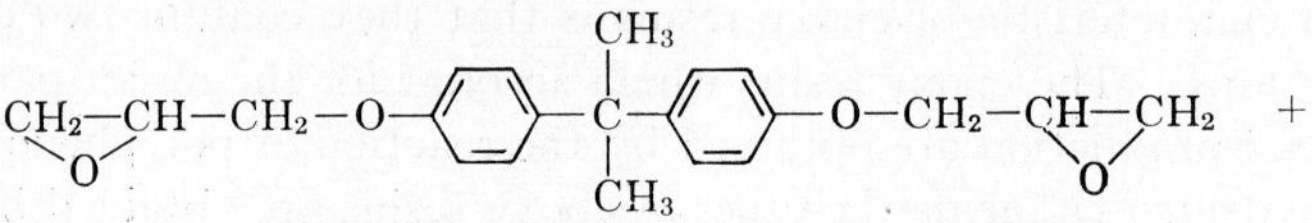

(III)

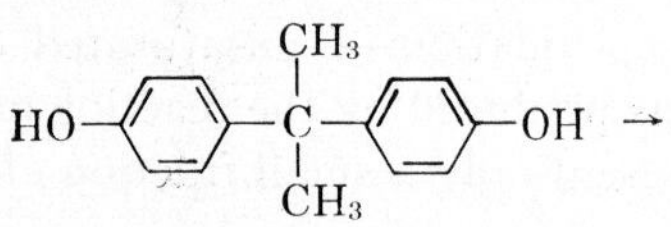

(20)

(I)

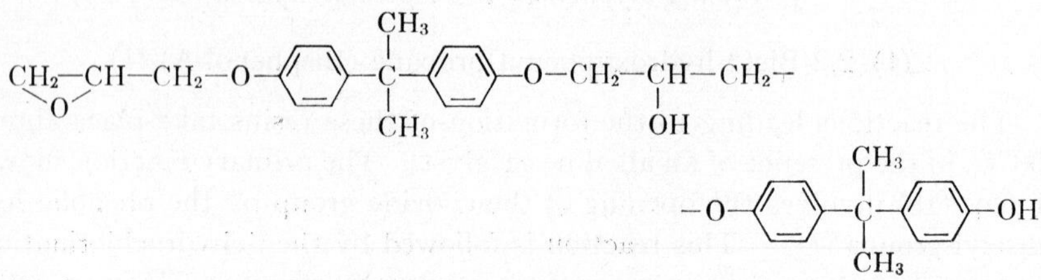

(IV)

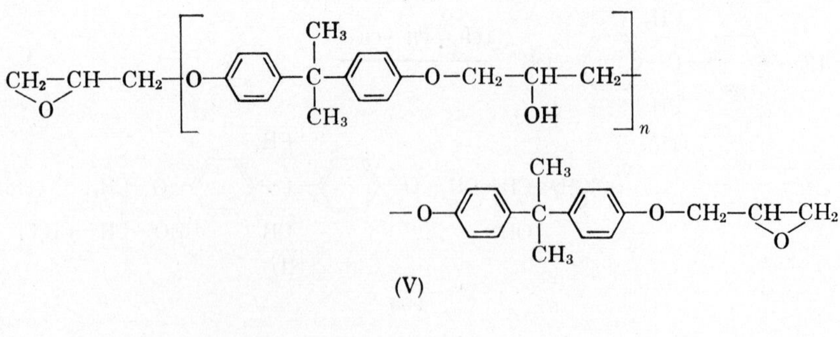

(V)

Further reaction with epichlorohydrin results in the formation of terminal epoxy groups as illustrated in the idealized structure (V).

Small percentages of other functional groups may also be present, such as glycerol monoether groups $-O-CH_2-CH(OH)-CH_2-OH$ derived from the hydration of glycidyl ether groups and glycerol chlorohydrin ether groups $-O-CH_2-CH(OH)-CH_2Cl$ obtained as a result of incomplete dehydrochlorination.

The liquid resins are prepared by using an excess of 6–8 moles of epichlorohydrin per mole of Bisphenol A (16). The solid, higher molecular weight resins are obtained by decreasing the amount of epichlorohydrin (17). Some of the epoxy resins with higher molecular weights of 3000–8000 are prepared by reacting a lower molecular weight epoxy resin with Bisphenol A (18).

The data in Table XI-2 show the effects of the changes of the ratio of epichlorohydrin to Bisphenol A on the physical characteristics of epoxy resins.

TABLE XI-2
Characteristics of Epoxy Resins as a Function of Epichlorohydrin/Bisphenol A Ratio

Epichlorohydrin, moles	Bisphenol A, moles	Melting point, °C. (Durrans)[a]	Epoxy equivalent, g. resin containing 1 g.-equiv. epoxide
6.0	1.0	Liquid	188
1.0	1.6	59	435
1.0	1.45	70	500
1.0	1.35	85	670

[a] See H. A. Gardner and G. G. Sward, *Paint Testing Manual,* 12th ed., Gardner Laboratory, Bethesda, Md., 1962, p. 367.

(2) Novolak Resins

A novolak resin is a low molecular weight condensation product of formaldehyde and a phenol or alkylphenol. An acidic condensation catalyst is used, and the resulting resin therefore contains no methylol groups.

Novolak resins react with epichlorohydrin by the same mechanisms as illustrated for Bisphenol A. The structure of epoxy resins made from novolak resins and epichlorohydrin can be presented by this idealized formula (VI) (19,20):

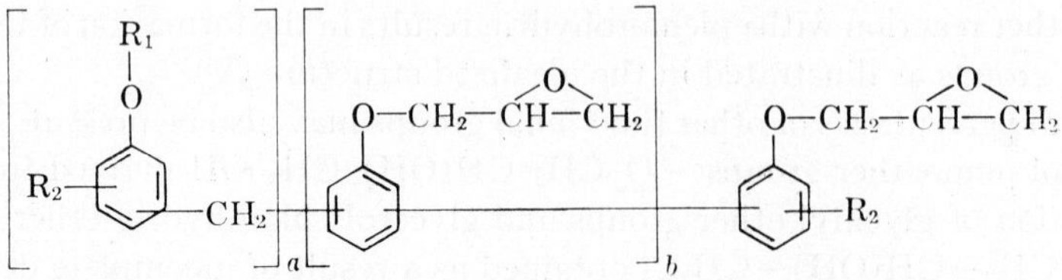

(VI)

where R_1 may be chlorohydrins, glycols, and polymeric ether segments, R_2 is CH_3 or H, a = 0.2–1.9, and b = 1.7–5.0. In contrast to the epoxy resins based on Bisphenol A which have close to two epoxy groups per molecule, the novolak-based epoxy resins can have up to six epoxy groups per molecule (Table XI-3).

(3) Other Polyphenols

Other polyphenols are used in the preparation of epoxy resins. However, these are limited to special applications. Two typical representatives of these resins have the structures (VII) and (VIII).

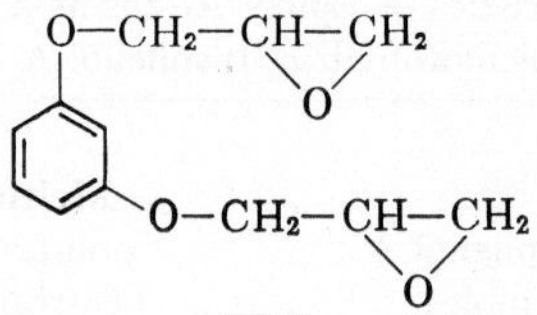

(VII)

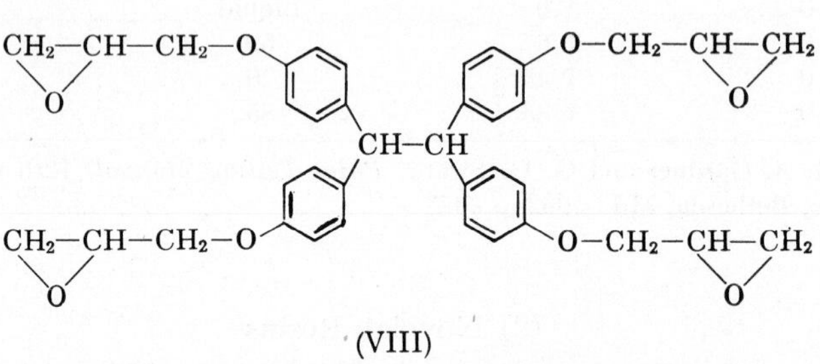

(VIII)

b. By Epoxidation of Unsaturated Compounds

This class of resin is the newest addition to the epoxy family. Some of the major representatives will be discussed in this section. However, many more will appear on the market in the coming years, since this approach of preparing epoxy resins has not been exploited as much as the earlier described approaches. (See also Chapter II-E.)

Several processes for producing peracetic acid used to epoxidize a variety of unsaturated compounds are now available. The selection of the process depends somewhat on the structural position of the double bond to be epoxidized. Two major processes are used commercially for epoxidation. In one, hydrogen peroxide is added to a mixture including acetic acid, the unsaturated compound to be epoxidized, and an acidic catalyst. Peracetic acid formed as an intermediate epoxidizes the unsaturated compound. The other process utilizes air to oxidize acetaldehyde in a suitable solvent

TABLE XI-3
Comparison of Epoxy Resins Based on Novolak Resins and Bisphenol A

Epoxy resin	Avg. mol. wt.	Avg. no. of epoxy groups per mole	Epoxide equiv.	Viscosity at 25°C., cpoise
Based on Bisphenol A	355	1.85	192	14,000
Based on Bisphenol A	900	1.80	465	Solid
Based on novolak resin (phenol–formaldehyde type)	600	3.3	180	Semisolid
Based on novolak resin (phenol–formaldehyde type)	485	2.6	177	Viscous liquid
Based on novolak resin (*o*-cresol–formaldehyde type)	540	2.7	200	Semisolid
Based on novolak resin (*o*-cresol–formaldehyde type)	1080	4.8	225	Solid
Based on novolak resin (*o*-cresol–formaldehyde type)	1270	5.4	235	Solid

to form acetaldehyde monoperacetate, which is cracked thermally to form peracetic acid. Acetic acid and acetaldehyde formed as by-products are removed in vacuum. Because the peracetic acid is converted into acetic acid during the epoxidation reaction, the overall process results in a conversion of acetaldehyde into the by-product acetic acid (21–23).

The oldest and most established application for such an epoxy resin is the use of epoxidized soya oil as a stabilizer for vinyl resins. The newer types of epoxidized olefins were also investigated for this purpose (24). Recently, epoxidized oils have found increased interest in the coating industry (25).

If one epoxidizes polybutadiene (IX) with peracetic acid, a resin with a simplified structural formula (X), results as shown in eq. (21).

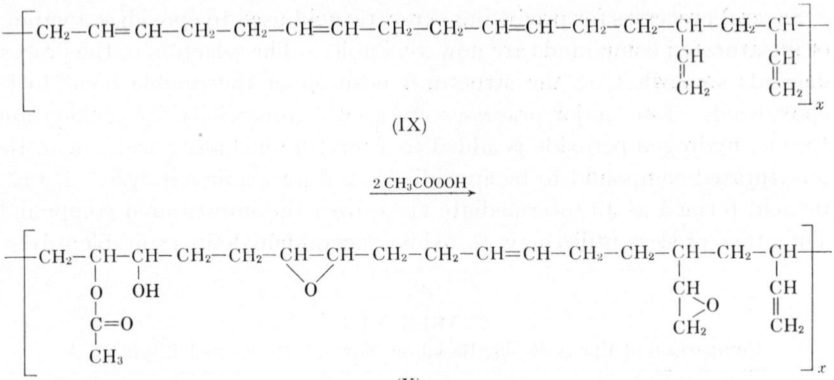

(IX)

(X)

(21)

Epoxy groups are located at terminal positions, at internal positions, and on branched chains along the hydrocarbon backbone. The molecule has additional reactive sites in the nonepoxidized vinyl groups. Thus, a vinyl monomer such as styrene can be coreacted with these epoxy resins (26).

The epoxidation of unsaturated cycloaliphatic esters yields another type of epoxy resin. By subjecting 6-methyl-3-cyclohexene carboxaldehyde (XI) to the Tishchenko reaction, 6-methyl-3-cyclohexenyl-1-methyl 6-methyl-3-cyclohexene 1-carboxylate (XII) is obtained (27) as in eq. (22).

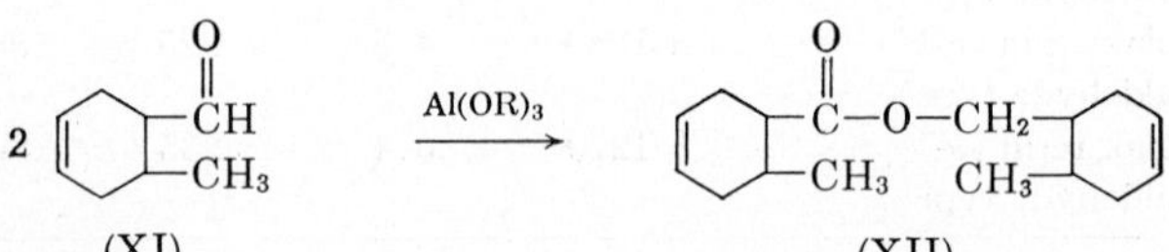

(XI) (XII)

(22)

The epoxidation can occur either by the acetaldehyde monoperacetate method or the peracetic acid method. The resulting product in eq. (23) is 3,4-epoxy-6-methylcyclohexylmethyl 3,4-epoxy-6-methylcyclohexanecarboxylate (XIII).

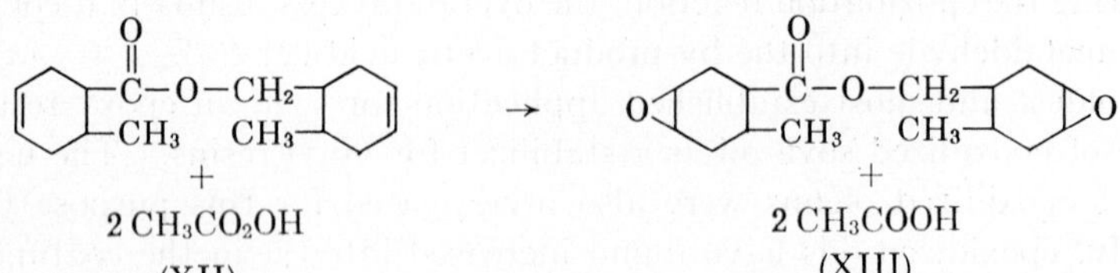

(XII) (XIII)

(23)

Many other epoxy resins produced by epoxidation of unsaturated compounds are commercially available. Due to their high heat resistance and good electrical properties, they are also considered for casting and filament winding applications. These compounds include limonene dioxide, 1-epoxyethyl-3,4-epoxycyclohexane, and dicyclopentadiene dioxide; typical structures include XIV–XVIII (28–31).

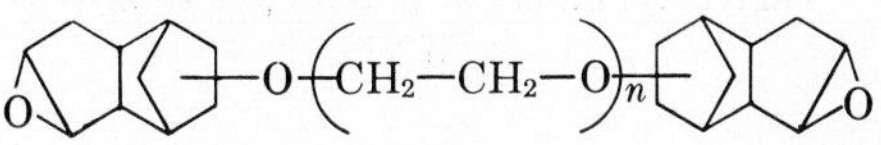

(XIV)

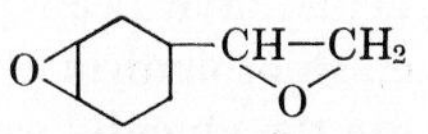

1-Epoxyethyl-3, 4-epoxycyclohexane

(XV)

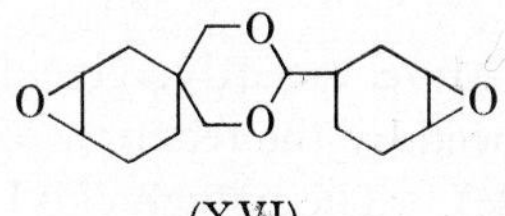

(XVI)

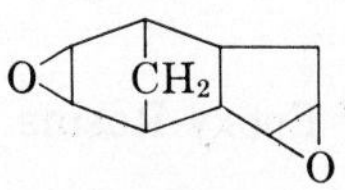

Dicyclopentadiene dioxide

(*endo*-isomer)

(XVII)

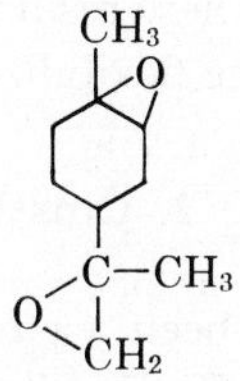

Limonene dioxide

(XVIII)

c. From Aliphatic Polyols and Epichlorohydrin

The commercial importance of these resins is small compared with that of the types discussed earlier. The major reason for this is probably that they cannot be used alone, but must be used in a mixture with aromatic or alicyclic epoxy resins in order that good physical properties may be obtained. *n*-Butyl glycidyl ether (XIX) is the most popular reactive diluent for aromatic epoxy resins.

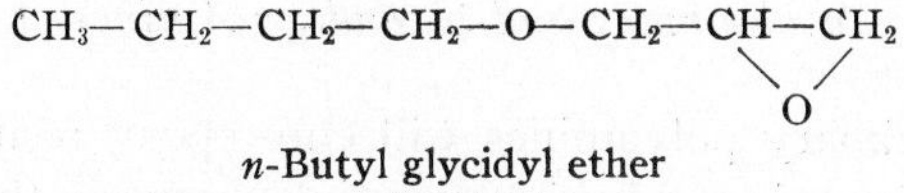

n-Butyl glycidyl ether

(XIX)

Some of the diglycidyl ethers of glycols for example, XX and XXI, are used as reactive flexibilizers (32a).

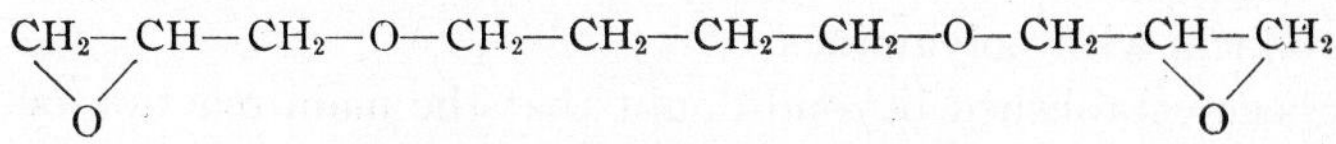

Diglycidyl ether of 1,4-butanediol

(XX)

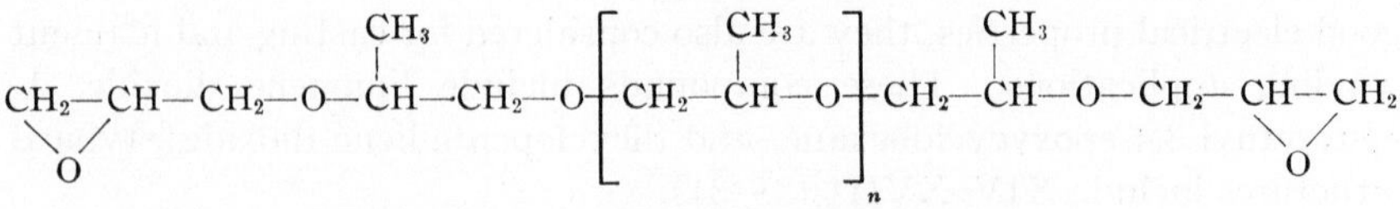

Diglycidyl ethers of polypropylene glycols
(XXI)

d. From Polycarboxylic Acids And Epichlorohydrin

More recently, glycidyl esters of polycarboxylic acids have been produced by the reaction of a polycarboxylic acid and epichlorohydrin (32b, 32c). The polyglycidyl esters most commonly used are the glycidyl esters of dimeric acids as obtained by the heat polymerization of dienoic fatty acids. These resins are mostly used in conjunction with other epoxy resins as reactive flexibilizers.

2. Crosslinking and Polymerization of Epoxy Resins

It has been a particularly challenging and difficult problem to develop methods for the determination of the mechanism, rate, and extent of the reaction that is commonly called the "cure" of epoxy resins.

The epoxy resins, after the addition of curing agent, pass from a liquid stage to a gel stage and eventually become insoluble and infusible (33,34). A method measuring the cure rates by refractometry was developed. Since epoxy resins shrink during cure, thereby increasing density and refractive index, the rate of cure can be expressed as refractometric cure rate (35). The disappearance of the infrared absorption bands for the epoxy groups can be used as a measure of cure rate (36). Epoxy content can also be determined in the cured resin by endgroup analysis (36).

a. Primary and Secondary Amines

Most of the primary polyamines will cure epoxy resins. The cure of epoxy resins consists of establishing crosslinks between the resin molecules to give a network structure. Since this crosslinked polymer is infusible and insoluble it is difficult to study the reaction mechanism. Therefore, most investigators used monofunctional epoxy resins which did not yield crosslinked products with polyamines.

It has been established beyond doubt that the main reaction occurs between the amine hydrogen and the epoxy groups (33,34,36–39), as shown in eq. (24).

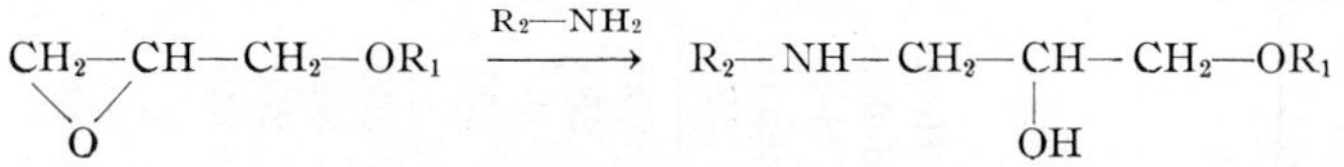
(24)

The secondary amino group formed reacts with the epoxy group at about the same rate as the primary amino group, unless steric hindrance is involved. As illustrated in eq. (25), the final product (XXII) contains ter-

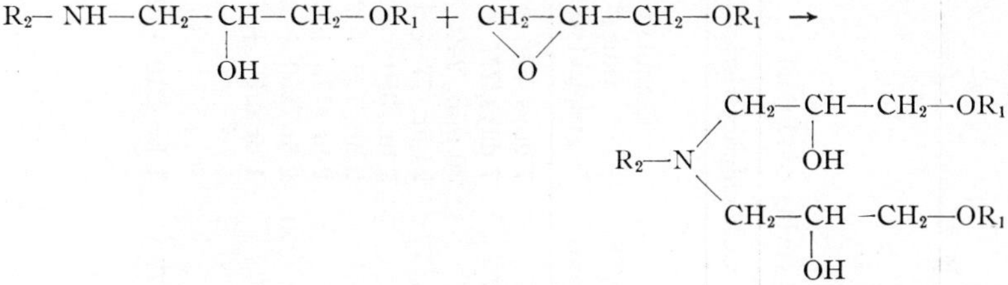
(XXII) (25)

tiary nitrogen and hydroxyl groups. The questions arise as to whether the tertiary nitrogen catalyzes the polymerization of the epoxy group and whether the hydroxyl group interacts with the epoxy group. The tertiary amines formed in this reaction have no appreciable catalytic effect on the polymerization of the epoxy group (40,41). This is probably due to steric hindrance in this type of tertiary amine.

The hydroxyl group does not participate in the reaction, but acts in some catalytic capacity. The addition reaction of amines to epoxy groups can be greatly accelerated by the addition of water, alcohol, and phenols.

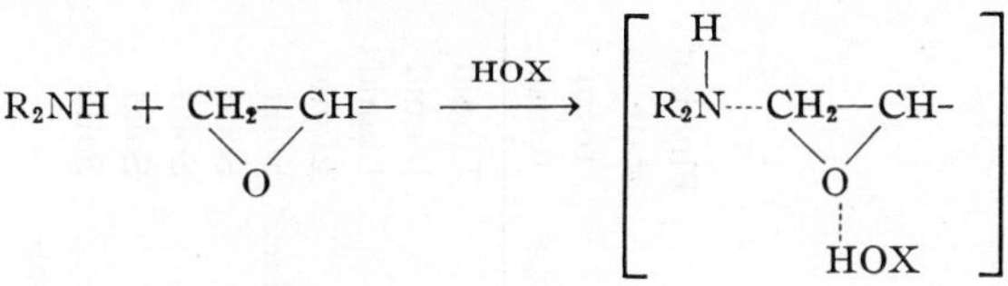
(26)

This may be explained by the termolecular mechanism proposed by Shechter (34), in which the hydrogen bonding in the transition state assists the opening of the epoxide ring.

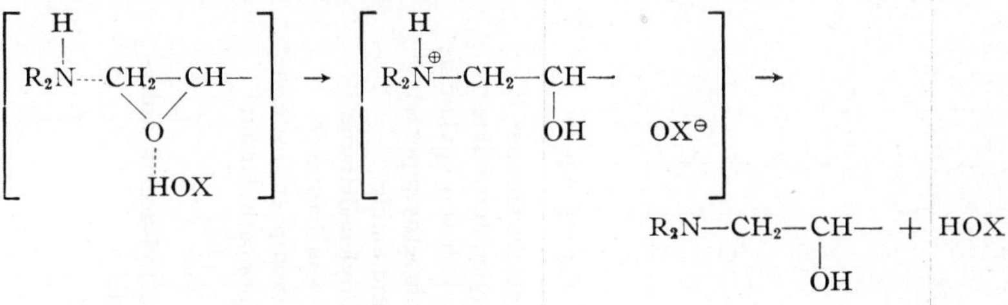
(27)

TABLE XI-4
Curing Agents for Epoxy Resins

Curing Agent	Chemical type	Physical state at room temp.	Recommended concentration range, parts/100 parts diglycidyl ether of Bisphenol A	Typical curing conditions: Curing temp. range, °F.	Cure characteristics: Gel, time/°F. (1 qt. mass)	Cure characteristics: Complete cure, time/°F. (typical schedule)	Heat deflection temp., °F.
Diethylenetriamine[a]	Polyamine	Liquid	10–12	60–300	30 min./77	7 days/77	250
Triethylenetetramine[b]	Polyamine	Liquid	11–13	60–300	30 min./77	7 days/77	250
Diethylaminopropylamine[c]	Polyamine	Liquid	4–8	80–300	3–4 hr./77	30 min./240	
N-Aminoethylpiperazine[d]	Polyamine	Liquid	20–23	80–300	20–30 min./77	24 hr./77 + 1 hr./300	250
Dicyandiamide[e]	Amide-Amine	Solid	4	300–350	1 yr./77	1 hr./350	
m-Phenylenediamine[f]	Polyamine	Solid	13–14	140–400	8 hr./77	2 hr./175 + 2 hr./300	300
Methylenedianiline[g]	Polyamine	Solid	28–30	140–400	8 hr./77	2 hr./175 + 2 hr./300	300
Diaminodiphenyl sulfone[h]	Polyamine	Solid	20–30	240–400	45–60 min./250	2 hr./250 + 2 hr./300	250
BF_3–monoethylamine[i]	Lewis acid–amine complex	Solid	2–4	240–400	6–9 mo./77	1 hr./250 + 2 hr./300	340
Dodecenylsuccinic anhydride[j]	Anhydride	Liquid	130–140	140–300	5–6 days/77	1 hr./210 + 2 hr./300	160

Nadic methyl anhydride[k]	Anhydride	Liquid	85–95	175–500	5–6 days/77	1 hr./250 + 4 hr./390; 24 hr./500	460
Phthalic anhydride[l]	Anhydride	Solid	70–80	200–300	5 min./250	1 hr./250 + 2 hr./300	300
Hexahydrophthalic anhydride[m]	Anhydride	Solid	75–85	200–400	20–30 min./175	1 hr./175 + 2 hr./300	265
Chlorendic anhydride[n]	Anhydride	Solid	100–120	200–400	10–15 min./250	1 hr./250 + 2 hr./300	355
Trimellitic anhydride[o]	Anhydride	Solid	30–40	210–400	30–60 min./250	1 hr./250 + 2 hr./300	460

[a] Fast cure, short pot life, good R.T. strength, low initial viscosity.

[b] Fast cure, short pot life, good R.T. strength, low initial viscosity.

[c] Excellent in adhesives, requires moderate heat cure, gives good moderate temperature strength. Longer pot life than diethylenetriamine and triethylenetetramine.

[d] Requires moderate heat cure, fast curing, low mix viscosity; gives castings with high impact strength.

[e] Long room temperature storage life coupled with fast high temperature cure in laminating and adhesive applications.

[f] Requires heat cure, imparts excellent high temperature and electrical properties and chemical resistance.

[g] Requires heat cure, imparts excellent high temperature and electrical properties, and chemical resistance.

[h] Excellent high temperature properties, high mix viscosity, excellent resistance to high humidity environment.

[i] Long pot life at R.T., good strength and heat resistance, cure rate highly dependent on temperature, good electrical properties.

[j] Long pot life at R.T., gives excellent electrical properties in castings and retains them above heat distortion temperature, imparts a degree of flexibility to castings.

[k] Low viscosity liquid at room temperature, long pot life, excellent for high temperature applications, requires extensive post cure.

[l] Insoluble below curing temperature, difficult to handle, used in electrical potting, inexpensive.

[m] Low melting point, gives low mix viscosity, long pot life, good electrical properties. Gives light-colored castings and laminates with good color stability to ultraviolet.

[n] Short pot life, gives castings of low flammability and high heat distortion.

[o] Good electrical properties, reacts very rapidly at high temperatures, good for high temperature applications.

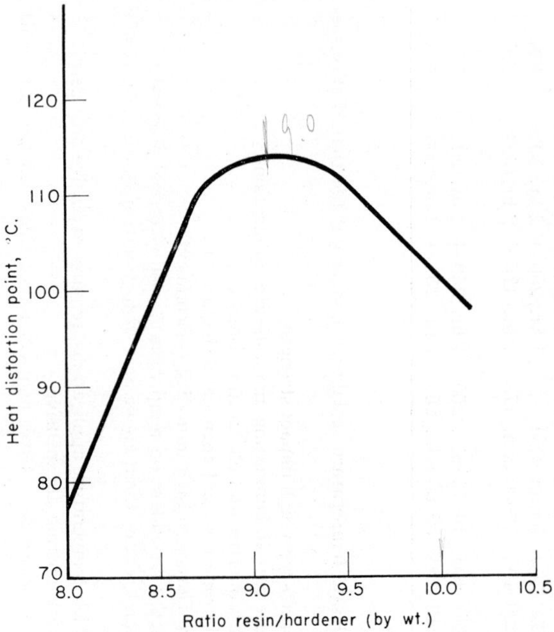

Fig. XI-1. Effect on heat distortion point of deviation from stoichiometric amounts of nine parts of resin to one part of diethylenetriamine. (Taken from ref. 40.)

The extent of the reaction of a polyamine with an epoxy resin varies with curing conditions (34,40). Not all of the epoxy groups react and up to 20% of all the epoxy groups may remain unreacted.

Ultimate physical properties such as hardness, solvent resistance, and strength values are usually obtained if stoichiometric amounts of polyamine and epoxy resins are used (assuming only reaction of the amine hydrogen with epoxide groups; if the hydroxyl groups were reacting with the epoxy groups, less amine would be required to give complete cure) (Fig. XI-1).

The properties of a cured epoxy resin differ with the type of polyamine used. In general, aliphatic polyamines react faster than aromatic polyamines, and the aromatic polyamines require higher reaction temperatures. Solvent resistance, heat distortion, and strength properties are generally higher for aromatic amine-cured epoxy resins than for aliphatic amine-cured resins. Table XI-4 summarizes some properties of epoxy resins cured with different types of amine hardeners (42).

The aliphatic amines are among the most potent skin irritants and sometimes cause allergic skin sensitization in humans. Therefore, many attempts have been made to modify the aliphatic amines to minimize this undesirable feature.

One approach consists in the reaction of aliphatic amines with alkylene oxides such as propylene oxide and ethylene oxide (41,43). Typical examples of the resulting hydroxyalkylpolyamines are *N*-hydroxyethyldiethylenetriamines. Cyanoethylation of polyamines was utilized to decrease the reactivity of aliphatic polyamines. The cyanoethylation reaction used to prepare these compounds occurs (40) according to eqs. (28) and (29).

$$NH_2—R—NH_2 + CH_2{=}CH—CN \rightarrow NH_2—R—NH—CH_2—CH_2—CN \quad (28)$$

$$NH_2—R—NH—CH_2—CH_2—CN + CH_2{=}CH—CN \rightarrow CN—CH_2—CH_2—NH—R—NH—CH_2—CH_2—CN \quad (29)$$

Many attempts have been made to reduce the reactivity of amines by the formation of chemical adducts which release the amine under the curing conditions. If an aliphatic amine reacts with a ketone, a ketimine is formed. Ketimines exhibit very low order of reactivity with epoxy resins in the absence of moisture. When water is introduced the polyamine is released into the system and crosslinks the epoxy resin (eq. 30). Ketimines containing free amine groups have levels of reactivity between pure ketimines and aliphatic polyamines. These types of curing agents are used mostly in moisture-curing coatings (44).

$$(R')(R'')C{=}N—R—N{=}C(R')(R'') + 2H_2O \rightleftarrows H_2N—R—NH_2 + 2R'—\overset{\overset{\displaystyle O}{\|}}{C}—R'' \quad (30)$$

A combination of a delayed amine cure and a catalyst cure is given by complexes of BF_3 with amines. The temperature at which the complex of BF_3 with amine decomposes depends upon the nature of the amine. The BF_3–monoethanolamine complex decomposes at temperatures above 90°C., whereas the BF_3–piperidine complex must be heated to above 135°C. to induce decomposition (45,46). This curing method is used in the preparation of glass-reinforced epoxy laminates and in casting operations.

The reaction product of an aromatic diamine with acetone results in a curing agent which, when mixed with an epoxy resin, has improved stability on storage as compared with aromatic polyamines (47).

Another type of a polyamine catalyst which has obtained commercial importance is prepared by the reaction of a polyamine with a dimeric acid. The dimeric acids result from the heat polymerization of dienoic fatty acids (especially 9,12-linoleic acid). The reaction mechanism is the same as for the aliphatic polyamines. However, the ratio of this polyamide hardener to epoxy resin is less critical than with aliphatic polyamine hardeners. The cured products are flexible due to the internal plasticization attributed to the basic character of the polyamide polyamine hardener (48).

Mixtures of coal tar and epoxy resins when cured with amines yield chemically resistant and tough coatings. The major use for this type of epoxy system is in pipe coatings, marine coatings, and coatings resistant to chemicals (49).

b. Tertiary Amines

Tertiary amines do not find widespread application as curing agents although pyridine, 2-vinylpiperidine, 2,4,6-tris(dimethylaminoethyl)phenol, and *o*- or *p*-dimethylaminoethylphenol can be used. The curing of epoxy resins with tertiary amines is effected catalytically by ionic polymerization through the epoxy groups. Polymerization of phenyl glycidyl ether with triethylamine suggests the reaction mechanism (33) shown in eqs. (31)–(35).

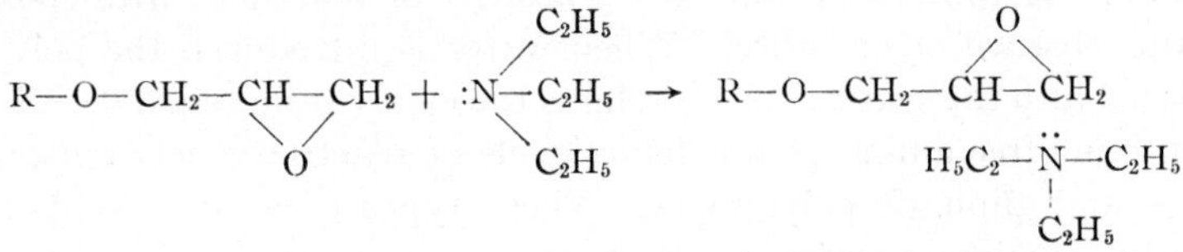

(31)

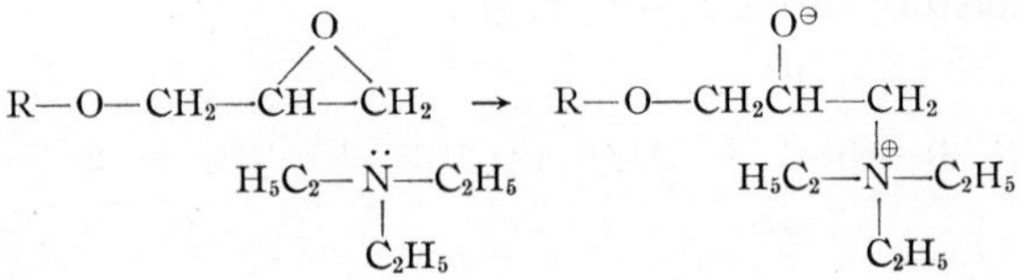

(32)

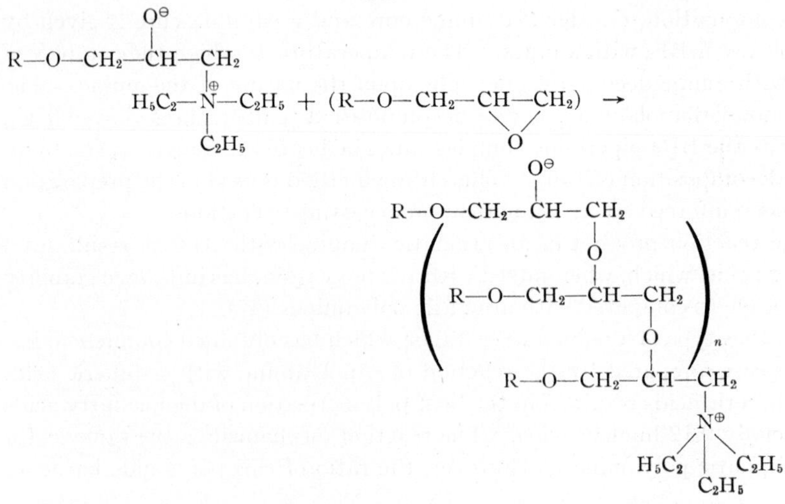

(33)

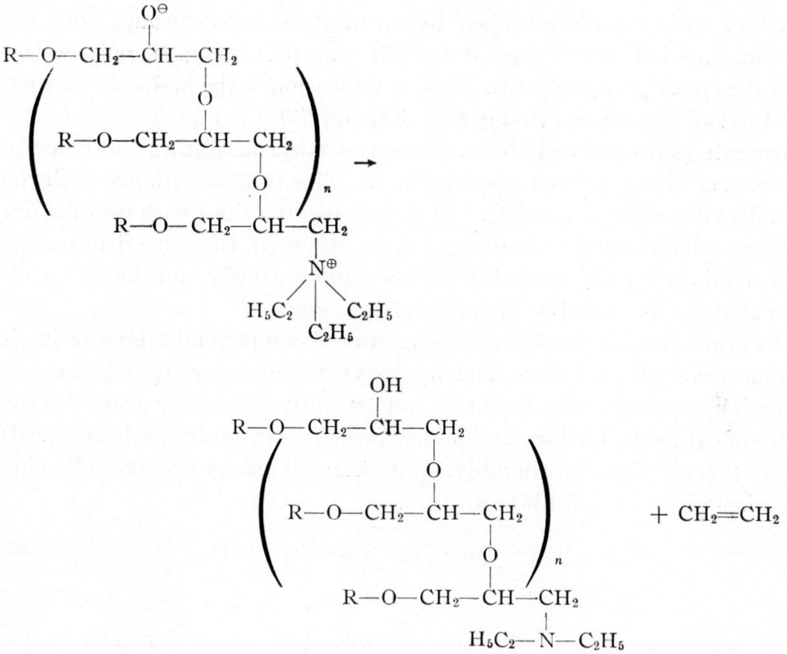

(34)

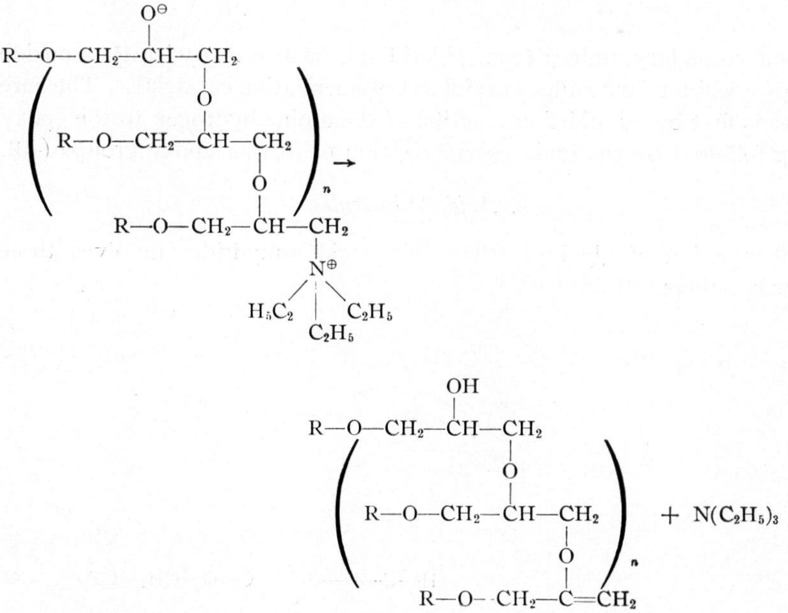

(35)

Tertiary amines probably react by opening the epoxy groups with the pair of unshared electrons (eqs. 31 and 32), thus promoting the polymerization of the epoxy group (eq. 33). The stabilization of the molecule may occur in the two ways illustrated in eqs. (34) and (35) (25,26).

Narracott (33) observed the formation of ethylene during the reaction and traces of nitrogen in the end product. This is in accordance with the mechanism described in eq. (34). Since polymer fractions with residual unsaturation which contain no nitrogen were observed, the second terminating mechanism (eq. 35) probably occurs simultaneously and, based on nitrogen analysis, is probably the predominant one.

The curing process involving polyfunctional commercial epoxy resins is much more complicated since both hydroxyl and epoxy groups are present. Although hydroxyl groups do not interact readily with epoxy groups in the absence of catalysts, tertiary amines (where no steric hindrance is involved) catalyze this reaction considerably. Shechter (34) suggested the following mechanism given in eqs. (36) and (37).

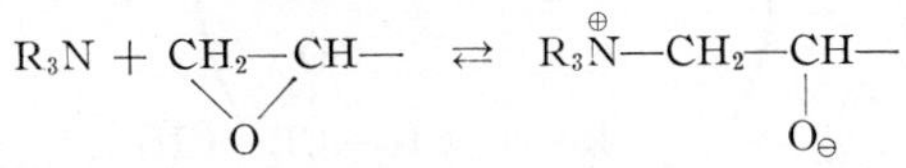
(36)

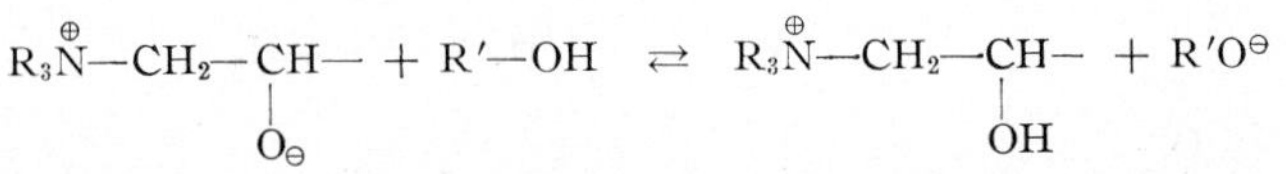
(37)

Some secondary amines (e.g., piperidine), on reacting with the epoxide groups, yield tertiary amines useful as polymerization catalysts. The cure proceeds first by an addition reaction of the amine hydrogen to the epoxy group followed by the ionic polymerization of further epoxy groups (40).

c. *Acid Anhydrides*

The reaction of glycidyl ethers with acid anhydrides involves three major reactions (50–56).

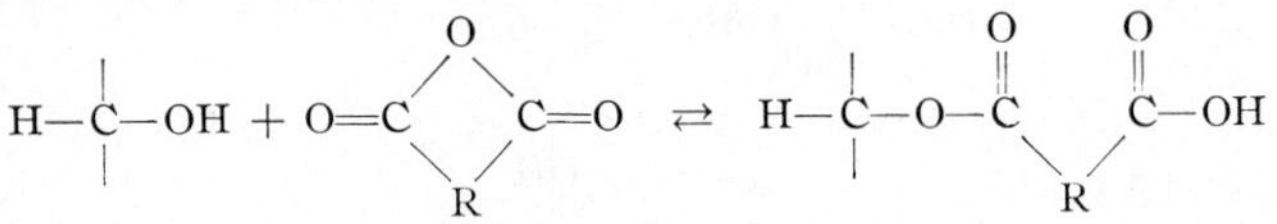
(38)

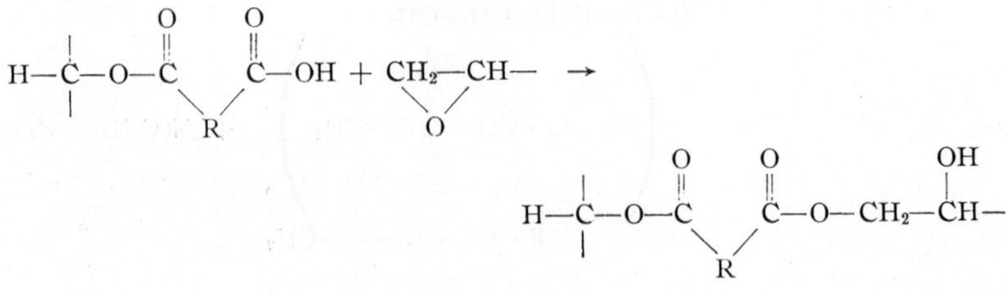
(39)

$$\text{H—}\underset{|}{\overset{|}{\text{C}}}\text{—OH} + \underset{\diagdown\text{O}\diagup}{\text{CH}_2\text{—CH—}} \rightarrow \text{H—}\underset{|}{\overset{|}{\text{C}}}\text{—O—CH}_2\text{—}\overset{\text{OH}}{\overset{|}{\text{CH}}}\text{—} + \text{other isomers} \quad (40)$$

Equation (38) shows a reversible reaction which does not contribute to the crosslinking process. The crosslinking occurs by esterification as in eq. (39) and etherification as in eq. (40).

Fisch et al. (52) determined the equilibrium of anhydride, hydroxyl, and monoester in eq. (38) and established the temperature dependence of the equilibrium. All three types of compounds are present in the cured resin. Reactions as shown in eqs. (39) and (40) occur simultaneously during the curing process (57). The ester formation in eq. (38) is favored by higher reaction temperature and by the addition of basic catalysts such as tertiary amines (57), quaternary ammonium salts of organic acids (58), BF_3 complexes of amines (59), alkali-metal salts of carboxylic acids, and metal alcoholates (60).

Fischer (61) showed that in the presence of a tertiary amine a terminal epoxide reacts exclusively with phthalic anhydride to form linear polyesters. The formation of polyether linkages is negligible in the absence of hydroxyl groups.

The ether formation shown in eq. (40) is catalyzed by acids or anhydrides. Tests on cured commercial resins (54) disclose that small amounts of monoether and anhydride groups are present, whereas hydroxyl, ether, and ester groups resulting from the crosslinking reaction are present in large amounts. While terminal epoxy groups such as in glycidyl ethers react with an anhydride to form predominately ester linkages, the more reactive internal epoxy groups in vinylcyclohexene oxide and alkyl epoxy stearates react only partially to form ester linkages. The rest of the epoxy groups polymerize to form polyethers.

d. Carboxylic Acids

In the reaction of a carboxylic acid with a glycidyl ether, four reactions can be expected (54).

$$\text{—COOH} + \underset{\diagdown\text{O}\diagup}{\text{CH}_2\text{—CH—}} \rightarrow \text{—COO—CH}_2\text{—}\underset{\text{OH}}{\underset{|}{\text{CH}}}\text{—} \quad (41)$$

$$\text{—COOH} + \text{—}\underset{\text{OH}}{\underset{|}{\text{CH}}}\text{—} \rightarrow \text{—}\underset{\text{OOC—}}{\underset{|}{\text{CH}}}\text{—} + \text{H}_2\text{O} \quad (42)$$

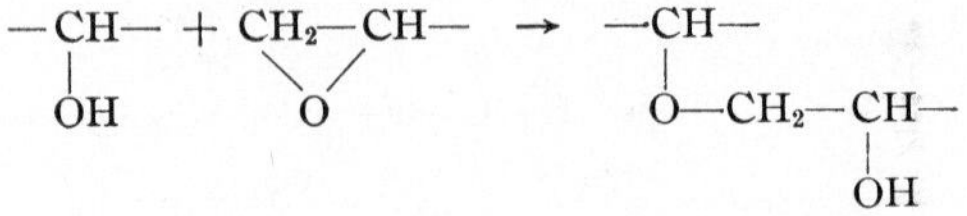
(43)

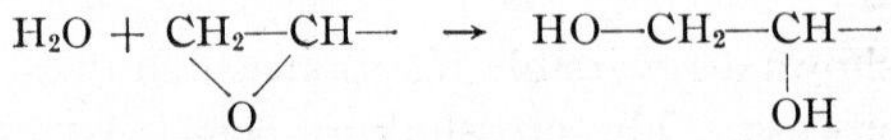
(44)

The reaction of an alcohol, an acid, and a glycidyl ether in the absence of a catalyst results principally in interaction between epoxy and hydroxyl groups, and between acid and hydroxyl groups, and to a much lesser extent in epoxide–acid esterification. If, however, a basic catalyst is present, the acid is rapidly consumed to form polyester linkages and then the reaction of epoxide with hydroxyl starts. This high order of selectivity can be explained by the reaction sequence in eqs. (45)–(47).

$$\text{RCOOH} + \text{Base} \rightarrow \text{RCOO}^{\ominus} \qquad (45)$$

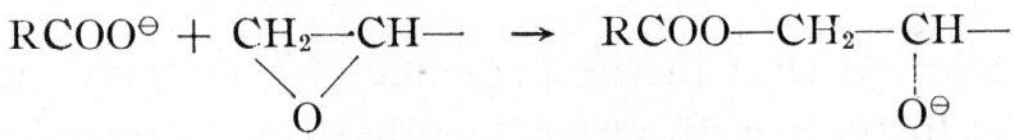
(46)

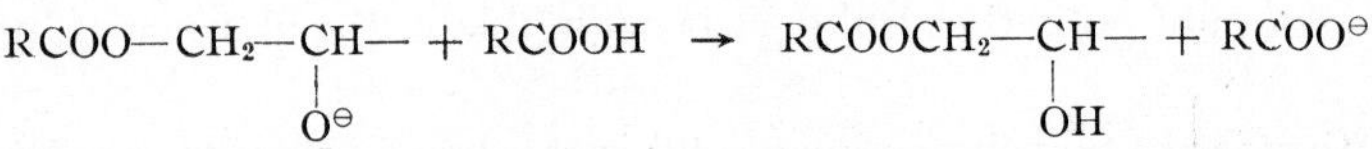
(47)

Monocarboxylic acids containing conjugated double bonds such as 2,4-hexadienoic acid have been found to be useful curing agents. The physical properties of the cured epoxy resins are equivalent to dibasic acid-cured epoxy resins. Two curing mechanisms are involved in this curing process. The carboxylic group reacts with the epoxy group in the usual manner, and the conjugated polyolefinic part of the curing agent reacts with unsaturated parts of other molecules, probably undergoing a Diels-Alder reaction.

e. Complexes of Lewis Acids

Recently, complexes of boron trifluoride and metal halides with polyether polyols have found use as curing agents for epoxy resins (62,63). The ether oxygen forms a weak complex with BF_3. In presence of epoxy groups, the boron trifluoride complexes with the ether oxygen of the epoxy group at room temperature initiating the cure at low temperatures. The polyols used to complex boron trifluoride have a dual function. They distribute the catalyst uniformly in the reaction mixture and they also participate in the curing reaction. The mechanism of this cure may be as shown in eqs. (48)–(50).

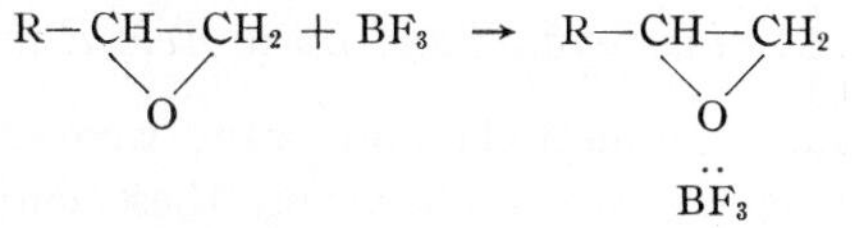

(48)

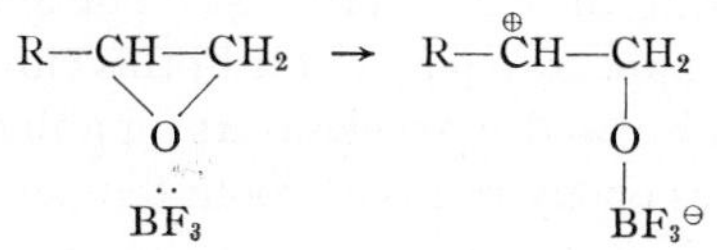

(49)

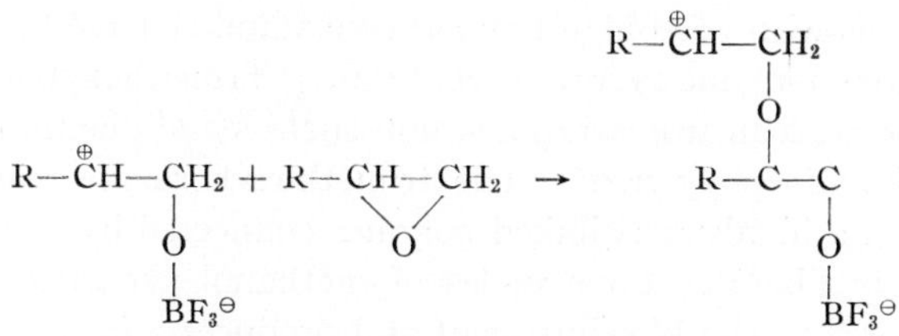

(50)

This type of curing agent was utilized in the development of halofluorocarbon-blown epoxy foams (62).

f. Polysulfides

The liquid polysulfide polymers used as crosslinking agents for epoxy resins are derived from the reaction of an alkaline polysulfide with a suitable dihalide. These materials are difunctional and are terminated with thiol groups. While the thiol groups are more reactive than the alcohol groups, additional catalysts are still necessary to obtain a satisfactory crosslinking reaction of a polysulfide polymer with an epoxy resin. These catalysts are usually tertiary amines such as 2,4,6-tris(dimethylaminomethyl)phenol and benzyldimethylamine. Polyamines such as diethylenetriamine are also useful as accelerators. The crosslinking of an epoxy resin with a polysulfide (64) is illustrated in equation (51).

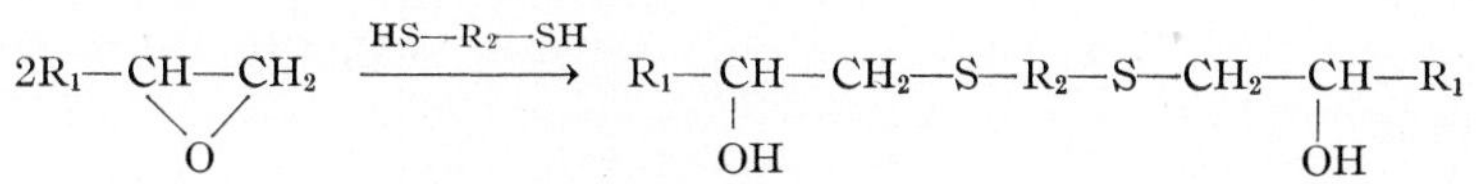

(51)

g. Aldehyde Condensation Resins

Phenol–formaldehyde, urea–formaldehyde, and melamine–formaldehyde resins have found extensive uses as crosslinking agents for epoxy resins in the coatings field. The crosslinking reaction most likely occurs through the methylol groups and results in the formation of new ether linkages (65–67).

h. Amine Boranes and Boric Acid Esters

Amine boranes, such as dimethylaminoborane, were suggested as primary curing agents with epoxy resins; however, these curing agents show a tendency to foam during the curing process. The amine and the boron segments of the molecule appear to play a role in this cure mechanism.

Amine boranes are also used as accelerators for anhydride cures (68). Trimethoxyboroxine cures epoxy resins at room temperature. This cure is of the acidic type (68).

Epoxy foams with good high temperature stability have been developed with trimethoxyboroxine as curing agent (69). Trimethoxyboroxine is used in conjunction with an aromatic polyamine such as *p,p'*-diaminodiphenylsulfone and a liquid epoxy resin. The trimethoxyboroxine reacts with the amine to form a highly crosslinked polymer connected by B–N bonds and simultaneously liberates three moles of methanol per mole of boroxine. The methanol acts as a blowing agent and produces a foam.

At elevated temperatures, the amine boroester cure occurs by means of a steric rearrangement which distributes the borate resonance and exposes an unshared electron pair on the nitrogen, for assisting in an epoxy ring cleavage as in eq. (52).

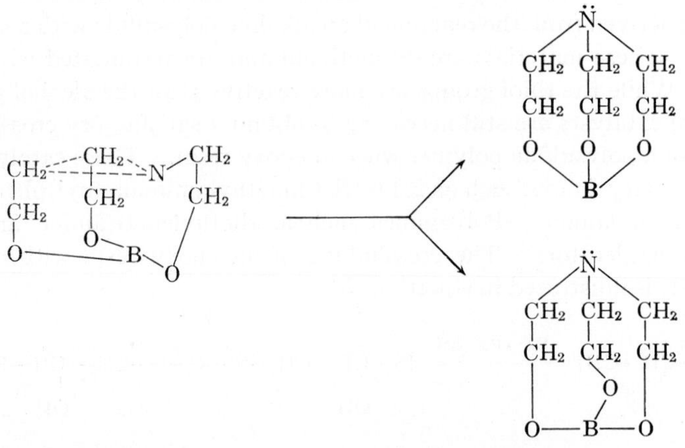

(52)

Amine boroesters are relatively stable at room temperature when admixed with epoxy resins (69).

Langer et al. combined borate esters and chelated titanium or phosphorous compounds to modify the properties of cured epoxy resins (70).

Boric acid esters derived from phenols such as tri-*m*- or *p*-cresyl borate (XXIII) are effective curing agents when used in conjunction with epoxy resins derived from the peracid epoxidation of polyolefins (71).

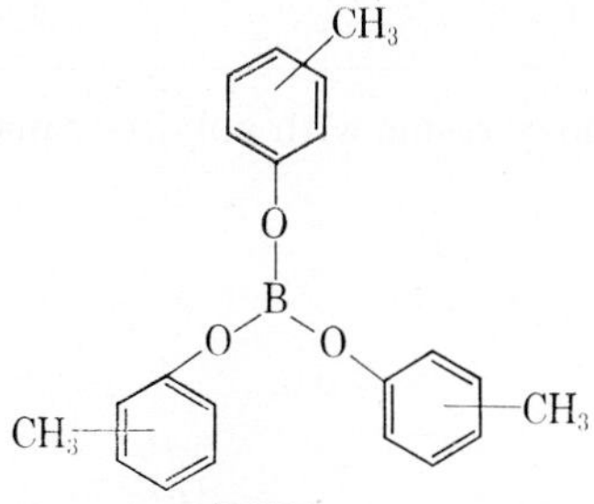

(XXIII)

Metaboric acid and B_2O_3 are also useful as curing agents (72).

i. Diisocyanates

The reaction of monoepoxides (1) and isocyanates to form oxazolidones (XXIV, XXV), shown in eq. (53), was reported by Speranza and Peppel (73) and Weiner (74). Gulbins et al. (75) investigated this reaction further

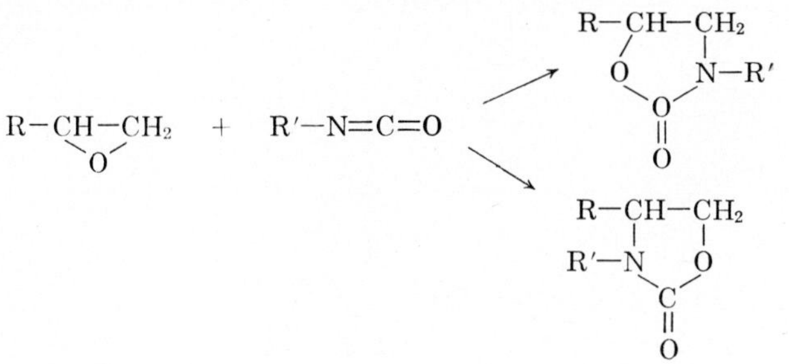

(XXIV)

(53)

(XXV)

and found that the 3,5-disubstituted oxazolidones (XXIV) are formed preferentially.

If this reaction is carried out with polyepoxides and polyisocyanates, crosslinking occurs due to the reaction of the isocyanate groups with the epoxide groups and the hydroxyl groups. The mechanism in eqs. (54) and (55) has been suggested for this reaction (75).

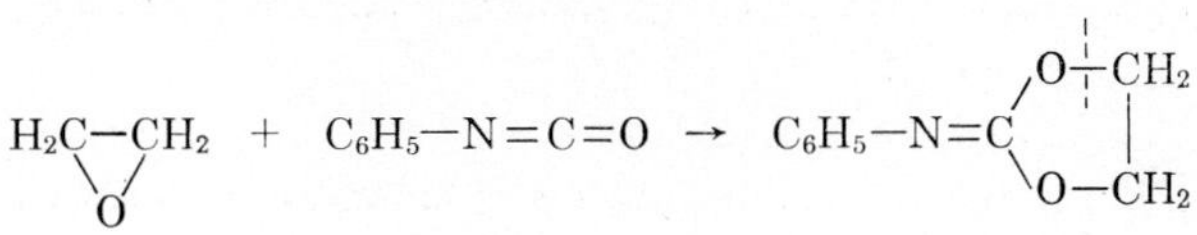

(54)

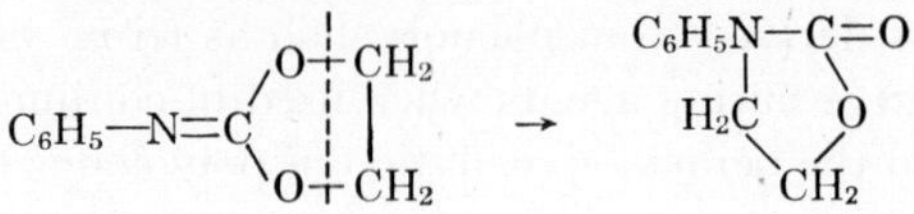
(55)

The crosslinking of epoxy resins with polyisocyanates has been described by Faerber (76).

C. POLYURETHANES AND RELATED ISOCYANATE POLYMERS

K. C. Frisch and H. C. Vogt

Wyandotte Chemicals Corporation

1. Introduction

The chemistry of isocyanates and of their addition products has been known since the beginning of modern synthetic organic chemistry. Wurtz (77), as early as 1849, successfully prepared aliphatic isocyanates by the reaction of organic sulfates with cyanates. The structure of these isocyanates was subsequently confirmed by Gautier (78). Wurtz also undertook a systematic study of the reactions of isocyanates, e.g., with alcohols and amines, thus observing many of the present day commercially important reactions. Hentschel (79) investigated the reaction between amines or their salts with phosgene to yield the isocyanate, a process which is essentially the basis of today's commercial manufacture of di- and polyisocyanates.

During the 1930's, Carothers at du Pont developed the high molecular weight polyamides which were successfully commercialized. Research subsequently initiated in Germany to find new fiber-forming reactions outside of the du Pont patents led in 1937 to the discovery of the polyaddition polymerization process by Otto Bayer and co-workers (80,81). At first polyureas were synthesized by the reaction of diisocyanates with diamines as shown in eq. (44).

$$O{=}C{=}N{-}(CH_2)_6{-}N{=}C{=}O + H_2N{-}(CH_2)_6{-}NH_2 \rightarrow \left[HN{-}(CH_2)_6{-}NH{-}\overset{\overset{\displaystyle O}{\|}}{C}{-}NH{-}(CH_2)_6{-}NH{-}\overset{\overset{\displaystyle O}{\|}}{C} \right]_n \qquad (44)$$

Polyurea

However, the resulting polyureas were insoluble and infusible and, hence, were not of interest as fibers or for plastics applications.

The reaction of dihydroxy compounds such as 1,4-butanediol with hexamethylene diisocyanate yielded a polyurethane which found limited use in Germany for fibers and bristles (Perlon U) and for plastics (Igamid U).

$$O{=}C{=}N{-}(CH_2)_6{-}N{=}C{=}O + HO{-}(CH_2)_4{-}OH \rightarrow \left[\overset{O}{\overset{\|}{C}}{-}NH{-}(CH_2)_6{-}NH{-}\overset{O}{\overset{\|}{C}}{-}O{-}(CH_2)_4{-}O \right]_n \qquad (45)$$

Polyurethane (Perlon U or Igamid U)

The development of polyurethanes for plastics, fibers, foams, adhesives, and coatings was actively pursued by Farbenfabriken Bayer (then a part of the I. G. Farbenindustrie) during World War II (80). The utilization of hydroxyl-terminated polyesters and the more inexpensive polyethers provided the final impetus to the full commercialization of the polyurethanes.

Urethanes are esters of carbamic acid, H_2NCOOR, and the urethane group has the characteristic configuration $>N{-}COO{-}$. The term "polyurethane" pertains to the polymer containing urethane linkages, even though other functional groups such as ester, ether, amide, urea, etc. may be present. These polymers are also designated as "urethane" or "isocyanate" polymers.

This chapter will primarily describe various polymer-forming reactions of diisocyanates or other intermediates resulting in the formation of polyurethanes or polyureas. Reactions of monofunctional isocyanates or of their products are included which could be used, if applied to difunctional reactions, for the preparation of polymers.

Monomeric compounds were also employed to elucidate the reaction sequences and chemical behavior observed in the more complex polymeric systems. The preparation of isocyanates is also briefly discussed because of their importance as reactants in the manufacture of polyurethanes and polyureas. The synthesis of isocyanates could also be applied to polymers containing functional groups such as the amino group which can be converted into the corresponding isocyanate polymers.

2. Preparation of Isocyanates

A number of methods for the preparation of isocyanates are reported in the literature. The majority of these can be conveniently classified according to the reactions involved: (*a*) phosgenation of amines or amine hydrochlorides; (*b*) decomposition of acid azides; (*c*) reactions of hydroxamic acids; (*d*) rearrangement of *N*-substituted amides; (*e*) double decomposition reactions between a cyanate and an ester of an inorganic acid or an organic or inorganic halide; (*f*) thermal decomposition of substituted ureas and urethanes; (*g*) miscellaneous reactions. The combination of desired physical and chemical properties with economic factors has confined the industrial production to about half a dozen different isocyanates.

TABLE XI-5
Typical Properties of Commercial Isocyanates[a]

Compound	Abbreviation	Mol. wt.	Melting point, °C.	Boiling point, °C./mm.	Specific gravity	Refractive index n_D^t	Manufacturer[b]
2,4-Tolylene diisocyanate	TDI	174	19.5–21.5	120/10	$1.22_{15.5}^{25}$	1.5654^{25}	A, B, C
Tolylene diisocyanate, 65/35 2,4–2,6 isomers	TDI	174	3.5–5.5	120/10	$1.22_{15.5}^{25}$	1.5666^{25}	A, B, C
Tolylene diisocyanate, 80/20 2,4–2,6 isomers	TDI	174	11.5–13.5	120/10	$1.22_{15.5}^{25}$	1.5663^{25}	A, B, C
4,4′-Diphenylmethane diisocyanate	MDI	250	37–38	194–199/5	1.19^{50}	—	B, C
1,6-Hexamethylene diisocyanate	HDI	168	—	140–142/21	$1.04_{15.5}^{25}$	1.4516	B
3,3′-Dimethoxy-4,4′-biphenyl diisocyanate, "dianisidine diisocyanate"	DADI	296	119–122	200–210/0.5	—	—	D
3,3′-Dimethyl-4,4′-biphenyl diisocyanate "tolidine diisocyanate"	TODI	264	69–71.5	—	1.20_4^{80}	—	D
3,3′-Dimethyldiphenylmethane 4,4′-diisocyanate	DMMDI	278	31.4	—	—	—	C
Polymethylene polyphenylisocyanate	PAPI	—	—	—	1.2_{20}^{20}	—	D

[a] Taken from ref. 119.

[b] Manufacturers: (A) E. I. du Pont de Nemours and Co.; (B) Mobay Chemical Co.; (C) National Aniline Division, Allied Chemical Corp.; (D) Carwin Chemical Co.

The most important commercial isocyanates are listed in Table XI-5. The reaction between primary amines (82,83) or their salts (79,84) and phosgene is the most common manufacturing procedure.

The reaction scheme for the preparation of aromatic diisocyanates proceeds in two stages as shown in eqs. (46).

$$H_2N{-}R{-}NH_2 + COCl_2 \rightarrow Cl{-}\overset{\overset{\displaystyle O}{\|}}{C}{-}NH{-}R{-}NH_2 \cdot HCl \qquad (46a)$$

$$Cl{-}\overset{\overset{\displaystyle O}{\|}}{C}{-}NH{-}R{-}NH_2 \cdot HCl + COCl_2 \xrightarrow{\Delta} O{=}C{=}N{-}R{-}N{=}C{=}O + 4HCl \qquad (46b)$$

These conversions may be carried out in various solvents, such as ethyl acetate, toluene, and *o*-dichlorobenzene, and the yields are generally in the 85–90% range (85). If the isocyanate does not have too high a boiling point, gas-phase reaction between an amine and phosgene at 180–400°C. in the presence of a catalyst has been successfully employed (82,86). This technique has been modified by isolating the carbamoyl chloride corresponding to the amine and decomposing it to the isocyanate (86).

Though side reactions are possible, the only one of any significance in the phosgenation reaction is the formation of the disubstituted urea. This has been almost eliminated in commercial processes by efficient mixing and by using a slight excess of phosgene in the vapor phase.

The preparation of aliphatic diisocyanates such as hexamethylene diisocyanate proceeds usually via the carbamate salt (87) as shown in eqs. (47).

$$H_2N{-}(CH_2)_6{-}NH_2 + CO_2 \rightarrow H_3\overset{+}{N}{-}(CH_2)_6{-}NH{-}CO\overset{-}{O} \qquad (47a)$$

$${}_3\overset{+}{N}{-}(CH_2)_6{-}NH{-}CO\overset{-}{O} + 2COCl_2 \rightarrow$$
$$Cl{-}\overset{\overset{\displaystyle O}{\|}}{C}{-}NH{-}(CH_2)_6{-}NH{-}\overset{\overset{\displaystyle O}{\|}}{C}{-}Cl + 2HCl + CO_2 \qquad (47b)$$

$$Cl{-}\overset{\overset{\displaystyle O}{\|}}{C}{-}NH{-}(CH_2)_6{-}NH{-}\overset{\overset{\displaystyle O}{\|}}{C}{-}Cl \xrightarrow{\Delta} O{=}C{=}N{-}(CH_2)_6{-}N{=}C{=}O + 2HCl \qquad (47c)$$

The Curtius rearrangement of acid azides (88), the Hofmann rearrangement of acid amides (89), and the Lossen rearrangement of hydroxamic acids (90) all appear to involve a similar intermediate which rearranges to the isocyanate (eq. 48).

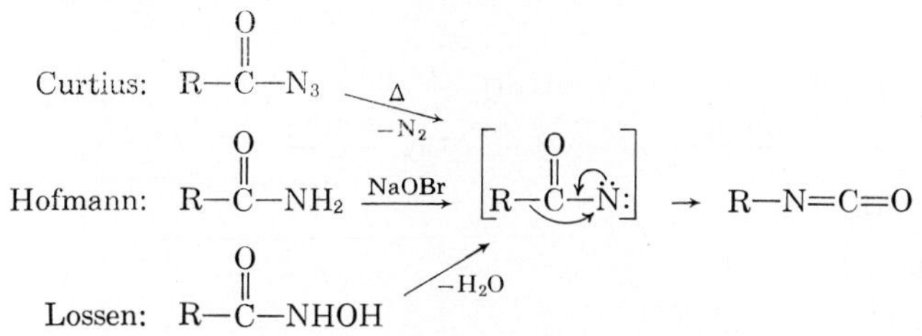

(48)

The Curtius reaction is useful primarily for the preparation of short-chain aliphatic diisocyanates (91–93), and unsaturated isocyanates (94,95). Since the Hofmann reaction is carried out in aqueous medium, the isocyanate must be water-insensitive (96). Iwakura, Taneda, and Uchida (97) successfully employed the Curtius rearrangement for the synthesis of tetramethylene diisocyanates from adipoyl dihydrazide and sodium nitrite (eq. 49). Because of the generally poor yields, the Lossen rearrangement is

$$H_2N{-}NH{-}\underset{\underset{O}{\|}}{C}{-}(CH_2)_4{-}\underset{\underset{O}{\|}}{C}{-}NH{-}NH_2 \xrightarrow[HCl]{NaNO_2}$$

$$N_3{-}\underset{\underset{O}{\|}}{C}{-}(CH_2)_4{-}\underset{\underset{O}{\|}}{C}{-}N_3 \rightarrow O{=}C{=}N{-}(CH_2)_4{-}N{=}C{=}O \quad (49)$$

not too frequently employed for the synthesis of isocyanates (90,98,99).

Double decompositions, e.g., the reaction of organic halides or sulfates with an inorganic cyanate, are generally hampered by poor yields and difficulties in isolation of the product. Better yields were claimed by employing high-boiling solvents such as dimethyl sulfone or dimethylformamide in the reaction of alkali or alkaline earth cyanates with organic halides such as xylylene dichlorides or dibromides and continually withdrawing vapors of the resulting isocyanates (100,101). The lower simple monoisocyanates, however, can be prepared in the laboratory in good yields by this technique (77,102,103). This preparative method is applicable to the synthesis of inorganic isocyanates (isocyanates with the NCO group attached to an element other than carbon) (104–109).

Tilley and Sayigh (110) reported that a number of *N-tert*-butyl-*N*-alkyl carbamoyl chlorides could be readily decomposed at low temperatures with or without ferric chloride catalyst to the corresponding alkyl isocyanates in good yields as shown in eq. (50). The *tert*-butylalkylamines employed were

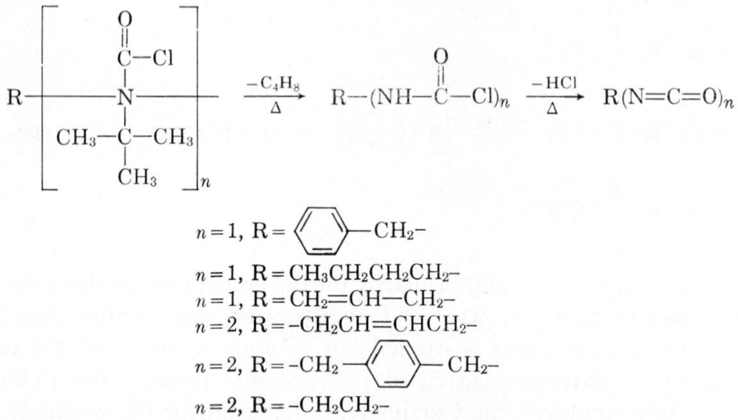

(50)

synthesized from *tert*-butylamine and the corresponding alkyl chlorides. The *tert*-butylalkylamines were then phosgenated to the *N*-*tert*-butylalkyl carbamoyl chlorides (110).

A recent procedure for the preparation of isocyanates was reported by Mukaiyama and Nohira (111). It consisted of the addition of a solution of a hydroxamic acid in ethyl acetate to a ketone dimer solution, also in ethyl acetate (eq. 51). The yields amounted to 78–86% for the first step while

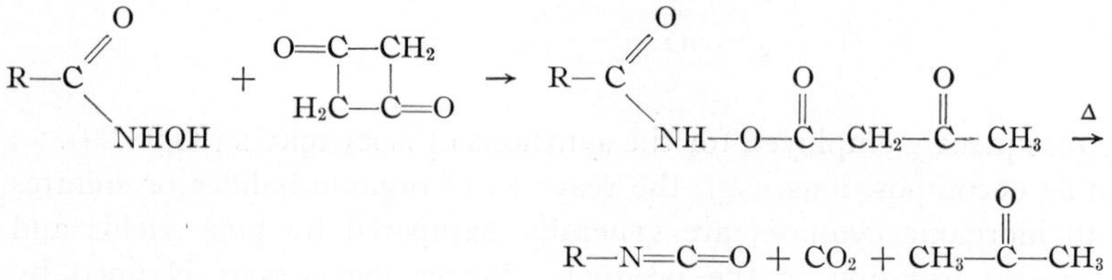

(51)

the decomposition to the isocyanates was achieved in yields in the range of 36–71% (112).

Very recently (113) a new synthesis was revealed for the preparation of mono- and diisocyanates by the addition of isocyanic acid to vinyl ethers.

$$R{-}O{-}CH{=}CH_2 + HNCO \rightarrow R{-}O{-}\underset{\underset{NCO}{|}}{CH}{-}CH_3 \qquad (52)$$

Likewise, propenyl and isopropenyl ethers added isocyanic acid to yield the corresponding 1-isocyanato-ethers (113).

Poly(vinyl isocyanate) was formed readily by the polymerization of vinyl isocyanate at room temperature (114). Poly(isopropenyl isocyanate) was formed in a similar manner from the isopropenyl isocyanate monomer.

These polymers were insoluble in common organic solvents but could be copolymerized with other vinyl monomers (114). Poly(vinyl isocyanate) was also reported by Jones, Zomlefer, and Hawkins (95), who prepared this polymer by the reaction of acrylyl chloride with sodium azide (eq. 53).

$$\underset{\displaystyle CH_2{=}CH}{\overset{\displaystyle COCl}{|}} + NaN_3 \rightarrow \left[CH_2{-}\underset{\displaystyle CH}{\overset{\displaystyle N{=}C{=}O}{|}}{-} \right]_n \qquad (53)$$

A great variety of other synthetic methods for preparing isocyanates are available, but they are of little practical or commercial importance (115–117). Urethanes and substituted ureas (82) thermally decompose to the isocyanate and are discussed in subsequent sections. The preparation of various isocyanates has been reviewed by several authors, notably by Saunders and Slocomb (118), Saunders and Frisch (119), and Petersen (120).

3. Reactions of Isocyanates

a. General

The electronic structure of the isocyanate group is indicative of the type of reactions the group may undergo. Staudinger and Endle (121) noted the similarity between isocyanates (—N=C=O) and ketenes (—C=C=O) in structure and chemical behavior. The subsequent discussions on the various reactions and chemistry of the isocyanate group will further exemplify the electronic structure of this group. A qualitative consideration of the resonance hybrids indicates that the electron density is high on the oxygen and least on the carbon, the nitrogen atom being intermediate with a net negative charge (122).

$$R{-}\ddot{N}{=}C{=}\ddot{O}: \leftrightarrow \underset{\text{minor}}{R{-}\overset{\ominus}{\underset{..}{\ddot{N}}}{-}\overset{\oplus}{C}{=}\ddot{O}:} \leftrightarrow \underset{\text{major}}{R{-}\ddot{N}{=}\overset{\oplus}{C}{-}\overset{\ominus}{\underset{..}{\ddot{O}}}:} \leftrightarrow R{-}\overset{\ominus}{\underset{..}{\ddot{N}}}{-}C{\equiv}\overset{\oplus}{\ddot{O}} \leftrightarrow R{-}\overset{\oplus}{N}{\equiv}C{-}\overset{\ominus}{\underset{..}{\ddot{O}}}:$$

Since isocyanates contain very electrophilic carbon atoms which are joined by double bonds to two electronegative atoms, the reactions of this group with compounds containing active hydrogens would be expected to involve the electrophilic carbon of the isocyanate. The attacking group would therefore contain a nucleophilic center. If steric factors are dismissed, then the presence of a strong electron-withdrawing group attached to the isocyanate group would tend to decrease the electron density on the carbon atom (i.e., increase the positive charge) and thus increase the susceptibility toward nucleophilic attack. Conversely, nucleophilic groups would tend to increase the electron density and therefore reduce the reactivity of the isocyanate group as seen in the series below (122):

$$O_2NC_6H_4\text{—} > C_6H_5\text{—} > p\text{-}CH_3C_6H_4\text{—} > p\text{-}CH_3OCH_2\text{—} > C_6H_{11}\text{—}$$

Likewise, as the nucleophilicity or base strength of the compound attacking the isocyanate group increases, its reactivity will increase as shown in the following series (122):

$$CH_3NH_2 > C_6H_5NH_2 > CH_3OH > C_6H_5OH > CH_3SH >$$ 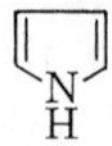

b. Reactions with Oxygen–Hydrogen Bond

The isocyanates are capable of reacting with a wide variety of organic and inorganic compounds containing active hydrogen atoms. In most cases simple addition occurs involving the migration of the active hydrogen atom to the nitrogen of the isocyanate. With the alcohol–isocyanate reaction, as seen in eq. (54), the effect of steric hindrance in the hydroxyl compound becomes especially pronounced:

$$R\text{—}N\text{=}C\text{=}O + R'\text{—}OH \rightarrow R\text{—}NH\text{—}\overset{\overset{\displaystyle O}{\|}}{C}\text{—}O\text{—}R' \quad (54)$$

At 25–50°C., secondary alcohols react only approximately 0.3 times as fast as the primary homologues, while tertiary alcohols react only 0.005 times as fast as the primary (123). The highly hindered triphenylcarbinol does not give the urethane derivative (124). If, in turn, the simpler aliphatic tertiary alcohols are employed, olefin formation becomes predominant (125,118) as shown in eq. (55).

$$2C_6H_5\text{—}N\text{=}C\text{=}O + (CH_3)_3C\text{—}OH \rightarrow$$
$$C_6H_5\text{—}NH\text{—}\overset{\overset{\displaystyle O}{\|}}{C}\text{—}NH\text{—}C_6H_5 + CO_2 + CH_3\text{—}\underset{\underset{\displaystyle CH_3}{|}}{C}\text{=}CH_2 \quad (55)$$

Investigations at the I. G. Farbenindustrie (now Farbenfabriken Bayer) led to the development of linear polyurethanes such as the reaction product of hexamethylene diisocyanate and 1,4-butanediol (eq. 56), known as Perlon U.

$$O\text{=}C\text{=}N\text{—}(CH_2)_6\text{—}N\text{=}C\text{=}O + HO\text{—}(CH_2)_4\text{—}OH \rightarrow$$
$$\text{+}(CH_2)_4\text{—}O\text{—}\overset{\overset{\displaystyle O}{\|}}{C}\text{—}NH\text{—}(CH_2)_6\text{—}NH\text{—}\overset{\overset{\displaystyle O}{\|}}{C}\text{—}O\text{+}_n \quad (56)$$

The preferred commercial method for the preparation of Perlon U type polyurethanes was to react a 0.5–3.0% excess of 1,4-butanediol with incremental amounts of hexamethylene diisocyanate. Since no solvent was generally employed, efficient mechanical mixing was required, especially

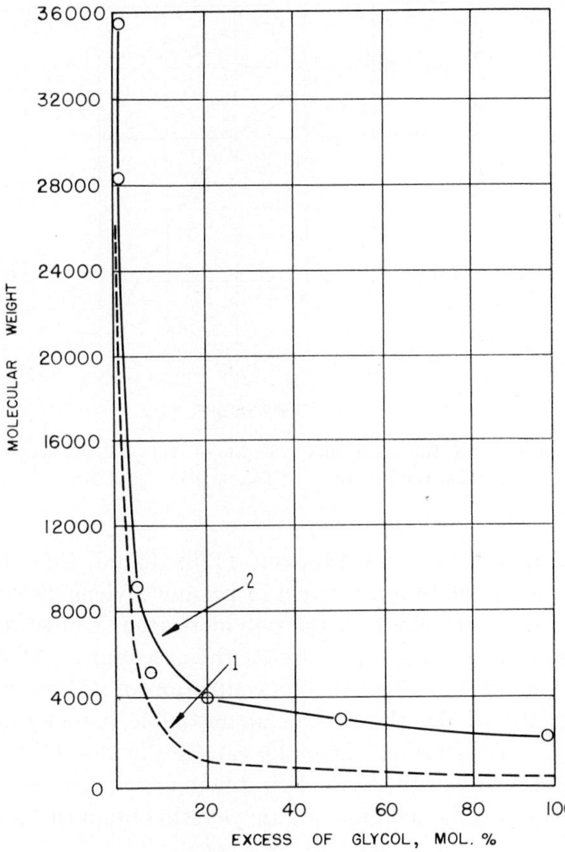

Fig. XI-2. Change in molecular weight of polyurethane under the effect of an excess of glycol: (*1*) calculated from viscosity data; (*2*) calculated according to Korshak and Golubev (126a). (Taken from ref. 126.)

during the latter stages of the polymerization when high viscosities were encountered. During the course of the reaction the temperature was increased to 190–195°C. and maintained at this level until the desired molecular weight had been obtained.

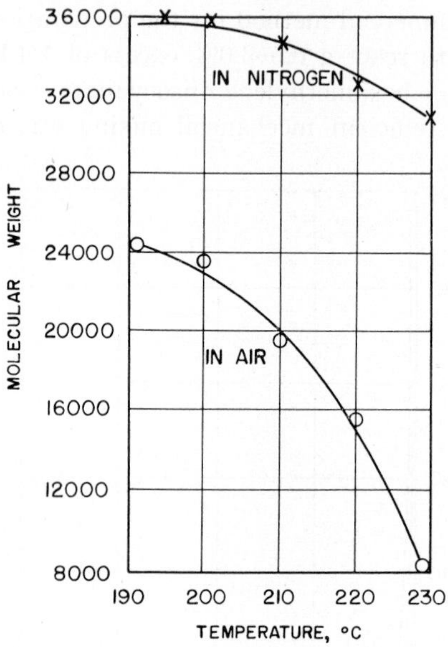

Fig. XI-3. Dependence of the molecular weight of the polyurethane on the final reaction temperature. (Taken from ref. 126.)

Korshak, Strepikheev, and Moiseev (126) found that the average molecular weight of the fusion product of hexamethylene diisocyanate and 1,4-butanediol was dependent on the polymerization temperature, as well as on the ratio of reactants, especially on the excess of α,ω-diol employed, see Figure XI-2 (126). When the concentration of diisocyanate was increased above 1% of the theoretical, an insoluble polymer was formed. Increasing the concentration threefold causes the insoluble polymer to become infusible. It was therefore desirable to use a slight excess of diol to prevent chain branching and crosslinking yet still obtain the desired molecular weight.

Korshak et al. have also observed (126) a strong influence of the initial reaction temperature and of free oxygen (air) during the reaction on the molecular weight of the linear polyurethane. In the presence of air, the molecular weight of the polyurethane dropped from 25,000 at 80°C. to approximately 14,000 at 180°C. while a polymer of 36,000 molecular weight at 80°C. under nitrogen only decreased to 33,000 with a 100°C. increase in temperature. Similarly, drastic decreases in molecular weight with respect to final polymerization temperatures were observed if the nitrogen atmos-

TABLE XI-6
Properties of Polyurethanes from Ethylene Glycol and Diisocyanates[a]

Reactant (diisocyanate)	Bulk properties: Inherent viscosity[b]	Polymer melt temp., °C.	Visual observations	Film properties (visual observations)
m-Phenylene diisocyanate	0.69 (*m*-Cresol)	185	White, moderately tough	Clear, somewhat brittle
2,4-Tolylene diisocyanate	0.45 (DMF)[c]	180	White, moderately tough	Clear, brittle
p-Phenylene diisocyanate	0.41 (H_2SO_4)	340	White, crumbly	
Durene diisocyanate	0.17 (H_2SO_4)	328	White, crumbly	
4,4′-diphenylmethane diisocyanate	1.01 (DMF)	255	White, tough	Clear, tough
Isopropylidenebis(4-phenyl isocyanate)	1.1 (DMF)	210	White, tough	Clear, tough
Bis(4-isocyanatophenyl) sulfone	0.82 (DMF)	224	White, tough	Clear, fairly tough
4,4′-Diphenyl ether diisocyanate	0.36 (DMF)	270	White, crumbly	Opaque, brittle
Biphenylene diisocyanate	0.67 (HMPA)[d]	388	White, tough	
3,3′-Dimethyl-4,4′-biphenylene diisocyanate	0.23 (H_2SO_4)	260	White, somewhat tough	Hazy, brittle
1,5-Naphthalene diisocyanate	0.14 (H_2SO_4)	304	White, crumbly	

[a] Taken from ref. 129.
[b] Measured at 30°C. at 0.5% concentration in the solvent listed.
[c] *N,N*-Dimethylformamide.
[d] Hexamethylphosphoramide.

phere was changed to air, as shown in Figure XI-3. Further control of molecular weight could also be exercised by introduction of monofunctional alcohols or amines such as heptyl alcohol or piperidine (126).

An alternate method for the preparation of Perlon U type materials is available based on a solvent-free process consisting of two steps (127). The initial condensation was carried out with only 80–90% of the theoretical concentration of hexamethylene diisocyanate to form a low molecular weight, fluid, isocyanate-terminated polymer. This material was then

TABLE XI-7
Properties of Polyurethanes from 4,4′-Diphenylmethane Diisocyanate and the *cis* and *trans* Glycols[a]

	1,4-Cyclohexanediol		1,4-Cyclohexanedimethanol	
Properties	*cis*	*trans*	*cis*	*trans*
Bulk				
Inherent viscosity	0.57	0.66	0.85	0.51
Polymer melt temp., °C.	230	308	227	220
$\bar{M}_n$	17,500 (η_{inh} = 0.57)[b]	16,000 (η_{inh} = 0.66)[b]		
		42,800 (η_{inh} = 1.72)[b]	50,000 (η_{inh} = 0.43)[b]	46,000 (η_{inh} = 0.41)[b]
Solubility in				
Tetrahydrofuran	Sol. cold	Insol.	Sol. cold	Sol. cold
Dioxane	Sol. hot	Insol.	Sol. cold	Sol. cold
1,1,2-Trichloroethane	Insol.	Insol.	Swollen	Insol.
Ethylene chlorohydrin	Sl. sol. hot	Insol.	Sol. hot, ppt. on cooling	Sol. hot, ppt. on cooling
Film[c]				
Water absorption, %	5.77	17.8	5.62	7.98
Fiber				
Tenacity, g./den.	1.8	3.3	0.6	0.9
Elongation, %	19	17	78	50
Initial modulus g./den.	20	38	9	16
Fiber stick temp., °C.	208	264	140	139
Moisture regain, %	5.93	14.52	3.99	5.87
Density, g./ml.	1.0137	1.2085	1.1691	1.2056

[a] Taken from ref. 130.

[b] Measured at 30°C. in *N,N*-dimethylformamide (c = 0.05).

[c] Clear, tough, amorphous films were cast from *N,N*-dimethylformamide solutions of the polyurethanes.

allowed to react further with the calculated concentration of isocyanate in special, heavy duty equipment to the desired molecular weight range.

During the early stages of Perlon U development, the use of dry chlorobenzene as a solvent (128), presented some difficulty in removing the last traces of solvent from the product and resulted in poor heat stability of the polymer during subsequent processing. Nevertheless, the resulting polymer had a melting point of 184°C. and a molecular weight of approximately 10,000, akin to the results exhibited by the polymer prepared by the direct reaction of the two components.

The solution polymerization of diisocyanates with ethylene glycol was described by Lyman (129). Essentially equal molar quantities of the diisocyanate and glycol were employed, and the reaction temperature was kept at 110–140°C. for 1–2 hr. The choice of the solvent greatly affected the yields as well as the molecular weights of the resulting polymers. Dimethyl sulfoxide, tetramethylene sulfone, and a mixture of dimethyl sulfoxide and 4-methyl-2-pentanone (50/50) as solvents were found to minimize the side reactions which influence the molecular weight. The properties of the polyurethanes prepared from ethylene glycol and various diisocyanates are summarized in Table XI-6 (129).

By employing the same technique of solution polymerization, the *cis* or *trans* isomers of 1,4-cyclohexanediol and 1,4-cyclohexanedimethanol were converted by reaction with 4,4′-diphenylmethane diisocyanate, to the corresponding *cis* and *trans* polyurethanes (130). Due to geometric reasons, the *trans*-1,4-cyclohexanediol isomer exhibited a lower degree of flexing than the *cis* isomer. Therefore, the stiffer, more linear polyurethane from the *trans* isomer would be expected to have a lower entropy of melting (i.e., higher melting point) than the polyurethane from the *cis* isomer. Lyman (130) observed that the *trans*-hexanediol-based urethane had a higher polymer melting temperature, decreased solubility, higher initial modulus and higher fiber stick temperature than the polymer prepared from the *cis* isomer. (See Table XI-7.)

Because of the presence of the methylene group between the cyclohexane ring and the hydroxyl oxygen, more rotation is possible resulting in a similar overall distortion for the *cis*- and *trans*-1,4-cyclohexanedimethanols. Thus, the chain flexibility between the two *cis* and *trans* polyurethanes would be expected to have similar entropies of melting or similar polymer melting points. Experimental results showed a remarkable similarity in the physical properties of the polyurethanes from *cis*- and *trans*-1,4-cyclohexanedimethanol (130) shown in Table XI-7.

Table XI-8 lists many of the more important diisocyanate-α,ω-diol interactions which yielded linear polyurethanes (131). Other examples of linear polyurethanes are found in additional tables.

The reaction of olefinic diols, such as *cis*- and *trans*-2-butene-1,4-diols, with hexamethylene diisocyanate was described by Marvel and Young (132). Some physical properties of the resulting polyurethanes are listed in Table XI-9.

TABLE XI-8

Linear Polyurethanes[a]

Diisocyanate	Diol	Melting point, °C.	Reference
$OCN(CH_2)_3NCO$	$HO(CH_2)_{10}OH$	105–108	273
$OCN(CH_2)_4NCO$	$HO(CH_2)_4OH$	193	80,81
"	$HO(CH_2)_6OH$	180	80,81,319
"	$HO(CH_2)_{10}OH$	171–173	80,319
$OCN(CH_2)_5NCO$	$HO(CH_2)_4OH$	159	80,81,319
"	$HO(CH_2)_6OH$	144–146	320
$OCN(CH_2)_6NCO$	$HO(CH_2)_2OH$	170	321
"	$HO(CH_2)_3OH$	155	321
"	$HOCH_2CHOHCH_3$	167	80
"	$HO(CH_2)_4OH$	183	80,81,133
"	$HOCH_2CH(CH_3)CH_2OH$	50	321
"	$HO(CH_2)_5OH$	151	80
"	$HOCH_2C(CH_3)_2CH_2OH$	120	321
"	$HO(CH_2)_2O(CH_2)_2OH$	120	80,225
"	$HO(CH_2)_2S(CH_2)_2OH$	129–134	80
"	$HO(CH_2)_6OH$	150	225
"	1,4-Cyclohexanediol	210	225
"	$HO(CH_2)_4O(CH_2)_4OH$	124	80
"	$HO(CH_2)_4S(CH_2)_4OH$	120–125	80
"	*m*-$(C_6H_4)(OH)_2$	150 (softens) 220 (dec.)	307
"	(*p*-$HOC_6H_4)_2C(CH_3)_2$	130 (softens) 230 (dec.)	307
"		158	80
"	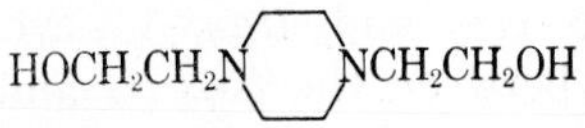	165	322
$OCN(CH_2)_7NCO$	$HO(CH_2)_4OH$	155–157	319
$OCN(CH_2)_8NCO$	$HO(CH_2)_4OH$	160	80,81,319
"	$HO(CH_2)_6OH$	153	80,81,319
"	1,4-Cyclohexanediol *cis*, *trans*	215–220	80
"	*trans*-1,4-Cyclohexanediol	250–255 (dec.)	80
"	1,4-$(HOCH_2)_2C_6H_4$	168	80
"	$HO(CH_2)_{10}OH$	144–146	319,323
$OCN(CH_2)_9NCO$	$HO(CH_2)_4OH$	136–140	80
$OCN(CH_2)_{10}NCO$	(*p*-$HOC_6H_4)_2C(CH_3)_2$	205	225
"	$HO(CH_2)_{10}OH$	138	225

(continued)

TABLE XI-8 (*continued*)

Diisocyanate	Diol	Melting point, °C.	Reference
$OCN(CH_2)_{11}NCO$	$HO(CH_2)_4OH$	143–146	80
"	$HO(CH_2)_5OH$	121–123	80
$OCN(CH_2)_{12}NCO$	$HO(CH_2)_{12}OH$	128	80
Cyclohexane-1,4-diisocyanate	$HO(CH_2)_4OH$	260 (dec.)	80
m-$C_6H_4(NCO)_2$	$HO(CH_2)_2OH$	185	129
"	$HO(CH_2)_6OH$	230	225
p-$(C_6H_4)(NCO)_2$	$HO(CH_2)_3OH$	340 (dec.)	129
2,4-$CH_3(C_6H_3)(NCO)_2$	$HO(CH_2)_2OH$	180	129
p,p'-$(OCNC_6H_4)_2CH_2$	$HO(CH_2)_2OH$	328	129
p,p'-$(OCNC_6H_4)_2CH_2$	2-Ethyl-1,3-hexanediol	140 (softens) 210 (dec.)	307
"	2-*n*-Butyl-2-ethyl-1,3-propanediol	110–120,160 (softens) 260 (dec.)	307
"	(*p*-$HOC_6H_4)_2C(CH_3)_2$	190–132 (softens) 260 (dec.)	307
p,p'-$(C_6H_4NCO)_2$	$HO(CH_2)_2OH$	388	129
$[3,4\text{-}CH_3(NCO)C_6H_4]_2$	$HO(CH_2)_2OH$	260	129
"	$HO(CH_2)_{10}OH$	215–219	80

[a] Taken from ref. 131.

The reaction of diols containing acetylenic bonds with hexamethylene diisocyanate (HDI) was reported by Marvel and Johnson (133). The preparation of these acetylenic polyurethanes was carried out by the reaction of 2-butyne-1,4-diol with HDI in chlorobenzene solution. The physical constants and some thermodynamic values are listed in Table XI-10. The polyurethane from 1,4-butanediol and HDI and mixtures of 1,4-butanediol and 2-butyne-1,4-diol with HDI were included in this table for com-

TABLE XI-9

Polyurethanes from Butenediols and Hexamethylene Diisocyanate[a]

Polymer	Inherent viscosity	Melting point, °C.	Second-order transition, °C.	Heat of fusion, cal.	Entropy of fusion, cal./deg.
cis	0.12	136	−39	4750	11.6
trans	0.19	177	−44	4250	9.5

[a] Taken from ref. 132.

parison purposes. As can be seen from Table XI-10 the presence of the triple bond caused lowering of the capillary melting point but increased the second order transition temperature, making the acetylenic polymer stiffer than the corresponding saturated polymer.

TABLE XI-10
Physical Constants and Thermodynamic Values for Polyurethanes of 1,4-Butanediol and 2-Butyne-1,4-diol and Mixtures[a]

Polyurethane diol, mole fraction						
Butanediol	Butynediol	Intrinsic viscosity	Capillary melting point, °C.	Second-order transition, °C.	Heat of fusion, cal.	Entropy of fusion, cal./deg.
1.0	0.0	0.25	176–177	−58	—	—
1.0	0.0	0.17	175	—	7000	15.7
0.8	0.2	0.17	163	—	—	—
0.2	0.8	0.19	128	—	—	—
0.0	1.0	0.17	146	—	4000	10.0
0.0	1.0	0.23	149–150	−45	—	—

[a] Taken from ref. 133.

Slezak et al. (134) employed long-chain polyacetylenic α,ω-diols, made from 1,7,13,19-eicosatetrayne, to prepare the corresponding polyurethanes with various diisocyanates. The following polyacetylenic diols were synthesized: 2,8,14,20-docosatetrayne-1,22-diol (I); 3,9,15,21-tetracosatetrayne-1,24-diol (II); 4,10,16,22-hexacosatetrayne-1,26-diol (III). The

$$HO{-}CH_2{-}C{\equiv}C{+}(CH_2)_4{-}C{\equiv}C{+}_3CH_2{-}OH$$
(I)

$$HO{-}CH_2{-}CH_2{-}C{\equiv}C{+}(CH_2)_4{-}C{\equiv}C{+}_3CH_2{-}CH_2{-}OH$$
(II)

$$HO{-}CH_2{-}CH_2{-}CH_2{-}C{\equiv}C{+}(CH_2)_4{-}C{\equiv}C{+}_3CH_2{-}CH_2{-}CH_2{-}OH$$
(III)

diisocyanates used in the reactions were tolylene diisocyanate (TDI); 4,4′-diphenylmethane diisocyanate (MDI); hexamethylene diisocyanate (HDI); 5,11-hexadecadiyne 1,16-diisocyanate, $OCN{+}(CH_2)_4C{\equiv}C{+}_2(CH_2)_4NCO$, (HDDDI); and hexadecane 1,16-diisocyanate (HDDI). The resulting polyurethanes were all hard, tough materials with the exception of the 5,11-hexadecadiyne 1,16-diisocyanate–I product, which was soft and waxy. The properties of these polyurethanes are listed in Tables XI-11 and XI-12 (134).

TABLE XI-11
Properties of Simple Polyacetylenic Polyurethanes[a]

Diisocyanate	Diol	Reaction time, hr.	Reaction temp., °C.	η_{inh} (25°C., DMF)	Softening range, °C.	Shore D hardness
TDI[b]	I	0.5	78[c]	0.65	274–287	72
TDI	II	12	110[d]	0.31	235–245	—
TDI	III	5	110	0.41	226–238	—
MDI[b]	I	22	98[e]	0.45	133–190	58
MDI	II	18	98	0.70	274–277	74
MDI	III	17	98	0.41	136–150	65
HDI[b]	I	20	98	0.37	250–283	43
HDI	II	19	98	0.62	150–280	50
HDI	III	19	98	0.38	126–138	65
HDDDI[f]	I	18	98	—	<50	—
HDDDI	II	18	98	0.17	70–75	—
HDDDI	III	18	98	0.19	70–80	—
HDDI[b]	I	72	110[g]	0.26[h,i]	280–300	—
HDDI	II	72	110	0.23[h,i]	335–345	—
HDDI	j	72	110	0.62[h]	160–360	—

[a] Taken from ref. 134.
[b] 99.7 + % pure.
[c] In benzene.
[d] In toluene.
[e] In heptane.
[f] 87% pure.
[g] In dimethylformamide.
[h] In *m*-cresol.
[i] Did not all dissolve.
[j] 1,24-Tetracosanediol.

The preparation of oligourethanes, i.e., polymers of a low degree of polymerization, was described by Kern and co-workers in a series of papers in which the so-called "duplication" procedure was used (135–138). The first step in the duplication procedure consists in the reaction of a large excess of a diol with a diisocyanate to yield urethane diols as shown in eq. (57).

$$\text{HO—R—OH} + \text{OCN—R'—NCO} + \text{HO—R—OH} \rightarrow$$

$$\underset{\text{(IV)}}{\text{HO—R—O—}\overset{\overset{\text{O}}{\|}}{\text{C}}\text{—NH—R'—NH—}\overset{\overset{\text{O}}{\|}}{\text{C}}\text{—O—R—OH}} \quad (57)$$

TABLE XI-12

Polyurethanes of Poly(propylene Glycol) and of Poly(acetylenic Diols) with Hexamethylene Diisocyanate and Trimethylolpropane[a,b]

	A	B	C	D	E
Diol	PPG[c]	PPG[c]	I	II	II
Cure temp., °C.	60	60	80	80	100
Cure, time, days	3	4	3	4	3
Avg. tensile strength, psi	1,300	1,250	3,490	3,650	2,140
Avg. tensile modulus, psi	450[d]	425[d]	—	12,400	5,650
Avg. elongation at break, %	1,380	1,120	1,200	95	160
Test speed, in./min.	5.0	5.0	20.0	0.5	0.5
No. specimens tested	3	3	1	3	3
Hardness					
Shore A	40	40	77	100	98
Shore D	—	—	—	73	54
Avg. B.t.u./lb.[e]	13,230	13,190	14,650	14,860	14,625
Avg. cal./g.[f]	7,351	7,328	8,140	8,256	8,126
Avg. density (26°C.), g./ml.	1.022	1.022	1.094	1.094	1.092
Avg. cal./ml.	7.513	7,489	8,905	9,032	8,874

[a] Taken from ref. 134.

[b] Poly(propylene glycol) of 2000 M.W. was used as received; HDI was distilled prior to use.

[c] Catalyzed by 10 mg. of ferric acetylacetonate per 0.01 mole of diol, and containing 1% *N*-phenyl-2-naphthylamine as antioxidant based on the combined weight of diol and triol.

[d] 100% modulus.

[e] Average of two values of gross heat of combustion including hydrogen to liquid water and nitrogen to nitric acid dissolved in water.

[f] Average B.t.u./lb. × 0.5556.

The resulting urethane diols (IV) are then reacted further with the diisocyanate by a similar chain extension as in eq. (58).

$$\text{IV} + \text{OCN—R'—NCO} + \text{IV} \rightarrow$$

$$\text{HO—R—O}\!\left[\overset{\text{O}}{\overset{\|}{\text{C}}}\text{—NH—R'—NH—}\overset{\text{O}}{\overset{\|}{\text{C}}}\text{—O—R—O}\right]_3\!\text{H} \quad (58)$$

(V)

The isolation of the products of the second step is relatively simple, since the products of the first step are soluble in methanol while the higher condensation products are not.

The third step (eq. 59) is a repetition of eq. (58) with the exception that the higher condensation products (V) are reacted with the diisocyanate.

$$\text{V} + \text{OCN—R'—NCO} + \text{V} \rightarrow$$

$$\text{HO—R—O}\!\left[\overset{\overset{\text{O}}{\|}}{\text{C}}\text{—NH—R'—NH—}\overset{\overset{\text{O}}{\|}}{\text{C}}\text{—O—R—O}\right]_7\text{H} \quad (59)$$

(VI)

Isolation of the products of this third step can be made by using aqueous formic acid (90–92%). The above steps can of course be repeated to give

TABLE XI-13
Oligourethanes (1st Step)[a]

Diisocyanate[b]	Diol[b]	Composition of oligomer	Mol. wt.	Melting point, °C.
$OCN(CH_2)_6$—NCO (h)	$HO(CH_2)_2OH$ (2)	2h2	292	95–97
"	$HO(CH_2)_4OH$ (4)	4h4	348	103–105
"	$HO(CH_2)_6OH$ (6)	6h6	405	106.5–107
1,5-Naphthalene diisocyanate (n)	$HO(CH_2)_2OH$	2n2	334	186.5–187.5
"	$HO(CH_2)_4OH$	4n4	390	176–176.5
"	$HO(CH_2)_6OH$	6n6	447	157–158
"	$HO(CH_2)_2$—O—$(CH_2)_2OH$ (5)	5n5	422	133–134.5
2,4-$(CH_3)(C_6H_4)(NCO)_2$ (t_a)	$HO(CH_2)_2OH$	$2t_a2$	298	137–138
"	$HO(CH_2)_4OH$	$4t_a4$	354	112.5–114
"	$HO(CH_2)_6OH$	$6t_a6$	410	61.5–63
2,6-$(CH_3)(C_6H_4)(NCO)_2$ (t_v)	$HO(CH_2)_2OH$	$2t_v2$	298	175–176
[3,4-$CH_3(NCO)C_6H_4]_2$ (p_o)	$HO(CH_2)_4OH$	$4p_o4$	445	147–149.5
"	$HO(CH_2)_2$—O—$(CH_2)_2OH$	$5p_o5$	477	92–93

[a] Taken from ref. 135.

[b] The abbreviations for the diisocyanates and diols are shown in parentheses, e.g. (h).

products of higher molecular weight. In Tables XI-13, XI-14, and XI-15 are listed reaction products obtained from reactions (57), (58), and (59) of the duplication procedure applied to 1,4-butanediol and hexamethylene diisocyanate (135).

Diol diurethanes derived from 1,4-butanediol and aromatic diisocyanates were also described by Kern and Thoma (136) and are shown in Table

TABLE XI-14
Oligourethanes (2nd Step)[a]

Diisocyanate[b]	Diol[b]	Composition of oligomer	Mol. wt.	Melting point, °C.
$OCN(CH_2)_6NCO$ (h)	$HO(CH_2)_2OH$ (2)	2h2h2h2	753	150.5–152
"	$HO(CH_2)_4OH$ (4)	4h4h4h4	865	155–157
"	$HO(CH_2)_6OH$ (6)	6h6h6h6	977	146–148
$OCN(CH_2)_6NCO$ + 2,4-$(CH_3)(C_6H_4)(NCO)_2$ (t_a)	$HO(CH_2)_4OH$	$4h4t_a4h4$	871	134–136
$OCN(CH_2)_6NCO$ + 1,5-Naphthalene diisocyanate (n)	$HO(CH_2)_4OH$	4h4n4h4	907	156–158.5
$OCN(CH_2)_6NCO$ + $[3,4\text{-}CH_3(NCO)C_6H_4]$	$HO(CH_2)_4OH$	$4h4p_04h4$	961	163.5–165

[a] Taken from ref. 135.
[b] The abbreviations for the diisocyanates and diols are shown in parentheses, e.g. (h).

TABLE XI-15
Oligomers and Polymers from 1,4-Butanediol and Hexamethylene Diisocyanate[a]

Composition[b]	Mol. wt.	Melting point, °C.	Yield, % theor.
4h4	348	103–105	90
$4(h4)_3$	865	155–157	95
$4(h4)_7$	1,898	170–173	50
$(h4)_n$	ca. 10,000	176–181	—

[a] Taken from ref. 136.
[b] Abbreviations: 1,4-butanediol = 4; hexamethylene diisocyanate = h.

TABLE XI-16
Diol Diurethanes from 1,4-Butanediol and Aromatic Diisocyanates[a]
$HO{-}(CH_2)_4{-}O{-}CO{-}NH{-}R{-}NH{-}CO{-}O{-}(CH_2)_4{-}OH$

R	Yield, %	Melting point, °C.
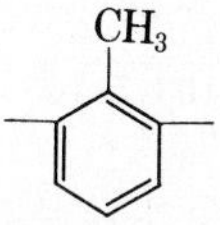	70	157–159
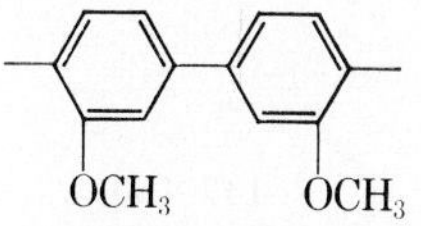	35–40	137.5
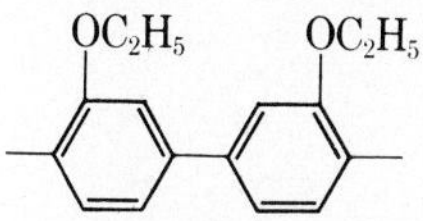	75–80	115–116
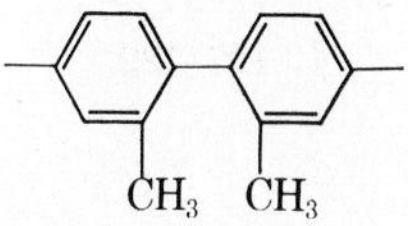	—	Oil

[a] Taken from ref. 136.

XI-16. Other diol diurethanes prepared by these authors had the general formula (VII) where R_1 consisted either of oxygen, sulfur, or variously

$$HO{-}(CH_2)_2{-}R_1{-}(CH_2)_2{-}O{-}CO{-}NH{-}R_2{-}NH{-}CO{-}O{-}(CH_2)_2{-}R_1{-}(CH_2)_2{-}OH \quad \text{(VII)}$$

substituted amine linkages and R_2 was either an aromatic or aliphatic radical.

Diol hexaurethanes were prepared by the reaction of diol diurethanes with various diisocyanates (136) according to eq. (60): The hexaurethanes

$$2HO{-}(CH_2)_4{-}O{-}CO{-}NH{-}(CH_2)_6{-}NH{-}CO{-}O{-}(CH_2)_4{-}OH + OCN{-}R_1{-}NCO \rightarrow$$
$$[HO{-}(CH_2)_4{-}O{-}CO{-}NH{-}(CH_2)_6{-}NH{-}CO{-}O{-}(CH_2)_4{-}O{-}CO{-}NH]_2R_1 \quad (60)$$

prepared in this manner are shown in Table XI-17.

The preparation of diol tetramide diurethanes by reaction of diol diamides with diisocyanates was described by Kern and Thoma (137). The diol diamides employed in the synthesis were made by the aminolysis of esters of dicarboxylic acids. A large excess of the diol diamides was then

TABLE XI-17
Diol Hexaurethanes[a]

R_1	Yield, %	Melting point, °C.
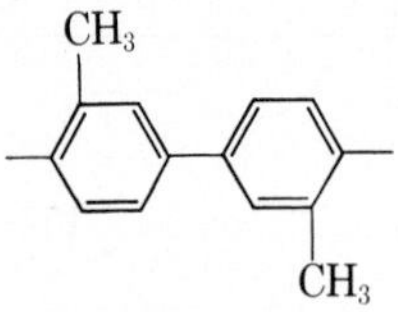	70	163.5–165
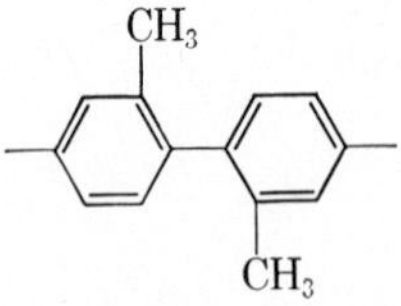	60	147–150
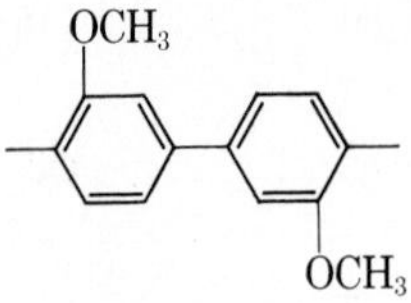	60	127–129
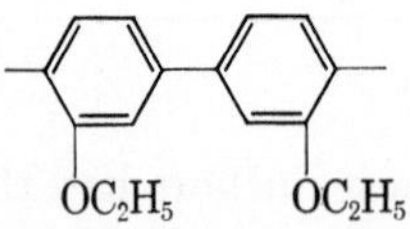	60	104–106

[a] Taken from ref. 136.

reacted with diisocyanates yielding the diol tetramide diurethanes as white, relatively high melting powders according to eq. (61).

$$\begin{array}{c} 2HO-(CH_2)_2-NH-CO-R_1-CO-NH-(CH_2)_2-OH + OCN-R_2-NCO \\ \downarrow \\ HO-(CH_2)_2-NH-CO-R_1-CO-NH-(CH_2)_2-O-CO-NH-R_2- \\ NH-CO-O-(CH_2)_2-NH-CO-R_1-CO-NH-(CH_2)_2-OH \end{array} \quad (61)$$

The diurethanes thus prepared are listed in Table XI-18. The separation of the diurethanes from the excess diol diamides was accomplished by extraction of the soluble diol diamides using water or methanol as solvent.

In order to determine the influence of the hydroxyl-bearing polymer on the properties of the final urethane, Schonfeld (139) reacted a series of α,ω-glycols with paraformaldehyde to yield low molecular weight polymers, bifunctional with respect to the hydroxyl group. These polyformals were reacted with tolylene diisocyanate and then converted by the addition of

TABLE XI-18
Diol–Tetramide Diurethanes[a]

R_1	R_2	Yield, %	Melting point, °C.
$-(CH_2)_4-$	$-(CH_2)_6-$	60	187–189
$-CH_2-$	$-(CH_2)_6-$	65	179–181
$-CH-CH(CH_3)_2$ (with bonds above and below the first CH)	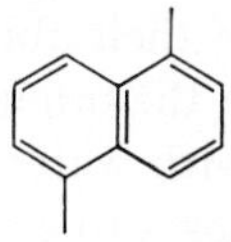	50	220–222
$-(CH_2)_4-$	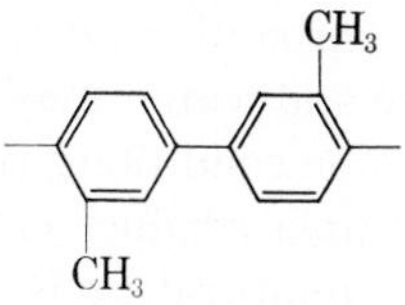	40	190–191.5

[a] Taken from ref. 137.

trimethylolpropane into crosslinked urethane elastomers with physical properties similar to those prepared from polyformals containing a varying number of methylene groups in the starting glycol.

Because of the possibility of obtaining highly energetic materials for use in explosive and propellano compositions, the preparation of polynitrocarbamates as well as of *N*-nitrocarbamates has been investigated (140, 141). These carbamates were conveniently prepared by the addition of either a nitroalcohol or nitroisocyanate with the appropriate isocyanate or alcohol, respectively. The nitro-containing alcohols were somewhat more acidic and therefore reacted less readily with isocyanates than ordinary alcohols. Addition was catalyzed, however, with a trace of ferric acetylacetonate (142), which was found to be the most effective catalyst for urethane formation in the presence of nitro groups. It also had the least effect on the rate of homopolymerization of nitrodiisocyanates (141). Boron trifluoride catalyst increased the rate of nitrourethane formation initially, but rapidly lost its effectiveness as the reaction proceeded.

The reaction between an isocyanate and a phenol is considerably slower than the reaction with aliphatic alcohols due to the decrease in the nucleophilicity of the hydroxyl group (phenol being more acidic than the aliphatic alcohols). The reaction between phenol and most isocyanates proceeds slowly at 50–75°C. (142,143). The presence of a substituent on the phenol nucleus, as expected, has a strong influence on the reaction rate. Electronegative substituents tend to retard the urethane-forming reaction, since the nucleophilic character of the hydroxyl has been further decreased. Picric acid, 2,4,6-trinitrophenol, does not react with isocyanate groups to give the urethane upon long heating under pressure (144). The lack of reactivity of the hydroxy group in trinitrophenol is credited both to the electronegative influence of the nitro group and also to the steric effect of the two *ortho* substituents. The phenol urethane derivatives have found commercial applications because of their ability to dissociate under the influence of heat and/or catalysts to the original isocyanate.

The reaction of an isocyanate with water proceeds first through an unstable intermediate which decomposes to give carbon dioxide and the substituted urea derivative. The carbamic acid, which is the initial reaction product between the isocyanate and water, may, however, undergo several reactions depending on the reaction conditions, the electronic structure, and steric factors, to give the final urea product (145). If the carbamic acid is very unstable or the reaction temperature is above 100°C., the acid decomposes with loss of carbon dioxide to the amine (146). The amine then reacts with the excess isocyanate to yield the substituted urea. The overall reaction is given in eq. (62c).

$$R{-}N{=}C{=}O + H_2O \rightarrow [R{-}NH{-}\overset{\overset{\displaystyle O}{\|}}{C}{-}OH] \rightarrow R{-}NH_2 + CO_2 \qquad (62a)$$

$$R{-}NH_2 + R{-}N{=}C{=}O \rightarrow R{-}NH{-}\overset{\overset{\displaystyle O}{\|}}{C}{-}NH{-}R \qquad (62b)$$

$$2R{-}N{=}C{=}O + H_2O \rightarrow R{-}NH{-}\overset{\overset{\displaystyle O}{\|}}{C}{-}NH{-}R + CO_2 \qquad (62c)$$

Initial studies of the rates of reaction of isocyanates with water show some similarities to that of the isocyanate–amine or isocyanate–alcohol reactions (147,148). The reaction is strongly catalyzed by various amines (149–151) and organometallic compounds (152–154). In the presence of strong acids, however, the amine salt is preferentially formed, which is unreactive toward the isocyanate (145) as shown in eq. (63).

$$R{-}N{=}C{=}O + H_2O + HCl \rightarrow [R{-}NH_3^{\oplus}]Cl^{\ominus} + CO_2 \qquad (63)$$

Similar conditions were observed when the reaction was carried out in the presence of a strong base (eq. 64). Sodium carbonate and the amine,

$$R{-}N{=}C{=}O + NaOH + H_2O \rightarrow R{-}NH{-}\overset{\overset{\displaystyle O}{\|}}{C}{-}O{-}Na \qquad (64a)$$

$$R{-}N{-}H{-}\overset{\overset{\displaystyle O}{\|}}{C}{-}O{-}Na + NaOH + H_2O \rightarrow R{-}NH_2 + Na_2CO_3 \qquad (64b)$$

rather than the urea derivative, were formed. This would suggest that an intermediate may well be the carbamic acid salt, if the conditions are sufficiently mild. This salt may liberate the amine at a slower rate than the rate at which the alkali attacks the isocyanate, or the base itself may react more rapidly with the —NCO group than does the weaker amine (145).

The careful treatment, in high dilution, of a polymethylene diisocyanate with water allowed the preparation of the cyclic ureas (155) as in eq. (65).

$$O{=}C{=}N{-}(CH_2)_n{-}N{=}C{=}O + H_2O \rightarrow H_2N{-}(CH_2)_n{-}N{=}C{=}O + CO_2 \quad (65a)$$

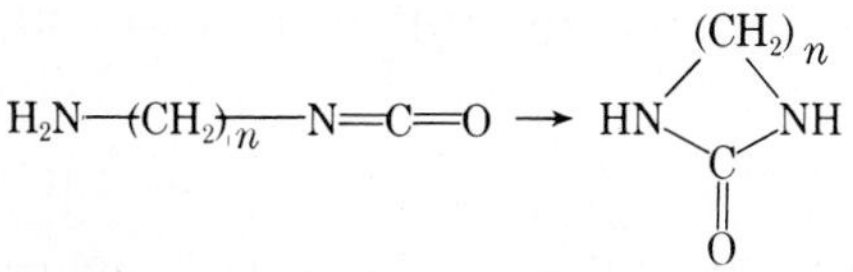

(65b)

When ethylene diisocyanate was treated with water, complete conversion to the cyclic urea was realized (156). Iwakura (156) was able to prepare linear *N,N'*-polymethyleneurea by the addition of water to the diisocyanate. The polymer was also synthesized from the diamine and the diisocyanate.

Organic carboxylic acid groups, due to the presence of an active hydrogen, react with isocyanates to yield unstable addition products, which generally decompose to the substituted amides (157). As was observed when isocyanates reacted with water, the environment as well as the electronic and steric factors play a pronounced role in the mode of decomposition as well as ease of formation. Organic acids vary considerably in their acid strength, and since the addition reaction is based on both the nucleophilicity of the active hydrogen compound and the electrophilicity of the carbon of the isocyanate, the ease and rate of carboxyl–isocyanate reactions may vary. As a general rule, the carboxylic acids are less reactive than primary hydroxyls or water toward isocyanates. Thus, a hydroxy aliphatic acid such as β-hydroxyisobutyric acid reacts preferentially at the hydroxyl site (158) (eq. 66). Aromatic hydroxyl groups, as was previously shown, are

$$R{-}N{=}C{=}O + HO{-}CH_2{-}CH(CH_3){-}C({=}O){-}OH \rightarrow R{-}NH{-}C({=}O){-}O{-}CH_2{-}CH(CH_3){-}C({=}O){-}OH \quad (66)$$

considerably less reactive than the aliphatic hydroxyl groups. They are also less reactive towards the isocyanate groups than aromatic carboxyl groups as demonstrated by the fact that *o*-, *m*-, and *p*-hydroxybenzoic acids yield the corresponding amides exclusively (159). Aliphatic isocyanates

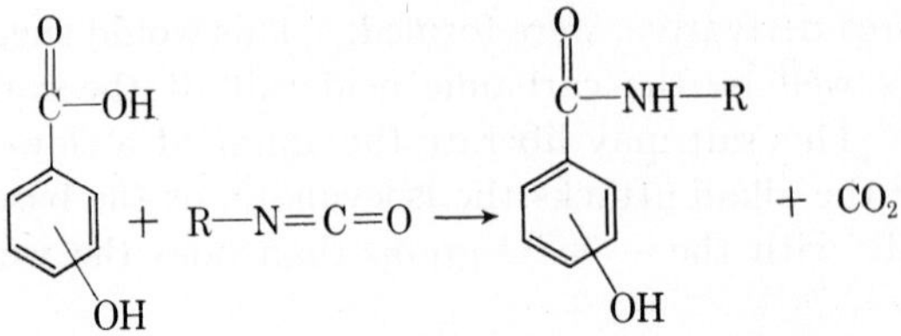
(67)

and aliphatic acids usually give unstable addition products which decompose to the substituted amides:

$$R{-}N{=}C{=}O + R'{-}\overset{\displaystyle O}{\overset{\|}{C}}{-}OH \rightarrow [R{-}NH{-}\overset{\displaystyle O}{\overset{\|}{C}}{-}O{-}\overset{\displaystyle O}{\overset{\|}{C}}{-}O{-}R'] \rightarrow R{-}NH{-}\overset{\displaystyle O}{\overset{\|}{C}}{-}R' + CO_2 \quad (68)$$

Strong organic acids, such as formic, cyanoacetic, and trichloroacetic acids react in an analogous manner. The reaction, however, between an isocyanate and a carboxylic acid may proceed by two different paths (160), as shown in eqs. (69) and (70). A mixture of products corresponding to

$$R{-}N{=}C{=}O + R'{-}\overset{\displaystyle O}{\overset{\|}{C}}{-}OH \rightarrow CO_2 + R'{-}\overset{\displaystyle O}{\overset{\|}{C}}{-}NH{-}R \quad (69)$$

$$2R{-}N{=}C{=}O + 2R'{-}\overset{\displaystyle O}{\overset{\|}{C}}{-}OH \rightarrow CO_2 + (R'{-}\overset{\displaystyle O}{\overset{\|}{C}}{-})_2O + R{-}NH{-}\overset{\displaystyle O}{\overset{\|}{C}}{-}NH{-}R \quad (70)$$

partial reaction by both paths may be observed. If conditions are sufficiently drastic, substituted ureas and carboxylic acid anhydrides may equilibrate to give two moles of the mixed amide and carbon dioxide (160). Fry (161) was able to show, by using C^{14}-carboxyl-labeled acids (eq. 71), that the carbon dioxide evolved during the isocyanate–acid reaction arises

$$R{-}N{=}\overset{*}{C}{=}O + R'{-}\overset{\displaystyle O}{\overset{\|}{C}}{-}OH \rightarrow [R{-}NH{-}\overset{\displaystyle O}{\overset{\|}{C}}{-}O{-}\overset{\displaystyle O}{\overset{\|}{C}}{-}R'] \rightarrow R{-}NH{-}\overset{\displaystyle O}{\overset{\|}{C}}{-}R' + \overset{*}{C}O_2 \quad (71)$$

from the isocyanate. These results favoring the decomposition of the addition product to carbon dioxide and the amide were in agreement with the behavior of isocyanates with other active hydrogen compounds and with the work of Krafft and Karstens (162) using benzoic acid and phenyl isothiocyanate.

The directions of the decomposition of mixed aromatic–aliphatic crystalline anhydride depend on both the temperature and the structure of the carboxylic acids. At low temperatures the decomposition favors the carbanilide, symmetrical carboxylic anhydride, and carbon dioxide, following simple first-order kinetics (163). At higher temperatures, the decomposition products are the *N*-substituted amides and carbon dioxide.

The condensation of diisocyanates with dioximes was reported by Campbell, Foldi, and Parrish (164). Four symmetrical dioximes, dimethylglyoxime, 1,4-cyclohexanedione dioxime, terephthaldehyde dioxime, and 2,6-pyridine dialdoxime, were reacted with a variety of diisocyanates. The reaction of 1,4-cyclohexanedione dioxime (VIII) and 4,4′-biphenylene diisocyanate is presented in eq. (72).

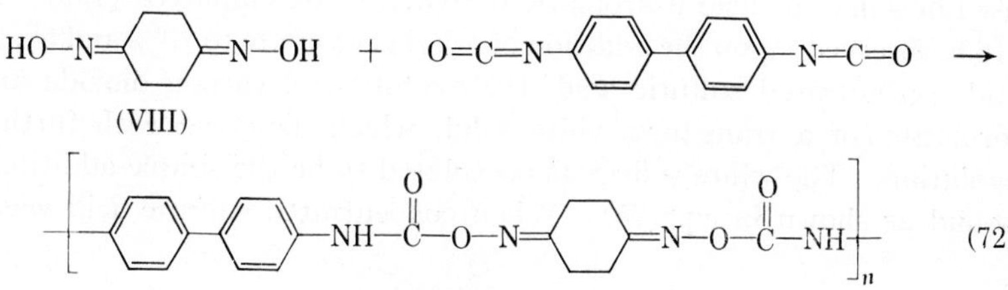
(VIII)

(IX) (72)

The general method of polymerization consisted of mixing dimethyl sulfoxide solutions of the diisocyanate and the dioxime, and heating the reaction mixture at 80–100°C. for about 2 hr. with nitrogen sparging. The isolation of the polymers was achieved by pouring the resulting mixture into water. Triethylamine and, in some instances, copper dichloride were found to be effective catalysts for these condensations.

The majority of these polymers, with some exceptions, such as the polymer (IX) shown above, were of low molecular weight and decomposed or charred at their melting points (164).

The simplest dihydroxyl material is hydrogen peroxide which reacts with an isocyanate to give the azine in low yields (165). The postulated reaction path (eq. 73) is via the bisperoxycarbamates which decompose with loss of carbon dioxide to the azines. Organic hydroperoxides, similarly, react

$$\mathrm{R{-}N{=}C{=}O + H_2O_2 \rightarrow [R{-}NH{-}\overset{\displaystyle O}{\overset{\|}{C}}{-}O{-}O{-}\overset{\displaystyle O}{\overset{\|}{C}}{-}NH{-}R] \rightarrow}$$

$$\mathrm{R{-}NH{-}NH{-}R + CO_2 \xrightarrow{H_2O_2} R{-}N{=}N{-}R} \qquad (73)$$

with isocyanates to give peroxycarbamates (166–168). These addition products readily decompose by a first-order, free radical mechanism to give carbon dioxide, an arylimino free radical, and an alkoxy or aralkoxy free radical (167); hydrazobenzene and azobenzene are the main products. In the presence of styrene, the decomposition products were able to initiate polymerization, suggesting the use of these peroxycarbamates as initiators of vinyl polymerization.

$$\mathrm{Ar{-}NH{-}\overset{\overset{\displaystyle O}{\|}}{C}{-}O{-}O{-}R} \rightarrow \mathrm{Ar{-}NH\cdot} + \mathrm{CO_2} + \mathrm{R{-}O\cdot} \qquad (74)$$

The "hydroxyl" groups present in sulfuric acid are capable of reacting with an isocyanate, to form either sulfamic acid if aliphatic isocyanates are used or sulfanilic acid if aromatic derivatives are employed (169). Bieber (169) observed, upon the addition of ethyl isocyanate to 20% and 5% oleum and concentrated sulfuric acid, the evolution of carbon dioxide and the formation of a transitory white solid, which dissolved with further gas evolution. The white solid was postulated to be the simple addition compound as shown in eq. (75). When concentrated sulfuric acid was used,

$$\mathrm{R{-}N{=}C{=}O} + \mathrm{H_2SO_4} \rightarrow [\mathrm{R{-}NH{-}\overset{\overset{\displaystyle O}{\|}}{C}{-}O{-}SO_3H}] \rightarrow \mathrm{CO_2} + \mathrm{R{-}NH{-}SO_3H} \qquad (75)$$

the major product was ethylamine acid sulfate accompanied by a 13% yield of ethylsulfamic acid. The water content of the concentrated sulfuric acid was greater than that required for hydrolysis of all the isocyanate employed.

Phosphorus acid derivatives form the expected anhydride, and, like the sulfur analogues, readily decompose with the liberation of carbon dioxide (170). Monoesters of orthophosphoric acid also give monocarbamoyl derivatives, as do hydroxysilanes (171,172) (eq. 76).

$$\mathrm{C_6H_5{-}\overset{\overset{\displaystyle O}{\uparrow}}{P}{-}(OH)_2} + \mathrm{R{-}N{=}C{=}O} \rightarrow \mathrm{C_6H_5{-}\overset{\overset{\displaystyle O}{\uparrow}}{P}(OH){-}O{-}\underset{\underset{\displaystyle O}{\|}}{C}{-}NH{-}R} \qquad (76)$$

Boronic acids readily react with diisocyanates, with the liberation of carbon dioxide, to yield a linear polymer (173). Boric acid, in turn, also reacts with diisocyanates to form boron- and nitrogen-containing polymers (174,175).

Greber and Jäger (176) reported the preparation of various silicon-containing polyurethanes by the reaction of organosilicon diols with diisocyanates in the absence of catalysts. The reaction of ω,ω′-bis-(γ-hydroxypropyl)polysiloxanes with various diisocyanates is represented schematically by eq. (77).

$$(y+1)\mathrm{O{=}C{=}N{-}R{-}N{=}C{=}O} + (y+1)\mathrm{HO{-}X{-}OH} \rightarrow$$

$$\mathrm{O{=}C{=}N}\left[\mathrm{R{-}NH{-}\overset{\overset{\displaystyle O}{\|}}{C}{-}O{-}X{-}O{-}\overset{\overset{\displaystyle O}{\|}}{C}{-}NH}\right]_y\mathrm{R{-}NH{-}\overset{\overset{\displaystyle O}{\|}}{C}{-}O{-}X{-}OH} \qquad (77)$$

where

$$\mathrm{X} = -(\mathrm{CH_2})_3{-}\underset{\underset{\displaystyle CH_3}{|}}{\overset{\overset{\displaystyle CH_3}{|}}{\mathrm{Si}}}\!-\!\left[\mathrm{O{-}Si}\right]_n\!-(\mathrm{CH_2})_3$$

The resulting polymers and some of their properties are listed in Table XI-19 (176). Knoth (177) reported the preparation of similar urethane polymers by the reaction of 1,3-bis(γ-hydroxypropyl) disiloxane with 2,5-tolylene diisocyanate.

TABLE XI-19
Properties of Polyurethanes Prepared from Polysiloxanediols and Various Diisocyanates[a]

Polysiloxane diol n	Diisocyanate R	Mol. wt. (ebull.)	Degree of polymerization ($\bar{y}$)	Melting point, °C.	Appearance
1	1,4-Phenylene	2200	4	105–120	Powder
2	1,4-Phenylene	2380	4	93–95	Powder
3	1,4-Phenylene	2860	4	71–78	Powder
4	1,4-Phenylene	3010	4	75–80	Rubber
1	1,5-Naphthalene	3450	7	140–150	Powder
2	1,5-Naphthalene	4700	8	95–105	Powder
3	1,5-Naphthalene	3530	5	95–105	Powder
4	1,5-Naphthalene	5200	7	90–95	Powder
2	4,4′-Diphenylmethane	5430	8	88–90	Rubber
2	4,4′-Dicyclohexylmethane	3170	5	85–88	Rubber
1	2,5-Tolylene	2880	6	165–177	Powder

[a] Taken from ref. 176.

Heating ω,ω'-bis(γ-hydroxypropyl) polysilmethylene with 1,4-phenylene diisocyanate in a 1:1 mole ratio at 80° C. for 20 hr. led to the formation of polyurethanes shown in eq. (78).

$$(y+1)\mathrm{O{=}C{=}N{-}R{-}N{=}C{=}O} + (y+1)\mathrm{HO{-}X{-}OH} \rightarrow$$
$$\mathrm{O{=}C{=}N}\left[\mathrm{R{-}NH{-}\overset{\overset{\displaystyle O}{\|}}{C}{-}O{-}X{-}O{-}\overset{\overset{\displaystyle O}{\|}}{C}{-}NH}\right]_y\mathrm{R{-}NH{-}\overset{\overset{\displaystyle O}{\|}}{C}{-}O{-}X{-}OH} \qquad (78)$$

where

$$\mathrm{R} = -\mathrm{C_6H_4}-,\ \mathrm{X} = -(\mathrm{CH_2})_3-\mathrm{Si(CH_3)_2}-\left[\mathrm{CH_2}-\mathrm{Si(CH_3)_2}-\right]_n(\mathrm{CH_2})_3-$$

These polymers and some physical characteristics are shown in Table XI-20 (176).

TABLE XI-20
Properties of Polyurethanes Prepared from Polysilmethylenediols and 1,4-Phenylene Diisocyanate[a]

Polysil-methylene diol n	Diisocyanate R	Mol. wt. (ebull.)	Degree of polymerization ($\bar{y}$)	Melting point, °C.	Appearance
1	1,4-Phenylene	4900	11	123–124	Powder
2	1,4-Phenylene	6750	13	124–125	Rubber
3	1,4-Phenylene	5070	8	79–85	Rubber
4	1,4-Phenylene	7050	10	75–80	Rubber

[a] Taken from ref. 176.

At an NCO/OH mole ratio of 2:1 in the reaction of polysiloxanediols with 1,4-phenylene diisocyanate, isocyanate-terminated prepolymers were obtained (176). Depending upon the reaction temperature (45–75°C.), prepolymers with a D.P. (degree of polymerization, $\bar{y}$) of 2 or 4–5, respectively, were formed. Representing schematically these prepolymers by O=C=N∿N=C=O, eq. (79) shows the formation of linear polymers when reacted with 1,3-bis-(γ-aminopropyl)disiloxane:

$$y\ \mathrm{O{=}C{=}N{\sim}N{=}C{=}O} + (y+1)\mathrm{H_2N{-}X{-}NH_2} \rightarrow$$
$$\mathrm{H_2N{-}X}\left[\mathrm{NH{-}\overset{\overset{\displaystyle O}{\|}}{C}{-}NH{\sim}NH{-}\overset{\overset{\displaystyle O}{\|}}{C}{-}NH{-}X}\right]_y\mathrm{NH_2} \qquad (79)$$

where

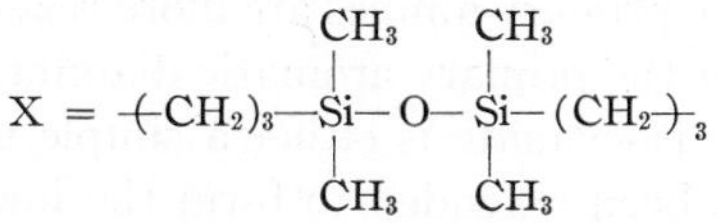

These polyurethane–urea polymers containing terminal amino groups are listed in Table XI-21 (176). When an excess of the isocyanate-terminated prepolymer was used in the above reaction, crosslinked resins were obtained.

TABLE XI-21
Properties of Urethane–Urea Polymers Prepared from Isocyanate-Terminated Polysiloxanes and Diamines[a]

Diisocyanate no.	Mol. wt. (ebull.)	Degree of polymerization ($\bar{y}$)	Melting point, °C.
234	2,350	2	115–125
242	2,700	2	105–108
235	3,420	2	90–94
182	9,970	4	180–200
211	11,200	5	200–210

[a] Taken from ref. 176.

Rubberlike polymers were obtained when difunctional organosilicon alcohols were reacted at 130–190°C. in the absence of solvent with either hexamethylene diisocyanate or tolylene diisocyanate (178). It was found that the glass transition temperature decreased as the number of silicon units (n) increased in the alcohol (X).

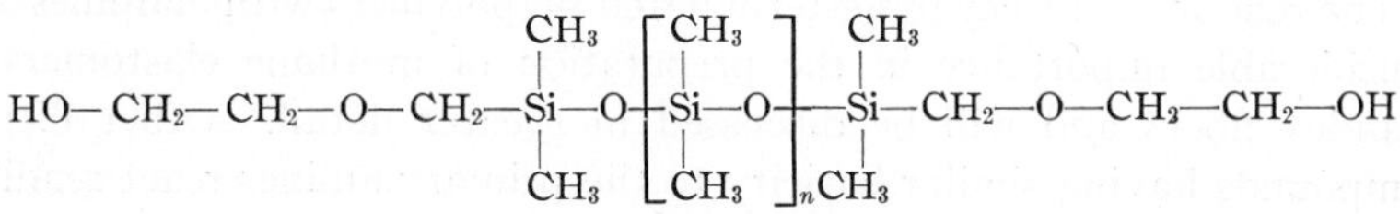

(X)

c. *Reactions with Nitrogen–Hydrogen Bond*

Though the polyfunctional hydroxyl compounds constitute the major industrial reactants for urethane-based polymers, the compounds containing the N–H grouping also share an important place. As would be expected, the stronger the basic character of the amine, the more reactive it is toward the isocyanate unless steric hindrance is pronounced (324). The simple difunctional aliphatic primary amines are more reactive than the secondary aliphatic diamines or the primary aromatic diamines (142,179–182). This holds true when the isocyanate is either a simple monomer, e.g., tolylene diisocyanate, or has been extended to form the low molecular weight isocyanate-terminated prepolymer. The typical reaction product, obtained at 0–25°C., of a primary diamine with a diisocyanate, is the linear poly(disubstituted urea).

$$O{=}C{=}N{-}R{-}N{=}C{=}O + NH_2{-}R{-}NH_2 \rightarrow$$

$$-NH-\overset{\displaystyle O}{\overset{\|}{C}}-NH-R\left(NH-\overset{\displaystyle O}{\overset{\|}{C}}-NH-R-NH-\overset{\displaystyle O}{\overset{\|}{C}}-NH-R\right)_n \qquad (80)$$

The reactivity of primary aromatic diamines with isocyanates can be reduced by introduction of bulky groups such as chlorine atoms in the ring *ortho* to the amine group. Typical "hindered" diamines are 4,4′-methylenebis(2-chloroaniline) and 3,3′-dichlorobenzidine (183,184).

Since the poly(disubstituted ureas), when prepared from an isocyanate and a primary amine, still contain an active hydrogen on each nitrogen, further interaction with isocyanate is possible. However, elevated temperatures are necessary to form biuret linkages (185–187).

$$R{-}N{=}C{=}O + R-NH-\overset{\displaystyle O}{\overset{\|}{C}}-NH-R \rightarrow \underset{\text{Biuret}}{R-NH-\overset{\displaystyle O}{\overset{\|}{C}}-\underset{\displaystyle R}{\underset{|}{N}}-\overset{\displaystyle O}{\overset{\|}{C}}-NH-R} \qquad (81)$$

Uncatalyzed reactions with ureas generally require temperatures of approximately 100°C. or higher to give a moderate rate.

The reactions of isocyanate-terminated prepolymers with diamines are of considerable importance in the preparation of urethane elastomers and spandex fibers and will be discussed in greater detail. Other nitrogen compounds having similar basicity to the primary amines react readily to form the corresponding addition polymers (142,188–190).

The reaction of hydrazine or hydrazine hydrate with diisocyanates yields linear polymers (polyureylenes) with the structures shown in eq. (82) (142,191).

$$H_2N{-}NH_2 + O{=}C{=}N{-}R{-}N{=}C{=}O \rightarrow \left[R-NH-\overset{\displaystyle O}{\overset{\|}{C}}-NH-NH-\overset{\displaystyle O}{\overset{\|}{C}}-NH\right]_n \qquad (82)$$

Hydrazine reacts with diisocyanate in solvents such as dimethylformamide or dimethyl sulfoxide to yield viscous solutions suitable for the casting of clear, tough films (191). Hydrazine hydrate can also be used because of the more rapid reaction of the isocyanate with the amine group than with water.

The reaction of diisocyanates with dihydrazides leads to the formation of poly(acylsemicarbazides) (191) as in eq. (83).

$$H_2N{-}HN{-}\overset{\overset{\displaystyle O}{\|}}{C}{-}R'{-}\overset{\overset{\displaystyle O}{\|}}{C}{-}NH{-}NH_2 + O{=}C{=}N{-}R{-}N{=}C{=}O \rightarrow$$

$$\left[R{-}HN{-}\overset{\overset{\displaystyle O}{\|}}{C}{-}HN{-}NH{-}\overset{\overset{\displaystyle O}{\|}}{C}{-}R'{-}\overset{\overset{\displaystyle O}{\|}}{C}{-}NH{-}NH{-}\overset{\overset{\displaystyle O}{\|}}{C}{-}NH\right]_n \quad (83)$$

Polymers were prepared from oxalyl-, isophthaloyl-, and terephthaloyldihydrazides with the use of 4,4′-diphenylmethane diisocyanate, tolylene, 3,3′-dimethylbiphenylene, and hexamethylene diisocyanate with dimethyl sulfoxide as solvent medium. Carbohydrazide, $NH_2{-}NH{-}CO{-}NH{-}NH_2$, also reacted with diisocyanates to yield linear polymers (191).

Similarly, ammonia reacted with diisocyanates (142,179,192) to yield a polymeric system (eq. 84).

$$R{-}N{=}C{=}O + NH_3 \rightarrow R{-}NH{-}\overset{\overset{\displaystyle O}{\|}}{C}{-}NH{-}\overset{\overset{\displaystyle O}{\|}}{C}{-}NH{-}R \quad (84)$$

Mixed difunctional amine-containing compounds such as amino acids are also capable of reacting with diisocyanates. At temperatures sufficiently low to minimize the reaction of the carboxylic acid group, the monoaddition product (i.e., urea derivative) from the sodium salt of an amino acid can be formed (193).

$$R{-}N{=}C{=}O + NH_2{-}R{-}\overset{\overset{\displaystyle O}{\|}}{C}{-}ONa \rightarrow R{-}NH{-}\overset{\overset{\displaystyle O}{\|}}{C}{-}NH{-}R{-}\overset{\overset{\displaystyle O}{\|}}{C}{-}ONa \quad (85)$$

Similar preferential reactions at the terminal amine can be achieved if the ester of the amino acid is used (194). Interestingly, the reaction can be inverted, so that the carboxylic acid group reacts and the amine remains free, by carrying out the reaction in an acid medium, the isocyanate group being relatively unreactive towards the ammonium ion. Thus, the two reactions can be combined, under neutral conditions and somewhat higher temperature to yield a polymeric material as well as a cyclic compound (195) as in eq. (86).

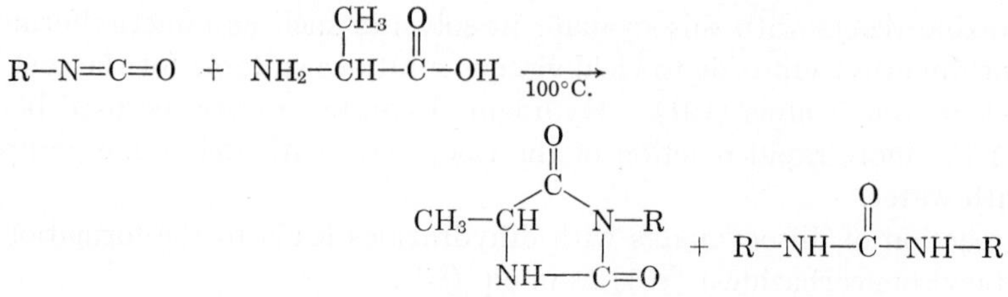

(86)

As would be anticipated, sodium aminosulfonic acids give the expected urea derivatives in an analogous manner to the aminocarboxylic acid system (196).

If an excess of hydroxylamine is sufficiently cooled and if the aryl isocyanate is carefully added, the urea is formed, indicating under these conditions that the nitrogen is more reactive towards isocyanate than the hydroxyl group (197):

$$C_6H_5{-}N{=}C{=}O + NH_2{-}OH \rightarrow C_6H_5{-}NH{-}\overset{\overset{\displaystyle O}{\|}}{C}{-}NH{-}OH \qquad (87)$$

The next most reactive position is the hydroxyl, which undergoes the typical reaction of alcohol–isocyanate to yield the urethane (197).

$$R{-}N{=}C{=}O + NH_2{-}OH \rightarrow R{-}NH{-}\overset{\overset{\displaystyle O}{\|}}{C}{-}NH{-}O{-}\overset{\overset{\displaystyle O}{\|}}{C}{-}NH{-}R \qquad (88)$$

Analogous to the hydroxylamine system are the aminoalcohols and the alkylene oxide addition products of the aminoalcohols.

The basic character of the N–H grouping strongly influences the reactivity towards urethane formation, if steric factors are discounted. It is, therefore, not surprising that the substitution of an electronegative group on the nitrogen usually reduces the rate of reaction with an isocyanate. The presence of an acyl grouping (an amide) causes, towards isocyanates, a moderate reaction rate at about 100°C. as compared to the extreme reactivity of the primary aliphatic amines at 0–25°C. If the reactions are carried out at moderate temperatures, the acylurea is obtained in good yields (142,160,198–200).

$$R{-}N{=}C{=}O + R{-}\overset{\overset{\displaystyle O}{\|}}{C}{-}NH_2 \rightarrow R{-}NH{-}\overset{\overset{\displaystyle O}{\|}}{C}{-}NH{-}\overset{\overset{\displaystyle O}{\|}}{C}{-}R \qquad (89)$$

If, however, severe conditions are employed, *N*-substituted amides undergo abnormal reactions (201).

$$R{-}\underset{\underset{O}{\|}}{C}{-}NH{-}CH_3 + C_6H_5{-}N{=}C{=}O \xrightarrow{190°C.} R{-}\underset{\underset{O}{\|}}{C}{-}NH{-}C_6H_5 \xrightarrow[200\text{–}220°C.]{C_6H_5{-}N{=}C{=}O} R{-}\underset{\underset{C_6H_5}{\overset{\|}{\underset{|}{N}}}}{C}{-}NH{-}C_6H_5 + CO_2 \quad (90)$$

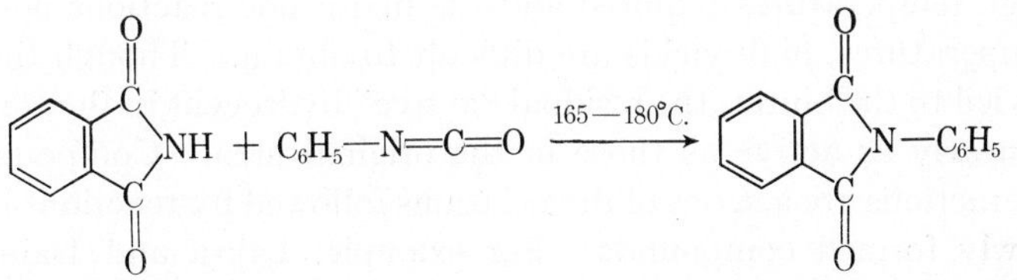

(91)

The use of Lewis acid catalysts (e.g., $AlCl_3$, $SnCl_4$) adversely influences the yields, while triethylamine has no catalytic influence (192).

The electronegativity of the sulfoxyl group in sulfonamide retards the reaction with isocyanates sufficiently to necessitate the use of the sodium salt of the sulfonamide (eq. 92) to increase the rate of reaction (142,202–204).

$$R{-}N{=}C{=}O + C_6H_5{-}SO_2{-}NH_2 \xrightarrow{NaOH} C_6H_5{-}SO_2{-}NH{-}\overset{\overset{O}{\|}}{C}{-}NH{-}R \quad (92)$$

Substitution by alkyl or aryl groups on the amide nitrogen of sulfonamide has prevented any interaction with isocyanates under conditions tried thus far. Reaction, however, was observed between phenyl isocyanate and an excess of dimethylformamide at 150°C. to give $C_6H_5{-}N{=}CH{-}N(CH_3)_2$ and CO_2 in 86% yield (205). Majewski (206) also reported a series of complex reaction products when a disubstituted amide was reacted with isocyanates.

Many of these amide–isocyanate interactions proceeded through postulated cyclic intermediates, accompanied by evolution of carbon dioxide. Subsequently formed condensation products were proved to undergo rearrangements to heterocyclic products which had greater thermodynamic stability.

Like the amides of carboxylic acids, the carbonyl group in urea strongly influences the reaction rates, and, like the amides, uncatalyzed reactions generally require temperatures of about 100°C. or higher to achieve a moderate reaction rate. The simple addition product of an isocyanate and a urea is a biuret (185–187) as shown by eq. (93).

$$R{-}N{=}C{=}O + R{-}NH{-}\overset{\displaystyle O}{\overset{\|}{C}}{-}NH{-}R \rightarrow R{-}NH{-}\overset{\displaystyle O}{\overset{\|}{C}}{-}\underset{\displaystyle R}{\underset{|}{N}}{-}\overset{\displaystyle O}{\overset{\|}{C}}{-}NH{-}R \quad (93)$$

As in the case of the amides, most tertiary amines apparently have little influence on reactions of ureas with isocyanates. Strong bases and certain metal compounds may be strongly catalytic (153). Because of the relatively high temperatures required and the many side reactions possible at these temperatures, high yields are difficult to obtain. Though the initial reactions led to the biuret, the residual "active" hydrogens in the compound may be nearly as active as those in the original urea. Compounded on these interactions are a series of dissociations followed by reactions between these newly formed compounds. For example, Lakra and Dains (187) reacted a 1:1 mole ratio of phenyl isocyanate and urea at 120°C. for 4 hr. and characterized seven products, as shown by eq. (94).

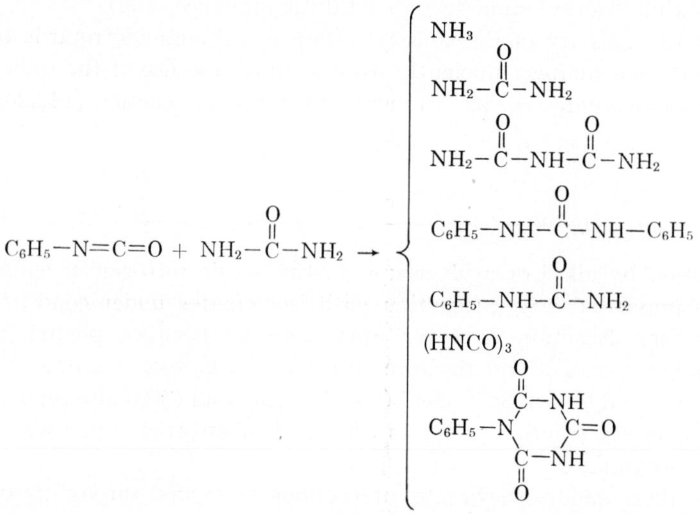

(94)

These products may all be explained by assuming dissociation of the urea to cyanic acid and ammonia, followed by reaction with the isocyanate grouping.

The reactions of isocyanate groups with urethanes lead to the substituted allophanate (eq. 95).

$$R{-}N{=}C{=}O + R{-}NH{-}\overset{\displaystyle O}{\overset{\|}{C}}{-}O{-}R \rightarrow \underset{\displaystyle R{-}NH{-}C{=}O}{\underset{|}{R{-}N}}{-}\overset{\displaystyle O}{\overset{\|}{C}}{-}O{-}R \quad (95)$$

For uncatalyzed systems, the temperature is approximately 20–40°C. above that necessary for reaction between urea and isocyanate. The reaction, like that of biuret formation, is not strongly catalyzed by most tertiary amines, but may be catalyzed by strong bases and certain metal compounds. As further analogy to the urea system, many side reactions arising by dissociation of the normal addition product are also realized (187,207). Equilibrium data showed greater stability of the allophanate linkage at lower temperatures and greater dissociation at higher temperatures (208).

The isocyanate group is also capable of reacting with almost any N—H-containing compounds, provided sufficiently vigorous conditions are employed. For example, imides (142,201), amidines (209), nitramines (181), phenylhydrazones (210,211), cyanamide (142,212), sulfimides (142), acylureas (187), thioureas (187), and others have been reacted with isocyanate-containing compounds to yield in the majority of cases the expected addition product.

The reaction of isocyanate groups with substituted ureas, urethanes and amides becomes of primary importance since it may lead to gelation and crosslinking during polymer forming reactions. However, by careful control of reaction conditions, minimizing or avoiding altogether these crosslinking reactions, high molecular weight linear macromolecules can readily be prepared.

The reaction of difunctional substituted amino boron compounds, e.g. bis(alkylamino)alkyl or aryl boron, with organic diisocyanates (eq. 96) yielded transparent, brittle substances which were stable in the air but hydrolyzed rapidly in boiling water (213).

$$\mathrm{R'{-}NH{-}\underset{}{\overset{\displaystyle R}{\overset{|}{B}}}{-}NH{-}R' + O{=}C{=}N{-}R''{-}N{=}C{=}O \rightarrow \left[{-}\underset{\underset{\displaystyle R'}{|}}{N}{-}\underset{\underset{\displaystyle R}{|}}{B}{-}\underset{\underset{\displaystyle R'}{|}}{N}{-}\overset{\overset{\displaystyle O}{\|}}{C}{-}NH{-}R''{-}NH{-}\overset{\overset{\displaystyle O}{\|}}{C}{-} \right]_n} \quad (96)$$

Depending on the type of substituents on the nitrogen, the linear polymers softened at 50–170°C., the softening point being lower, the smaller the alkyl group.

The investigation was expanded to include the reactions of boron-substituted borazoles with hexamethylene diisocyanate to give linear as well as three dimensional polymers (214) depending on the mole ratio of reactants as in eq. (97).

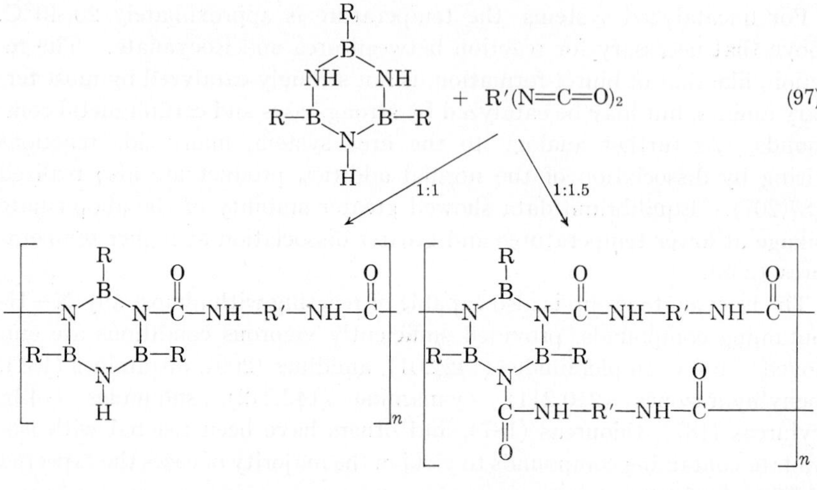

(97)

Though these polymers softened above 300°C., the stability of the polymers in boiling water was similar to that of the alkylamino boron-based polymers.

During an investigation of the polymer forming reaction of a diamine with a macro-bis(chloroformate), Foldi and Campbell (215) obtained low molecular weight materials. Analysis of the product permitted the investigators to develop a novel method for the preparation of copolymers of polyurethane and polycarbonate by degrading a high molecular weight polycarbonate to a low molecular weight urethane bisphenol polymer

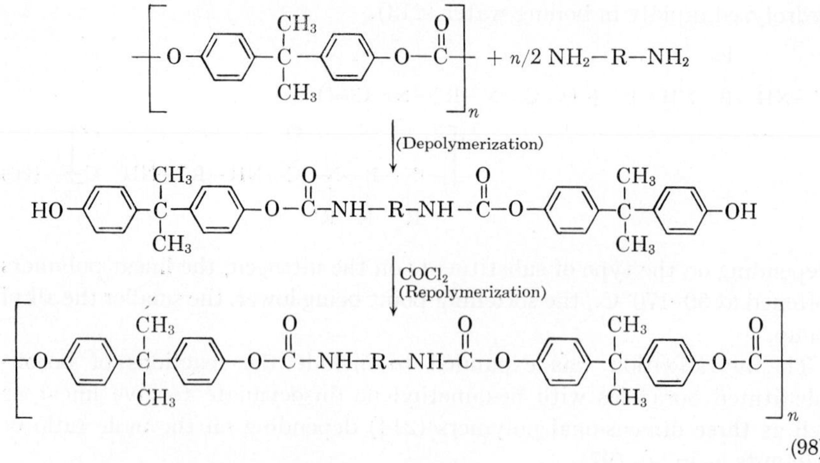

(98)

followed by repolymerization with phosgene. This can be shown in idealized form in eq. (98).

The general method of preparation was to treat a dichloromethane solution of commercial poly(diphenylolpropane carbonate) with a solution of the diamine in the same solvent. The subsequent coupling reaction with phosgene was carried out with pyridine as acid acceptor. In general, these copolymers were soluble in methylene chloride. Film strips and fibers prepared from a methylene chloride solution could be drawn two to three times in the range of 50–100°C. (215). The properties of the copolymers which were prepared are summarized in Table XI-22.

TABLE XI-22
Properties of Diphenylolpropane Carbonate–Urethane Copolymers[a]

Diamine	Amt. modified, %	η_{inh} (TCE/phenol)	Polymer melt temperature, °C.	Remarks
Piperazine	20	0.64	230–240	Clear, strong film easily drawn 2.5–3× at 50° C.
Piperazine	50	0.60	260	Clear, strong film drawn 2× in hot water.
Piperazine	75	0.31		
Hydrazine	10	Insol.		
Hydrazine	50	Insol.	240	Insoluble or swells in usual solvents.
Ethylenediamine	50	0.45	215	Strong film, drawable 2× at 50–70°C.
Hexamethylenediamine	50	0.63	152	Strong film drawn 2× at 40–60°C.
p-Xylenediamine	50	0.57	202	Strong film drawn 2× at 50–70°C.

[a] Taken from ref. 215.

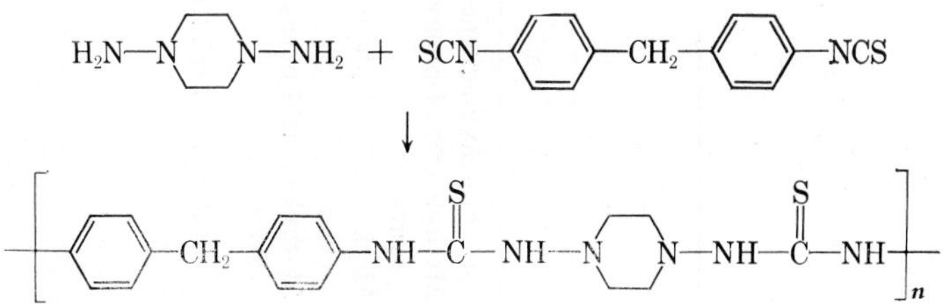

(99)

TABLE XI-23
Preparation of Polythiosemicarbazides[a]

A	Wt. A, g.	B	Wt. B, g.	Vol. dimethyl sulfoxide, ml.	Yield, g.	η_{inh} in dimethyl sulfoxide	Polymer melt temperature, °C.
4,4′-Diphenylmethane diisocyanate	37.5	N,N′-Diaminopiperazine	17.4	500	51	0.49	320
Methylenebis(4-phenyl isothiocyanate)	40	N,N′-Diamino-2,5-dimethylpiperazine	20.4	500	62	0.84	270
Methylenebis(4-phenyl isothiocyanate)	5.64	1,4-Diaminocyclohexane	2.28	75	7	0.40	210
Methylenebis(4-phenyl isothiocyanate)	5.64	Piperazine	1.72	75	7.3	0.26	290

[a] Taken from ref. 216.

By the reaction of a diisothiocyanate, such as 4,4′-diphenylmethane diisothiocyanate with *N,N′*-diaminopiperazine, Campbell and Tomic (216) were able to prepare high molecular weight polythiosemicarbazides (eq. 99).

Polymerizations were carried out in dimethyl sulfoxide, in which the polymer was readily soluble, to give very viscous solutions, which could be cast to clear, tough, colorless films or wet-spun to fibers (Table XI-23). Both drawn and undrawn film samples were completely amorphous. The polymer reacted readily with various metal ions to give metallic chelates (216).

d. *Reactions with Carbon–Hydrogen Bond*

The highly unsaturated —N=C=O group is capable of reacting with compounds containing carbon–hydrogen bonds in which the hydrogen is sufficiently reactive to be replaced with sodium. Thus, compounds containing methylene groups activated by carbonyl, ester, nitrile, and nitro, undergo reactions with isocyanates as a result of nucleophilic attack by the carbanions on the isocyanate group (142,217,218). The normal reaction products are substituted amides (142,219), as shown in eq. (100).

$$\mathrm{R{-}N{=}C{=}O} + \overset{\oplus}{\mathrm{Na}}\left[\overset{\ominus}{\mathrm{C}}\mathrm{H}(\overset{\overset{\displaystyle\mathrm{O}}{\|}}{\mathrm{C}}{-}\mathrm{O}{-}\mathrm{C_2H_5})_2\right] \rightarrow \mathrm{R{-}NH{-}}\overset{\overset{\displaystyle\mathrm{O}}{\|}}{\mathrm{C}}\mathrm{{-}CH(}\overset{\overset{\displaystyle\mathrm{O}}{\|}}{\mathrm{C}}\mathrm{{-}O{-}C_2H_5)_2} \quad (100)$$

In an analogous manner, amides can readily be prepared from interaction of the isocyanate with nitroalkanes (220–222) or acetoacetic esters (221).

Similar to the nucleophilic addition of hydrogen cyanide to carbonyl-containing compounds is the addition of hydrogen cyanide to isocyanates to give the cyanoformamides (223,224).

$$\mathrm{C_6H_5{-}N{=}C{=}O + HCN} \rightleftharpoons \mathrm{C_6H_5{-}NH{-}}\overset{\overset{\displaystyle\mathrm{O}}{\|}}{\mathrm{C}}\mathrm{{-}C{\equiv}N} \quad (101)$$

As would be expected, the cyanoformamides decompose back to the starting reactants at approximately 120–130°C. (142). These nucleophilic reactions require for optimum conditions basic catalysis such as tertiary amines or alkaline carbonates as well as solvents such as toluene (142,224). However, if the reaction is carried out in the absence of a solvent, the cyclic monoimide of diphenylparabanic acid is formed (223), as shown in eq. (102).

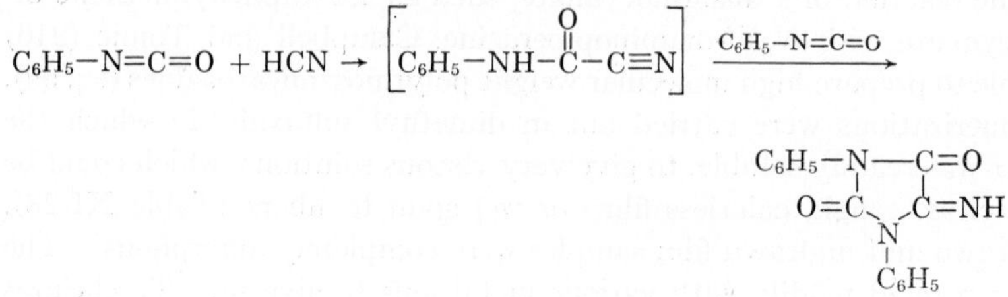
(102)

e. Reactions with Sulfur–Hydrogen Bond

Polythiolcarbamates (polyurethanes in which the ether oxygen atom has been replaced by sulfur)

$$\left(\overset{\displaystyle O}{\overset{\|}{C}}-NH-R-NH-\overset{\displaystyle O}{\overset{\|}{C}}-S-R'-S \right)_n$$

were originally synthesized by Catlin (225) and Bayer and co-workers (226). Dyer and Osborne (227) prepared and characterized several types of polythiolcarbamates by adapting either the addition of mercaptans to isocyanates (228) or the condensation of bischlorothiolformates with amines (229).

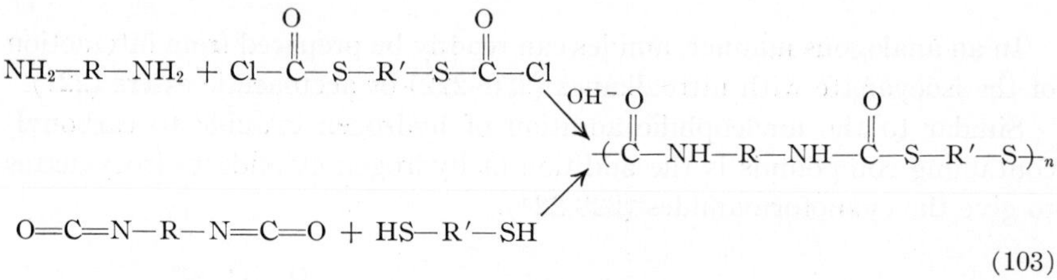
(103)

Higher molecular weight polymers were generally obtained by the interfacial polycondensation techniques (230–232).

The polymerization of diisocyanates with dimercaptans was catalyzed by means of a tertiary amine. The polymerization was carried out in a solvent mixture of chlorobenzene and *o*-dichlorobenzene (80:20). The polymer was isolated by precipitation with methanol and purified by reprecipitation from dimethylformamide in methanol. The pure polythiolcarbamates

TABLE XI-24
Polythiolcarbamates from Diisocyanates and Dimercaptans[a]

Isocyanate	Dimercaptan	Catalyst	Yield, %[b]	Melting point (corr.), °C.[c]	$[\eta]$[d]	Film[e]	Solubility, g./100 ml. at 25°C.[f]
MDI	$HS—(CH_2)_4—SH$	TPA[g]	83	238–241	0.25	Pliable	1(0.31),3(hot)
	$HS—(CH_2)_6—SH$	TPA	73–82	228–230	0.14–0.16	Brittle	1,2,3(hot),5
	$HS—(CH_2)_{10}—SH$	TPA	75	207–208	0.18	Powdery	1,3(hot)
	p-$HS—CH_2C_6H_4CH_2—SH$	TPA	87	253–256	0.11	Brittle	1,2,3
	$HS—CH(CH_3)CH_2CH_2CH(CH_3)—SH$	TPA	35	171–173	0.11	Brittle	1,2,3
	$HS—CH_2C(CH_3)_2CH—SH$	Dabco[h]	61	198–202	0.13	Pliable	1,2,3,5
	$HS—CH_2CO_2CH_2CH_2OCOCH_2—SH$	TPA	25	159–161	0.05	Brittle	1,2,3,4
HDI	$HS—(CH_2)_4—SH$	TPA	87	186–190	0.17[i]	None	1(0.07),3(hot)
	$HS—(CH_2)_6—SH$	Dabco	49	184–187	0.33[i]	Powdery	1(0.04),2,3(hot)
	p-$HS—CH_2C_6H_4CH_2—SH$	Dabco	77	160–173	0.32[i]	None	1(0.07),3(hot)
	$HS—CH_2CO_2CH_2CH_2OCOCH_2—SH$	Dabco	10	99–102	0.05	None	1,3,4

[a] Taken from ref. 227.
[b] After two reprecipitations.
[c] On Fisher block.
[d] Intrinsic viscosity in dimethylformamide at 30°C.
[e] From dimethylformamide.
[f] Solvents: 1 is dimethylformamide; 2 is *N*-methyl-2-pyrrolidone; 3 is dimethyl sulfoxide; 4 is nitrobenzene; 5 is tetramethylurea.
[g] Tri-*n*-propylamine.
[h] 1,4-Diazabicyclo-[2.2.2]-octane.
[i] Inherent viscosity of saturated solution.

TABLE XI-25
Polythiolcarbamates from Bischlorothiolformates and Diamines[a]

Y of ClCOS—Y—SCOCl	X of NH_2—X—NH_2	Yield, %[b]	Melting point, (corr.), °C.[c]	η_{inh}[d]	Film[e]	Solubility, g./100 ml. at 25°C.[f]
—$(CH_2)_6$—	—$C_6H_4CH_2C_6H_4$—[g,h]	73	228–230	0.30[i]	Pliable	1,2 (hot)
—$(CH_2)_4$—	—$(CH_2)_6$—	31	180–182	0.35	Powdery	1(0.09),3 (hot)
—$(CH_2)_6$—	—$(CH_2)_6$—	58	194–196	1.18	None	1(0.01)
—$CH_2C_6H_4CH_2$—	—$(CH_2)_6$—	32	213–215	0.50	Brittle	1(0.04),3 (hot)
—$CH_2C(CH_3)_2CH_2$—	—$(CH_2)_6$—	38	211–213	0.25	Pliable	1,2,4[j]

[a] Take from ref. 227.
[b] After two reprecipitations.
[c] On Fisher block.
[d] Saturated solution in dimethylformamide at 30°C.
[e] From dimethylformamide.
[f] Solvents: 1 is dimethylformamide; 2 is dimethyl sulfoxide; 3 is tetramethylurea; 4 is dioxane.
[g] C_6H_4 is *p*-phenylene.
[h] A small amount of Duponol G detergent added to polymerization.
[i] Intrinsic viscosity.
[j] Reprecipitated from dioxane and water.

were generally obtained (227) as white powders in 50–80% yield (see Tables XI-24 and XI-25).

The polythiolcarbamates were extremely insoluble, even in highly polar solvents. The melting points of the sulfur analogues were, in general, higher than those of the corresponding oxygen-containing polyurethanes. However, the polythiolcarbamates turned yellow in light and decomposed in hot solvents and aqueous base (227).

The reaction between phenyl isocyanate and 1-butanethiol and 1-dodecanethiol, in toluene solution in the presence of triethylamine as a catalyst, was described by Dyer and Glenn (233). They reported that these reactions followed approximately second-order kinetics during the early stages and exhibited product catalysis as the reactions progressed. However, no product catalysis occurred in the absence of triethylamine. Likewise, no product catalysis was found in the amine-catalyzed reaction between phenyl isocyanate and 2-methylpropane-2-thiol in xylene solution. The reaction of the thiols with the isocyanate was first-order with respect to the concentration of the amine. Yields were almost quantitative with amine catalysis (233,234).

In an analogous manner thiophenols (228) and mercaptobenzothiazoles (235) interact with isocyanates to yield the expected addition products.

Malootian (236) has reported the preparation of polymers by the reaction of tolylene diisocyanate with liquid mercaptan-terminated polysulfides (LP-2). An alkaline environment was necessary for rapid conversion. Curing of thiol-terminated polymers with polyisocyanates yielded products having compression set and hardness equivalent to the values obtained by effective crosslinking of thiol-terminated polysulfide polymers by oxidative systems (237). Mitchell (238) developed a series of isocyanate-terminated prepolymers based on polysulfide thiol-terminated polymers which on subsequent addition of water and amine catalyst resulted in a cured polymer system.

Hydrogen sulfide, similar to water, readily reacts with isocyanates to yield the substituted urea and carbonyl sulfide (142).

$$R{-}N{=}C{=}O + H_2S \rightarrow R{-}NH{-}\overset{\overset{\large O}{\|}}{C}{-}NH_2 + COS \qquad (104)$$

Jackson (239) reported the interaction of metal hydrogen sulfide with isocyanates to give stable, water-soluble adducts of the type —NH—CO—S—M.

An interesting poly(sulfide–urethane) polymer was synthesized by Iwakura et al. (240) from an α,ω-dichlorourethane and sodium tetrasulfide in methanol. The dichloro-terminated polyurethane was prepared (eq. 105) by the reaction of either ethylene chlorohydrin or 4-chloro-1-butanol with poly(methylene diisocyanate). The polyurethane polysulfide was a

$$\text{O—C=N—}(\text{CH}_2)_n\text{—N—C=O} + 2\text{Cl—}(\text{CH}_2)_m\text{—OH} \rightarrow$$

$$\text{Cl—}(\text{CH}_2)_m\text{—O—}\overset{\text{O}}{\overset{\|}{\text{C}}}\text{—NH—}(\text{CH}_2)_n\text{—NH—}\overset{\text{O}}{\overset{\|}{\text{C}}}\text{—O—}(\text{CH}_2)_m\text{—Cl} \xrightarrow{\text{Na}_2\text{S}_4}$$

$$\left[\text{S}_4\text{—}(\text{CH}_2)_m\text{—O—}\overset{\text{O}}{\overset{\|}{\text{C}}}\text{—NH}(\text{CH}_2)_n\text{NH—}\overset{\text{O}}{\overset{\|}{\text{C}}}\text{—O—}(\text{CH}_2)_m\right]_x \quad n = 3, 4, 6, 8 \quad m = 2, 4 \qquad (105)$$

transparent and elastic compound, which, when masticated with zinc oxide and vulcanized, had good elongation, strength and resistance to chemicals.

f. Reactions with Other Active Hydrogens

Since isocyanates contain very electrophilic carbon atoms which are joined by double bonds to two electronegative atoms, it is not at all surprising that nucleophilic addition reactions are prevalent. As has already been observed, hydrogen cyanide adds to organic isocyanates to yield the cyanoformamides (142,223,224). Similarly, halogen acids readily add to form the carbamoyl halides (241,242).

$$\text{R—N=C=O} + \text{HX} \rightleftharpoons \text{R—NH—}\overset{\text{O}}{\overset{\|}{\text{C}}}\text{—X} \qquad (106)$$

The carbamoyl chlorides are stable at room temperature, but dissociate back to the starting materials as the temperature increases. At about 90–110°C. dissociation becomes nearly complete (86). The other carbamoyl halides behave in a similar fashion. Carbamoyl halides may be observed during the preparation of isocyanates by interaction of an amine with phosgene, if the reaction conditions are sufficiently mild.

$$\text{R—NH}_2 + \text{COCl}_2 \searrow$$
$$\text{R—NH—}\overset{\text{O}}{\overset{\|}{\text{C}}}\text{—Cl} + [\text{HCl}] \qquad (107)$$
$$\text{R—N=C=O} + \text{HCl} \nearrow$$

It therefore becomes necessary to remove the hydrogen chloride from the reaction medium.

The organic carbamoyl halides are sufficiently reactive to undergo interaction with active hydrogen-containing materials to give the typical isocyanate-active hydrogen compound addition product, accompanied with hydrogen halide evolution, as shown in eq. (108).

$$R{-}NH{-}CO{-}Cl + R'{-}OH \rightarrow R{-}NH{-}\overset{\overset{O}{\|}}{C}{-}OR' + HCl \qquad (108)$$

A typical carbonyl addition product was observed when aliphatic or aromatic isocyanates were treated with aqueous alkali bisulfites (142).

$$R{-}N{=}C{=}O + NaHSO_3 \rightarrow \left[R{-}NH{-}\overset{\overset{O}{\|}}{C}{-}SO_3^{\ominus}\right]Na^{\oplus} \qquad (109)$$

Since, however, water is also able to react with isocyanate groups to give amines and ureas, considerable formation of side products is encountered. Amines are also capable of reacting with the bisulfite addition products to give the urea derivative (142).

The reaction of vinyl isocyanate with sodium or acetone bisulfite to yield the vinyl isocyanate adduct (XI) was described by Schulz and Hartmann (243).

$$CH_2{=}CH{-}N{=}C{=}O + NaHSO_3 \rightarrow CH_2{=}CH{-}N{=}\overset{\overset{OH}{|}}{C}{-}SO_3Na \rightleftharpoons \underset{\text{(XI)}}{CH_2{=}CH{-}NH{-}CO{-}SO_3Na} \qquad (110)$$

The bisulfite addition compound of vinyl isocyanate (XI) was stable in aqueous solution and polymerized in the presence of ammonium persulfate as catalyst at 20°C. for 4 hr. to yield a white, soluble, hygroscopic polymer (XII).

$$\underset{\text{(XII)}}{\left[CH_2{-}\underset{\underset{NH-CO-SO_3Na}{|}}{CH}\right]_n}$$

The soluble polymer reacted further with amines such as cyclohexylamine to give the poly(*N*-vinyl-*N'*-cyclohexylurea) (XIII).

$$\underset{\text{(XII)}}{\left[CH_2{-}\underset{\underset{NH-CO-SO_3Na}{|}}{CH}\right]_n} \xrightarrow{C_6H_{11}NH_2} \underset{\text{(XIII)}}{\left[CH_2{-}\underset{\underset{NH-CO-NH-C_6H_{11}}{|}}{CH}\right]_n} \qquad (111)$$

In order to ascertain the extent to which hydrogen, activated solely by the hyperconjugation in an olefin, $H{-}CH_2{-}CR{=}CR_2$, can undergo the reactions of "classically" activated hydrogen, e.g., $H{-}CH_2{-}C{=}O$, the reaction between olefins and phenyl isocyanate was investigated by Baker and Holdsworth (244). When this type of olefin was allowed to react with phenyl isocyanate in the presence of anhydrous stannic chloride under rigidly anhydrous conditions, small amounts of *N,N′,N″*-triphenylbiuret were isolated. Baker and Holdsworth postulated that the necessary hydrogen arose from the olefin.

The addition of dialkyl phosphonates to unsaturated groups such as carbonyl or imine or to activated carbon–carbon unsaturated groups has been extensively investigated (245,246). The high reactivity of the isocyanate group toward nucleophilic reagents has already been discussed. Dialkyl phosphonates react directly with aliphatic isocyanates in the absence of bases at temperatures on the order of 135°C. (247).

Fox and Venezky (246) have shown that isocyanates and dialkyl phosphonates react readily in the presence of bases to form carbamoylphosphonates.

$$R{-}N{=}C{=}O + H{-}\overset{\overset{\displaystyle O}{\uparrow}}{P}(OR')_2 \xrightarrow{\text{base}} R{-}NH{-}\overset{\overset{\displaystyle O}{\|}}{C}{-}\overset{\overset{\displaystyle O}{\uparrow}}{P}(OR')_2 \qquad (112)$$

Trialkylamines, α-picoline, sodium cyanide, and sodium carbonate were found to be effective catalysts in reaction (112).

In general, the reaction of isocyanates with acids of phosphorus and their esters that contain a P—H group and no strongly acidic hydrogen yields carbamoylphosphonates which are fairly stable in the presence of water (247–250). However, with the aryl derivatives, the course of hydrolysis in acid or base depends on the substituent present in the aryl group (246). Hydrolysis of phenylphosphinic and phenylphosphonic carbamoyl derivatives gives high yields of the corresponding acid (170).

$$C_6H_5{-}\underset{\underset{\displaystyle H}{|}}{\overset{\overset{\displaystyle O}{\uparrow}}{P}}{-}OH + RNCO \rightarrow C_6H_5{-}\underset{\underset{\displaystyle OH}{|}}{\overset{\overset{\displaystyle O}{\uparrow}}{P}}{-}\overset{\overset{\displaystyle O}{\|}}{C}{-}NH{-}R \xrightarrow{H^+} C_6H_5{-}\overset{\overset{\displaystyle O}{\uparrow}}{P}(OH)_2 \qquad (113)$$

The reaction of isocyanates to give the monocarbamoyl derivatives has been carried out with a monoalkylphosphinic acid, alkyl monoalkylphosphinate, and secondary phosphine (250).

The reaction of aryl isocyanates with phosphines produces tricarbamoylphosphines (250), as in eq. (114).

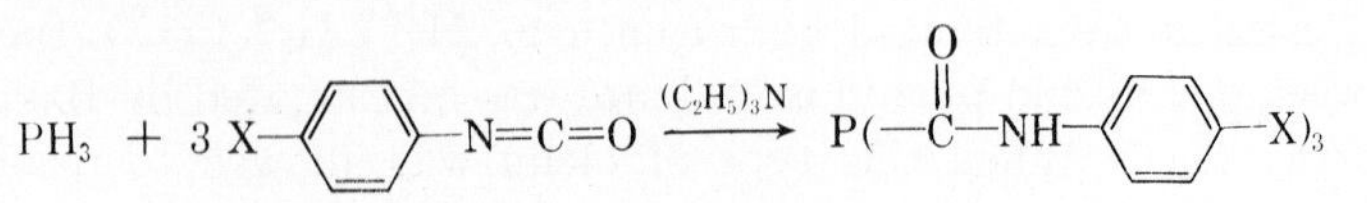

(114)

where

$$X = H, Cl, NO_2$$

The yields were 13, 55, and 100% for the H-, Cl-, and NO_2-substituted tricarbamoylphosphines, respectively. The intermediate mono- and dicarbamoyl phosphines were not detected. The triscarbamoyl phosphines were thermally stable in the solid state up to 200°C. The reaction of 2,4-tolylene diisocyanate with phosphine proceeded only slowly, and no definite product was isolated (250).

g. Miscellaneous Reactions

Methyl isocyanate, when catalyzed with triethylphosphine, reacts (eq. 115) with carbon dioxide to give 3,5-dimethyl-2,4,6-triketo-1,3,5-oxdiazine in 60–70% yield, the remainder being the polymerization product of methyl isocyanate (trimethylisocyanurate) (251,252).

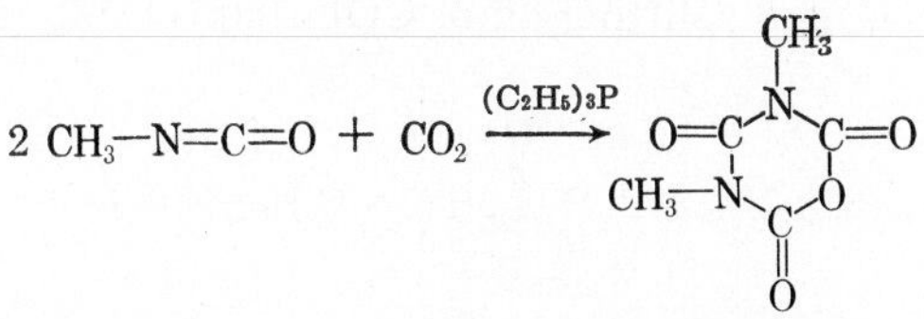

(115)

Attempts to bring about a reaction of methyl isocyanate with carbon disulfide, carbon oxysulfide, phenyl isothiocyanate, acetonitrile, quinone, nitromethane, acetylene, ethylene, or amylene under similar conditions were unsuccessful.

The reaction of methyl isocyanate with aldehydes, aldoketenes, and cyanic acid yielded only the homopolymer of these compounds and the trimethylisocyanurate (253). Carbon oxysulfide and methyl isocyanate in the presence of triethylphosphine also did not give the thio ring compound (251). This reaction seems to be specific for both the methyl isocyanate and carbon dioxide.

The reaction between the sodium salt of nitromethane and phenyl isocyanate has been found to give *o*-nitroacetanilide and nitromalonamide (221,254). These reactions have been extended to give a series of *N*-substituted α-nitroacetanilides and α-carbethoxy-α-nitroacetanilides (220).

Mukaiyama and Hoshino (222) have reported the interesting reactions of isocyanates with primary nitroparaffins, such as nitroethane, 1-nitropropane, and phenylnitromethane, in the presence of catalytic amounts of tertiary alkyl amine to give *sym*-disubstituted urea, furoxane, and carbon dioxide in excellent yields as in eq. (116). The generally expected addition

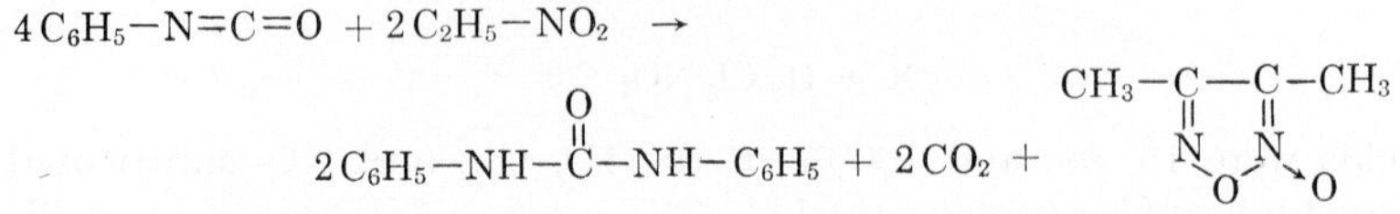

(116)

compounds of *N*-substituted α-nitro fatty acid amides were not formed. The reaction was postulated to proceed through the intermediate amine and nitrile oxide, formed by the decomposition of the addition compound of isocyanate and *aci*-nitroparaffin with spontaneous evolution of carbon dioxide. The furoxane was expected to arise by the dimerization of nitrile oxide. This reaction was not observed in the absence of tertiary alkyl amines or when tertiary nitroparaffins were employed (222).

Phenyl isocyanate has been reported to react with sulfur tetrafluoride to yield phenylimido sulfur difluoride (255). It was assumed that the first step consisted of the addition of SF_4 to the carbon-nitrogen bond, followed by a rearrangement and splitting off of COF_2 (eq. 117).

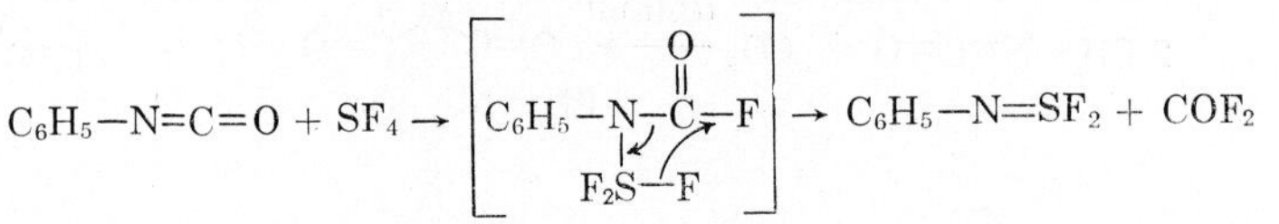

(117)

h. Blocking and Deblocking

The blocking of the isocyanate group is employed in cases where it is desirable to have a system that is stable at room temperature, but which would react at elevated temperatures as a reactive isocyanate with any hydroxyl-containing material present. Of particular industrial importance are blocked urethanes for coating applications, especially for wire enamels and similar uses. In order to meet the requirements for blocking and subsequent deblocking at elevated temperatures, materials have to be employed which form derivatives such as urethanes, capable of regenerating the free isocyanate group on heating and which would not undergo undesirable side reactions (e.g., by decomposition into various fragments other than the original components from which they were formed) which would reduce in effect the amount of free isocyanate available when desired. Blocked isocyanates are also referred to as "capped" isocyanates or as "splitters."

The most widely used blocked isocyanates are urethanes derived from phenol. On heating to 150–200°C. they regenerate the isocyanate as shown in eq. (118).

$$R{-}N{=}C{=}O + C_6H_5{-}OH \rightleftharpoons R{-}NH{-}\overset{\overset{\displaystyle O}{\|}}{C}{-}O{-}C_6H_5 \qquad (118)$$

The "splitting" of a urethane linkage in the presence of alcohols (or polyols) could be considered mere thermal dissociation. However, it is more likely that an addition to the carbonyl group takes place, similar to a transesterification reaction.

$$R{-}NH{-}\overset{\overset{\displaystyle O}{\|}}{C}{-}O{-}C_6H_5 + R'{-}OH \rightleftharpoons \left[R{-}NH{-}\underset{\underset{\displaystyle R'OH}{|}}{\overset{\overset{\displaystyle O}{|}}{C}}{-}O{-}C_6H_5 \right] \rightleftharpoons R{-}NH{-}\overset{\overset{\displaystyle O}{\|}}{C}{-}O{-}R' + C_6H_5{-}OH \qquad (119)$$

An investigation by Reilly and Orchin (256) on the dissociation of selected ureas, urethanes, and biurets supports this suggested mechanism. As would be expected, however, steric as well as electronic factors influence the ease with which a urethane bond is dissociated. Urethanes from aro-

TABLE XI-26

Splitting of Blocked Hexamethylene Diisocyanate[a]

Active hydrogen compound	Splitting temp., °C.
HCN	120–130
Ethyl malonate	130–140
Acetylacetone	140–150
Ethyl acetoacetate	140–150
1-Phenyl-3-methyl-5-pyrazolone	150
Hydroxylamine	160
Aryl mercaptans	160
Caprolactam	>160
Pyrocatechol	>160
Aliphatic mercaptans	160–180
Monomethylaniline	170–180
Acetone oxime	180
Diphenylamine	180
Phenol	180
2,4-Diisobutylphenol	>180
Isooctylphenol	>180
4-Hydroxybiphenyl	>180
6-Hydroxytetralin	>180
α-Pyrrolidone	>180

[a] Taken from ref. 142.

matic isocyanates and phenols are attacked by aliphatic amines but not by hydroxyl-containing compounds at room temperature. On the other hand, urethanes derived from aromatic isocyanates and alcohols are stable towards aliphatic amines under the same conditions (257). The dissociation may, indeed, be forced to the isocyanate by removal of a volatile component. These reactions are also subject to mild catalysis, such as by tertiary amine salts of organic acids (258) and dibutyltin dicarboxylates (259), which may permit deblocking at lower temperatures.

In order to obtain an indication of the ease of dissociation of various active hydrogen containing compounds, the temperature at which an aliphatic "blocked" diisocyanate was made available to react with and cross-link a partially hydrolyzed cellulose acetate (Cellit test) was determined by Petersen (142) (Table XI-26).

Iwakura and Hayashi (260) prepared a series of addition compounds based on tetramethylene diisocyanate or 4,4′-diphenylmethane diisocyanate and phenol, *m*-cresol, diethyl malonate, ethyl acetoacetate, ethyl cyanoacetate, α-pyrrolidinone, and ε-caprolactam. A qualitative test for the ease of thermal dissociation based on diamine interaction resulted in similar data to those of the Cellit test reported by Petersen (142).

Dreyfus (261) prepared polymers by reacting phenol-blocked diisocyanates with diols, diamines, aminoalcohols, and dicarboxylic acids.

i. Dimerization

Dimers may be considered as the simplest polymers. It would be expected that the isocyanate group, being a highly unsaturated group, is capable of undergoing self-condensation to yield dimers, as well as trimers and higher molecular weight polymers. In the case of the aliphatic isocyanates, however, dimers have not been obtained, and only trimers have been isolated.

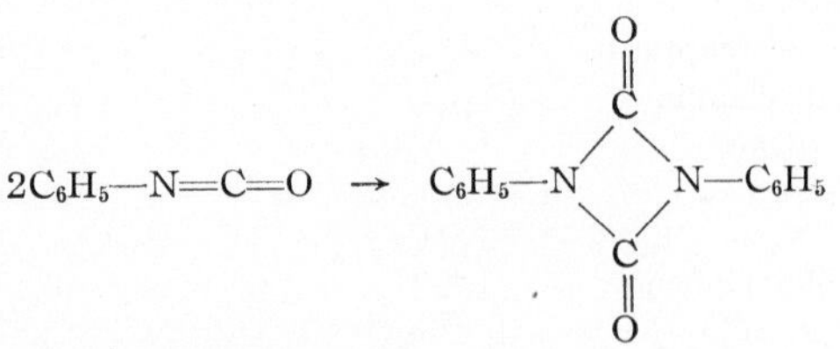

(120)

The rate of self-polymerization to dimers or "uretidine diones" is dependent on electronic or steric influences in the compound or substituents. The rate of dimerization of many aromatic isocyanates is greatly retarded if *ortho* substituents are present, while compounds such as 4,4′-diphenylmethane diisocyanate dimerize slowly on standing, even without a catalyst. Dimerization is strongly catalyzed by trialkylphosphines (262–265) and mildly by tertiary amines (266–268). The reactivity of the phosphine catalysts is strongly influenced by the type of substituents on the phosphorus atom. Trialkylphosphines are the most active catalysts for dimerization. Replacement of one alkyl group by aryl (i.e., dimethylphenylphosphine) greatly reduces the catalytic activity (269). Further substitution by aryl groups progressively reduces the efficiency, while triphenylphosphine exhibits no catalytic activity.

Even though the dimer formed by self-condensation of phenyl isocyanate has long been known (270), and although the formula has been assumed to be XIV, some consideration has been given to an alternate structure (XV)

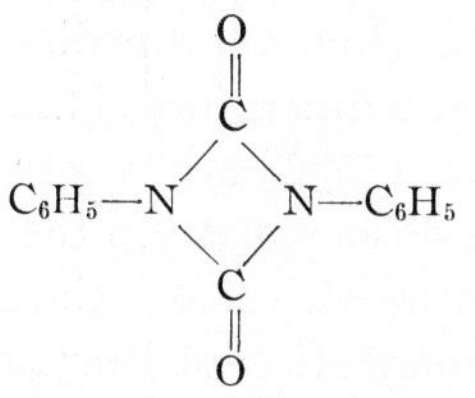

(XIV)

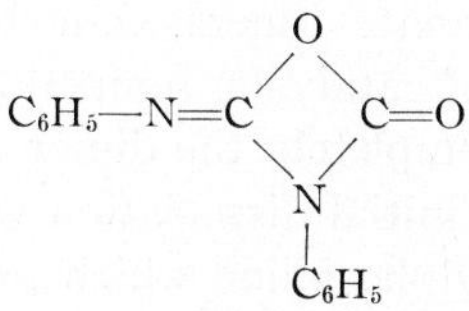

(XV)

based primarily on a few isolated reactions of the dimer (267,271). X-ray diffraction data (271), ebullioscopic results (262), as well as chemical confirmation (264,265) suggest that the symmetrical diketo form (XIV) is favored.

The formation of "mixed dimers" by the reaction of equimolar concentrations of two isocyanates has also been reported (82). When an isothiocyanate is mixed with an isocyanate, e.g., α-naphthyl isocyanate and phenyl isothiocyanate, four products were obtained, including α-naphthyl isothiocyanate, after 14 hr. at 215–225°C. The formation of these products could be explained through the equilibrium of the "mixed dimer" to the corresponding isocyanates and isothiocyanates (272), as shown in eq. (121).

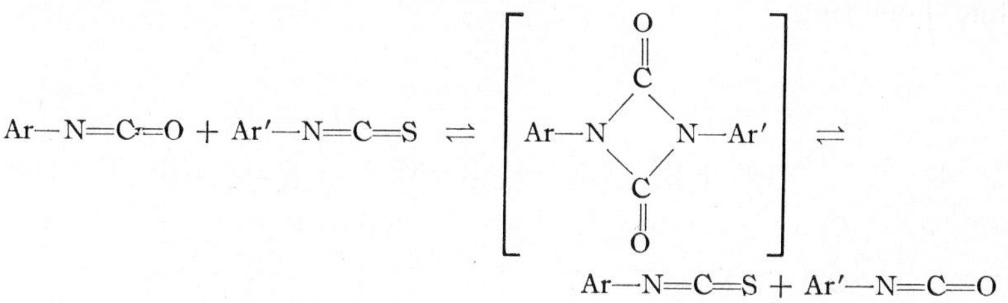

(121)

Trimethylene diisocyanate, prepared by the action of nitrous acid on the hydrazide of glutaric acid, was reported to solidify to a transparent mass after a week, yielding a polymeric dimer (273).

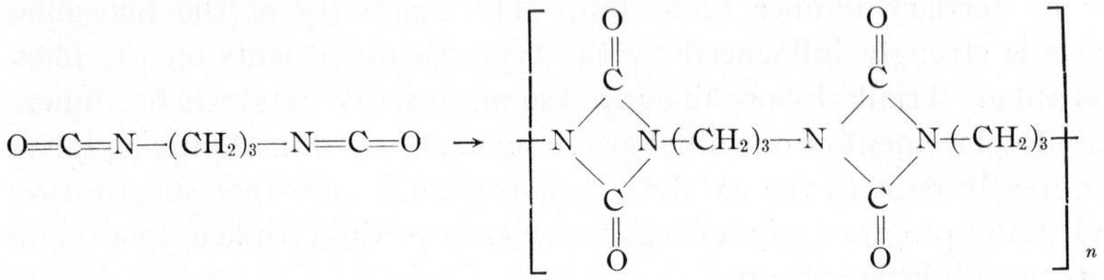
(122)

The chemistry of isocyanate dimers has been summarized by Siefken (82), Arnold, Nelson, and Verbanc (122), and Taub and McGinn (274).

Isocyanate dimerization is an equilibrium reaction, the conversion to dimer increasing as the temperature decreases. However, the dissociation of the isocyanate dimers occurs only at elevated temperatures (122). In the absence of catalysts, temperatures as high as 175°C. are necessary to dissociate completely the dimer of 2,4-tolylene diisocyanate to the monomer, although initial dissociation was noticed at 150°C. (275). Catalysts such as triethylphosphine which promote the dimerization of isocyanates, also affect the dissociation of the uretidine dione (82).

The isocyanate dimer may be considered to contain a urea linkage and therefore should undergo similar reactions with active hydrogen compounds. Thus, alcohols slowly cleave the four-membered ring to give the allophanate (263).

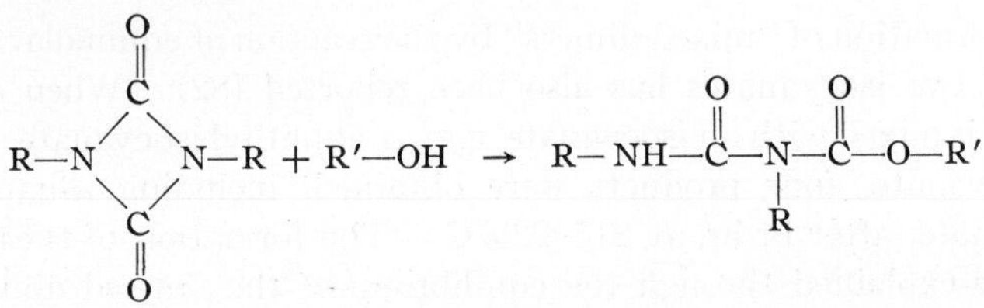
(123)

Ammonia or aliphatic amines give the expected biuret by cleaving the uretidine dione ring.

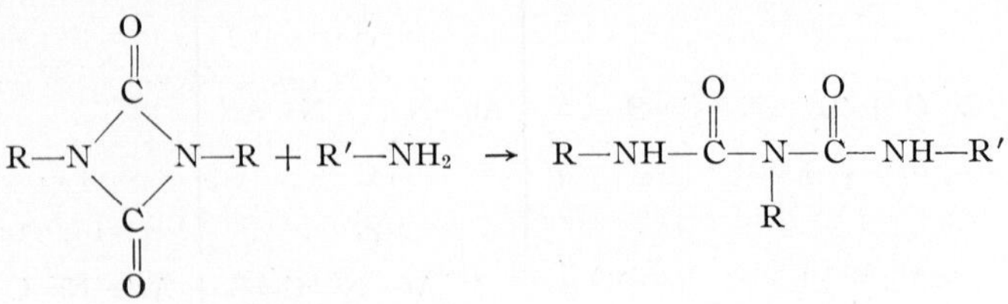
(124)

In order to effect reaction with phenols and mercaptans, higher temperatures are required. In this case the reaction (eq. 125) may proceed by regeneration of the isocyanate and subsequent reaction with the reactants (265).

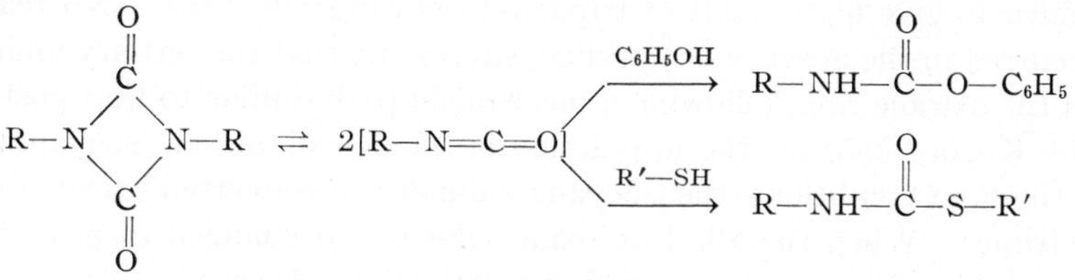

(125)

j. Trimerization

Hofmann (264), as early as 1870, reported that methyl and ethyl isocyanate formed a stable trimer when treated with triethylphosphine. It soon became evident that aromatic isocyanates also formed trimers as well as dimers as shown in the preceding section. Independent syntheses from isocyanuric acid with diazomethane (276) and from phenylcyanamide (264) yielded the same product as that realized from the catalytic reaction with phenyl isocyanate.

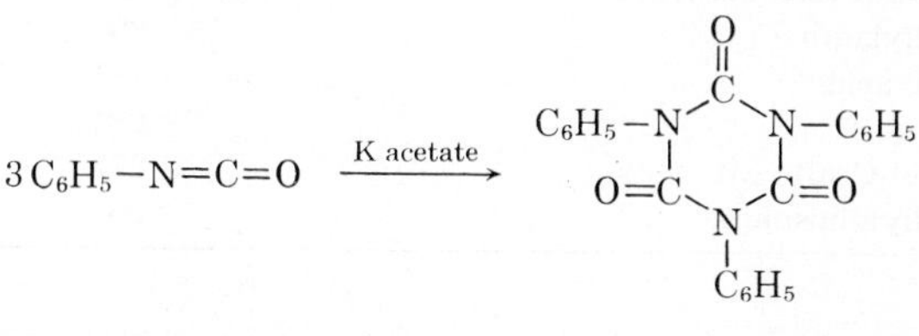

(126)

Isocyanates, such as *tert*-butyl isocyanate, reportedly do not trimerize, even in the presence of such active catalysts as triethylamine, presumably due to steric hindrance (277). In a similar manner, the presence of *ortho* substituents on an aromatic isocyanate greatly reduces the ease of trimerization.

Havekoss (278) reported that a large number of soluble compounds of elements in groups 1, 2, 3, 4, 5, 6, and 8 induced trimerization of either aromatic or aliphatic isocyanates. Other catalysts which have been used to promote trimerization are listed in Table XI-27.

It was found by Kogon (285) that the reaction between phenyl isocyanate and ethyl alcohol at 125°C. in the presence of *N*-methylmorpholine as catalyst led to the trimer in excellent yields. In the absence of the tertiary amine catalyst, and employing the same reaction conditions, a mixture of α,γ-diphenyl allophanate and phenyl isocyanate dimer was formed.

Phenyl isocyanate in the presence of pyridine catalyst and an oxirane such as ethylene oxide, propylene oxide, styrene oxide, and epichlorohydrin, was shown to give high yields of triphenyl isocyanurate (286). No reaction occurred in the absence of pyridine, suggesting that the tertiary amine opened the oxirane ring, following a mechanism path similar to that postulated by Kogon (285) for the interaction of an alcohol and an isocyanate. Under the same conditions, the isocyanate dimer was converted irreversibly to the trimer. When the alkylene oxide solvent was changed to benzene, ligroin, or chloroform, no trimerization reaction was observed.

TABLE XI-27
Catalysts Promoting Trimerization

Catalyst	Reference
Sodium formate	279
Sodium carbonate	279
Sodium methoxide	221
Sodium benzoate in DMF	282
Potassium acetate	279
Calcium acetate	263
Titanium tetrabutyrate	283
Triethylamine	280
Oxalic acid	281
Oxygen	284
Friedel-Crafts catalysts	275
Triethylphosphine	264

The slow trimerization of phenyl isocyanate at room temperature by means of metal carboxylates was reported by Kogon (288). Lead and cobalt derivatives were found to be the most active catalysts.

The reaction of TDI and hexamethylene diisocyanate with ethylene carbonate, in the presence of *N*-methylmorpholine as catalyst, was shown to produce three-dimensional polymers, termed polyisocyanurates (287).

The chemistry of isocyanate trimers has been reviewed by Taub and McGinn (274), while the rates of dimerization and trimerization of TDI have recently been determined by Davis (289).

Extensive literature is available on the various chemical modifications and reactions to which the derivatives of 1,3,5-triazines (the basic ring system of isocyanate trimers) may be subjected (274,290,291). Because of the high thermal as well as chemical stability of this ring system, research has recently been initiated into potential reactions forming polymers containing the triazine ring.

Treatment of substituted triazines with potassium hydroxide causes an almost quantitative transformation to the expected trialkylbiuret (292), while anhydrous hydrogen chloride gives the isocyanate only in poor yield (293). Thermal decomposition of triphenyl isocyanurate gives the corresponding carbodiimide (294), as shown in eq. (127).

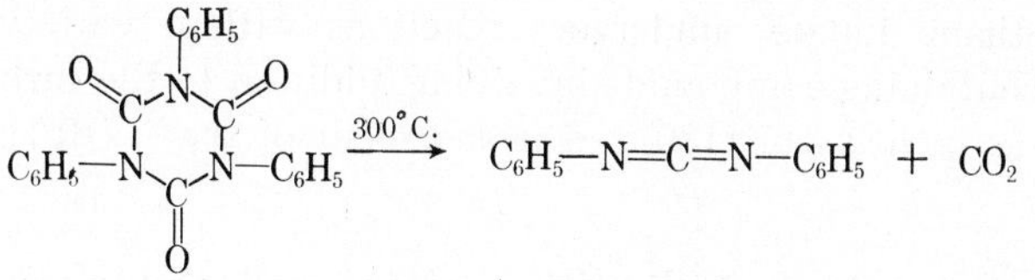

(127)

4. Reactions of Polyurethanes

a. Thermal Degradation

The thermal stability of polyurethanes depends upon the structure of the polymer. Polyurethanes from primary and secondary alcohols undergo degradation very slowly at 150–200°C. while urethanes from tertiary alcohols decompose at temperatures as low as 50°C. The presence of other reactants and particularly of catalysts has a considerable influence on the stability of the urethane polymer. In general, the thermal degradation may take place via alternate routes leading to different end products (256, 295–300). The first of these is represented by the dissociation of the urethane to alcohol and isocyanate as in eq. (128). This reaction has been

$$\mathrm{R{-}NH{-}\overset{O}{\overset{\|}{C}}{-}O{-}R'} \rightleftharpoons \mathrm{R'{-}OH + R{-}N{=}C{=}O} \qquad (128)$$

used in some instances to prepare the isocyanate from the corresponding urethane. Urethanes based on phenol dissociate more readily than alcohols (at about 150°C.), as has been discussed in greater detail under "blocked" isocyanates.

Another type of thermal degradation of the urethane has been reported to lead to the formation of an olefin and a primary amine (297).

$$\mathrm{R{-}NH{-}\overset{O}{\overset{\|}{C}}{-}O{-}CH_2{-}CH_2{-}R'} \rightarrow \mathrm{R'{-}CH{=}CH_2 + R{-}NH_2 + CO_2} \qquad (129)$$

Decomposition to the olefin and a primary amine occurs at elevated temperatures (200–300°C.) and takes place preferentially if the alcohol formed in the reaction is easily dehydrated to the corresponding olefin (298). This would lead to chain rupture in the case of a urethane polymer. Thermal degradation of the urethane with formation of secondary as well as primary amines in addition to the olefin formation has been described by Dyer, Newborn, and Wright (298).

b. Reactions with Active Hydrogens

The urethane linkage undergoes reactions with a variety of active hydrogen-containing compounds involving addition to the carbonyl group (187,256), as seen in eq. (130). Displacement of the —OR′ group takes

$$\mathrm{R{-}NH{-}\overset{\overset{\displaystyle O}{\|}}{C}{-}OR' + Z{-}H \rightleftharpoons \left[R{-}NH{-}\underset{\underset{\displaystyle ZH}{|}}{\overset{\overset{\displaystyle O}{|}}{C}}{-}OR' \right] \rightleftharpoons R{-}NH{-}\overset{\overset{\displaystyle O}{\|}}{C}{-}Z + R'{-}OH} \tag{130}$$

place more readily with aryloxy than with alkoxy groups.

The reaction of urethanes with alcohols are analogous to transesterification reactions, with the equilibrium favoring the formation of aliphatic rather than aromatic urethanes.

$$\mathrm{R{-}NH{-}\overset{\overset{\displaystyle O}{\|}}{C}{-}O{-}R' + R''{-}OH \rightleftharpoons R{-}NH{-}\overset{\overset{\displaystyle O}{\|}}{C}{-}O{-}R'' + R'{-}OH} \tag{131}$$

The reaction of urethanes with amines leads to formation of substituted ureas with the equilibrium strongly in favor of the latter.

$$\mathrm{R{-}NH{-}\overset{\overset{\displaystyle O}{\|}}{C}{-}OR' + R''{-}NH_2 \rightleftharpoons R{-}NH{-}\overset{\overset{\displaystyle O}{\|}}{C}{-}NH{-}R'' + R'{-}OH} \tag{132}$$

Phenyl *N*-phenylcarbamate reacted with dibutylamine at temperatures as low as 40°C. (256). On the other hand, urethanes derived from aromatic isocyanates were reported not to react readily with aliphatic amines at low temperatures, although the reaction proceeded at an appreciable rate at 100–150°C. (257).

Mukaiyama et al. (301–303) have studied the reaction of urethanes at 130–170°C. with a 10:1 molar excess of active hydrogen compounds such as amines, carboxylic acids, and aminoalcohols. Since the reaction conditions were such as to fit pseudo first-order kinetics, the rate-determining step was assumed to be the dissociation of the urethane into the corresponding isocyanate as shown in eq. (128). It was also found that the rate of reaction between urethanes and amines increased with the base strength of the amine

(301). Likewise, the reaction rate with carboxylic acids increased with the acid strength of the carboxylic acid.

Gaylord and Sroog (304) investigated the reaction of some disubstituted carbamates with alcohols using sodium alkoxide as a catalyst. With *N,N*-dialkyl and *N*-alkyl-*N*-aryl ethylcarbamates, new carbamates formed on alcoholysis. This reaction was similar to the ester exchange type of reaction, pictured in eq. (131). However, *N,N*-diaryl ethylcarbamate under the same reaction conditions yielded the carbonate in 62% yield (305), as shown in eq. (133).

$$(C_6H_5)_2{-}N{-}\overset{\overset{\Large O}{\|}}{C}{-}OC_2H_5 + (CH_3)_2CH{-}CH_2OH \xrightarrow{NaOR} [(CH_3)_2CH{-}CH_2{-}O]_2CO + (C_6H_5)_2NH \quad (133)$$

When benzyl alcohol was used in this reaction, dibenzyl ether was the principal product, presumably due to decarboxylation of the formed dibenzy carbamate.

The urethane linkage has excellent resistance toward hydrolysis and is more resistant than the ester group. Flexible urethane foams based on polyethers were found to exhibit outstanding resistance to hydrolysis, while the polyester-based foams underwent hydrolysis under the same reaction conditions, as determined by a noticeable drop in physical properties (306).

Dyer and Bartels (307) reported that polyurethanes prepared from aliphatic diols and diisocyanates were unaffected by 1% sodium hydroxide at 50°C., although the corresponding phenol analogues were attacked. Quantitative determinations of the hydrolysis products indicated the presence of carbon dioxide, a diamine, a phenol, and a polyurea. The latter was shown to result from the action of the diamine with unreacted polyurethane.

5. Reactions of Substituted Ureas

a. Thermal Degradation

The dissociation of substituted ureas into the corresponding isocyanates takes place at relatively high temperatures. Diphenylurea was shown to dissociate 99% at 370°C. (eq. 134).

$$C_6H_5{-}NH{-}\overset{\overset{\Large O}{\|}}{C}{-}NH{-}C_6H_5 \rightleftharpoons C_6H_5{-}N{=}C{=}O + C_6H_5{-}NH_2 \quad (134)$$

The phenyl isocyanate can be recovered in yields of up to 71% on addition of hydrogen chloride, which combines with the amine to form the salt and prevents recombination of the isocyanate and the amine (308). Similarly, methyl isocyanate was obtained in nearly quantitative yields by heating *N*-diphenyl-*N'*-methylurea to 240–290°C. (82).

The presence of acid catalysts has also a considerable influence on the thermal stability of substituted aliphatic ureas. Di-*tert*-alkylureas in the presence of acid catalysts decomposed to yield olefins which may subsequently polymerize (295). In the absence of acid or even in the presence of alkali, di-*tert*-butylurea sublimed at 250°C. with little sign of decomposition.

Iwakura and Ishizuka (273) observed that poly(ethylene trimethylene)-urea decomposes into *N,N'*-ethyleneurea and *N,N'*-trimethyleneurea as shown in eq. (135). Poly(octamethylene trimethylene)urea decomposed on

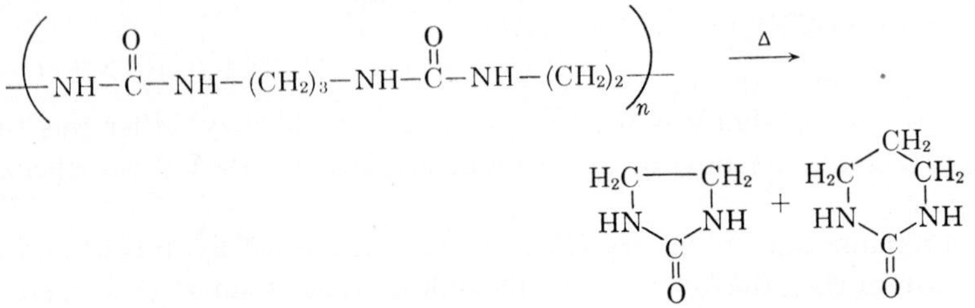

(135)

heating to *N,N'*-trimethyleneurea via the aminopropyl isocyanate.

b. Reactions with Active Hydrogens

Substituted ureas, like urethanes, undergo reactions with compounds containing active hydrogen. Although, as in the case of the urethane interactions, dissociation may play a role, addition reactions to the carbonyl group, analogous to transesterification reactions, are prevalent (187,247, 309).

$$R{-}NH{-}\overset{\overset{\displaystyle O}{\|}}{C}{-}NH{-}R' + Z{-}H \rightleftharpoons \left[R{-}NH{-}\underset{\underset{\displaystyle ZH}{|}}{\overset{\overset{\displaystyle O}{|}}{C}}{-}NH{-}R' \right] \rightleftharpoons R{-}NH{-}\overset{\overset{\displaystyle O}{\|}}{C}{-}Z + R'{-}NH_2 \quad (136)$$

The reactions of substituted ureas with alcohols and amines can be represented as shown in eqs. (137) and (138).

$$R{-}NH{-}\overset{\overset{\displaystyle O}{\|}}{C}{-}NH{-}R' + R''{-}OH \rightleftharpoons R{-}NH{-}\overset{\overset{\displaystyle O}{\|}}{C}{-}O{-}R'' + R'{-}NH_2 \quad (137)$$

$$R{-}NH{-}\overset{\overset{\displaystyle O}{\|}}{C}{-}NH{-}R' + R''{-}NH_2 \rightleftharpoons R{-}NH{-}\overset{\overset{\displaystyle O}{\|}}{C}{-}NH{-}R'' + R'{-}NH_2 \quad (138)$$

Mukaiyama et al. (155,187,310–313) investigated the reactions of substituted ureas with dicarboxylic acids at 140–160°C. and with alcohols at 160–190°C. in the presence of a large excess of the active hydrogen compounds. The nucleophilic addition reactions of fatty acids with urea were studied kinetically by following the carbon dioxide evolution (314). The rate of dissociation, which was first-order with respect to urea, increased as the acidity of the solvent acid increased. The introduction of a strong acid either accelerated or retarded the reaction, depending upon the concentration. The catalytic effect of the acids was postulated to be due to the formation of the conjugate acid of urea, and the decelerating effect of excess strong acid was ascribed to a further protonation of urea. The dissociation of urea (eqs. 139 and 140) probably proceeded through the con-

$$H_2N{-}\overset{\overset{\displaystyle O}{\|}}{C}{-}NH_2 \underset{-H^{\oplus}}{\overset{+H^{\oplus}}{\rightleftharpoons}} H_2N{-}\overset{\overset{\displaystyle O}{\|}}{C}{-}\overset{\oplus}{N}H_3 \underset{-H^{\oplus}}{\overset{+H^{\oplus}}{\rightleftharpoons}} H_3\overset{\oplus}{N}{-}\overset{\overset{\displaystyle O}{\|}}{C}{-}\overset{\oplus}{N}H_3 \qquad (139)$$

$$H_2N{-}\overset{\overset{\displaystyle O}{\|}}{C}{-}\overset{\oplus}{N}H_3 \xrightarrow{-NH_3} H_2\overset{\oplus}{N}{-}C{=}O \xrightarrow{-H^{\oplus}} H{-}N{=}C{=}O \qquad (140)$$

jugate acid to yield the isocyanate. The isocyanic acid, in turn reacted with the large excess of organic acid to form carbon dioxide and the amides of the acid, probably through an intermediate anhydride (157,160,315). Cyclic ureas, upon heating, dissociated into ω-aminoalkyl isocyanates (155). Rate constants of the thermal dissociation in fatty acid solvent showed an increase, depending on the ring size, in the order 5, 6, 15, 7, 8. The decomposition of substituted ureas in organic carboxylic acids, as would be expected, was dependent upon the nature and acid strength of the acid solvent. Similar results for the reactions of substituted ureas at 120–135°C. with propionic acid were reported by Magee and Daniels (316). They also observed that the rate of carbon dioxide evolution was first order with regard to the concentration of substituted urea, and was faster for aryl-substituted ureas than for *sym*-dimethylurea. Urea itself exhibited second-order kinetics under these conditions.

The thermal dissociation of ureas in alcohol was studied by making use of the relatively rapid reaction between the isocyanate formed and the alcoholic solvent to force the reaction to completion (310,312). The rates, as previously observed with analogous systems, were first order with respect to urea. The rates generally increased with the basicity of the alcohol; the order being ethylene glycol > glycerol > anisyl alcohol > benzyl alcohol > 1,2-propanediol > diethylene glycol, triethylene glycol > 1,4-butanediol. These rates, however, were lower in the alcohols than in organic carboxylic acids. The role of the solvent, as in the previous cases, was interpreted in terms of its ability to protonate one nitrogen of the urea and to remove a proton from the other.

Because of the large excess of reacting solvent used in all of these studies, the reactions appeared to follow pseudo first-order kinetics but it seems probable that the reactions may well be second-order as reported by Reilly and Orchin (256).

Davis, Blanchard, and Underwood (317,318) noted that ureas reacted with each other in an equilibration type of reaction, called "dearrangement," when treated with an amine.

$$R{-}NH{-}\overset{O}{\overset{\|}{C}}{-}NH{-}R + R'{-}NH{-}\overset{O}{\overset{\|}{C}}{-}NH{-}R' \rightleftharpoons 2R{-}NH{-}\overset{O}{\overset{\|}{C}}{-}NH{-}R' \quad (141)$$

Ureas generally hydrolyze in the presence of alkali to carbon dioxide and amines. However, diaryl-substituted ureas exhibit excellent resistance to hydrolysis, as demonstrated by carbon dioxide-blown polyether urethane foams which contain these linkages (306).

6. Chemistry of Industrial Polyurethanes

In this section a brief description is given of the chemistry of urethane foams, elastomers, coatings, and fibers, currently the most important commercial polyurethanes. For a more detailed discussion of these urethane products the reader is referred to reference books such as those by Saunders and Frisch (119,131), Dombrow (320), Mueller (321), and Frisch and Davis (322). In addition, numerous review articles, covering each class of these urethane polymers, have appeared in literature.

The basic chemical reactions, occurring during the preparation of urethane foams, elastomers, coatings, fibers, etc., have already been described. However, the reaction sequence in the formation of these polymers is very important since some of these reactions are regulated in such a manner as to proceed either almost simultaneously or in distinct separate phases.

a. Foams

In the preparation of foams three types of systems may be employed: (*a*) prepolymer; (*b*) semi- or quasi-prepolymer; (*c*) one-shot.

In the prepolymer method, the hydroxyl-terminated polyether or polyester is first reacted with an excess of diisocyanate to yield an isocyanate-terminated prepolymer.

$$\underset{\substack{\text{Polyether}\\ \text{or}\\ \text{polyester}}}{HO{-}R{-}OH} + \underset{\text{Diisocyanate}}{2O{=}C{=}N{-}R_1{-}N{=}C{=}O} \rightarrow$$

$$\underset{\text{Prepolymer}}{O{=}C{=}N{-}R_1{-}NH{-}\overset{\overset{\displaystyle O}{\|}}{C}{-}O{-}R{-}O{-}\overset{\overset{\displaystyle O}{\|}}{C}{-}NH{-}R_1{-}N{=}C{=}O} \quad (142)$$

In the subsequent foaming reaction, the prepolymer then reacts with water, in the presence of catalysts, surfactants and, occasionally, fillers and miscellaneous additives. The reaction with water produces higher molecular weight polymers containing substituted urea linkages with liberation of carbon dioxide, which is the active blowing agent for flexible foams.

$$nO{=}C{=}N{-}R_1{-}NH{-}\overset{\overset{\displaystyle O}{\|}}{C}{-}O{-}R{-}O{-}\overset{\overset{\displaystyle O}{\|}}{C}{-}NH{-}R_1{-}N{=}C{=}O + nH_2O \rightarrow$$

$$\left[NH{-}\overset{\overset{\displaystyle O}{\|}}{C}{-}NH{-}R_1{-}NH{-}\overset{\overset{\displaystyle O}{\|}}{C}{-}O{-}R{-}O{-}\overset{\overset{\displaystyle O}{\|}}{C}{-}NH{-}R_1\right]_n + nCO_2 \quad (143)$$

The density of the foam is controlled by the amount of blowing agent (CO_2) formed. Fluorocarbons such as trichlorofluoromethane may be used as auxiliary blowing agents in formulations where flexible foams of very low density are desired. The majority of rigid foams currently employ trichlorofluoromethane as the sole blowing agent because of lower costs and greatly improved thermal insulating factor (K-factor).

If an excess of free diisocyanate is present in the prepolymer and elevated temperatures are used, crosslinking reactions may occur, such as the formation of allophanate and biuret linkages (eqs. 81 and 95).

A favored method to introduce crosslinks into the foam polymer is to employ tri- or higher functional polyols such as poly(oxypropylene) adducts of glycerol, trimethylolpropane, pentaerythritol, sorbitol, α-methyl glucoside, and sucrose. Generally, di- and trifunctional resins are used for flexible foams while polyols of higher functionality and lower equivalent weights are utilized in rigid foams. An idealized structure (XVI) for a typical "triol-branched" polymer is shown.

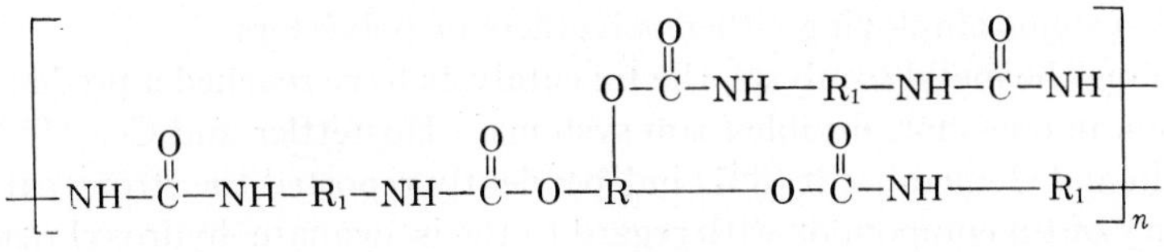

(XVI)

In the preparation of a semi- or quasi-prepolymer, only a portion of the polyether or polyester is reacted with the diisocyanate, resulting in a low molecular weight polymer dissolved in a large excess of isocyanate. This semi-prepolymer is then reacted at the time of foaming with the remainder of the polyol, in the presence of water or fluorocarbon, catalysts and surfactant. Semi-prepolymer systems are widely used for rigid foams where complete prepolymers would be difficult to handle because of the high viscosities resulting from the reaction between low equivalent weight polyols and di- and polyisocyanates.

The one-shot method provides for simultaneous mixing of the polyol(s), di- or polyisocyanate, water, and/or fluorocarbon, catalysts, and surfactant (usually nonionic surfactants or silicone copolymers). This process is at present favored in the manufacture of flexible foams and is gaining increasing acceptance in the preparation of rigid foams.

Catalysts employed in the preparation of urethane foams play an important role in the formation of foams but are also significant factors in the development of foam properties. Both the type and concentration of catalyst(s) are of prime importance in regulating the isocyanate–hydroxyl reaction (chain propagation) and the isocyanate–water reaction (crosslinking) at such a rate that a proper balance exists. Only then can the blowing agent be entrapped efficiently and the polymer have sufficient strength to prevent shrinkage or even foam collapse. The most common catalysts are tertiary amines and metal catalysts, notably organotin compounds.

The tertiary amines serve as catalysts for both the isocyanate–hydroxyl and isocyanate–water reactions. Both base strength of the amine and steric factors are considered to be the keys for the relative activity of these catalysts. In general, the catalyst activity increases with increasing base strength and with decreasing steric shielding of the amine nitrogen (149, 323). The most common catalysts are *N*-alkyl morpholines, *N,N'*-dialkyl piperazines, aliphatic mono- and diamines, and more recently 2,2,2-diazabicyclooctane (Dabco). The latter is of special importance in the manufacture of one-shot flexible foams (151,325,326). Tertiary amines are being used for both flexible and rigid foams, for one-shot or prepolymer-based systems employing either polyethers or polyesters.

Among the metal catalysts, the tin catalysts have reached a predominant position in one-shot, flexible foam systems. Hostettler and Cox (153) and Britain and Gemeinhardt (327) independently reported the strong catalytic activity of tin compounds with regard to the isocyanate–hydroxyl reaction. The most common organotin compounds used are stannous octoate, stannous oleate, dibutyltin dilaurate, and dibutyltin di-2-ethylhexoate.

The relative reaction rates of phenyl isocyanate with *n*-butanol, water, and diphenylurea, uncatalyzed and catalyzed with different tertiary amine and tin catalysts, are shown in Table XI-28 (153).

TABLE XI-28
Relative Reaction Rates of Phenyl Isocyanate with *n*-Butanol, Water, and Diphenylurea[a]
(Solvent: Dioxane, 70°C.)

Catalyst	Catalyst concn., *M*	Relative rates: Butanol	Water	Diphenylurea
None	—	1.0	1.1	2.2
N-Methylmorpholine	0.025	40	25	10
Triethylamine	0.025	86	47	4
N,N,N′,N′-Tetramethyl-1,3-butanediamine	0.025	260	100	12
1,4-Diazabicyclo[2.2.2]octane (Dabco)	0.025	1200	380	90
Tri-*n*-butyltin acetate	0.00025	800	140	80
Di-*n*-butyltin diacetate	0.00025	5600	980	120

[a] Taken from ref. 153.

Combinations of tin catalysts and tertiary amines exhibit a synergistic effect as seen in Table XI-29 (328). Combination catalyst systems are most widely used in one-shot, flexible foam systems.

TABLE XI-29
Order of Catalytic Activity for Isocyanate–Hydroxyl Reaction[a]
(Urethane)

Catalyst	Concentration, phr	Order of activity[b]
Uncatalyzed reaction		1
Stannous oleate (SnOle)	0.1	25
Dibutyltin dilaurate (DBTDL)	0.1	280
Dibutyltin di-2-ethylhexoate (DBTDEH)	0.1	300
Stannous octoate (SnOct)	0.1	1270
DBTDL	0.1 + 0.1 Dabco	860
DBTDEH	0.1 + 0.1 Dabco	870
SnOct	0.1 + 0.1 Dabco	2110

[a] Taken from ref. 328.
[b] Relative to rate of an uncatalyzed reaction.

In addition to the catalysts mentioned above, impurities in the isocyanate or polyols used may exert a considerable catalytic influence. Alkaline and metal impurities in the polyols act as catalysts, while acidic impurities in the isocyanate and polyols may reduce the overall catalytic effect by neutralizing part of the added catalyst. An excellent review on the catalysis in isocyanate reactions has recently issued (329).

b. Elastomers

Solid urethane elastomers are generally prepared by a series of steps involving: (*a*) preparation of a low molecular weight prepolymer; (*b*) chain extension to a higher molecular weight polymer; (*c*) crosslinking or curing. In some instances, such as the one-shot technique, the prepolymer formation may be eliminated. In the preparation of urethane elastomers to be processed on thermoplastic machinery, the polymer is designed in such a fashion that crosslinking does not take place at all or only to a slight degree after a period of postcuring.

The preparation of prepolymers has been discussed under the part on foams. In some cases, not only isocyanate-terminated but also hydroxyl-terminated prepolymers are being used, depending upon the NCO/OH ratio employed in the prepolymer preparation.

In order to convert the low molecular weight prepolymers to higher molecular weight polymers, difunctional, active hydrogen-containing compounds are used as chain extenders. Foremost among these are water, glycols and diamines. Chain extension with water and diamines yields substituted urea linkages while glycols form urethane linkages.

A majority of polyester–urethane elastomers are based on adipate polyesters, 4,4′-diphenylmethane diisocyanates (MDI), and a glycol such as 1,4-butanediol. Polyether-based elastomers usually consist of either poly(1,4-oxybutylene) glycols or poly(oxypropylene) glycols, a "hindered" aromatic diamine such as 4,4′-methylenebis(2-chloroaniline) and TDI. Polyether urethane elastomers may also be prepared by a combination of polyether diols and triols and TDI, thus containing only urethane linkages; the tensile properties of these elastomers, however, are generally inferior to those of polyether-based elastomers containing both urethane and urea linkages. However, for the manufacture of urethane sealing and caulking compounds which can be regarded as low modulus elastomers, the polyether diol or triol-based isocyanate-terminated prepolymers are chain-extended with either polyether triols or diols (330).

A variety of crosslinking reactions may be employed in the formation of thermosetting urethane elastomers. In the presence of an excess of isocyanate and elevated temperatures (generally about 100°C. or higher), the active hydrogen on the urethane and urea groups (formed in the chain extension step), react to yield allophanate (XVII) and biuret (XVIII) crosslinks, respectively.

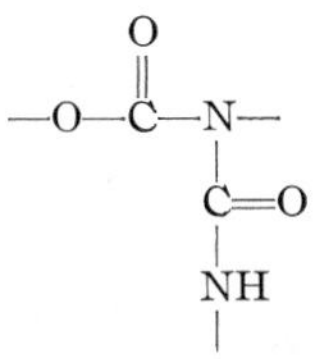

(XVII)

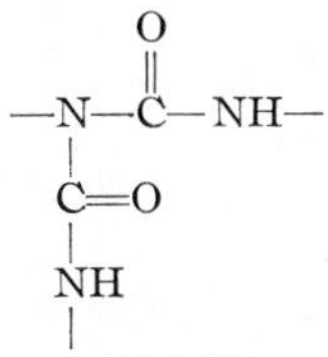

(XVIII)

Hydroxyl-terminated prepolymers can be cured by reaction with di- or triisocyanates, yielding urethane crosslinks. A different type of crosslinking is through vulcanization of unsaturated groups present in the polyester or polyether moiety of the prepolymer (331–333).

Another type of cure is represented by crosslinking a urethane gum stock based on either polyethers or polyesters and 4,4′-diphenylmethane diisocyanate (334). The use of peroxides such as dicumyl peroxide leads to crosslinking, presumably through formation of free radicals on the methylene group of MDI (XIX).

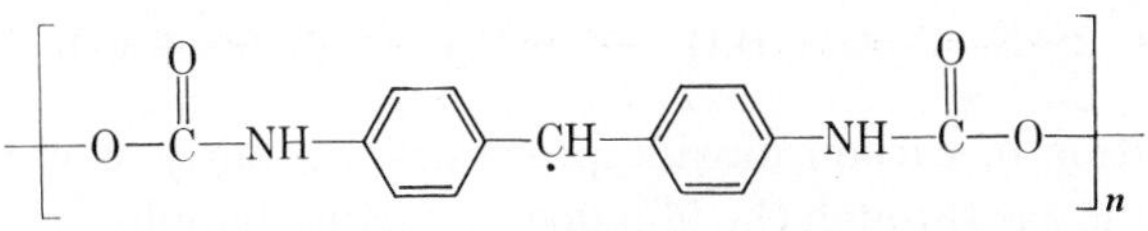

(XIX)

C. *Coatings*

Urethane coatings fall generally into two categories: (*a*) one-component coatings; (*b*) two-component coatings. The one-component coatings include urethane oils (isocyanate modified drying oils), isocyanate-terminated prepolymers (cured with moisture), and blocked isocyanate coatings (cured with heat). The two-component coatings are isocyanate-terminated prepolymers cured with polyols or isocyanate-terminated prepolymers cured with catalyst.

Urethane oils are the reaction products of hydroxyl-containing drying oil derivatives with diisocyanates. Generally, a mixed hydroxy ester is first prepared by the alcoholysis of a drying oil such as linseed oil with a polyol, e.g., trimethylolpropane, followed by reaction with the diisocyanate as in eq. (144). Since the drying oil portion of the urethane oil

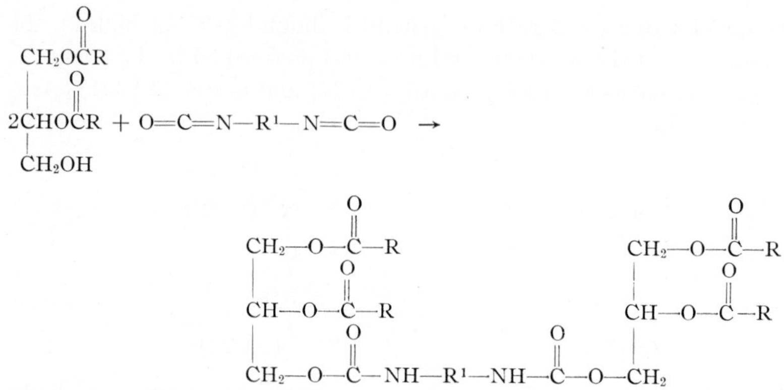

(144)

"Urethane oil"

contains double bonds, curing is effected by oxidation involving the methylene groups adjacent to the double bonds (335,336).

Isocyanate-terminated prepolymers are gaining increasingly wider acceptance as one-component, clear coatings for wood and other subtrates. Curing takes place by reaction with the moisture in the air which can be represented schematically as in eq. (145).

$$2\sim\!N{=}C{=}O + H_2O \rightarrow \sim\!NH{-}\overset{\displaystyle O}{\overset{\|}{C}}{-}NH\!\sim + CO_2 \tag{145}$$

The evolution of carbon dioxide proceeds at a fairly slow rate, so that diffusion of the gas through the film does not cause bubble formation. The rate depends upon the humidity as well as the temperature.

"Blocked" isocyanates are being used where a short bake cycle at elevated temperatures is desired such as in wire enamels. The principle of blocking and deblocking of isocyanates has been discussed. Phenol has been the most widely used blocking agent because the resulting blocked isocyanates can be deblocked at lower temperatures than those derived from alcohols. Certain catalysts, particularly organotin salts, lower the splitting temperature and time.

The chemistry of the two-component coatings has been covered in the discussion of urethane foams and elastomers, since the preparation of prepolymers for coatings is essentially the same as that for foams or elastomers. The curing by means of polyols results in urethane crosslinks. However, if this reaction is slow, as at low temperatures, the terminal isocyanate groups may also react with the moisture from the air, resulting in urea linkages. This side reaction can be eliminated by employing either higher temperatures or catalysts for the isocyanate–hydroxyl reaction, e.g., metal catalysts.

Isocyanate-terminated prepolymers may also be cured directly by means of catalysts such as tertiary amines or combinations of these with metal naphthenates.

d. Fibers

Urethane fibers were among the first commercial urethane products and were developed originally by Bayer (80). The reaction of hexamethylene diisocyanate and 1,4-butanediol led to the formation of Perlon U, which found limited use as fibers and bristles.

$$O{=}C{=}N{-}(CH_2)_6{-}N{=}C{=}O + HO{-}(CH_2)_4{-}OH \rightarrow \left[HN{-}(CH_2)_6{-}NH{-}\overset{\overset{\displaystyle O}{\|}}{C}{-}O{-}(CH_2)_4{-}O{-}\overset{\overset{\displaystyle O}{\|}}{C} \right]_n \quad (146)$$

Perlon U

Similarly, by varying the chain length and the nature of the diisocyanate and of the diol, other fiber-forming linear polyurethanes were obtained. The preparation and properties of linear polyurethanes, many of which are suitable for the formation of fibers, have been described.

Another class of urethane fibers which has already reached considerable commercial importance is the spandex fibers. These are elastomeric fibers consisting of polymers which contain at least 85% segmented polyurethane. The term "segmented" refers to an alternate arrangement of "soft" and "hard" components. Generally, the soft segments consist of either polyether or polyester urethane blocks which impart elasticity. The hard segments, usually made up of aromatic and urea groups, and in some instances, urethane groups, provide for strong hydrogen bonding or primary crosslinks which tie the elastic chains together and prevent stress decay. The composition of the spandex fibers can be varied considerably, depending upon the nature of the polymer segments. In addition to urethane groups they may contain urea, hydrazide, amide, sulfonamide, and other functional groups (337–340).

Elastomeric urethane fibers were first reported by Windemuth (341). Isocyanate-terminated prepolymers based on polyesters and aliphatic diisocyanates were spun into an aqueous piperazine solution yielding fibers which required a long curing time.

In the United States, spandex fibers were developed based on either polyesters or polyethers. The synthesis of the polymer takes place in several steps and is represented schematically in eq. (147) where HO~~P~~OH represents a polyester or polyether. The first step is the reaction of the hydroxyl-terminated polyester or polyether with a diisocyanate, preferentially TDI or MDI, to yield an isocyanate-terminated prepolymer:

$$2\ \mathrm{HO{\sim}P{\sim}OH} + 3\ \mathrm{O{=}C{=}N{-}R{-}N{=}C{=}O} \rightarrow$$

$$\mathrm{O{=}C{=}N{-}R{+}NH{-}\overset{\overset{O}{\|}}{C}{-}O{\sim}P{\sim}O{-}\overset{\overset{O}{\|}}{C}{-}NH{+}R{-}N{=}C{=}O} \quad (147)$$

In some instances the prepolymer formation may be carried out in two steps, e.g., reacting the dihydroxy compound first with TDI to give a hydroxy-terminated adduct which subsequently reacts with MDI to yield an isocyanate-terminated prepolymer as shown in eqs. (148).

$$2\ \mathrm{HO{\sim}P{\sim}OH} + \underset{\text{(TDI)}}{\mathrm{O{=}C{=}N{-}R{-}N{=}C{=}O}} \rightarrow$$

$$\mathrm{HO{\sim}P{\sim}O{-}\overset{\overset{O}{\|}}{C}{-}NH{-}R{-}NH{-}\overset{\overset{O}{\|}}{C}{-}O{\sim}P{\sim}OH} \quad (148a)$$

$$\mathrm{HO{\sim}P{\sim}O{-}\overset{\overset{O}{\|}}{C}{-}NH{-}R{-}NH{-}\overset{\overset{O}{\|}}{C}{-}O{\sim}P{\sim}OH} + 2\ \underset{\text{(MDI)}}{\mathrm{O{=}C{=}N{-}R'{-}N{=}C{=}O}} \rightarrow$$

$$\mathrm{O{=}C{=}N{-}R'{-}NH{-}\overset{\overset{O}{\|}}{C}{-}O{\sim}P{\sim}O{-}\overset{\overset{O}{\|}}{C}{-}NH{-}R{-}NH{-}}$$
$$\mathrm{\overset{\overset{O}{\|}}{C}{-}O{\sim}P{\sim}O{-}\overset{\overset{O}{\|}}{C}{-}NH{-}R'{-}N{=}C{=}O} \quad (148b)$$

If the isocyanate-terminated prepolymer is represented schematically by OCN~U~NCO, where U is the polyurethane chain, chain extension of the prepolymers takes place preferentially with diprimary aliphatic diamines to yield urethane-urea polymers as shown in eq. (149).

$$3\ \mathrm{O{=}C{=}N{\sim}U{\sim}N{=}C{=}O} + 2\ \mathrm{H_2N{-}R{-}NH_2} \rightarrow$$

$$\mathrm{[NH{\sim}U{\sim}NH{-}\overset{\overset{O}{\|}}{C}{-}NH{-}R{-}NH{-}\overset{\overset{O}{\|}}{C}{-}NH{\sim}U{\sim}NH{-}}$$
$$\mathrm{\overset{\overset{O}{\|}}{C}{-}NH{-}R{-}NH{-}\overset{\overset{O}{\|}}{C}{-}NH{\sim}U{\sim}NH{-}\overset{\overset{O}{\|}}{C}]_n} \quad (149)$$

The polymers are usually spun in the form of highly viscous solutions, the techniques employed for cellulose acetate or polyacrylonitrile fibers being used. Melt polymerization has also been used in the preparation of spandex fibers, but this process is more difficult to control due to the danger of gel formation and crosslinking.

A somewhat different type of process is employed for the manufacture of certain polyester-based spandex fibers (342–345).

The isocyanate-terminated prepolymer from the adipate ester and MDI is first extruded in a fine stream and is then converted into a solid thread by use of a two-stage curing process. The liquid prepolymer is transformed into a solid by reaction with a diamine such as hexamethylenediamine or ethylenediamine. The resulting threadlike product still contains a liquid core of uncured prepolymer and an outer solid shell consisting of urea-chain extended polymer. Usually, 0.5% of a nonionic or anionic wetting agent is added to the setting bath to allow for uniform setting on the extruded filament surface. The thread after winding on spools or packages is then subjected to a final cure in water at 55–65°C. and at a pressure of 80–100 psi. The water penetrates the outer casing of the filament and reacts with the isocyanate groups of the liquid core to form urea groups.

Another method for preparing elastic urethane fibers consists of extension of the thermoplastic elastomers into fibers which can be oriented under tension (346–348).

References

A. Polysulfides

1. Fettes, E. M., J. S. Jorczak, and J. R. Panek, *Ind. Eng. Chem.*, **46**, 1539 (1954).
2. Patrick, J. C., and H. R. Ferguson, U. S. Patent 2,466,963 (to Thiokol Chemical Corp.), Apr. 12, 1949; *Chem. Abstr.*, **43**, 5636h (1949).
3. Fettes, E. M., U. S. Patent 2,606,173 (to Reconstruction Finance Corp.), Aug. 5, 1952; *Chem. Abstr.*, **47**, 349g (1953).
4. Fettes, E. M., U. S. Patent 2,676,165 (to Thiokol Chemical Corp.), Apr. 10, 1954; *Chem. Abstr.*, **48**, 9110c (1954).
5. Bender, H. L., A. G. Farnham, and J. W. Guyer, U. S. Patent 2,731,437 (to Union Carbide and Carbon Co.), Jan. 17, 1956; *Chem. Abstr.*, **50**, 7503d (1956).
6. Carpenter, G. D., G. Gregory, S. H. Kalfayan, and I. P. Seegman, U. S. Patent 2,964,503 (to Products Research Co.), Dec. 13, 1960; *Chem. Abstr.*, **55**, 7885d (1961).
7. Gregory, G., and I. P. Seegman, U. S. Patent 2,787,608 (to Products Research Co.), Apr. 2, 1957; *Chem. Abstr.*, **51**, 9202d (1957).
8. Barth, W. L. A., U. S. Patent 2,727,883 (to Aero Service Corp.), Dec. 20, 1955; *Chem. Abstr.*, **50**, 13496h (1956).
9. Fettes, E. M., and J. A. Gannon, U. S. Patent 2,789,958 (to Thiokol Chemical Corp.), Apr. 23, 1957; *Chem. Abstr.*, **51**, 17239f (1957).
10. Minnesota Mining & Mfg. Co., British Patent 787,022, Nov. 27, 1957.
11. Bender, H. L., A. G. Farnham, and J. W. Guyer, U. S. Patent 2,849,416 (to Union Carbide Corp.), Aug. 26, 1958; *Chem. Abstr.*, **52**, 19258d (1958).
12. Mitchell, A., III, U. S. Patent 2,814,600 (to E. I. du Pont de Nemours & Co.), Nov. 26, 1957; *Chem. Abstr.*, **52**, 42316 (1958).
13. Peters, H., German Patent 1,027,395 (to Phoenix Gummi), Apr. 3, 1958; *Chem. Abstr.*, **54**, 15988i (1960).

14. Patrick, J. C., and H. R. Ferguson, U. S. Patent 2,646,415 (to Reconstruction Finance Corp.), July 21, 1953; *Chem. Abstr.*, **47,** 10276i (1953).
15. Ruderman, I. W., and E. M. Fettes, *J. Am. Chem. Soc.*, **71,** 2264 (1949).

B. Epoxides

16. Werner, E. G. G., and E. Farenhorst, U. S. Patent 2,467,171 (to Shell Development Company), Apr. 12, 1949; *Chem. Abstr.*, **43,** 5421h (1949).
17a. Greenlee, S. O., U. S. Patent 2,582,985 (to Devoe and Raynolds Co.), Jan. 22, 1952; *Chem. Abstr.*, **46,** 4275d (1952).
17b. Greenlee, S. O., U. S. Patent 2,615,007 (to Devoe and Raynolds Co.), Oct. 21, 1959; *Chem. Abstr.*, **49,** 10637a (1955).
18. Greenlee, S. O., U. S. Patent 2,615,008 (to Devoe and Raynolds Co.), Oct. 21, 1959; *Chem. Abstr.*, **49,** 10637c (1955).
19. Dow Chemical Co., Technical Bulletin, Dow Epoxy Novolak D. E. N. 438.
20. Koppers Co., Inc., Tar Products Division, Technical Bulletin E-103, Sept. 2, 1960.
21. Bludworth, J. E., U. S. Patent 2,314,385 (to Celanese Corp. of America), Mar. 23, 1943; *Chem. Abstr.*, **37,** 5081^9 (1943).
22. Phillips, B., F. C. Frostick, and P. S. Starcher, U. S. Patent 2,804,473 (to Union Carbide Corp.), Aug. 27, 1957; *Chem. Abstr.*, **52,** 2051h (1958).
23. Greenspan, F. P., and R. J. Gall, U. S. Patent 2,919,283 (to Food Machinery and Chemical Corp.), Dec. 29, 1959; *Chem. Abstr.*, **54,** 7189a (1960).
24. McGuigan, J. P., *Offic. Dig. Federation Soc. Paint Technol.*, **34,** 939 (1962).
25. Budde, W. M., U. S. Patent 3,050,480 (to Archer-Daniels-Midland Co.), Aug. 21, 21, 1962; *Chem. Abstr.*, **57,** 15277f (1962).
26. Greenspan, F. P., and A. E. Pepe, U. S. Patent 3,030,336 (to Food Machinery and Chemical Corp.), Apr. 17, 1962.
27. Frostick, F. C., and B. Phillips, U. S. Patent 2,716,123 (to Union Carbide Corp.), Aug. 23, 1955; *Chem. Abstr.*, **50,** 7852f (1956).
28. Niederhauser, W. D., U. S. Patent 2,543,419 (to Rohm and Haas Co.), Feb. 27, 1951; *Chem. Abstr.*, **45,** 8038b (1951).
29. Batzer, H., and E. Nickles, *Chimia* (*Aarau*), **16,** 57 (1962).
30. McGary, C. W., and C. T. Patrick, U. S. Patent 2,985,616 (to Union Carbide Corp.), May 23, 1961.
31. Greenspan, F. P., U. S. Patent 3,073,792 (to Food Machinery and Chemical Corp.), Jan. 15, 1963; *Chem. Abstr.*, **59,** 10306d (1963).
32a. Wiles, Q. T., and H. A. Newey, U. S. Patent 2,528,932 (to Shell Development Co.), Nov. 7, 1950; *Chem. Abstr.*, **45,** 1816g (1951).
32b. Erickson, J. G., U. S. Patent 2,567,842 (to American Cyanamid Co.), Sept. 11, 1951; *Chem. Abstr.*, **46,** 4561b (1951).
32c. Maerker, G., H. A. Monroe, Jr., and W. S. Port, *J. Appl. Polymer Sci.*, **7,** 301 (1963).
33. Narracott, E. S., *Brit. Plastics*, **26,** 120 (1953).
34. Shechter, L., J. Wynstra, and R. P. Kurkjy, *Ind. Eng. Chem.*, **48,** 94 (1956).
35. Dannenberg, H., *SPE* (*Soc. Plastics Engrs.*) *J.*, **15,** 875 (1959).
36. Dannenberg, H., and W. R. Harp, *Anal. Chem.*, **28,** 86 (1956).
37. Smith, I. T., *Polymer*, **2,** 95 (1961).
38a. O'Neill, L. A., and C. P. Cole, *J. Appl. Chem.* (*London*), **6,** 356 (1956).

38b. O'Neill, L. A., and C. P. Cole, *J. Appl. Chem.* (*London*), **6,** 399 (1956).
39. Lissner, O., *Farbe Lack.*, **66,** 14 (1960); *Chem. Abstr.*, **54,** 11511a (1960).
40. Allen, F. J., and W. M. Hunter, *J. Appl. Chem.* (*London*), **7,** 86 (1957).
41. Ingberman, A. K., and R. K. Walter, *J. Polymer Sci.*, **28,** 468 (1958).
42. Shell Chemical Co., Technical Bulletin, SC:62-60.
43. Union Carbide Corp., British Patent 792,187, Mar. 19, 1958; *Chem. Abstr.*, **52,** 17796a (1958).
44. Shell International Research Maat. N.V., British Patent 905,725, Sept. 12, 1962; *Chem. Abstr.*, **58,** 9293d (1963).
45. Greenlee, S. O., U. S. Patent 2,717,885 (to Devoe and Raynolds Co.), Sept. 13, 1955; *Chem. Abstr.*, **50,** 2207b (1956).
46. Parry, H. L., and W. A. Hubbard, U. S. Patent 2,824,083 (to Shell Development Co.), Feb. 18, 1958; *Chem. Abstr.*, **52,** 8621f (1958).
47. Smith, C. M., and D. E. Graham, U. S. Patent 3,032,526 (to General Aniline and Film Corp.), May 1, 1962; *Chem. Abstr.*, **57,** 3630g (1962).
48. Renfrew, M. M., and H. Wittcoff, U. S. Patent 2,705,223 (to General Mills, Inc.), Mar. 29, 1955; *Chem. Abstr.*, **50,** 2206i (1956).
49. Whittier, F., and R. J. Lawn, U. S. Patent 2,765,288 (to Pittsburgh Coke and Chemical Co.), Dec. 28, 1956; *Chem. Abstr.*, **51,** 1625g (1957).
50. Castan, P., U. S. Patent 2,324,483 (to Gebr. De Trey A. G.), July 20, 1943; *Chem. Abstr.*, **38,** 185^4 (1944).
51. Fisch, W., and W. Hofmann, *J. Polymer Sci.*, **12,** 497 (1954).
52. Fisch, W., W. Hofmann, and J. Koskikallio, *J. Appl. Chem.* (*London*), **6,** 429 (1956).
53. Dearborn, E. C., R. M. Fuoss, and A. F. White, *J. Polymer Sci.*, **16,** 201 (1955).
54. Shechter, L., and J. Wynstra, *Ind. Eng. Chem.*, **48,** 86 (1956).
55. Fisch, W., and W. Hofmann, *Plastic Technol.*, **28,** (8), 28 (1961).
56. Tanaka, Y., and H. Kakiuchi, *J. Appl. Polymer Sci.*, **7,** 1063 (1963).
57. Wear, R. L., and R. L. Bowman, U. S. Patent 3,052,650 (to Minnesota Mining and Manufacturing Co.), Sept. 4, 1962.
58. Devoe and Raynolds Co., British Patent 896,601, May 16, 1962; *Chem. Abstr.*, **57,** 13930g (1962).
59. Carey, J. E., U. S. Patent 2,839,495 (to Shell Development Co.), June 17, 1958; *Chem. Abstr.*, **52,** 21236h (1958).
60a. Proops, W. R., and G. W. Fowler, French Patent 1,284,559 (to Union Carbide Corp.), Jan. 8, 1962.
60b. Proops, W. R., and G. W. Fowler, French Patent 1,282,227 (to Union Carbide Corp.), Dec. 11, 1961.
61. Fischer, R. F., *J. Polymer Sci.*, **44,** 155 (1960).
62. Wismer, M., and W. R. Hydro, U. S. Patent 3,051,665 (to Pittsburgh Plate Glass Co.), Aug. 28, 1962).
63. CIBA., British Patent 882,360, Nov. 15, 1961; *Chem. Abstr.*, **58,** 3571f (1963).
64. Fettes, E. M., and J. A. Gannon, U. S. Patent 2,789,958 (to Thiokol Chemical Corp.), Apr. 23, 1957; *Chem. Abstr.*, **51,** 17239e (1957).
65. Greenlee, S. O., U. S. Patent 2,521,911 (to Devoe and Raynolds Co.), Sept. 12, 1950; *Chem. Abstr.*, **45,** 1380b (1951).
66. Greenlee, S. O., U. S. Patent 2,511,913 (to Devoe and Raynolds Co.), June 20, 1950. *Chem. Abstr.*, **44,** 8696d (1950).

67. Greenlee, S. O., U. S. Patent 2,528,359 (to Devoe and Raynolds Co.), Oct. 31, 1950; *Chem. Abstr.*, **45**, 2261b (1951).
68. Lee, H., and K. Neville, *SPE* (*Soc. Plastics Engrs.*) *J.*, **16**, 315 (1960).
69a. Imperial Chemical Industries, Ltd., British Patent 910,899 (by H. Brunner and M. J. Waghorn), Nov. 21, 1962; *Chem. Abstr.*, **58**, 3564g (1963).
69b. Chen, H. H., and A. C. Nixon, paper presented at 144th Meeting of the American Chemical Society, Los Angeles, Calif., Mar. 31–Apr. 5, 1963.
70. Langer, S. H., I. N. Elbling, A. B. Finestone, and W. R. Thomas, *J. Appl. Polymer Sci.*, **5**, 370 (1961).
71. U. S. Borax and Chemical Corp., Belgian Patent 609,522, Apr. 24, 1962; *Chem. Abstr.*, **57**, 11385f (1962).
72. Imperial Chemical Industries, Ltd., British Patent 912,115 (by H. Brunner), Dec., 5, 1962; *Chem. Abstr.*, **58**, 5841g (1963).
73. Speranza, G. P., and W. J. Peppel, *J. Org. Chem.*, **23**, 1922 (1958).
74. Weiner, M. L., *J. Org. Chem.*, **26**, 951 (1961).
75. Gulbins, K., G. Benzing, R. Maysenholder, and K. Hamann, *Chem. Ber.*, **93**, 1975 (1960).
76. Faerber, G., U. S. Patent 2,959,571 (to Deutsche Solvay-Werke G.m.b.H.), Nov. 8, 1960; German Patent 1,002,945, Feb. 21, 1957; *Chem. Abstr.*, **53**, 23088a (1959).

C. Polyurethanes and Related Isocyanate Polymers

77. Wurtz, A., *Ann.*, **71**, 326 (1849).
78. Gautier, A., *Ann.*, **149**, 311 (1869).
79. Hentschel, W., *Ber.*, **17**, 1284 (1884).
80. Bayer, O., *Angew. Chem.*, **A59**, 257 (1947); *Chem. Abstr.*, **42**, 6160c (1948).
81. I. G. Farbenindustrie A.-G., German Patent 728,981 (by O. Bayer, H. Rinke, W. Siefken, L. Orthner, and H. Schild), Nov. 12, 1942; *Chem. Abstr.*, **38**, 381[6] (1944).
82. Siefken, W., *Ann.*, **562**, 75 (1949).
83. Petersen, S., and H. F. Piepenbrink in Houben-Weyl, *Methoden der Organischen Chemie*, E. Müller, ed., Vol. VIII, George Thieme-Verlag, Stuttgart, 1952, pp. 75–246.
84. Gattermann, L., and G. Schmidt, *Ann.*, **244**, 30 (1888).
85. Shriner, R. L., W. H. Horne, and R. F. B. Cox in *Organic Syntheses*, A. H. Blatt, ed., Vol. II, Wiley, New York, 1943, p. 453.
86. Slocombe, R. J., E. E. Hardy, J. H. Saunders, and R. L. Jenkins, *J. Am. Chem. Soc.*, **72**, 1888 (1950).
87. DeBell, J. M., W. C. Goggin, and W. E. Gloor, *German Plastics Practice*, DeBell and Richardson, Springfield, Mass., 1946, p. 301.
88. Smith, P. A. S., in *Organic Reactions*, R. Adams, W. E. Bachmann, L. F. Fieser, R. Johnson, and H. R. Snyder, eds., Vol. III, Wiley, New York, 1946, Chap. 9.
89. Montagne, M., and T. Guilmart, *Bull. Soc. Chim.*, **12**, 836 (1945); *Chem. Abstr.*, **40**, 5696[4] (1946).
90. Yale, H. L., *Chem. Rev.*, **33**, 209 (1943).
91. Roesch, R., and M. H. Gold, *J. Am. Chem. Soc.*, **73**, 2959 (1951).

92. Curtius, T., G. v. Brüning, and H. Derlon, *J. Prakt. Chem.*, **125,** 63 (1930); *Chem. Abstr.*, **24,** 3230 (1930).
93. Curtius, T., and W. Hechtenberg, *J. Prakt. Chem.*, **105,** 289 (1923); *Chem. Abstr.*, **17,** 2868 (1923).
94. Coffman, D. D., U. S. Patent 2,334,476 (to E. I. duPont deNemours & Co.), Nov. 16, 1944; *Chem. Abstr.*, **38,** 2772[2] (1944).
95. Jones, G. D., J. Zomlefer, and K. Hawkins, *J. Org. Chem.*, **9,** 500 (1944).
96. Pyman, F. L., *J. Chem. Soc.*, **103,** 852 (1913).
97. Iwakura, Y., Y. Taneda, and S. Uchida, *J. Appl. Polymer Sci.*, **5,** 108 (1961).
98. Cupery, M. E., U. S. Patent 2,346,665 (to E. I. duPont de Nemours & Co.), Apr. 18, 1944; *Chem. Abstr.*, **38,** 5845[6] (1944).
99. Dickey, J. B., J. M. Straley, and T. E. Stanin, U. S. Patent 2,394,597 (to Eastman Kodak Co.), Feb. 12, 1946; *Chem. Abstr.*, **40,** 3848[3] (1946).
100. Himel, C. M., and L. M. Richards, U. S. Patent 2,866,801 (to Ethyl Corp.), Dec. 30, 1958; *Chem. Abstr.*, **53,** 9145i (1959).
101. Schaeffer, W. D., U. S. Patent 3,017,420 (to Union Oil Co. of Calif.), Jan. 16, 1962; *Chem. Abstr.*, **57,** 664i (1962).
102. Slotta, K. H., and L. Lorenz, *Ber.*, **58B,** 1320 (1925).
103. Hill, A. J., and W. M. Degnan, U. S. Patent 2,379,486 (to American Cyanamid Co.), July 3, 1945; *Chem. Abstr.*, **40,** 175[5] (1946).
104. Anderson, H. H., *J. Am. Chem. Soc.*, **72,** 193 (1950).
105. Anderson, H. H., *J. Am. Chem. Soc.*, **72,** 196 (1950).
106. Forbes, G. S., and H. H. Anderson, *J. Am. Chem. Soc.*, **70,** 1043, 1222 (1948).
107. Klein, D. X., U. S. Patent 2,532,559 (to E. I. duPont deNemours & Co.), Dec. 5, 1950; *Chem. Abstr.*, **45,** 3409d (1951).
108. Jenkins, L. H., and D. S. Sears, U. S. Patent 2,873,171 (to Virginia-Carolina Chemical Corp.), Feb. 10, 1959; *Chem. Abstr.*, **53,** 18864c (1959).
109. Goubeau, J., and H. Gräbner, *Chem. Ber.*, **93,** 1379 (1960).
110. Tilley, J. N., and A. A. R. Sayigh, *J. Org. Chem.*, **28,** 2076 (1963).
111. Mukaiyama, T., and H. Nohira, *Angew. Chem.*, **73,** 510 (1961).
112. Mukaiyama, T., and H. Nohira, *J. Org. Chem.*, **26,** 782 (1961).
113. McClanahan, J. L., and J. L. Harper, *Chem. Ind. (London)*, **1963,** 1280.
114. Hart, R., *Bull. Soc. Chim. Belges*, **65,** 291 (1956); *Chem. Abstr.*, **51,** 13762d (1957).
115. Schweitzer, C. E., U. S. Patent 2,409,712 (to E. I. duPont deNemours & Co.), Oct. 22, 1946; *Chem. Abstr.*, **41,** 1239f (1947).
116. Hofmann, A. W., *Ber.*, **3,** 653 (1870).
117. Wenker, H., *J. Am. Chem. Soc.*, **58,** 2608 (1936).
118. Saunders, J. H., and R. J. Slocombe, *Chem. Rev.*, **43,** 203 (1948).
119. Saunders, J. H., and K. C. Frisch, *Polyurethanes: Chemistry and Technology*, High Polymer Series, Vol. XVI, Part I, Interscience, New York, 1962, pp. 17–28.
120. Petersen, S., Ref. 83, pp. 119–137.
121. Staudinger, H., and R. Endle, *Ber.*, **50,** 1042 (1917).
122. Arnold, R. G., J. A. Nelson, and J. J. Verbanc, *Chem. Rev.*, **57,** 47 (1957).
123. Davis, T. L., and J. M. Farnum, *J. Am. Chem. Soc.*, **56,** 883 (1934).
124. Knoevenagel, E., and A. Schürenberg, *Ann.*, **297,** 138 (1897).
125. Karmas, G., U. S. Patent 2,574,484 (to Ortho Pharmaceutical Corp.), Nov. 13, 1951; *Chem. Abstr.*, **46,** 7123g (1952).

126. Korshak, V. V., Y. A. Strepikheev, and A. F. Moiseev, *Plasticheskie Massy*, **1961** (7), 13; Soviet Plastics **1961** (7), 13; *Chem. Abstr.*, **56**, 4937e (1962).
126a. Korshak, V. V., and V. V. Golubev, *Izv. Akad. Nauk SSSR Otd. Khim. Nauk*, **1946**, 185; *Chem. Abstr.*, **43**, 142c (1949).
127. Alexander, P., and C. S. Whewell, "Some Aspects of Textile Research in Germany," BIOS Final Report No. 1472, H. M. Stationery Office, London, 1947; PB 87939.
128. Ref. 87, p. 303.
129. Lyman, D. J., *J. Polymer Sci.*, **45**, 49 (1960).
130. Lyman, D. J., *J. Polymer Sci.*, **55**, 507 (1961).
131. Saunders, J. H., and K. C. Frisch, *Polyurethanes: Chemistry and Technology*, High Polymer Series, Vol. XVI, Part II, Interscience, New York, N. Y., 1964.
132. Marvel, C. S., and C. H. Young, *J. Am. Chem. Soc.*, **73**, 1066 (1951).
133. Marvel, C. S., and J. H. Johnson, *J. Am. Chem. Soc.*, **72**, 1674 (1950).
134. Slezak, F. B., J. P. Stallings, D. H. Wagner, and J. H. Wotiz, *J. Org. Chem.*, **26**, 3137 (1961).
135. Kern, W., and W. Thoma, *Makromol. Chem.*, **11**, 10 (1953).
136. Kern, W., and W. Thoma, *Makromol. Chem.*, **16**, 89 (1955).
137. Kern, W., and W. Thoma, *Makromol. Chem.*, **16**, 108 (1955).
138. Kern, W., H. Kalsch, K. J. Rauterkus and H. Sutter, *Makromol. Chem.*, **44/46**, 78 (1961).
139. Schonfeld, E., *J. Polymer Sci.*, **59**, 87 (1962).
140. Frankel, M. B., *J. Chem. Eng. Data*, **7**, 410 (1962).
141. Fischer, J. R., *Tetrahedron Suppl.*, **19**, (1), 97 (1963).
142. Petersen, S., *Ann.*, **562**, 205 (1949).
143. Leuckart, R., and M. Schmidt, *Ber.*, **18**, 2338 (1885).
144. Gumpert, F., *J. Prakt. Chem.*, **32**, 278 (1885).
145. Naegeli, C., A. Tyabji, L. Conrad, and F. Litman, *Helv. Chim. Acta*, **21**, 1100 (1938); *Chem. Abstr.*, **33**, 539 (1939).
146. Shkapenko, G., G. T. Gmitter, and E. E. Gruber, *Ind. Eng. Chem.*, **52**, 605 (1960).
147. Morton, M., and M. A. Deisz, paper presented at the 130th Meeting of the American Chemical Society, Atlantic City, N. J., Sept. 16–21, 1956.
148. Morton, M., M. A. Deisz, and M. Ohta, "Degradation Studies on Condensation Polymers," U. S. Dept. of Commerce Report PB-131795, March 31, 1957.
149. Alzner, B. G., and K. C. Frisch, *Ind. Eng. Chem.*, **51**, 715 (1959).
150. Farkas, A., and K. G. Flynn, *J. Am. Chem. Soc.*, **82**, 642 (1960).
151. Farkas, A., G. A. Mills, W. E. Erner, and J. B. Maerker, *Ind. Eng. Chem.*, **51**, 1299 (1959).
152. Cox, E. F., and F. Hostettler, paper presented at the 135th Meeting of the American Chemical Society, Boston, Mass., Apr. 5–10, 1959.
153. Hostettler, F., and E. F. Cox, *Ind. Eng. Chem.*, **52**, 609 (1960).
154. Wolf, H. W., Jr., Foam Bulletin, "Catalyst Activity in One-Shot Urethane Foam," E. I. du Pont de Nemours & Co., March 16, 1960.
155. Ozaki, S., T. Mukaiyama, and K. Uno, *J. Am. Chem. Soc.*, **79**, 4358 (1957).
156. Iwakura, Y., *Kobunshi Kagaku*, **4**, 91 (1947); *Chem. Abstr.*, **45**, 2711 (1951).
157. Dieckmann, W., and F. Breest, *Ber.*, **39**, 3052 (1906).
158. Blaise, E. E., and I. Hermann, *Ann. chim. phys.*, **17**, 371 (1909); *Chem. Abstr.*, **4**, 763 (1910).

159. Humnicki, W., *Roczniki Chem.*, **11**, 674 (1931); *Chem. Abstr.*, **26**, 5556 (1932).
160. Naegeli, C., and A. Tyabji, *Helv. Chim. Acta*, **17**, 931 (1934); *Chem. Abstr.*, **29**, 1074[9] (1935).
161. Fry, A., *J. Am. Chem. Soc.*, **75**, 2686 (1953).
162. Krafft, F., and H. Karstens, *Ber.*, **25**, 452 (1892).
163. Parker, J. A., J. J. Thomas, C. L. Zeise, E. A. Peterson, and R. P. Dryden, paper presented at the 132nd Meeting of the American Chemical Society, New York, N. Y., Sept. 8–13, 1957.
164. Campbell, T. W., V. S. Foldi, and R. G. Parrish, *J. Appl. Polymer Sci.*, **2**, 81 (1959).
165. Esser, H., K. Rastädter, and G. Reuter, *Chem. Ber.*, **89**, 685 (1956).
166. Davies, A. G., and K. J. Hunter, *J. Chem. Soc.*, **1953**, 1808.
167a. O'Brien, E. L., F. M. Beringer, and R. B. Mesrobian, *J. Am. Chem. Soc.*, **79**, 6238 (1957).
167b. O'Brien, E. L., F. M. Beringer, and R. B. Mesrobian, *J. Am. Chem. Soc.*, **81**, 1506 (1959).
168. Pedersen, C. J., *J. Org. Chem.*, **23**, 252 (1958).
169. Bieber, T. I., *J. Am. Chem. Soc.*, **75**, 1405 (1953).
170. Fox, R. B., and W. J. Bailey, *J. Org. Chem.*, **25**, 1447 (1960).
171. Astakhin, V. V., I. P. Losev, and K. A. Andrianov, *Dokl. Akad. Nauk SSSR*, **113**, 581 (1957); *Chem. Abstr.*, **51**, 14582i (1957).
172. Astakhin, V. V., I. P. Losev, and K. A. Andrianov, *Zh. Obsch. Khim.*, **29**, 904 (1959); *Chem. Abstr.*, **54**, 1371f (1960).
173. Upson, R. W., U. S. Patent 2,517,944 (to E. I. duPont deNemours & Co.), Aug. 8, 1950; *Chem. Abstr.*, **44**, 10378a (1950).
174. Aries, R. S., U. S. Patent 2,931,831 Apr. 5, 1960; *Chem. Abstr.*, **54**, 15314c (1960).
175. Aries, R. S., U. S. Patent 2,945,841, July 19, 1960; *Chem. Abstr.*, **54**, 23426i (1960).
176. Greber, G., and S. Jäger, *Makromol. Chem.*, **57**, 150 (1962).
177. Knoth, W. H., U. S. Patent 2,983,744 (to E. I. duPont deNemours & Co.), May 9, 1961; *Chem. Abstr.*, **55**, 22132i (1961).
178. Andrianov, K. A., and L. I. Makarova, *Vysokomolekul. Soedin.*, **3**, 966 (1961); *J. Polymer Sci.*, **59**, S50, (1962).
179. Davis, T. L., and F. Ebersole, *J. Am. Chem. Soc.*, **56**, 885 (1934).
180. Naegeli, C., A. Tyabji, and L. Conrad, *Helv. Chim. Acta*, **21**, 1127 (1938); *Chem. Abstr.*, **33**, 540[3] (1939).
181. Scholl, R., and K. Holdermann, *Ann.*, **345**, 376 (1907).
182. Stoutland, O., L. Helgen, and C. L. Agre, *J. Org. Chem.*, **24**, 818 (1959).
183. Athey, R. J., *Ind. Eng. Chem.*, **52**, 611 (1960).
184. Sampson, A. J., and C. F. Blaich, Jr., paper presented before the Division of Rubber Chemistry, American Chemical Society, Buffalo, N. Y., May 4–6, 1960.
185. Blitz, H., and A. Beck, *Ber.*, **58B**, 2187 (1925).
186. Kühn, B., and E. Hentschel, *Ber.*, **21**, 504 (1888).
187. Lakra, H., and F. B. Dains, *J. Am. Chem. Soc.*, **51**, 2220 (1929).
188. Curtius, T., and A. Burkhardt, *J. Prakt. Chem.* [2], **58**, 205 (1898).
189. Gelderen, M. J. v., *Rec. Trav. Chim.*, **52**, 979 (1933); *Chem. Abstr.*, **28**, 4406[2] (1934).
190. Pacilly, C. C. P., *Rec. Trav. Chim.*, **55**, 101 (1936); *Chem. Abstr.*, **30**, 4835[8] (1936).

191. Campbell, T. W., V. S. Foldi, and J. Farago, *J. Appl. Polymer Sci.*, **2**, 155 (1959).
192. White, H. C., and F. W. Bergstrom, *J. Org. Chem.*, **7**, 497 (1942).
193. Paal, C., *Ber.*, **27**, 974 (1894).
194. Schultz, E. M., *J. Am. Chem. Soc.*, **69**, 1056 (1947).
195. Kühn, B., *Ber.*, **17**, 2880 (1884).
196. Inukai, K., Y. Maki, and T. Ueda, *Repts. Govt. Ind. Research Inst., Nagoya*, **1**, 176 (1952); *Chem. Abstr.*, **50**, 3332f (1956).
197. Fischer, E., *Ber.*, **22**, 1930 (1889).
198. Busch, M., G. Blume, and E. Pungs, *J. Prakt. Chem.*, **79**, 513 (1909); *Chem. Abstr.*, **4**, 898 (1910).
199. French, H. E., and A. F. Wirtel, *J. Am. Chem. Soc.*, **48**, 1736 (1936).
200. Wiley, P. F., *J. Am. Chem. Soc.*, **71**, 1310 (1949).
201. Wiley, P. F., *J. Am. Chem. Soc.*, **71**, 3746 (1949).
202a. Kurzer, F., *J. Chem. Soc.*, **1951**, 1258.
202b. Kurzer, F., *Chem. Rev.*, **50**, 1 (1952).
203. Petersen, S., *Chem. Ber.*, **83**, 551 (1950).
204. Roth, J. S., and E. F. Degering, *J. Am. Chem. Soc.*, **67**, 126 (1945).
205. Weiner, M. L., *J. Org. Chem.*, **25**, 2245 (1960).
206. Majewski, T. E., Ph.D. Thesis, Univ. of Delaware, 1960; *Dissertation Abstr.*, **21**, 2483 (1961).
207. Bennet, W. B., J. H. Saunders, and E. E. Hardy, paper presented at the Alabama Academy of Sciences, Tuscaloosa, Ala., April 1954.
208. Kogon, I. C., *J. Org. Chem.*, **24**, 83 (1959).
209. Pinner, A., *Ber.*, **23**, 2923 (1890).
210. Caldwell, W. A., J. Chapman, H. W. Goodwin, and F. J. Wilson, *J. Chem. Soc.*, **1932**, 2086.
211. Minunni, G., and S. D'Urso, *Gazz. Chim. Ital.*, **58**, 808 (1928); *Chem. Abstr.*, **23**, 3681 (1929).
212. Slotta, K. H., and R. Tschesche, *Ber.*, **62B**, 137 (1929).
213. Korshak, V. V., N. I. Bekasova, V. A. Zamyatina, and G. I. Aristarkhova, *Vysokomolekul. Soedin.*, **3**, 521 (1961); *J. Polymer Sci.*, **59**, S12 (1962).
214. Korshak, V. V., V. A. Zamyatina, N. I. Bekasova, Ma Zhui-Zhan, *Vysokomolekul. Soedin.*, **3**, 525 (1961); *J. Polymer Sci.*, **59**, S12 (1962).
215. Foldi, V. S., and T. W. Campbell, *J. Polymer Sci.*, **56**, 1 (1962).
216. Campbell, T. W., and E. A. Tomic, *J. Polymer Sci.*, **62**, 379 (1962).
217. Coenen, M., *Ber.*, **80**, 546 (1947).
218. Mumm, O., H. Hinz, and J. Diederichsen, *Ber.*, **72B**, 2107 (1939).
219. Dieckmann, W., J. Hoppe, and R. Stein, *Ber.*, **37**, 4627 (1904).
220. Boyd, R. N., and R. Leshin, *J. Am. Chem. Soc.*, **75**, 2762 (1953).
221. Michael, A., *Ber.*, **38**, 22 (1905).
222. Mukaiyama, T., and Y. Hoshino, *J. Am. Chem. Soc.*, **82**, 5339 (1960).
223. Dieckmann, W., and K. Kämmerer, *Ber.*, **38**, 2977 (1905).
224. Dieckmann, W., and K. Kämmerer, *Ber.*, **40**, 3737 (1907).
225. Catlin, W. E., U. S. Patent 2,284,637 (to E. I. duPont deNemours & Co.), June 2, 1942.
226. Bayer, O., BIOS Report No. C22/4495, Interrogation of O. Bayer, 1946.
227. Dyer, E., and D. W. Osborne, *J. Polymer Sci.*, **47**, 361 (1960).
228. Snape, H. L., *Ber.*, **18**, 2428 (1885).

229. Rivier, H., *Bull. Soc. Chim.* [4], **1,** 733 (1907); *Chem. Abstr.*, **1,** 3004 (1907).
230. Morgan, P. W., and S. L. Kwolek, *J. Polymer Sci.*, **40,** 299 (1959).
231. Wittbecker, E. L., and P. W. Morgan, *J. Polymer Sci.*, **40,** 289 (1959).
232. Wittbecker, E. L., and M. Katz, *J. Polymer Sci.*, **40,** 367 (1959).
233a. Dyer, E., and J. F. Glenn, *J. Am. Chem. Soc.*, **79,** 366 (1957).
233b. Dyer, E., J. F. Glenn, and E. G. Lendrat, *J. Am. Chem. Soc.*, **26,** 2919 (1961).
234. Goldschmidt, H., and A. Meissler, *Ber.*, **23,** 253 (1890).
235. Seeger, N. V., and T. G. Mastin U. S. Patent 2,764,592 (to Goodyear Tire and Rubber Co.), Sept. 25, 1956; *Chem. Abstr.*, **51,** 765f (1957).
236. Malootian, M. H., *Electron. Equipment Eng.*, **4,** (7), 2 (1956).
237. Berenbaum, M. B., in *Polyethers*, N. G. Gaylord, ed., High Polymer Series, Vol. XIII, Part III, Interscience, New York, 1962, p. 85.
238. Mitchell, A., III, U. S. Patent 2,814,600 (to E. I. duPont deNemours & Co.), Nov. 26, 1957; *Chem. Abstr.*, **52,** 4231b (1958).
239. Jackson, H. E., and Imperial Chemical Industries, British Patent 599,177, Mar. 5, 1948; *Chem. Abstr.*, **42,** 7331f (1948).
240. Iwakura, Y., T. Hori, K. Suzuki, T. Wakasugi, and G. Kobayashi, *Kogyo Kasaku Zasshi*, **59,** 564 (1956); *Rubber Chem. Technol.*, **33,** 416 (1960); *Chem. Abstr.*, **52,** 3728c (1958).
241. Buckley, G. D., H. A. Piggott, and A. J. E. Welch, *J. Chem. Soc.*, **1945,** 864.
242. Gal, M. H., *Bull. Soc. Chim.*, **6,** 437 (1866).
243. Schulz, R. C., and H. Hartmann, *Makromol. Chem.*, **55,** 227 (1962).
244. Baker, J. W., and J. B. Holdsworth, *J. Chem. Soc.*, **1945,** 724.
245. Pudovik, A. N., *Usp. Khim.*, **23,** 547 (1954); *Chem. Abstr.*, **49,** 8788i (1955).
246. Fox, R. B., and D. L. Venezky, *J. Am. Chem. Soc.*, **78,** 1661 (1956).
247. Reetz, T., D. H. Chadwick, E. E. Hardy, and S. Kaufman, *J. Am. Chem. Soc.*, **77,** 3813 (1955).
248. Pudovik, A. N., I. V. Konovalova, and R. E. Krivonosova, *Zh. Obshch. Khim.*, **26,** 3110 (1956); *Chem. Abstracts*, **51,** 8642e (1957).
249. Pudovik, A. N., and A. V. Kuznetsova, *Zh. Obshch. Khim.*, **25,** 1369 (1955); *Chem. Abstr.*, **50,** 4808b (1956).
250. Buckler, S. A., *J. Org. Chem.*, **24,** 1460 (1959).
251. Slotta, K. H., and R. Tschesche, *Ber.*, **60B,** 295 (1927).
252. Slotta, K. H., and L. Lorenz, *Ber.*, **58B,** 1320 (1925).
253. Slotta, K. H., and R. Tschesche, *Ber.*, **60B,** 1021 (1927).
254. Steinkopf, W., and H. M. Daege, *Ber.*, **44,** 497 (1911).
255. Glemser, O., *Angew. Chem.*, **75,** 697 (1963).
256. Reilly, C. B., and M. Orchin, paper presented at the 130th Meeting of the American Chemical Society, Atlantic City, N. J., Sept. 16–21, 1956.
257. Hudson, G. A., J. C. Hixenbaugh, E. R. Wells, J. H. Saunders, and E. E. Hardy, *Offic. Dig. Federation Soc. Paint Technol.*, **32,** 213 (1960); *Chem. Abstr.*, **54,** 21783b (1960).
258. Bunge, W., K. H. Mielke, and F. Möller, U. S. Patent 2,886,555 (to Farbenfabriken Bayer A.-G.), May 12, 1959; *Chem. Abstr.*, **54,** 1926g (1960).
259. Hudson, G. A., Mobay Chemical Company, private communication.
260. Iwakura, Y., and K. Hayaski, *Yuki Gosei Kagaku Kyokai Shi*, **16,** 533 (1958); *Chem. Abstr.*, **53,** 1200b (1959).
261. Dreyfus, H., U. S. Patent 2,568,885 (to Celanese Corp. of America), Sept. 25, 1951; *Chem. Abstr.*, **46,** 1808h (1952).

262. Blair, J. S., and G. E. P. Smith, Jr., *J. Am. Chem. Soc.*, **56,** 907 (1934).
263. Frentzel, W., *Ber.*, **21,** 411 (1888).
264. Hofmann, A. W., *Ber.*, **3,** 761 (1870).
265. Hofmann, A. W., *Ber.*, **4,** 246 (1871).
266. Lyons, J. M., and R. H. Thompson, *J. Chem. Soc.*, **1950,** 1971.
267. Raiford, L. C., and H. B. Freyermuth, *J. Org. Chem.*, **8,** 230 (1943).
268. Snape, H. L., *J. Chem. Soc.*, **49,** 254 (1886).
269. Speranza, G. P., and W. J. Peppel, *J. Org. Chem.*, **23,** 1922 (1958).
270. Hofmann, A. W., *Ann. Suppl.*, **1,** 57 (1861).
271. Gaylord, N. G., and J. H. Crowdle, *Chem. Ind.* (*London*), **1955,** 145; *Chem. Abstr.*, **49,** 8902a (1955).
272. Case, L. C., *Nature*, **183,** 675 (1959).
273. Iwakura, Y., and Y. Ishizuka, *Kobunshi Kagaku*, **4,** 97 (1947); *Chem. Abstr.*, **45,** 2711 (1951).
274. Taub, B., and C. E. McGinn, *Dyestuffs*, **42,** 263 (1958).
275. Bayer, O., BIOS Final Report No. 719 "Interview with Professor Otto Bayer," July 1946; PB 45246.
276. Slotta, K. H., and R. Tschesche, *Ber.*, **60B,** 301 (1927).
277. Brauner, B., *Ber.*, **12,** 1874 (1879).
278. Havekoss, H., "Polymerization of Diisocyanates," PB Report 73894, Frames 4709–18, Apr. 10, 1942.
279. Hofmann, A. W., *Ber.*, **18,** 764 (1885).
280. Hofmann, A. W., *Jahresber. Fortschritte Chem.*, **1862,** 335.
281. Bailey, J. R., and A. T. McPherson, *J. Am. Chem. Soc.*, **39,** 1322 (1917).
282. Balon, W. J., U. S. Patent 2,801,244 (to E. I. duPont deNemours & Co.), July 30, 1957; *Chem. Abstr.*, **51,** 18016d (1957).
283. Laakso, T. M., and D. D. Reynolds, *J. Am. Chem. Soc.*, **79,** 5717 (1957).
284. Farbenfabriken Bayer A.-G. (by H. Kleiner, H. Havekoss, and F. v. Spulak) German Patent 872,618, Nov. 25, 1941; *Chem. Zentr.*, **125,** 7572 (1954).
285. Kogon, I. C., *J. Org. Chem.*, **23,** 1594 (1958).
286. Jones, J. I., and N. G. Savill, *J. Chem. Soc.*, **1957,** 4392.
287. Tsuzuki, R., K. Ichikawa, and M. Kase, *J. Org. Chem.*, **25,** 1009 (1960).
288. Kogon, I. C., *J. Org. Chem.*, **26,** 3004 (1961).
289. Davis, A., *Makromol. Chem.*, **66,** 196 (1963).
290. Sidgwick, N. V., *The Organic Chemistry of Nitrogen*, The Clarendon Press, Oxford, 1937.
291. Rapoport, L., and E. M. Smolin, s-*Triazines and Derivatives*, The Chemistry of Heterocyclic Compounds Series, Interscience, New York, 1959.
292. Kruger, R., *J. Prakt. Chem.* [3], **42,** 473 (1890).
293. Schaefer, F. C., and E. K. Drechsel, U. S. Patent, 2,580,468 (to American Cyanamid Co.), Jan. 1, 1952; *Chem. Abstr.*, **46,** 7117c (1952).
294. Stolle, R., *Ber.*, **41,** 1125 (1908).
295. Bortnick, N., L. S. Luskin, M. D. Hurwitz, and A. W. Rytina, *J. Am. Chem. Soc.*, **78,** 4358 (1956).
296. Blohm, H. W., and E. I. Becker, *Chem. Rev.*, **51,** 471 (1952).
297. Dyer, E., and G. C. Wright, *J. Am. Chem. Soc.*, **81,** 2138 (1959).
298. Dyer, E., G. E. Newborn, Jr., and G. C. Wright, paper presented at the First Delaware Science Symposium, Feb. 15, 1958.

299. Dyer, E., and G. E. Newborn, Jr., *J. Am. Chem. Soc.*, **80**, 5495 (1958).
300. Swerdloff, J., and S. B. McFarlane, paper presented at the 126th Meeting of the American Chemical Society, New York, N. Y., Sept. 12–17, 1954.
301. Mukaiyama, T., and Y. Hoshino, *J. Am. Chem. Soc.*, **78**, 1946 (1956).
302. Mukaiyama, T., and M. Iwanami, *J. Am. Chem. Soc.*, **79**, 73 (1957).
303. Mukaiyama, T., S. Motoki, and Y. Hamada, *Bull. Chem. Soc. Japan*, **26**, 49 (1953); *Chem. Abstr.*, **48**, 3770c (1954).
304. Gaylord, N. G., and C. E. Sroog, *J. Org. Chem.*, **18**, 1632 (1953).
305. Gaylord, N. G., *J. Org. Chem.*, **25**, 1874 (1960).
306. Saunders, J. H., S. Steingiser, P. G. Gemeinhardt, A. S. Morecroft, and E. E. Hardy, *J. Chem. Eng. Data Ser.*, **3**, 153 (1958).
307. Dyer, E., and G. W. Bartels, Jr., *J. Am. Chem. Soc.*, **76**, 591 (1954).
308. Bennet, W. B., J. H. Saunders, and E. E. Hardy, *J. Am. Chem. Soc.*, **75**, 2101 (1953).
309. Hoshino, T., T. Mukaiyama, and H. Hoshino, *J. Am. Chem. Soc.*, **74**, 3097 (1952); *Bull. Chem. Soc. Japan*, **25**, 392, 396 (1952); *Chem. Abstr.*, **48**, 5132a (1954).
310. Mukaiyama, T., *Bull. Chem. Soc. Japan*, **28**, 253 (1935); *Chem. Abstr.*, **52**, 3708a (1958).
311. Mukaiyama, T., S. Ozaki, and T. Hoshino, *Bull. Chem. Soc. Japan*, **27**, 578 (1954); *Chem. Abstr.*, **49**, 13900f (1955).
312. Mukaiyama, T., S. Ozaki, and Y. Kobayashi, *Bull. Chem. Soc. Japan*, **29**, 51 (1956); *Chem. Abstr.*, **50**, 13775b (1956).
313. Ozaki, S., and T. Nagoya, *Bull. Chem. Soc. Japan*, **30**, 444 (1957); *Chem. Abstr.*, **52**, 3708c (1958).
314. Mukaiyama, T., and T. Matsunaga, *J. Am. Chem. Soc.*, **75**, 6209 (1953).
315. Iwakura, Y., and K. Yoneshima, *Nippon Kagaku Zasshi*, **70**, 151 (1949); *Chem. Abstr.*, **45**, 6583a (1951).
316. Magee, E. M., and F. Daniels, *J. Am. Chem. Soc.*, **79**, 829 (1957).
317. Davis, T. L., and K. C. Blanchard, *J. Am. Chem. Soc.*, **45**, 1816 (1923).
318. Davis, T. L., and H. W. Underwood, Jr., *J. Am. Chem. Soc.*, **44**, 2595 (1922).
319. Rinke, H., H. Schild, and W. Siefken, U. S. Patent 2,511,544 (to Alien Property Custodian), June 13, 1950; *Chem. Abstr.*, **44**, 8699a (1950).
320. Dombrow, B., *Polyurethanes*, Reinhold, New York, 1957.
321. Müller, E., in Houben-Weyl, *Methoden der Organischen Chemie*, Vol. XIV, Part II, George Thieme, Stuttgart, Germany 1963, Chapter A_2 III.
322. Frisch, K. C., and S. Davis, in *Polyethers*, N. Gaylord, ed., High Polymer Series, Vol. XIII, Part I, Interscience, New York, 1963, Chap. VI.
323. Baker, J. W., and J. B. Holdsworth, *J. Chem. Soc.*, **1947**, 713.
324. Baker, J. W., and D. N. Bailey, *J. Chem. Soc.*, **1957**, 4652, 4663.
325. Farkas, A., G. A. Mills, W. E. Erner, and J. B. Maerker, *J. Chem. Eng. Data*, **4**, 334 (1959).
326. Farkas, A., and P. W. Hill, *Mod. Plastics*, **37**, (6), 107 (1960).
327. Britain, J. W., and P. G. Gemeinhardt, *J. Appl. Polymer Sci.*, **4**, 207 (1960).
328. Wolfe, H. W., Jr., E. I. duPont de Nemours & Co., Elastomer Foam Bulletin "Tin Catalyst Activity in Urethane Foam," Feb. 24, 1961.
329. Farkas, A., and G. A. Mills, in *Advances in Catalysis*, D. D. Eley, P. W. Selwood, and P. B. Weisz, eds., Vol. XIII, Academic Press, New York, N. Y., 1962, Chap. 6.

330. Damusis, A., J. M. McClellan, H. G. Wissman, C. W. Hamilton, and K. C. Frisch, *Ind. Eng. Chem. Prod. Res. Develop.*, **1**, 269 (1962).
331. Rinke, H., *Angew. Chem. Intern. Ed. Engl.*, **1**, 419 (1962); *Rubber Chem. Technol.*, **36**, 719 (1963).
332. Farbenfabriken Bayer A.-G. German Patent 863,403 (by E. Müller, O. Bayer, and H. F. Piepenbrink), Jan. 19, 1953.
333. Ogden, W. G., *Rubber World*, **136**, 537 (1957).
334. Gruber, E. E., and O. C. Keplinger, *Ind. Eng. Chem.*, **51**, 151 (1959).
335. Farmer, E. H., G. F. Bloomfield, A. Sundralingam, and D. A. Sutton, *Trans. Faraday Soc.*, **38**, 348 (1942); *Rubber Chem. Technol.*, **15**, 756 (1942).
336. Farmer, E. H., and D. Sutton, *J. Chem. Soc.*, **1942**, 139.
337. Benning, A. F., U. S. Patent 2,948,707 (to E. I. du Pont de Nemours & Co.), Aug. 9, 1960; *Chem. Abstr.*, **54**, 23402c (1960).
338. Koller, C. R., U. S. Patent 2,813,776 (to E. I. du Pont de Nemours & Co.), Nov. 19, 1957; *Chem. Abstr.*, **52**, 3388i (1958).
339. Steuber, W., U. S. Patent 2,813,775 (to E. I. du Pont de Nemours & Co.), Nov. 19, 1957; *Chem. Abstr.*, **52**, 3388g (1958).
340. Steuber, W., U. S. Patent 2,935,372 (to E. I. du Pont de Nemours & Co.), May 3, 1960; *Chem. Abstr.*, **54**, 15989c (1960).
341. Farbenfabriken Bayer A.-G., German Patent 826,641 (by E. Windemuth) Jan. 3, 1952; *Chem. Abstr.*, **52**, 7776h (1958).
342. Kohrn, R. C., D. G. Slovin, and F. L. Bliven, U. S. Patent 2,953,839 (to United States Rubber Co.), Sept. 27, 1960.
343. Kohrn, R. C., D. G. Slovin, and F. L. Bliven, U. S. Patent 3,009,762 (to United States Rubber Co.), Nov. 21, 1961.
344. Slovin, D. G., U. S. Patent 3,009,765 (to United States Rubber Co.) Nov. 21, 1961.
345. Urs, V. S., U. S. Patent 3,009,764 (to United States Rubber Co.) Nov. 21, 1961; *Chem. Abstr.*, **56**, 11847e (1962).
346. Schollenberger, C. S., H. Scott, and G. R. Moore, *Rubber World*, **137**, 549 (1958).
347. Pigott, K. A., J. W. Britain, W. Archer, B. F. Frye, R. J. Cote, and J. H. Saunders, *Ind. Eng. Chem. Prod. Res. Develop.*, **1**, 28 (1962).
348. Farbenfabriken Bayer A.-G., German Patent 831,772 (by E. Müller, H. F. Piepenbrink, F. Schmidt, and E. Weinbrenner), Feb. 18, 1952.

Chapter XII

SURFACE REACTIONS

D. J. ANGIER

Ethicon, Inc.

The chemical reactions occurring at the surfaces of polymers may be classified into two general categories. First, undesirable deleterious reactions occur through interaction of the surface with its environment, often referred to as aging or weathering. Such unwanted reactions are not included in this chapter. The second category, embracing deliberate and planned chemical modifications, comprises two parts: interpolymerization by energetic or chemical means and standard chemical reactions at the polymer surface.

First, what is meant by surface? Ideally, such a reaction is one involving only those polymer chains directly on the surface, i.e., approximately 10^{-7} cm. in depth. If the writer were to employ this yardstick, this chapter would indeed be very short. The more practical interpretation employed includes those reactions occurring predominantly in the surface region, and not homogeneously through the polymeric substrate, i.e., the so-called topographical reactions. As a further refinement, the surface modification is carried out on the final form of the substrate. Thus, for example, the chlorination of a fine suspension of polyethylene is excluded, since the polymer is subsequently worked to its final shape, while chlorination of the film is included.

Obviously, whether or not the modification is confined to the surface region depends a great deal on the conditions and extent of the reaction employed. The writer has, therefore, confined the text to reported reactions which appear to be at the surface and has resisted the impulse to include those which would be topographical if conditions were to be changed.

In general, surface modifications have been carried out on films and textile fibers, the governing principle being to modify the surface without significantly altering the physical properties of the substrate. It is often found that when the shaped object is modified homogeneously, there is a severe loss in physical properties.

Utilization of reactions confined to the surface region is becoming increasingly widespread. Fibers have been modified to improve feel, washability, dye retention, antistatic properties, and abrasion. Surface treated films, particularly polyethylene, have resulted in improved scuff resistance, printability, permeability to liquids and vapors, solvent resistance, and adhesion.

The first section of the chapter deals with radiochemical interpolymerization in terms of the more important reaction parameters and outlines the basic requirements for surface reactions. The second section includes interpolymers initiated by chemical means, while the final area outlines the more conventional chemical reactions that have been employed.

A. SURFACE GRAFTING BY IRRADIATION

The formation of block (linear) or graft (branched) interpolymers (as discussed in an earlier chapter) depends on the effect of irradiation on the polymer. It appears that, under vacuum, when no α-methylenic hydrogen is present, scission occurs (1) by the rearrangement shown in eq. (1).

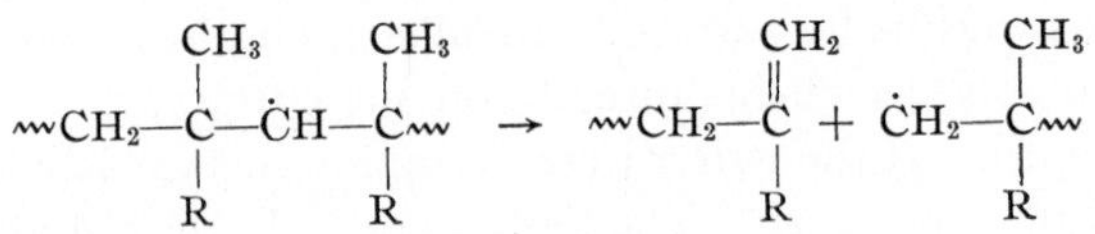

(1)

TABLE XII-1
Effect of Irradiation of Polymers in Vacuum

Polymer	Predominant effect	Reference
Polytetrafluoroethylene	Scission	2
Poly(methyl methacrylate)	"	3
Cellulose	"	2
Nylon	"	5
Polytrifluorochloroethylene	"	2
Polyethylene	Crosslinking	3
Polypropylene	"	3
Poly(vinyl chloride) (in air)	"	6
Poly(vinyl alcohol) (+ trace H_2O)	"	5
Polyacrylonitrile	"	3
Polyvinylpyrrolidone	"	7

In the presence of monomer, it is reasonable to assume that linear interpolymers would be formed. Generally, when an α-methylenic hydrogen is present in the backbone, crosslinking occurs; hence graft polymers would be formed (2). Heats of polymerization are generally higher for those polymers which crosslink (3).

The presence of oxygen, however, may change the reaction. For example, it has been reported that on γ-irradiation up to 7 Mrad, nylon degrades *in vacuo* but crosslinks in air (4). The predominating reactions upon irradiation *in vacuo* for most of the polymers included in this text are given in Table XII-1. For more detailed and extensive literature on the effect of irradiation on polymers, the reader is referred to other texts (8,9) as well as Chapters XIII-C and IX-A. For reasons of brevity and in accordance with common misuse, the writer has taken the liberty of using the term "graft" to include both linear and branched structures. With the exception of solution properties, the distinction between linear and branched interpolymers is probably very fine.

Two units of dose are employed in the literature, rep (Roentgen equivalent physical) and rad. The latter is defined as a unit of dose of any irradiation resulting in the absorption of 100 ergs per gram of absorber. The use of rep is gradually being discontinued and is no longer recognized by the ICRU as a unit of absorbed dose. Since both, as measured by Fricke dosimetry, differ only by 5%, and taking into account the inherent errors in the measurement of dose, rep has been directly converted to rad for conformity.

The efficiency of grafting depends on the relative susceptibilities of the monomer and polymer to the ionizing energy. If the G value (number of radicals formed per 100 e.v. of adsorbed ionizing energy) for the monomer is much greater than that of the polymer, homopolymerization will predominate, unless the monomer contains an inhibitor which cannot diffuse into the polymeric substrate (10). It is generally assumed that the G value of a

TABLE XII-2

G Values of Various Polymers (Monomers)

Monomer	*G* value	Reference
Styrene	1.6	11
Acrylonitrile	2.7	11
Methyl acrylate	23.5	11
Methyl methacrylate	27.5	11
Vinyl acetate	33.0	11
Isobutene(polyethylene)	5–6	12
N-Vinylpyrrolidone	15.0	13

polymer is the same as that of its monomer. Table XII-2 presents G values for various polymers. Owing to the chemical analytical difficulties involved, no G value is available for polytetrafluoroethylene. Due to possible energy exchange reactions, grafting by simultaneous irradiation of monomer and polymer does not appear to be a simple function of the relative G values (14).

It has recently been reported that polyethylene grafted at 25°C. with mixtures of styrene and methyl methacrylate, 4-vinylpyridine, or acrylonitrile contained far less styrene than expected from the respective monomer reactivity ratios. This anomaly, compounded by the fact that styrene is far more soluble in polyethylene than the other monomers used, was not explained (15).

1. Requirements for Surface Grafting

The primary requirement is, of course, a low solubility of the monomer in the base polymer. This may be aided by use of a nonswelling solvent for the polymer. Generally, as grafting proceeds, monomer penetration will be more readily effected, most monomers being solvents for their own polymer. At this point, the reaction may become diffusion controlled and sometimes may be confined only to the surface zone by hindering such diffusion. Low temperatures, high degrees of crystallinity, low monomer concentrations, and high rates of monomer consumption favor this end. In special cases, the susceptibility of the monomer (and hence its polymer) to irradiation is much greater than the substrate, and then grafting outward rather than inward will result. If low energy of penetration is used, the reaction is, of necessity, confined to the surface.

Five general methods of irradiation grafting have been employed: (*a*) simultaneous irradiation of polymer in contact with monomer; (*b*) irradiation of a polymer predipped in monomer; (*c*) preirradiation of polymer (in absence of oxygen) followed by exposure to monomer (this method, while yielding less homopolymer, is less efficient than *a*; consequently, higher doses are required, and this may result in greater damage to substrate); (*d*) preirradiation of the polymer in air to form peroxides, and their subsequent decomposition in the presence of monomer; (*e*) simultaneous irradiation of a polymer in the presence of a second polymer or nonmonomer, or preirradiation of a polymer with subsequent addition of a polymer or nonmonomer.

The first three methods will be jointly discussed in terms of the reaction parameters outlined above. The last two methods are more conveniently treated separately as shown in TableXII–4.

2. Initial Monomer Penetration

The following systems exemplify the effect of radiation grafting when the initial penetration or wetting of the monomer into the substrate is negligible.

a. Polytetrafluoroethylene–Vinyl Acetate

This system was studied kinetically by Restaino and Reed (16). Sheets of polytetrafluoroethylene were immersed in vinyl acetate, degassed and irradiated with γ-rays with intensities varying from 15 to 460 Krad/hr. The process is free radical in nature, and hydroquinone retards grafting when present in the monomer. In addition, Schneider (17) found polytetrafluoroethylene to be paramagnetic after irradiation *in vacuo*. Restaino and Reed showed that the rate of grafting was independent of initial film thickness; and hence dependent only on surface area, the main criterion for surface grafting (Fig. XII-1).

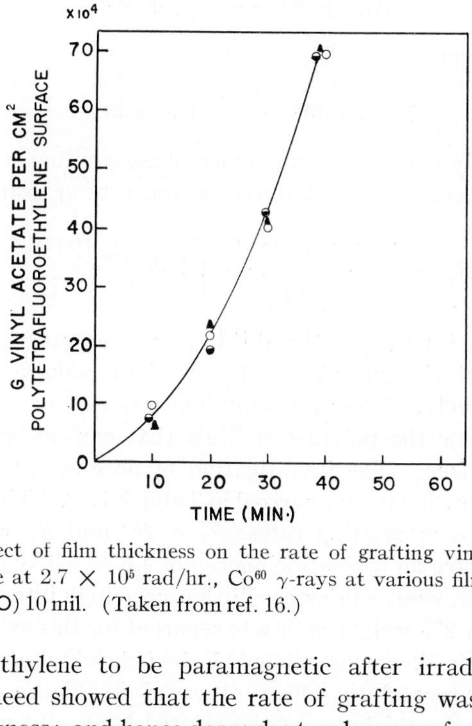

Fig. XII-1. Effect of film thickness on the rate of grafting vinyl acetate to polytetrafluoroethylene at 2.7 × 10^5 rad/hr., Co^{60} γ-rays at various film thicknesses: (▲) 3 mil; (◒) 5 mil; (O) 10 mil. (Taken from ref. 16.)

The kinetic scheme proposed is shown in eqs. (2)–(7).

Polymer radical formation:

$$P\text{\textasciitilde\textasciitilde} \xrightarrow{I} R\cdot \tag{2}$$

Monomer radical formation:

$$\mathrm{M} \xrightarrow{I} \mathrm{M}\cdot \tag{3}$$

Graft propagation:

$$\mathrm{R}\cdot + \mathrm{M} \xrightarrow{K_p} \mathrm{R}_x\cdot \tag{4}$$

Graft polymer formation:

$$\mathrm{R}_x\cdot + \mathrm{R}_y\cdot \xrightarrow{K_t} P_g \tag{5}$$

Monomer transfer:

$$\mathrm{R}_z\cdot + \mathrm{M} \xrightarrow{K_{tr,m}} \mathrm{P}_g + \mathrm{M}\cdot \tag{6}$$

Polymer transfer:

$$P_g + \mathrm{M}\cdot \xrightarrow{K_{tr,p}} \mathrm{R}_u\cdot + \mathrm{M} \tag{7}$$

Assuming steady state in the monomer phase and nonsteady conditions in the substrate, eq. (8) was derived for the rate of grafting, R_g, where

$$R_g = \frac{K_p \mathrm{I}^{1/2} G_m [\mathrm{M}]^{3/2}}{(2K_t)^{1/2}} \left[1 + \frac{G_p\ [\mathrm{P}]}{G_m\ [\mathrm{M}]}\right]^{1/2} \tag{8}$$

$t > 30$ sec., I is the intensity, [P] and [M] are concentrations of polymer and monomer, respectively, and G_m and G_p are the G values of monomer and polymer, respectively. The same equation was derived assuming steady-state conditions for the polymer radicals that can initiate grafting, i.e., those on the surface. The investigation of dose rate, temperature, and monomer concentration is summarized in Table XII-3. The results showed these relationships of grafting rates: $R_i \propto I^{1/2}$ and $R_g \propto [\mathrm{M}]^{3/2}$ (eq. 8). Arrhenius plots gave an activation energy of 4.6 ± 0.4 kcal./mole, in good agreement with previous workers. With a very high intensity of 1 Mrad/min. for 1 min., a 2% weight gain was reported for this system (18). The resulting surface is then more amenable to poly(vinyl alcohol)-based adhesives. The autocatalytic effect observed in Figure XII-3 and the determination of the thickness of the grafted layer (19) will be described later.

Physical data for films of polytetrafluoroethylene grafted with 5.9% poly(vinyl acetate) have been reported, revealing no significant change in tensile properties as shown in Table XII-4.

TABLE XII-3
Effect of Temperature, Dose Rate, and Monomer Concentration on the Rate of Grafting Vinyl Acetate to 3-mil Polytetrafluoroethylene[a]

Dose rate $\times 10^{-4}$, rad/hr.	Molar concn. of vinyl acetate in ethyl acetate	Temperature, °C.	Initial rate, % graft/min.	Rate $\times 10^4$ / Intensity$^{1/2}$	Rate $\times 10^3$ / [Monomer]$^{3/2}$
		A. Effect of Intensity			
1.5	7	20	0.042	3.4	
7.0	7	20	0.133	5.0	
15.9	7	20	0.185	4.7	
27.0	7	20	0.256	4.8	
46.0	7	20	0.475	5.4	
		B. Effect of Temperature			
27.0	10.8	5	0.156		
27.0	10.8	20	0.310		
27.0	10.8	40	0.385		
27.0	10.8	59	0.500		
		C. Effect of Monomer Concentration			
27.0	10.8	20	0.310		8.8
27.0	7.0	20	0.256		7.3
27.0	5.0	20	0.105		9.3
27.0	3.0	20	0.050		9.6
27.0	2.0	20	0.022		7.5

[a] Taken from ref. 16.

TABLE XII-4
Effect of Grafting 5.9% Vinyl Acetate to Polytetrafluoroethylene[a]

Sample	Tensile strength, kg./cm.^{2}
Control, unirradiated	126
Control, 58,000 rad	116
Graft, 58,000 rad	119

[a] Taken from ref. 19.

b. Polytetrafluoroethylene–Styrene

Ballantine et al. (20) found that surface grafting occurred when films of polytetrafluoroethylene were immersed in styrene and subjected to γ-irradiation from a Co^{60} source. The amount of graft formed was, within certain experimental limitations, independent of the thickness of the film.

With 10% styrene grafted on to the surface, peel strength to an adhesive tape was improved 2.2-fold (21). When the monomer is in the vapor phase, less homopolymerization and increased grafting per unit dose have been reported (22,23).

c. Miscellaneous Polytetrafluoroethylene Grafts

Polytetrafluoroethylene has been grafted with acrylonitrile in the liquid (20) and vapor phase (22,23), also with divinylbenzene, α-chloroacetic acid and acrylic acid (24). At the dose rates used (>10^4 rad/hr.), all the above materials can be considered surface grafts. However, at considerably lower dose rates (<2,000 rad/hr.), homogeneous grafting has been reported (25).

d. Polyethylene–Acrylonitrile

Polyethylene films, 4 mil thick, were irradiated when immersed in the pure monomer, a saturated aqueous solution, and a solution in dimethylformamide which is a solvent for polyacrylonitrile (20). Dose rates were in the range of 6.7–30 × 10^4 rad/hr. (Fig. XII-2). Pure acrylonitrile gave the fastest rate. Surprisingly, the saturated aqueous solution grafted more rapidly than the dimethylformamide solution, despite the much higher monomer concentration in the latter. It was suggested that the higher

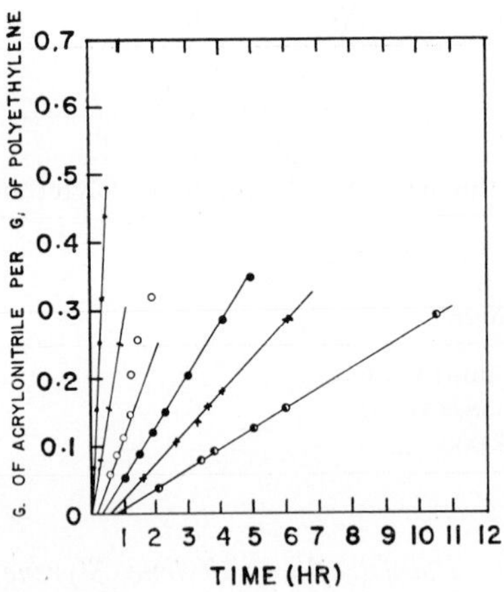

Fig. XII-2. Effect of dose rate and concentration on rate of grafting of acrylonitrile to 4 mil polyethylene, Co^{60} γ-rays: (◐) 25% volume in DMF, 67 Krad/hr.; (×) 25% volume in DMF, 170 Krad/hr.; (●) 25% volume in DMF, 300 Krad/hr.; (O) saturated water solution, 180 Krad/hr.; (×) 100%, 183 Krad/hr.; (•) 100%, 248 Krad/hr. (Taken from ref. 20.)

rate of grafting in the aqueous system might be a consequence of the OH and H radicals formed; this, however, implies their attacking the polyethylene film.

A 23% weight increase was recorded when irradiation was carried out for 48 hr. at 1800 rad/hr. The films produced were harder and more resistant to boiling water. Since the monomer cannot readily diffuse into the grafted surface layer, even at this lower dose rate, significant penetration of the substrate is unlikely (26). Physical properties and permeabilities of these grafts have been measured; results are shown in Tables XII-5 and XII-6.

TABLE XII-5
Properties of 4 mil Polyethylene Films Grafted with Acrylonitrile[a]

Graft, %	Density, g./ml.	Elongation, %	Tensile strength, psi	Elastic modulus, psi
0	0.909	630	1890	14,400
12	0.933	518	2460	21,870
18	0.933	580	2310	23,500

[a] Taken from ref. 20.

TABLE XII-6
Permeabilities of Polyethylene–Acrylonitrile Grafts at 30°C.[a]

Graft, %	Permeability, cc. STP/cm./mm./cm. Hg × 10^9		
	N_2	O_2	CO_2
0	2.0	7.0	28.0
1.8	1.7	5.7	25.4
9.3	1.3	—	17.1
20.8	1.1	3.2	13.6
31.3	0.7	2.2	9.7

[a] Taken from ref. 27.

e. Poly(vinyl Alcohol)

The importance of monomer penetration or wetting of the film surface is particularly apparent from the experimentation with grafting to poly(vinyl alcohol). Films of poly(vinyl alcohol) have been irradiated with γ-rays or x-rays while immersed in methyl methacrylate, styrene, and acrylonitrile to give what appears to be predominantly surface-grafted products. Sakurada, Okada, and Kugo (28) noted that, if perfectly dry films were used with styrene and methyl methacrylate, virtually no grafting occurred up to 3.4 Mrad. If, however, water was present to swell the film, monomer could penetrate; and the amount of grafting became significant. The possibility that ionized water fragments could also initiate grafting was also suggested; but the former explanation seems more logical, particularly in the light of later findings.

Chapiro and Stannett (29) found that a considerable depth of penetration could be achieved with styrene in the presence of water and with dioxane as solvent. The grafting results were correlated with the adsorption isotherms measured for this system and were related to the increased swelling of the film by water. Various methanol solutions of methyl methacrylate were employed by Szántó and Gál (30) utilizing x-radiation intensity of 3.6×10^4 rad/hr. They reported that, for doses up to 4×10^4 rad and concentrations of methanol above 40% and below 60%, monomer can penetrate the film of poly(vinyl alcohol) to achieve high levels of grafting. With pure methyl methacrylate, a dose of 2.5 Mrad results in only 5–10% grafting, presumably at the surface. With styrene the extent of grafting is proportional to the surface area.

Dry poly(vinyl alcohol) films irradiated in the presence of acrylonitrile as a liquid (28) and as a vapor (31) resulted in little grafting ($\leq$6 Mrad). Significant grafting is observed only with cotton–acrylonitrile when the monomer wets or is adsorbed by the fibers, with methanol–water as swelling agent (32).

3. Effect of Relative G Values

Autoacceleration has been observed in several systems and may arise from two causes. First, if the polymer which has been grafted on to the substrate is significantly more susceptible to irradiation (higher G value), or if its monomer is unable to penetrate the substrate, the effective locus of grafting will change to the newly formed polymer as the reaction proceeds. Since the concentration of the newly formed polymer is related to the grafting rate, the reaction approaches zero-order kinetics (eq. 8), and an autocatalytic effect results. The Trommsdorf-Norrish effect, which occurs when termination is suppressed by either occlusion or immobility of radicals due to the internal viscosity of the medium, is a second possibility. With the exception of the grafting of styrene on to polyethylene in the presence of a nonsolvent such as methanol (33), all other reported examples of autoacceleration are attributed to the former phenomenon.

Restaino and Reed (16), investigating the autoacceleration observed with polytetrafluoroethylene and vinyl acetate ($G = 33$) (Figs. XII-3 and XII-5), eliminated the gel effect by increasing the viscosity of the reaction medium. Up to 15% of poly(vinyl alcohol) was added to the monomer during grafting without significant change in rate. Similar autoacceleration effects were observed with polytetrafluoroethylene grafted with 20% aqueous *N*-vinylpyrrolidone ($G = 15$) (21) and methyl methacrylate ($G = 27.5$) (20).

The result of grafting methyl methacrylate ($G = 27.5$) to polyethylene ($G \simeq 6$) is given in Figure XII-4. The initial grafting rates, as can be seen in the figure, are proportional to the square root of the intensity, but as

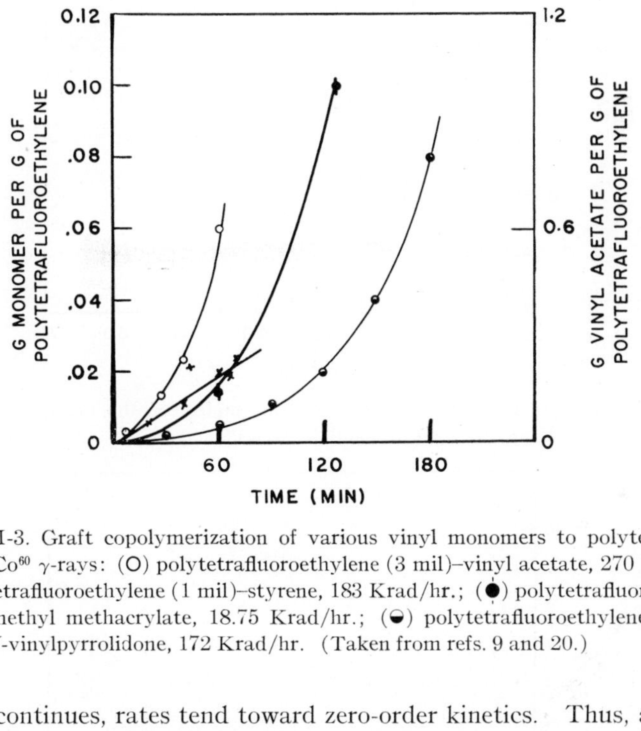

Fig. XII-3. Graft copolymerization of various vinyl monomers to polytetrafluoroethylene, Co^{60} γ-rays: (O) polytetrafluoroethylene (3 mil)–vinyl acetate, 270 Krad/hr.; (×) polytetrafluoroethylene (1 mil)–styrene, 183 Krad/hr.; (●) polytetrafluoroethylene (10 mil)–methyl methacrylate, 18.75 Krad/hr.; (◒) polytetrafluoroethylene (1 mil)–20% aq. *N*-vinylpyrrolidone, 172 Krad/hr. (Taken from refs. 9 and 20.)

grafting continues, rates tend toward zero-order kinetics. Thus, although monomer is able to diffuse into the film more readily by virtue of the initial grafting, in practice further interpolymerization takes place predominantly on the already grafted side chains. Since poly(methyl methacrylate) undergoes scission on irradiation, considerable homopolymer would be expected and has been found. At higher doses and dose rates, Pinner and Wycherley (34) found it difficult to prepare grafts containing more than 15% poly(methyl methacrylate), large amounts of homopolymer being formed.

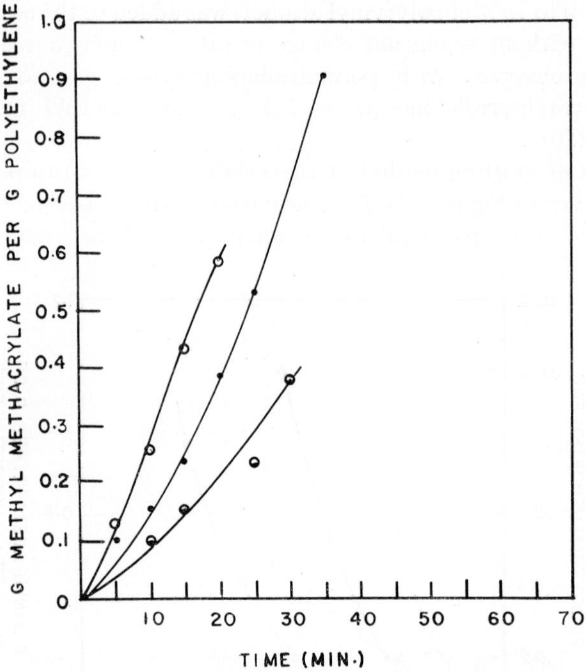

Fig. XII-4. Effect of dose rate on rate of grafting methyl methacrylate to 4 mil polyethylene: (O) 160 Krad/hr.; (●) 67 Krad/hr.; (◒) 20 Krad/hr. (Taken from ref. 20.)

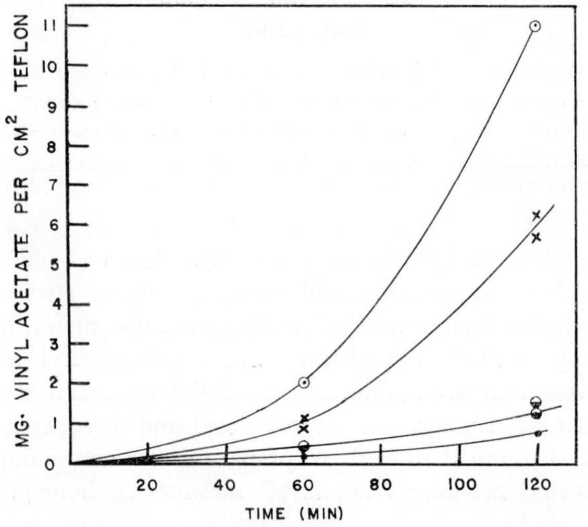

Fig. XII-5. Effect of temperature on grafting vinyl acetate to polytetrafluoroethylene, 37 Krad/hr. γ-rays: (●) 25°C.; (◒) 30°C.; (×) 45°C.; (⊙) 55°C. (Taken from ref. 19.)

Chapiro (35) observed marked autoacceleration when poly(vinyl chloride) was grafted with methyl methacrylate. The classical requirement of $R_g \propto I^{1/2}$ still held, however.

When polytetrafluoroethylene was grafted with styrene ($G = 2$) as shown in Figure XII-3, and polyethylene ($G = 6$) with acrylonitrile ($G = 2.7$) as shown in Figure XII-2, no autoacceleration was noted (20).

4. Effect of Rate of Diffusion of Monomer

It has already been pointed out that, even though the monomer may initially have a very limited solubility in the polymeric substrate, as grafting proceeds the monomer may further infiltrate the grafted area, insomuch as most monomers are solvents for their own polymers. Thus, if the monomer can diffuse into the polymer more quickly than it is consumed and no extreme differences in G values exist, grafting will proceed in toward the center of the substrate. If, however, monomer is consumed more rapidly than it can diffuse inward, the reaction becomes diffusion-controlled.

Restaino (36) pointed out that the limiting swelling value of acrylonitrile in polyethylene is less than 0.4% and that the diffusion rate in a 10 mil film is 2.5×10^{-6} g./g. film/cm.^{2}/min. When this figure is applied to the previously discussed polyethylene–acrylonitrile system (20), monomer consumption is 10^2–10^3 times greater than diffusion would permit, and surface grafting only must ensue.

Dobó, Somogyi, and Lakner (19), investigating the polytetrafluoroethylene–vinyl acetate system, found a pronounced change of grafting rate with temperature as shown in Figure XII-5. Since rates of polymerization initiated by irradiation are relatively insensitive to temperature changes, the observed increase in rate was attributed to increased swelling of the film by the monomer.

The radiation chemical grafting of styrene and methyl methacrylate in various solvents to poly(vinyl chloride) has been studied (35). It was deduced that with styrene alone or methyl methacrylate dissolved in benzene or carbon tetrachloride, the reactions were diffusion-controlled. From a study of the swelling of the films, it was concluded that diffusion-controlled grafting would predominate in those systems that took several hours or more to reach swelling equilibrium.

Chapiro (25) has prepared homogeneous grafts of polytetrafluoroethylene with styrene and methyl methacrylate. Experimental conditions were so chosen that consumption of monomer was slower than its rate of diffusion. Low dose rates were employed, <2000 rad/hr., with increased temperature and monomer concentration to aid diffusion. To allow further time for monomer penetration, the samples were intermittently irradiated. By these techniques, coherent samples containing up to 90% polystyrene were obtained. The dimensions of films increased geometrically up to this point, then disrupted. Optical and swelling measurements indicated the homogeneity of the grafts produced. Two patents (37,38) cover the use of the intermediate irradiation technique, the first specifically describing polytetrafluoroethylene grafted with styrene, methyl methacrylate, and isoprene.

Mock and Vanderkooi (39) evolved a rigorous mathematical treatment, with experimental verification, for the diffusion-controlled grafting of styrene on to ethyl cellulose. Neglecting homopolymer formed by chain transfer (low for this system), the authors showed that the kinetic chain length distribution of the grafted polymer throughout the substrate $V_{x,t}$ was given by:

$$V_{(x,t)} = (K_p/K_t^{1/2})^{1/2} K^{1/2} C_{(x,t)} \tag{9}$$

where K is the rate of formation of radicals *in vacuo*, determined by paramagnetic resonance, and $C_{(x,t)}$ is the concentration of monomer after irradiation for time t.

5. Preirradiation in the Absence of Oxygen

When polymers are subjected to irradiation, particularly below their second-order transition temperature, "trapped" free radicals are formed. In the presence of oxygen, diperoxides and hydroperoxides may be formed. In the absence of oxygen, the "trapped" radicals are capable of initiating polymerization of an added vinyl monomer. Generally, such polymerizations tend to lead to a more homogeneous distribution of the graft polymer, since reaction rates are usually slower than those prepared by simultaneous irradiation of monomer and polymer, and also less homopolymer will be formed. There are, however, several examples of surface grafted materials within this category.

Bevington and Eaves (40) subjected 15 den. monofilaments of nylon to γ-irradiation *in vacuo* and then exposed the polymer to C^{14}-labeled acrylonitrile. They were thus able to measure the extremely small degrees of grafting that resulted. They found that a limiting value of grafting was achieved for a given preirradiation dose (Fig. XII-6). Furthermore, for a given dose, the extent of grafting was not a linear function of time of ex-

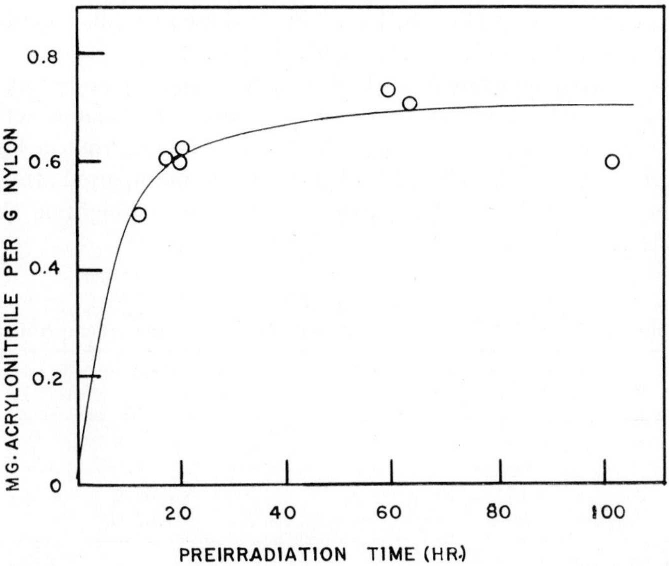

Fig. XII-6. Grafting of C^{14} acrylonitrile to nylon preirradiated 60 min. with nominal 100 c. source. Exposure to vapor at 78–79 mm. Hg, 18.5–19.5°C. (Taken from ref. 40.)

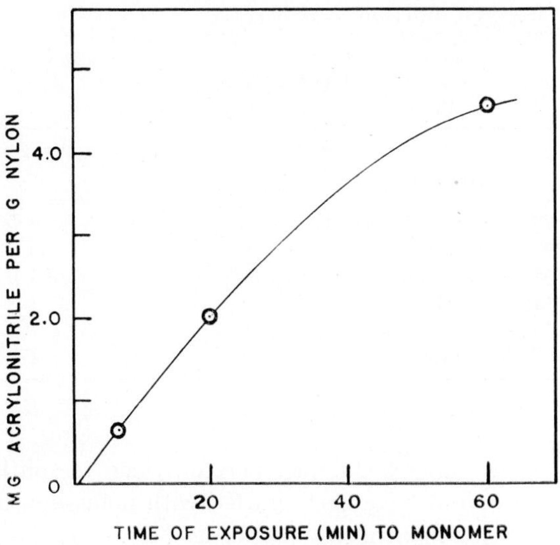

Fig. XII-7. Grafting of C^{14} acrylonitrile to nylon preirradiated 17 hr. *in vacuo* with nominal 100 c. source. Exposed to vapor at 73.5 mm. Hg, 19.5°C. (Taken from ref. 40.)

posure to the monomer (Fig. XII-7). From these facts, it is evident that grafting occurred at, or close to, the surface layer.

Nylon has been preirradiated (1 Mrad), subsequently stored at various temperatures, and then immersed in 80% aqueous potassium acrylate at room temperature (41). The lower the storage temperature, the higher the final degree of grafting. The radical activity was unimpaired after storage for 60 days at −80°C. The amount of increase in weight is shown in Table XII-7.

TABLE XII-7
Stability of Free Radicals from Irradiated Nylon at Various Temperatures[a]

Storage temperature, °C.	Wt. gain, %
20	0.9
0	4.9
−15	57.0
−80	67.0

[a] Taken from ref. 41.

Polyethylene was similarly irradiated, then immersed for 36 hr. in various monomers at room temperature. The amount of grafting as shown by gain in weight is given in Table XII-8.

TABLE XII-8
Preirradiation Polyethylene Grafts[a]

Monomer	Wt. gain, %
20% Potassium acrylate	9.5
Acrylonitrile	55.0
Methyl acrylate	24.0
Methacrolein	4.3
Vinylidene chloride	4.6
Vinyl acetate	4.6

[a] Taken from ref. 41.

By means of the same technique, poly(ethylene terephthalate), polyacrylonitrile, and cotton have been grafted with potassium acrylate, with distinct improvements in antistatic properties (41).

Nylon, preirradiated under nitrogen and then dipped into degassed aqueous acrylamide, surface grafted with no loss of strength (4). When preirradiated in air and then heated with monomer, more homogeneous grafts were obtained; the product could be dyed more evenly but had considerably lower tensile strength.

6. Effect of Crystallinity

Polyethylene was irradiated under nitrogen ($\leqslant 5$ Mrad) and then immersed in degassed styrene (42). The reaction continued up to 10 days, with a 55% increase in weight. At low temperatures, linear polyethylene grafted more slowly and less completely than the branched polyethylene. At higher temperatures, the reverse was observed; the increase in grafting of the linear product was attributed to release of trapped free radicals within the crystalline regions. Such grafts were shown by x-ray diffraction and hot stage microscopy to be more homogeneous than those prepared by simultaneous irradiation of the polymer–monomer mixture (43).

Since styrene has an appreciable solubility in polyethylene, homogeneous grafts might be expected. However, for simultaneous irradiation, Hoffman et al. (44) showed this reaction to be diffusion controlled at 10–20°C. but not at 70°C., when monomer can readily penetrate the crystallites. Resulting grafts appeared stratified and cavitated, presumably due to the accumulation and swelling of the monomer in the amorphous region (21). From birefringence studies of oriented polyethylene films, it has been observed that, initially, grafting of styrene took place in the microcavities. When these were filled, however, the microcrystallites began to be destroyed (45).

The permeabilities of polyethylene grafted with styrene have been recorded (27). As grafting proceeded, gas permeability first decreased as the amorphous regions were filled in, then increased as the crystalline regions

TABLE XII-9
Permeabilities of Low Density Polyethylene–Styrene Graft Polymers at 30°C.[a]

Graft, %	Permeability, cc./cm.^{2}/sec./mm./cm. Hg $\times 10^9$		
	N_2	O_2	CO_2
0	2.0	7.0	28.0
4.8	1.5	4.8	22.5
20.9	0.9	3.5	14.9
41.3	1.1	4.3	20.2
Polystyrene	0.3		8.8

[a] Taken from ref. 27.

were destroyed. The permeability to gases of polyethylene grafted with varying amounts of styrene is shown in Table XII-9.

While none of the above can be considered surface grafts, they serve to illustrate the importance of crystallinity, with ensuing impenetrability, in surface reactions.

7. Thickness of Grafted Layer

Dobó, Somogyi, and Lakner (19) grafted vinyl acetate, methyl methacrylate, and vinylpyridine on to polytetrafluoroethylene. The thickness of the grafted layer was determined by coloring it with a suitable dye and examining the surface and cross sections of the grafted film. Grafts from vinyl acetate responded best to this treatment. Below 2% grafting, the surface was not completely covered; but, after 6–10%, homogeneously dyed surfaces were obtained. The thickness of the grafted (dyed) layer was proportional to the extent of grafting as shown in Table XII-10. In accordance with previous discussion, the thickness of the grafted layer is

TABLE XII-10
Thickness of Grafted Layer of Vinyl Acetate, Methyl Methacrylate, and Vinylpyridine on Polytetrafluoroethylene[a]

Monomer	Dose rate, Krad/hr.	Irradiation time, hr.	Temp., °C.	Graft, mg./cm.^{2}	Average thickness, %[b]
		Effect of Temperature			
Vinyl acetate	18.75	2	25	0.51	33
		2	45	2.15	43
		2	55	3.87	56
	37.00	2	55	11.64	100
		Effect of Dose Rate			
Vinyl acetate	18.75	2	45	2.15	43
	37.00	1		1.62	22
	18.75	2	55	3.87	56
	37.00	1		2.23	41
		Other Monomers			
Methyl methacrylate	37.00	1	35	1.12	23
		2		1.17	25
Vinylpyridine		3		0.91	17

[a] Taken from ref. 20.

[b] Average depth of grafted layer, each side, relative to original polytetrafluoroethylene thickness.

TABLE XII-11
Thickness of Grafted Layer in Grafting of Acrylonitrile to Polyvinylpyrrolidone Film[a]

Thickness of film, mm.	Acrylonitrile, vol.-% in benzene[b]	Grafted polyacrylonitrile, mg./cm.^{2}	Thickness of grafted layer, mm.
0.23	10	1.8	0.096
	19	5.4	0.23
0.42	10	2.1	0.068
	19	6.8	0.155
0.70	10	2.7	0.081
	19	6.1	0.152

[a] Taken from ref. 46.
[b] Immersed 14 hr. in monomer prior to irradiation at 1.6×10^5 rad/hr.

increased by higher temperatures and lower dose rates. Of the monomers investigated, vinyl acetate most readily grafted, vinylpyridine least.

Henglein and Schnabel (46) irradiated films of polyvinylpyrrolidone immersed in solutions of acrylonitrile in benzene. These grafts adsorb up to 20 times their own weight when swollen in methanol, and the surface layer increases up to 5 times in area without rupture. If these films are first sliced through, the ungrafted substrate can be dissolved. The thickness and composition of the residual grafted layer can then be determined and is listed in Table XII-11. From surface dosimetry and the known G value of the substrate, the authors computed that, for grafting confined only to the surface layer (10^{-7} cm.), the average molecular weight of the side chains of polyacrylonitrile would be 2.5×10^8. Assuming a more reasonable value of 2.5×10^3, penetration would be 10^{-2} cm., of the same order shown in Table XII-11. As verification, film 0.23 mm. thick was found to be homogeneously grafted.

Similar experiments were carried out by dipping films of poly(methyl methacrylate) into solutions in methanol of acrylonitrile and vinylpyrrolidone, and then irradiating (47). After an initial induction period, a linear relationship was found between the amount of graft and the square root of the time of immersion. Furthermore, for a given immersion time, the thickness of the grafted layer was independent of the subsequent irradiation dose.

When a 2-mm. film was immersed in 30% acrylonitrile in methanol for 50 hr., the sample was homogeneously swollen. Homogeneous grafts prepared in this manner were compared with surface grafts (immersed for shorter periods) of similar composition. Rather surprisingly, both exhibited almost identical swelling in chloroform.

8. Presence of Oxygen during Irradiation

When films of polyvinylpyrrolidone were irradiated immersed in acrylonitrile dissolved in chloroform or benzene in the presence of oxygen, little or no homopolymer was observed (46). However, the grafting rate is little affected by the presence of air as shown in Table XII-12. Apparently,

TABLE XII-12
Grafting Acrylonitrile to Polyvinylpyrrolidone Film in the Presence and Absence of Oxygen[a]

Dose rate, rad/hr. for 16 hr.	Acrylonitrile, vol.-%	Atmosphere over solution	Grafted polyacrylonitrile, mg./cm.^{2}
2×10^4	19	Argon	9.7
		Air	7.1
4.3×10^4	19	Argon	10.6
		Air	8.4
1.6×10^5	10	Argon	8.8
		Air	6.6

[a] Taken from ref. 46.

oxygen can diffuse quickly through the liquid medium but much more slowly into the film itself. Grafts prepared in the presence of oxygen had a soft, rubbery surface of lightly grafted polyvinylpyrrolidone. In the absence of oxygen, tough, hard surfaces were observed.

9. Low Energy Grafting

High energy irradiation passes completely through the sample, producing free radicals which, if no monomer is present, will either dismutate or crosslink. In either case, the net effect is to change the physical properties of the substrate, often disadvantageously. Clearly then, for surface reactions, low energy irradiation might be used, leaving the physical properties of the substrate essentially unchanged. In addition, the limited penetration tends to confine the grafting reaction to the surface layers.

Oster (48) has utilized these principles for a wide range of polymer–monomer combinations. Sources emitting ultraviolet in the 200–300 mμ range, such as carbon arc lamps and low pressure mercury vapor resonance germicidal lamps, were used with care being taken to avoid undue heating of the sample. Such lamps may give off irradiation below 200 mμ; for prolonged exposure, a filter was used to prevent excessive damage

TABLE XII-13
Ultraviolet Grafting of Various Substrates[a]

Base polymer	Activator	Monomer	Time	Sample
Polyethylene, 2 mil	0.5% Benzophenone	Acrylamide (40% aq.)	10 sec.	A
Polyethylene (high density), 1 mil	5% Dibenzyl disulfide	Acrylamide (10% aq.)	10^{-3} sec.	
Poly(ethylene terephthalate), 1 mil	"	"	"	
Polyacrylonitrile fiber	2% Diphenylamine	Acrylic acid (50% aq.)	10 min.	B
Nylon 66 fiber	0.2% Benzophenone	Vinylpyridine (50%) Vinylpyrrolidone (50%)	7 min.	C
Natural rubber film	Methyl ethyl ketone	Acrylamide (saturated aq.)	10 sec.	D
Paper	5% Benzophenone	*N*-Octylacrylamide (10% aq.)	1 hr.	E
Wood	"	*N*-Octylacrylamide (3% aq.)	1 hr.	
Regenerated cellulose	10% Benzophenone	*N*-Octylacrylamide (10% aq.)	1 min.	F

[a] Taken from ref. 48.

to the substrate. Activators, such as acetophenone, benzyl disulfide, ninhydrin, and alkaline cystine were either swollen into, mechanically dispersed, or painted onto the surface of the polymer. Such materials, absorbing in the 200–300 mμ range, are thought to react on irradiation with a labile hydrogen in the polymer backbone, thereby providing grafting sites when monomer is present. When 0.1–1.0% of such a material is present, the grafting rate is increased enormously, and very short irradiation times are required to effect significant polymerization. This is apparent from Table XII-13. If the films are thin enough, sufficient energy is transmitted to graft both surfaces; otherwise, the irradiated surface only is grafted.

All experiments were carried out in the absence of oxygen; and while no attempt was made to substantiate that grafting had taken place, undoubtedly the surface characteristics of the film were drastically changed. Sample A (Table XII-13) could be marked with water-based inks and readily retained a cast film of gelatin. Sample B had a greater affinity to basic dyes; C to acid dyes, with less static retention. The surface of a natural rubber slab after treatment (sample D) became hydrophobic, adhering strongly to cotton fibers. Paper (Sample E) became greasy and nonwetting; while Sample F, when irradiated through a stencil, retained ink only on the illuminated area.

Fibers and films of polyethylene and polyamides have been similarly grafted with benzoin as the activator (49). The substrate was grafted by illumination in the presence of methyl methacrylate vapor. A coating of 0.01–1.7 mil was deposited on polyethylene film in 5–200 min.

Polypropylene fibers containing benzophenone were first grafted with epoxy monomers, such as glycidyl methacrylate or acrylate, or epoxy-containing copolymers, utilizing ultraviolet irradiation, then treated with an ethanolamine (e.g., diethanolamine) (50). Such fibers can then be colored with direct, acid or basic dyes.

10. Miscellaneous Direct Surface Grafting

Polyethylene has been grafted with acrylic acid, by both simultaneous irradiation (51) and preirradiation (52). The sodium salt of the graft was reported to have a higher softening temperature and less static retention.

Improved heat-resistant films with lower coefficient of friction were obtained when polyethylene was irradiated in contact with a 3:1 volume mixture of ethylene and sulfur dioxide.

Nylon has been grafted with styrene to give a tenting material more resistant to water after weathering (54), with methacrylic acid to improve solvent resistance (55), and with acrylamide to improve coloring with basic dyes (56). Shinohara (57) grafted various monomers on nylon 66 and measured the loss factor (tan δ). Despite the higher relaxation temperature of acrylonitrile (100°C.), there was little change in the loss factor at the α' peak (80°C.), supporting the previously discussed surface grafting for this system (40).

Most common vinyl monomers have been grafted to fibers and films of poly(vinyl chloride) (23,51) in liquid and vapor phases to impart heat resistance and dyeability (58).

Gaylord (59) employed a novel method for confining grafting to the surface. A polymer was irradiated in the presence of an initiator, such as aqueous hydrogen peroxide or azobisisobutyronitrile. It is envisaged that the initiator upon exposure to radiation decomposes and, by attacking the polymer surface, forms initiation sites for subsequent grafting in the absence of air. A wide range of polymer–monomer systems was surface-grafted in this manner.

Kobayashi (60) has reported that, when cellulose is preirradiated in aqueous hydrogen peroxide, polymeric hydroperoxides were formed.

TABLE XII-14
Surface-Grafted or Diffusion-Controlled Graft Polymers Prepared by Irradiating Monomer–Polymer Mixtures

Polymer	Monomer grafted	Intensity, rad/hr. × 10^5	Total dose × 10^5, rad	Grafted monomer, wt.-%	Reference
Polytetrafluoroethylene	Acrylonitrile	—	0.63	1.3	21
	Vinyl acetate	3.0	2.5	61.0	61
	Styrene	1.72	1.83	24.4	21
	Styrene	3.0	15.0	17.0	21
	Styrene	3.0	15.0	22.9	21
	Styrene	3.0	15.0	18.4	21
	Acrylic acid	3.0	0.75	37.0	61
	N-Vinylpyrrolidone	1.72	5.16	5.0	21
Poly(ethylene terephthalate)	Styrene		135.0	8.8	21
Polyethylene	4-Vinylpyridine[a]	1.72	1.72	40.0	61
	Acrylic acid	3.0	0.75	37.0	61
	Methyl methacrylate	1.72	0.43	29.5	21
	Acrylonitrile (25 vol.-% in DMF)	3.0	9.0	16.6	61
Polytrifluorochloroethylene	Vinylidene chloride	0.3	30.0	2.5	34
	Acrylic acid	3.0	0.75	6.0	61
	Acrylonitrile	3.0	0.75	1.0	61
	Styrene	3.00	72.00	3.4	61
	Vinyl acetate[a]	3.00	3.00	11.0	61
Poly(methyl methacrylate)	Acrylonitrile (20 vol.-% in MeOH, after 16 hr. immersion)	0.25	3.75	6.5	46
	Vinylpyrrolidone (40 vol.-% in MeOH after 24 hr. immersion)	0.20	1.00	2.95	46
Poly(vinyl alcohol)	Styrene	3.00	114.00	2.95	61
	Vinyl acetate[a]	3.00	3.00	1.9	61
Polyvinylpyrrolidone	Acrylonitrile (25 vol.-% in benzene)	1.6	32.0	20.00	47
	Acrylonitrile (13 vol.-% in benzene)	1.6	32.00	7.00	47
Nylon	Styrene	—	311.00	10.5	61
Poly(vinyl chloride) fiber	Acrylic acid (25% aq.)	—	1.86	0.9	51

[a] Monomer undistilled.

These were used to initiate graft copolymerization of styrene with a mixture of methanol and water to facilitate penetration of monomer. If the styrene is maintained outside the cotton fiber, little grafting is observed.

Other systems, considered essentially surface grafts from the conditions of their preparation, are given in Table XII-14.

11. Preirradiation in Oxygen

In general, preirradiation in air to form peroxides followed by heating in monomer leads to more homogeneous grafting than the previously described methods, but for comparison and convenience is included in this chapter. Subsequent grafting reactions are generally carried out at higher temperatures, favoring diffusion of the monomer. In addition, there is not the effect encountered in simultaneous grafting when the monomer has a significantly greater G value than the substrate. At first glance, it might be expected that the peroxidation technique might lead to more homopolymerization, but this depends on the nature of the reaction product of the irradiation-induced polymeric free radicals with oxygen.

Chapiro (62) has pointed out that, on irradiation of polyethylene in air, mainly diperoxides are formed.

$$PH \xrightarrow{I} P\cdot + H\cdot \tag{10}$$

$$P\cdot + O_2 \rightarrow PO_2\cdot \tag{11}$$

$$2\ PO_2\cdot \rightarrow PO_2P + O_2 \tag{12}$$

$$\text{or } PO_2\cdot + P\cdot \rightarrow PO_2P \tag{13}$$

In polypropylene, hydroperoxide formation is favored by the presence of the α-methylenic hydrogen.

$$PrH \xrightarrow{I} Pr\cdot + H\cdot \tag{14}$$

$$Pr\cdot + O_2 \rightarrow PrO_2\cdot \tag{15}$$

$$PrO_2\cdot + H\cdot \rightarrow PrO_2H \tag{16}$$

In support of these postulates, preirradiation in air followed by irradiation *in vacuo* and subsequent exposure to monomer does not lead to grafting. The radiation-sensitive peroxides are destroyed. Further evidence was provided by Burlant (63), who found that irradiation in oxygen led to a maximum and steady peroxide concentration. Peroxidized nylon and poly(ethylene terephthalate) are stable at room temperature for at least

24 hr. (64). Shinohara and Tomioka (65) have claimed, however, that on irradiation in air using higher dose rates not all radicals formed were peroxidized. This was based on evidence that grafting of styrene occurred well below the decomposition temperatures of the peroxides. On storage, the irradiated films gradually lost their free radical character, combining with oxygen (E_a = 20 kcal./mole).

Comparative studies of grafting acrylonitrile to linear polyethylene and polypropylene are reported (66). For the same preirradiation dose, polypropylene initially grafts more quickly than polyethylene, particularly at lower temperatures (25°C.). Polyethylene grafted below 110°C., the assumed melting point of the crystallites, had an activation energy of 17.5 kcal./mole. Above this temperature, the activation energy changed abruptly to 9 kcal./mole. No such change was observed with polypropylene (E_a = 8.0 kcal./mole), the grafting temperature employed being below the melting point of the crystallites (170°C.).

Extraction of the graft polymers revealed considerably more homopolymer from polypropylene, as would be expected from decomposition of a hydroperoxide. Swelling and optical examination showed that grafting occurred mainly in the amorphous regions of polyethylene, but became increasingly more homogeneous above 110°C. Since the hydroperoxide decomposes at a lower temperature, the polypropylene system is diffusion-controlled.

Hazenberg et al. (67) utilized similar techniques, employing an additional redox catalyst, but were unable to graft styrene at room temperature. Unexpectedly, less grafting was observed with polypropylene at 70°C. than with polyethylene. Washing peroxidized polyethylene with a non-solvent, then heating in acrylonitrile vapor, reportedly reduced the amount of homopolymer by 83% (68).

A number of systems which grafted predominantly on the surface have been prepared by irradiation peroxidation. Sykes and Thomas (69), investigating the dyeing of nylon, polyacrylonitrile, poly(ethylene terephthalate), and polypropylene grafted with 4-vinylpyridine, found peripheral penetration only. Peroxidized polyethylene, heated first in vinylidene chloride, then in ethylene, had the feel and surface characteristics of the base polymer, but was impermeable to air (70).

Nylon, poly(vinyl chloride), and polystyrene were grafted with acrylonitrile, and polystyrene, polyethylene and poly(methyl methacrylate) with aqueous acrylamide. Peroxidation was carried out with both γ-rays and neutrons (71). Cellulose triacetate, irradiated 125 hr. at 25 Krad/hr. in air, then heated 8 hr. at 80°C. in styrene, increased 11% in weight (72).

12. Irradiation of Polymer–Nonmonomer Systems

In recent years, considerable work has been reported in the patent literature on surface modification of polymeric substrates by simultaneous or pre-irradiation in the presence of nonpolymerizable materials. Free radicals produced on the substrate are capable of either directly interacting with the coating or cross terminating with free radicals formed in the coating. It may be beneficial to protect the substrate by using just sufficient irradiation energy to penetrate through to the surface of the base polymer.

Poly(ethylene terephthalate) was coated with poly(ethylene oxide) from solution, dried, degassed, and subjected to 10 K.e.v. electrons at 0.01 w. sec./cm.^{2} for 2 hr. After a 20 hr. ethanol extraction to remove the poly(ethylene oxide), the film retained a 1.5% increase in weight. The surface resistivity was reduced from $10^{12.9}$ to $10^{10.9}$. It could be argued that, since poly(ethylene oxide) crosslinks on irradiation, it may not be chemically bonded to the surface. However, a weight increase from similar experiments with regenerated cellulose coated with poly(vinylidene chloride), which degrades, proved interpolymer formation. Polyethylene was also coated with poly(ethylene oxide) and with poly(vinyl chloride); poly(ethylene terephthalate) was coated with poly(vinyl chloride). Poly(ethylene terephthalate) has been thinly coated with natural rubber and subjected to ultraviolet irradiation. The coating could not be dissolved

TABLE XII-15
High Intensity Radiation of Polymer–Polymer Systems

Substrate	Coating	Dose, Mrad	Reference
Nylon	Polychlorostyrene	40	75
	Poly(vinylidene chloride/vinyl acetate)	40	75
	Poly(methoxynonaethyleneoxyethyl methacrylate)	40	75
	Poly(ethylene glycol)	40	75
Wool	Poly(ethylene glycol)	40	76
Silk	Poly(ethylene glycol)	40	76
Rubber	Poly(ethylene glycol)	40	76
Polytetrafluoroethylene	Poly(ethylene glycol)	27	77
Poly(methyl methacrylate)	Poly(allyl methacrylate)	20	77
Poly(styrene-*co*-butadiene)	Poly(oxyethylene glycol)	10	77
Polyethylene	Poly(ethylene glycol)	—	52

with a good solvent for rubber and exhibited good adhesion to the substrate surface (74).

Higher penetrating 2 M.e.v. electrons, with doses of 10–40 Mrad, intermittently administered to prevent excessive heating, have been used to graft on the surface of numerous fibers. The samples were either wrapped in aluminum foil to prevent excessive oxidation or else degassed. At the extremely high dose rates used, insufficient oxygen can diffuse through the sample to significantly interfere with the radical processes. The systems that have been reported are shown in Table XII-15. The treatment of the fibers and films variously gave improved oil, scratch, stain, and wash resistance; surface conductivity; water repellency; softness to hand; and dyeability.

TABLE XII-16
Irradiation of Polymer–Nonmonomer Systems

Base	Coating	Irradiation type	Reference
Nylon	Hexamethylenediamine	2 M.e.v. electrons	75
Polyacrylonitrile	Dodecafluoroheptyl alcohol	"	77
Nylon	Palmitic acid	α-particles	52
Polyethylene	Glycerol	"	52

Polyethylene film was preirradiated *in vacuo* (20 min., 250 w. sec./cm.^{2}) and, within 90 sec., spread-coated with poly(ethylene oxide) of 6,000 molecular weight at 100°C. Heating was continued for 1 hr. under nitrogen. After rigorous extraction with a solvent, the coated polyethylene had a net gain of 0.15% in weight compared to a noncoated control. The wettability of the film increased, as measured by the sliding drop angle technique. Poly(ethylene terephthalate) and nylon were similarly treated, with resultant improvement in softness, resilience, and dyeability (78).

The loss of weight on air-heating (150°C.) a varnish-coated polyethylene is markedly reduced by preirradiation (15 Mrad) prior to varnishing (79).

Several examples of irradiation grafting of salts and other low molecular weight compounds have been patented. Preirradiated nylon and cotton have been exposed to C^{14}-labeled β-methoxyethanol at −78°C. for 16 hr., and polyethylene was exposed to amyl alcohol. An increase of approximately 0.2% by weight in all three cases was observed (78). Similar results are summarized in Table XII-16.

Nylon fibers impregnated with a 25% aqueous solution of maleic anhydride or various unsaturated acids, when subjected to 40 Mrad of 2 M.e.v. electrons, exhibited an 8% weight gain after washing. When then reacted with a detergent, a further 7% weight gain was reported. The resistance of the treated fiber to cigarette burns and to melting is strikingly improved. When treated with acid to free the detergent, these benefits are lost, but may be restored by further immersion in detergent. Various metal salts may be used in place of the detergent (80).

The hand, feel, and resistance to washing of nylon, polyethylene, and poly(ethylene terephthalate) were improved by irradiation of high (81) and low (82) penetration in the presence of 5% aqueous solutions of various salts, e.g., stannous chloride, calcium fluoride, or aluminum hydroxide. Up to a 5.6% weight increase was observed.

The joining (cold welding) of similar and dissimilar surfaces has been achieved by employing the techniques of irradiation grafting. By first treating the surfaces to be joined with lithium or boron compounds, pressing them tightly together, and subjecting them to thermal neutrons, bond strengths greater than 120 kg./cm.^{2} were achieved. The key to the process lies in the fact that, although lithium and boron have relatively low cross sections, the resulting isotopes have extremely short half-lives (0.89 and 0.03 sec., respectively). The decomposition products lead to high yields of α-particles, thereby confining radical production to the immediate vicinity of the bonding surfaces. Little overall damage to the bulk product ensues. Materials that have been bonded this way include polytetrafluoroethylene to polystyrene and poly(methyl methacrylate), polyethylene to polystyrene and poly(methyl methacrylate), and polystyrene to poly(methyl methacrylate) (83).

Sections of vulcanized polysiloxane elastomers containing carbon black brought into intimate contact with a thin layer of the elastomer without black, have been cold-welded by γ-irradiation (4 Mrad) (84).

From the data presented in this section, it is evident that considerable technological improvements have already been made, but even greater advances may be anticipated, particularly in textiles.

B. CHEMICAL SURFACE GRAFTING

Surface interpolymers have been produced by chemical means, chiefly by employing peroxidation and ozonolysis techniques as the means of forming the sites for initiation on the substrate.

1. Chemical Peroxidation

A great deal of work has been reported on the peroxidation and subsequent grafting of polypropylene and its copolymers with ethylene (85–88). The highly crystalline isotactic form of this polymer which is 85% insoluble in boiling heptane is almost impermeable to oxygen. Peroxidation is, therefore, primarily confined to the surface. To further this end, the amorphous content may be reduced by extraction with ether before grafting.

Studies of the thermal degradation of polypropylene at 250°C. in the absence of oxygen revealed that chain scission occurred (89). If the sample was preheated at 180°C. in high vacuum, the thermal stability at 250°C. was improved. The presence of hydroperoxides in the polymer was reported. Their decomposition, yielding hydroxyl groups, was activated by the presence of copper.

The peroxidation of polypropylene is generally carried out by heating for several hours at 60–120°C. under oxygen or air at 1–10 atm. pressure. Isotactic polypropylene treated in this manner had 0.03–0.5% oxygen content, with no change in physical properties, as shown in Table XII-17.

TABLE XII-17
Effect of Peroxidation of Isotactic Polypropylene[a]

Peroxidation, wt.-% O_2	Tensile strength, kg./mm.^{2}	Elongation, %
Control	20.0	27.0
0.05	18.4	27.8
0.20	20.0	25.0

[a] Taken from ref. 85.

As expected, amorphous polypropylene is far more readily oxidized. After 7 hr. heating at 70°C. under 3 atm. of air, the peroxide content, determined by iodine titration, was 0.48%. A 30% reduction in molecular weight was observed. The isotactic form, similarly treated, yielded only 0.05% oxygen, with little chain degradation (85). It is reported that the peroxidation rate is accelerated by the presence of *tert*-butyl hydroperoxide vapor in air (90).

Grafting occurs when the peroxidized fiber or film is contacted and heated with the liquids or vapors of a wide variety of vinyl monomers. The amount of grafting with various monomers is shown in Table XII-18.

Tensile strengths, based on the cross section of the original substrate, remain almost constant even for highly grafted samples. Elongations generally increase. The grafted component exerts little influence on physical properties until heated sufficiently to flux. Vinyl esters could not be grafted directly in this manner. However, vinyl acetate and vinyl chloroacetate have been grafted as copolymers with acrylonitrile (92). The above graft polymers generally exhibited excellent dyeability, some improved wettability, and, with butyl acrylate, a tacky surface.

Polypropylene peroxidized with air has been treated with triethylaluminum, which adheres to the surface and permits subsequent dyeing

TABLE XII-18
Grafting of Thermally Peroxidized Polypropylene

Peroxide content, % O_2	Monomer	Temperature, °C.	Time, hr.	Wt. gain, %	Wt. grafted %[a]	Reference
0.3	4-Vinylpyridine	80–85	2.5	—	10.6	88
0.25	2-Vinylquinoline	85	6	—	8	88
0.35	Vinylpyrrolidone	83	5	—	7.5	88
0.4	Acrylonitrile–4-vinylpyridine (1:1)	75	4	—	8	88
0.2	Methyl methacrylate	75	3	38	24	87
0.2	Methyl methacrylate (40% in toluene)	75	15	—	21	87
0.03	Styrene	70	24	163	—	87
0.5	Styrene	75	24	—	10	87
0.03	Methyl acrylate	70	20	65	—	87
0.03	Acrylic acid, (25% aq.)	60	30	—	10	87
0.08	Methyl methacrylate–3-isopropenylpyridine	80	7	—	—	91
—	Butyl acrylate (50% IPA)	80	3	—	4	87

[a] After solvent extraction of homopolymer.

(93). It was recently reported that polyamides and polyesters may be grafted by first heating in air at 80–90°C., then with vinyl monomers at 65–80°C. (94).

Interpolymers may be formed by solution impregnation of the fibers with chemical initiators, such as azobisisobutyronitrile and benzoyl peroxide. For example, after treatment with 0.6% benzoyl peroxide in benzene and evaporation, polypropylene was heated 2 hr. at 85°C. with styrene in the absence of air. After solvent extraction, 10% chemically bound polystyrene was retained (95). When the peroxide was washed out before contact with the monomer, no increase in weight was observed.

Sheets of polyethylene have been impregnated with benzoyl peroxide. After preheating in air, the polymer was heated *in vacuo* with methyl methacrylate. The grafting rate increased with preheating time, and decreased with the length of time between preheating and heating with the monomer (96).

Strong adhesion and crease resistance were imparted to a polyethylene sheet printed with a poly(vinyl chloride)-based paint by dipping in a benzene solution of dibenzoyl peroxide and heating to 100°C. for 15 min. (97).

When polyethylene is oxidized with nitric oxide or fuming nitric acid, sites for initiating grafting are formed (98). For example, a filament of polyethylene, after 30 min. heating at 70°C. in fuming nitric acid, gained 0.8% weight. When further heated in methyl methacrylate vapors for 4 hr. at 100°C. and extracted with methyl ethyl ketone, a 21% weight gain was recorded.

2. Chemical Grafting via Ozone

Treatment of polyethylene, polypropylene, poly(vinyl chloride), and polyamide films or fibers with ozone produces sites capable of further initiating graft copolymerization. The simplest mechanism to envisage is the formation of ozonides at points of unsaturation in the polymer. However, this can be hardly true in the case of the polyamides. In addition, the extent and rapidity of grafting by this method suggest that other active species, perhaps peroxides, are formed.

Polyethylene film has been treated with 15% ozone in oxygen at 25°C. up to 1 hr. at 0.5 psi (99). The ozonized films were stored up to 184 hr. at room temperature with no loss of grafting efficiency. When heated for 30 min. at 120°C. with acrylonitrile, the product contained 72.5% bound polyacrylonitrile. Even though the heating is carried out above the melting point of polyethylene, it is still difficult to imagine the film as anything but substantially surface grafted. Similar experiments with vinylpyrrolidone yield films which could be readily dyed. Homopolymerization may be reduced by using an equal mixture of cupric oxychloride and cuprous oxide added to the monomer (100).

A comparison of grafting by preozonization and preirradiation has been reported (99). After the pretreatment, films of polyethylene were heated 2 hr. at 120°C. in acrylonitrile, then extracted with dimethylformamide. The amount of bound polyacrylonitrile is shown in Table XII-19.

Vinylidene chloride has been surface-grafted to polyethylene by rapidly passing a film of polyethylene through a chamber containing 1.5% ozone,

TABLE XII-19
Comparison of Irradiation and Ozonization Initiation of Polyethylene–Acrylonitrile Graft Copolymers[a]

Treatment	Bound polyacrylonitrile, %
5 Mrad	61.0
1.5% O_3 for 5 hr.	85.8
5 Mrad 1.5% O_3 for 5 hr.	91.5

[a] Taken from ref. 99.

then heating in the monomer vapor at 95°C. By the same technique, vinyl acetate was grafted to cotton, acrylonitrile to poly(vinyl chloride) (101), and vinylpyridine to isotactic polypropylene (102).

Detailed studies of the ozonization of poly(vinyl chloride) (18 mg. O_3/l. O_2) revealed a maximum concentration of 1.0×10^{-4} mole peroxide/g. When decomposed at 25°C., the rate was determined as 4.6×10^{-7} sec.$^{-1}$, with an activation energy of 19.8 kcal./mole. The decomposition was accelerated by hydrogen chloride and by vinylidene chloride, but diminished by the presence of acrylonitrile. A decrease in molecular weight was observed. Rates of grafting were as follows: acrylic acid > vinylidene chloride > methyl acrylate > methyl methacrylate > acrylonitrile > styrene > vinyl acetate.

Polyamides, polylactams, and poly(ethylene terephthalate) have been grafted by this technique with a variety of vinyl monomers (103–106). The amount of graft formed was greatly reduced when highly oriented polyamide films were used (104). The locus of grafting is apparently confined to the surface region.

The wettability of open-cell polyurethane sponge has been improved by superficial ozonolysis, surface grafting with vinyl acetate, and subsequent hydrolysis (107).

3. Miscellaneous Methods

The pyrolysis of polytetrafluoroethylene leads to breakage of carbon–carbon bonds, $E_a = 74$ kcal./mole, and results in the formation of free radicals (108). Deacon (109), utilizing this reaction, rapidly heated polytetrafluoroethylene to 400°C., then immersed the film in styrene. The pyrolysis-induced free radicals initiated the growth of a coating of polystyrene which could be readily bonded to aluminum foil.

Polyethylene films or tubing have been thinly coated with tetrafluoroethylene by heating with the monomer in an aqueous solution of ammonium perfluorocarboxylate and persulfate. The monomer was maintained under 300 psi pressure (49).

Cellulose fabrics, esterified or etherified with unsaturated acids or alcohol on the surface, may be further modified by surface copolymerization with an additional monomer (110). Little or no loss of tensile strength was observed. The fabrics obtained were wash-fast, resilient, and the threads not bonded together.

C. CHEMICAL TREATMENT OF SURFACES

Recognition of the benefits of surface treatment of polymers is not confined to the interpolymer field. Numerous examples of more conventional chemical treatments abound in the literature, usually in patent form. In the field of textiles and adhesives, considerable technology has been evolved. It is not always apparent whether many of the treatments employed are actually chemical interactions with the polymer surface rather than physical deposition. With this reservation, examples are presented of the various types of chemical reaction which appear to be essentially topographical.

1. Oxidation

Most surface oxidation reactions have been carried out on polyethylene film. Studies of the thermal oxidation of polymer by Baum (111) revealed that initially hydroperoxides are formed. As the reaction proceeds, a maximum concentration is achieved, then the hydroperoxide catalyzes the production of aldehydes and ketones, and finally of acids and esters (112). Simultaneous crosslinking and scission occur (111).

When subjected to a corona discharge, polyethylene loses weight, the loss being independent of the film thickness. At first carbonyl groups appear, reach a maximum concentration, and then readily detectable oxalic acid and ethylene glycol appear on the surface (113). Hougen (114) has advanced an ionic mechanism in an attempt to explain this phenomenon, which does not occur with γ- and neutron-irradiation.

Treatment of polyethylene with ozone yields a less wettable, faintly acid surface. Carboxylic acids and ketones are found, with a slight overall increase in weight (113).

Various surface oxidation techniques have been employed to impart adhesion and printability to polyethylene film. Extrusion into air, rapidly followed by a hot quenching bath containing hydrogen peroxide, nitrous acid, or alkaline hypochloride, gives a printable surface (115). Alternatively, the film may be subjected to various discharges in air, such as a Tesla coil, corona (116–118), or ultraviolet irradiation just below the melting point (119). Carbon black has been incorporated in the last case to confine the reaction to the surface (120).

Spectroscopic examination reveals the formation of carbonyl and olefinic groups which disappear when the treated film is rubbed with a moist tissue (118). Subjecting the film to an oxidizing flame renders polyethylene (121, 122) and poly(ethylene terephthalate) (123) printable, as does treatment with 0.1% ozone in the presence of ultraviolet light (124,125).

Arbit, Greisser, and Haine (126) showed that the adhesion of polyethylene film to other materials depends on the degree of surface oxidation. When manufactured in the absence of air, adhesion was negligible. The higher processing temperatures now possible with linear polyethylene (> 325°F.) cause sufficient oxidation of the surface so that further treatment is unnecessary (127).

An interesting method of determining the degree of hydrophilic functional groups present on the surface has been recently described (128). After treating polyethylene film with pyrosulfuric acid (25% SO_3) and chlorine, the washed and dried films were immersed in aqueous methylene blue solution. After thorough washing with water, the surface-adherent dye was removed with alcoholic hydrogen chloride. The optical density at 666 mμ, under given conditions, was referred to as the MBR value. Values are summarized in Table XII-20.

Protein films, deposited from solution, adhered well to treated polyethylene when MBR values were in the range 0.08–0.250.

When pretreated with chromic acid, both polyethylene (129) and polypropylene (130) exhibit markedly greater adhesion to polar polymers. The

TABLE XII-20
MBR Values of Surface-Oxidized Polyethylene Film[a]

Time, sec.	Treatment	MBR value
	Untreated	0.050
5	Pyrosulfuric acid	0.183
30	Pyrosulfuric acid	0.224
300	Chlorine	0.054
600	Chlorine	0.063
1800	Chlorine	0.082

[a] Taken from ref. 128.

former, subsequently thinly coated with a vinylidene chloride terpolymer, was impermeable to oxygen and more resistant to grease, oil, abrasion, and high temperatures (131).

The greasy feel of polyethylene can be removed by a 2 min. immersion in a bath containing fuming nitric acid and concentrated hydrochloric acid, followed by neutralization and washing. Oxidation of the side chains is postulated (132).

A sevenfold increase in the adhesion of polytetrafluoroethylene to a pressure-sensitive tape has been recorded, by subjecting the former to ultraviolet irradiation for 60 sec. at low pressure, then exposing to air (133).

2. Acid or Alkali Treatment

The exposure of polyethylene film to concentrated sulfuric acid, hydrochloric acid, and 30% sodium hydroxide at 50°C. has little or no effect, but concentrated nitric acid causes embrittlement (134). At higher temperatures (150°C.), however, sulfonation occurs (135). When treated at 50°C. with 8% oleum, polyethylene fabric may be dyed with crystal violet and readily discharges static electricity as shown in Table XII-21.

After sulfonation with fuming sulfuric acid, polyethylene films have been treated first with ethylenediamine, then with a terpolymer of vinylidene chloride, acrylonitrile, and acrylic acid (136). When vinylpyridine replaced the acrylic acid (137), treatment with diamine was unnecessary. Such films exhibited better clarity, scuff resistance, and reduced permeabilities to gases and vapors.

Various lacquers may be strongly bonded to polyethylene by pretreating the latter with 95% chlorosulfonic acid for a few seconds. After hydrolysis in air and drying, the lacquer is applied (138).

TABLE XII-21
Static Discharge of Polyethylene Fabric after Treatment with 8% Oleum at 50°C.[a]

Treatment time, min.	Discharge time, sec.[b]
Control	>5000
5	240
10	60
15	30
50	0

[a] Taken from ref. 135.

[b] Time required to discharge an electroscope charged to 1000 v.

By treating polyethylene containers first with fluorosulfonic acid, then aqueous alkali, the surface is permanently colored amber. These vessels may then be used to store light-sensitive compounds (139).

A 30 sec. dip in trichloroacetic acid, enhanced by the presence of chromic or chromate salts, renders the surface of poly(ethylene terephthalate) strongly adhesive to polyethylene and polyamides (140).

Linear polypropylene has been surface-modified by first rapidly treating the film with chlorinating, sulfonating, or chlorosulfonating agents. After washing, the film is treated with an amine or imine and may then be used as a base for photographic gelatin coatings (141).

Hydrophobic surfaces, such as polystyrene, and phenol–formaldehyde resins have been modified by exposure, for a few minutes at room temperature, to the liquid or vapors of fuming sulfuric acid, sulfur trioxide, or chlorosulfonic acid. The surface is unimpaired, even optically, and antifogging lenses have been prepared in this way. Improved adhesion, coloring with basic dyes (142), and antistatic properties (143) have been reported.

Depending on the time of treatment with concentrated nitric acid, polymethacrylates may be rendered progressively opaque (144).

Polyacrylonitrile fibers, surface-hydrolyzed by boiling 10 min. in 2% caustic solution, are readily amenable to sulfonate dyes (145). Wool fibers and fabrics have been shrink-proofed by treatment with nonswelling solutions of acids or alkalis (146).

High polystyrene–butadiene resins, polyisobutylene, and natural rubber, first lightly abraded at the surface, then treated with sulfuric acid, boiling hydrochloric acid, or alkaline potassium permanganate, have increased wettability and adhesion to polar cements (147).

3. Halogenation

Modification of polyethylene film has been carried out by exposure to the vapor or solutions of chlorine, usually in the dark. The optimum degree of substitution is reported to be 25–100 mg. chlorine/100 cm.^{2} At this level, the original transparency is unaffected, while dielectric heat-sealability, dyeability (148), and printability (149) are improved. After chlorination and coating with a vinylidene chloride latex, a film "impermeable to aromas" results (150).

The treatment of preformed polyethylene bottles with fluorine gas at room temperature for 12 hr. resulted in a weight gain of 3.5%. When the bottles were filled with an alkyl caprolactam, the unmodified containers lost 5.7% by weight after 40 days. The fluorinated vessels lost only 0.4% and had no residual odor after washing (151).

Bromination or chlorination of abraded natural rubber and polyisobutylene surfaces increases adhesion to polar adhesives such as those based on nitrocellulose (147). Polyethylene, chlorosulfonated with a mixture of SO_2/Cl_2 with a molecular excess of SO_2 under ultraviolet irradiation, then may be printed by the relief, intaglio, or flat process (152).

4. Silicon Derivatives

A variety of thermoplastics have been treated with alkyl or alkenyl halosilanes. Generally, the materials become opaque, but improved heat, stain, and scratch resistance is reported. The thermoplastic is first immersed in the organohalosilane at an elevated temperature, removed, and the coating allowed slowly to hydrolyze in air (153). By similarly employing hydroxyl- or amine-containing organosilanes with glass cloth used for laminating, an increase in the static bending strengths of 25–45% was found (154).

Cellulose esters, such as acetate and butyrate, may be treated with the vapors of dimethyldichlorosilane, then hydrolyzed. The thin, chemically bonded silane surface can then strongly adsorb metal atoms and may be further coated by drawing through a photographic silvering solution (155).

5. Miscellaneous Treatments

Polymers of tetrafluoroethylene and trifluorochloroethylene exhibit both extreme inertness to most chemicals and good physical properties. However, use of these polymers as protective coatings was initially limited by their lack of bonding with conventional adhesives.

Polytetrafluoroethylene, when briefly treated with 1% sodium in liquid ammonia, darkens at the surface. If the immersion is prolonged, the surface becomes carbonized and brittle. After 1–5 sec. immersion, the treated darkened surfaces may be strongly bonded with conventional adhesives to metals and other materials (156). Such films may be nickel-plated, then soldered, and find uses in high temperature capacitors (157). When coated with a lead–zinc–silver alloy, the resistivity is low enough for electrical shielding purposes but high enough for use as extended area heating elements (158).

Similarly, polytrifluorochloroethylene has been treated with solutions of Li, Na, Ca, Ba, or Mg in liquid ammonia. The surface-modified materials are readily adherent to conventional polar adhesives (159), can be metallized (160), and can be used as a backing for a pressure-sensitive tape (161). In addition, polytetrafluoroethylene may be bonded to other materials after 5 min. treatment with sodium–naphthalene in dimethyl glycol, under nitrogen (162). Microscopic examination of the films after 2–3 sec. immersion showed the penetration to be less than 10^{-4} cm. There is no change in the diffraction pattern, dielectric constant, or dissipation factor (163). While polyethylene, poly(vinyl fluoride) and polytetrafluoroethylene are inert to refluxing butylamine (164), polychlorotrifluorethylene can be surface-modified with a variety of amines. The films were refluxed for 0.5–18 hr. with sodium hydroxide solutions of amines, such as 4-diallylethylamine, containing functional groups capable of further reaction with the chosen adhesive (165).

Natural rubber and other polymers containing reactive hydrogen may be surface reacted with aliphatic diazo compounds such as bisazodicarboxylic acid esters. The treated surface was then pressed against a metal plate spread with a diisocyanate. The bond was considerably stronger than that obtained with the diisocyanate alone (166). A mixture consisting primarily of diisocyanates and a benzoyl compound, when reacted on the surface of, for example, poly(vinyl fluoride), yields an ultraviolet-absorbing surface with consequently improved weathering properties (167). Active hydrogens have been induced on the surface of poly(ethylene terephthalate) both by hydrolysis with 2% sodium hydroxide and reduction with lithium aluminum hydride. The reaction is carried out until there is a weight loss of 0.5–2%. When further treated with various diisocyanate–polyglycol reaction products, the fabrics are free from objectionable static charge (168).

A series of reactions on the surface of methyl methacrylate–maleic anhydride copolymers has been reported (169). Heptane or methanol was used as a solvent to reduce surface swelling. Half-esters of heptane-soluble alcohols were formed by heating up to 16 hr. at 70°C. with 0.5% sodium carbonate. Amination was reported with most common primary and secondary amines after 45 min. immersion at 25°C., yielding materials with hard, clear surfaces. After hydrolysis of the copolymer with potassium hydroxide, various metals salts were formed, giving improved scratch resistance. Similarly, salts formed on the surface of copolymers of acrylic acid with methyl methacrylate and methyl acrylate, such as Cu^{++}, Ni^{++}, UO_2^{++}, result in improved abrasion, heat, and solvent resistance (170).

Increased tensile, resistance to heat deformation and adhesion of ink are reported for surface-crosslinked linear polyethylene. This is achieved by spraying the surface with 1% solutions of peroxides or ammonium persulfate and then heating. Reduced swelling and stress cracking are also claimed (171).

References

1. Alexander, P., A. Charlesby, and M. Ross, *Proc. Royal Soc. (London)*, **A223**, 892 (1954); *Chem. Abstr.*, **48**, 8079f (1954).
2. Lawton, E. J., A. M. Bueche, and J. S. Balwit, *Nature*, **172**, 76 (1953); *Chem. Abstr.*, **47**, 12003d (1953).
3. Wall, L., *J. Polymer Sci.*, **17**, 141 (1955).
4. Okamura, S., T. Iwasaki, Y. Kobayashi, and K. Hayashi, *Large Radiation Sources Industry Proc. Conf. Warsaw 1959*, Vol. 1, p. 459.
5. Okamura, S., T. Manabe, S. Futami, T. Iwasaki, A. Nakajima, K. Odan, H. Inagaki, and I. Sakurada, *Proc. 2nd Intern. Conf. Peaceful Uses Atomic Energy, Geneva 1958*, Vol. 29, United Nations, 1958, p. 176.
6. Charlesby, A., *Plastics (London)*, **18**, 142 (1953).
7. Henglein, A., *J. Phys. Chem.*, **63**, 1852 (1959).
8. Swallow, A. J., *Radiation Chemistry of Organic Compounds*, Pergamon Press, New York, 1960.
9. Bovey, F. A., *The Effects of Ionizing Radiation on Natural and Synthetic High Polymers*, Polymer Reviews Series, Vol. I, Interscience, New York, 1958.
10. Chapiro, A., and M. Magat, Canadian Patent 620,826 (to Centre National de la Recherche Scientifique), May 23, 1961.
11. Prevot-Bérnas A., A. Chapiro, C. Cousin, Y. Landler, and M. Magat, *Discussions Faraday Soc.*, **12**, 98 (1952); *Chem. Abstr.*, **48**, 8079d (1954).
12. Miller, A. A., E. J. Lawton, and J. S. Balwit, *J. Phys. Chem.*, **60**, 599 (1956).
13. Bouby, L., A. Chapiro, M. Magat, E. Migirdicyan, A. Prevot-Bérnas, L. Reinisch, and J. Sebban, *Proc. 1st Intern. Conf. Peaceful Uses Atomic Energy, Geneva, 1955*, Vol. 7, United Nations, 1956, p. 526.
14. Graham, R. K., M. S. Gluckman, and M. J. Kampf, *J. Polymer Sci.*, **38**, 417 (1959).
15. Odian, G., A. Rossi, E. Ratchik, and T. Acker, *J. Polymer Sci.*, **54**, S11 (1961).
16. Restaino, A. J., and W. N. Reed, *J. Polymer Sci.*, **36**, 499 (1959).
17. Schneider, E. E., *J. Chem. Phys.*, **23**, 978 (1955).
18. T. I. (Group Services) Ltd., British Patent 864,893 (by S. H. Pinner), Apr. 12, 1961.
19. Dobó, J., A. Somogyi, and E. Lakner, *Plaste Kautschuk*, **8**, 393 (1960); *Chem. Abstr.*, **55**, 14969c (1961).
20. Ballantine, D., P. Colombo, A. Glines, B. Manowitz, and D. Metz, Brookhaven National Lab. Report BNL, 414, T-18 (1956).
21. Ballantine, D. S., A. Glines, D. J. Metz, J. Behr, R. B. Mesrobian, and A. J. Restaino, *J. Polymer Sci.*, **19**, 219 (1956).
22. Takamatsu, T., *Rika Gaku Kenkyusho Hokoku*, **37**, 1 (1961); *Chem. Abstr.*, **55**, 25350f (1961).

23. Shinohara, K., and T. Takamatsu, *Rika Gaku Kenkyusho Hokoku*, **36**, 652 (1960); *Chem. Abstr.*, **55**, 21657b (1961).
24. Hardy, G., and J. Dobó, *Chem. Prumsyl*, **9**, 215 (1959); *Chem. Abstr.*, **53**, 15629i (1959).
25. Chapiro, A., *J. Polymer Sci.*, **34**, 481 (1959).
26. Centre National de la Recherche Scientifique, British Patent 801,528, Sept. 17, 1958; *Chem. Abstr.*, **53**, 23080d (1959).
27. Myers, A. W., C. E. Rogers, V. Stannett, M. Szwarc, G. S. Patterson, Jr., A. S. Hoffman, and E. W. Merrill, *J. Appl. Polymer Sci.*, **4**, 159 (1960).
28. Sakurada, I., T. Okada, and E. Kugo, *Doitai to Hoshasen*, **2**, 296 (1959); *Chem. Abstr.*, **53**, 15635c (1959).
29. Chapiro, A., and V. Stannett, *Intern. J. Appl. Radiation Isotopes*, **8**, 614 (1960); *Chem. Abstr.*, **55**, 17070c (1961).
30. Szánto, I., and K. Gál, *J. Polymer Sci.*, **53**, 321 (1961).
31. Société des Usines Chimiques Rhône-Poulenc, French Patent 1,181,893, June 19, 1959; *Chem. Abstr.*, **54**, 26017e (1960).
32. Usmanov, Kh. U., B. I. Aikhodzhaev, and U. Azizov, *Mezhdunar. Simpozium po Makromolekul. Khim. Dokl. Moscow 1960, Sektsiya*, **3**, 344; *Chem. Abstr.*, **55**, 10956a (1961).
33. Odian, G., A. Rossi, and E. Trachtenberg, paper presented at the 137th meeting of the American Chemical Society, Cleveland, Ohio, Apr. 5–14, 1960.
34. Pinner, S. H., and V. Wycherley, *Plastics* (*London*), **22**, 503 (1957).
35. Chapiro, A., E. Goethals, and A. Jendrichowska-Bonamour, *J. Chim. Phys.*, **57**, 787 (1960); *Chem. Abstr.*, **55**, 6023a (1961).
36. Harwood, J., H. Hausner, J. Morse, and W. Rauch, *Effect of Radiation on Materials*, Reinhold, New York, 1958, p. 257.
37. Centre National de la Recherche Scientifique, British Patent 883,728, Dec. 6, 1961; *Chem. Abstr.*, **57**, 1089f (1962).
38. Société Anon. des Manufactures des Glaces et Produits Chimiques de Saint-Gobain, Chauny & Cirey, French Patent 1,147,722 (by J. Gabilly and M. Jobard), Nov. 28, 1957; *Chem. Abstr.*, **54**, 2819b (1960).
39. Mock, R. A., and W. N. Vanderkooi, *J. Polymer Sci.*, **56**, 69 (1962).
40. Bevington, J. C., and D. E. Eaves, *Nature*, **178**, 1112 (1956).
41. E. I. duPont deNemours & Co., British Patent 845,897–8, Aug. 24, 1960.
42. Ballantine, D., A. Glines, G. Adler, and D. J. Metz, *J. Polymer Sci.*, **34**, 419 (1959).
43. Ballantine, D., D. J. Metz, J. Gard, and G. Adler, *J. Appl. Polymer Sci.*, **1**, 371 (1959).
44. Hoffman, A. S., E. R. Gilliland, E. W. Merrill, and W. H. Stockmayer, *J. Polymer Sci.*, **34**, 461 (1959).
45. Lipatova, T. E., Yu. S. Lipatov, and N. L. Tutaeva, *Vysokomolekul. Soedin.*, **3**, 184 (1961); *Chem. Abstr.*, **55**, 26520d (1961).
46. Henglein, A., and W. Schnabel, *Makromol. Chem.*, **25**, 119 (1958).
47. Henglein, A., W. Schnabel, and K. Heine, *Angew. Chem.*, **70**, 461 (1958).
48. Oster, G., British Patent 856,884, Dec. 21, 1960; *Chem. Abstr.*, **55**, 13907f (1961).
49. Burk, R. E., and E. H. Price, U. S. Patent 2,999,772 (to E. I. duPont deNemours & Co.), Sept. 12, 1961; *Chem. Abstr.*, **56**, 588h (1962).
50. New Japan Nitrogenous Fertilizer Co., Ltd., Japanese Patent 23810(61), Dec. 18, 1961.

51. E. I. duPont deNemours & Co., British Patent 875,131, Aug. 16, 1961; U. S. Patent 2,999,056; *Chem. Abstr.*, **56,** 4991c (1962).
52. E. I. duPont deNemours & Co., British Patent 839,483, June 29, 1960; *Chem. Abstr.*, **55,** 2183a (1961).
53. E. I. duPont deNemours & Co., Belgian Patent 603,086, Appl. Apr. 24, 1961.
54. Richardson, R., paper presented at the 9th Canadian High Polymer Forum, Toronto, Ontario, Oct. 1959.
55. Roberts, R., *Rubber Plastics Age*, **40,** 145 (1959).
56. Nippon Rayon Co., Ltd., Japanese Patent 4250(61) (by M. Tsuruta, S. Okamura, F. Kobayashi, and T. Iwasaki), Apr. 27, 1961; *Chem. Abstr.*, **55,** 25365a (1961).
57. Shinohara, Y., *J. Appl. Polymer Sci.*, **1,** 251 (1959).
58. Levine, C. A., U. S. Patent 2,979,447 (to Dow Chemical Co.), Apr. 11, 1961; *Chem. Abstr.*, **55,** 24123f (1961).
59. Gaylord, N. G., U. S. Patent 2,907,675 (to E. I. duPont deNemours & Co.), Oct. 6, 1959; *Chem. Abstr.*, **55,** 24102a (1961).
60. Kobayashi, Y., *J. Polymer Sci.*, **51,** 359 (1961).
61. Restaino, A., and W. Reed, The Martin Co. Radiation Effect Unit, Progress Report II E. R. 8519, 13 (1956).
62. Chapiro, A., *J. Polymer Sci.*, **34,** 439 (1959).
63. Burlant, W. J., and D. H. Green, *J. Polymer Sci.*, **28,** 252 (1958).
64. Cline, E. T., U. S. Patent 2,956,899 (to E. I. duPont deNemours & Co.), Oct. 18, 1960; *Chem. Abstr.*, **55,** 6918f (1961).
65. Shinohara, Y., and K. Tomioka, *J. Polymer Sci.*, **44,** 195 (1960).
66. Chapiro, A., *J. Polymer Sci.*, **48,** 109 (1960).
67. Minnema, L., J. F. A. Hazenberg, L. Callaghan, and S. H. Pinner, *J. Appl. Polymer Sci.*, **4,** 246 (1960).
68. B. X. Plastics Co. Ltd., British Patent 871,572 (by R. R. Smith, D. C. M. Mann, and J. F. Salmon), June 28, 1961; *Chem. Abstr.*, **55,** 25373f (1961).
69. Sykes, J. A. W., and J. K. Thomas, *J. Polymer Sci.*, **55,** 721 (1961).
70. Houillères du Bassin-du-Nord et du Pas-de-Calais, French Patents 1,160,106–8, July 8, 1958; *Chem. Abstr.*, **54,** 23446d (1960).
71. Centre Nationale de la Recherche Scientifique, British Patent 809,838, Mar. 4, 1959; *Chem. Abstr.*, **53,** 11894i (1959).
72. B. X. Plastics Co. Ltd., British Patent 863,211 (by R. R. Smith), Mar. 22, 1961; *Chem. Abstr.*, **55,** 18198e (1961).
73. E. I. duPont deNemours & Co., British Patent 801,479, Sept. 17, 1958; *Chem. Abstr.*, **53,** 4815c (1959).
74. Minnesota Mining and Manufacturing Co., British Patent 848,917, Sept. 21, 1960.
75. E. I. duPont deNemours & Co., British Patent 838,412, June 22, 1960; *Chem. Abstr.*, **54,** 25866i (1960).
76. E. I. duPont deNemours & Co., British Patent 834,557, May 11, 1960; *Chem. Abstr.*, **54,** 25870i (1960).
77. E. I. duPont deNemours & Co., British Patent 820,120, Sept. 16, 1959; *Chem. Abstr.*, **54,** 5161c (1960).
78. Graham, B., U. S. Patent 2,940,869 (to E. I. duPont deNemours & Co.), June 14, 1960; *Chem. Abstr.*, **54,** 21787c (1960).
79. Esso Research and Engineering Co., British Patent 784,624, Oct. 9, 1957; *Chem. Abstr.*, **52,** 14219f (1958).

80. E. I. duPont deNemours & Co., British Patent 838,413, June 22, 1960; *Chem. Abstr.*, **54,** 25867e (1960).
81. E. I. duPont deNemours & Co., British Patent 802,620, Oct. 8, 1958.
82. E. I. duPont deNemours & Co., British Patent 802,621, Oct. 8, 1958.
83. Barkalov, I. M., V. I. Gol'danskii, and B. G. Dzantiev, Russian Patent 129,015, June 1, 1960; *Chem. Abstr.*, **55,** 1091a (1961).
84. General Electric Co., British Patent 871,784, June 28, 1961; *Chem. Abstr.*, **55,** 26523g (1961).
85. Montecatini, S.p.A., British Patent 843,190, Aug. 4, 1960; *Chem. Abstr.*, **55,** 2180e (1961).
86. Montecatini S.p.A., British Patent 850,471, Oct. 5, 1960; *Chem. Abstr.*, **55,** 9894d (1961).
87. Natta, G., E. Beati, and F. Severini, U. S. Patent 3,020,174 (to Montecatini S.p.A.), Feb. 6, 1962.
88. Bonvicini, A., A. Monaci, and V. Cappuccio, Canadian Patent 618,950 (to Montecatini S.p.A.), Apr. 25, 1961.
89. van Schooten, J., and P. W. O. Wijga in *High Temperature Resistance and Thermal Degradation of Polymers, Monograph 13,* Soc. Chem. Ind., London, 1961, p. 432.
90. Beati, E., F. Severini, and S. Toffano, *J. Polymer Sci.*, **51,** 455 (1961).
91. Montecatini S.p.A., Italian Patent 602,489, Appl. Jan. 1, 1958; *Chem. Abstr.*, **56,** 1612h (1962).
92. Cappuccio, V., A. Monaci, and A. Bonvicini, Canadian Patent 632,551 (to Montecatini S.p.A.), Dec. 12, 1961.
93. Minsker, K. S., and I. Z. Shapiro, *Tr. po Khim. i Khim. Tekhnol.*, **3,** 609 (1960); *Chem. Abstr.*, **55,** 24094g (1961).
94. Mozgova, K. K., V. V. Korshak, and M. A. Shkolina, Russian Patent 131,084, Aug. 20, 1960; *Chem. Abstr.*, **55,** 6048g (1961).
95. Montecatini S.p.A., British Patent 878,523, Oct. 4, 1961; *Chem Abstr.*, **56,** 8960a (1962).
96. Okamura, S., and T. Manabe, *Bull. Chem. Soc. Japan*, **33,** 1526 (1960); *Chem. Abstr.*, **55,** 13903d (1961).
97. Farbwerke Hoechst A. G., German Patent 1,084,175 (by A. H. Grimminger), June 23, 1960; *Chem. Abstr.*, **55,** 27979c (1961).
98. Rieke, J. K., and C. Moore, U. S. Patent 2,987,501 (to Dow Chemical Co.), June 6, 1961; *Chem. Abstr.*, **55,** 25374b (1961).
99. Dow Chemical Co., British Patent 825,680, Dec. 16, 1959; *Chem. Abstr.*, **54,** 9361i (1960).
100. Urchick, D., U. S. Patent 3,008,920 (to Dow Chemical Co.), Nov. 14, 1961; *Chem. Abstr.*, **56,** 4973b (1962).
101. Polyplastic, German Patent 1,100,286 (by Y. Landler and P. Lebel), Appl. Oct. 11, 1958; *Chem. Abstr.*, **56,** 2588d (1962).
102. Polyplastic, British Patent 883,793, Dec. 6, 1961; *Chem. Abstr.*, **57,** 3638c (1962).
103a. Korshak, V. V., K. K. Mozgova, and M. A. Shkolina, *Vysokomolekul. Soedin.*, **1,** 1573 (1959); *Chem. Abstr.*, **54,** 14755c (1960).
103b. Korshak, V. V., K. K. Mozgova, and M. A. Shkolina, *Vysokomolekul. Soedin.*, **1,** 1604 (1959); *Chem. Abstr.*, **54,** 14755f (1960).
104. Korshak, V. V., K. K. Mozgova, and M. A. Shkolina, *Vysokomolekul. Soedin.*, **1,** 1364 (1959).

105. Korshak, V. V., K. K. Mozgova, and M. A. Shkolina, *Dokl. Akad. Nauk SSSR*, **122,** 609 (1958); *Chem. Abstr.*, **53,** 1812a (1959).
106. Korshak, V. V., and K. K. Mozgova, Russian Patent 116,268, Jan. 19, 1959; *Chem. Abstr.*, **53,** 19460g (1959).
107. Polyplastic, French Patent 1,176,772 (by Y. Landler and P. Lebel), Apr. 15, 1959; *Chem. Abstr.*, **54,** 25970a (1960).
108. Friedman, H., U. S. Dept. Com. Office Tech. Serv. PB Report 145182.
109. Deacon, R., *Res. Correspondence*, **9,** S 22 (1956).
110. Fetscher, C. A., U. S. Patent 2,789,030 (to Cluett, Peabody & Co., Ind.), Apr. 16, 1957; *Chem. Abstr.*, **51,** 10085d (1957).
111. Baum, B., *J. Appl. Polymer Sci.*, **2,** 281 (1959).
112. Beachell, H. C., and G. W. Tarbet, *J. Polymer Sci.*, **45,** 451 (1960).
113. Cooper, G. D., and M. Prober, *J. Polymer Sci.*, **44,** 397 (1960).
114. Hougen, L., *Nature*, **188,** 577 (1960).
115. Wolinski, L. E., U. S. Patent 2,878,519 (to E. I. duPont deNemours & Co.), Mar. 24, 1959; *Chem. Abstr.*, **53,** 12745c (1959).
116. Berthold, G. H., and A. S. Mancib, U. S. Patent 2,859,480 (to Olin Mathieson Chemical Corp.), Nov. 11, 1958; *Chem. Abstr.*, **53,** 5749h (1959).
117. Société Anon. du Blanc Omya, French Patent 1,195,383, Nov. 17, 1959; *Chem. Abstr.*, **54,** 21862c (1960).
118a. Rossmann, K., *J. Polymer Sci.*, **19,** 141 (1956).
118b. Rossmann, K., *J. Polymer Sci.*, **21,** 565 (1956).
119. Siemens-Schuckertwerke A. G., German Patent 1,023,880 (by E. Sauter, G. Buerklin, and E. Karsten), Feb. 6, 1958; *Chem. Abstr.*, **54,** 21860c (1960).
120. Mannesmann A. G., German Patent 1,106,069 (by H. Niklas), May 4, 1961; *Chem. Abstr.*, **55,** 26539i (1961).
121. Loukomsky, S. A., U. S. Patent 2,767,103 (to Plax Corp.), Oct. 16, 1956; *Chem. Abstr.*, **51,** 4057h (1957).
122. Grow, H. J., J. H. Prichard, and W. D. Paist, U. S. Patent 2,795,820 (to Celanese Corp. of America), June 18, 1957; *Chem. Abstr.*, **51,** 13466b (1957).
123. Imperial Chemical Industries Ltd., British Patent 788,365 (by W. E. F. Gates), Jan. 2, 1958; *Chem. Abstr.*, **52,** 9657f (1958).
124a. Wolinski, L. E., U. S. Patent 2,805,960 (to E. I. duPont deNemours & Co.), Sept. 10, 1957; *Chem. Abstr.*, **52,** 1684f (1958).
124b. Wolinski, L. E., U. S. Patent 2,801,446 (to E. I. duPont deNemours & Co.), Aug. 6, 1957; *Chem. Abstr.*, **52,** 6845c (1958).
124c. Wolinski, L. E., U. S. Patent 2,801,447 (to E. I. duPont deNemours & Co.), Aug. 6, 1957; *Chem. Abstr.*, **52,** 6845d (1958).
125. Imperial Chemical Industries Ltd., British Patent 802,974 (by W. E. F. Gates), Oct. 15, 1958; *Chem. Abstr.*, **53,** 7623h (1959).
126. Arbit, H. A., E. E. Greisser, and W. A. Haine, *Tappi*, **40,** 161 (1957); *Chem. Abstr.*, **51,** 7715e (1957).
127. Swerlick, I., U. S. Patent 2,941,254 (to E. I. duPont deNemours & Co.), June 21, 1960; *Chem. Abstr.*, **54,** 20332b (1960).
128. Bersin, T., and A. Müller, U. S. Patent 2,979,422, Apr. 11, 1961; *Chem. Abstr.*, **55,** 20510f (1961).
129. Schrader, W. H., and M. J. Bodner, *Plastics Technol.*, **3,** 988 (1957); *Chem. Abstr.*, **52,** 3394h (1958).

130. Gevaert Photo-Produkten N. V., Belgian Patent 569,129, Nov. 1, 1958; *Chem. Abstr.*, **53,** 1836a (1959).
131. Keller, T. W., C. W. Garvin, and J. G. McMillan, U. S. Patent 2,968,576 (to Howard Plastics, Inc.), Jan. 17, 1961; *Chem. Abstr.*, **55,** 12944d (1961).
132. Elliott, J. C., U. S. Patent 2,934,457 (to Bjorksten Research Laboratories, Inc.), Apr. 26, 1960; *Chem. Abstr.*, **54,** 16021h (1960).
133. Minnesota Mining & Manufacturing Co., British Patent 868,463, May 17, 1961; *Chem. Abstr.*, **56,** 592b (1962).
134. Ranalli, F., *Materie Plastiche,* **20,** 503 (1954); *Chem. Abstr.*, **49,** 663h (1955).
135. Walles, W. E., U. S. Patent 2,937,066 (to Dow Chemical Co.), May 17, 1960; *Chem. Abstr.*, **54,** 17905c (1960).
136. Walles, W. E., and H. G. Hahn, U. S. Patent 2,786,780 (to Dow Chemical Co.), Mar. 26, 1957; *Chem. Abstr.*, **51,** 10125h (1957).
137. Hahn, H. G., and W. E. Walles, U. S. Patent 2,786,783 (to Dow Chemical Co.), Mar. 26, 1957; *Chem. Abstr.*, **51,** 10125i (1957).
138. Nelson, J. A., Jr., and W. K. Vollmer, U. S. Patent 2,879,177 (to Union Carbide Corp.), Mar. 24, 1959; *Chem. Abstr.*, **53,** 11889f (1959).
139. Gilbert, E. E., and C. B. Miller, U. S. Patent 2,793,964 (to Allied Chemical & Dye Corp.), May 28, 1957; *Chem. Abstr.*, **51,** 13466a (1957).
140. Kalle & Co. A. G., German Patent 1,068,008 (by W. Brandt), Oct. 29, 1959; *Chem. Abstr.*, **55,** 16002c (1961).
141. Montecatini S.p.A., British Patent 868,159, May 17, 1961; *Chem. Abstr.*, **55,** 25378d (1961).
142. Staudinger, H. P., and H. M. Hutchinson, U. S. Patent 2,400,720 (to Distillers Co. Ltd.), May 21, 1946; *Chem. Abstr.*, **40,** 5295[3] (1946).
143. Dixon, R. R., and D. E. Baldwin, U. S. Patent 2,727,831 (to Westinghouse Electric Corp.), Dec. 20, 1955; *Chem. Abstr.*, **50,** 8248i (1956).
144. Bicker, R., and R. Winter, *Rev. Sci. Instr.*, **28,** 843 (1957); *Chem. Abstr.*, **52,** 8615h (1958).
145. Compagnie Francaise des Matières Colorantes, French Patent 1,057,729 (by A. Baron, L. Wallner, and M. Vinson), Mar. 10, 1954; *Chem. Abstr.*, **52,** 19153f (1958).
146. Takeda Chemical Industries Ltd., Japanese Patent 3200('61) (by K. Tamari and J. Kinukawa), Appl. Mar. 7, 1957; *Chem. Abstr.*, **56,** 15879d (1962).
147. Voyutskii, S. S., P. A. Rebinder, E. S. Khoroshaya, and S. I. Shur, *Dokl. Akad. Nauk SSSR,* **73,** 747 (1950); *Chem. Abstr.*, **45,** 899e (1951).
148. Imperial Chemical Industries Ltd., British Patent 581,717 (by J. R. Myles and D. Whittaker), Oct. 22, 1946; *Chem. Abstr.*, **41,** 1889f (1947).
149. Henderson, W. F., U. S. Patent 2,502,841 (to Visking Corp.), Apr. 4, 1950; *Chem. Abstr.*, **44,** 5613e (1950).
150. Farbwerke Hoechst A. G., British Patent 836,793, June 9, 1960; *Chem. Abstr.*, **54,** 26001f (1960).
151. Joffre, S. P., U. S. Patent 2,811,468 (to Shulton Inc.), Oct. 29, 1957; *Chem. Abstr.*, **52,** 2453g (1958).
152. Schneemann K.-G., German Patent 1,046,634 (by L. Jänecke and H. Lantermann), Dec. 18, 1958; *Chem. Abstr.*, **55,** 4218a (1961).
153. Baum, B., and J. Harding, U. S. Patent 2,921,870 (to Union Carbide Corp.), Jan. 19, 1960; *Chem. Abstr.*, **54,** 9356i (1960).

154. Avrasin, Ya. D., A. Ya. Korolev, and Ya. I. Mindlin, *Plasticheskie Massy*, **1960** (7), 31; *Chem. Abstr.*, **55**, 6027d (1961).
155. Martinson, L. E., and K. H. Sun, U. S. Patent 2,464,143 (to Eastman Kodak Co.), Mar. 8, 1949; *Chem. Abstr.*, **43**, 4520d (1949).
156. E. I. duPont deNemours & Co., British Patent 793,731, Apr. 23, 1958; *Chem. Abstr.*, **52**, 21241i (1958).
157. British Dielectric Research Ltd., British Patent 816,641 (by D. S. Margolis), July 15, 1959; *Chem. Abstr.*, **54**, 966g (1960).
158. Montecatini S.p.A., British Patent 841,334, July 13, 1960; *Chem. Abstr.*, **55**, 1068a (1961).
159. E. I. duPont deNemours & Co., British Patent 806,422, Dec. 23, 1958; *Chem. Abstr.*, **53**, 11890e (1959).
160. Kelley, F. M., U. S. Patent 2,898,228 (to E. I. duPont deNemours & Co.), Aug. 4, 1959; *Chem. Abstr.*, **53**, 23098f (1959).
161. Fields, R. T., U. S. Patent 2,946,710 (to E. I. duPont deNemours & Co.), July 26, 1960; *Chem. Abstr.*, **55**, 6939c (1961).
162. Rappaport, G., U. S. Patent 2,809,130 (to General Motors Corp.), Oct. 8, 1957; *Chem. Abstr.*, **52**, 2460b (1958).
163. Nelson, E., T. Kilduff, and A. Benderly, *Ind. Eng. Chem.*, **50**, 329 (1958).
164. Bro, M. I., *J. Appl. Polymer Sci.*, **1**, 310 (1959).
165. Cox, R. P., L. L. Yaeger, and R. W. Buetow, U. S. Patent 2,788,306 (to Pittsburgh Plate Glass Co.), Apr. 9, 1957; *Chem. Abstr.*, **51**, 10125f (1957).
166. Phoenix Gummiwerke A.-G., German Patent 930,655 (by W. Stegemann and G. Reuter), July 21, 1955; *Chem. Abstr.*, **52**, 17813d (1958).
167. Brasure, D. E., U. S. Patent 2,970,066 (to E. I. duPont deNemours & Co.), Jan. 31, 1961; *Chem. Abstr.*, **55**, 12925c (1961).
168. Collins, R. J., U. S. Patent 2,955,954 (to E. I. duPont deNemours & Co.), Oct. 11, 1960; *Chem. Abstr.*, **55**, 4044b (1961).
169. Seymour, R. B., I. Branum, Jr., and F. W. Hayward, *Ind. Eng. Chem.*, **41**, 1483 (1949).
170. Seymour, R. B., and I. Branum, Jr., *Ind. Eng. Chem.*, **41**, 1481 (1949).
171. Farbwerke Hoechst A. G., German Patent 1,056,822 (by A. Fischer, W. Müller, and H. Beuschel), May 6, 1959; *Chem. Abstr.*, **55**, 7917c (1961).

Chapter XIII

OXIDATIVE REACTIONS

W. L. Hawkins and F. H. Winslow

Bell Telephone Laboratories

A. INTRODUCTION

Atmospheric oxygen penetrates and reacts with porous regions in unprotected polymers exposed to photo or thermal radiation. Under moderate conditions, thermal reactions are usually referred to as *autoxidation.* For example, oxidative reactions are often autocatalytic, and have rates which depend on chemical composition, molecular structure, and morphology. It is the intricate interplay of these and other effects that governs the drying of paints, the deterioration of rubber and plastics, the spoilage of foods, and a multitude of other polymeric oxidations.

Despite the importance and prevalence of oxidative reactions, their chemistry remained a mystery until the late 1920's and early 1930's, when research on model compounds and rubber led to development of the concept of oxidation as a free radical, chain mechanism. It is now generally agreed that polymeric hydrocarbons, in particular the addition polymers, oxidize by this mechanism. Oxidation of most polymers usually results in deterioration of mechanical strength and dielectric properties, but oxidation may, as in the case of cellulose, be used to improve or regenerate certain physical properties of the polymer.

Although similarities are found in the oxidative reactions of many polymers, there are sufficient variations to warrant discussion of these reactions by polymer types, with emphasis on the polymeric hydrocarbons which have been the main subject of oxidation studies.

B. POLYMERIC HYDROCARBONS

Polymeric hydrocarbons oxidize by a free radical, chain mechanism similar to that proposed by Bolland and Gee (1) for the oxidation of volatile hydrocarbons. The mechanism which adequately accounts for the oxidative reaction of polymeric hydrocarbons such as polyethylene (Fig. XIII-1) is summarized in the series of reaction steps shown in reactions (1–9), where RH denotes polymer.

Initiation:

$$RH \xrightarrow{k_1} R\cdot \tag{1}$$

Propagation:

$$R\cdot + O_2 \xrightarrow{k_2} ROO\cdot \tag{2}$$

$$ROO\cdot + RH \xrightarrow{k_3} ROOH + R\cdot \tag{3}$$

Chain branching:

$$ROOH \xrightarrow{k_4} RO\cdot + HO\cdot \tag{4}$$

$$RO\cdot + RH \xrightarrow{k_5} ROH + R\cdot \tag{5}$$

$$HO\cdot + RH \xrightarrow{k_6} HOH + R\cdot \tag{6}$$

Termination:

$$2\,R\cdot \xrightarrow{k_7} \text{Inert products} \tag{7}$$

$$2\,ROO\cdot \xrightarrow{k_8} \text{Inert products} \tag{8}$$

$$R\cdot + ROO\cdot \xrightarrow{k_9} \text{Inert products} \tag{9}$$

The initiation rate (k_1) is extremely slow for saturated polymeric hydrocarbons in the dark and at room temperature. It is generally agreed that polymeric radicals (R·) are formed by absorption of heat, ultraviolet light, high energy radiation, mechanical stress, or by reaction of the polymer with radicals from a foreign source, but the exact mechanism of these reactions is not fully understood. Shelton and Vincent (2) and Bateman et al. (3) have suggested that in most polymers peroxide decomposition as indicated in reaction (4) is the principal source of radicals which initiate oxidation. Low concentrations of peroxides and other impurities are usually formed in polymers during processing. Shelton has observed a change in rate during the initial stages of oxidation which he attributes to the onset of bimolecular decomposition as the hydroperoxide accumulates.

Most polymeric hydrocarbons oxidize at an appreciable rate when exposed to ultraviolet radiation and/or elevated temperature. Outdoor weathering of polyethylene, for example, causes both dielectric and mechanical failure of the polymer in less than two years (4,5). Both polyethylene and polypropylene oxidize at an appreciable rate in the dark at 60°C. (6). Photooxidation of polyethylene is evident after only a few months of outdoor exposure (4,5). Ions of certain metals also increase the initiation rate by catalyzing hydroperoxide decomposition, presumably by homolytic cleavage into radicals. Copper is one of the active catalysts for polyolefin oxidation. The effect is far greater with polypropylene, poly-1-butene, and related polyolefins having large concentrations of tertiary carbon atoms in the main chain than it is with polyethylene. Certain catalyst residues, occluded in the polymer during polymerization, are active oxidative catalysts.

Once radicals have been generated within the polymer, rapid reaction with oxygen occurs forming peroxy radicals (eq. 2). This reaction depends, of course, on the availability of oxygen, and consequently is limited both by sample thickness and by the relative diffusion rates of molecular oxygen and volatile oxidation products. Hydrogen abstraction by peroxy radicals (eq. 3) leads to hydroperoxide formation. The overall propagation rate depends on the rate of hydrogen abstraction, which is usually much slower than the rate of formation of peroxy radicals (k_2) in the preceding step.

Hydroperoxides have been detected in the initial stages of autoxidation by infrared spectroscopy (7,8) and by iodometric titration (9). Numerous secondary products accumulate as the reaction proceeds, several of which have been identified by their characteristic infrared absorption (8). Decomposition of hydroperoxides on tertiary carbon atoms leads to cleavage of carbon-carbon bonds as in reaction (10), where R denotes a branch on the main chain.

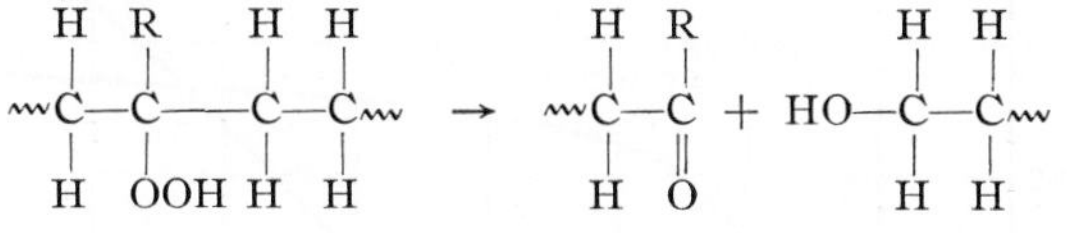
(10)

In the decomposition of simple tertiary hydroperoxides, it is the larger group which usually breaks away and so by analogy cleavage at a branch point in the polymer chain should be anticipated. Homolytic decomposition of hydroperoxides (eq. 4) produces a net increase in the number of radicals capable of initiating new chains (eqs. 5 and 6) by abstraction of hydrogen atoms from the polymer. It has been shown that homolytic decomposition of hydroperoxides coincides with the autocatalytic stage in the oxidation of simple hydrocarbons.

In the absence of added inhibitors, oxidation is terminated by several interactions represented by eqs. (7)–(9). Radical concentration apparently declines by coupling, disproportionation, and/or by reactions with inhibiting products of the oxidation. The effect of inhibitors and various stabilization mechanisms are discussed later in this chapter.

1. Saturated Polymers

Polymers, represented by the structure

in which R is any combination of hydrogen, alkyl, or aryl, are saturated except for endgroups or occasional molecular imperfections. These polymers, which are generally referred to as the polyolefins, might be expected to have about the same resistance to oxidation as the simple paraffins. In fact, when polyethylene first became commercially available, it was anticipated that this new polymer would have great inherent stability. Experience, however, soon proved the converse. It is now, of course, recognized that weathering of polyolefins results from reaction with atmospheric oxygen in the presence of sunlight or at elevated temperatures.

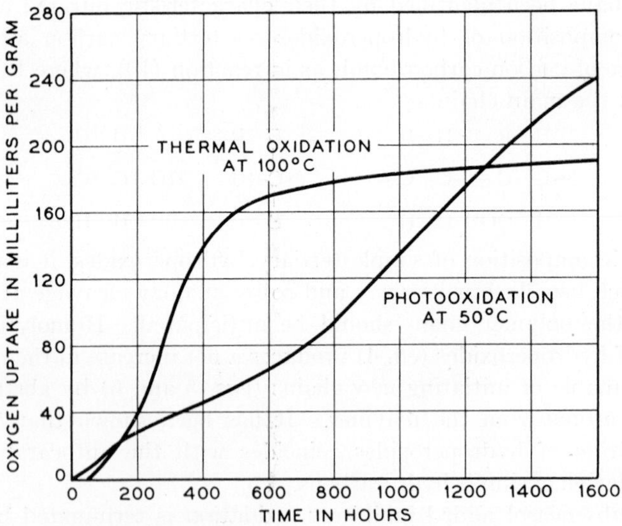

Fig. XIII-1. Difference between thermal and photooxidation of a branched polyethylene.

The earth's atmosphere absorbs almost all solar radiation with a wavelength less than 3000 A. Since saturated paraffins absorb only in the region below 2000 A, it has been proposed (10–12) that the susceptibility of polyethylene to photooxidation is related to structural abnormalities such as carbonyl groups or unsaturation. Photo- and thermal oxidation apparently proceed by the same general mechanism, but usually differ in initiation rate and distribution of reaction products. For example the photooxidation rate curve of polyethylene at 50°C. in Figure XIII-1 shows no noticeable induction period, and only a slight autocatalytic effect in contrast to the thermal reaction of this polymer at 100°C.

Susceptibility to oxidation depends both on molecular structure and on the arrangement (morphology) of molecules in the solid polymer. The effect of structure is represented by the relative oxidative resistance of the following series of polymers:

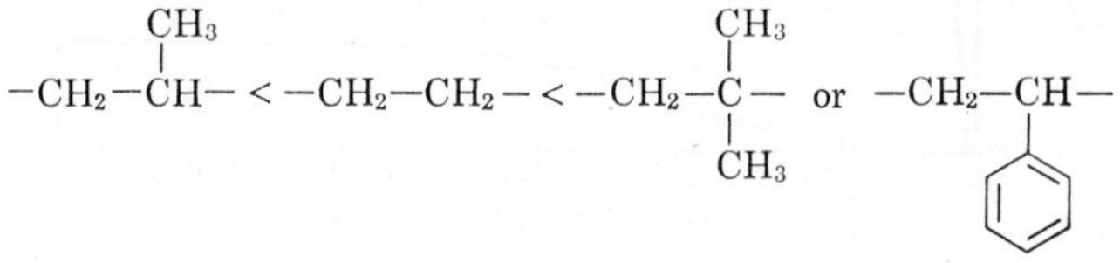

where the oxidative resistance increases from left to right.

Hydrogens bonded to tertiary carbons are more readily removed by radical reactions than those on secondary carbon atoms. Thus, polypropylene oxidizes more rapidly than linear polyethylene (6) as shown in Figure XIII-2. Polyisobutylene, with fewer methylene groups, partially shielded by inert methyl groups, is much more stable than polyethylene. Polystyrene, on the other hand, has the same frequency of branching as does polypropylene and yet it oxidizes extremely slowly at 100°C. The necessity for caution in making comparisons between polymers and related model compounds is clearly evident in the comparison of polystyrene with cumene. Cumene oxidizes readily at 80°C., while molten polystyrene oxidizes only slowly at 140°C. Moreover, polyisopropylstyrene is highly vulnerable to oxidation (13). Since hydrogens on tertiary carbons are the principal sites of oxidative attack in branched polymers, it has been proposed that the stability of polystyrene arises partly from shielding effects of the phenyl group (14), and perhaps partly from loss in resonance energy caused by unfavorable orientation of crowded phenyl groups attached to the main chain (15). Evidence obtained by Hansen (14) supports the shielding mechanism since oxidation stability of the polymers in Table XIII-1 decreases abruptly with an increase in the number of methylene

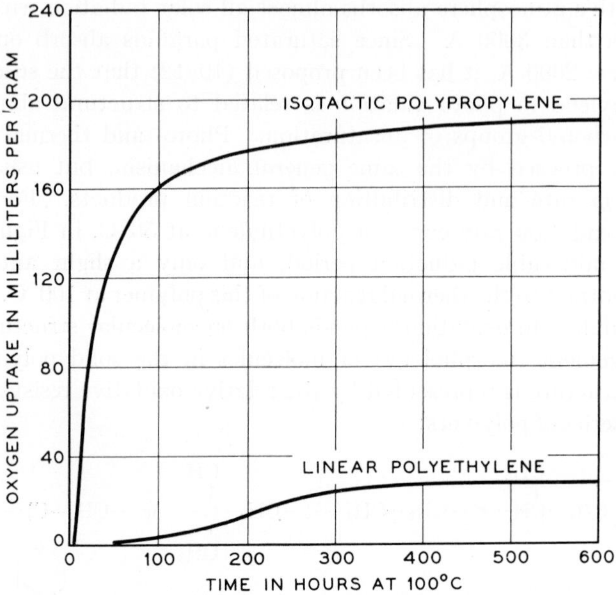

Fig. XIII-2. Comparison of oxidation behavior of polypropylene and linear polyethylene.

groups separating the phenyl groups from the main chain. The facile photooxidation of polystyrene (16) is further evidence that the reaction is not diffusion-dependent but that stability is a chemical property of the polymer.

Oxidation of polymeric hydrocarbons causes discoloration and rapid loss of mechanical and dielectric strength. For example, the elongation at break of a typical branched polyethylene decreases from 570 to 40% as the combined oxygen content of the polymer increases to only a mere 1%. Apparently, only a small fraction of the polymer molecules break, during the reaction, since almost complete recovery of mechanical strength is attained by redistributing ruptured and unreacted molecules through remilling the sample (17,18). The nature of the change in physical properties during oxidation reflects the relative rates of crosslinking and chain scission. If chain scission predominates, there will be a continuous reduction in molecular weight, indicated by an increase in melt viscosity. Alternatively, when crosslinking predominates, gel formation leads to a rapid decrease in melt viscosity. Both processes often occur simultaneously, and their relative rates vary with different polymers and with oxidation conditions. Scission is the dominant reaction in polypropylene oxida-

TABLE XIII-1
Oxidation Stability of Polystyrene and Related Polymers

		Induction period, hr.	
Polymer	Structure	At 80°C.	At 110°C.
Polystyrene	$—CH_2—CH(C_6H_5)—$	—	>10,000
Poly-3-phenyl-1-propene	$—CH_2—CH(CH_2C_6H_5)—$	>10,000	1,900
Poly-4-phenyl-1-butene	$—CH_2—CH((CH_2)_2C_6H_5)—$	500	30
Poly-6-phenyl-1-hexene[a]	$—CH_2—CH((CH_2)_4C_6H_5)—$	200	13

[a] Tacky at room temperature.

tion, where the melt viscosity increases sharply during milling of the unprotected polymer in air (19). In the case of polyethylenes, the ratio of crosslinking to chain scission may be somewhat higher. Since oxygen-containing groups are polar, there is a direct increase in power factor, dielectric constant, and surface conductivity with increasing content of combined oxygen.

The rate at which oxygen diffuses into semicrystalline polymers is influenced by morphology and the surface/volume ratio as well as other factors. The change in oxidation pattern of polyethylene with increasing sample thickness is shown in Figure XIII-3. Carbon dioxide, water, and oxidized polymer are the main oxidation products. As the reaction proceeds, the outer surface of the polymer sample becomes more highly oxidized than the inner regions because the availability of oxygen depends on the reaction rate and the relative diffusion rates of oxygen and oxidation products. Apparently the compact crystalline regions in polyethylene and polypropylene are inaccessible to oxygen since the cumulative oxygen uptake is roughly proportional to the volume fraction of amorphous regions in these polymers (6). For example, highly crystalline linear polyethylene, crystallized from a dilute solution in xylene in the form of a finely divided powder, combines with less oxygen than a

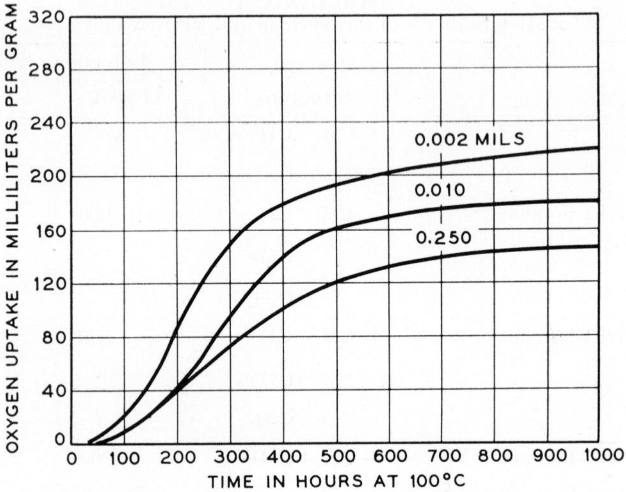

Fig. XIII-3. Effect of thickness on the oxidation rate of branched polyethylene.

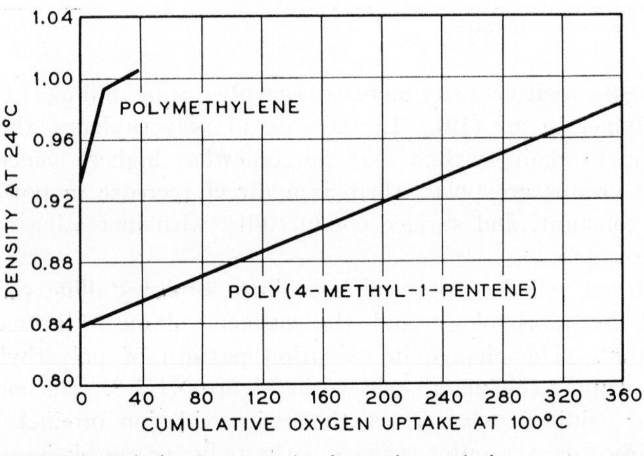

Fig. XIII-4. Relation between density and cumulative oxygen uptake.

compression-molded sheet of the same polymer at 100°C. On the other hand, oxygen seems to freely pervade polyolefins like poly-4-methyl-1-pentene which possess crystalline and amorphous regions of nearly the same density (20). Chain cleavage during the early stage of oxidation permits severed chains to crystallize, as shown in Figure XIII-4, wherein the x-ray crystallinity of the polymethylene increases from 67% to greater than 95% during a cumulative oxygen uptake of about 15 ml./g.; yet no

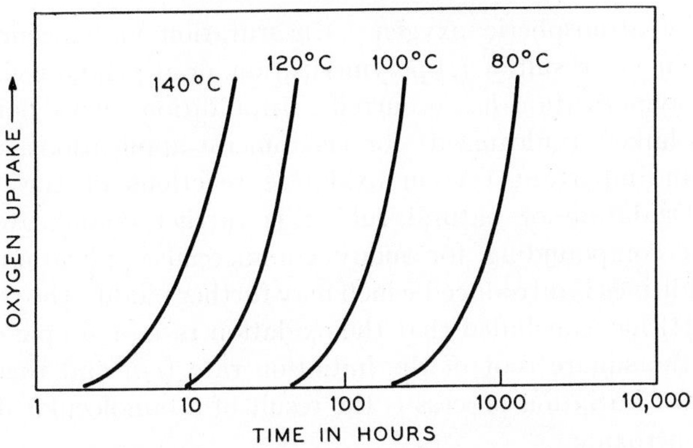

Fig. XIII-5. Effect of temperature on the oxidation rate of branched polyethylene.

change in density is observed during prolonged heating of the same polyethylene in nitrogen at 100°C. The juncture of the two slopes in the density–oxygen absorption plots (Fig. XIII-4) corresponds to the point at which crystallization ceases. Since the densities of amorphous and crystalline regions in poly-4-methyl-1-pentene are nearly identical, density increase, like oxygen content, is directly proportional to oxygen absorption. For a further description of the relationship between chemical reactivity and morphology of the polymers see Chapter I-C.

The effect of temperature on the oxidation of a branched polyethylene is shown in Figure XIII-5. A wide range of activation energies for the oxidative reaction of uninhibited polymeric hydrocarbons has been reported. Burnett (21) obtained a value of 18 kcal./mole over the temperature range of 40–100°C. At higher temperatures, between 120 and 170°C., Grieveson, Howard, and Wright (22) and Notley (23) reported overall activation energies of 33 and 55 kcal./mole, respectively. Reactions at 170°C. are presumably diffusion-dependent, even in the incipient stages of oxidation.

2. Diene Polymers

Another group of polymers, formed from dienes, includes both the synthetic and natural elastomers. Their oxidative reactions, like those previously described, proceed by a free radical chain mechanism in which peroxides are important intermediates. They differ sufficiently from the polyolefins in oxidative reactions, however, to warrant separate consideration. Diene polymers are characterized by the regular occurrence of ethylenic unsaturation, and are therefore vulnerable to attack by ozone as well as by atmospheric oxygen. Unsaturation may occur either in the main chain as a result of 1,4 polymerization, or as pendant vinyl groups where 1,2 polymerization has occurred. In addition, diene polymers are usually crosslinked (vulcanized) for elastomeric applications, and crosslinks play an important role in oxidative reactions of the vulcanized polymers. Oxidation of natural rubber is further complicated by the fact that in compounding for many commercial applications, a wide variety of additives is introduced which may further modify the reactions.

Shelton (24) has concluded that the oxidation rate of simple olefins is a function of the square root of the initiation rate (r_i), and therefore, the only important initiation process is the result of a bimolecular decomposition of hydroperoxide.

$$2\text{ROOH} \xrightarrow{k_1} \text{RO}\cdot + \text{ROO}\cdot + \text{H}_2\text{O} \tag{11}$$

with $r_i = k_1[\text{ROOH}]^2$. In the initial stages of oxidation, a first-order decomposition occurs which is then superceded by the second-order decomposition as peroxide concentration increases. Bateman and Hughes (25) have obtained evidence for the existence of a hydrogen-bonded dimer of hydroperoxides using infrared techniques. Shelton (24) has summarized reactions of peroxide decomposition in model systems as shown in eq. (12).

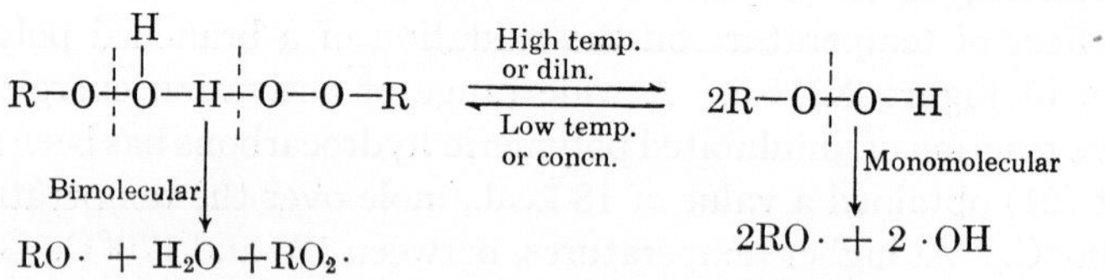

(12)

Rugg (26) has also observed that peroxide absorption in the infrared, obtained with oxidized polyethylene at elevated temperatures, disappears at room temperature and has suggested that in this polymer there may be an association of hydroperoxide groups.

It is difficult and often misleading to interpret oxidative reaction of diene polymers solely on the basis of results obtained with model compounds. Considerable work has been reported (24,25,27) on the structure, decomposition, and isomerization of the peroxides of simple dienes. When properly interpreted these studies have been useful guides to reactions of polymers. The oxidation of diene polymers, however, is considerably more complex than that of the simple dienes. In addition to the effect of unsaturation on the reactions, there is substantial evidence to indicate that oxidation is influenced by the presence of crosslinks (24,28), either introduced in vulcanization or formed during the oxidative reaction. Pendant vinyl groups formed by 1,2 addition are particularly suited to crosslinking reactions (24), as shown in eq. (13).

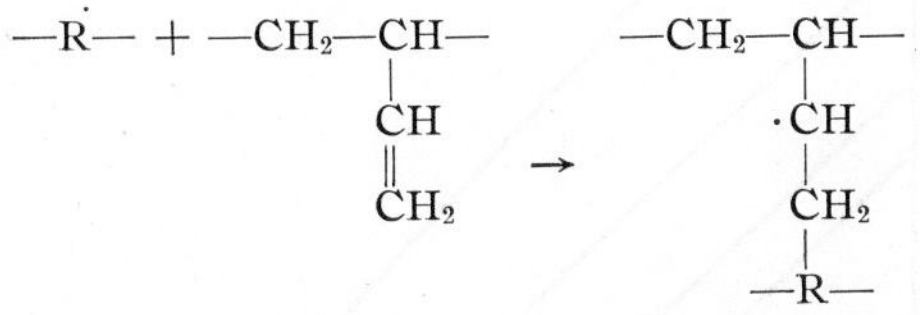

(13)

Reactions such as these leading to crosslinking are favored at lower temperatures and by low concentration of oxygen since oxygen reacts rapidly with hydrocarbon radicals forming peroxy radicals which then react preferentially by hydrogen abstraction. In addition to the carbon–carbon crosslinks formed by this reaction, it has been demonstrated that carbon-loaded rubber forms crosslinks in which the pigment becomes an integral part of the bond between polymer molecules (24), and sulfur crosslinks, of course, are intentionally introduced during vulcanization. Each type of crosslink probably influences oxidative reactions to a different degree by activation of adjacent groups on the main chains and/or by reactions of the crosslink itself. It is thus convenient to discuss the oxidation of diene polymers by first examining the mechanisms proposed for the uncured polymer without the complication of crosslinks, and then to discuss the more complex reactions of the vulcanized polymers.

The rate at which diene polymers react with oxygen increases with temperature as shown (24) in Figure XIII-6. From the linear relationship of rate to $1/T$, activation energies ranging from 23.6 to 26.0 kcal./mole have been calculated for a variety of rubber compounds. Degradation of uncured rubber under oxidative conditions has been measured by breaking down the polymer on a two-roll mill to a predetermined change in physical properties, as for example, Mooney viscosity (28). When this technique is applied over a range of temperature, the viscosity reaches a maximum value at about 130°C. (Fig. XIII-7). The breakdown is dependent on oxygen, and does not follow the typical rate curve of oxygen uptake (dashed line) at the lower temperatures. The rapid increase in viscosity below 130°C. is the result of mechanical shearing of polymer chains at the lower temperatures producing radicals which react rapidly with oxygen before recombination is possible (28). Physical rupture under applied stress promotes oxidation of elastomers in a manner somewhat analogous to the stress cracking of rubber on exposure to ozone.

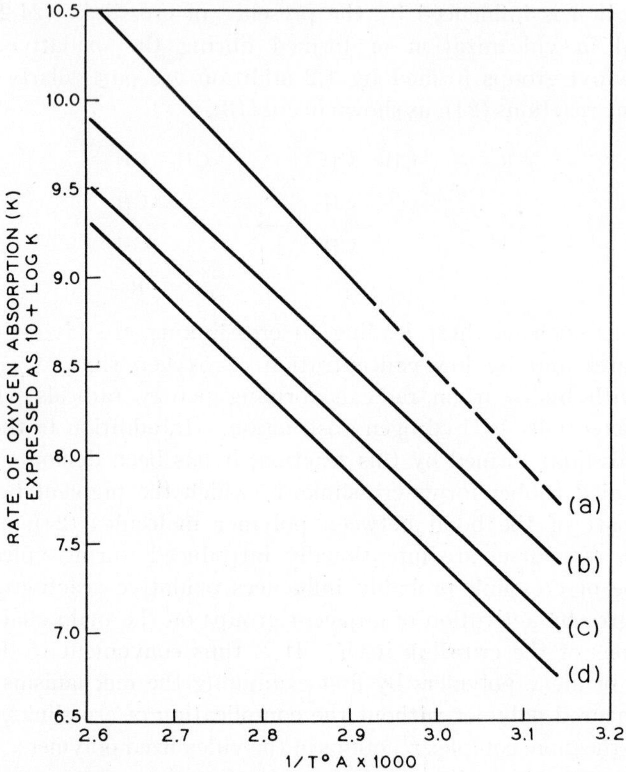

Fig. XIII-6. Effect of temperature on the oxidation rate of elastomers: (*a*) uninhibited Hevea black; (*b*) inhibited Hevea black; (*c*) Hevea gum; (*d*) GR-S black.

The rate of scission of elastomers can be estimated by relating oxygen uptake to the ratio of initial to final viscosity of the sample. Results obtained by different techniques support the conclusion that the efficiency of chain scission is greater at higher temperatures, although there is not good quantitative agreement between some of the methods. It is apparent, nonetheless, that a direct correlation does exist between oxygen uptake and the extent of chain scission, and that the rate of scission is dependent both on temperature and on oxygen concentration. Changes in modulus afford a sensitive method for estimating the relative rates of chain scission and crosslinking at different temperatures. At the lower temperature, crosslinking is the predominant reaction in Hevea black stock at 200% elongation (Fig. XIII-8), and at higher temperatures,

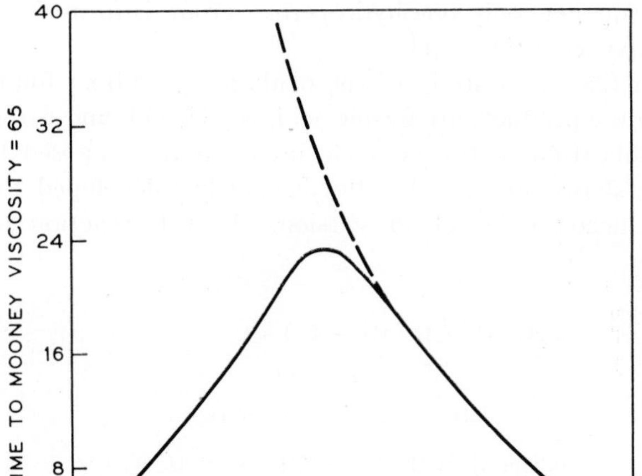

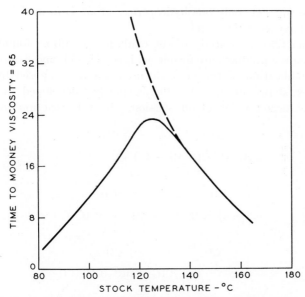

Fig. XIII-7. Rate of breakdown of a hydrocarbon rubber during milling in air over a temperature range. (Taken from ref. 28.)

scission predominates with an approximate balance between these competing reactions indicated in the intermediate range (29).

At present, it has not been established conclusively whether chain scission is a primary reaction during oxidation associated with the initiation, or whether it is a side reaction arising from products of the primary oxidative reaction. Attempts to settle this controversy have centered around the structure of the hydroperoxide formed in the reaction and the role of peroxides in chain scission. Several mechanisms have been suggested in which chain scission results from decomposition of hydroperoxides (24). Though not supported by direct evidence, it has been suggested (30) that chain scission is associated with the propagation step of the primary oxidative reaction. A number of possible peroxide structures have been proposed to account for the products formed when rubber is oxidized (28). The older concept of direct attack of oxygen at the double bond to form a four-membered cyclic peroxide has not been generally accepted. Recently Cortyl-Lacau (31) has proposed a diperoxy radical as the key intermediate which could lead to chain scission, a stable cyclic diperoxide, or crosslinked products. Bolland and Hughes (32) have suggested a cyclic peroxide to account for their observation that in the oxidation of squalene only one hydroperoxy group is formed for each two molecules of oxygen which react.

Bevilacqua (28), in a study of the oxidation of rubber found that the principal volatile products are formic acid, acetic acid, and carbon dioxide. Using a modification of the peroxide intermediate proposed by Bolland and Hughes, shown in eqs. (14) Bevilacqua has developed the series of reactions to account for chain scission. In this reaction mechanism,

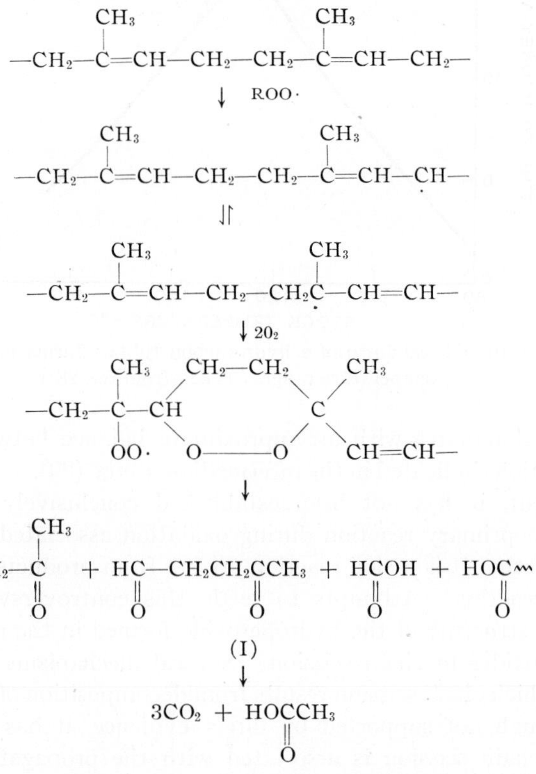

(14)

one isoprene unit is destroyed for each scission, and eventual decomposition of this unit yields the five of six carbons which appear as volatile products. A product generally agreed to be levulinaldehyde (I) has been isolated from aged rubber (28,33,34). The endgroups on polymer residues (35) also agree with this suggested mechanism. Recently, Bevilacqua, English, and Gall (36) have identified acetaldehyde, methyl formate, propionaldehyde, acetone, methanol, methacrolein, ethanol,

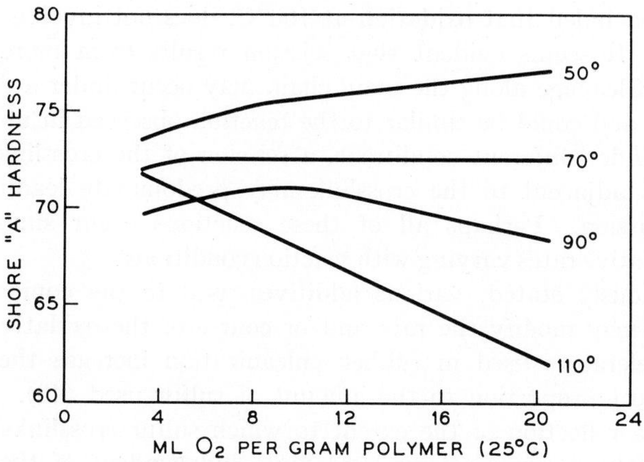

Fig. XIII-8. Relationship between oxygen uptake of Hevea black stock and Shore A hardness. (Taken from ref. 29.)

butanone and butenone, several of which can be accounted for through decomposition of the proposed cyclic peroxy intermediate.

Still unresolved is the question of the role of crosslinks in chain scission. Actually three possibilities exist: (*a*) a random scission in which crosslinks have no effect; (*b*) scission of the crosslink which would tend to revert the polymer to its uncured state; (*c*) scission of the main chain at or near the point of crosslinking. Bueche (37) has developed a theoretical differentiation between random scission and cleavage of crosslinks, and an interpretation of stress decay data (38–40) based on this theory appears to support the conclusion that crosslinks are broken during low temperature aging of rubber. This conclusion is further supported by the work of Berry and Watson (38), who have measured the rates of relaxation and found that they are different for peroxide- and sulfur-cured natural rubber. Mercurio and Tobolsky (41), however, have obtained widely different stress relaxations for sulfur vulcanizates of a series of different polymers, leading them to conclude that oxidative scission occurs predominantly along the isoprene chains and not at crosslinks. Bevilacqua (28) has observed that the amount of oxygen required for chain scission increases as the number of crosslinks diminishes and interprets this as an indication that both chains and crosslinks undergo scission. The rate of scission in the vicinity of a crosslink would, of course, vary with the method of vulcanization. Based on studies of the amount of soluble fraction formed during oxidation of cured natural rubber, Horikx

(42) has concluded that oxidation at 100°C. does not involve opening of crosslinks. It seems evident that scission results from more than one reaction. Cleavage along the main chain may occur under a given set of conditions, and could be similar to the reaction observed in unvulcanized rubber. Under different conditions, a scission of the crosslink or of the main chain adjacent to the crosslink may predominate leading to non-random scission. Perhaps all of these reactions occur simultaneously with the relative rates varying with reaction conditions.

As previously stated, various additives used in the compounding of elastomers may modify the rate and/or course of the oxidative reaction. Sulfur accelerators used in rubber vulcanization increase the oxidation rate in direct proportion to the amount of sulfur used (43). This may indeed be a reflection of the extent to which sulfur crosslinks accelerate scission of the polymer chains, and quite independent of the ability of elemental sulfur and certain sulfur compounds to inhibit oxidation. Shelton (24) points out that, whereas *tert*-butyl disulfide is unreactive toward oxygen at 100°C., allyl sulfide reacts rapidly, and suggests that structures

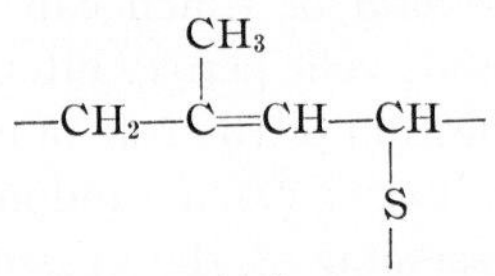

(II)

such as II could account for the accelerated aging of sulfur-vulcanized rubber stocks. This is also in agreement with observations (24) that saturated elastomers containing sulfur are resistant to aging.

3. Stabilization

In 1918, Moureu and Dufraisse (44) discovered that trace amounts of certain compounds which they called "antioxygens" retarded autoxidation of many organic materials. The observed effect was explained by Christiansen (45), who deduced that autoxidation is a chain reaction, and that the additives reported by Moureu and Dufraisse functioned as chain terminators. Then in 1934, Bäckström (46) suggested that the chain reaction could be explained by a free radical mechanism. Thus, the background for a mechanism of stabilizer action has been known for some time. The technology of stabilization for commercially significant polymers has advanced rapidly in the intervening years. Complete reaction mechanisms accounting for the observed effects with all types of stabilizers, however, are not as yet fully understood. Since only traces of stabilizer or prooxidant have a profound effect on oxidation, an accurate analysis of reaction mechanisms is possible only when both the stabilizer and the substrate are extremely pure. In most polymers it is not possible to obtain the required degree of purity, and side reactions have undoubtedly contributed to the difficulty in establishing reaction mechanisms.

It is now generally agreed that both thermal and light-induced oxidation of polymeric hydrocarbons proceed by a free radical, chain reaction. This reaction can be terminated or retarded by stabilizers at any of several different stages. Very effective control often results when combinations of stabilizers are used in which the individual components inhibit the reaction at separate stages. Certain combinations stabilize the polymer to a greater degree than anticipated from the additive effect of the components (47)—a phenomenon referred to as synergism. Other combinations are characterized by an antagonistic interaction between the components (48). A stabilizer for one polymer may act as a prooxidant at different concentrations (24) or in another polymer. The mechanism of stabilization is further complicated by the fact that some stabilizers react in more than one way to inhibit oxidation. Stabilization can be effective in the initiation, propagation, or chain branching stages of oxidation. In this discussion, stabilizers will be related to the particular stage in the reaction at which they function primarily.

a. Control of Rate of Initiation

In polymers which are free of initiating impurities, oxidation presumably is initiated when a few molecules attain an excited state and are eventually converted to radicals. The energy required for this activation results from application of physical stress, heat, ultraviolet radiation, or bombardment with high energy particles. The rate of initiation may be suppressed in several ways. Light screens, carbon black being a notable example, reduce the quanta of ultraviolet radiation which reach the bulk of the sample.

Ultraviolet absorbers preferentially absorb light in those wavelengths particularly detrimental to the polymer, and dissipate the absorbed energy in nondestructive ways. Substituted benzophenones and esters of salicylic acid have been widely used to inhibit photooxidation. Tamblyn and co-workers (49) have reviewed the reactions of ultraviolet absorbers, emphasizing various reactions through which absorbed energy can be dissipated. Where metallic impurities catalyze initiation, chelating compounds can be used to deactivate these catalysts (14). Inherent stability of some polymers may be attributed to their molecular structure. Each of these mechanisms for controlling the rate of initiation results in a reduction in the number of radicals available for propagation.

b. Chain Termination

Alkyl radicals formed in the initiation stage react rapidly with oxygen, yielding peroxy radicals which in turn abstract hydrogen from the polymer in a chain reaction (eq. 3). This reaction, unless terminated or retarded, leads eventually to rapid degradation of the polymer. Radical acceptors afford one means of deactivating propagating radicals. The role of carbon black as a radical trap has been proposed by Szwarc (50) but Spackman (51) has shown that unpaired spins in carbon black do not participate in covalent bond formation. Direct addition of ROO· to an aromatic ring or formation of a π-complex (52,53) with an aromatic system may serve to trap radicals. Relatively stable radicals also inhibit oxidation, presumably through coupling reactions (54).

The most common class of commercial stabilizers for inhibiting oxidation of hydrocarbon polymers consists of compounds containing labile hydrogen which function as chain terminators in thermal oxidation, but are much less effective in photooxidation (eq. 15). In practice HA sta-

$$\text{ROO}\cdot + \text{HA} \rightarrow \text{ROOH} + \text{A}\cdot \qquad (15)$$

bilizers never completely inhibit the reaction (Fig. XIII-9*a*), a measurable amount of oxidation proceeding throughout the induction period until the stabilizer becomes exhausted. Oxidation then proceeds at a rate

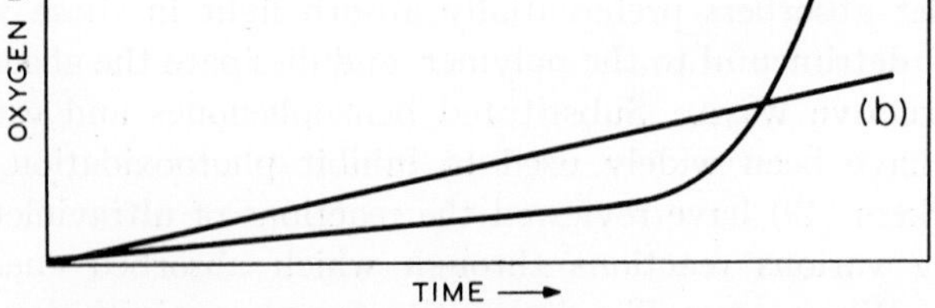

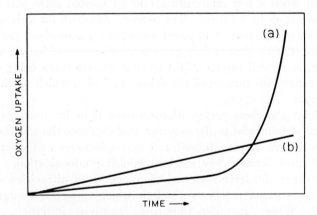

Fig. XIII-9. Typical rate curves for inhibited and retarded oxidation.

comparable with that of the uninhibited polymer. The amount of oxygen which reacts with the polymer during the induction period depends on the chain transfer potential of A· or the efficiency with which the antioxidant reacts with and terminates propagating radicals. In those instances where A· functions as a transfer agent, oxidation may proceed at a constant, retarded rate with no evidence of autocatalysis (Fig. XIII-9*b*).

Several important classes of compounds function as chain terminators. The most important types are the hindered phenols and the secondary amines. Since donation of labile hydrogen to ROO· is an oxidative reaction, HA stabilizers are themselves vulnerable to oxidation. Antioxidant effectiveness is increased by alkylating at one or both positions *ortho* to the hydroxyl group. Especially effective in this respect are *tert*-butyl groups. Biphenolic stabilizers, effective in both polyolefins and in elastomers, have been developed in which two aromatic moieties are bridged by carbon or by sulfur (Structure III), in which R and R′ are alkyl.

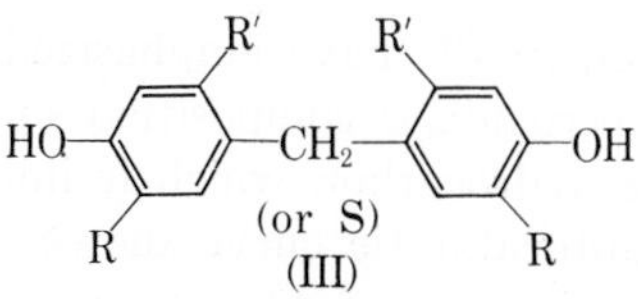

(III)

Carbon black, which also inhibits oxidation of polyolefins, has been described as a giant phenol in which reactive hydroxyl (or quinone) groups attached to the condensed aromatic structure are responsible for inhibiting the oxidation. Carbon black, modified to increase the number of such active groups, is a very effective stabilizer for polyolefins (55,56). In rubber, however, where it is used for reinforcement, high loadings of carbon black sometimes accelerate oxidation (24). At lower concentrations an inhibiting effect has been reported. The existence of an optimum range has been reported for other antioxidants (24). It has been suggested by several investigators that naturally occurring antioxidants in rubber are absorbed by carbon black, thus reducing the inherent stability of the polymer.

Considerable controversy has centered around the mechanism by which HA stabilizers inhibit oxidation. Removal of the labile hydrogen by peroxy radicals has been indicated by studies of Shelton (2) and others. Failure to detect an isotope effect with deuterated amines, however, has lead some investigators (52,57,58) to conclude that hydrogen abstraction is not the primary step. Pederson (59) has proposed a mechanism in which donation of an electron by the stabilizer is the key step in the reaction. Hammond et al. (53,57) postulated a π-complex between ROO· and the aromatic ring as a first and reversible step leading eventually to loss of labile hydrogen. Ingold and Howard (60), however, have shown that deuterated phenols exchange rapidly with traces of moisture which possibly accounts for failure of some investigators to detect an isotope effect. Shelton and co-workers (2), in reexamining the stabilization of carefully purified *cis*-1,4-polyisoprene with deuterated amines and phenols have demonstrated that isotope effects do occur when concentration of the inhibitor and oxidation temperature are controlled. Failure to detect an isotope effect is also attributed to the competitive, direct oxidation of inhibitor with its accompanying isotope effect. Isotope effects as high as 10.6 have been observed by adding D_2O to maintain the deuterium level (60). Thus, the abstraction of hydrogen as the primary step in stabilization with labile hydrogen donors appears to be confirmed.

c. Peroxide Deactivation

Shelton (2) and Bateman (3) have emphasized the important role of radicals generated by peroxide decomposition on the oxidation rate of polymers. In a simple hydrocarbon which is initially free of peroxides, oxidation follows the autocatalytic curve shown in Figure XIII-9. Analysis of the peroxide content as oxidation progresses shows that there is an accumulation of peroxides which reaches a maximum as oxidation approaches the autocatalytic stage. Decomposition of peroxides, apparently by an autocatalytic reaction, then occurs at a rapid rate with the concentration falling off to a small, limiting value. Presumably, simultaneous formation and decomposition of peroxides takes place throughout the reaction at competitive rates. Radicals formed by the rapid decomposition of peroxides are believed to be responsible for the increase in oxidation rate (autocatalysis), and this stage of the reaction is usually referred to as chain branching. In polymer oxidation, most of the initiation probably results from radicals generated by peroxide decomposition. These radicals also react with and deactivate HA inhibitors. Thus effective stabilization results when peroxide decomposition into radicals is prevented.

Two mechanisms have been proposed for peroxide deactivation. Using squalene as a model for rubber and alkylsulfoxides as inhibitors, Bateman and co-workers (3) have found that the concentration of peroxide in the oxidized hydrocarbon is reduced only slowly by addition of sulfoxides. They have proposed a molecular association between the peroxide and the

S═O group as the mechanism by which peroxides are deactivated. This mechanism is supported by their observation that addition of stearic acid, which is known to bond with S═O groups, reduces the effectiveness of the sulfoxide inhibitors. However, elemental sulfur, disulfides, and their various oxidation products are very effective decomposers of hydroperoxides (61). In oxidizing cumene, which forms a well-defined hydroperoxide and has been used as a model for saturated hydrocarbon polymers, it has been shown (62) that addition of sulfur compounds rapidly and completely decomposes the hydroperoxide, even at temperatures as low as 40°C. Products of decomposition of cumene hydroperoxide in the presence of sulfur compounds indicate a heterolytic decomposition into nonradical products.

It is apparent from several investigations that disulfides do not in themselves inhibit oxidation. Apparently the disulfides are oxidized as peroxides accumulate in the substrate, thiolsulfinates being the first product as in eq. (16). Under conditions at which the thiolsulfinates are

$$\text{RSSR} \rightarrow \text{RSSOSR} \tag{16}$$

sufficiently stable, they probably function as the active antioxidant. Barnard and co-workers (63) have shown that *n*-butyl-*n*-butane thiolsulfinate effectively inhibits oxidation at 75°C. of squalene in contrast to its precursor, *n*-butyl disulfide, which inhibits only after an appreciable amount of oxygen has reacted with the substrate. A similar, delayed reaction has been reported (61) with naphthyl disulfide as the stabilizer in branched polyethylene. Phenylbenzenethiosulfinate, however, is unstable at temperatures at which it has been used as a stabilizer. Several acidic products are formed by decomposition of this thiolsulfinate, and it has been suggested (61) that one or several of these products are responsible for the rapid, catalytic decomposition of hydroperoxides. Some diperoxides and those formed in diene compounds, however, are not as susceptible to this decomposition.

Apparently the mechanism by which sulfur compounds deactivate peroxides is not the same in all polymers. Deactivation by formation of a molecular complex may be the predominant mechanism for those polymers whose peroxides are not readily decomposed. In saturated hydrocarbons, which oxidize primarily through a hydroperoxidic intermediate, decomposition of the peroxide into nonradical products apparently predominates. The actual stabilizer formed from such sulfur compounds as the disulfides may also vary with the oxidation temperature.

d. Synergistic Stabilizer Combinations

Combinations of stabilizers have been reported whose effectiveness is considerably greater than would be anticipated from the combined effect of the several components. Synergistic combinations of ultraviolet absorbers with thermal antioxidants have been used (64) to improve the outdoor weathering of polymers. Combinations of carbon black with elemental sulfur, thiols, and disulfides show a pronounced synergistic effect in stabilizing polyolefins against thermal oxidation (47). Recently, combinations of typical chain terminators with peroxide decomposers have been used effectively.

Since inhibition can be effected at any of several stages in the oxidative reaction, combinations which suppress oxidation at different steps in the reaction are particularly effective. For example, a chain terminator may suppress the rate of initiation, but as each oxidative chain is terminated, a molecule of peroxide is formed. If peroxides accumulate and then decompose into radicals, oxidation not only becomes autocatalytic but the chain terminator is rapidly consumed. But in the presence of a peroxide deactivator (or its precursor), additional radicals do not form by homolytic decomposition of peroxides. The chain terminator is preserved, and excellent stabilization results. Combinations of disulfides with carbon black or with typical chain terminators show a high degree of synergism in protecting saturated polymeric hydrocarbons against thermal oxidation. It has been suggested (62) that the chain terminator stabilizes the polymer in the early stages of oxidation until sufficient active peroxide-decomposer has accumulated, by oxidation of the disulfide, to control the more damaging chain-branching reaction.

The good weathering properties of natural rubber are due in part to the presence of foreign materials in the latex which apparently inhibit oxidation. These so-called "natural antioxidants" consist in part of nonhydrocarbon impurities, e.g., proteins or acidic plant products, which may act as chelating agents and thus reduce the metal-catalyzed oxidation. Extraction of the natural antioxidants reduces the oxidative stability of natural rubber to a point where it is comparable to that of synthetic elastomers. Chelating agents have also been used to stabilize polypropylene against copper-catalyzed oxidation (14).

The importance of inhibiting the oxidative reaction of polymeric hydrocarbons to insure adequate service life is generally recognized. It should be emphasized, however, that polymeric hydrocarbons vary in their ease of oxidation under different conditions of exposure, even though the basic reactions may be similar. In practice, therefore, it is advisable to design the stabilizer (or combination of stabilizers) to the requirements of the individual polymer as well as to the conditions at which the material is to be exposed. Loss of antioxidant by evaporation or extraction also contributes to antioxidant failure (65).

The various reactions by which stabilizers terminate the oxidation of hydrocarbon polymers are summarized as follows:

(*a*) light screening or ultraviolet absorption; (*b*) radical trapping, including π-complex formation and aromatic substitution; (*c*) hydrogen donation or electron donation to ROO·; (*d*) deactivation of prooxidants, e.g., metallic impurities, (*e*) decomposition of peroxides into inert products. Individual stabilizers can function by more than one of these reactions. For example, phenols, though normally considered as HA stabilizers, also decompose peroxides, and carbon black has been reported to function as a radical acceptor, an HA stabilizer, and a peroxide decomposer.

C. HALOGEN-CONTAINING POLYMERS

Poly(vinyl chloride) and its copolymers represent special problems in stability since they decompose with loss of hydrogen chloride at temperatures as low as 150°C. The rate of hydrogen chloride evolution ac-

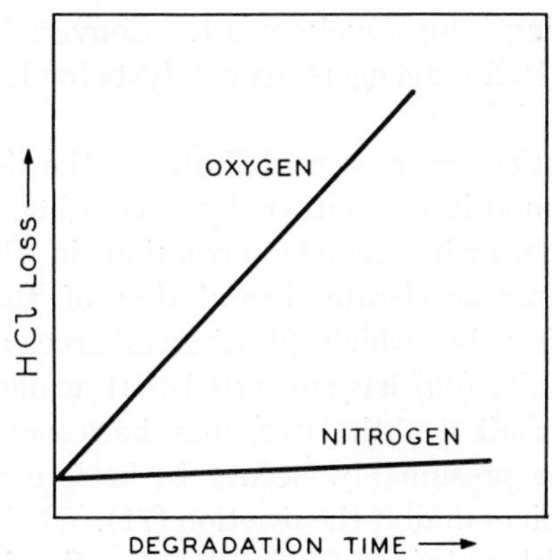

Fig. XIII-10. Effect of oxygen on hydrogen chloride loss from poly(vinyl chloride).

celerates with increasing oxygen pressure (Fig. XIII-10) and is affected by various structural abnormalities such as branching (66), unsaturation, and oxygen-containing groups derived from peroxide breakdown during polymerization or from subsequent reaction of the polymer with atmospheric oxygen.

Loss of hydrogen chloride during heating in nitrogen is accompanied by rapid discoloration of the polymer. The appearance of color after only slight loss of hydrogen chloride has been ascribed (67) to a zip reaction producing a linear polyene structure by elimination of adjacent HCl groups in rapid succession. Discoloration is attributed to the development of conjugated unsaturation. Continued reaction results in extensive crosslinking.

Exposure to oxygen during the early stages of discoloration causes temporary bleaching. Then, as loss of hydrogen chloride progresses in air, a rapid and irreversible color formation takes place. Baum (68) has reported that loss of hydrogen chloride is autocatalytic in the presence of air and attributes the phenomenon to catalysis by hydrogen chloride of the homolytic cleavage of hydroperoxides.

Photooxidation arises primarily from the absorption of ultraviolet radiation by unsaturated or carbonyl groups. Reaction of the polymer with air produces additional hydroperoxide, carbonyl and carboxyl groups which further promote degradation by lowering the dissociation energy of adjacent C—Cl bonds.

Both ionic and free radical degradation reactions are apparently involved (68). Antioxidants reduce the rate of HCl release but are ineffective in preventing color development. Conversely, the heavy metal salts act at once as HCl scavengers, as catalysts for HCl evolution and as color stabilizers.

Oxidation of plasticizers may contribute to the degradation of poly(vinyl chloride) compositions, either by increasing the rate at which plasticizer loss occurs, or by secondary reactions in which oxidative products of the plasticizer accelerate degradation of the polymer (69,70). The exact mechanism by which plasticizers accelerate degradation is not known, but Murfitt (69) has suggested that acidic oxidation products of plasticizers (e.g., dialkyl phthalates) may be responsible for this effect. Plasticizer oxidation presumably occurs by a free radical mechanism, since phenols and amines inhibit the reaction (71).

In comparison with poly(vinyl chloride), the fluorine-containing polymers like poly(vinyl fluoride) are remarkably stable to photooxidation. Unprotected polytetrafluoroethylene shows no signs of deterioration after more than twenty years of outdoor exposure in New Jersey. Even at temperatures of 200°C. or more, polytetrafluoroethylene is resistant to attack by atmospheric oxygen or by strong oxidizing agents like nitric acid. The bulky fluorine atoms completely shield the carbon chain from access to oxygen.

Neoprene, a halogen-containing elastomer, is considerably more resistant than polybutadiene to thermal oxidation. Since the two polymers differ only in the pendant atoms attached to vinylene carbon, the increased stability of neoprene is attributed to the presence of a chlorine atom in each repeating unit.

D. MISCELLANEOUS POLYMERS

Oxidation is a general reaction both of addition and condensation polymers. Considerable empirical data have been accumulated on the effect of oxygen on many polymers, but reaction mechanisms have not been investigated as extensively as in the polymers previously discussed. In general, however, a polymer comprised in part of hydrocarbon segments may undergo the free radical chain reaction described previously. The reaction would, of course, be modified by other chemical groups, either in the main chain or as side groups.

1. Vinyl Polymers

The oxidative stability of polystyrene in contrast to polyethylene and polypropylene has been attributed to the presence of bulky phenyl groups at regular intervals along the polymer chain. Several other vinyl polymers are comparable with polystyrene in their resistance to oxidation. Poly(methyl methacrylate) does not oxidize appreciably in the dark at 130°C. (72). Jellinek (73) attributes a retarding effect to electrophilic groups including Cl, CN, C_6H_5, and CO. Electron donor groups, i.e., CH_3, apparently promote oxidation. This generalization would account for the stabilizing effect of chlorine in neoprene. At higher temperatures or on exposure to ultraviolet radiation, both polystyrene and the polymethacrylates oxidize more rapidly with accompanying loss in mechanical properties. Under these conditions, oxidation probably occurs by a mechanism similar to that described for hydrocarbon polymers. Oxidation of poly(vinyl chloride) and related halogen-containing polymers has been discussed previously.

2. Condensation Polymers

It is usually difficult to separate oxidative from hydrolytic reactions in condensation polymers. Acidic products of the oxidation can catalyze hydrolysis of polyesters (74) and polyamides. Oxidative products of cellulose also appear to be more susceptible to oxidation than the parent polymer. In the presence of alkali, cellulose is sensitive to direct oxidation by air (75), but thermal oxidation under neutral conditions is quite slow. The overall effect of oxidation is a gradual reduction in molecular weight which probably results from secondary hydrolytic reactions. The fact that oxidation is accelerated by moisture (76,77) supports the hypothesis that an interplay of hydrolysis and oxidation is responsible for degradation. Oxidation can occur at any of the several hydroxyl groups in each repeating unit, and there is evidence of carboxyl formation at relatively low temperatures. Oxidation occurs somewhat more rapidly under ultraviolet radiation. In the early stages of the reaction, bleaching may occur, but eventually discoloration and loss in mechanical properties take place. Both carboxyl and carbonyl groups have been detected in cellulose oxidized by exposure to sunlight (78).

Polyglycols oxidize by a short branch, free radical mechanism in which peroxides are important intermediates (79). Salts of transition metals, e.g., cupric chloride, catalyze the oxidation of polyglycols of high molecular weight (80), although Lloyd (79) has shown that these same salts inhibit oxidation of diethylene glycol and, to a lesser extent, polyglycols of low molecular weight (ca. 600). Lloyd has proposed that the metal ion and the peroxide form a complex by a reaction which competes with the normal homolytic peroxide decomposition. As the molecular weight increases and the number of endgroups diminishes, autocatalysis becomes predominant.

The polymeric polysulfides which contain sulfur in the main chain are unusually stable to oxidation. Acidic products formed during degradation apparently suppress autooxidation by preventing the accumulation of hydroperoxides.

3. Polyamides

Oxidation of polyamides at or above 140°C. leads to formation of branched, three-dimensional structures accompanied by deterioration of mechanical properties and a slight change in chemical composition (81). Crosslinking in the early stages of oxidation apparently occurs as indicated by improvement in toughness (82). Oxidation of the aliphatic segments of polyamides probably follows a mechanism similar to that developed for polymeric hydrocarbons. Amide groups linking the repeating units like the glycosidic linkages of cellulose are vulnerable to hydrolysis and scission at these points under oxidative conditions could account for some of the apparent degradation. Ultraviolet-induced oxidation of polyamides results in discoloration and loss in mechanical strength. Achhammer, Reinhart, and Kline (83) have reviewed the effect of weathering on the physical and electrical properties of polyamides.

References

1a. Bolland, J. L., and G. Gee, *Trans. Faraday Soc.*, **42,** 236 (1946).

1b. Bolland, J. L., *Proc. Roy. Soc. (London)*, **186,** 218 (1946); *Chem. Abstr.*, **40,** 6956^4 (1946).

2. Shelton, J. R., and D. N. Vincent, *J. Am. Chem. Soc.*, **85,** 2433 (1963).
3. Bateman, L., M. Cain, T. Colclough, and J. I. Cunneen, *J. Chem. Soc.*, **1962,** 3570.
4. Wallder, V. T., W. J. Clarke, J. B. DeCoste, and J. B. Howard, *Ind. Eng. Chem.*, **42,** 2320 (1950).
5. Biggs, B. S., and W. L. Hawkins, *Mod. Plastics*, **31** (1), 121 (1953).
6. Hawkins, W. L., W. Matreyek, and F. H. Winslow, *J. Polymer Sci.*, **41,** 1 (1959).
7. Rugg, F. M., J. J. Smith, and R. C. Bacon, *J. Polymer Sci.*, **13,** 535 (1954).
8. Luongo, J. P., *J. Polymer Sci.*, **42,** 139 (1960).
9. Manasek, Z., D. Berek, M. Micko, M. Lazar, and J. Pavlinec, *Vysokomolekul. Soedin.*, **3,** 1104 (1961); *Rubber Chem. Technol.*, **36,** 532 (1963).
10. Burgess, A. R., in *Polymer Degradation Mechanisms*, Circular 525, National Bureau of Standards, Washington, D. C., 1953, p. 149.
11. Pross, A. W., and R. M. Black, *J. Soc. Chem. Ind. (London)*, **69,** 113 (1950); *Chem. Abstr.*, **44,** 8160d (1950).
12. Vale, C. P., and W. G. K. Taylor, *Chem. Ind. (London)*, **1961,** 268.
13. Metz, D. J., and R. B. Mesrobian, *J. Polymer Sci.*, **16,** 345 (1955).
14. Hansen, R. H., W. H. Martin, and T. DeBenedictis, *Trans. Inst. Rubber Ind.*, **39,** No. 6, T301 (1963).
15. Tryon, M., and L. A. Wall, *J. Phys. Chem.*, **62,** 697 (1958).
16. Matheson, L. A., and Boyer, R. F., *Ind. Eng. Chem.*, **44,** 867 (1952).
17. Kavafian, G., *J. Polymer Sci.*, **24,** 499 (1957).
18. Winslow, F. H., and W. L. Hawkins, in *Crystalline Olefin Polymers*, R. Raff and K. W. Doak, eds., High Polymer Series, Vol. 20, Part 1, Interscience, New York, 1964, Chap. 15, to be published.
19. Gilroy, H. M., Bell Telephone Laboratories, private communication.
20. Griffith, J. H., and B. G. Rånby, *J. Polymer Sci.*, **44,** 369 (1960).
21. Burnett, J. D., *Compt. Rend. Congr. Intern. Chim. Ind. 31^e^ Liege, 1958* (Pub. as Ind. Chim. Belge, Suppl.), **2,** 319 (Pub. 1959); *Chem. Abstr.*, **54,** 4125e (1960).
22. Grieveson, B. M., R. N. Haward, and B. Wright, in *Thermal Degradation of Polymers*, Monograph No. 13, Society of Chemical Industry, London, 1961, p. 429.
23. Notley, N. T., *Trans. Faraday Soc.*, **58,** 66 (1962); *Chem. Abstr.*, **57,** 7454c (1962).
24. Shelton, J. R., *Rubber Chem. Technol.*, **30,** 1251 (1957).
25. Bateman, L., and (Mrs.) H. Hughes, *J. Chem. Soc.*, **1952,** 4594.
26. Rugg, F. M., J. J. Smith, and R. C. Bacon, *J. Polymer Sci.*, **13,** 535 (1953).
27. Bateman, L., H. Hughes, and A. L. Morris, *Discussions Faraday Soc.*, **1953** (14), 190; *Chem. Abstr.*, **48,** 432f (1954).
28. Bevilacqua, E. M., *Rubber Age (N. Y.)*, **80** (2), 271 (1956).
29. Shelton, J. R., F. J. Wherley, and W. L. Cox, *Ind. Eng. Chem.*, **45,** 2080 (1953); *Rubber Chem. Technol.*, **27,** 120 (1954).

30. Bateman, L., *Trans. Inst. Rubber Ind.*, **26,** 246 (1950); *Chem. Abstr.*, **45,** 1369d (1951).
31. Cortyl-Lacau, J., *Rev. Gen. Caoutchouc*, **30,** 819 (1953); **31,** 473 (1954); *Rubber Chem. Technol.*, **28,** 746 (1955).
32. Bolland, J. L., and H. Hughes, *J. Chem. Soc.*, **1949,** 492.
33. McGavack, J., and O. W. Lundstedt, *Rubber Age* (*N. Y.*), **67,** 431 (1950); *Chem. Abstr.*, **44,** 8149g (1950).
34. Whitby, G. S., *India Rubber J.*, **63,** 742 (1922); *Chem. Abstr.*, **16,** 4093 (1922).
35. Naylor, R. F., *Trans. Inst. Rubber Ind.*, **19,** 45 (1944); *Chem. Abstr.*, **39,** 1565^4 (1945).
36. Bevilacqua, E., E. English, and J. Gall, paper presented at the Metropolitan Regional Meeting of the American Chemical Society, Newark, N. J., Jan. 28, 1963.
37. Bueche, A. M., *J. Chem. Physics*, **21,** 614 (1953).
38. Berry, J. P., and W. F. Watson, *J. Polymer Sci.*, **18,** 201 (1955).
39. Baxter, S., P. D. Potts, and H. A. Vodden, *Ind. Eng. Chem.*, **47,** 1481 (1955).
40. Robinson, H. W. H., and H. A. Vodden, *Ind. Eng. Chem.*, **47,** 1477 (1955).
41. Mercurio, A., and A. V. Tobolsky, *J. Polymer Sci.*, **36,** 467 (1959).
42. Horikx, M. M., *J. Polymer Sci.*, **19,** 445 (1956); *Rubber Chem. Technol.*, **29,** 1166 (1956).
43. Cox, W. L., and J. R. Shelton, *Ind. Eng. Chem.*, **46,** 2237 (1954).
44. Moureu, C., and C. Dufraisse, *Chem. Rev.*, **3,** 113 (1926).
45. Christiansen, J. A., *J. Phys. Chem.*, **28,** 145 (1924).
46. Bäckström, H. L. J., *Z. Physik. Chem.*, **B25,** 99 (1934); *Chem. Abstr.*, **28,** 4294^2 (1934).
47. Hawkins, W. L., V. L. Lanza, B. B. Loeffler, W Matreyek, and F. H. Winslow, *J. Appl. Polymer Sci.*, **1,** 43 (1959).
48. Hawkins, W. L., R. H. Hansen, W. Matreyek, and F. H. Winslow, *J. Appl. Polymer Sci.*, **1,** 37 (1959).
49. Chaudet, J. H., G. C. Newland, H. W. Patton, and J. W. Tamblyn, *SPE* (*Soc. Plastics Engrs.*) *Trans.*, **1,** 26 (1961).
50. Szwarc, M., *J. Polymer Sci.*, **16,** 367 (1955).
51. Spackman, J. W. C., *Chem. Ind.* (*London*), **1961,** 1532.
52. Boozer, C. E., and G. S. Hammond, *J. Am. Chem. Soc.*, **76,** 3861 (1954).
53. Hammond, G. S., J. N. Sen, and C. E. Boozer, *J. Am. Chem. Soc.*, **77,** 3244 (1955).
54. Biggs, B. S., and W. L. Hawkins, paper presented at the Annual Meeting of the Scientific Advisory Committee of the Preservation and Deterioration Center, Washington, D. C., May, 1957.
55. Hawkins, W. L., and F. H. Winslow, *Plastics Inst.* (*London*), *Trans. J.*, **29** (81), 82 (1961).
56. Hawkins, W. L., M. A. Worthington, and F. H. Winslow, *Proc. Conf. Carbon, 4th, Buffalo 1959*, Pergamon Press, New York, 1960, p. 63; *Rubber Age* (*N. Y.*), **88,** 279 (1960).
57. Hammond, G. S., C. E. Boozer, C. E. Hamilton, and J. N. Sen, *J. Am. Chem. Soc.*, **77,** 3238 (1955).
58. Ingold, K. U., *Chem. Rev.*, **61,** 563 (1961).
59. Pedersen, C. J., *Ind. Eng. Chem.*, **48,** 1881 (1956).
60. Ingold, K. U., and J. A. Howard, *Nature*, **195,** 280 (1962).

61. Hawkins, W. L., and Mrs. H. Sautter, *Chem. Ind. (London)*, **1962**, 1825.
62. Hawkins, W. L., paper presented at The Symposium on Thermal Stability, Battelle Memorial Inst., Dec. 1963.
63. Barnard, D., L. Bateman, E. R. Cole, and J. I. Cunneen, *Chem. Ind. (London)*, **1958**, 918.
64. DeCroes, G. C., and J. W. Tamblyn, *Mod. Plastics*, **29** (8), 127 (1952).
65. Hawkins, W. L., M. A. Worthington, and W. Matreyek, *J. Appl. Polymer Sci.*, **3**, 277 (1960).
66. Cotman, J. D., Jr., *Ann. N. Y. Acad. Sci.*, **57**, 417 (1953); *Chem. Abstr.*, **48**, 4288b (1954).
67. Boyer, R. F., *J. Phys. Chem.*, **51**, 80 (1947).
68. Baum, B., *SPE (Soc. Plastics Engrs.) Trans.*, **17**, 71 (1961).
69. Murfitt, H. C., *Brit. Plastics*, **33**, 578 (1960).
70. Delfosse, P., *Rubber Plastics Age*, **40**, 941 (1959).
71. Murphy, C. M., and H. Ravner, *Ind. Eng. Chem.*, **44**, 1607 (1952).
72. Mesrobian, R. B., and A. V. Tobolsky, *J. Polymer Sci.*, **2**, 463 (1947).
73. Jellinek, H. H. G., ed., *Degradation of Vinyl Polymers*, Academic Press, New York, 1955, p. 214.
74. McMahon, W., H. A. Birdsall, G. R. Johnson, and C. T. Camilli, *J. Chem. Eng. Data*, **4**, 57 (1959).
75. Ott, E., and H. M. Spurlin, eds., *Cellulose and Cellulose Derivatives*, High Polymer Series, Vol. V, Interscience, New York, 1954, p. 101.
76. Waller, R. C., K. C. Bass, and W. E. Roseveare, *Ind. Eng. Chem.*, **40**, 138 (1948).
77. Wiegerink, J. G., *J. Res. Natl. Bur. Std.*, **25**, 435 (1940).
78. Launer, H. F., and W. K. Wilson, *J. Res. Natl. Bur. Std.*, **30**, 55 (1943).
79. Lloyd, W. G., *J. Polymer Sci.*, **1A**, 2551 (1963).
80. McGary, C. W., Jr., *J. Polymer Sci.*, **46**, 51 (1960).
81. Rafikov, S. R., and R. A. Sorokina, *Vysokomolekul. Soedin.*, **3**, 21 (1961); *Chem. Abstr.*, **55**, 26580i (1961).
82. Fuller, C. S., U. S. Patent 2,364,204 (to Bell Telephone Labs., Inc.), Dec. 5, 1944; *Chem. Abstr.*, **40**, 5014 (1946).
83. Achhammer, B. G., F. W. Reinhart, and G. M. Kline, Ref. 10, p. 253.

Chapter XIV

MECHANOCHEMICAL REACTIONS

W. F. Watson

Rubber and Plastics Research Association of Great Britain

A. INTRODUCTION

The large majority of chemical reactions are thermal reactions, the necessary energy being supplied as heat. Equivalent forms of energy give rise to electrochemical and photochemical reactions. Reactions which are induced by direct acquisition of mechanical energy on a molecular scale can by analogy conveniently be termed "mechanochemical" reactions.

It is only in recent years that mechanochemical mechanisms have been established by critical experiment (1) although, to be discussed presently, they have long been proposed and are at the basis of mastication, the earliest processing operation of the rubber industry. They are particularly of concern with polymers as can be readily pictured as follows.

Let us take the stirring of a low molecular weight liquid as an application of mechanical energy to a system. The molecules of the liquid do not offer enough resistance to the shear forces at normal shear rates to absorb activation energy for reaction. The energy absorbed is dissipated in the ready moving of the molecules to new positions:

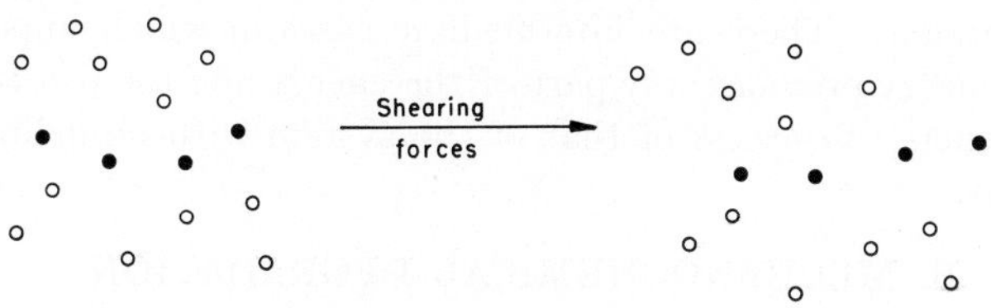

The same shear rates with polymers imposes very much higher amounts of energy. The entangled chain structure also tends to localize this energy in bonds near the centers of the chains, and with normal polymer-mixing

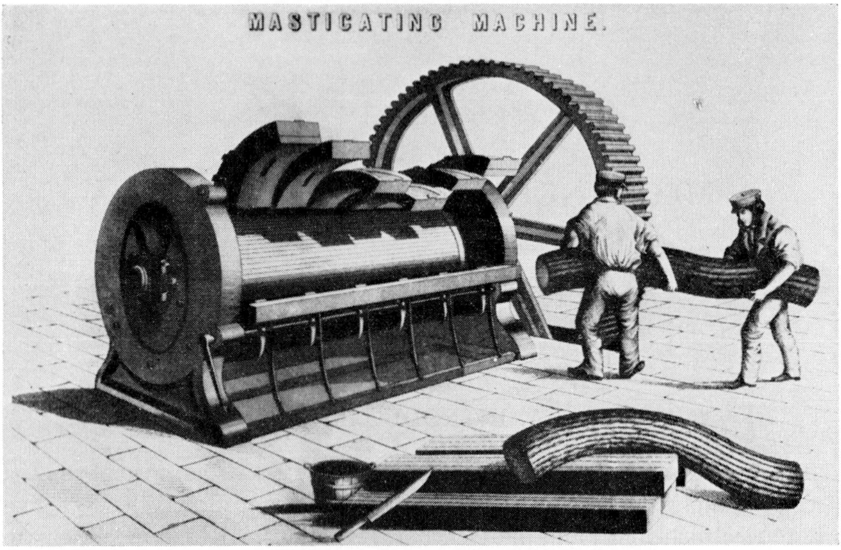

Fig. XIV-1. Illustration of masticator in Hancock's *Personal Narrative.* (Taken from ref. 2.)

equipment the energy imposed can exceed the bond strength. Further, this degradative reaction causes marked changes in physical properties,

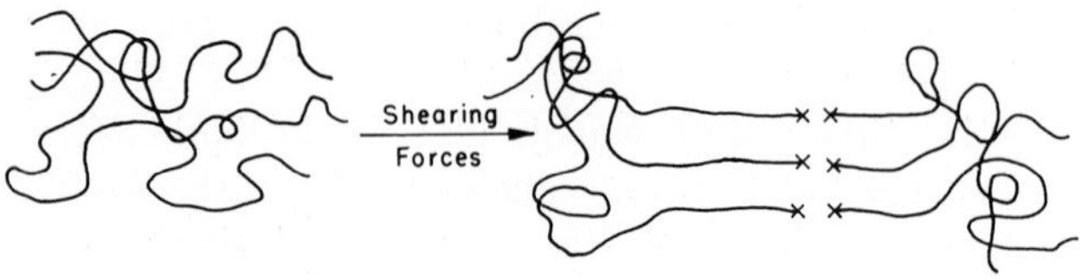

although only a fraction of a per cent of the chemical bonds may be involved in reaction. This simplified picture represents a wholly mechanochemical reaction. There are intermediate cases in which imposition of mechanical energy provides only part of the energy and the rest is supplied by thermal energy in excess of that of the system with no deliberate addition of heat.

B. MECHANOCHEMICAL DEGRADATION

1. Natural Rubber

In 1820 Thomas Hancock found that the passing of natural rubber between spiked rollers did not shred it, as he had expected, but coalesced

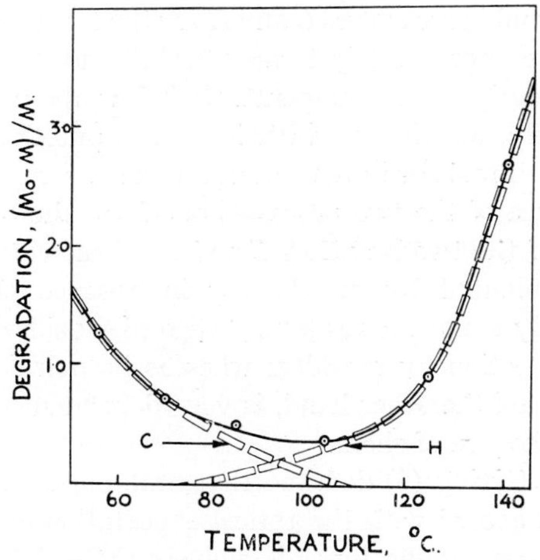

Fig. XIV-2. Efficiency of mastication of natural rubber at different temperatures. (Taken from ref. 1.)

it together into a softer and more coherent mass. As he asserted, this discovery "was unquestionably the origin and commencement of the india-rubber manufacture" and was soon followed by the first large machines of the industry such as the masticator (Fig. XIV-1) illustrated in his *Personal Narrative* (2).

Hancock observed that it required the mechanical energy of a strong man to masticate a charge of about 2 oz. of rubber and that the softening was related to the energy input and the temperature. An understanding of the process had to await the demonstration by Staudinger that natural rubber was one of a class of high polymer substances (3). Staudinger also showed from osmotic molecular weight measurements of raw and masticated rubber that the softening was attributable to polymer degradation (4). He further demonstrated that polymer molecules could be degraded mechanically by forcing polymer solutions through fine jets (5).

Mechanochemical mechanisms thereafter rather lost favor due to the occurrence also during mastication of natural rubber of thermal oxidative breakdown and a concentration of attention in explaining away all results by this one mechanism. The co-occurrence of the two reactions can clearly be seen in the U-shaped efficiency–temperature curve of Figure XIV-2, where efficiency of mastication is expressed by the fractional increase in number of polymer molecules, $[(1/M) - (1/M_0)]/(1/M_0)$, produced in a given time under standard machine working. The whole curve is a composite one which would give curves *C* and *H* for the two reactions separately. These processes are appropriately termed "cold" and "hot" mastication in view of their predominance at temperatures below about 80°C. and above 130°C., respectively, and in line with industrial practice of effecting degradation on cold roll mills or in hot internal mixers.

The independence of the two processes one from the other is evidenced by the positions of the two branches *C* and *H* of the composite curve (1). Branch *H* is eliminated by masticating in absence of oxygen. It is also moved laterally toward lower temperatures by oxidation catalysts and in the opposite direction by retarders whereas branch *C* is unaffected by these. Branch *C*, on the other hand, is very dependent on shear rate and does not exist in absence of shear.

Kauzmann and Eyring (6) deduced that Staudinger's mechanochemical mechanism was in accord with theoretical expectation and they expressed the degradation more specifically as homolysis of C—C bonds of the polymer backbone to free radicals:

$$\text{R—R} \xrightarrow[\text{Forces}]{\text{Shearing}} 2\text{R}\cdot \tag{1}$$

Experimental support for and extension of this mechanism by Watson and co-workers (1,7) has now established that mechanodegradation as expressed by eq. (1) is the primary step in cold mastication. The reactive radicals produced then undergo normal thermal reactions. With oxygen normally present during mastication in air, the radicals form peroxy radicals, and these are terminated by hydrogen abstraction from nonrubber constituents or from other rubber molecules

$$\text{R}\cdot + \text{O}_2 \rightarrow \text{RO}_2\cdot \rightarrow \text{RO}_2\text{H} \tag{2}$$

in propagating an oxidation chain reaction (cf. Chapter XIII).

It follows from this mechanism that polymer reactions such as radical recombination and branching on other polymer chains should occur in absence of oxygen:

$$2\text{R}\cdot \rightarrow \text{R—R} \tag{3}$$

$$\text{R}\cdot + \text{R—R} \rightarrow \text{R—}\underset{}{\overset{\text{R}\atop|}{\text{}}}\text{R} \tag{4}$$

These can account for the long-standing observations of Busse (8) and Cotton (9) of no softening of natural rubber on masticating while keeping air excluded from the masticator by a stream of nitrogen or carbon dioxide. (Plausible misinterpretations at the time in ascribing these significant results

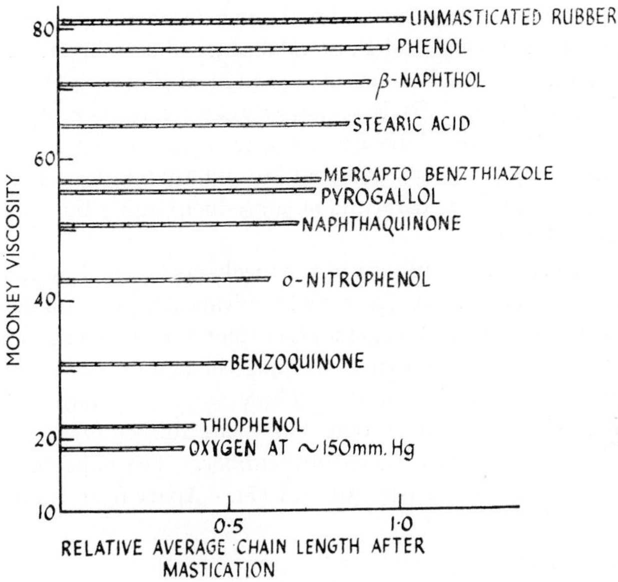

Fig. XIV-3. Efficiencies of some radical scavengers in stabilizing the mechanodegradation of natural rubber.

as showing that oxygen played a similar role in both cold and hot mastication did in fact turn attention from mechanochemistry.)

A prediction of the mechanochemical reaction step (1) is that many other substances should function as does oxygen as a polymer-radical scavenger to consummate degradation. This has been amply borne out by masticating, in an inert atmosphere, natural rubber containing 1 or 2% of compounds known to be reactive toward radicals of the type produced by polymer-chain rupture (1). An example is thiophenol (eq. 5).

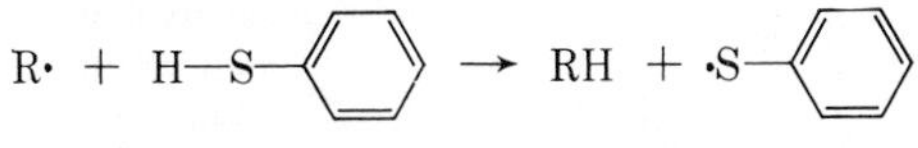

(5)

Incorporation of 1% of this chemical in the rubber results in a rate of degradation on masticating in an inert atmosphere equal to that in air. Here the alternative scavenger and oxygen are mopping up virtually all the polymer radicals and so rendering the rate determined and limited by the rate of mechanochemical rupture, that is by the shearing forces imposed. Other reactive scavengers also yield this limiting maximum rate. Less reactive scavengers do not compete so effectively with reactions of type

(3) and (4) and so give rates of breakdown intermediate between those with oxygen or thiophenol and those in absence of scavenger. A diagrammatic representation of efficiency is presented in Figure XIV-3 for typical radical scavengers (10). (It is of importance for rubber processing that many so-called "peptizers" are radical scavengers as well as promoters of oxidative scission during hot mastication and that radical scavengers do not necessarily need to be catalysts of subsequent aging but indeed can be oxidation retarders.)

The argument above is support of the mechanochemical mechanism from physical measurements. A chemical confirmation was forthcoming (7) through the use of two scavengers which met the stringent requirements of an unambiguous detection when forming the end unit of polymer chains of some thousand monomer units. These were 1,1-dinaphthyl disulfide labeled with S^{35} used with styrene–butadiene rubber and 1,1′-diphenyl-2-picrylhydrazyl (DPPH) with natural rubber. The expected stoichemical equations are shown in eqs. (6) and (7). Apart from qualitative evi-

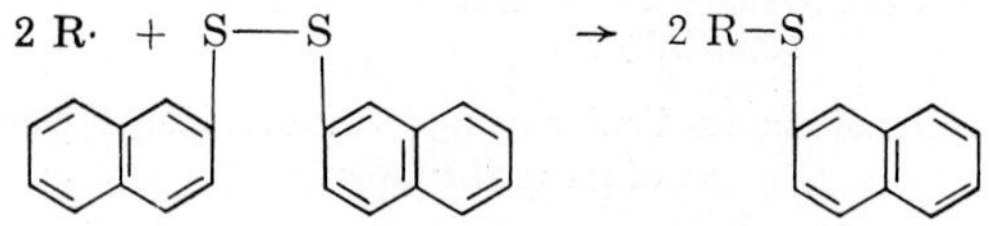

(6)

$$\text{R}\cdot + \text{DPPH} \rightarrow \text{R–DPPH} \qquad (7)$$

TABLE XIV-1
Confirmation of the Mechanochemical Mechanism of Degradation of Rubbers by Cold Milling

Rubber	Radical scavenger	Extent of degradation from osmotic mol. wt. measurements, new chain ends/g. rubber × 10^{-18}	Attachment of radical scavenger fragments, no./g. rubber × 10^{-18}
Poly(styrene-*co*-butadiene)	Dinaphthyl-disulfide	18.4	17.6
		18.8	18.6
cis-Polyisoprene	DPPH	4.8	3.0
		6.0	5.0
		6.8	6.4
		9.0	8.3
		9.8	9.1

Fig. XIV-4. Two models of unirotor mixer.

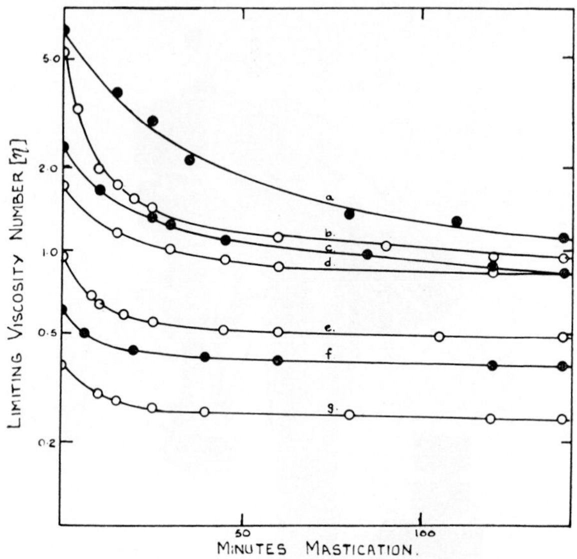

Fig. XIV-5. Mechanodegradation of typical polymers: (*a*) poly(methyl methacrylate) at 185°C.; (*b*) poly(methyl methacrylate) with 16% benzene at 12°C.; (*c*) cellulose acetate with 25% methyl acetate at 12°C.; (*d*) polystyrene at 130°C.; (*e*) polystyrene with 16% benzene at 12°C.; (*f*) poly(vinyl acetate) at 90°C.; (*g*) poly(vinyl acetate) with 16% benzene at 12°C.

dence of chemical attachment to the rubber, the measured uptake of scavenger was qualitatively in agreement with extent of degradation measured physically within experimental error of the molecular weight measurements (Table XIV-1).

2. Other Polymers

As with the history of natural rubber, observations have long been made on the effect of mechanical working on other polymers. Staudinger and Heuer (4) and Staudinger and Dreher (5) were the first to show clearly that mechanical treatment caused polymer degradation. They demonstrated that polystyrenes of different initial molecular weight were degraded by ball milling and after a prolonged period reached a constant molecular weight. Hess, Steurer, and Fromm (11) and Hess and Steurer (12) confirmed the observations on polystyrene and further found that cellulose, silk, and starch pounded in a swing mill lost crystallinity and likewise decreased in molecular weight to a steady value. Mechanisms of mechanochemical scission have since been put forward for the grinding of cellulose (13), starch

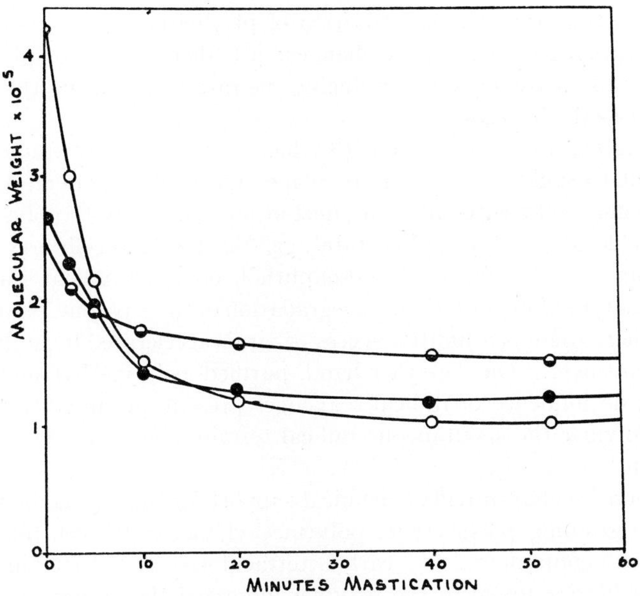

Fig. XIV-6. Mechanodegradation of rubbers to their limiting molecular weights: (O) natural rubber; (●) chloroprene rubber; (◒) styrene–butadiene rubber.

(14), and albuminous substances (15–17). Degradation under mechanical action has been noted for a great variety of polymers including vinyl polymers such as poly(methyl methacrylate) and polyethylene; phenol-aldehyde, polyester, and polyamide condensate resins; naturally occurring casein, copal resins, shellac, and glue (18).

Mechanodegradation of thermoplastic polymers has been studied in some detail by use of the convenient uni-rotor mixers (19) portrayed in Figure XIV-4. The general pattern of degradation is illustrated in Figures XIV-5 and 6 for typical polymers at temperatures at which they are in a rubbery state and on plasticizing to give a suitably deformable mixture at room temperature.

The dependence of degradation on the various parameters of the system is in line with a mechanochemical mechanism (18). Raising the temperature under standard conditions of rate of shear does not give the Arrhenius dependence but a much smaller change which may in fact be a decrease in rate of degradation with rise in temperature due to the concomitant decrease in viscosity reducing the work done in deforming the polymer. The more rapid degradation with polymer of higher molecular weight can be attributed to the same cause. Addition of plasticizer also affects the degradation in accord with viscosity changes; a higher content of plasticizer or one of greater softening effect reducing the rate. Increasing the rate of shear increases the breakdown.

The recombination reaction, eq. (3), has in no case been found to be predominant to such an extent as to reduce markedly the overall breakdown on mechanical treatment in an inert atmosphere. With polystyrene, poly(vinyl chloride), poly(vinyl acetate), gelatin (20), and cellulose acetate (18), the presence of oxygen, thio-β-naphthol, or other radical scavenger increases the rate of degradation. Degradation of these polymers on a two-roll mill, where there is a limited access of air, is accelerated by addition of a soluble scavenger. On the other hand, purified poly(methyl methacrylate) shows no influence of radical scavenger present, presumably because with this polymer the spontaneous radical termination is not by polymer combination.

Baramboim (21) has provided chemical support for the mechanochemical reaction by grinding polystyrene, poly(methyl methacrylate), and poly(vinyl acetate) containing 2–3% carbon tetrachloride at −10°C. in a steel ball mill. Chlorine found in the polymer indicated the occurrence of the secondary reactions (8) and (9).

$$R\cdot + CCl_4 \rightarrow R{-}Cl + \cdot CCl_3 \qquad (8)$$

$$R\cdot + \cdot CCl_3 \rightarrow R{-}CCl_3 \qquad (9)$$

Characterization of the radicals produced on mechanical treatment of a range of polymers has recently been achieved (22). Polymer samples were milled with a conical bit and the turnings, still in a hermetically sealed manipulator, inserted in an EPR spectrometer. EPR spectra of the radicals produced on the polymer surfaces by the milling were thus observed. For poly(methyl methacrylate), the spectrum of radical I was measurable for several hours at 77°K. *in vacuo* but that of the more reactive radical II was not observed. Raising the air pressure to 0.1 mm.

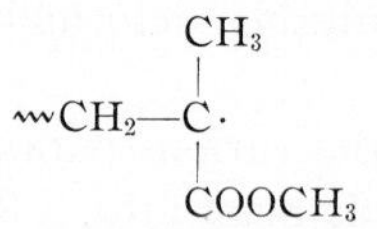
(I)

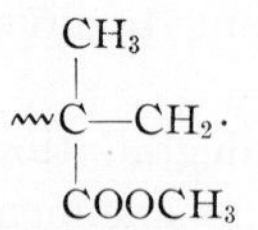
(II)

Hg caused the disappearance in a few minutes of the spectrum of I and development of the spectrum of the peroxy radical, which in its turn disappeared after some 40 min. at 77°K. Only the peroxy radical was detected with polyisoprene, polystyrene, and polytetrafluoroethylene.

Berlin (23) envisages mechanodegradative reactions involving heterolytic scission to form polymeric ions with silicates, glass, asbestos, feldspar, mica, and other minerals. He further suggests their consideration with regard to proteins and polysaccharides in living processes. Mullins and Watson (24) have shown that the high temperature breakdown of natural rubber in oxygen is also shear-dependent and suggest here an acceleration by added mechanical energy of the normal thermal bimolecular reactions of oxidative scission. Kargin and Plate (25) have created, by grinding, active sites on inorganic crystalline substances such as common salt, quartz, and graphite. Yet a further almost unexplored field is the cutting and other mechanical operations in metal working, where certain observations appear to fit in well with a primary mechanochemical reaction (26).

C. SITE OF MECHANOCHEMICAL SCISSION

The weakest bonds in the monomeric units of natural rubber are the C—C bonds midway between the 1,5 double bonds due to the resonance energy of the two alkenyl radicals on scission.

$$\sim\!\!\overset{\displaystyle CH_3}{\overset{|}{C}}\!=\!CH\!-\!H_2C\!-\!CH_2\!-\!\overset{\displaystyle CH_3}{\overset{|}{C}}\!=\!CH\!\sim \;\rightarrow\; \sim\!\!\overset{\displaystyle CH_3}{\overset{|}{C}}\!=\!CH\!-\!H_2C\cdot + \cdot CH_2\!-\!\overset{\displaystyle CH_3}{\overset{|}{C}}\!=\!CH\!\sim \qquad (10)$$

Alkenyl radicals of this type are prone to recombination, hence the occurrence of eq. (3) with natural rubber. Again, hydrogen abstraction by these primary alkenyl radicals from other polyisoprene molecules gives a chemical description of the branching reactions of eq. (4). The high efficiency of oxygen as scavenger is also in line with its reactivity toward alkenyl radicals during thermal oxidation (27).

The rupturable bond in most other polymers cannot be so certainly specified. Suitably disposed groups for resonance in the radicals probably also determine the site of rupture in the other 1,5-dienes, *cis*-polybutadiene, polychloroprene, poly(butadiene-*co*-styrene) and poly(butadiene-*co*-acrylonitrile). The wide range of polymers discussed above shows, however, that there are few if any chemical-structure limitations to the polymers which will undergo mechanochemical rupture.

The site of scission with respect to the whole polymer chain is an important feature, in that it determines both the rate of degradation and the properties of the polymer which depend on its molecular weight distribution. The expectation with many thermal reactions is of equal probability of scission along the polymer chain, giving an approach toward a "random," i.e., Flory's "most probable" (28), molecular weight distribution. This is not so with mechanochemical scission; nonrandom scission takes place with reactions of this class.

Polymers under shear initially degrade at a relatively rapid rate and quite shortly level off to a limiting, still quite high, molecular weight. Taking a typical experience, natural rubber on cold mastication decreases in molecular weight to, say, one half in a few minutes and has a molecular weight of the order of 70,000 in 20 min., below which the molecular weight is not sensibly reduced over an extended period of mastication. Figures XIV-5 and XIV-6 illustrate the rate phenomena for typical polymers in their rubbery state.

These observations are explicable by a highly preferential rupture of bonds in central sections of molecules a sufficient distance—about 35,000 in molecular weight for natural rubber—from either end (III):

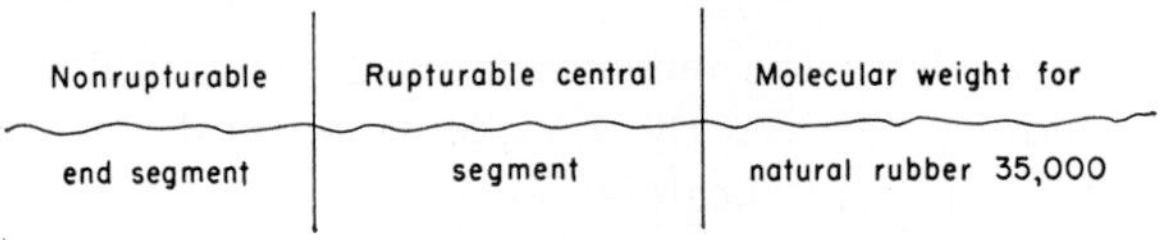

(III)

When molecules are lower in chain length than a fairly well-defined size, which is twice the length of nonrupturable end segment, they no longer degrade under the shear conditions applied. In practice it is found that the limiting molecular weight on degradation is not greatly lowered on increasing the shear within the limits of conventional mixing equipment. (For example, "depolymerized" rubber of molecular weight about 10,000 cannot be commercially produced by cold milling.)

This nonrandom rupture restricted to central sections of the molecules above a minimum molecular weight leads to a molecular weight distribution narrower than the random one. The high molecular weight tail of the distribution curve found in an unmilled sample of polychloroprene disappeared, and fractions close to the average increased in size (29). Milling for 5 min. sufficed to reduce the ratio of weight-average to number-average molecular weight from 2.87 to 1.84, while the number-average itself fell only from 8.8×10^4 to 7.8×10^4. Milling for a further 55 min. reduced the ratio to 1.65 and the number-average molecular weight to 6.1×10^4.

An illustration of the effect of nonrandom rupture on physical properties is provided by the solution viscosity of masticated rubber (30). As the proportion of molecules of relatively long chain length in masticated rubber is lower than that of a more random distribution, the solution vis-

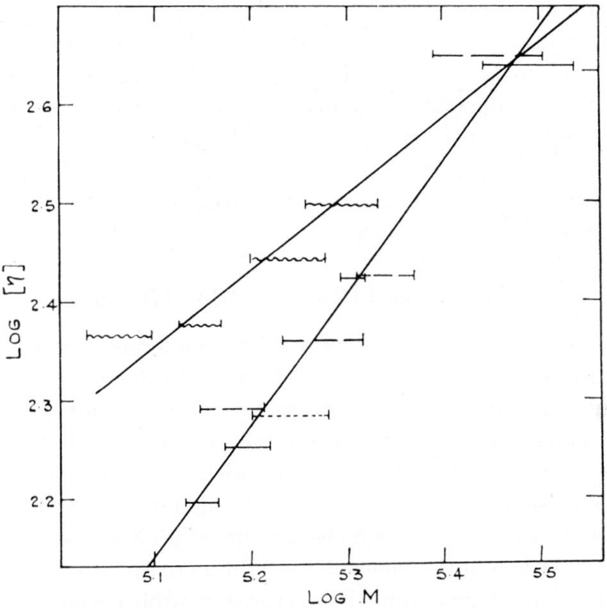

Fig. XIV-7. Viscosity–osmotic molecular weight relationships for natural rubber: (∿∿) thermally degraded in air as thin films at 140°C.; (——) masticated at 55°C.; (- - - - -) masticated at 120°C.; (– – –) masticated at 140°C.

cosity is markedly lower than for rubber degraded by thermal oxidation to the same value of number-average molecular weight (Fig. XIV-7).

A theoretical treatment of energy distribution among polymer bonds on cavitation of dilute polymer solutions by ultrasonic radiation leads to the conclusion in qualitative harmony with the above experimental results that bonds in the center of polymer molecules acquire disproportionate amounts of energy (31). More direct theoretical support comes from an analysis (32) indicating that central sections of the longer molecules in bulk polymer acquire higher amounts of energy, mainly due to these molecules not being able to disentangle sufficiently under shear to dissipate the mechanical work in movement.

The energetics of mechanodegradation of polymer solutions (33,34) give an energy consumption some thousands of times that of the bond strengths of the ruptured bonds. This is, of course, not surprising and is similar to thermal activation of bond rupture, where again energy distribution and concentration above a critical value in individual bonds and not total values are directly relevant. Energy consumption decreases with increasing polymer concentration; for example, from a value of 450 × 10³ kcal./mole bonds ruptured for polyisobutylene at 5% concentration in *n*-hexadecane at 40°C. to 250 × 10³ kcal./mole for a 20% solution. Approximate calculations are sufficient to indicate that intramolecular processes of energy accumulation (31) in rupturing bonds are ruled out and that intermolecular processes (32) need to be invoked to give a buildup of sufficient energy in rupturing bonds and for dissipation of energy stored in many neighboring bonds on scission (34).

D. CROSSLINKING REACTIONS

It has been mentioned that natural rubber undergoes secondary branching reaction steps on mastication in an inert atmosphere. The rubber after a small amount of mastication still has the high Huggins' k' solution viscosity parameter of a soluble branched polymer and a bulk viscosity higher than of the original polymer, as illustrated by the data of Table XIV-2. Rigorous exclusion of radical scavengers, including oxygen, yielded on mastication a gelled rubber which became solubilized on further mastication (35). Although the molecular weight increased, the tensile strengths of vulcanizates produced from the masticated rubber were only one-tenth of those for the rubber lightly masticated in air, presumably due to branching depressing crystallization on stretching.

TABLE XIV-2

Duration of mastication under nitrogen, min.	k' value	Bulk viscosity, Wallace Plastimeter units
0	0.49	68
2	—	75
3	0.49	76
5	—	74
7	—	60
10	0.50	52

The common synthetic elastomers prepared from styrene–butadiene, chloroprene, and acrylonitrile are all readily insolubilized on mastication in absence of radical scavengers (Fig. XIV-8). The chemistry of these reactions has not been elucidated; the greater crosslinking tendency compared with natural rubber may probably be explained similarly to that on

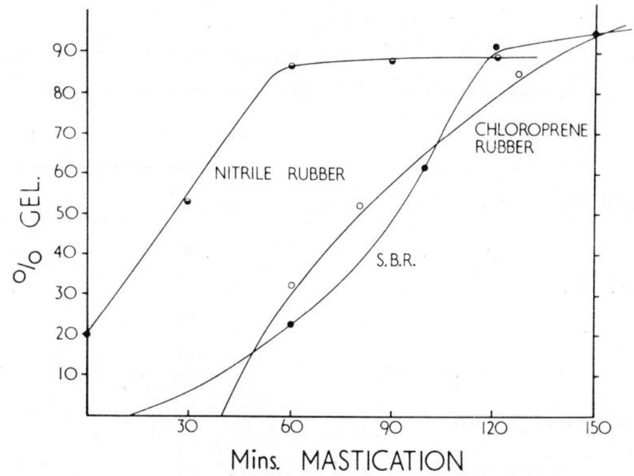

Fig. XIV-8. Gelation on the mastication of some rubbers in the absence of radical scavengers.

oxidation or other radical attack. Butyl rubber degrades only slowly under mechanical treatment and does not form gel.

Gelation of natural and the other rubbers does not appear to take place during normal factory processing. The degradation of the common synthetic elastomers is, however, slower than of natural rubber of comparable viscosity. In part, this is due to oxygen being a less efficient scavenger for the polymeric radicals and thus not allowing realization of the potential degradation by the machine. Addition of mercaptan or other very reactive scavenger accelerates degradation in such cases. As an illustration, the initial Mooney viscosity of 97 of a styrene–butadiene rubber was reduced to 81 under normal milling in air and to 68 and 65, respectively, with 1% thiophenol and benzoquinone present.

The radical scavengers so far considered simply stabilize ruptured fragments of polymer molecules at their degraded chain lengths. Another group of radical scavengers promotes branching. Maleic anhydride is one of this group. Natural rubber milled in air or in nitrogen after incorporation of 1 or 2% of this compound becomes first elastic and insoluble and then quite suddenly is transformed to a brittle product which sputters alarmingly from the mill (36). Here the maleic anhydride adds to the primary polymeric radical to give a secondary radical very reactive toward carbon–carbon double bonds:

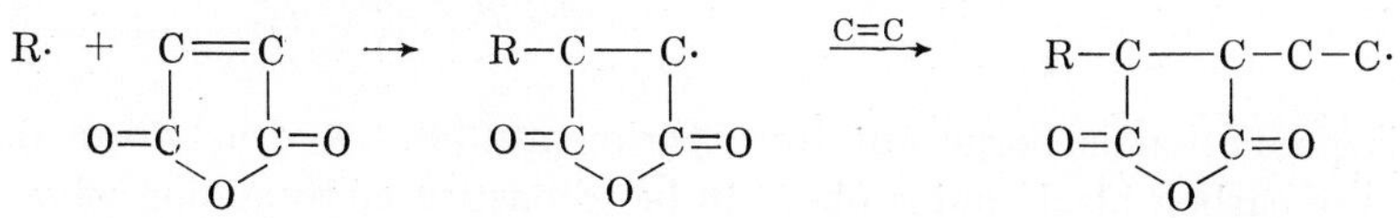

(11)

TABLE XIV-3
Crosslinking Radical Scavengers at Molar Concentrations Equivalent to 1% Benzoquinone in Natural Rubber after 30 min. Mastication at 55°C.

Compound	Gel, %	
	In N_2	In Air
Chloranil	80	81
Maleic anhydride	75	0
m-Aminophenol	45	45
p-Aminophenol	37	0
Benzidine	50	82
Trimethylene dimercaptan	73	0
p-Nitrophenol	11	0
m-Nitrophenol	1	0
Trinitrophenol	0	4
m-Nitroaniline	15	0
Cobalt naphthenate (0.0051 mole Co)	9	0

Other additives which crosslink natural rubber on cold mastication are listed in Table XIV-3.

1. Fillers

Mechanical processing is in large measure performed in order to incorporate various fillers among other compounding ingredients into rubbers. It is then pertinent to enquire whether filler mixing and dispersing is a wholly physical process or whether the filler can participate in the mechanochemical reactions taking place. Considering first carbon blacks, these possess on their surface various functional groups (37) which may act as radical scavengers. If, further, some of these groups serve to attach polymer chains to carbon black particles, degradation of attached chains and further reaction with the multifunctional black particles would eventually produce rubber–carbon black gel:

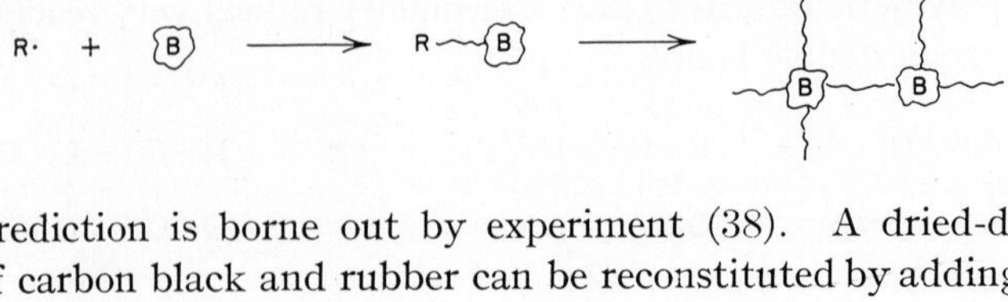

This prediction is borne out by experiment (38). A dried-down dispersion of carbon black and rubber can be reconstituted by adding solvent.

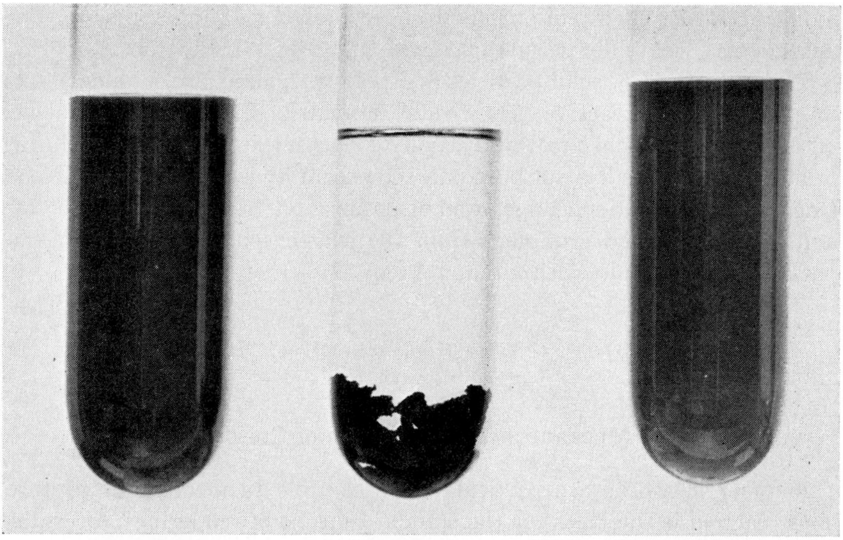

Fig. XIV-9. Carbon gel on milling natural rubber–carbon black dispersions: (*a*) dissolution of original dispersion in benzene; (*b*) carbon gel after one pass through a two-roll mill; (*c*) dissolution of milled dispersion containing added radical scavenger.

If, however, the dry mixture is first passed once through the nip of a two-roll mill, the black no longer disperses in the solvent but is held bound to a fraction of the rubber in a rubber–carbon black gel in a solution of the rest of the rubber which remains indefinitely water-clear (Fig. XIV-9). DPPH (0.1%) completely prevents this gel formation, as do other reagents normally present or specially added for this purpose. The capacity for gel formation increases inversely with particle size of black of a given type, furnace blacks give more gel than channel blacks and lamp black gives hardly any gel.

Rubber–carbon gel formed either during cold mastication or by thermal reaction on hot mastication reduces the flow of the unvulcanized rubber to an extent of industrial significance. It has to be emphasized that there is, on the other hand, no immediate tie-up between gel formation and reinforcement of properties of the vulcanizate (39) during the preparation of which any chemical effects which may contribute to reinforcement are more likely to develop during the heat-treatment stage of production.

Fine silica and silicate fillers give filler-gel formation parallel to that of carbon blacks (40). Gel has also been detected in polyethylene–carbon black mixtures (41). Coarser fillers, which are added mainly to give stiffening rather than reinforcement of tensile strength and abrasion resistance, do not yield filler gels on mastication.

These reactions of solid particles in a polymer matrix are secondary to a mechanochemical reaction step within the matrix. The likely prevalence of direct mechanochemical activation of the surface of particles during grinding operations has not been checked except by isolated investigations. One such investigation (42) showed that silica, on grinding under alcohols and ethers, attached groupings from the solvent on the surfaces of the particles, for example, with *n*-butanol (eq. 12):

$$-\overset{|}{\underset{|}{\mathrm{Si}}}-\mathrm{O}-\overset{|}{\underset{|}{\mathrm{Si}}}- + \mathrm{C_4H_9OH} \rightarrow -\overset{|}{\underset{|}{\mathrm{Si}}}-\mathrm{OH} + \mathrm{C_4H_9O}-\overset{|}{\underset{|}{\mathrm{Si}}}- \qquad (12)$$

2. Mechanochemical Scission of Crosslinks

Polymer networks are particularly susceptible to mechanical rupture. This reaction is the basis for the standard means of rendering processable by milling rubber which has "set-up" during storage either in the raw or compounded state. For example, a sample of styrene–butadiene rubber had its gel content decreased from 64 to 44, 25, and 0% on milling for 0.5, 1, and 2 min., respectively (43).

An interesting case is poly(vinyl chloride) at extrusion temperatures. Thermal reactions tend to form a branched network which is simultaneously being degraded mechanically by the machine. Kargin, Slonimskii, and coworkers term this "chemical flow" and suggest that it must be taken into account in establishing optimum processing conditions and properties of the processed polymer (44).

E. FORMATION OF BLOCK COPOLYMERS

1. Blending of Polymers

The mechanical rupture mechanism suggests that if two polymers are masticated together they may form a block polymer fraction either by combination of polymeric radicals of different types or branching of a polymer radical on to a polymer molecule of the other type (eqs. 13 and 14).

$$\mathrm{R}\cdot + \mathrm{S}\cdot \rightarrow \mathrm{R}-\mathrm{S} \qquad (13)$$

$$\mathrm{R}\cdot + \mathrm{S}-\mathrm{S} \rightarrow \mathrm{S}\overset{\mathrm{R}}{\overset{|}{-}}\mathrm{S} \qquad (14)$$

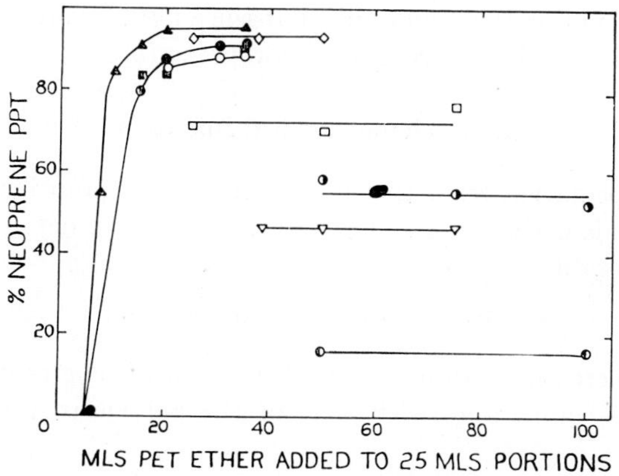

Fig. XIV-10. Selective precipitation of polychloroprene from a 50:50 blend with natural rubber: (▲) unmilled; (◇) 2 hr. in air; (●) 50 min. under N_2; (□) 2 hr. under N_2; (▽) 6 hr. under N_2; (◐) 12 hr. under N_2; (◑) 12 hr. under N_2 in an internal mixer.

These reactions may well occur on occasion during polymer blending, as with high styrene/high acrylonitrile–butadiene blends, and butyl rubber and polyethylene blends (45).

They have been confirmed to take place by experiments designed to test this expectation. Blends of purified natural rubber with polybutadiene (46), poly(butadiene-*co*-styrene), poly(butadiene-*co*-acrylonitrile), and polybutadiene (47) all gave gels containing a high proportion of both rubbers on masticating together under nitrogen. The sol fractions exhibited properties characteristic of block polymers, in that a major proportion of either of the polymers remained in a milky suspension in a solvent mixture in which one homopolymer was soluble and the other was cleanly precipitated. The presence of a radical scavenger prevented gel formation and gave quantitative precipitation into homopolymer fractions (Fig. XIV-10). Block polymer formation was also demonstrated by the binding of natural rubber into a vulcanizate of polychloroprene with the use of a metal oxide recipe which does not crosslink the natural rubber.

A wider survey of rubber–nonrubber polymer systems has shown that nitrile rubber forms interpolymer on blending with phenol–formaldehyde and epoxy resins and refined coal tar (48). A small proportion of nitrile rubber confers elasticity to the resin, whereas a small proportion of resin stiffens the rubber without materially reducing its extensibility. Blends of poly(vinyl chloride) with phenol–aldehyde resin gave only homopolymeric mixtures when iodine was added as scavenger but some 20% of the resin bound to the poly(vinyl chloride) in its absence (49). Poly(vinyl chloride) also forms a block polymer with polychloroprene (50).

2. Mechanochemical Initiation

Another expectation from the mechanism of mechanochemical scission into free radicals is that mechanical treatment of polymer–monomer mixtures under suitable conditions should lead to addition polymerization.

$$R\cdot + M \rightarrow R{-}M{-}M{-}M{-}M\cdot \tag{15}$$

The initiator here differs from the usual free-radical generator in being of a molecular size comparable with that of the polymerized monomer and

TABLE XIV-4A
Monomers as Noncrosslinking Radical Scavengers on Natural Rubber Mastication[a]

Additive	After 15 min. mastication		After 30 min. mastication		After 60 min. mastication	
	$[\eta]$	k'	$[\eta]$	k'	$[\eta]$	k'
None	2.19	0.54	1.82	0.53	1.67	0.58
Oxygen (air)	1.47	0.43	1.38	0.44	1.21	0.44
Methyl methacrylate, 5%	1.74	0.46	1.60	0.45	1.37	0.46
Methyl methacrylate, 1%	1.95	0.46	1.70	0.47	1.43	0.46
Styrene, 1%	2.11	0.48	—	—	1.55	0.49
Vinyl acetate, 5%	2.15	0.53	1.84	0.47	1.59	0.49

[a] Taken from ref. 51.

TABLE XIV-4B
Monomers as Crosslinking Radical Scavengers on Natural Rubber Mastication[a]

Additive	Mastication conditions	Gel	
		%	Swelling
Chloroprene, 1%	15 min., N_2	45	20
	30 min., N_2	43	20
	15 min., Air	20	54
Acrylonitrile, 1%	5 min., N_2	66	12
	15 min., N_2	80	7
	15 min., Air	63	10
Methacrylic acid, 1%	5 min., N_2	34	34
	15 min., N_2	43	27
	15 min., Air	30	37

[a] Taken from ref. 51.

Fig. XIV-11. Production of natural rubber–poly(methyl methacrylate) block polymer with the use of an extruder.

thereby yielding a block polymer product. The simplest mechanism of eq. (15) suggests a linear and not a graft type of block polymer.

Suitable monomers must be reasonably active radical scavengers. This is shown (51) to be the case (Tables XIV-4A, XIV-4B) for several common monomers, where their presence in small amounts does not complicate the degradation evidence of radical scavenger action with significant further polymerization.

Free radical scavengers must not be present in amounts sufficient to terminate a substantial proportion of the ruptured chains or of the propagating radicals. In practice, the simple expedient of flushing an internal mixer with inert gas or the normal working of an extruder (52) frequently removes oxygen to an adequate extent (Fig. XIV-11). Acetone extraction for natural rubber and similar purification procedures for synthetic rubbers are normally required. Many other synthetic and natural polymers as available require no purification.

Figure XIV-12 illustrates the typical shape of polymerization curve for a liquid monomer which gives a hard polymer. The initial relatively slow polymerization rate is attributable to the softness of the initial polymer–monomer mixture requiring the least work from the machine operating at a constant shear. The rate on onset of polymerization rapidly increases

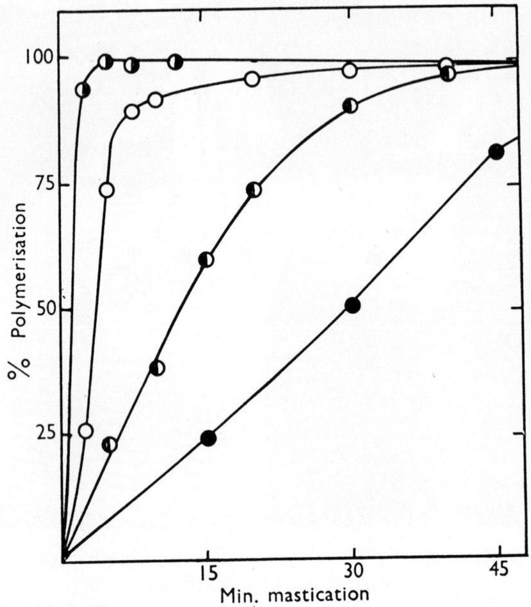

Fig. XIV-12. Polymerization by mastication of monomers at 0.33 ml./g. concentration in acetone-extracted smoked sheet: (◑) methacrylic acid; (O) methyl methacrylate; (◐) chloroprene; (●) styrene.

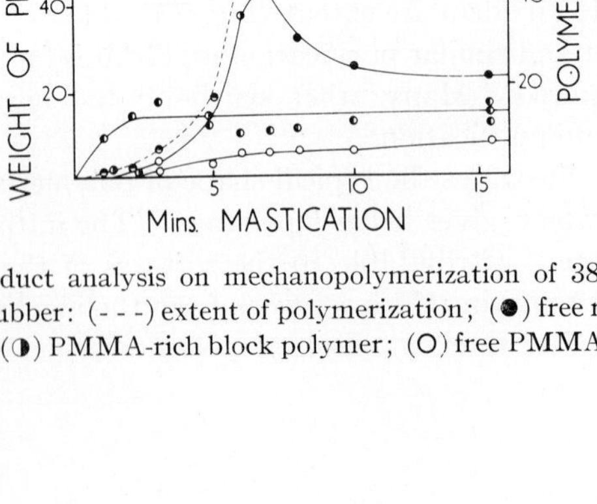

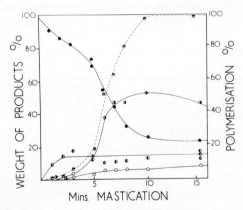

Fig. XIV-13. Product analysis on mechanopolymerization of 38.5% methyl methacrylate in natural rubber: (- - -) extent of polymerization; (●) free rubber; (◐) rubber-rich block polymer; (◑) PMMA-rich block polymer; (O) free PMMA.

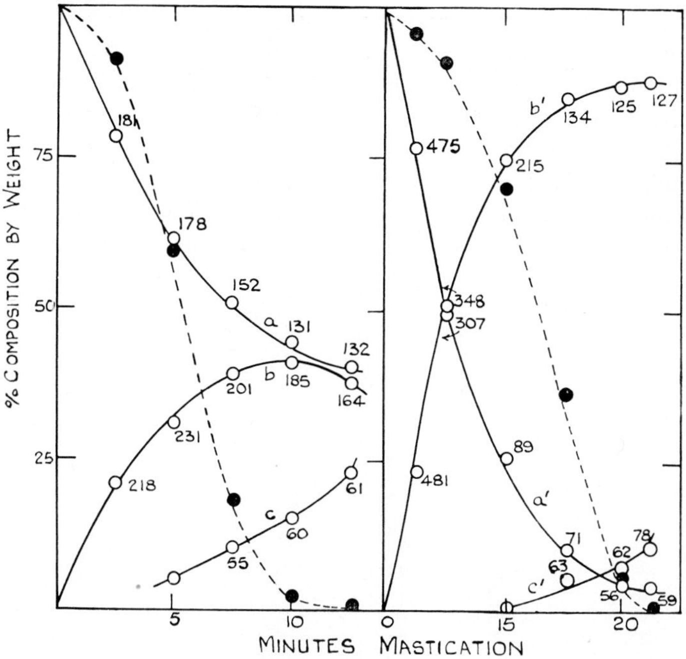

Fig. XIV-14. Composition during the mastication of initially (left) 24% methyl methacrylate in polystyrene, and (right) 38% styrene in poly(methyl methacrylate): (*a*) free polystyrene; (*b*) block polymer; (*c*) free poly(methyl methacrylate); (*a'*) free poly(methyl methacrylate); (*b'*) block polymer; (*c'*) free polystyrene; (- -) % unpolymerized monomer. The numbers on the curves are the limiting viscosity numbers of the appropriate samples. (Taken from ref. 54.)

until virtually complete conversion of monomer in line with increasing work done by the machine. The influence of monomer concentration, shear rate, temperature, and solvent addition can all be qualitatively described in terms of their effect on the work done by the masticator (51).

The separation of the constituents after polymerization by mastication of methyl methacrylate in natural rubber is shown for one monomer concentration in Figure XIV-13. Separative procedures with free polymer and block polymer are tricky and require cross-checking by independent methods (53). Fractional precipitation of the dissolved product gave three fractions, homopolymeric (free) poly(methyl methacrylate), a block polymer fraction, and a coprecipitate of free rubber with a rubber-rich portion of block polymer. Free rubber could be extracted by petroleum ether from the other constituents. It is seen in Figure XIV-13 that the free natural rubber content decreased to about 20% of the original, the free rubber remaining being of low molecular weight. The bulk of the polymerized monomer ended up in the block polymer fractions. A proportion of the free polymer appears to have been formed by shear of previously formed block polymer.

A similar product analysis is given in Figure XIV-14 for polystyrene–methyl methacrylate and poly(methyl methacrylate)–styrene (54). The alternative systems show some interesting differences. In particular, the

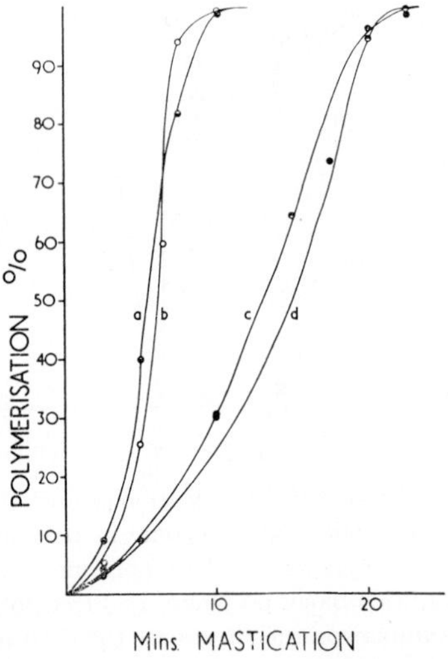

Fig. XIV-15. Mechanopolymerization of monomers in thermoplastic substances: (*a*) polystyrene with 24% methyl methacrylate; (*b*) poly(vinyl acetate) with 23% methyl methacrylate; (*c*) poly(methyl methacrylate) with 30% styrene; (*d*) poly(vinyl acetate) with 23% styrene.

former system yields more of the monomer in free polymer after mastication.

The polymeric structure of block polymer formed has been investigated in greatest detail for natural rubber–poly(methyl methacrylate) (55). The separated block polymer was analyzed with respect to composition, number-average molecular weight, ozonolysis to leave only the plastic segments, and autoxidation of the rubber segments. The general picture is that of a block polymer molecule containing one or two rubber and polymerized monomer segments of molecular weights 100,000–200,000 on masticating to complete polymerization.

Mechano-initiated polymerization occurs very readily with nonrubbery polymers, including the common thermoplastics (56), as shown in Figure XIV-15. The rate is frequently increased by adding small amounts of inorganic salts and other powders (57). As with mechanodegradation, the polymer component can be chosen from a wide range, including natural polymers such as starch, glue, and casein (57). The initial mixture need not be in a coherent deformable mass so long as the machine used can apply the necessary shearing energy. Indeed the polymer component itself can be dispensed with and replaced by powders including common salt and quartz (25).

References

1. Pike, M., and W. F. Watson, *J. Polymer Sci.*, **9,** 229 (1952).
2. Hancock, T., *Personal Narrative of the Origin and Progress of the Caoutchouc or India-Rubber Manufacture in England.* Longmans, 1857.
3. Staudinger, H., *Ber.*, **63,** 931 (1930).
4. Staudinger, H., and W. Heuer, *Ber.*, **67,** 1159 (1934).
5. Staudinger, H., and E. Dreher, *Ber.*, **69,** 1091 (1936).
6. Kauzmann, W., and H. Eyring, *J. Am. Chem. Soc.*, **62,** 3113 (1940).
7. Ayrey, G., C. G. Moore, and W. F. Watson, *J. Polymer Sci.*, **19,** 1 (1956).
8. Busse, W. F., and E. N. Cunningham, in *Proc. Rubber Technol. Conf. 1st, London, 1938,* T. R. Dawson and J. R. Scott, eds., Institution of the Rubber Industry London, p. 288.
9. Cotton, F. H., *Trans. Inst. Rubber Ind.*, **6,** 487 (1931); *Chem. Abstr.*, **26,** 872 (1932).
10. Watson, W. F., *Trans. Inst. Rubber Ind.*, **29,** 32 (1953); *Chem. Abstr.*, **47,** 4116h (1953).
11. Hess, K., E. Steurer, and H. Fromm, *Kolloid-Z.*, **98,** 148, 290 (1942); *Chem. Abstr.*, **36,** 5581[6] (1942).
12. Hess, K., and E. Steurer, *Z. Physik. Chem. (Leipzig)*, **193,** 234 (1944); *Chem. Abstr.*, **40,** 6939[5] (1946).
13. Clark, J. d'A., in *Cellulose and Cellulose Derivatives,* E. Ott, ed., High Polymers Series, Vol. V, 1st ed., Interscience, New York, 1943, p. 364.
14. Shul'man, M. S., and S. M. Lipatov, *Kolloidn. Zh.*, **14,** 135 (1952); *Chem. Abstr.*, **46,** 6522h (1952).
15. Cohen, H. R., *Arch. Biochem.*, **4,** 145 (1944); *Chem. Abstr.*, **39,** 313[1] (1945).
16. Edwards, B., and J. I. Routh, *J. Biol. Chem.*, **154,** 593 (1944); *Chem. Abstr.*, **38,** 6305[4] (1944).
17. Pavlov, S. A., and N. K. Baramboim, *Kolloidn. Zh.*, **11,** 420 (1949); *Chem. Abstr.*, **44,** 2822a (1950).
18. Ceresa, R. J., and W. F. Watson, *J. Appl. Polymer Sci.*, **1,** 101 (1959).
19. Watson, W. F., and D. Wilson. *Rubber Plastics Age*, **38,** 982 (1957).
20. Baramboim, N. K., *Zh. Fiz. Khim.*, **32,** 1049 (1958); RABRM Transl. 721; *Chem. Abstr.*, **52,** 2121h (1958).

21. Baramboim, N. K., *Zh. Fiz. Khim.*, **32,** 806 (1958); DSIR Transl. RTS 1092; *Chem. Abstr.*, **52,** 2122f (1958).
22. Bresler, S. E., S. N. Zhurkov, E. N. Kazbekov, E. M. Saminskii, and E. E. Tomashevskii, *Zh. Teckhn. Fiz.*, **29,** 358 (1959); *Rubber Chem. Technol.*, **33,** 462 (1960).
23. Berlin, A. A., *Dokl. Akad. Nauk SSSR,* **110,** 401 (1956); *Chem. Abstr.*, **51,** 14378f (1957).
24. Mullins, L., and W. F. Watson, *J. Appl. Polymer Sci.*, **1,** 245 (1959).
25. Kargin, V. A., and N. A. Plate, *Vysokomolekul. Soedin.*, **1,** 330 (1959); RABRM Transl. 777; *Chem. Abstr.*, **53,** 19437c (1959).
26. Shaw, M. C., *J. Appl. Mech.*, **15** (1), 37 (1948).
27. Bateman, L., *Quart. Rev. (London),* **8,** 147 (1954).
28. Flory, P. J., *Principles of Polymer Chemistry,* Cornell Univ. Press, Ithaca, New York, 1953, p. 321.
29. Angier, D. J., W. T. Chambers, and W. F. Watson, *J. Polymer Sci.*, **25,** 129 (1957).
30. Zurabyan, S. I., N. G. Karapetyan, and A. N. Lyubimova, *Izv. Akad. Nauk Arm., SSR, Khim. Nauk, Ser. Techn. Nauk,* **12,** 15 (1959); RABRM Transl. 840; *Chem. Abstr.*, **53,** 16573i (1959).
31. Frenkel, Y., *Acta. Physicochim. USSR,* **19,** 51 (1944); *Chem. Abstr.*, **39,** 1340 (1945).
32. Bueche, F., *J. Appl. Polymer Sci.*, **4,** 101 (1960).
33. Morris, W. J., and R. Schnurmann, *Nature,* **160,** 674 (1947).
34. Bestul, A. B., *J. Chem. Phys.*, **32,** 350 (1960).
35. Dogadkin, B. A., and V. N. Kuleznev, *Kolloidn. Zh.*, **20,** 674 (1958); *Chem. Abstr.*, **53,** 2671c (1959).
36. Le Bras, J., *Rev. Gen. Caoutchouc,* **19,** 43 (1942); *Chem. Abstr.*, **38,** 2844^2 (1944).
37. Garten, V. A., and D. E. Weiss, *Australian J. Chem.*, **8,** 68 (1955); *Chem. Abstr.*, **50,** 5276f (1956).
38. Watson, W. F., *Ind. Eng. Chem.*, **47,** 1281 (1955).
39. Watson, J. W., *Trans. Inst. Rubber Ind.*, **32,** 204 (1956); *Chem. Abstr.*, **51,** 8468e (1957).
40. Watson, W. F., in *Proc. Rubber Technol. Conf. 3rd, London, 1954,* T. H. Messenger, ed., Institution of the Rubber Industry, London, p. 553.
41. Kargin, V. A., N. A. Plate, V. G. Zhuravleva, and V. P. Shivaev, *Vysokomolekul. Soedin.*, **3,** 650 (1961); RAPRA Transl. 922.
42. Deuel, H., and R. Gentili, *Helv. Chim. Acta,* **39,** 1586 (1956); RABRM Transl. 809; *Chem. Abstr.*, **51,** 2442f (1957).
43. Baker, W. O., R. W. Walker, and N. R. Pope, U. S. War Prod. Board Report No. CR-352.
44. Kargin, V. A., T. I. Sogolova, G. L. Slonimskii, and E. V. Reztzova, *Zh. Fiz. Khim.*, **30,** 1903 (1956); RABRM Transl. 568.
45. Davis, H. G., W. L. Durette, and E. C. Johnson, U. S. Patent 2,656,297 (to B. B. Chemical Co.), Oct. 20, 1953; *Chem. Abstr.*, **49,** 5888^1 (1955).
46. Angier, D. J., and W. F. Watson, *J. Polymer Sci.*, **18,** 129 (1955).
47. Angier, D. J., and W. F. Watson, *Trans. Inst. Rubber Ind.*, **33,** 22 (1957); *Chem. Abstr.*, **51,** 18676b (1957).

48. Kargin, V. A., B. M. Kovarskaya, L. I. Golubenkova, M. S. Akutin, and G. L. Slonimskii, *Khim. Prom.*, **1957** (2) 77; *Chem. Abstr.*, **51,** 18686i (1957).
49. Berlin, A. A., G. S. Petrov, and V. F. Prosvirkina, *Khim. Nauk. i. Prom.*, **2,** 522 (1957); RABRM Transl. 615; *Chem. Abstr.*, **52,** 4235 (1958).
50. Rubber and Plastics Research Assoc. of Great Britain, British Patent 888,231 (by E. Shaw and W. C. Wake), Jan. 31, 1962; *Chem. Abstr.*, **56,** 10352h (1962).
51. Angier, D. J., and W. F. Watson, *J. Polymer Sci.*, **20,** 235 (1956).
52. Angier, D. J., E. Farlie, and W. F. Watson, *Trans. Inst. Rubber Ind.*, **34,** 8 (1958); *Chem. Abstr.*, **52,** 10624f (1958).
53. Ceresa, R. J., in *Techniques of Polymer Characterisation*, P. W. Allen, ed., Butterworths, London, 1959, p. 231.
54. Angier, D. J., R. J. Ceresa, and W. F. Watson, *J. Polymer Sci.*, **34,** 699 (1959).
55. Angier, D. J., and W. F. Watson, *J. Polymer Sci.*, **25,** 1 (1957).
56. Angier, D. J., R. J. Ceresa, and W. F. Watson, *Chem. Ind. (London)*, **1958,** 593.
57. British Rubber Producers' Research Assoc., British Patent 836,053 (by R. J. Ceresa, D. J. Elliott, and W. F. Watson), June 1, 1960; *Chem. Abstr.*, **54,** 21849e (1960).

Information concerning translations made by the Rubber and Plastics Research Association of Great Britain (RAPRA), formerly called the Research Association of the British Rubber Manufacturers (RABRM), can be obtained by writing the Secretary of the Rubber and Plastics Research Association of Great Britain, Shawbury, Shrewsbury, Shropshire, England.

Chapter XV

FIBER-REACTIVE DYES

DAVID TABER and E. E. RENFREW

Koppers Co., Inc.

H. E. TIEFENTHAL

Armour Industrial Chemical Co.

A. INTRODUCTION AND HISTORY

Dyeing is a process for imparting uniform permanent or semipermanent color to various materials. These materials may be animal, vegetable, or synthetic fibers, paper, wood, plastic, metal, etc. Because in most cases the material to be dyed is a polymer, dyeing by virtue of a chemical reaction between functional groups of the dyestuff and functional groups of the polymer constitutes a valid reason for inclusion of a discussion of fiber-reactive dyes in a work concerned with the chemical reactions of polymers.

Dyeing has been practiced since prehistoric times for reasons of religious and ritual significance, protective coloration, identification, uniformity, singularity, or estheticism, of which the last certainly has been the most impelling.

Through most of its long history, dyeing was an empirical art. Until midway in the nineteenth century the dyeing of fibers and fabrics was brought about almost exclusively by the use of minerals or of extracts of animal and vegetable materials. The only textiles of any importance were made from the natural protein fibers, wool and silk, and the natural cellulosic fibers, cotton and linen.

Perhaps few organic chemical disciplines can recognize and date their origins as accurately as can synthetic dyestuff chemistry, which was born on August 26, 1856, with the granting of an English patent covering the preparation of a violet dyestuff for silk to William Henry Perkin (1). Subsequent investigations by many persons have led to the discovery of thousands of other dyes represented by such classifications as triarylmethane, azo, sulfur, quinone, and phthalocyanine (2,3).

Simultaneous with the expansion of the knowledge of new dyes was the development of new techniques and equipment with which to carry out the dyeing operations. The introduction in 1911 of the reconstituted cellulose now known as viscose rayon brought about no great change in dyeing methods since the fiber was chemically the same as cotton; it did, however, herald the present era in which modified natural polymers and truly synthetic fibers are increasingly important. The introduction of secondary cellulose acetate after World War I, and more recently, synthetics such as polyamides, polyesters, and polyacrylonitrile, required the development of modified types of dyes and application techniques.

All methods of dyeing involve presenting the fiber or fabric to a liquid containing the coloring material. The liquid normally is water; the coloring material either is dissolved, or is capable of being dissolved by the addition of chemicals, or is present in fine suspension. Concomitant with the dyeing is a decrease in the dye concentration of the liquid phase, indicating a preferential sorption of the dye by the fiber. The dyeing so produced must possess some resistance to further handling in water, including washing. Simple imbibition of the colored liquor does not qualify under the definition; even if color remains in the fiber after drying, such stains are largely removed by a washing treatment.

The principles which are involved in dyeing with non-fiber-reactive dyes have been considered to involve one or more of the following (4,5):

(*a*) Soluble dyestuffs are sorbed at active sites in the fiber by reversible attachment which may be due to ionization, hydrogen bonding, or aggregation. Examples of such dyes are the direct dyes for cotton and the acid dyes for wool.

(*b*) Soluble materials are accepted by the fiber by mechanisms similar to (*a*) and are rendered insoluble subsequently by chemical reaction. An example is the vat dyes for cellulosic fibers, which are solubilized by reduction in aqueous alkali and insolubilized by oxidation after dyeing. Another example is the acid dyestuffs for wool which can be after-chromed to give dyeings with improved fastness to wet treatments.

(*c*) Insoluble dyestuffs are synthesized from intermediates already in place in the fiber. Examples are the azoics, which are formed by coupling; oxidation bases, which undergo oxidation to form dyes; and the "phthalogens," which react in the fiber to form phthalocyanines (6).

(*d*) Water-insoluble dyes are extracted from aqueous dispersion to form solid solutions with the fibers. This mechanism is limited to the synthetic fibers.

Almost a century after the preparation of the first synthetic dye, another dyeing principle, fiber reactivity, was introduced. This principle involves the reaction of a functional group of a dyestuff with a site on the fiber to form a covalent link between the dye molecule and the substrate. Whereas most other dyeings can be considered as physical combinations, dyeings produced by fiber-reactive dyes are different structures of matter, since they are new molecules produced by synthesis, and as such must be recognized to be members of several new series of chemical compounds.

Although useful fiber-reactive dyes are comparatively new offerings to the textile trade, the concept of a system in which a colored structure is attached by a chemical bond to a fiber molecule is not new. The report of an early study on such a dye-cellulose combination was made in 1895 by Cross and Bevan (7) as part of the research program on cellulose that had led to their discovery, with Beadle, of the viscose reaction (8). The reactions used to produce the chemically linked dyestuff are shown in Eq. (1), in which

$$\text{CellOH} \rightarrow \text{CellO}^-\text{Na}^+ \rightarrow \text{CellOCOC}_6\text{H}_4\text{NO}_2 \rightarrow \text{CellOCOC}_6\text{H}_4\text{NH}_2 \rightarrow$$
$$\text{CellOCOC}_6\text{H}_4\text{N}_2{}^+\text{Cl}^- \xrightarrow{\text{C}_6\text{H}_5\text{N(CH}_3)_2} \text{CellOCOC}_6\text{H}_4\text{N{=}NC}_6\text{H}_4\text{N(CH}_3)_2 \quad (1)$$

CellOH represents cellulose. The red cellulose-dye compound was said to be very fast to washing.

Variations on this idea were examined and reported during succeeding years (9–11). Despite the obvious impracticability due to the many steps in the operation, the idea was recognized as sound, and additional patents related to the scheme were published (12,13).

Of the ester linkages investigated, probably the most important are the cellulose esters of aryl sulfonic acids. In 1932, the preparation of the structure I was described (14).

$$\text{CellO}{-}\overset{\overset{\displaystyle\text{O}}{\uparrow}}{\underset{\underset{\displaystyle\text{O}}{\downarrow}}{\text{S}}}{-}\text{ArNH}_2$$

(I)

The $—NH_2$ on the aryl radical was then diazotized and coupled to yield the colored compound. Some dyestuffs capable of producing sulfonic ester links with cellulose are commercially promising today. They are water-soluble, colored molecules containing the sulfonyl fluoride group.

Probably the most important fiber-reactive dyes for cellulosics now in use are those derived from cyanuric chloride. Two general structures which

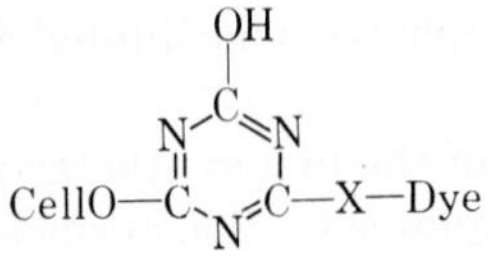

(II)

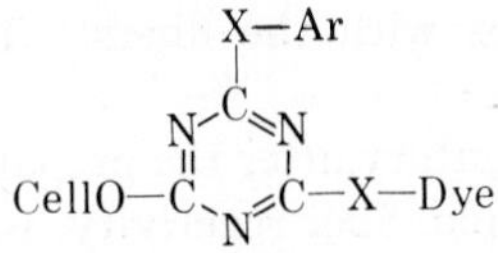

(III)

include most of the dyeings produced are represented by II and III. Ar is usually a substituted aryl fragment; X is usually imino, but can be oxygen or sulfur. The best known dyes of this type are the cyanuric chloride derivatives marketed under the trade marks Procion (Imperial Chemical Industries) and Cibacron (Ciba). Similar dyes containing the chloropyrimidine nucleus also are available; Drimarene (J. R. Geigy) and Reactone (Sandoz, Ltd.) are names under which two lines are offered.

An early description of cellulose linked to a colored material through the *sym*-triazine and other hetero rings is given in a patent granted in 1932 to Haller and Heckendorn (15). These inventors first applied cyanuric chloride to the cotton under conditions such that only one chlorine reacted, then brought about reaction between the remaining chlorines and suitable functions which were integral parts of colored molecules. The technique was tedious and uneconomical and never was used commercially. The present system, in which a dye–cyanuric chloride reaction product is permitted to react with alkali cellulose, is much more practical because of its simplicity. The dyeings (i.e., the dye-cellulose combinations) obtained with Cibacrons and Procions when considered as species of chemical compounds, thus are similar to those produced by the earlier method of Haller and Heckendorn.

A structure in which cellulose was bonded chemically to a colored structure through an ether link was reported by Peacock in 1926 (16). Cellulose was nitrobenzylated with *p*-nitrobenzyltrimethylammonium chloride, and the nitro group was reduced. Diazotization followed by coupling gave a colored compound of which IV is typical.

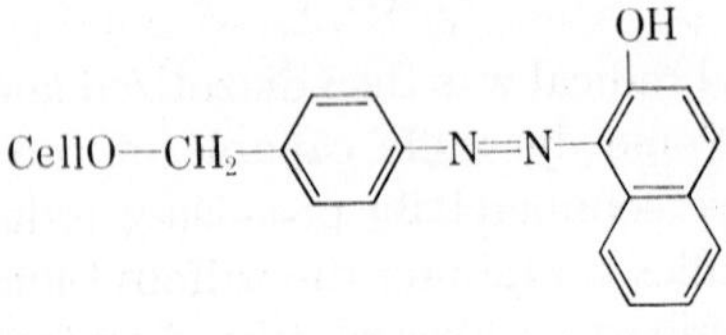

(IV)

Because of the ease with which such a molecule might be expected to be removed by hydrolysis, Peacock did not feel that the attachment of a dyestuff molecule by means of an ester grouping would be of much value. Peacock's judgment was at least partially wrong, since, as has been noted previously, fiber-reactive dyes with a sulfonic ester link have been described. His judgment that potentially valuable materials might result from the use of the ether linkage has been amply borne out by the excellent performance of the Remazol family of dyes. These dyes of Farbwerke Hoechst are discussed in more detail later.

The first to describe a dyestuff capable of reacting with cotton was Günther, who in 1925 patented a material prepared by coupling diazotized sulfanilic acid with anthranilic acid and treating the product with phosgene. The resulting colored isatoic anhydride derivative was said to possess the property of chemically combining with cellulose (17). Dyes based on this fiber-reactive group have not been developed commercially.

Some work of great significance to the progress of fiber-reactive dyes and dyeing was done in the laboratories of Farbwerke Hoechst during the 1940's. This dealt with the preparation and method of applying dyes containing the 2-sulfatoethylsulfonyl group, from which a vinylsulfonyl group is said to form during the dyeing. One of the publications describing this work is a United States patent (18) which was issued in 1954 to Heyna and Schumacher. In the disclosure part of this patent, the statement is made that "...the vinyl group in *statu nascendi* may possibly enter into reaction with the reactive groups of the fiber." Quite understandably, no attempt was made in the patent to present proof of covalent linkages, since such proof was not necessary to support the claims, all of which relate to the dyeing method. However, the application methods described and the properties which were noted for the dyeings produced, leave little doubt that the inventors had a good understanding of the nature of the dyeings they obtained. The Remazol and related fiber-reactive dyes of the vinylsulfone type which have been aggressively investigated and marketed by Farbwerke Hoechst are outgrowths and extensions of the work.

Another important milestone on the road to the commercial acceptance of fiber-reactive dyes was a paper by Guthrie presented in 1951 on dyestuffs bonded to cellulose through ether links (19,20). Preformed dye molecules containing a reactive group (in this case, $ArOCH_2CH_2Cl$) were caused to contact cotton under alkaline conditions such that the structure $ArOCH_2$-CH_2OCell was formed. The dye structures used by Guthrie to prove this point are not representative of present commercial fiber-reactive dyes. The importance of his work must be recognized as considerable, since he was the "first person ever to speak in public about cotton-reactive dyes which he synthesized himself" (21).

Many other fiber-reactive systems have been proposed. A few have had acceptance for specialized purposes such as textile printing and as dyes for noncellulosic fibers, particularly wool and nylon. Some of these types will be considered in subsequent portions of this chapter.

B. APPLICATION OF FIBER-REACTIVE DYES

In the few years which have passed since their introduction to the textile trade, fiber-reactive dyes have been well accepted. Because of the wide variations in the kinds of fiber-reactive groups and in the chromophoric systems to which they are attached, no generalization can encompass all the characteristics which have brought about this acceptance. Two positive factors which have been present in many cases are the brightness of the dyeings produced and the economy of the dyeing operation.

The most important dyestuffs for cotton which have been useful historically are those classified as vat dyes, direct dyes, and azoic component dyes. Each of these classes has many useful members, and all classes will, no doubt, continue to play a part in the dyeing of cellulosics. Each dye in each class has some good and some bad features. For example, direct colors of the triarylmethane or related types are usually bright, but not very lightfast. Those of the polyazo type are less bright and require considerable handling to produce acceptable shades. Vat dyes on the whole give dyeings of the highest order of washfastness and excellent resistance to bleaching and to light. However, they are expensive and often quite dull, and the dyeing operations are complex and require careful control. Azoics produce dyeings of generally good performance and brightness, but the shades which are available are somewhat limited. Since the azoic dyestuffs are built up on the cloth by the combination of the azoic components, the dyeing operation involves a considerable outlay in labor and equipment. None of the previously known classes of dyes thus can answer all the requirements of the dyer. Neither do fiber-reactives, but they do offer some different and attractive features.

Probably the principal advantage in the dyeing of yard goods with fiber-reactive dyes is the saving in labor costs. The equipment used is not highly specialized, and the operations of padding with dissolved dye and alkali and salt, followed by a short curing time (1–5 min.) at high temperature (up to about 150°C.) provide a rapid dyeing method.

Fiber-reactive dyes are relatively expensive on a poundage basis, but the saving in labor due to the rapidity of the dyeing operation makes their use especially economical for preparing pastels and light backgrounds for prints. The percentage of fixation is lower when heavier shades are dyed, and the cost of scouring off the unfixed dye becomes more important, along with the greater proportion of wastage of the comparatively high-priced dye. (Techniques of dyeing fiber-reactives in heavier shades have been developed. They are considered briefly in the section of this chapter dealing with resin finishing.)

Dyeings made with fiber-reactive dyes usually are bright. One reason for this is that the colored structures are quite simple, and since they are united with the molecules of the fiber in chemical combination, the resistance to washing does not depend to any extent on the size of the dye molecule, as is the case with direct colors and with vat dyes. This usefulness of relatively small structures permits the selection of such chromophoric systems as the monoazos, which are characterized by fewer and sharper peaks in the absorption spectra; absorption patterns of this nature are evidenced as bright shades. The small number of chemical steps required to synthesize the smaller molecules also plays a part in the resulting brightness, there being fewer opportunities for isomers and other impurities to be formed and carried through into the final product. Such impurities inevitably act to make the absorption curve more diffuse and the dyeing less bright. Furthermore, in some cases fiber-reactive dyes perform better than some conventional dyes when after-treated with certain resin finishes.

Some of the fiber-reactive dyes show lightfastness and chlorine-fastness properties which are lower than normally found in quality dyestuffs. This is not surprising, since, as has been mentioned, the chromophoric systems are often simple azo structures and the action of the fading agent on any part of the chromophoric system easily changes the color. As time goes on, it is to be expected that dyes of greater fastness will be introduced.

The methods by which fiber-reactive dyes are applied vary, since they depend on the equipment, the type of dye used, and the chemical and physical character of the goods to be colored. A typical application of a fiber-reactive dye would include steps such as the following: (*1*) The cloth is run into and out of a trough containing a solution of the dye and passed between rollers to squeeze out excess solution. (This is the operation of "padding." It is a major element in continuous dyeing with many types of dyes. The equipment is well developed and widely used.) (*2*) The cloth is dried. Although the fabric is colored at this point, the color is not well fixed and can be considered a stain caused by imbibition of a colored solution. (*3*) The fabric is padded with a solution containing a salt or urea, and an alkali. (*4*) With or without drying, the cloth is subjected to a curing at an elevated temperature with live steam or between rollers heated to about 150°C. (5) The cloth is soaped and rinsed to remove unfixed dye and the other chemicals used in the operation, then dried.

A printing operation with fiber-reactive dyestuffs utilizes steps related to those above. A printing paste, which contains a dye, water, a thickening agent, alkali salts, and materials to modify the surface properties of the cloth as desired, is applied locally to an area on the cloth. Additional colors are put in place in successive applications, usually from engraved rollers. The cloth is heated to bring about reaction of the cellulose with the reactive dye. Soaping, rinsing, and drying complete the operation.

C. COMMERCIAL TYPES OF FIBER-REACTIVE DYES FOR COTTON

Two major types of fiber-reactive dyes for cellulosic materials have been developed commercially.

The first is characterized by a structure which is a vinyl sulfone or which can be converted readily to a vinyl sulfone. Reaction occurs by a Michael addition, and may be represented as in eq. (2), where Ar is a colored frag-

$$ArSO_2CH{=}CH_2 + Cell{-}OH \rightarrow Cell{-}OCH_2CH_2SO_2Ar \qquad (2)$$

ment and contains groups, usually sulfonic acid groups, which confer water-solubility to the molecule. The structures most often used are actually of the type $ArSO_2CH_2CH_2OSO_3Na$; Ar represents a wide variety of structures in which the principal chromophoric systems are azo, anthraquinone, and phthalocyanine.

The only line of dyes of this type are the Remazols, manufactured and sold by Farbwerke Hoechst and its affiliated companies. Under license, Du Pont markets some of these dyes under the trade name "Cavalite." The structure of each of the Remazols has not been officially announced. The Levafix dyes (formerly Permafix) of Farbenfabriken Bayer are believed to have a related structure (170): $ArSO_2NHCH_2CH_2$-OSO_3Na. Dyes and some textile chemicals representing most shades have been selected from pertinent patents and are shown in Table XV-1.

The more recently introduced Primazin dyes (Badische Anilin-u. Soda-Fabrik) have the acrylamido group as the reactive entity.

A second important generic type of fiber-reactive dye which has found commercial acceptance comprises heterocyclic nitrogen compounds to which colored structures and active halogen atoms are attached. They react with cellulose by substitution of a chlorine atom (eq. 3). Ar is a colored

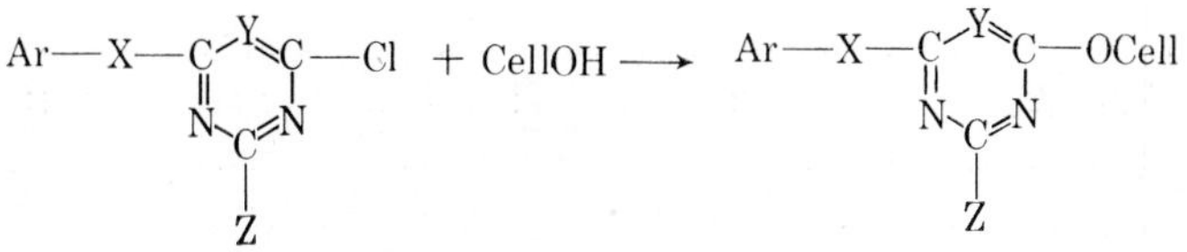

(3)

radical which may bear solubilizing groups; X is a linking group such as oxygen or sulfur, but most often is imino; Y is nitrogen or methine; Z is an organic group which may or may not carry a chromophore, or which may be a substituent such as amino, hydroxyl, or chloro.

The dichlorotriazines in which Y is nitrogen and Z is chlorine were among the first practical fiber-reactive dyes. The great reactivity of the first of the two chlorines causes the dyes to fix to the fiber under comparatively mild conditions. However, the high reactivity also shortens the shelf life of the dye and the stability of printing pastes made from dyes of this type. Furthermore, the competing reaction of hydrolysis may occur in the dye bath to form unreactive colored bodies which must later be removed by washing.

Trade names of some of the commercially available cotton dyes of this haloheterocyclic type are listed in Table XV-2.

Virtually all the chromophoric systems useful in textile chemistry can be incorporated into these fiber-reactive structures. A spectrum of dyes of the chlorotriazine types contain such colored residues as those listed in Table XV-3.

The same chromophoric systems are useful in the series of dyes based on chloropyrimidines. Generalized formulas of this type are V, VI, VII, and VIII.

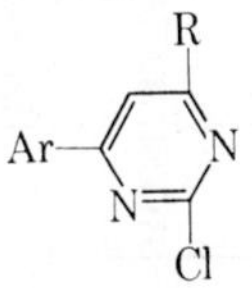

(V)

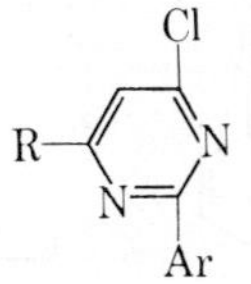

(VI)

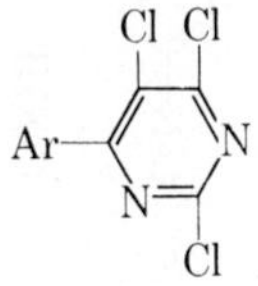

(VII)

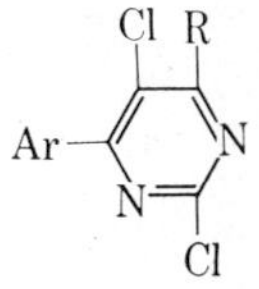

(VIII)

In these formulas, Ar is a chromophoric group derived from such structures as azo, anthraquinone, phthalocyanine, phthaloperinone, nitrodiarylamine, and stilbene; Ar usually contains ionic water-solubilizing groups, since the dye molecule must have an appreciable solubility in water. Linkage to the pyrimidine nucleus is through nitrogen, oxygen, or sulfur. The group R may or may not be colored and is perhaps most often chlorine, in which case the molecule has two chlorines. Dyestuffs bearing three chlo-

TABLE XV-1
Reactive Dyes and Textile Auxiliaries Containing the Vinyl Sulfone Group or Precursor

Use or color	Structure	Structural type	Reference
Water repellent (colorless)	$C_{18}H_{37}SO_2CH_2CH_2OSO_3Na$	Long chain aliphatic group	18
Moth resistant (colorless)	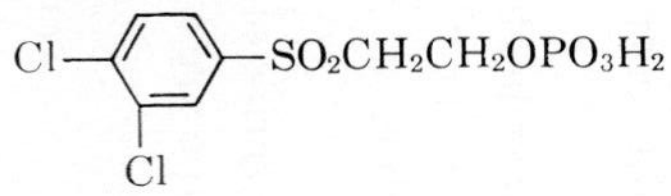	Halogenated aromatic group	18
Greenish-yellow	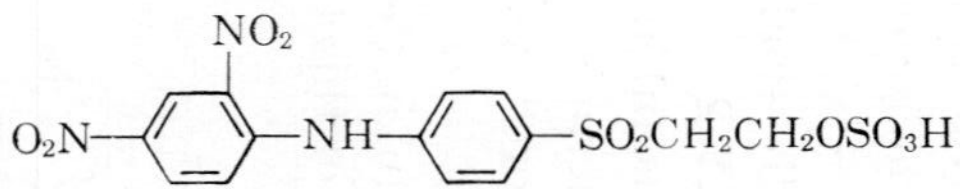	Nitrodiphenylamine	18
Yellow	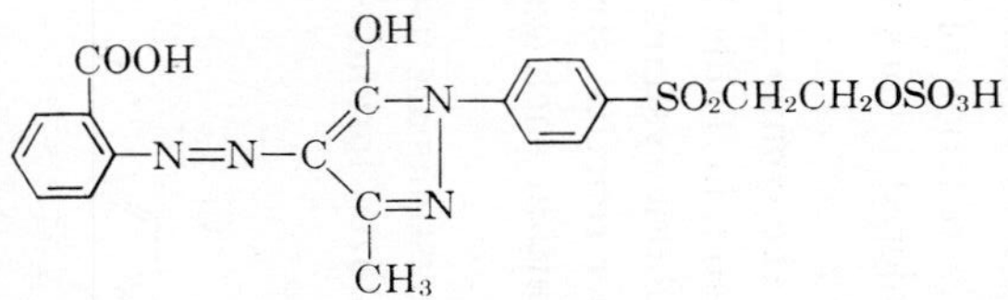	Monoazo	172
Yellow	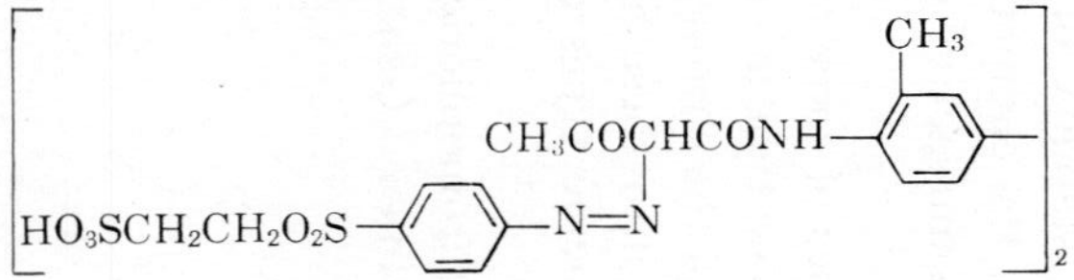	Disazo	18
Yellow	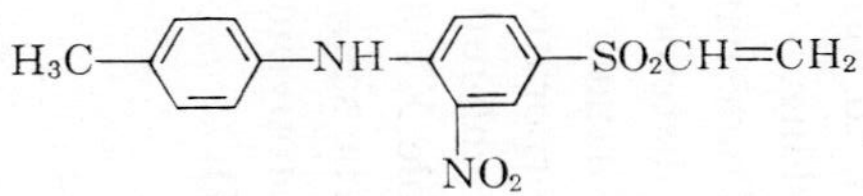	Nitrodiphenylamine	173

Orange	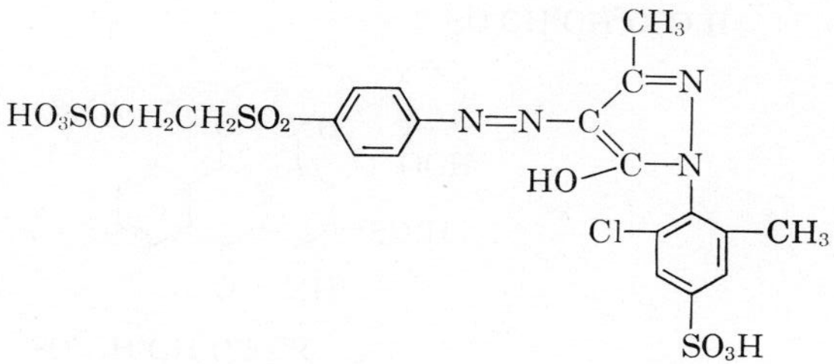	Monoazo	18
Red	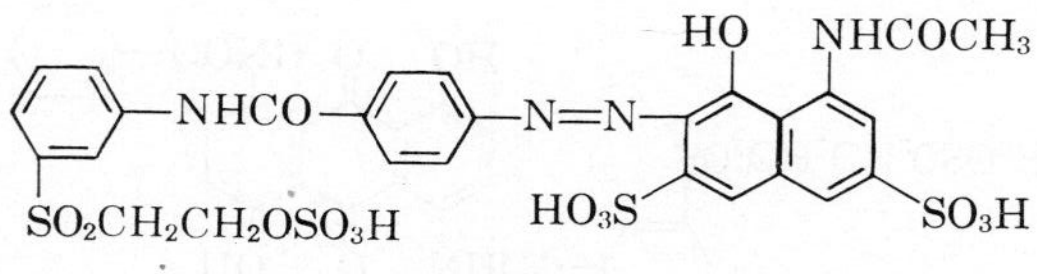	Monoazo	174
Red	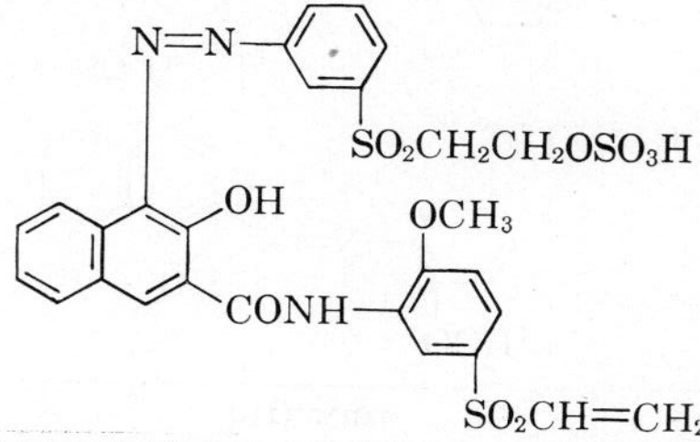	Monoazo	18

(continued)

TABLE XV-1 (*continued*)

Use or color	Structure	Structural type	Reference
Red	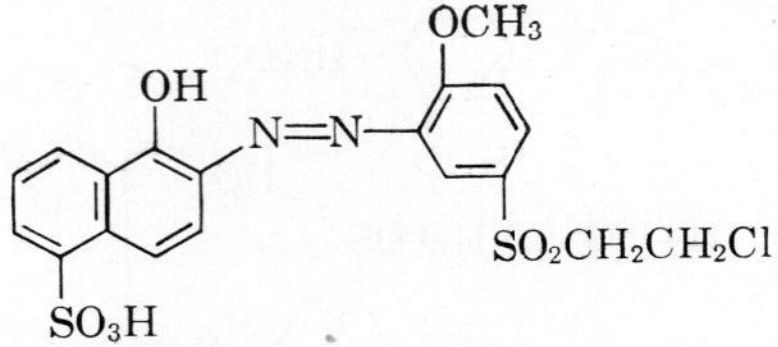	Monoazo	175
Violet	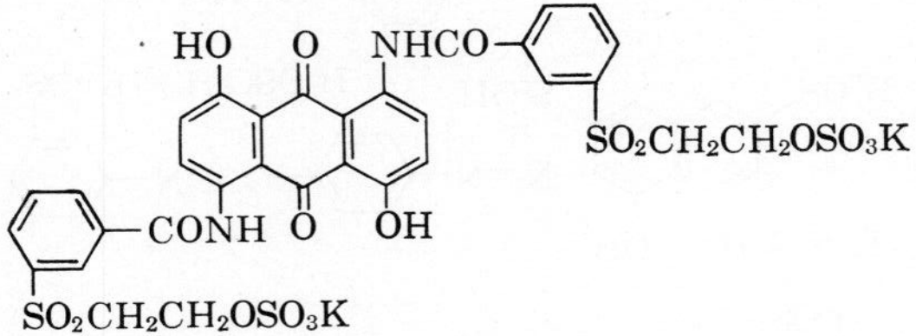	Anthraquinone	18
Blue	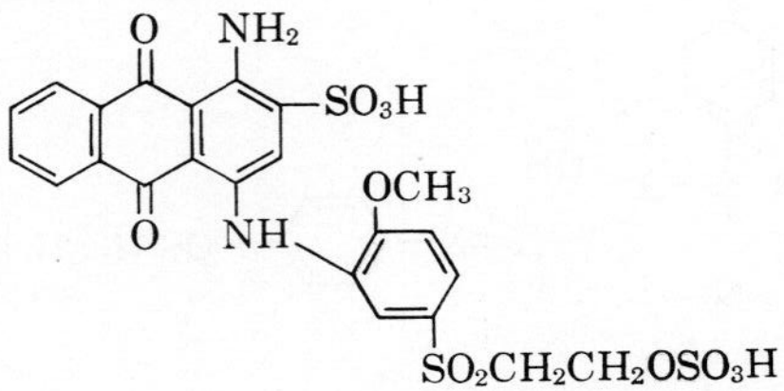	Anthraquinone	18

Blue	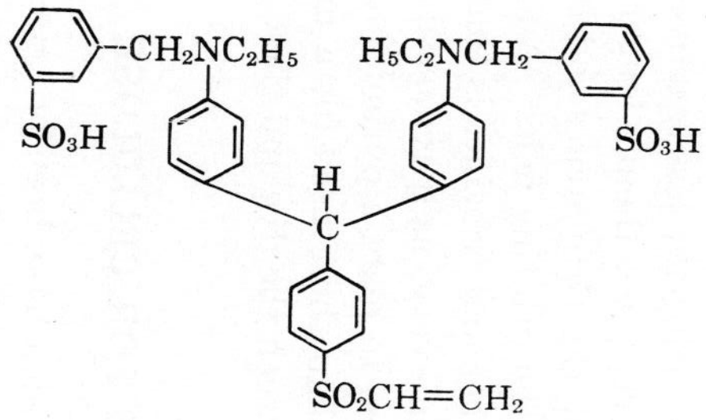	Triarylmethane	176
Blue	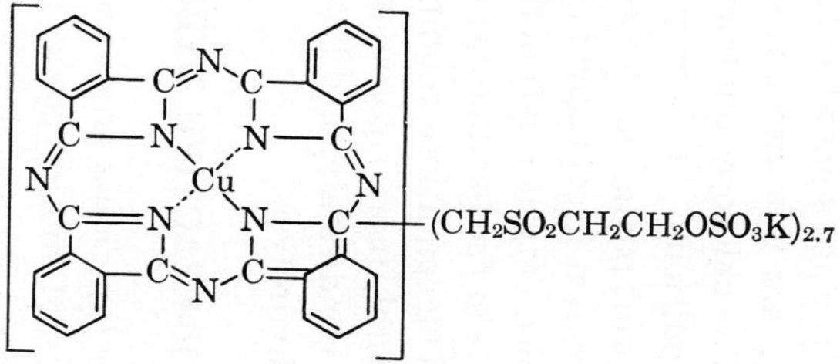	Phthalocyanine	18
Brown	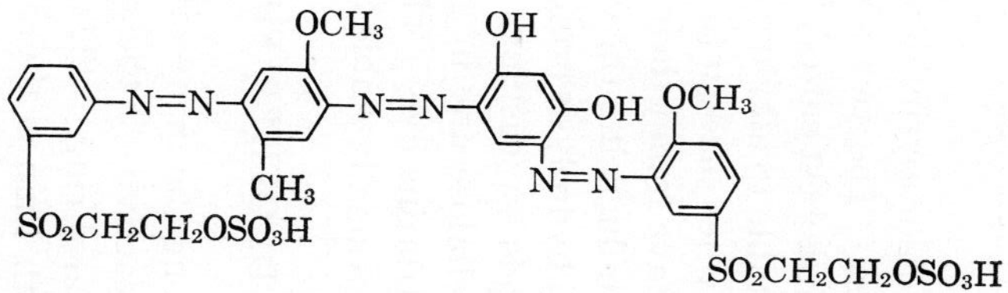	Trisazo	18

rine atoms on the pyrimidine ring (i.e., derived from tetrachloropyrimidine) are also known, as indicated by VII; the Drimarenes and Reactones are said to be of this type (22,23). The chlorine in the 5 position does not take part in the reaction by which the dye is attached to cellulose (24).

TABLE XV-2
Trade Names of Some Heterocyclic Fiber-Reactive Dyes

Name	Manufacturer	Chemical type
Procion	Imperial Chemical Industries, Ltd.	Dichloro-*sym*-triazine
Procion H	Imperial Chemical Industries, Ltd.	Monochloro-*sym*-triazine
Cibacron	Ciba Ltd.	Monochloro-*sym*-triazine
Drimarene	Sandoz Ltd.	Chloropyrimidine
Reactone	J. R. Geigy A.-G.	Chloropyrimidine

The chloropyrimidine dyes are somewhat less reactive than the chlorotriazines. The two series are not direct rivals, since each has uses for which it is best suited. The chloropyrimidines, being the less reactive, are more stable to alkaline conditions. This property gives them a longer useful life when made into a print paste, and indeed, the Drimarenes and Reactones have found their greatest acceptance in the printing field. Another factor influencing the choice between pyrimidines and triazines is that the unfixed hydrolysis products of the pyrimidines are very easily removed from the goods by washing. The conditions required to react a pyrimidine dye with cellulose are, in general, more rigorous than those used for a monochlorotriazine dye. The bond established between the dye and the cotton is exceptionally stable to hydrolysis.

D. OTHER FIBER-REACTIVE DYES FOR CELLULOSE

Among the many other functional groups which have been proposed for fiber reactivity is the sulfonyl fluoride group, especially when it is attached to an aryl ring. This group is much less susceptible to hydrolysis in the dyebath than is the sulfonyl chloride group. Dyeings can be made from the "long bath" (in which the dye is exhausted from the solution onto the fiber by the addition of salt, after which reaction with the cellulose is brought about by increasing the alkalinity and raising the temperature), or by the padding methods described previously. The usual methods for printing fiber-reactive dyes are also workable in this series. The new group formed is that of a sulfonic ester of cellulose shown in eq. (4). The ester

$$ArSO_2F + CellOH \rightarrow ArSO_2OCell \tag{4}$$

link which is formed is surprisingly resistant to washing and other wet treatments conducive to hydrolysis, but is probably not as resistant as the esters formed from the chloroheterocyclics and the ethers arising from the vinylsulfonyl type (25–27). No commercial line of dyes for cotton based on this functional group has yet been widely distributed, nor has extensive composition-of-matter patenting occurred. A patent assigned to Cassella Farbwerke (28) and several from the laboratories of Imperial Chemical Industries (29,30) describe application methods for such dyes.

Typical of the structures described are the greenish-yellow dye IX, the orange-red dye X, and the bluish-red dye XI.

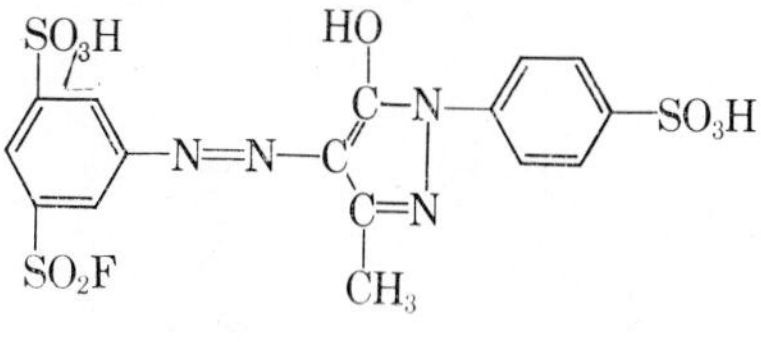

(IX)

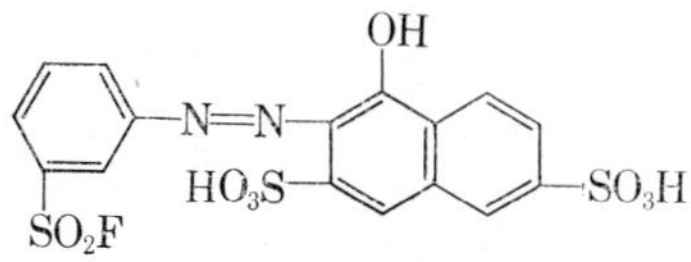

(X)

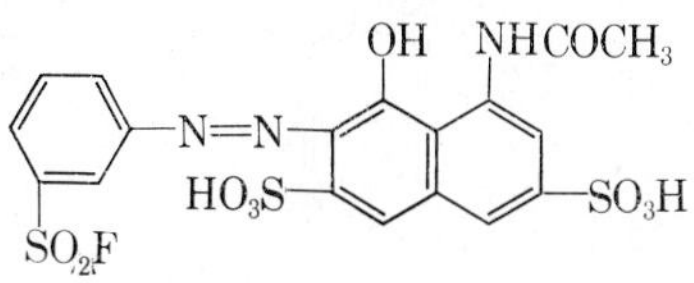

(XI)

Fiber-reactive dyes in which the reactive center is an *N*-(substituted ethyl)sulfamyl group have been reported. English patents have been issued to both Badische Anilin- & Soda-Fabrik (31,32) and to Imperial Chemical Industries (33) for water-soluble anthraquinones bearing the *N*-(2-chloroethyl)sulfamyl group. These are exemplified by formulas XII and XIII; XII yields blue shades; XIII gives dull green dyeings on cotton (page 1132).

Azo structures also have been reported. Examples are the orange dye XIV and the red dye XV of BASF (34,35); typical of azo structures which can be premetallized or which can be metallized after dyeing is one (XVI) claimed by Farbenfabriken Bayer (36).

TABLE XV-3
Reactive Dyes Containing the Chloro-*sym*-Triazinyl Group

Use or color	Structure	Structural type	Reference
Fluorescent brightener (colorless)	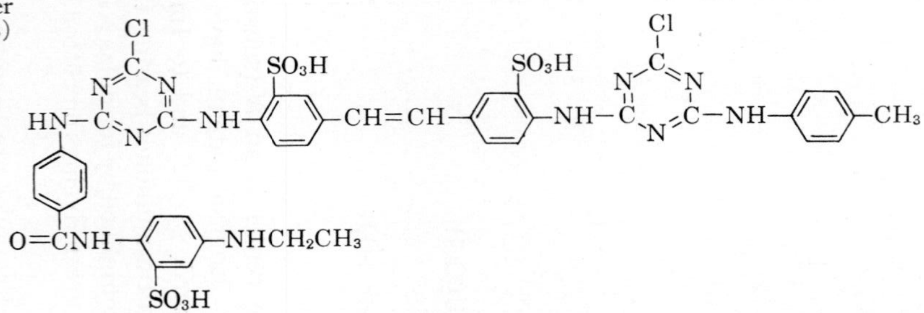	Stilbene	177
Greenish yellow	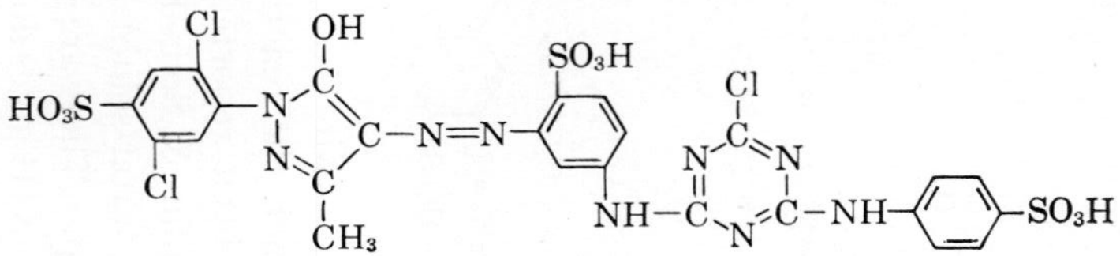	Monoazo	178
Yellow	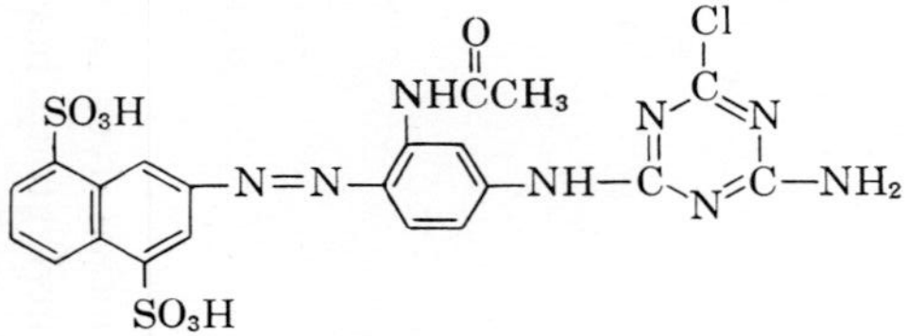	Monoazo	179
Yellow	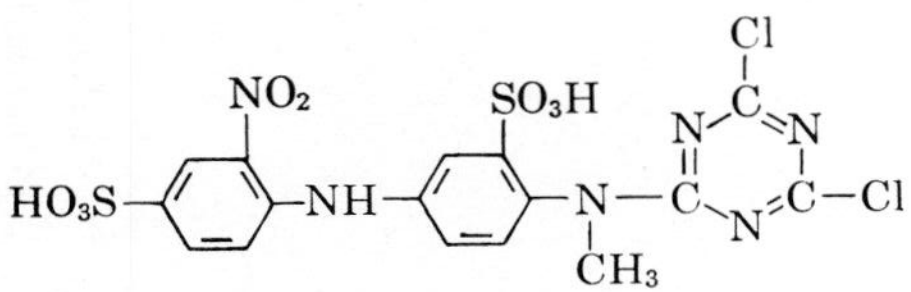	Nitrodiphenylamine	180

Orange	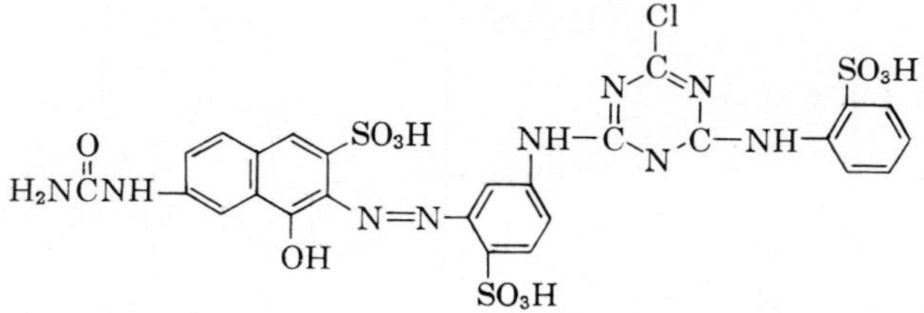	Monoazo	178
Orange	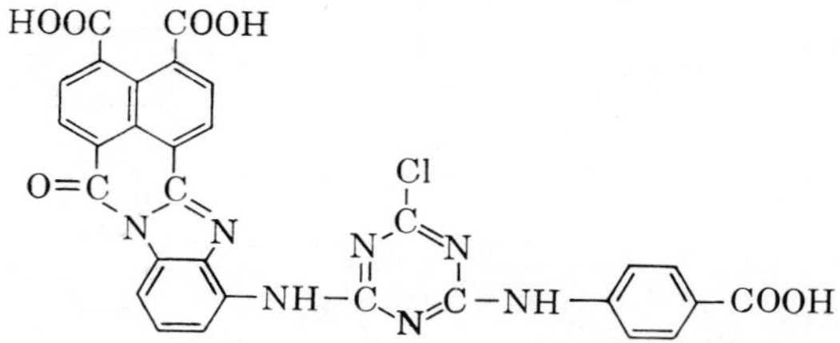	Perinone	181
Scarlet	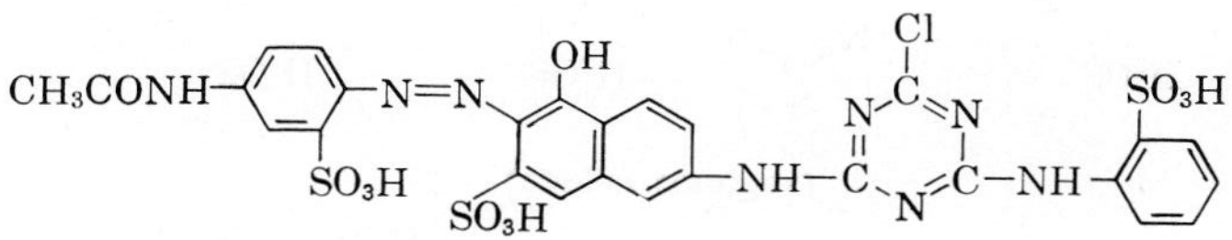	Monoazo	182
Red	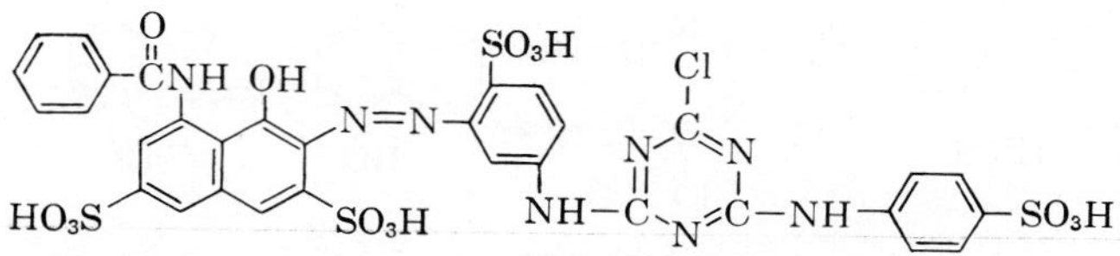	Monoazo	182

(continued)

TABLE XV-3 (*continued*)

Use or color	Structure	Structural type	Reference
Rubine	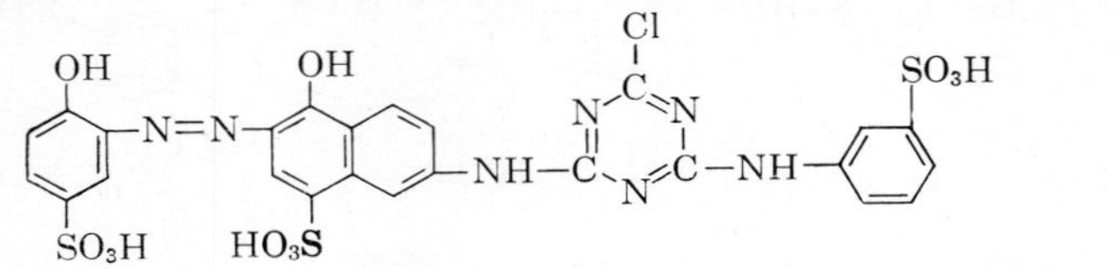 (copper complex)	Metallized monoazo	183
Blue	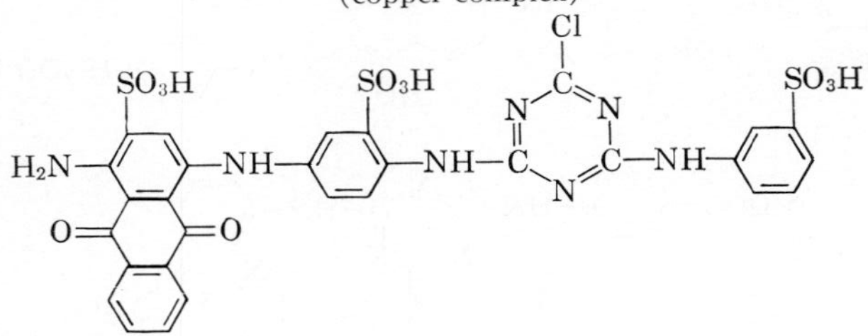	Anthraquinone	184
Greenish blue	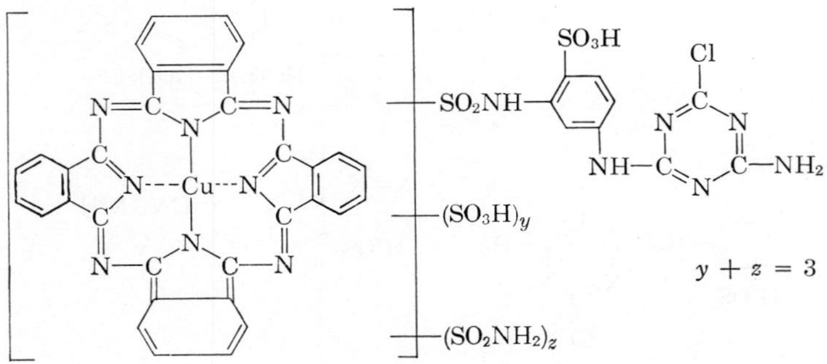	Phthalocyanine	

Green	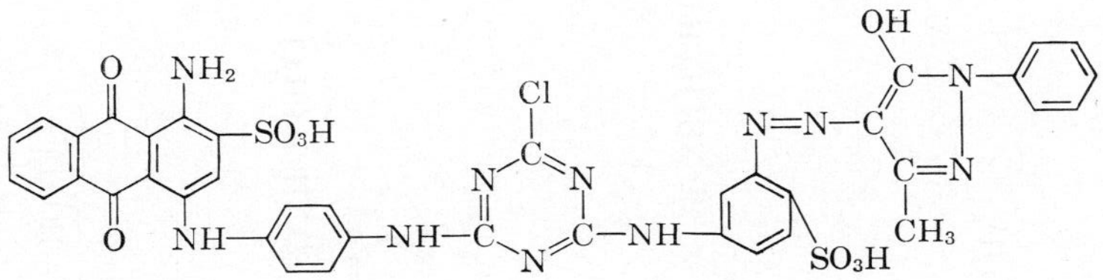	Azo and anthraquinone	185
Green	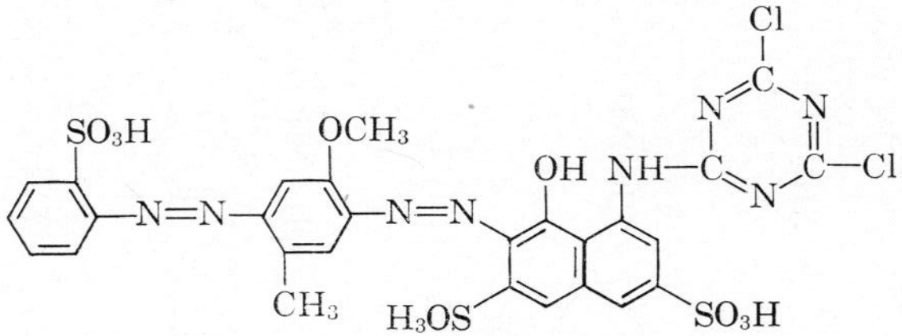 (copper complex)	Metallized disazo	185
Black	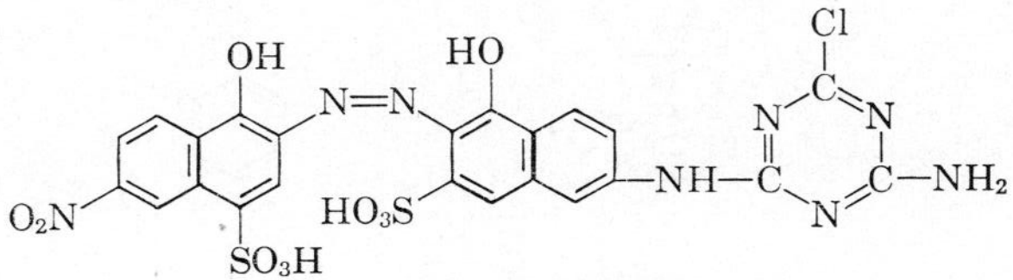 (mixed chrome and cobalt complex	Metallized monoazo	186

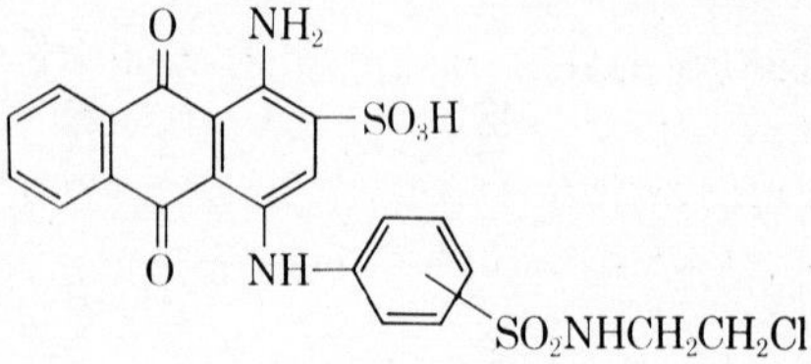

(XII)

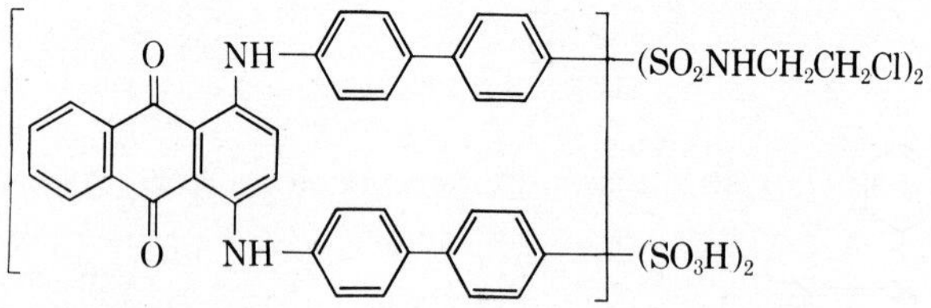

(XIII)

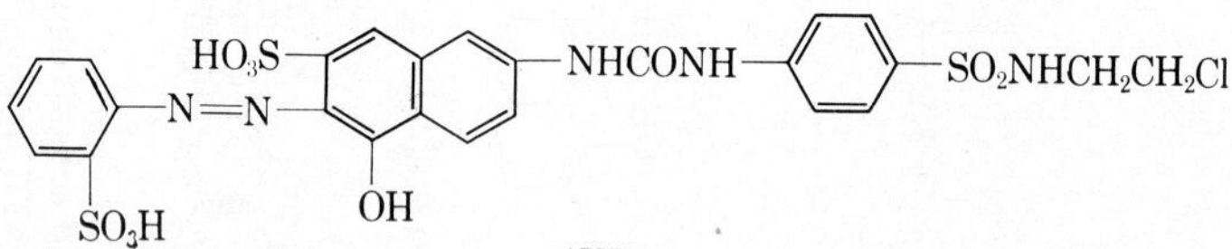

(XIV)

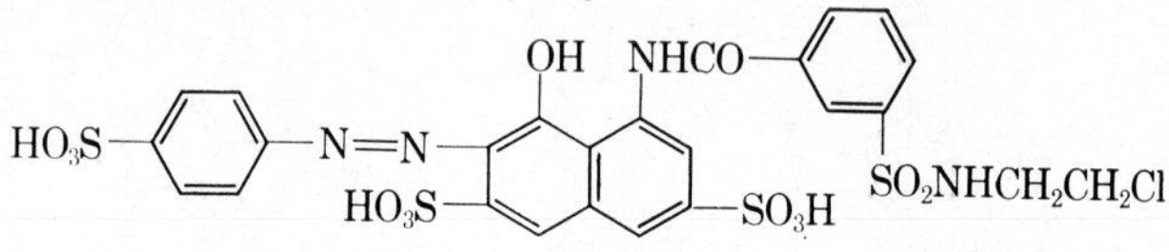

(XV)

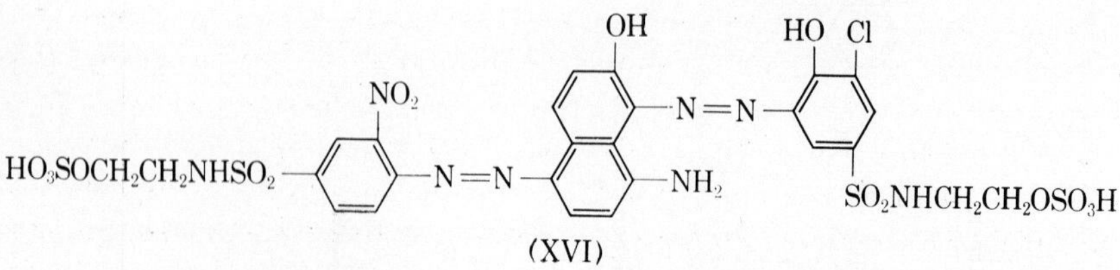

(XVI)

The beautiful greenish-blue color and good stability of phthalocyanine is used in this series as in all the others (37–40).

Nitrodiphenylamine structures (XVII) also have been patented (41); only yellow and orange shades can be obtained with this chromophore.

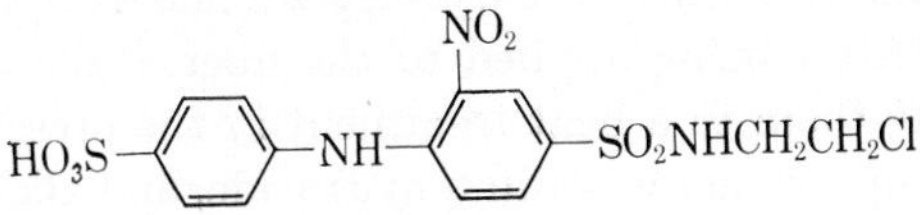

(XVII)

Reactive coupling components have been described (42); an example is XVIII. The component is applied on the cloth by the usual alkaline padding method, and fixed by heating and drying. The soaped and rinsed material is printed with a thickened diazotized component (an example is XIX), and coupling takes place to provide, in this case, orange-patterned areas.

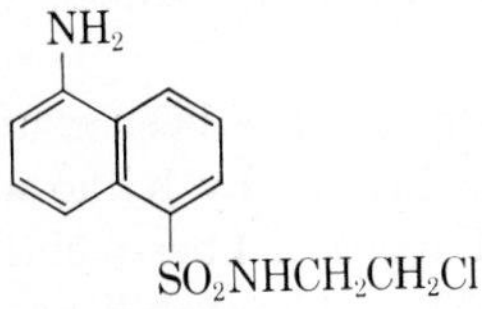

(XVIII)

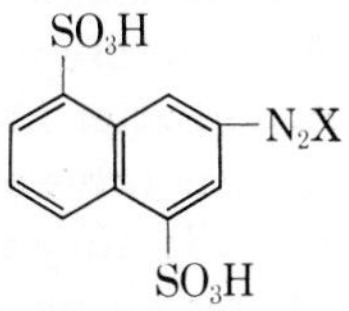

(XIX)

There are many references in the patent literature to dyes which bear aliphatic acylamido groups in which the acyl group is halogenated on the α or β carbon. In earlier patents (43–49) such dyes are described merely as water-soluble acid colors for wool. In later patents, it is recognized that the materials are useful on other fibers, including cellulosics (50–52). Thus, a patent issued to Ciba Ltd. in 1951 (53) which deals with 2-chloropropionamido-substituted dyes states, "The products are useful for dyeing and printing a wide variety of materials, for example, those of animal origin such as silk and especially wool, and also various artificial fibers, for example, those of animalized artificial silk, superpolyamide fibers or superpolyurethane fibers and especially polyhydroxylated fibrous materials which may be synthetic as, for example, in the case of regenerated cellulose, or natural materials, for example, cellulose, linen, and especially cotton." The description or method by which the dyeings are made implies that reaction is taking place: "After being applied to the fiber...the dyestuffs can be fixed by subjecting them to a heat treatment in the presence of an alkali, for example, sodium carbonate, sodium hydroxide, and alkaline earth metal hydroxide, or trisodium phosphate."

In addition to the water-soluble azo dyes, examples of other chromophores have been reported. Among them are anthraquinones, acridones, and thioxanthones (54), and phthalocyanines (55,56). Closely related dyes in which β-sulfatopropionamide groups provide the reactive centers also have been described (57).

Dyestuffs bearing acrylamido groups have been disclosed and claimed as fiber-reactive dyes (58–60), together with other materials in which amino groups have been reacted with acrylic radicals which may be substituted (61–64).

The chloroacetamido group also has been examined for fiber reactivity. The Japanese research teams headed by Kitao which have published data on investigations on several types of fiber-reactive dyes have studied azo dyes containing this group (65). The stabilities of dyeings on wool, nylon, silk, cotton, and viscose rayon were examined, and evidence for the presence of covalent dye–fiber linkage was gathered. There are numerous other references to dyes containing this structure in the journal literature and in patents which issued both before and after fiber reactivity was recognized. In many newer patents, the dye structures are simply described as being useful on wool when properly applied; they undoubtedly do provide dyeings of conventional washfastness by virtue of their sulfonic acid groups. Apparently there is little interest at present in promoting such structures as fiber-reactives for cellulosic materials (66–68).

Colored vinyl ketones (69) and colored chloromethyl ketones (70) also have been reported. Neither class is important at present.

Many references have been made to dyestuffs containing halohydrin and epoxy groups. The dyes are applied like other fiber-reactives: they are padded onto the fiber from water solution and fixed by heating in the presence of alkali. Many groups have been suggested, among them 2,3-epoxypropylamino (71), 2,3-epoxypropoxyl (72), 2,3-epoxythiopropoxyl (73), 3-chloro-2-hydroxypropylamino (74), 3-chloro-2-hydroxypropoxyl (71), 3-chloro-2-hydroxythiopropoxyl (73), *N*-(3-chloro-2-hydroxypropyl)-sulfamyl

(74), and the analogous bromine compounds. The structures may be idealized as XX and XXI, in which Ar is a colored organic residue such as azo, anthraquinone, or phthalocyanine and bears water-solubilizing groups; Z is oxygen, sulfur, sulfonyl, imino, or sulfamyl, and X is chlorine or bromine.

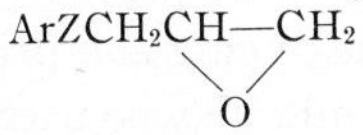

(XX)

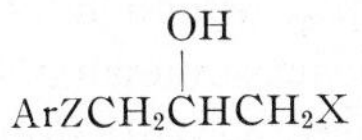

(XXI)

Among the many patents and articles dealing with dyes which can join with cellulose through ether links, an important one is the 1952 paper by Guthrie of the Southern Regional Research Laboratory of the U. S. Department of Agriculture (20), mentioned earlier. This describes dyes of the types $ArOCH_2CH_2Cl$ and $ArOCH_2CH_2OSO_3H$ and the method by which they are applied to cellulose to give structures of the type $CellOCH_2CH_2OAr$. Guthrie's paper contains one of the earliest clear statements that covalent links can be formed by reacting a suitably constituted structure with cotton, and describes experiments which establish the suggestion as fact. This was by no means the first dye–cellulose combination, of course. The significance of the Guthrie work was that it established the feasibility of preparing a preformed colored material which could be fastened to cotton under conditions which would harm neither the dye nor the cotton.

Guthrie's work was the subject of a patent application which issued in 1956 (75). The dye structures are not unusual azo structures; typical is the one made from diazotized *p*-(2-chloroethoxy)aniline and chromotropic acid (eq. 5), which yields purplish-red dyeings on cotton. The patent claims deal only with the process of dyeing, and not with the structures of the dyes or the dyed goods.

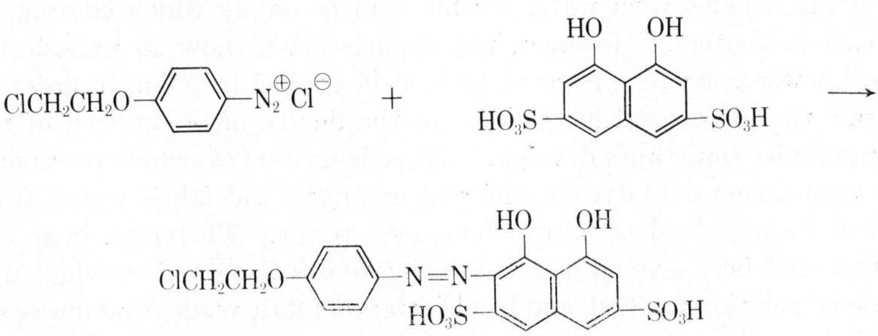

(5)

Other groups which have been suggested as being fiber-reactive or which may be inferred to be fiber-reactive include azide (76), thiocyanotriazinyl

(77), isothiocyanate (78), nitroaryl fluorides (79), urethanes (80), and ethylene imine (81).

E. FIBER-REACTIVE DYES FOR NONCELLULOSIC FIBERS

All of the examples which have been mentioned contain groups which make the dyes at least somewhat soluble in an aqueous system, a requirement if the dyes are to be truly useful in the dyeing and printing of unmodified cellulosic fibers. Many of the dyes could also be used for dyeing wool and nylon. The usefulness on wool of dyes containing sulfonic acid groups has been known for many decades. The conditions of dyeing wool are different from those used for cotton, since the alkaline conditions which are used to fix reactive dyes to cotton not only would inhibit dyeing, but would cause serious damage to the wool. Acid would have to be added to the bath to bring about dyeings of acceptable depth. Dyeing would take place whether fiber-reactive systems were present or not, since sulfonic acid groups alone would hold the dye to the fiber.

All of the fiber-reactive systems which have been described above can be built into dyestuffs which are not soluble in water. Insoluble dyes, if properly selected, are useful for dyeing some of the synthetic fibers from disperse baths. The finely divided dye in the bath is extracted from the bath into the fiber in much the same way organic materials are removed from water by ether or benzene. Disperse dyes, not necessarily those with fiber-reactive centers, have been used to dye hydrophobic fibers made from secondary cellulose acetate, cellulose triacetate, nylon, poly(ethylene terephthalate), polyacrylonitrile, and other polymers almost from the time such fibers were introduced.

Fiber reactivity as now known does not appear to be useful for any of the hydrophobic fibers with the important exception of nylon. Nylon can be dyed in fast shades with water-soluble acid dyestuffs which contain no fiber-reactive centers. However, the dyeings often show an undesirable feature known as barré. Because tension is applied to nylon in order to cold-draw the fiber, local inequalities in the degree of orientation of the macromolecules sometimes develop. These lengths of overdrawn or underdrawn yarn accept acid dyes in different amounts, and fabric woven from them will show striped or barré effects as a result. Therefore, in recent years there has been a trend in nylon dyeing to use disperse dyes which dye by the solid solution method, and level better on fabric made from unevenly drawn nylon. There are no strong ionic bonds established in this case as there are when acid dyes are used, and consequently the fabrics show less fastness to washing.

The use of fiber reactivity appears to be a logical way to solve this problem and has been widely investigated. Dyes containing fiber-reactive centers such as those described earlier but which contain no water-solubilizing groups are dispersed by milling with suitable agents and applied to the fiber from the disperse bath in the usual way. Alkali and heat are applied, and reaction takes place with the amino radicals present as endgroups, or perhaps with imido nitrogens. Whatever the actual structure of the nylon–dyestuff composition, there is no question that barré can be minimized in dyeings which have considerably improved fastness to wet treatments (82).

Probably the best known name among dispersed colors of the fiber-reactive type are the Procinyls of the Imperial Chemical Industries and affiliates. The exact structures for individual dyes have not yet become

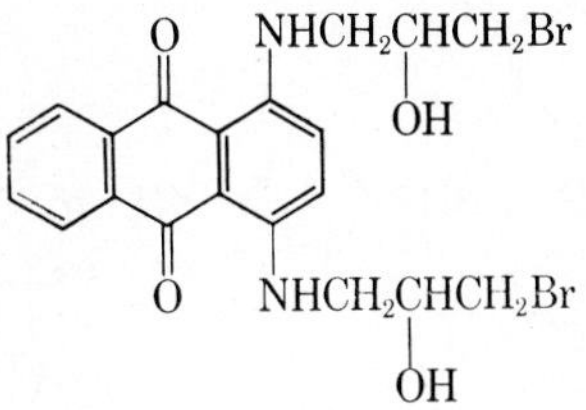

(XXII)

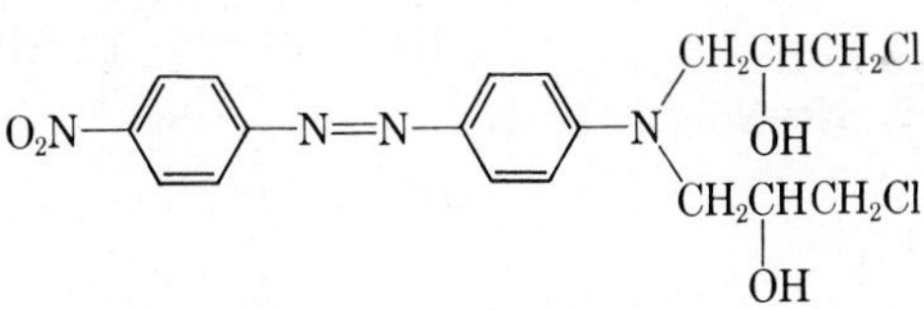

(XXIII)

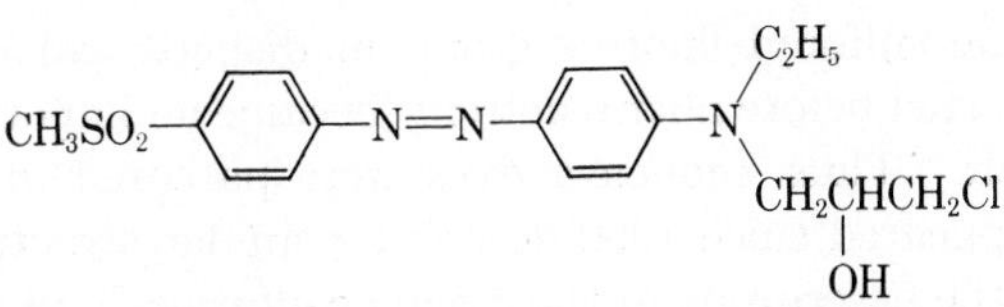

(XXIV)

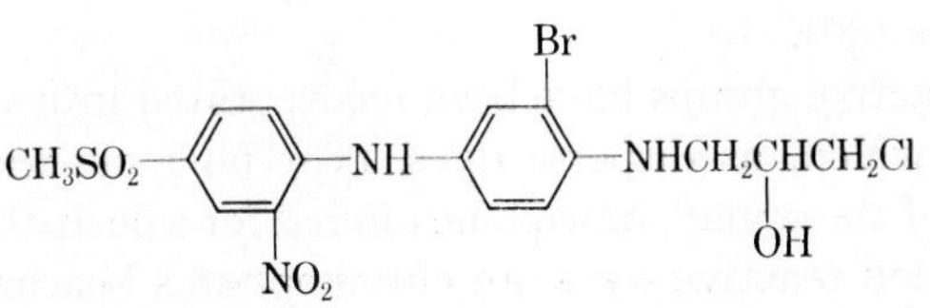

(XXV)

common knowledge. However, it is possible that structures such as these selected from the patent literature may be typical:

The 3-halo-2-hydroxypropylamino group has been attached to disperse dyes of the anthraquinone series (83,84) (XXII), the azo series (85–87) (XXIII and XXIV), and a nitrodiphenylamine (89) (XXV). The closely related oxiranyl function also has been described (88).

Disperse dyes which are fiber-reactive by virtue of a cyanuric chloride residue have been reported. The important chromophores have been utilized in this series too. Typical are such anthraquinone derivatives as XXVI (90) and azo materials such as XXVII (91,92). Disperse dyes utilizing the chloropyrimidine reactive center also are known (93).

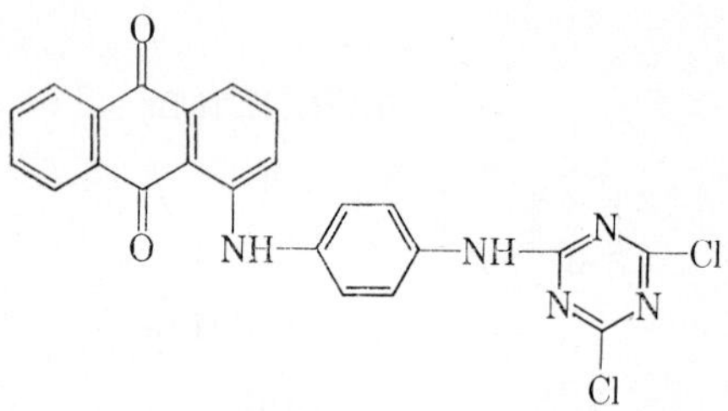

(XXVI)

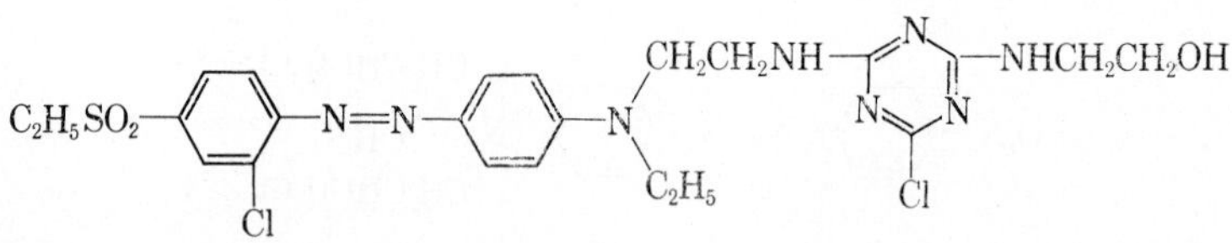

(XXVII)

The use of the sulfonyl fluoride group in disperse colors for cellulose acetate was reported before fiber reactivity became an important field of industrial research. Thus, monoazo dyes were patented in 1948 (94–96). Patents have appeared since 1960 describing similar structures for use on nylon in which the description of the dyeing conditions and the declaration of improved fastness to washing strongly imply the formation of sulfur–nitrogen linkages (30).

Other fiber-reactive groups have been incorporated into various chromophoric systems which, as disperse dyes, bear no ionic water-solubilizing groups. Some of these may, indeed, be offered for sale at the present time. Among these nylon-reactive dyes are chromophores bearing vinylsulfonyl or potential vinylsulfonyl groups (97), haloacyl dyes (98,99), haloacylimido dyes (100,101), hydroxylalkylsulfamyl dyes (102), haloacylamido dyes (103), acrylamido dyes (104), β-haloethyl sulfide dyes (105), haloalkoxyl dyes (106), azophosphonic acid esters (107), and haloalkylsulfamyl dyes (102, 108,109).

Although several of these fiber-reactive groups have been attached to a phthalocyanine nucleus, such materials probably are not useful as disperse dyes for nylon because the size and shape of the chromophoric structure probably would preclude effective dissolution in the polyamide, which is a requisite of disperse dyes.

F. FIBER-REACTIVE DYES AND RESIN FINISHES

Fiber-reactive dyes do not fix completely (100%) to the cellulosic material because of the competing reaction of hydrolysis. In light and medium shades, the usual fixation of 75–80% can be tolerated, and the unfixed dye can be removed readily in a simple soaping and rinsing operation. In dyeing heavier shades, the comparatively large amount of dye which has not reacted with the fiber or which has reacted with water to yield nonreactive dyes requires more elaborate washing arrangements for complete removal.

Applying a dye and a resin finish simultaneously offers a method which utilizes nearly all of the fiber-reactive dye. Furthermore, an economy is effected in that dyeing and finishing can be done in one operation. The crease-resisting resins which are widely used for "minimum-care" or "wash-and-wear" cottons have, in the past, usually required a separate application step. Dimethylolurea (XXVIII) and tetramethylolglyoxal diurein (XXXIII) are typical of the resin-precondensates used in crease proofing.

Dimethylolurea

$$HOCH_2NHCONHCH_2OH$$

(XXVIII)

Trimethylolmelamine

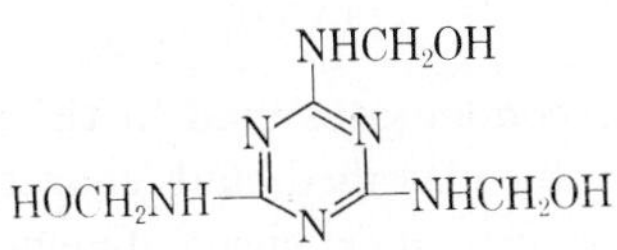

(XXIX)

Dimethylolethylene urea

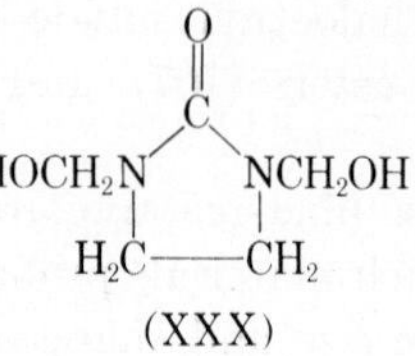

(XXX)

Dimethylol-*N*-methyltriazone

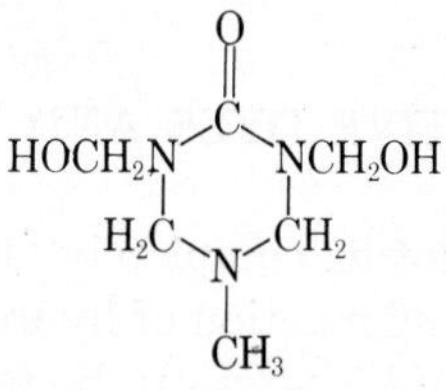

(XXXI)

Dimethylolglyoxal monourein

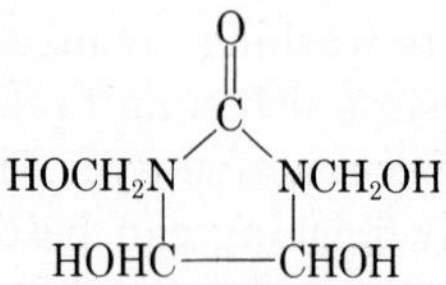

(XXXII)

Tetramethylolglyoxal diurein

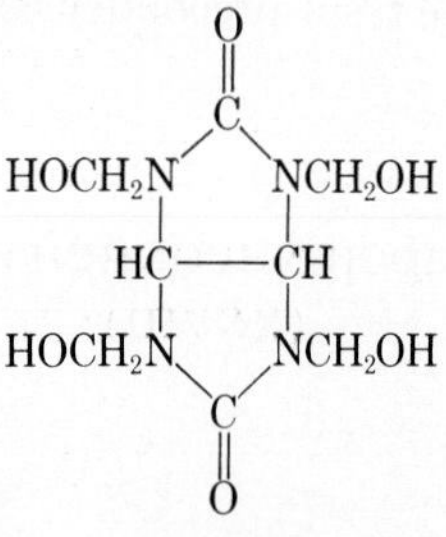

(XXXIII)

The principal resin precondensates used in the resin-finishing of cotton (cf. Chapter XVI) can be classified and characterized as follows: (*a*) methylolureas, which produce inexpensive finishes of limited durability (XXVIII); (*b*) methylolmelamines, from which durable finishes can be obtained (XXIX); (*c*) cyclic urea derivatives (XXX–XXXIII), including dimethylolethylenethioureas, dimethylol-*N*-(alkyl or aryl)triazone, dimethylolglyoxal monourein, and tetramethylolglyoxal diurein.

Durable finishes are obtained from these. Types (*a*) and (*b*) give high molecular weight, insoluble polymers, whereas the methylolated cyclic ureas give polymers of comparatively low molecular weight which derive their durability not so much by forming an insoluble encasement or sheath around the fiber, as by reacting with the cellulose.

Either acid or base can be used to catalyze the formation of the resin from the precondensate. The action is substantially this: the dye colors the resin, and the resin coats the fiber. Those conditions which remove the resin from the goods also remove all of the dye (110). Formation of dye–resin bonds and resin–cellulose bonds occurs. Thus, the application of both the dye and the finish can be carried out in a single operation to yield a result comparable to that obtained by dyeing followed by resin aftertreatment.

A typical scheme is this. The fabric is run through a padding solution containing a fiber-reactive dye, a resin precondensate, an alkaline catalyst, and some surface-activity modifiers to control such factors as viscosity, foam, and dye migration. The goods pass through nip rolls to squeeze out excess solution and go directly into any of several drying systems, such as a hot-box containing infrared lamps. An arrangement to hold the goods in open width is used in the drying steps; one such apparatus is known as a tenter. Reaction between the chemicals on the padded material is brought about by a baking or curing step; temperatures of 145–165°C. usually are used. An efficient washing-off step to remove unfixed dye and resin is essential. However, utilization of the padded dye is considerably more complete here than it is in the conventional fiber-reactive dyeing, perhaps due to the more intimate contact between the resin and dye. Even in full shades, fixations of over 90% can be achieved, and the production of such depths in goods is economically attractive (111).

G. MECHANISMS FOR THE REACTION OF FIBER-REACTIVE DYES WITH CELLULOSE

Depending on the nature of the reactive group, several general mechanisms are possible for the reaction of fiber-reactive dyes with cellulose. Of the dyes available commercially, the Procions, Cibacrons, Drimarenes, and Reactones involve the substitution of chlorine by the cellulose anion, probably by a straightforward S_N2 reaction (eq. 6). With few exceptions

$$\text{CellO}^{\ominus} + \begin{array}{c}\diagdown\!\!\diagdown\\ \text{C—Cl}\\ \diagup\end{array} \rightarrow \text{CellO—}\begin{array}{c}\diagup\!\!\diagup\\ \text{C}\\ \diagdown\end{array} + \text{Cl}^{\ominus} \tag{6}$$

this undoubtedly describes the behavior of the vast majority of fiber-reactive structures described so far and has been the subject of most of the papers published on the mechanism of fiber-reactivity.

A second type involves the addition of cellulose anion to an activated double bond, e.g., vinylsulfonyl (112). This is an example of the well-known Michael reaction in which the sulfone group causes a polarization of the double bond as shown in eq. (7). Although dyes of the Remazol type

$$\text{—CH=CH—}\overset{\displaystyle \text{O}^{\ominus}\atop|}{\underset{\|\atop\displaystyle \text{O}}{\text{S}^{\oplus}}}\text{—} \leftrightarrow \text{—}^{\oplus}\text{CH—CH=}\overset{\displaystyle \text{O}^{\ominus}\atop|}{\underset{|\atop\displaystyle \text{O}^{\ominus}}{\text{S}^{\oplus}}}\text{—} \tag{7}$$

contain a 2-sulfatoethylsulfonyl structure, $\text{—SO}_2\text{CH}_2\text{CH}_2\text{OSO}_3{}^{\ominus}\text{Na}^{\oplus}$, as the reactive entity, it is believed that reaction of these materials with cellulose is preceded by the splitting out of sodium sulfate and formation of a vinyl sulfone (112) as in eq. (8). When alkali is added slowly to a

$$\text{ArSO}_2\text{CH}_2\text{CH}_2\text{OSO}_3\text{Na} + \text{NaOH} \rightarrow \text{ArSO}_2\text{CH=CH}_2 + \text{Na}_2\text{SO}_4 + \text{H}_2\text{O} \tag{8}$$

solution of such a dye, the pH rises only to 10–10.5 until the stoichiometric amount of alkali is exceeded, whereupon the pH rises abruptly. However, this experiment by no means rules out the possibility that Remazol dyes also react with cellulose by nucleophilic displacement of the sulfate group. A similar situation exists with respect to the 3-chloropropionamides, since it is possible that in the presence of alkali, hydrogen chloride may be eliminated to form an acrylamide (eq. 9), which is known to be fiber-reactive (113).

$$\text{—NHCOCH}_2\text{CH}_2\text{Cl} \xrightarrow{-\text{HCl}} \text{—NHCOCH=CH}_2 \tag{9}$$

The reaction of cellulose with an isothiocyanate may involve a Michael addition to form a thionocarbamate (eq. 10).

$$\text{—N=C=S} + \text{CellO}^{\ominus}\text{—} \leftrightharpoons \text{—N=}\overset{\displaystyle \text{S}^{\ominus}\atop|}{\text{C}}\text{OCell} \xrightarrow{\text{H}_2\text{O}} \text{—NH}\overset{\displaystyle \text{S}\atop\|}{\text{C}}\text{OCell} \tag{10}$$

The reaction of dyes containing the acyl azide group perhaps involves the Curtius reaction, i.e., a preliminary loss of nitrogen, followed by rearrangement of the resulting neutral fragment to isocyanate and reaction of this with cellulose to form a carbamate, as shown in eqs. (11) and (12).

$$-\overset{\overset{\displaystyle O}{\|}}{C}-N=\overset{\oplus}{N}=\overset{\ominus}{N} \xrightarrow{-N_2} [-\overset{\overset{\displaystyle O}{\|}}{C}-N-] \rightarrow -N=C=O \qquad (11)$$

$$-N=C=O + CellO^{\ominus}- \rightleftharpoons -N=\overset{\overset{\displaystyle O^{\ominus}}{|}}{C}OCell \xrightarrow{H_2O} -NH\overset{\overset{\displaystyle O}{\|}}{C}OCell \qquad (12)$$

Although isocyanates by themselves are too hydrolytically unstable to be useful as reactive dyes (114), their generation *in situ* apparently permits reaction with cellulose to occur at a rate considerably greater than reaction with water. This is not too surprising, since Procion dyes, which also are unstable to hydrolysis, react preferentially with cellulose under the conditions employed in the dyebath. The causes for this phenomenon will be discussed later.

H. EVIDENCE FOR THE COVALENT BONDING OF REACTIVE DYES TO FIBERS

There is nothing novel in the idea of modifying cellulose by chemical reaction. This concept is the basis of several processes of considerable commercial importance; one may cite as examples the synthesis of viscose rayon and of cellulose acetate. There is no reason, then, for doubting that even complicated molecules such as dyes, if suitably constructed, may combine with cellulose to form covalent bonds. Nevertheless, much effort has been spent to establish the presence of a chemical link between the reactive dye and cellulose, both for scientific interest and for practical implications.

The mechanism whereby a dye is attached to a fiber through the formation of a covalent bond is radically different from the mechanisms involved in traditional dyeing. As has been discussed, the latter may involve forming strong hydrogen bonds between dye and substrate or precipitating an initially soluble dye within the fiber. Although it is not possible to predict whether a particular direct dye or vat dye will be suitable for a given purpose, enough is known about the properties of direct and vat dyes to permit the dye chemist to propose structures likely to be useful. In order to achieve a comparable level of sophistication in the field of reactive dyes, it was necessary to establish unequivocally the precise means whereby the dyes are bonded to the fiber. If the bonding is chemical, there should be no restriction on the type of colored structure which can be attached to the reactive species, and reactive dyes of such diverse types as azo, anthraquinone and phthalocyanine, should be possible. Such has been found to be the case.

If what is involved is a chemical reaction with a fiber containing an abundance of nucleophilic groups, for example, hydroxyl, the search for new types of reactive dyes becomes a search for materials capable of participating in such reaction. All of the known fiber-reactive dyes contain at least one group which can react with nucleophilic reagents or which can give rise to such a group. In practice, the development of new fiber-reactive groups has not awaited a rigorous proof of covalent bonding between dye and fiber. During much of the history of the fiber-reactive concept an intuitive feeling that a chemical reaction was involved supplied sufficient justification for a search for suitable materials.

Perhaps most important from the dyer's point of view, the elucidation of the mechanism of reactive dyeing has been important in establishing methods for using the new dyes in the mills. Such matters as the effect of reaction variables in the dyeing process, methods for obtaining maximum color yields in the dyeing, and information of importance to the user of the dyed fabrics, have been placed on a reasonably firm basis, and not left entirely to trial-and-error methods.

Several techniques have been used to establish the presence of a covalent bond between reactive dye and fiber. In this regard, the Procions and Cibacrons have been investigated most extensively of the dyes available commercially. Although reactive dyes for wool and nylon are sold, the dyeing of cotton is the most important application for these materials, and for this reason much of the work which has been reported concerns the reaction with cellulose. The following have been presented as evidence for the occurrence of a chemical reaction between dye and fiber.

(*1*) Reactive dyes cannot be extracted from dyed cotton with boiling solvents such as pyridine, *o*-chlorophenol, or chloroform (115). In like fashion, nylon which has been dyed with conventional dyes can be stripped with boiling chlorobenzene, propanol, or aqueous pyridine (82), but this is not the case with reactive dyeings. The implication is that unlike disperse, direct, acid, or azoic dyes, reactive dyes are not held in the fiber mechanically or by adsorption or salt formation.

(*2*) When nylon which has been dyed with a conventional disperse dye is dissolved in *o*-chlorophenol and the solution is added to propanol, the nylon is precipitated and the dye is found in the liquid phase. A similar treatment of nylon dyed with a Procinyl dye (i.e., a disperse reactive dye containing a reactive halogen) does not separate the dye, which remains on the precipitated fiber (82). This result would be expected if the dye were bound chemically to the fiber.

(*3*) The solubility of cellulose dyed with a Procion dye, i.e., a dye containing a dichloro-*sym*-triazinyl group, in cuprammonium hydroxide, is greatly reduced (115–119), suggesting that a crosslinking reaction has occurred. The implication of this finding will be discussed later. Schwertassek (120) has observed a similar decrease in the solubility of such dyed fibers in certain sulfuric acid solutions.

(*4*) Wool which has been dyed with a dye containing two vinyl sulfone groups or two monochloro-*sym*-triazinyl groups exhibits a much lower solubility in urea–bisulfite solutions than does untreated wool (121,122). This also indicates crosslinking.

(*5*) In the presence of alkali, reaction occurs between cellulose and cyanuric chloride (123), a finding which augments the several pieces of evidence that dyes containing chloro-*sym*-triazinyl residues also react with cotton.

(*6*) A method which has received much attention is based upon the fact that when an azo dye is treated with a reducing agent such as alkaline sodium hydrosulfite, the azo bond is reduced, forming two fragments:

$$\mathrm{ArN{=}NAr'} \rightarrow \mathrm{ArNH_2} + \mathrm{H_2NAr'} \qquad (13)$$

Since the color of such a dye is due to the azo linkage, the fragments are colorless. This technique is of technical importance to the dyer, who uses the term "discharge" to describe the operation. It is apparent that if a fiber dyed with a reactive azo dye were subjected to such treatment, one of the fragments would be removable, either by simple soaping or by solvent extraction, while the other, if it is bound to the fiber, would resist removal Because each of the products from the reduction contains a diazotizable amino group, it should be possible to subject the reduced, washed and colorless fiber to nitrous acid and form a diazonium salt, and by immersing the treated fiber in a solution of a coupling component, to form a new dye. Just as the original dyeing, the new dyeing should resist soaping and solvent extraction. A generalized sequence of reactions is given in eq. (14).

$$\mathrm{ArN{=}NAr'OCell} \xrightarrow{\mathrm{H_2}} \mathrm{ArNH_2} + \mathrm{H_2NAr'OCell} \xrightarrow{\mathrm{HNO_2}}$$

$$\mathrm{Cl^-N_2^+Ar'OCell} \xrightarrow{\mathrm{Ar''OH}} \mathrm{Ar''N{=}NAr'OCell} \qquad (14)$$

Such behavior has been observed with cellulose and nylon which had been dyed with reactive dyes (82,112,115), and supplies one of the strongest pieces of evidence that reactive dyes combine chemically with these fibers. Indeed, it has been possible to synthesize a reactive dye on cellulose in a stepwise manner by first reacting the cloth with a colorless fragment containing both a diazotizable amine and a dichloro-*sym*-triazinyl group, diazotizing, and coupling. The properties of the dyed fiber (color, resistance of the dye to removal) were the same as when the preformed dye was reacted with cotton (119).

(*7*) One of the most elegant proofs of covalent linkage of reactive dye with cellulose is due to Krazer and Zollinger, who studied a reactive dye containing the sulfofluoride group, —SO_2F (124). Reaction of this structure with a hydroxyl group of cellulose forms a sulfonate ester, diagnosed by reaction with sodium iodide in acetone (125).

(*8*) An argument suggesting chemical reaction is that fixation of reactive dyes does not occur unless the pH of the dyeing system is suitable. Wool dyed with a vinyl sulfone dye can be stripped of its color by soaping or solvent extraction unless the dyeing is effected at a pH greater than 5 (122, 126,127). The pH dependence of the reactive dyeing of cellulose has been studied in some detail (118,128–138).

(*9*) The rate of acetylation of cellulose which has been dyed with difunctional reactive dyes is markedly less than for undyed cellulose, indicating a lesser availability of hydroxyl groups (139).

(*10*) Although the infrared absorption spectra of monochloro-*sym*-triazinyl dyes is too complicated to permit a reliable interpretation of the spectra of powdered cellulose which has been dyed with such coloring agents, it was possible to obtain suitable spectra by using the reaction product of cellulose with simpler molecules containing the monochloro-*sym*-triazinyl structure (140). Absorption bands at 8.8–9.1 μ, indicative of the —C—O—C— grouping, and found in a simpler alkaloxy-*sym*-triazine, were observed. Simultaneously, the intensity of the 2.9 μ band, a band due to the hydroxyl groups of cellulose, decreased in intensity, as would be expected if hydroxyl groups were consumed.

(*11*) Microbiological degradation of cellulose dyed with a Procion or a Remazol dye resulted in the formation of a colored, water-soluble fraction from which, after acid hydrolysis, glucose was obtained, indicating a chemical attachment of dye to cellulose (141). In a separate experiment, the infrared spectrum of glucose reacted with a Remazol dye was found to be identical to the spectrum of the colored acid hydrolyzate of cellulose dyed with the same material (142). Viscose rayon dyed with a dye containing the β-sulfatoethylsulfonyl group was subjected to acid hydrolysis, and products were isolated in which the dye was attached to glucose and cellulose (143).

(*12*) Modifying a reactive group so that it no longer can react readily with nucleophilic reagents destroys its ability to dye cotton by conventional reactive dyeing techniques. For example, if the chlorine atoms in a dichloro-*sym*-triazinyl dye are replaced by hydroxyl groups, the dye no longer is fiber-reactive (115,144). Similarly, unlike the vinylsulfonyl group, the 2-hydroxyethylsulfonyl group has been claimed not to be fiber-reactive (112). More recently, dyes containing 2-hydroxyethylsulfonyl residues have been claimed to be fiber-reactive (171).

(*13*) Procion dyes are known to react with primary and secondary alcohols (145,146), an observation which is consistent with the presumed reaction of such dyes with cellulose.

In addition to solubility tests which suggest that wool and nylon undergo chemical reaction with reactive dyes (*1*, *2*, and *4* above), chemical evidence of fiber-reactivity is available.

(*14*) Nylon which was dyed with an azo dye containing a chloro-*sym*-triazinyl residue was exposed to a reducing medium to decolorize the cloth (82). After washing, treatment of the cloth with cold nitrous acid followed by exposure to a phenol caused the cloth to become colored again. This observation is explicable on the basis that the original dye was covalently bound to the fiber and that the reduction left a colorless amine fragment attached to the nylon. It will be recalled that similar experiments were reported for cellulose (item *6* above).

(*15*) Treating a nylon model compound, $C_4H_9NHCO(CH_2)_4CONH(CH_2)_6NHCONHC_4H_9$, with Procinyl Orange G gave a product which could not be decolorized by treatment with charcoal or with solvents which would remove unreacted dye (82). The possibility that the dye reacted with the urea grouping of the model compound is problematical, but evidence of reaction was obtained with reactive dye and dibenzoylhexamethylenediamine, which, of course, does not contain a urea-type residue. On the other hand, the reports of Russian workers (127,147,148), who, using both dichloro-*sym*-triazinyl and 2-sulfatoethylsulfonyl dyes, obtained reaction with α-amino acids but not with their acylated derivatives, suggests that the precise nature of the reaction of reactive dyes with polyamides is not entirely clear.

(*16*) Chromatographic analysis indicated that, in addition to combining with the amino groups of wool, the vinylsulfonyl groups of Remazol dyes may also react with the phenolic hydroxyl groups of tyrosine residues (126).

I. MECHANISM OF REACTIVE DYEING

At first glance, several aspects of reactive dyeing seem difficult to understand. It is known, for example, that substituted chloro-*sym*-triazines are readily hydrolyzed in hot, alkaline water (149). Why, then, should some Cibacron or Procion dyes react with cellulose to the extent of 80% or better in hot water containing alkali? In addition, alkyl esters of sulfonic acids are readily susceptible to hydrolysis, and indeed are so reactive as to be useful alkylating agents, yet a dye attached to cellulose through a sulfonate grouping is quite stable to hot, dilute alkali. Moreover, although the reactive group may be the same in any given group of dyes, comparatively trivial changes in the structure of the colored portion of the molecule may cause pronounced differences in the extent to which the dyes are fixed.

Sufficient information is available, however, to permit an understanding of these apparently anomalous findings. For convenience, the several aspects of the overall problem are grouped separately. Because many of the published studies have originated in the laboratories of Imperial Chemical Industries, Ltd., the bulk of the work concerns the chemistry of Procion dyes which contain a chloro- or dichloro-*sym*-triazinyl residue.

1. Cellulosic Fibers Reacted with Chloro-*sym*-Triazinyl Dyes

a. Position of Attachment of Dye to Cellulose

By studying the reaction of *p*-toluenesulfonyl chloride with cellulose, Gardner and Purves (150) concluded that the ratio of the first-order rate constants of the hydroxyl groups at C_6, C_2, and C_3 of cellulose in this reaction was 23.4:2.16:0.106. An inspection of the structure of cellulose (XXXIV) shows that the enormously greater reactivity of the hydroxyl group at C_6 is due to two factors: it is sterically more accessible than the others and, unlike the groups at C_2 and C_3, is primary rather than secondary.

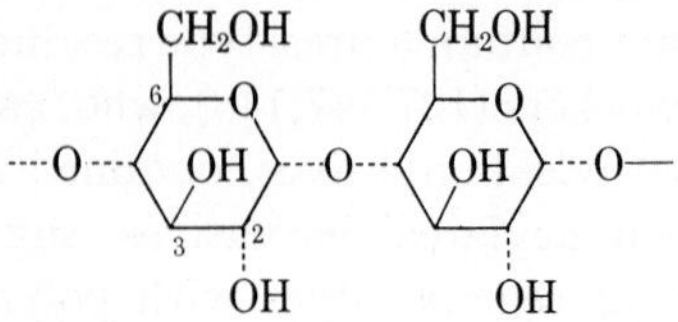

(XXXIV)

The greater reactivity of primary as compared to secondary alcohols in nucleophilic substitution reactions with, for example, acid chlorides (151), is well known.

Dawson and co-workers (145,146), studying the rates of reaction of dichloro- and monochloro-*sym*-triazinyl dyes with both *n*-propyl and isopropyl alcohols, found that the ratio of the rate constants for the reaction of a dichloro-*sym*-triazinyl dye (Procion Brilliant Red 2B) with *n*-propanol and isopropanol, respectively, was 3.7. For a monochloro-*sym*-triazinyl type of dye (Procion Brilliant Red H3B), the ratio was 15.2. These results indicate that reaction undoubtedly occurs mostly at the C_6 atom of cellulose. Dichloro-*sym*-triazinyl dyes are more reactive with cellulose than are monochloro-*sym*-triazinyl dyes, a situation which is to be expected in view of the finding of Ackermann and Dussy (152) that the rate constant for the reaction of XXXV with ethoxide is 550×10^5 sec.$^{-1}$, whereas for XXVI the value is 37×10^5 sec.$^{-1}$ It can be concluded, therefore, that Dawson's

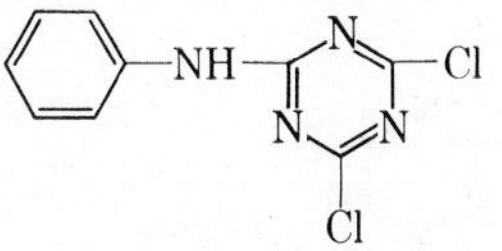

(XXXV)

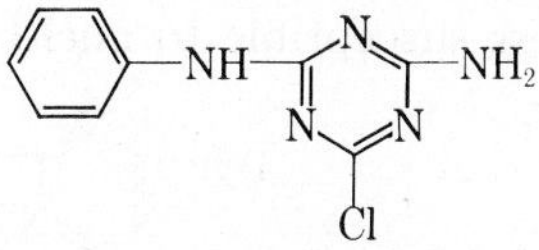

(XXXVI)

data mean that the more reactive the dye, the greater is its reactivity toward secondary hydroxyl groups. Conclusive evidence that reaction does occur with both primary and secondary hydroxyl functions of cellulose was obtained by Daruwalla and Subramaniam (153) by reacting oxidized cellulose with reactive dyes. Dinitrogen tetroxide oxidizes only C_6, while periodate oxidizes C_2 and C_3. Both modifications could be dyed. It has been shown that glucose can be dyed with Remazol (142) and with dichloro-*sym*-triazinyl dyes (146).

When cellulose is reacted with a dichloro-*sym*-triazinyl dye, there may be one dye molecule for every 5000–7500 anhydroglucose units (146).

Approximately 75% of a sulfofluoride dye was bound to primary hydroxyl groups of cellulose, while 25% was linked to secondary hydroxyl groups (124), indicating a different degree of reactivity with the primary and secondary hydroxyl groups of cellulose than was obtained with tosyl chloride.

b. Stability of Reactive Dyes to Hydrolysis

The success of a reactive dyeing depends greatly, but not exclusively, on the extent to which hydrolysis of the dye occurs. Since the ideal case of quantitative reaction of dye with cellulose is met infrequently, if at all, a certain proportion of dye always is lost. Of the commercial dyes, the chloro-*sym*-triazinyl type has received most attention in this regard.

Hydrolysis increases with increasing pH, but not uniformly (146).

For the reaction indicated by eq. (15), log k_1 increases linearly with temperature (146). Dyes of type XXXVIII are but slightly reactive to cellulose, a result which has been interpreted by Wegmann (119) as being due to keto–enol tautomerism (eq. 16). By destroying the conjugation of the

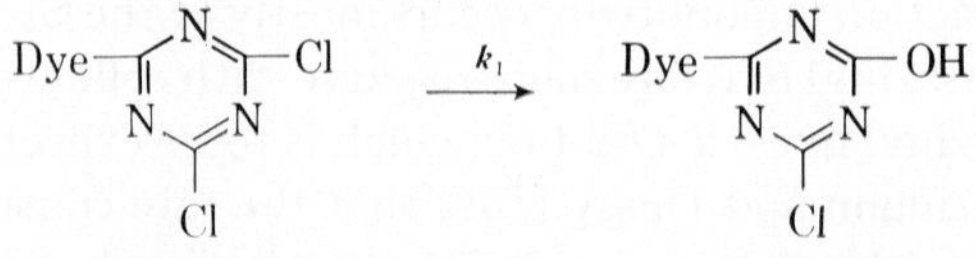 (15)

(XXXVII) (XXXVIII)

three electronegative nitrogen atoms, ketonization would make the C—Cl bond less susceptible to nucleophilic attack.

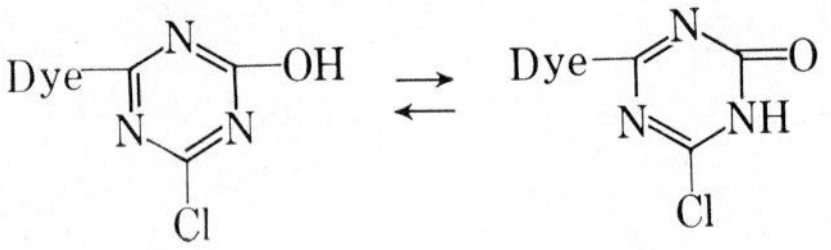 (16)

(XXXVIII) (XXXIX)

The rate of alkaline hydrolysis of dichloro-*sym*-triazinyl compounds was found to be a first-order reaction and to increase with increasing electrolyte concentration (146).

In addition to these factors, the hydrolysis rate depends on the overall structure of the dye (130). Since this also is true for the rate of reaction with the fiber, the effect of dye structure is discussed below.

c. *Factors in Reactive Dyeing*

(1) Affinity of the Dye for the Fiber

The concept of affinity has been treated at length by Vickerstaff (154). Mathematically, affinity can be represented by eq. (17)

$$-\Delta\mu^\circ = RT \ln (D)\phi/(D)\sigma \tag{17}$$

for an equilibrium system in which the dye forms an ideal solution in both the water phase (σ) and the fiber phase (ϕ). The difference in standard chemical potential, $-\Delta\mu^\circ$, which is a quantitative measure of affinity, represents the tendency of a dye to move from its standard state in solution to its standard state on the fiber. A complete discussion of the affinity of dyes for fibers is beyond the scope of this chapter, but it can be said that the structure of the dye and the fiber, as well as the presence of materials such as electrolytes, affect the affinity.

In general, the greater the affinity of a dye, the greater the exhaustion, i.e., the extent to which the dye migrates into the fiber. Vickerstaff (115) has discussed the affinities of some reactive Procion dyes on viscose rayon, pointing out some of the practical consequences. A recent treatment of the calculation of the affinities of dyes from alkaline solutions is given by Sumner (133).

(2) Diffusion of the Dye Into the Fiber

A significant characteristic of a dye is the rate at which it diffuses into the fiber. The size and shape of the dye molecule, as well as its affinity for the fiber, will determine the ease with which the dye can penetrate. Since "diffusion is a stepwise process from one adsorption site to another" (115), the greater the affinity the more difficult will it be for a dye molecule to be displaced from a site, and the lower will be the diffusion coefficient. The relationship is shown in the data in Table XV-4, published by Vickerstaff (115).

TABLE XV-4
Relationship Between Affinity and Diffusion Coefficient for Procion Dyes[a]

Reactive dye	Affinity for viscose rayon at 30°C., cal.	Diffusion coefficient in viscose film (30°C. and 5 g. NaCl/l.), $cm.^2/sec. \times 10^8$
Procion Yellow RS	−4100	2.4
Procion Brilliant Red 2BS	−2500	25.0
Procion Blue 3GS	−2400	20.0

[a] Taken from ref. 115.

The presence of salt in the dyebath increases the extent of adsorption of dye by neutralizing the electrical surface charge on the substrate, which might otherwise prevent the formation of hydrogen bonds between dye and fiber (155). Under conditions of high alkalinity, fixation can occur so rapidly that dye molecules have no opportunity to diffuse into the fiber, and so-called "ring dyeing" occurs on the fiber surface (135). This circumstance is avoided in the mill by a suitable choice of conditions.

d. Rate of Reaction of Dye with Fiber

(1) Effect of pH

One of the astonishing features of reactive dyeing is that in the presence of alkali, dyeing, rather than hydrolysis of the reactive moiety, occurs preferentially.

The reason is that in an alkaline bath, the pH within a cellulosic fiber is higher than the pH of the bath (118,131,134,137). The data shown in Table XV-5 have been published for cotton and viscose rayon immersed in alkaline water (118). Sumner (131–133) has examined the interaction of cellulose with alkali, and concluded that in the presence of alkali, cellulose is ionized and behaves as a weak acid. This finding is consistent with Neale's calculation of the dissociation constant of the hydroxyl groups in cellulose, 1.84×10^{-14} at 25°C. (156), i.e., greater than the dissociation constant of water.

TABLE XV-5

pH of Cotton and Viscose Immersed in Alkaline Water[a]

Fiber	pH of bath	pH within fiber
Cotton	11.23	12.36
Viscose	10.84	12.35

[a] Taken from ref. 118.

By considering the equilibria involved when cellulose is immersed in an aqueous solution of sodium hydroxide and sodium chloride, Sumner was able to develop equations which make it possible to calculate the amount of hydroxide ion (and thereby the concentration of cellulose anion) sorbed from a dyebath (133). These calculations have been extremely useful in studying the rate of reaction of reactive dyes with ionized cellulose. An equation due to Danckwerts (157) has been simplified by Sumner (131) to eq. (18) and applied to the problem of reactive dyeing. Here Q is the

$$Q = c[t + (^1/_2k)]\,(Dk)^{1/2} \tag{18}$$

amount of dye diffusing through unit area of surface, c is the equilibrium surface concentration of dye, which can be calculated from the thermodynamic affinity, D is the diffusion coefficient, t is the duration of the experiment, and k is the reaction constant of dye with cellulose. Under the experimental conditions used (films of viscose were employed) (130), it was possible to equate Q with the amount of dye fixed to the cellulose. The reaction of a viscose film with a Procion dye was found to be complete in less than 15 sec. (135). For an undisclosed dichloro-*sym*-triazinyl dye, the equation was used to obtain pseudo first-order reaction constant ratios $k_{\text{cellulose}}/k_{\text{water}}$. By correcting these values to allow for cellulose anion, bimolecular reaction constant ratios $k_{\text{CellO}^-}/k_{[\text{OH}^-]}$ were obtained. In the pH range 9.46–12.73, the ratios were found to be nearly constant and close to unity (actually, 1.14 ± 0.14) (130,131,158). This means that the reactivities of the dye with hydroxide and with cellulose anion are essentially identical. If this is so, why should dyeing occur to a significant extent? The two reasons were mentioned earlier: the affinity of the dye for the fiber, because of which the dye can be 500 times as concentrated in the fiber as in the water phase, and the increased degree of ionization of cellulose compared to that of water.

The greater importance of affinity as compared with diffusion and reactivity is apparent from the simplified Danckwerts equation, for the latter variables are square-root terms rather than logarithmic. Since a high affinity generally is accompanied by a low diffusion coefficient, these factors must be balanced for a dye to be useful.

Since at higher pH a greater number of the hydroxyl groups in cellulose will be ionized, it is to be expected that the fixation of dye will increase with increasing pH. That this is indeed the case has been known for some time (135). However, as was mentioned previously, the hydrolysis of the dye also increases with increasing pH. A plot of per cent fixation of several Procion dyes with respect to pH shows that fixation passes through a maximum, then falls off (135). Both the rate at which fixation increases and the position of the maximum are unique for each dye. Decreasing fixation beyond the maximum can be attributed to hydrolysis of the dye, since the hydrolysis is markedly pH-dependent whereas the diffusion rate is only slightly dependent upon pH. The rate of increase of fixation with pH as well as the position of maximum fixation, undoubtedly are functions of the structure of the dye, reflected in the affinity and the diffusion coefficient.

(2) Effect of Temperature

Not only does increasing the temperature at any pH result in an increase in the hydrolysis of reactive dye, it also increases the diffusion coefficient of a dye into a fiber (159), whereas affinity decreases with temperature (160). However, the effect of temperature on hydrolysis and diffusion is such that these two effects nearly cancel one another (135), and the limiting variable is the affinity. Therefore, the per cent of any dye which is fixed from a bath containing both dye and alkali should be independent of temperature, an expectation which has been confirmed experimentally (135). In practice however, the dye usually is placed on the fiber at room temperature so as to induce the maximum amount of dye to penetrate, and the colored fiber is exposed to alkali in a second step, i.e., after diffusion has occurred. Under these conditions and with a dichloro-*sym*-triazinyl dye, increasing the temperature of the alkaline treatment results in a lower degree of fixation because the hydrolysis of sorbed dye is increased (115).

(3) Effect of Time

The per cent fixation of a Procion dye was found to increase with time (135), a relationship which is predicted by the Danckwerts equation.

(4) Effect of Added Electrolytes

The significance of electrolytes in the dyebath was mentioned briefly before. In a two-stage dyeing process in which the colored and dried fiber is fixed with alkali, omission of the electrolyte (sodium chloride or sodium sulfate) results in desorption of dye from the fiber. Electrolytes have been said to increase the pH difference between the bath and the fiber (128).

(5) Nature of the Fiber

Under uniform conditions, the per cent fixation of a Procion dye by cellulosic fibers decreases in the order viscose rayon, mercerized cotton, cotton (115), a sequence which is general for direct dyes and is ascribed to differences in the total micellar surface available for the sorption of dye and to the electrical charges on the fibers (161).

(6) Structure of the Colored Moiety

For a given series of mono- or dichloro-*sym*-triazinyl dyes, the rate of reaction with simple alcohols is markedly dependent upon the structure of the colored group to which the reactive group is attached. For example, reference can be made again to the study of Dawson, Fern, and Preston (146) on the ratio of the rates of reaction of some monochloro-*sym*-triazinyl dyes with *n*-propanol and isopropanol (Table XV-6). Since the reactive moiety is the same for these four dyes, the difference in the reaction rates must be due to the colored segment of the dye. Unfortunately, the precise structures of these materials have not been disclosed. Consequently, little more can be said about the contribution of the colored end of the dye to the reactivity of the dye. Some insight into what may be occurring can be obtained by considering the data of Ackermann and Dussy (152) mentioned earlier, in which the displacement of chloride by ethoxide from chloro-*sym*-triazines was shown to be markedly dependent upon the nature of the substituents on the triazine ring. Both inductive and resonance effects appear to be involved, and, in fact, the order of the influence of the substituent

TABLE XV-6
Reactivity of Some Procion Dyes with Alcohols[a]

Procion dye	Ratio of rates (primary/secondary)
Brilliant Red 2B	3.7
Red G	5.9
Brilliant Blue R	6.6
Yellow R	7.2

[a] Taken from ref. 146.

group on the ease of displacement parallels that found for nucleophilic aromatic substitution (162).

Luttringhaus (163) has presented data which show the marked dependence upon dye structure of the degree of fixation of several vinylsulfonyl dyes for cotton and rayon. Here too, the dyes are indicated by trade name only, but the variations in fixation would appear to be largely, if not solely, due to the structure of the dye.

(7) Structure of the Colorless Moiety

In the class of monochloro-*sym*-triazinyl dyes, where both colored and colorless residues are attached to the triazine ring (the Cibacron and Procion H types), the reactivities of the dyes were found to decrease as the basicities of the substituent groups decreased (164). This situation is entirely similar to that found for the colored moieties.

(8) Steric Considerations

The geometry and dimensions of the dye molecule apparently have an effect on the extent of fixation. Zollinger (114,165–167) has examined homologous dyes in the dichloro- and monochloro-*sym*-triazinyl series in which the colored portion is separated from the reactive group by 0–2 methylene groups. The per cent fixation increased in the order 0, 1, 2, a result which was interpreted to mean that the steric requirements for the transition state involved in the displacement of a chloride ion by cellulose anion are more readily met if the reactive group can move around a flexible grouping without shifting the entire molecule. The latter would be difficult because the colored portion, which contains sulfonic acid and other polar groups, is bound too tightly to the substrate. It is Zollinger's belief that similar considerations are involved in reactions with dyes containing oxirane or vinylsulfonyl groups as the reactive portions.

2. Cellulosic Fibers Reacted with Remazol Dyes

In general, the variables discussed above for the Procion dyes have similar effects in the Remazol series (128,136). Unlike the Procion dyes (73), however, the rate of hydrolysis of Remazol dyes is not dependent upon the concentration of electrolyte (128).

3. Reactive Dyes for Nylon

The Procinyl dyes, which are disperse dyes containing a reactive halogen, are applied to nylon at an acid pH (3.54–4.0), then fixed at an alkaline pH (10–10.5). Most of the data pertinent to this series of dyes have been presented by Scott and Vickerstaff (82). The effects of some variables on the dyeing of polyamides sometimes are very different from their effects on the dyeing of cellulose. For example, electrolyte concentration has only a trivial effect on the dyeing of nylon, unlike the situation with respect to cotton. Also, the exhaustion, which is the extent to which dye migrates from the bath into the fiber, is independent of pH. This is fortunate, since it permits one to apply dye to the fiber at pH's where the reactive group is quite stable. In a fashion similar to the reaction of Procion dyes with cellulose, the fixation increases with increasing pH, then levels off.

Because it reflects the rate of diffusion of dye into the fiber, exhaustion increases with temperature, but only to a point, then levels off. Fixation increases with temperature.

4. Crosslinking of Cellulose

It was mentioned previously that crosslinking of a substrate can occur if the reactive group is difunctional. An examination of scale models indicates that when the second chlorine atom of a dichloro-*sym*-triazine is displaced by cellulose, reaction is more likely to involve a hydroxyl group of a second cellulose chain than a hydroxyl group in the same anhydroglucose unit or in another unit of the same chain (146).

5. Hydrolysis of Reactive Dyeings

Based on the behavior of several esters of cyanuric chloride to acid and alkaline hydrolysis, Mur, Gorbunova, and Korolev (168) concluded that reaction involved acyl–oxygen cleavage.

Benz (169) investigated the hydrolysis of reactive dyeings in which several types of dyes were used. The dyes contained the same chromophore and differed only in the structure of the reactive grouping. The extent of hydrolysis was dependent both on the nature of the reactive group and on the nature of the atom linking this group to the chromophore. Thus, an azo dye linked to a dichloropyrimidyl residue through a nitrogen atom gave a dyeing of cellulose which was more resistant to alkaline hydrolysis than was the analogous dye in which oxygen was the connecting atom. It should be pointed out that whereas the hydrolysis of a dyeing made with chloro-*sym*-triazinyl or chloropyrimidyl dyes is a saponification reaction, the hydrolysis of a dyeing made from a Remazol dye probably involves the reversal of a Michael addition (eq. 19):

$$—SO_2CH_2CH_2OCell \xrightarrow{OH^-} —SO_2\overset{\ominus}{C}HCH_2Cell \longrightarrow —SO_2CH{=}CH_2 + Cello\overset{\ominus}{—} \quad (19)$$

Ulrich (117) and Wegmann (164) also have studied the hydrolytic stability of reactive dyeings. Elöd and Nakahara (129) have found that the "desorption" of fixed dye from cellulose (actually hydrolysis of a covalent bond to cellulose) was first-order, and developed a kinetic expression (eq. 20) to describe the reaction,

$$\log (A - x/A) = -kt \quad (20)$$

where A is the amount of fixed dye at time t, x is the amount of dye "desorbed" in time t, and k is a reaction constant.

It is possible that the hydrolytic stability of the dye–fiber bond is due partly to its relative inaccessibility to attacking anions. This may explain the surprising stability of the $DyeSO_2$—OCell bond.

References

1. Perkin, W. H., British Patent 1984, Aug. 26, 1856.
2. Venkataraman, K., *The Chemistry of Synthetic Dyes*, Academic Press, New York, 1952.
3. Lubs, H. A., *The Chemistry of Organic Dyes and Pigments*, Reinhold, New York, 1955.
4. Vickerstaff, T., *The Physical Chemistry of Dyeing*, Oliver and Boyd, London, 1954.
5. Rattee, I. D., "Historical Introduction," in *Procion Dyestuffs in Textile Printing*, Imperial Chemical Industries Ltd., Dyestuffs Division, 1960.
6. Gund, F., *J. Soc. Dyers Colourists*, **69**, 671 (1953).
7. Cross, C. F., and E. J. Bevan, *Researches on Cellulose*, 1895, p. 34.
8. Cross, C. F., E. J. Bevan, and C. Beadle, British Patent 8700, May 7, 1892.
9. Achroeter, G., *Ber.*, **39**, 1559 (1906).
10. Textilwerk Horn A.-G., British Patent 195,619, Mar. 20, 1923; *Chem. Abstr.*, **17**, 3613 (1923).
11. I. G. Farbenindustrie A.-G., British Patent 322,556, Sept. 15, 1928; *Chem. Abstr.*, **24**, 2883 (1930).

12. CIBA Ltd., British Patent 363,897, Feb. 21, 1930; through *Chem. Abstr.*, **27**, 1767 (1933).
13. Dinklage, R., British Patent 398,279, Sept. 4, 1936; *Chem. Abstr.*, **28**, 1531[6] (1934).
14. Dinklage, R., French Patent 735,343, Apr. 18, 1932; *Chem. Abstr.*, **27**, 1166 (1933).
15. Haller, R., and A. Heckendorn, U. S. Patent 1,886,480 (to CIBA), Nov. 8, 1932; *Chem. Abstr.*, **27**, 1519 (1933).
16. Peacock, D. H., *J. Soc. Dyers Colourists*, **42**, 53 (1926); *Chem. Abstr.*, **20**, 1325 (1926).
17. Günther, F., U. S. Patent 1,567,731, Dec. 29, 1925; *Chem. Abstr.*, **20**, 3820 (1926).
18. Heyna, J., and W. Schumacher, U. S. Patent 2,670,265 (to Farbwerke Hoechst A.-G.), Feb. 23, 1954; *Chem. Abstr.*, **48**, 7914a (1954).
19. Guthrie, J. D., *Am. Dyestuff Reptr.*, **40**, 643 (1951).
20. Guthrie, J. D., *Am. Dyestuff Reptr.*, **41**, 13 (1952); *Chem. Abstr.*, **46**, 5319e (1952).
21. Sommer, E. P., *Am. Dyestuff Reptr.*, **20**, 895 (1958); *Chem. Abstr.*, **53**, 3699h (1959).
22. Heslop, R. N., N. Legg, J. F. Mawson, W. E. Stephen, and J. Wardleworth, U. S. Patent 2,935,506 (to Imperial Chemical Industries, Ltd.), May 3, 1960; *Chem. Abstr.*, **54**, 16853d (1960).
23. Schumacher, H., *Melliand Textilber.*, **41**, 1548 (1960); *Chem. Abstr.*, **55**, 9883a (1961).
24. Capponi, M., E. Metzger, and A. Giamarra, *Am. Dyestuff Reptr.*, **50**, 505 (1961); *Chem. Abstr.*, **55**, 19245i (1961).
25. Maruyama, T., T. Kitao, I. Kushiro, N. Kuroki, and K. Konishi, *Kogyo Kagaku Zasshi*, **63**, 997 (1960) (English Abstract).
26. Maruyama, T., T. Kitao, S. Kubo, N. Kuroki, and K. Konishi, *Kogyo Kagaku Zasshi*, **63**, 1000 (1960) (English Abstract).
27. Maruyama, T., T. Kitao, T. Ono, N. Kuroki and K. Konishi, *Kogyo Kagaku Zasshi*, **64**, 327 (1961) (English Abstract).
28. Cassella Farbwerke Mainkur A.-G., British Patent 827,570, Feb. 10, 1960; *Chem. Abstr.*, **54**, 12605a (1960).
29. Imperial Chemical Industries, Ltd., British Patent 819,320 (by W. Baird, D. K. Lawman, W. E. Stephen, and C. D. Weston), Sept. 2, 1959; *Chem. Abstr.*, **54**, 10343b (1960).
30. Imperial Chemical Industries, Ltd., British Patent 824,690 (by H. R. Hadfield, and R. H. Ricketts), Dec. 2, 1959; *Chem. Abstr.*, **54**, 8100c (1960).
31. Eisele, J., W. Federkiel, R. Gehm, W. Rohland, C. Schuster, E. Stöckl, and A. Tartter, German Patent 1,066,682 (to Badische Anilin- & Soda-Fabrik A.-G.), (Oct. 8, 1959); *Chem. Abstr.*, **55**, 14926b (1961); corresponds to British Patent 868,743, May 25, 1961.
32. Badische Anilin- & Soda-Fabrik A.-G., British Patent 868,744, May 25, 1961.
33. Imperial Chemical Industries, Ltd., British Patent 847,142 (by C. H. Reece and J. Wardleworth), Sept. 7, 1960; *Chem. Abstr.*, **55**, 7858c (1961).
34. Rohland, W., E. Stöckl, F. Graser, A. Tartter, C. Schuster, R. Gehm, J. Eisele, and W. Federkiel, German Patent 1,083,957 (to Badische Anilin- & Soda-Fabrik

A.-G.), June 23, 1960; *Chem. Abstr.*, **55,** 22839e (1961); corresponds to British Patent 868,745, May 25, 1961.
35. Badische Anilin- & Soda-Fabrik A.-G., British Patent 876,496 (by W. Rohland, and E. Stöckl), Sept. 6, 1961; *Chem. Abstr.*, **56,** 13054e (1962).
36. Farbenfabriken Bayer A.-G., British Patent 875,888, Aug. 23, 1961; *Chem. Abstr.*, **56,** 14438f (1962).
37. Imperial Chemical Industries, Ltd., British Patent 826,689 (by V. D. Poole and J. Wardleworth), Jan. 20, 1960; *Chem. Abstr.*, **54,** 13673b (1960).
38. Badische Anilin- & Soda-Fabrik A.-G., British Patent 848,782 (by A. Tartter), Sept. 21, 1960; *Chem. Abstr.*, **55,** 9891e (1961).
39. Tartter, A., F. Graser, W. Rohland, E. Stöckl, C. Schuster, R. Gehm, J. Eisele, and W. Federkiel (to Badische Anilin- & Soda-Fabrik A.-G.), German Patent 1,066,684, Oct. 8, 1959; *Chem. Abstr.*, **55,** 17028a (1961); corresponds to British Patent 868,746, May 25, 1961.
40. Badische Anilin- & Soda-Fabrik A.-G., British Patent, 868,747 May 25, 1961; *Chem. Abstr.*, **56,** 1559i (1962).
41. Imperial Chemical Industries, Ltd., British Patent 821,963 (by F. H. Slinger), Oct. 14, 1959; *Chem. Abstr.*, **55,** 1007a (1961).
42. Badische Anilin- & Soda-Fabrik A.-G., British Patent 865,305 (by W. Rohland, E. Stöckl, J. Eisele, and W. Federkiel), Apr. 12, 1961; *Chem. Abstr.*, **55,** 24040i (1961).
43. Fleishhauer, R., and A. Muller, U. S. Patent 2,213,697 (to General Aniline & Film Corp.), Sept. 3, 1940; *Chem. Abstr.*, **35,** 1234^9 (1941).
44. Knight, A. H., and W. E. Stephen, U. S. Patent 2,384,750 (to Imperial Chemical Industries, Ltd.), Sept. 11, 1945; *Chem. Abstr.*, **40,** 2993^4 (1936).
45. Knight, A. H., and W. E. Stephen, U. S. Patent 2,384,751 (to Imperial Chemical Industries, Ltd.), Sept. 11, 1945; *Chem. Abstr.*, **40,** 2993^7 (1946).
46. Knight, A. H., and W. E. Stephen, U. S. Patent 2,384,752 (to Imperial Chemical Industries, Ltd.), Sept. 11, 1945; *Chem. Abstr.*, **40,** 2993^9 (1946).
47. Knight, A. H., and W. E. Stephen, U. S. Patent 2,384,753 (to Imperial Chemical Industries, Ltd.), Sept. 11, 1945; *Chem. Abstr.*, **40,** 2994^3 (1946).
48. Knight, A. H., and W. E. Stephen, U. S. Patent 2,384,754 (to Imperial Chemical Industries, Ltd.), Sept. 11, 1945; *Chem. Abstr.*, **40,** 2994^5 (1946).
49. Knight, A. H., and W. E. Stephen, U. S. Patent 2,384,755 (to Imperial Chemical Industries, Ltd.), Sept. 11, 1945; *Chem. Abstr.*, **40,** 2994^6 (1946).
50. Riat, H., and F. Oesterlein, U. S. Patent 2,906,748 (to CIBA Ltd.), Sept. 29, 1959; *Chem. Abstr.*, **54,** 12600d (1960).
51. Illy, H., German Patent 1,110,347 (to CIBA Ltd.), Oct. 31, 1958; *Chem. Abstr.*, **56,** 3600f (1962); corresponds to U. S. Patent 2,984,659, May 16, 1961.
52. CIBA Ltd., British Patent 870,047, June 7, 1961; *Chem. Abstr.*, **56,** 1561d (1962).
53. CIBA Ltd., British Patent 845,567, Aug. 24, 1960; *Chem. Abstr.*, **55,** 7851f (1961); corresponds to U. S. Patent 2,973,351, Feb. 28, 1961.
54. Stauble, M., and K. Weber, U. S. Patent 2,989,540 (to CIBA Ltd.), June 20, 1961; *Chem. Abstr.*, **55,** 25270g (1961).
55. Kitao, T., N. Kuroki, and K. Konishi, *Kogyo Kagaku Zasshi*, **63,** 137 (1960); *Chem. Abstr.*, **56,** 13050d (1962).
56. Cassella Farbwerke Mainkur A.-G., British Patent 874,355, Aug. 21, 1961.
57. Badische Anilin- & Soda-Fabrik A.-G., Belgian Patent 593,868, Feb. 8, 1961; *Derwent Belgian Patents Rept.*, **74B,** C 19, Apr. 28, 1961.

58. Badische Anilin- & Soda-Fabrik A.-G., British Patent 858,183 (by J. Eisele, W. Federkiel, G. Krehbiel, H. Krzikalla, G. Lange, and H. Pohlemann), Jan. 11, 1961; *Chem. Abstr.*, **55**, 11862a (1961).
59. Badische Anilin- & Soda-Fabrik A.-G., British Patent 858,184, (by J. Eisele, W. Federkiel, G. Lange, G. Krehbiel, and H. W. Stein), Jan. 11, 1961.
60. Badische Anilin- & Soda-Fabrik A.-G., British Patent 862,318 (by G. Lange), Mar. 8, 1961; *Chem. Abstr.*, **55**, 22839c (1961).
61. Frey, W., U. S. Patent 2,779,772 (to Saul and Co.), Jan. 29, 1957; *Chem. Abstr.*, **51**, 4724b (1957).
62. CIBA Ltd., British Patent 848,742, Sept. 21, 1960; *Chem. Abstr.*, **55**, 11872h (1961).
63. Sandoz S. A., Belgian Patent 584,832, Mar. 16, 1960; *Derwent Belgian Patents Rept.*, **63B**, A 12, Apr. 22, 1960.
64. Stahel, P., K. Seitz, and H. Riat, German Patent 1,083,779 (to CIBA Ltd.), June 23, 1960; through *Chem. Abstr.*, **55**, 21607a (1961).
65. Kitao, T., N. Kuroki, and K. Konishi, *Kogyo Kagaku Zasshi*, **63**, 133 (1960); *Chem. Abstr.*, **56**, 13050a (1962).
66. Clingestein, H., and K. Dobmaier, U. S. Patent 2,019,844 (to General Aniline Works), Nov. 5, 1935; *Chem. Abstr.*, **30**, 1574[5] (1936).
67. Kvalnes, D. E., U. S. Patent 2,374,157 (to E. I. du Pont de Nemours and Co.), Apr. 17, 1945; *Chem. Abstr.*, **39**, 5502[4] (1945).
68. Schwander, H. R., J. P. Jung, and P. Hindermann, U. S. Patent 2,975,167 (to J. R. Geigy A.-G.), Mar. 14, 1961; *Chem. Abstr.*, **55**, 15940g (1961).
69. Kitao, T., N. Kuroki, and K. Konishi, *Bull. Univ. Osaka Prefect.*, **7A**, 85 (1959) (in English); *Chem. Abstr.*, **54**, 25836c (1960).
70. Badische Anilin- & Soda-Fabrik A.-G., British Patent 831,371, Mar. 30, 1960; *Chem. Abstr.*, **54**, 20228e (1960).
71. CIBA Ltd., British Patent 868,026, May 17, 1961; *Chem. Abstr.*, **55**, 27908b (1961).
72. Badische Anilin- & Soda-Fabrik A.-G., Belgian Patent 585,005, May 25, 1960; *Derwent Belgian Patents Rept.*, **66A**, C19, July 15, 1960.
73. Imperial Chemical Industries, Ltd., British Patent 854,962 (by G. Booth and F. Hall), Nov. 23, 1960; *Chem. Abstr.*, **55**, 11872a (1961).
74. Imperial Chemical Industries, Ltd., Belgian Patent 581,359, Feb. 1960; *Derwent Belgian Patents Rept.*, **62B**, C22, May 4, 1960.
75. Guthrie, J. D. (to the United States of America), U. S. Patent 2,741,532, Apr. 10, 1956; *Chem. Abstr.*, **50**, 11681f (1956).
76. Tanabe, K., and A. Nasuno, *Sen-i Gakkaishi*, **16**, 235 (1960); *J. Soc. Dyers Colourists*, **76**, 608 (1960); *Chem. Abstr.*, **54**, 13669a (1960).
77. Imperial Chemical Industries, Ltd., British Patent 852,911 (by R. Price and C. E. Vellins), Nov. 2, 1960; *Chem. Abstr.*, **55**, 22851d (1961).
78. Farbenfabriken Bayer A.-G., Belgian Patent 598,651 Apr. 14, 1961; *Derwent Belgian Patents Rept.*, **76B**, A19, June 30, 1961.
79. Imperial Chemical Industries, Ltd., British Patent 882,001 (by A. H. Berrie, G. Booth, and I. Durham), Nov. 8, 1961; *Chem. Abstr.*, **56**, 8962h (1962).
80. Anon., *Textile World*, **111** (12), 79 (1961).
81. Benz, J., L. Schneider, and H. Siegrist, U. S. Patent 3,035,043 (to Sandoz Ltd.), May 15, 1962.

82. Scott, D. F., and T. Vickerstaff, *J. Soc. Dyers Colourists,* **76,** 104 (1960). *Chem. Abstr.,* **55,** 21595a (1961).
83. Imperial Chemical Industries, Ltd., British Patent 833,832 (by V. Boyd and C. H. Reece), May 4, 1960.
84. Boyd, V., and C. H. Reece, U. S. Patent 2,989,548 (to Imperial Chemical Industries, Ltd.), June 20, 1961; *Chem. Abstr.,* **55,** 22848i (1961).
85. Atkinson, J. R., G. Booth, E. L. Johnson, W. P. Mills, and Imperial Chemical Industries, Ltd., British Patent 856,899, Dec. 21, 1960; *Chem. Abstr.,* **55,** 13862i (1961).
86. Imperial Chemical Industries, Ltd., British Patent 855,715 (by J. R. Atkinson, P. W. Barker, G. Booth, and E. L. Johnson), Dec. 7, 1960; *Chem. Abstr.,* **55,** 11863i (1961).
87. Imperial Chemical Industries, Ltd., British Patent 868,468 (by J. R. Atkinson, P. W. Barker, G. Booth, and E. L. Johnson), May 17, 1961.
88. Imperial Chemical Industries, Ltd., (by B. N. Parsons and E. Waters), British Patent 875,106, May 8, 1959; *Chem. Abstr.,* **56,** 3686a (1962).
89. Imperial Chemical Industries, Ltd., British Patent 877,666 (by B. N. Parsons and E. Waters), Sept. 20, 1961; *Chem. Abstr.,* **56,** 8963h (1962).
90. Imperial Chemical Industries, Ltd., British Patent 802,935 (by C. H. Reece, R. N. Heslop, and F. Lodge), Oct. 15, 1958; *Chem. Abstr.,* **53,** 7611b (1959).
91. Imperial Chemical Industries, Ltd., British Patent 833,396 (by R. Baker, H. R. Hadfield, E. L. Johnson, and W. E. Stephen), Apr. 21, 1960; *Chem. Abstr.,* **55,** 3077i (1961); corresponds to U. S. Patent 2,964,520, Dec. 13, 1960.
92. Imperial Chemical Industries, Ltd., British Patent 825,377 (by R. Baker, H. R. Hadfield, E. L. Johnson, and W. E. Stephen), Dec. 6, 1959; *Chem. Abstr.,* **54,** 11495h (1960); corresponds to U. S. Patent 2,953,560, Sept. 20, 1960.
93. Sandoz S. A., Belgian Patent 595,565, Jan. 16, 1961; *Derwent Belgian Patents Rept.,* **73B,** A24, Mar. 24, 1961.
94. Lecher, H. Z., R. P. Parker, and C. M. Hofmann, U. S. Patent 2,436,697 (to American Cyanamid Co.), Feb. 24, 1948; *Chem. Abstr.,* **42,** 3969e (1948).
95. Parker, R. P., and C. M. Hofmann, U. S. Patent 2,427,995 (to American Cyanamid Co.), Sept. 23, 1947; *Chem. Abstr.,* **42,** 375i (1948).
96. Lecher, H. Z., R. P. Parker, and C. M. Hofmann, U. S. Patent 2,437,644 (to American Cyanamid Co.), Mar. 9, 1948; *Chem. Abstr.,* **42,** 6125f (1948).
97. Imperial Chemical Industries, Ltd., Belgian Patent 592,883, Jan. 12, 1961; *Derwent Belgian Patents Rept.,* **73A,** C24, Mar. 22, 1961.
98. Imperial Chemical Industries, Ltd., British Patent 879,263 (by P. W. Barker), Oct. 11, 1961; *Chem. Abstr.,* **57,** 8698e (1962).
99. Imperial Chemical Industries Ltd., British Patent 868,471 (by B. McKnight and F. H. Slinger), May 17, 1961; *Chem. Abstr.,* **56,** 1567a (1962).
100. Bolliger, H., Canadian Patent 595,979 (to CIBA Ltd.), Apr. 12, 1960.
101. Bolliger, H., U. S. Patent 2,799,673 (to CIBA Ltd.), July 16, 1957; *Chem. Abstr.,* **51,** 17179g (1957).
102. Bolliger, H., U. S. Patent 2,766,231 (to CIBA Ltd.), Oct. 9, 1956; *Chem. Abstr.,* **51,** 3148c (1957).
103. Knight, A. H., U. S. Patent 2,384,749 (to Imperial Chemical Industries, Ltd.), Sept. 11, 1945; *Chem. Abstr.,* **40,** 2992[4] (1946).
104. Sandoz S. A., Belgian Patent 594,910, Jan. 2, 1961; *Derwent Belgian Patents Rept.,* **73A,** A13, Mar. 22, 1961.

105. Imperial Chemical Industries, Ltd., Belgian Patent 587,423, Aug. 1960; *Derwent Belgian Patents Rept.*, **68B**, C17, Oct. 18, 1960.
106. Imperial Chemical Industries, Ltd., British Patent 835,819 (by F. Lodge), May 25, 1960; *Chem. Abstr.*, **55**, 3076d (1961).
107. Suckfull, F., and H. Haubrick, German Patent 1,008,313 (to Farbenfabriken Bayer A.-G.), May 16, 1957; *Chem. Zentr.*, **129**, 1990 (1958).
108. Imperial Chemical Industries, Ltd., British Patent 862,269 (by G. Booth, G. T. Douglas, J. S. Hunter, and E. L. Johnson), Mar. 8, 1961.
109. CIBA S. A., Belgian Patent 594,666, Mar. 2, 1961; *Derwent Belgian Patents Rept.*, **75B**, C2, June 2, 1961.
110. Sarantis, E. N., et al., *Am. Dyestuff Reptr.*, **49**, 810 (1960); *Chem. Abstr.*, **55**, 999a (1961).
111. Rattee, I. D., *J. Soc. Dyers Colourists*, **78**, 69 (1962).
112. Bohnert, E., *J. Soc. Dyers Colourists*, **75**, 581 (1959); *Chem. Abstr.*, **54**, 6131f (1960).
113. Wegmann, J., *Textil-Praxis*, **13**, 1056 (1958); *Chem. Abstr.*, **53**, 6621a (1959).
114. Zollinger, H., *Angew. Chem.*, **73**, 125 (1961); *Chem. Abstr.*, **55**, 8864h (1961).
115. Vickerstaff, T., *J. Soc. Dyers Colourists*, **73**, 237 (1957); *Chem. Abstr.*, **51**, 12495h (1957).
116. Chitale, A. G., and A. Y. Kulkarni, *J. Textile. Inst. Trans.*, **51**, 484 (1960); *Chem. Abstr.*, **55**, 8869f (1961).
117. Ulrich, P., *Teintex*, **24**, 237 (1959); *Melliand Textilber.*, **41**, 86 (1960); see also *Chem. Abstr.*, **53**, 17517b (1959).
118. Vickerstaff, T., *Textil-Rundschau*, **13**, 267 (1958).
119. Wegmann, J., *Melliand Textilber.*, **39**, 1006 (1958); *Chem. Abstr.*, **53**, 721f (1959).
120. Schwertassek, K., *Faserforsch. Textiltech.*, **9**, 321 (1958); *J. Textile Inst. Abstr.*, **50**, 280 (1959); *Chem. Abstr.*, **53**, 10769b (1959).
121. Manchester, F., *J. Soc. Dyers Colourists*, **74**, 421 (1958); *Chem. Abstr.*, **52**, 12405e (1958).
122. Osterloh, F., *Melliand Textilber.*, **41**, 1533 (1960); *Chem. Abstr.*, **55**, 8868g (1961).
123. Warren, J., J. D. Reid, and C. Hamalainen, *Textile Res. J.*, **22**, 584 (1952).
124. Krazer, B., and H. Zollinger, *Helv. Chim. Acta*, **43**, 1513 (1960); *Chem. Abstr.*, **55**, 17013b (1961).
125. Oldham, J. W. H., and J. K. Rutherford, *J. Am. Chem. Soc.*, **54**, 366 (1932).
126. Osterloh, F., *Textil-Praxis*, **15**, 734 (1960); *J. Textile Inst. Abstr.*, **51**, A512 (1960).
127. Virnik, A. D., and M. A. Chekalin, *Tekhnol. Tekstil'n. Prom.*, **1960**, No. 6, 109; *J. Soc. Dyers Colourists*, **77**, 463 (1961).
128. Bohnert, E., and R. Weingerten, *Melliand Textilber.*, **40**, 1036 (1959); *Chem. Abstr.*, **54**, 903f (1960).
129. Elöd, E., and Y. Nakahara, *Melliand Textilber.*, **41**, 567 (1960); *Chem. Abstr.*, **54**, 16838d (1960).
130. Preston, C., and A. S. Fern, *Chimia (Aarau)*, **15**, 177 (1961).
131. Sumner, H. H., *Dyer*, **123**, 29 (1960); *Chem. Abstr.*, **54**, 9299d (1960).
132. Sumner, H. H., *J. Roy. Inst. Chem.*, **84**, 389 (1960).
133. Sumner, H. H., *J. Soc. Dyers Colourists*, **76**, 672 (1960); *Chem. Abstr.*, **55**, 5960c (1961).

134. Vickerstaff, T., *Melliand Textilber.*, **39**, 905 (1958); *Chem. Abstr.*, **52**, 19145e (1958).
135. Vickerstaff, T., *Am. Dyestuff Reptr.*, **47**, 33 (1958); *Chem. Abstr.*, **54**, 10329e (1960).
136. von der Eltz, H. V., and F. Osterloh, *Melliand Textilber.*, **40**, 1443 (1959); *Chem. Abstr.*, **54**, 5093e (1960).
137. Weston, C. D., *Hexagon Digest*, **25**, 3 (1957) (Imperial Chemical Industries, Ltd.).
138. Vickerstaff, T., *Dyer*, **126**, 166 (1961); *Am. Dyestuff Reptr.*, **50** (22), 22 (1961).
139. Einsele, U., *Melliand Textilber.*, **42**, 427 (1961); *Chem. Abstr.*, **55**, 14921f (1961).
140. Rath, H., and M. Passler, *Melliand Textilber.*, **42**, 789 (1961); *Chem. Abstr.*, **55**, 22835f (1961).
141. Stamm, O. A., H. Zollinger, H. Zähner, and E. Gäumann, *Helv. Chim. Acta*, **44**, 1123 (1961); *Chem. Abstr.*, **56**, 1629a (1962).
142. Bohnert, E., *Melliand Textilber.*, **42**, 1156 (1961); *Chem. Abstr.*, **56**, 7533a (1962).
143. Chekalin, M. A., *Textil'n. Prom.*, **21**, 40 (1961); *Chem. Abstr.*, **55**, 20439c (1961).
144. Fox, M. R., *Am. Dyestuff Reptr.*, **47**, 413 (1958); *Chem. Abstr.*, **52**, 12404e (1958).
145. Dawson, T. L., *J. Soc. Dyers Colourists*, **74**, 584 (1958).
146. Dawson, T. L., A. S. Fern, and C. Preston, *J. Soc. Dyers Colourists*, **76**, 210 (1960); *Chem. Abstr.*, **54**, 14695g (1960).
147. Bogoslovskii, B. M., A. D. Virnik, and M. A. Chekalin, *Izv. Vysshikh Uchebn. Zavedenii Tekhnol. Legkoi Prom., No.* **4**, 80 (1960); *J. Soc. Dyers Colourists*, **77**, 229 (1961); *Chem. Abstr.*, **55**, 997i (1961).
148. Virnik, A. D., and M. A. Chekalin, *Zhur. Vses. Khim. Obshchestva im. D. I. Mendeleeva*, **6**, 236 (1961); *Chem. Abstr.*, **55**, 18114i (1961).
149. Fierz-David, H., and M. Matter, *J. Soc. Dyers Colourists*, **53**, 424 (1937); *Chem. Abstr.*, **32**, 783[2] (1938).
150. Gardner, T. S., and C. B. Purves, *J. Am. Chem. Soc.*, **64**, 1539 (1942).
151. Norris, J. F., and A. A. Ashdown, *J. Am. Chem. Soc.*, **47**, 837 (1925).
152. Ackermann, H., and P. Dussy, *Melliand Textilber.*, **42**, 1167 (1961); *Chem. Abstr.*, **56**, 7929g (1962).
153. Daruwalla, E. H., and P. Subramaniam, *J. Soc. Dyers Colourists*, **74**, 296 (1958); *Chem. Abstr.*, **52**, 10586h (1958).
154. Ref. 4, pp. 100–103.
155. Ref. 4, p. 231ff.
156. Neale, S. M., *J. Textile Inst.*, **20**, T373 (1929); *Chem. Abstr.*, **24**, 3110 (1930).
157. Danckwerts, P. V., *Trans. Faraday Soc.*, **46**, 300 (1950).
158. Rattee, I. D., *Endeavour*, **20**, 154 (1961); *Chem. Abstr.*, **55**, 22834g (1961).
159. Ref. 4, p. 160.
160. Ref. 4, p. 214.
161. Ref. 4, p. 215ff.
162. Berliner, E., and L. C. Monack, *J. Am. Chem. Soc.*, **74**, 1574 (1952).
163. Luttringhaus, H., *Am. Dyestuff Reptr.*, **50**, 248 (1961); *Chem. Abstr.*, **55**, 11855h (1961).
164. Wegmann, J., *J. Soc. Dyers Colourists*, **76**, 205 (1960); *Chem. Abstr.*, **54**, 14695f (1960).
165. Zollinger, H., in *Review of Textile Progress*, Vol. 11, Butterworths, London, 1960, p. 215.

166. Zollinger, H., *Am. Dyestuff Reptr.*, **49**, 142 (1960); *Chem. Abstr.*, **54**, 9301g (1960).
167. Zollinger, H., *Chimia* (*Aarau*), **15**, 186 (1961).
168. Mur, V. I., Zh. A. Gorbunova, and A. I. Korolev, *Zh. Vses. Khim. Obshchestva im. D. I. Mendeleeva*, **6**, 586 (1961); *Chem. Abstr.*, **56**, 10328e (1962).
169. Benz, J., *J. Soc. Dyers Colourists*, **77**, 734 (1961); *Chem. Abstr.*, **56**, 15633i (1962).
170. Panchartek, J., Z. J. Allan and J. Poshocil, *Collection Czech. Chem. Commun.*, **27**, 268–75 (1962); *Chem. Abstr.*, **57**, 2369a (1962).
171. Randall, D. I., S. A. Buc, and H. B. Freyermuth, U. S. Patent 3,094,516 (to General Aniline & Film, Inc.), June 18, 1963.
172. Heyna, J., O. Hensel, and W. Schnorrenberg, U. S. Patent 2,728,762 (to Farbwerke Hoechst A.-G.), Dec. 27, 1955; corresponds to German Patent 925,121, Mar. 14, 1955; *Chem. Abstr.*, **50**, 4520d (1956).
173. Heyna, J., A. Carl, and H. D. Wagner, U. S. Patent, 2,784,204 (to Farbwerke Hoechst A.-G.), Mar. 5, 1957; *Chem. Abstr.*, **51**, 13407g (1957).
174. Heyna, J., K. Sommer, A. Siebert, and K. Berner, U. S. Patent 3,008,950 (to Farbwerke Hoechst A.-G.), Nov. 14, 1961; *Chem. Abstr.*, **56**, 11757a (1962).
175. Heyna, J., and W. Schumacher, U. S. Patent 2,743,267 (to Farbwerke Hoechst A.-G.), Apr. 24, 1956; *Chem. Abstr.*, **50**, 13453c (1956).
176. Heyna, J., and W. Schumacher, U. S. Patent 2,657,205 (to Farbwerke Hoechst A.-G.), Oct. 27, 1953; *Chem. Abstr.*, **48**, 3037i (1954).
177. Gold, H., and S. Petersen, U. S. Patent 2,764,583 (to Farbenfabriken Bayer A.-G.), Sept. 25, 1956; *Chem. Abstr.*, **51**, 4447a (1957).
178. Fasciati, A., R. Gunst, H. Riat, and K. Seitz, U. S. Patent 2,945,021 (to CIBA Ltd.), July 12, 1960; *Chem. Abstr.*, **56**, 8885i (1962).
179. Fasciati, A., R. Gunst, H. Riat, and K. Seitz, U. S. Patent 2,945,022 (to CIBA Ltd.), July 12, 1960; *Chem. Abstr.*, **55**, 22843d (1961).
180. Imperial Chemical Industries, Ltd., British Patent 838,338 (by H. T. Howard, F. H. Slinger, and J. Wardleworth), June 22, 1960; *Chem. Abstr.*, **55**, 3078e (1961).
181. Stäuble, M., U. S. Patent 2,949,467 (to CIBA Ltd.), Aug. 16, 1960; *Chem. Abstr.*, **55**, 4975a (1961).
182. Stephen, W. E., U. S. Patent 2,892,828 (to Imperial Chemical Industries, Ltd.) June 30, 1959; corresponds to British Patent 785,120, Oct. 23, 1957; *Chem. Abstr.*, **52**, 3353i (1958).
183. Menzi, K., F. Oesterlein, and B. Ruetimeyer, U. S. Patent 2,929,809 (to CIBA Ltd.), Mar. 22, 1960; *Chem. Abstr.*, **54**, 16846h (1960).
184. Heslop, R. N., U. S. Patent 2,907,762 (to Imperial Chemical Industries, Ltd.), Oct. 6, 1959; corresponds to British Patent 772,030, Apr. 10, 1957; *Chem. Abstr.*, **51**, 13406h (1957).
185. CIBA Ltd., British Patent 849,115, Sept. 21, 1960; *Chem. Abstr.*, **56**, 1561g (1962).
186. Oesterlein, F., U. S. Patent 2,943,085 (to CIBA Ltd.), June 28, 1960; *Chem. Abstr.*, **55**, 3995h (1961).

Chapter XVI

CHEMICAL FINISHING OF CELLULOSIC FIBERS

W. A. Reeves and J. D. Guthrie

Southern Utilization Research and Development Division,
U. S. Department of Agriculture

For centuries, cellulosic textile fibers such as cotton have been scoured, bleached, mercerized, and dyed, but these processes do not necessarily involve formation of stable primary valence bonds between the chemical compounds used and the cellulose. It is only recently that much scientific or commercial interest has been shown in chemical processes in which the reactant combines with the cellulose by primary valence bonds, or in some instances forms polymers within the fibers. The purpose of this chapter is to describe some of these processes, to indicate some of the physical and chemical changes that they produce, and to relate these to useful properties such as flame resistance, heat stability, crease resistance, and resistance to microorganisms. In general, only those processes that impart durable changes that are not removed by laundering are included.

A. SMOOTH-DRYING AND CREASE-RESISTANT FABRICS

Chemical finishes that impart improved smooth-drying and crease-resistant properties to cellulosic fabrics have been developed during the past 30 years. The ultimate goal of this type of finish is to produce fabrics for household and especially apparel items that dry smooth after laundering and remain free of wrinkles during use. The goal has not been reached, but considerable progress has been made. It is probable that more research and development have been done in this area during the past 15 years than in any other concerned with finishing of cellulosic fabrics. This research has enabled fabrics of cotton and rayon to compete favorably with newer synthetic fabrics having a natural tendency to dry smooth and resist wrinkling. The use of these finishes led to the consumption of over one million bales of cotton during 1961 that would not have been used otherwise.

1. Theoretical Concepts

The various kinds of cellulosic fibers are similar in that they are made up of long chain molecules of cellulose. In most cases the molecules are closely associated into small groups known as microfibrils. In the case of the cotton fiber, these microfibrils are about 0.015 μ wide and perhaps one third as thick. In addition, the naturally occurring fibers, such as cotton, can be separated into concentric lamellae that are about 0.1 μ thick and are apparently continuous throughout the length of the fiber (1). These lamellae are made of about five layers of microfibrils.

Slippage or relative movement between the cellulose chains or between the larger structural units of the fibers occurs when a bending force of sufficient magnitude is placed upon the fiber in a fabric. Secondary valence bonding forces present in the fiber tend to resist or prevent the slippage but once it occurs the secondary valence forces re-form in new locations and then tend to maintain the fiber or the fabric in the bent or wrinkled condition. Thus, in order to produce smooth-drying and wrinkle-resistant fabrics it is necessary to stabilize the structural components of the fiber. Stabilization is accomplished by crosslinking cellulose chains. The crosslinks are generally made through primary valence bonds, though secondary or hydrogen bonds may contribute.

Crosslinking has been generally accepted as the factor responsible for crease recovery and smooth-drying properties. There is good evidence that crosslinks of covalent bonds are responsible for the major portion of the crease recovery imparted by the commercially used chemical finishes. These finishes make use of compounds which are di- or polyfunctional with respect to reaction with cellulose. Monofunctional compounds that are closely related to them impart little or no conditioned crease recovery when reacted with cellulosic fibers under similar conditions. Those polyfunctional reagents that form bonds with cellulose that are resistant to alkaline hydrolysis make the fibers insoluble in cuprammonium hydroxide. This is a good indication of crosslinking, especially when the low degree of reaction used for these finishes is taken into consideration. Crosslinks of hydrogen bonds can contribute to crease recovery. The increase in hydrogen bonding caused by drying an air-equilibrated fabric is shown by a significant increase in the crease recovery of the fabric.

Other factors also influence the properties of crease recovery and smooth drying of cellulosic fabrics. Perhaps the most important of these is the moisture content of the fabric or state of swelling of the fiber at the time crosslinking covalent bonds are formed. If a fabric is in a relatively dry or collapsed state at the time the crosslinks are formed, the resultant fabric will exhibit both conditioned and wet crease recovery. On the other hand, if the fabric is wet or swollen at the time the crosslinks are formed, the fabric may exhibit little or no increased conditioned crease recovery but can exhibit crease recovery when wet (2). The state of swelling at the time of crosslinking does not alter significantly the line drying properties which are more closely related to wet crease recovery. The above statements are true especially for cotton fabrics reacted with sufficient crosslinking reagent to produce on the average up to one crosslink in about 20 anhydroglucose units.

2. Test Methods

Several related methods for determining crease recovery are in use, and additional ones are being suggested (3–7). A general description of the methods follows. A rectangular fabric specimen not more than 1 × 2 in. is creased by folding. A weight of about 500 g., but ranging from 400 to 2000 g., is placed upon the creased fabric to cause a bending strain of up to 100%. The strain is maintained for about 5 min. and is then released. The amount the fabric recovers in 5 min. is referred to as the crease recovery. Most emphasis has been placed upon determining the crease recovery of fabrics conditioned in an atmosphere of 65% relative humidity and 70°F. Values obtained under these conditions are generally referred to as dry or conditioned crease recovery. During recent years considerable significance has been attached to the crease recovery values obtained by testing fabrics while they are completely wet. These values are generally referred to as wet crease recovery.

Other test methods provide information on the smooth-drying properties of fabrics (8–10). One of these tests was developed by a committee of American Association of Textile Chemists and Colorists and is used extensively (10). It is carried out on square 15 × 15 in. samples after they have been laundered and dried. The test specimens are compared with standard fabrics or three-dimensional replicas of standard fabrics while they are illuminated by a light striking at a low angle. The standards have varying degrees of wrinkling. Fabrics equivalent to a freshly ironed sample with essentially no wrinkles receive a rating of 5. A rating of 3 is moderately good and a rating of 1 is very poor.

3. Crosslinking Agents

The finisher of today has many crosslinking agents from which to choose. They vary considerably in chemical constitution but are similar in that they are water-soluble and of low molecular size so that they can penetrate the cellulosic fibers. These agents may be monomeric compounds or very low molecular weight polymers. They have two or more groups that are reactive with cellulosic hydroxyls, especially at elevated temperatures and under the influence of catalysts.

The crosslinking agents are generally reacted with cotton and other cellulosic fabrics by a very rapid process. The most common procedure is known as the pad, dry, and cure process. In this process the fabric is padded or wet-out in a solution containing the crosslinking agent, a catalyst, usually a softener, and often a number of other auxiliary chemicals. The wet fabric is dried and cured. Drying time is about 1 min. at about 100°C., and curing time about 1–2 min. at 145–165°C. There is generally little or no reaction between the cellulose and the crosslinker during the drying step. Most of the reaction occurs during the curing.

Newer application techniques are in limited use. One of these is called wet process, because the crosslinking agent reacts with the cellulose while the fiber is wet. The fiber may be wet with either a swelling or nonswelling liquid.

The crosslinking reaction can occur with hydroxyls on different molecules of cellulose or with the hydroxyls on the same molecule. Its effectiveness in imparting crease resistance is dependent chiefly upon the extent of intermolecular crosslinking. Some polymerization of the crosslinking agent generally occurs inside the fiber as well as on its surface. Surface resin imparts stiffness to the fiber. The average crosslink produced by reacting dimethylolurea with cotton by the pad, dry, and cure process contains about two urea groups. Dimethylolethyleneurea produces crosslinks that contain on the average 1.5 ethyleneurea groups. It is difficult to produce water-insoluble polymers from dimethylolethyleneurea. Other crosslinking agents, especially the amidomethylol compounds, probably also form crosslinks that contain dimer and polymer units as well as single unit crosslinks.

a. Amidomethylol Finishing Agents

The crosslinking agents formed by reacting formaldehyde with amido compounds are currently the most important group of compounds for producing crease resistance and smooth drying. These agents are generally inexpensive, easily produced, and stable for long periods in aqueous solution; many of them impart very good crease resistance and smooth-drying properties to cellulosic fabrics.

Since reaction between amidomethylol compounds and cellulose takes place at a very slow rate with heat when uncatalyzed, catalysts are always used to assure adequate reaction during the short cure period. The catalysts are generally either protonic or Lewis acids, although bases may be used with certain compounds of this group. The amidomethylol compounds are more easily catalyzed than most of the other crosslinking agents to be described. The acidic catalysts may be free acids, such as lactic, tartaric, or formic, but in most cases they are latent Lewis acids, such as magnesium chloride and zinc nitrate. The following common catalysts are arranged in approximate order of increasing effectiveness: ammonium phosphate, ammonium sulfate, amine hydrochloride, magnesium chloride, zinc nitrate, and zinc fluoborate.

The amount of these amidomethylol crosslinking agents that must be attached to the fabric to produce rather significant improvements in the fabric properties is about 5% of the fabric weight for cotton and about 10% for rayon. The differences in the required amount added is generally thought to be related to the higher ratio of amorphous to crystalline cellulose in rayon.

(1) Ureas

The methylolureas were among the first crosslinking agents to be used to impart crease resistance. The reaction of dimethylolurea (I) with cellulose can be used to illustrate the crosslinking reaction between amidomethylol compounds and cellulose:

$$\underset{\text{(I)}}{HO{-}CH_2{-}\overset{\displaystyle H}{\overset{|}{N}}{-}\overset{\displaystyle O}{\overset{\|}{C}}{-}\overset{\displaystyle H}{\overset{|}{N}}{-}CH_2{-}OH} + Cell{-}OH \xrightarrow{H^+}$$

$$Cell{-}O{-}\left(CH_2{-}\overset{\displaystyle H}{\overset{|}{N}}{-}\overset{\displaystyle O}{\overset{\|}{C}}{-}\overset{\displaystyle H}{\overset{|}{N}}\right)_n{-}CH_2{-}OCell + H_2O \quad (1)$$

The methylolureas are often methylated with acidified methanol to produce methoxymethylureas, such as bismethoxymethylurea (II), to retard polymerization of the aqueous agents before use and during reaction with cellulose. In the presence of acid catalysts at elevated temperatures the

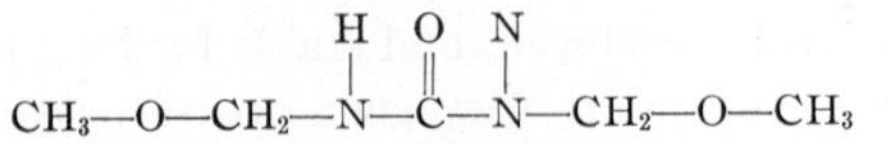

(II)

methoxy derivative regenerates the cellulose-reactive methylolurea.

Other methylol- and methoxymethylureas are produced and used. Products containing as low as 1.3 moles of formaldehyde per mole of urea are used to impart special effects. The trisubstituted ureas are said to exist. The methylol- and the methoxymethylureas are usually reacted with cellulose through acid catalysis; however, these crosslinking agents may also be catalyzed with bases, such as sodium carbonate, although industry has never practiced this extensively.

(2) Cyclic Alkyleneureas

These tetrasubstituted *N,N'*-urea derivatives have been used to a considerable extent by the industry to produce crease-resistant cottons. A typical example of this group is 1,3-bis(hydroxymethyl)-2-imidazolidinone (III), better known as dimethylolethyleneurea. These com-

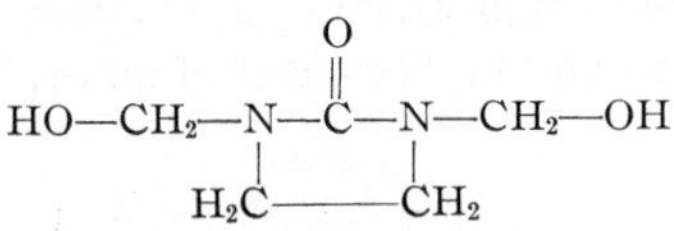

(III)

pounds have a greater tendency to react with cellulose than to polymerize since they do not contain reactive amido hydrogens. During acid-catalyzed reactions with cellulose some of the methylol groups are lost, but rarely enough to form water-insoluble polymers as is often the case with the methylolureas. Other crosslinking agents of this group are: 1,3-bis(methoxymethyl)-2-imidazolidinone, 1,3-bis(hydroxymethyl)-4,5-dihydroxy-2-imidazolidinone, 1,3-bis(hydroxymethyl)tetrahydro-2(1-*H*)-pyrimidinone, and 1,3-bis(hydroxymethyl)tetrahydro-5-hydroxy-2(1-*H*)-pyrimidinone.

(3) Triazones

Compounds having the basic chemical structure (IV) are commonly referred to as triazones. In structure IV, R is an alkyl or substituted alkyl group; it is most commonly an ethyl or hydroxyethyl group. The tertiary nitrogen in these compounds makes them substantially different from the compounds discussed earlier in this section. Larger amounts of acid

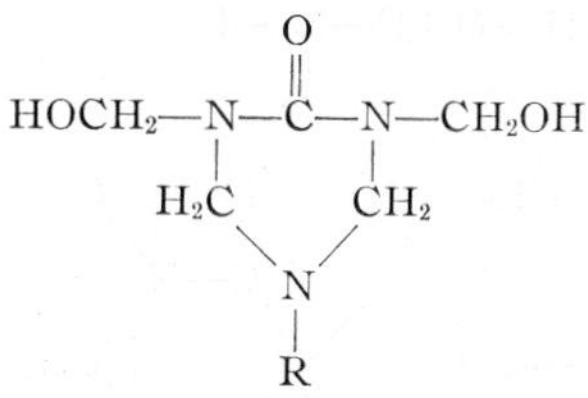

(IV)

1,3-Bis(hydroxymethyl)-tetrahydro-5-R-*sym*-triazin-2(1*H*)-one

catalyst are needed to promote reaction with cellulose because the catalyst is partially neutralized by the basic amine group. The tertiary nitrogen helps to prevent loss in strength when the fabric is bleached with hypochlorite and subsequently ironed. It apparently neutralizes the acid resulting from chloramide decomposition. During the bleaching process the hypochlorite reacts with NH groups which are usually available to a small extent in amidomethylol finishes. Heat decomposes the chloramide through a free radical mechanism. The chlorine radical extracts a proton from some available source, and then the resulting hydrochloric acid attacks the cellulose hydrolytically if it is not taken from the system by a tertiary amine group or other means.

(4) Uron

The preparations sold commercially as dimethylol uron (V) apparently are a mixture of products. The commercial products tend to split off

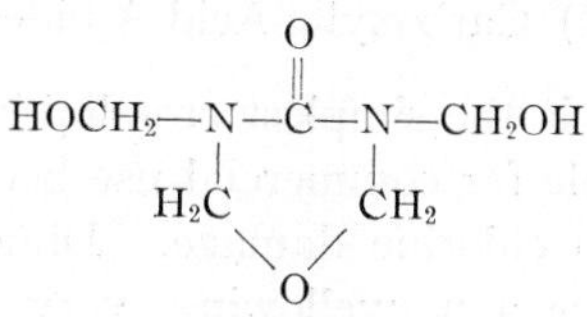

(V)

formaldehyde when reacted with cellulosic fabrics resulting in a finish that has poor resistance to acid hydrolysis, but if freshly distilled uron is methylolated and reacted with cotton the finish has comparatively greater resistance to acid. It is not known what material is present in the commercial product that makes this difference.

(5) Triazines

The methylol and the methoxymethyl derivatives of melamine form a group of finishing agents known as triazines. A typical representative

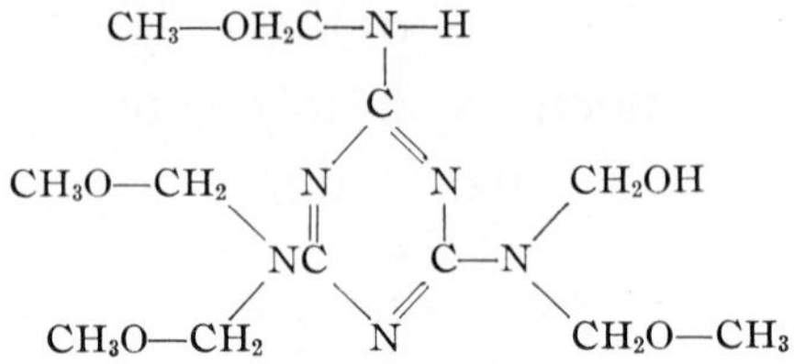

(VI)

of this group is tetramethoxymethylmethylolmelamine (VI). The compounds of this group containing low ratios of formaldehyde to triazine, such as trimethylolmelamine, produce finishes that yellow when exposed to sodium hypochlorite. The chromophore apparently results from the formation of dichloramides (—NCl_2). Aqueous solutions of the methylolmelamines containing low ratios of formaldehyde have a strong tendency to form insoluble polymer at the same time reaction with cellulose occurs.

(6) Carbamates

The carbamates are a newer group of crosslinking agents. One of the earliest of these to be suggested for commercial use is the *N,N*-dimethylol tetramethylene biscarbamate. A more recently announced group, the alkyl monocarbamates, especially ethyl and methyl carbamate, appear to have greater potential (11). These monocarbamates react with two moles of formaldehyde to form *N,N*-dimethylol derivatives.

(7) Carboxylic Acid Amides

Dimethylolformamide is the simplest crosslinking agent of this group, although it is not suitable for commercial use because the fabric finished with it is susceptible to chlorine damage. Dimethyloladipamide reacts with cellulose to produce a nonyellowing, very durable finish. A particularly good amide crosslinker is tris(*N*-hydroxymethyl carbamoylethyl)-amine (12). Because of the tertiary nitrogen, care must be taken to assure proper catalysis for reaction with cellulose. Either the system is acidified before the latent acid catalyst is added or excess catalyst is added to overcome the neutralizing effect of the amine.

b. Acetals

The acetals useful in crosslinking cellulose are made by reacting formaldehyde with polyols. Typical examples are pentaerythritol bisformal (VII) and diethyleneglycol formal (VIII). Reaction of acetals with

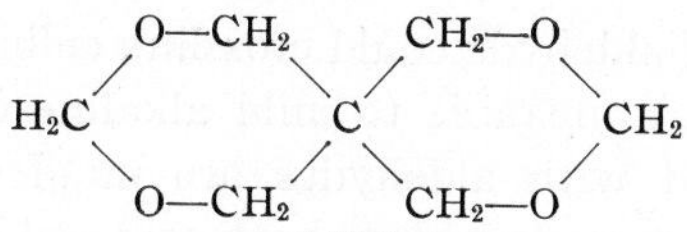

(VII)

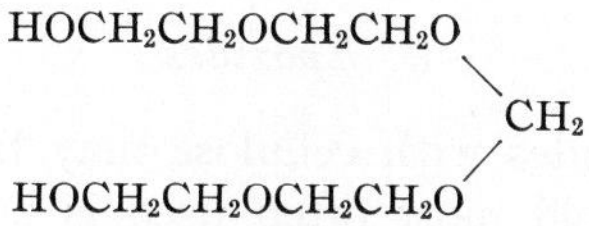

(VIII)

cellulose is acid-catalyzed. The reaction proceeds first through de-acetalization to cleave the acetal, followed by reaction with cellulose. Generally, stronger acid catalysts are needed with the acetals than with the amidomethylol compounds. A mixture of aluminum and magnesium chlorides is an effective catalyst.

c. Aldehydes

This group includes mono- and dialdehydes. Formaldehyde and glyoxal are the simplest and most studied of this group. The crosslinks produced with these compounds can be very effective in producing crease resistance and smooth-drying properties. Reaction with cellulose to form the hemiacetal proceeds rapidly, but to produce an acetal crosslink, strong acid catalysts such as magnesium chloride or zinc nitrate are required. The use of these compounds by the industry for finishing cotton has lagged because of excessive strength loss obtained by the pad, dry, cure application technique. Some have explained the excessive strength loss by the short crosslinks. Others have attributed it to the strong acidic catalysts needed to promote reaction with the cellulose. Newer techniques of application have produced fabrics with better strength but still somewhat weaker than obtained with amidomethylol compounds.

The results obtained with dialdehydes are about comparable to those obtained with formaldehyde. In both cases the stable crosslink is through a single carbon atom, as illustrated with formaldehyde and glyoxal (IX and

$$\text{Cell—O—CH}_2\text{—O—Cell}$$

(IX)

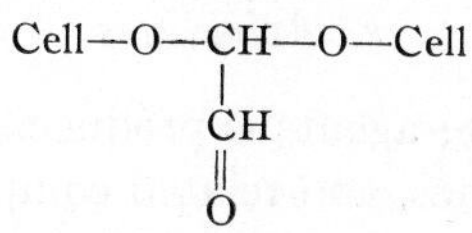

(X)

X, respectively). A dialdehyde could crosslink cellulose through hemiacetal bonds but these are unstable to mild alkaline conditions. The durable finishes produced with aldehydes are unaffected by hypochlorite bleach. They are also very durable to both acid and base hydrolysis.

d. Epoxides

The reaction of epoxides with cellulose may be catalyzed with either acids or bases. The acid most often used is zinc fluoborate. Weaker latent acid catalysts are inefficient. Sodium and potassium hydroxides are sometimes used when only wet crease recovery is desired. Typical examples of epoxides of this group are 1,3-diglycidyl glycol (XI) and vinylcyclohexene diepoxide (XII). Epichlorohydrin has been reacted

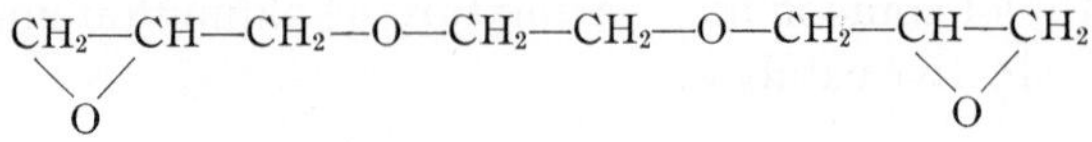

(XI)

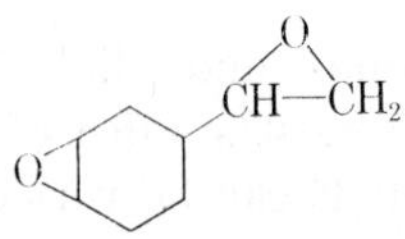

(XII)

with cotton in the presence of a strong base to produce wet crease recovery. Although it has only one epoxide group, a second can be formed under the conditions used for reaction. Similarly, 1,3- and 1,2-dichloropropanol react with cellulose. When these chlorohydrins are used commercially for imparting wet crease recovery in cotton, an amidomethylol agent is used to pretreat or aftertreat to impart dry crease recovery.

The crosslinks produced by reacting epoxides with cellulose are very durable to both acidic and basic hydrolysis. Cotton finished with epoxides can be bleached without fear of discoloration or other ill effects. Cost of the epoxides and problems in applying chlorohydrins have been the main deterrents to extensive use of these compounds in the production of wash-wear cottons.

e. Aziridines

This group of crosslinking agents is produced by reacting alkylenimines with isocyanates, acid halides, and related compounds. Typical examples are tris(1-aziridinyl)phosphine oxide (XIII), commonly referred to as

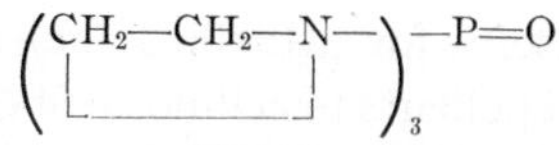

(XIII)

APO, and hexamethylenebis-*N*-*N'*-ethyleneurea (XIV). The reaction

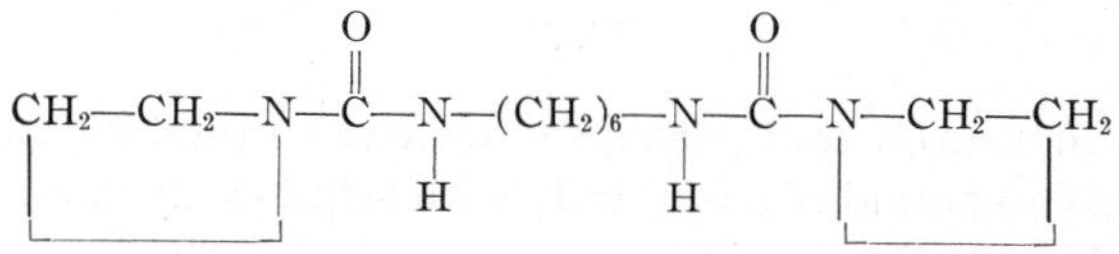

(XIV)

of these compounds with cellulose is catalyzed best with zinc fluoborate. One of the compounds of this group, APO, is very durable to acidic and basic hydrolysis and can produce extremely good crease recovery and smooth-drying properties in cotton fabrics (13). All of these compounds studied produce fabrics that yellow when exposed to hypochlorite bleaches and heated as by ironing. This essentially limits the use of these compounds to the finishing of dyed fabrics.

The aziridine ring is opened readily by acids, so that polymer formation accompanies the reaction with cellulose. Although the crosslinks produced with these compounds contain an amide group, the finishes are very resistant to acidic and basic hydrolysis.

f. Sulfone and Sulfonium-Containing Compounds

There has been considerable interest in the use of divinyl sulfone for crosslinking cellulosic fabrics, especially cotton. Since divinyl sulfone is toxic and is undesirable to handle in a finishing plant, various heat-unstable adducts of the compound have been made for this use. One of these bis(2-hydroxyethyl) sulfone (XV), which may be considered a

$$HOCH_2CH_2SO_2CH_2CH_2OH$$
(XV)

water adduct of divinyl sulfone, is used extensively. Urea, formaldehyde, phenols, alcohols, and many other compounds form heat-unstable adducts with divinyl sulfone. The adducts require an alkaline catalyst to promote decomposition and subsequent reaction with cellulose. The heat of cure causes at least partial reversal of the adduct reaction and the resulting activated olefinic group reacts with cellulose through a Michael condensation.

Since the activated olefinic group of sulfones reacts with many compounds that contain an active hydrogen, it is apparent that this group of compounds can be useful for attaching many materials, such as dyes, humectants, and water repellents to cellulosic fibers.

The disodium salt of tris(2-sulfato-ethyl)sulfonium inner salt (XVI)

$$[NaO(O)_2SOCH_2CH_2]_2\text{—}\overset{+}{S}\text{—}CH_2CH_2OS(O)_2O^-$$

(XVI)

is being used in Europe and perhaps elsewhere to produce smooth-drying fabrics. This compound reacts readily with cellulose at room temperature under strongly alkaline conditions to produce ether derivatives. In such systems, cotton is swelled at the time of crosslinking so that wet crease recovery is good, but dry recovery is poor. For this reason a second crosslinking treatment is applied to impart dry crease recovery.

4. Other Fiber and Fabric Properties Affected by Crosslinking

The strength of cellulosic fabrics is of primary importance. It is usually measured in terms of either tensile or tear strength. Crosslinking processes that produce improved dry or conditioned crease recovery cause a reduction of these properties in cotton but affect rayon differently. In the case of cotton fabrics, tensile or breaking strength is reduced about one-third when crosslinking agents are applied in sufficient quantity to produce about 240–270° crease recovery. The tear strength is usually reduced even more. Considerable research has been done seeking crosslinking agents and processing techniques that would avoid a loss in strength. The research has shown that all crosslinking agents applied by the pad, dry, cure process to impart dry or conditioned crease recovery reduce tear and tensile strength. Crosslinking agents of different lengths were included in these studies. There is an inverse linear relationship between crease recovery imparted to a fabric and per cent strength retained. This is approximately true up to the point where maximum crease recovery is obtained, but does not mean that all crosslinkers that impart a certain crease recovery (warp + filling) cause exactly the same strength loss since small differences are obtained for different crosslinking agents. These differences can usually be attributed to variation in extent of hydrolysis of the cellulose caused by different catalysts. The greatest changes in the strength/crease recovery ratio can be made by altering the process of application of crosslinking agents.

Crosslinking the cellulose molecules in rayon fabrics causes little loss in breaking strength and often even increases it as much as 20%. On the other hand, tear strength is reduced nearly as much as is observed with cotton fabrics. For some reason, rayon is less susceptible than cotton to damage caused by acidic catalysts.

Water of imbibition, moisture regain, dye uptake, and density are affected by crosslinking cellulosic fabrics. The first three of these properties are decreased when the crosslinks are formed while the fibers are in a collapsed or nonswollen condition, but are increased when the crosslinks are formed while the fibers are in a swollen condition. The density is decreased when the fibers are crosslinked under either set of conditions, but is decreased more if the fibers are crosslinked while swollen. Crosslinking increases dimensional stability and reduces permanent set of fibers and fabrics. Crosslinked fabrics shrink less when laundered. They also return more nearly to their original dimension when elongated by force.

B. FLAME-RESISTANT FINISHES

A fabric is said to be flame-resistant if it does not continue to flame when removed from the source of ignition. Such fabrics are used in garments worn in occupations involving exposure to flames or sparks, in combat clothing such as aviators' flight suits, and in tents and tarpaulins. It is a general safety requirement that draperies and upholstery used in places of assembly be flame-resistant. Flame resistance would be of value in mattress covers, bed sheets, and in certain clothing of women and children.

Cellulosic fabrics are made flame-resistant by applying chemical treatments which are classified as either nondurable or durable. The nondurable treatments are based on water-soluble compounds such as borax, boric acid, and ammonium phosphate, sulfate, or sulfamate. These are removed by laundering, and must be renewed whenever the fabric is cleaned. Emphasis in this chapter will be placed upon durable flame-retardant treatments which are based on (*a*) the chemical modification of the cellulose by etherification or esterification, and (*b*) the deposition of insoluble materials, especially polymers, in or on the fibers. The deposited material, in some instances, may form chemical bonds with the cellulose, resulting in greater durability. To be classified as durably flame-resistant, a fabric should pass the vertical flame test after a specified number and kinds of launderings. In such tests the fabric, held in a suitable frame, is exposed to a Bunsen flame of specified height for a given length of time. After removal of the flame, the time of after-flaming, the time that the char may glow, and the char length are noted. Interpretation and details of this test differ considerably in various countries (14,15).

1. Mechanism of Flame Retardancy

The effect of high temperature on cellulose is to break it down into a solid char, volatile liquids or tars and gases. The so-called tar is composed chiefly of levoglucosans, along with carbonyl and unsaturated compounds. There is considerable experimental support for the idea that flame retardants for cellulosic fibers act by catalytically promoting a dehydration reaction, altering the course of the decomposition to produce a smaller amount of inflammable volatile materials and a greater amount of solid, carbonaceous char. The ideal treatment should cause dehydration of the cellulose on heating to produce only carbon and water vapor. A current theory states that most flame retardants for cellulose are Lewis acids or are capable of forming such acids at the temperature of burning celluloses and that these act catalytically via a carbonium ion mechanism (16). It has been suggested that flame retardants act by combining with the cellulose at burning temperatures to form compounds or complexes that decompose differently and at a lower temperature than untreated cellulose (17). All known flame retardants lower the decomposition temperature of cellulose.

The glowing of the carbonaceous char after the cellulose ceases to flame must be decreased or eliminated in flame-retardant fabrics for most uses. This glowing is distinct from flaming and depends on different reactions. When carbon is oxidized, two reactions are possible.

$$C + {}^{1}/_{2}O_2 \rightarrow CO \quad \Delta H = -26.4 \text{ kcal./mole} \tag{2}$$

$$C + O_2 \rightarrow CO_2 \quad \Delta H = -94.4 \text{ kcal./mole} \tag{3}$$

A glow retardant is believed to act catalytically by favoring the first reaction so that the heat produced is insufficient to maintain the glowing. Phosphorus compounds are outstanding as anti-glow agents for cellulose (18). It is well known that carbon chars containing small amounts of phosphates or pyrophosphates are resistant to prolonged heating in air. This anti-glow action of phosphorus compounds is an important reason for their use as flame retardants for cellulose and as additives to non-phosphorus flame retardants.

2. Durable Flame-Retardant Treatments

The properties of an ideal, durable flame retardant for cellulosic fabrics are: (*a*) it should impart flame resistance and glow resistance adequate for the intended use; (*b*) it should not be removed by laundering, last for the life of the fabric, and be stable to storage, light and weather; (*c*) it should have no irritating effect on the skin, nor should it give off toxic fumes when charred; (*d*) it should add little weight to the fabric, have no adverse effect on fabric properties, and preferably improve such properties are tensile and tear strength, hand, drape, color, air permeability, and abrasion resistance; (*e*) it should be applied by use of ordinary textile finishing equipment and not be hazardous to those applying it; (*f*) it should be inexpensive. No known flame retardant meets all these ideal requirements, but some approach rather closely, and others are adequate for the particular use for which they are designed.

A flame retardant extensively used on fabric for tents and tarpaulins contains antimony oxide and chlorinated paraffins (19). The formulations used are said also to contain calcium carbonate to neutralize any hydrochloric acid that might form from the chlorinated paraffins, carbon black or other light-screening pigment, and copper naphthenate to protect against microorganism. It is applied from a hydrocarbon solvent and adds 60% or more to the weight of the fabric. Millions of yards of military fabrics were treated with this retardant during World War II. The resulting fabrics were flame-resistant, water-resistant, rot-resistant, and weather-resistant. The chief disadvantage of this type of flame retardant for its intended use is the high amount required, adding seriously to transportation requirements. The possible toxicity of the chlorinated paraffins and other components preclude its use in clothing. Canvas treated with it has been reported to be useable after exposure to light and weather for five years, while untreated canvas failed in less than one year.

Another type of flame retardant in current use contains antimony oxide and poly(vinyl chloride) or poly(vinylidene chlorides). Plasticizers, such as phosphate esters, may be added to the formulations to decrease stiffening and to control afterglow. The anti-glow and flame-resistant properties may also be improved by combining this retardant with certain flame retardants based on phosphorus-containing polymers. Flame-retardants of this type are used to some extent in the United States and in Europe in military and protective clothing. Disadvantage of treatments of this type may be poor fabric hand, reduced tear strength, and rather high add-ons.

Durability of the type of flame retardant just described probably does not depend on chemical combination of the retardant with the cellulose, but rather on the deposition of insoluble materials. The flame retardants of greatest current interest and potential value are those that involve some chemical combination of the retardant with the cellulose. These are of two types: (*a*) those that involve formation of true partial phosphorus-containing esters or ethers of cellulose, and (*b*) those that are based on the application of phosphorus-containing monomers which form polymers or copolymers in or on the cellulose, and simultaneously react or graft polymerize with it. Examples of the first type are the phosphate esters of cellulose (20) and an ether called phosphonomethylated cotton (21). Both of these have the serious disadvantage of being flame-resistant only as the ammonium salt or free acid, undergoing ion exchange when laundered to give their calcium, magnesium, or sodium salts, which are not flame-resistant. The second type, phosphorus-containing polymers grafted to the cellulose, are of considerable use and interest throughout the world. Several of the more important ones will be described in some detail.

A rather unusual phosphorus compound, tetrakis(hydroxymethyl)-phosphonium chloride (THPC), will react to form polymers with most compounds that are capable of reacting with aqueous formaldehyde. These compounds include urea and melamine and their methylol derivatives. A formulation used extensively (22) consists of an aqueous solution containing THPC, methylolmelamine, urea, triethanolamine and sometimes a softener. The solution is applied by padding, followed by drying, curing at an elevated temperature and washing. It appears to be well suited to fabrics with not too tight a weave that have a weight of 8 oz./yd.^{2} or more. About 16% weight add-on is sufficient to impart adequate flame resistance to such fabrics, but with lighter fabrics greater add-ons are required, at which levels fabric strength sometimes decreases below acceptable values. This treatment also imparts glow resistance, crease resistance, shrinkage control, and mildew resistance. Certain bromine-containing polymers, the bromoform adducts of triallyl phosphate (23) or of allyl phosphononitrilates (24) act synergistically with this THPC retardant to improve its effectiveness, but so far these combinations have not been used extensively, largely because of cost.

Since the THPC–methylolmelamine flame retardant is not particularly suitable for lighter weight fabrics due to losses in strength and also the stiffening associated with extensive polymer formation, crosslinking, and crease-proofing action on the cellulose, ways were sought to avoid these effects. It was found that substitution of a treatment with ammonia (25,26) for the curing step largely eliminated the crosslinking and stiffening effects, making the treatment suitable for light weight fabrics and also for cotton flannelette fabrics of particular interest in children's night clothing.

Another phosphorus-containing monomer of importance in flame-retardant treatments of cellulosic fabrics is tris(1-aziridinyl)phosphine oxide

(APO) (27). This compound reacts readily with cellulose and THPC to form a polymer which is a very effective flame retardant. An aqueous solution containing equimolecular amounts of APO and THPC, along with triethanolamine to prevent both acid degradation and premature polymerization, is applied to the fabric, followed by drying, curing at an elevated temperature, and washing. Adequate flame resistance is obtained with 8-oz. cotton fabric at add-ons of about 10%. The treatment is also suitable for lighter weight fabrics; the tear strength is reduced slightly, but much less than with the THPC–methylolmelamine heat-cure treatment. Increased crease resistance, shrink resistance, and rot resistance are imparted by the APO–THPC treatment which comes very close to meeting the requirements of an ideal flame retardant for cellulosic fabrics, aside from cost. Chemical companies predict much lower prices for both THPC and APO, with increased production and improved processes.

C. WATER- AND OIL-REPELLENT FINISHES

A water-repellent fabric is one composed of fibers that have a water-repellent surface, usually brought about by coating the surface of the fiber with a hydrophobic type of compound or by attaching hydrophobic groups to the fibers. A water-repellent fabric is different from a waterproof fabric in that its interstices are not closed, leaving it quite permeable to air and water vapor; a waterproof fabric is one in which the interstices are filled with a water-impermeable material, resulting in a continuous surface of very low vapor permeability. A similar distinction should be made between oil-repellent and oilproof fabrics. Permeability to water vapor is an important comfort factor in water-repellent garments or in oil-resistant fabrics intended for clothing.

1. Principles of Water and Oil Repellency

When a drop of water, oil, or other liquid touches a solid surface it may take on a spherical shape if it does not wet the surface, it may flatten and form a thin film if it wets the surface, or it may take on forms intermediate between these extremes. The tendency of a solid to resist wetting is a function of the chemical nature of its surface, the roughness of its surface, the porosity of the surface, and the presence on the surface of molecules that alter the surface energy. The angle of contact formed by the tangent to the drop at the point of contact with the surface (angle measured through the liquid) is related to the repellency of the surface and the surface tension of the liquid. When the angle of contact is under

90 degrees the surface is said to be wettable with the particular liquid, and when the angle is over 90 degrees the surface is said to be nonwettable or repellent. A consideration of the energy relationship of the drop–surface system (28) shows that the equilibrium condition is due to the surface energies, γ_{sa}, γ_{la}, γ_{sl}, where γ_{sa} is the free surface energy per square centimeter of the solid in contact with air, γ_{la} is the free surface energy per square centimeter of the liquid in contact with air (numerically and dimensionally equivalent to the surface tension), and γ_{sl} is the free surface energy per square centimeter of the solid in contact with the liquid. At equilibrium the following relationship holds, where θ is the contact angle:

$$\gamma_{sa} = \gamma_{la} \cos \theta + \gamma_{sl} \tag{4}$$

Since the work of adhesion W, a measure of the wetting tendency, is given by

$$W = \gamma_{sa} + \gamma_{la} - \gamma_{sl} \tag{5}$$

it follows that:

$$W = \gamma_{la} (1 + \cos \theta) \tag{6}$$

From this it is clear that the smaller the work of adhesion (the larger the contact angle), the smaller will be the wettability and the greater the repellency.

2. Methods of Evaluating Water and Oil Repellency

Although a study of contact angles is of importance in the study of behavior of liquids on solid surfaces, textile fibers and fabrics do not present ideal surfaces, making necessary other methods for evaluating water and oil repellency and, from a practical standpoint, resistance to rain. Simple, practical tests for measuring the water and oil repellency of textiles have been devised. These are based on the penetration or lack of penetration of the fabric surface by drops of liquids of graduated surface tensions and are designed to evaluate the repellency of the fiber and fabric surfaces *per se* and not the practical resistance of the fabric to rain or to oily stains, which present more complicated problems involving fabric properties in addition to the repellency of the surfaces. It has been shown that for any homologous series of organic liquids, a plot of the cosine of the contact angle observed in the wetting of low energy solids versus the surface tension of the liquid results in a straight line. The intercept of this straight line plot with the line $\cos \theta = 1$ (contact angle 0°) has been defined as the critical surface tension of the solid. Thus, in order for any liquid to wet a surface, the surface tension of the liquid must be less than the critical surface tension of the solid surface. However, critical surface tensions measured on closely packed organic films cast on smooth, clean, nonporous surfaces are always lower than observed with the same films applied to textiles, since these do not present ideal surfaces. Despite this shift in level of wettability, the relationship between the chemical structure of surfaces and their critical surface tension correlates well enough with behavior to serve as the basis for a much used test for oil repellency (29) in which mixtures of mineral oil and *n*-heptane of various surface tensions are placed as drops on fabrics and the rate of penetration or lack of penetration observed. Based on similar considerations, a drop penetration test for water repellency has also been devised (30).

Although repellency of the surface is a major factor in water-resistant fabrics, other fabric properties and various external factors, such as the energy with which the rain drops strike the fabric, are involved. Numerous tests for evaluating the practical water-resistance of textiles are available. Among those most used are the spray test, rain test, falling drop penetration test, Bundesman water-repellency test, Suter hydrostatic test, and dynamic absorption test. A review of such test methods is available (31). Due to the complexity of textiles and because these tests do not all measure the same properties, it is customary to base the evaluation of water-repellent fabrics on several of these tests. Details of some of those most frequently used are available in the yearbooks of the American Association of Textile Chemists and Colorists or in methods of the American Society for Testing Materials.

3. Water-Repellent Treatments

Water-repellent treatments for cellulosic fibers may be placed into three classes: (a) those based on metallic salts and oxides, which usually involve the deposition of aluminum or zirconium soaps or the application of paraffin wax emulsified with aluminum acetate, (*b*) those based on the formation of a polymer or copolymer in or on the fibers, or on the deposition of a polymer on the fibers, and (*c*) those in which there is some chemical union between the repellent and the cellulose. Oil-repellent treatments may be similarly classified. A review of the extensive literature through October 1947 on imparting water-repellency to textiles by chemical methods has been published (32). Of the many repellent treatments described in the literature, only selected examples of current use or interest which involve deposition of a polymer or a chemical union with the cellulose will be discussed in this chapter.

An important group of water repellents is based on the deposition of silicon-containing organic polymers, usually dimethyl and methyl hydrogen silicones which contain chains that may be represented by $[—Si(CH_3)_2OSiH(CH_3)O—]_n$. The chain length and ratio of H to CH_3 varies with the intended use, a high proportion of H being favored in water repellents for cellulosic textiles. Silicones are usually applied from solution in organic solvents or from emulsions. Further polymerization and oxidative crosslinking at the hydrogen atoms occur under the action of elevated temperatures and catalysts. Zirconium salts are often used as catalysts and to increase the effectiveness of the treatments. The alkyl groups orient themselves outward on the fibers to present a surface with a sufficiently low energy to give good water repellency. The durability to laundering and dry cleaning is not particularly good. This may be improved by adding *N*-methylol type compounds to the formulations to form copolymers with the silicone. A silicone material made by simultaneous polymerization of tetravinylsilane and methyl hydrogen siloxane is of current interest as a durable water repellent for textiles (33).

Water repellency may be obtained by the copolymerization of *N*-methylol compounds (the so-called wash-wear resins) with compounds having long alkyl groups, such as stearamide. Other reactive long-chain compounds such as *N*-*n*-octadecyl aziridine may be similarly used. Aziridine compounds of this type may also be reacted directly with the cellulose to impart water repellency.

A water-repellent treating agent in widespread current use which involves some union with the cellulose is Zelan or Velan, the active ingredient of which is stearoamidomethylpyridinium chloride, $C_{17}H_{35}CONHCH_2N^+C_5H_5Cl^-$. It is said to react at curing temperatures to form $C_{17}H_{35}CONHCH_2O$—cellulose. Substitutions of one stearamido group per 150 anhydroglucose units have been obtained (34), which accounts for the durable portion of the water repellency. The nondurable part of the water repellency imparted by this treatment is due to the deposition of some stearamidomethyl compounds, such as distearamidomethane, in the fibers. Other long-chain quaternary compounds are available and are probably used also to impart durable water repellency.

4. Oil-Repellent Treatments

Although long-chain hydrocarbons or silicones applied or attached to cellulose surfaces present a closely packed array of $—CH_3$ groups to give surfaces of low enough surface energy to repel water, repellency to mineral or vegetable oils is not obtained. A surface of significantly lower surface energy, such as is provided by —CF_3 groups, is needed. Since, in the absence of surfactants or other complicating factors, oil repellency is only a higher level of the same property as water repellency, most oil-repellent surfaces are also water-repellent. At the present state of knowledge, practical oil repellency is obtainable only with certain fluorochemicals (29). The more effective of these contain perfluorocarbon groups of four or more carbon atoms. It is important that these chains terminate with a —CF_3 group, since this group in a closely packed smooth surface gives a critical surface tension of 6 dynes/cm., the least wettable surface ever recorded, while a surface composed of —CF_2H groups gives a value of only 15 dynes/cm. This is carried over into practical observations on textile surfaces, —CF_3 compounds giving high oil repellency as indicated by wetting with hydrocarbon liquids of 22 dynes/cm. or less, while similar compounds terminated with —CF_2H groups give low oil repellency, being wet with oils having a surface tension of 28 dynes/cm. or less.

Oil repellency as well as water repellency may be imparted to cellulosic textiles by application of perfluorooctanoic acid by means of its chromium or aluminum complexes. This acid or other perfluoro acids also may be esterified with cellulose to produce oil repellency. However, none of these methods produce repellency that is very durable to dry cleaning or laundering. Durable oil and water repellency may be obtained by attaching perfluoro groups to cellulose by ether linkage. For example, the partial 1,1-dihydroheptafluorobutoxyhydroxypropyl and 1,1-dihydropentadecafluorooctoxyhydroxypropyl ethers of cellulose import durable oil- and water-repellent properties, but are said to be too expensive for practical use (35).

Currently available practical methods for obtaining durable oil repellency in textiles depend on the deposition of polymers containing perfluoro groups. For example, 1,1-dihydroperfluorooctanol, $C_7F_{15}CH_2OH$, may be reacted with acrylic acid and the resulting monomer polymerized to form the polyacrylate (29). This type of polymer exhibits water and oil repellency when applied to fibrous substrates. A commercial product widely used to impart oil and water repellency is said to be of this type. Durability may be increased and cost lowered by blending this fluorochemical with commercially available quaternary-type water repellents, as demonstrated by the U. S. Quartermaster Corps in development of their Quarpel oil- and water-repellent treatment for military and other textiles (36).

D. WEATHER-RESISTANT FINISHES

Cellulosic fabrics, especially those of cotton, are used in tents, tarpaulins, awnings, truck covers, and for other outdoor applications where they are subject to degradation by sunlight, microorganisms, and other factors. Two extensive reviews of this subject were published recently (37,38). Because of the extent of damage caused by sunlight and microorganisms, ways of preventing it have been developed. Although only part of the protective methods involve chemical reaction with the cellulose, the degrading effects of microorganisms and sunlight are manifested through reactions of the cellulose molecule.

1. Theoretical Concepts

a. Actinic Degradation

The exact mechanism through which the degradation of cellulose takes place is perhaps not yet known but is generally agreed to result from an oxidation reaction. Two kinds of reaction, photolysis and photosensitization, may be involved when cellulose is degraded by light. Irrespective of the reaction, ultraviolet light with wavelengths in the range of about 2500–4000 A. is most degrading. Wavelengths of less than 2700 A. are absorbed by the earth's atmosphere and are therefore not important from a practical point of view.

When sufficient light of the proper wavelength is absorbed by cellulose to cause disruption of a chemical bond, the reaction is referred to as photolysis. Cellulose absorbs most strongly in the shortwave ultraviolet region where the energy transfer is most capable of promoting reaction. Only ultraviolet radiation of less than about 3000 A. causes photolysis. Carbonyl groups present to a small extent in purified or bleached cellulose absorb light quanta. The absorbed light is either dissipated as heat or light, or it is transmitted along the cellulose chain to promote degradation by oxidation of alcoholic groups or cleavage of glucosidic bonds. As depolymerization occurs through cleavage of the molecules, more carbonyl groups are made available for absorption of light and, as a consequence, the rate of photolysis increases.

Most actinic damage to cellulosic fibers is through photosensitization. Solar radiation ranging from 2700 A. up to and even including the shorter visible light can activate this type of reaction. In this process some substance present in the cellulose either as an additive or as an impurity absorbs light in the initial step. Subsequent steps may follow either of two mechanisms. According to one mechanism the absorbed energy is transferred to oxygen present in the surrounding atmosphere, yielding activated oxygen or ozone. The activated oxygen then reacts with water vapor to produce hydrogen peroxide which oxidizes the cellulose. According to the second mechanism, the absorbing substance takes a hydrogen atom from the cellulose molecule after which oxygen adds to the cellulose to yield a peroxy radical. Decomposition of the peroxy radical will either break the cellulose chain or produce a carbonyl group in the chain. If a carbonyl group forms, the cellulose is more susceptible to further degradation by light and to cleavage when exposed to alkali solutions.

The substances present in cellulosic fabrics that absorb and transmit solar energy are referred to as sensitizers. They are often such materials as dyes and pigments. The effects of photosensitization will vary, depending on the amount of moisture and oxygen present.

b. Effects of Microorganisms

The two general types of microorganisms that cause the degradation of cellulose are bacteria and fungi. These microorganisms require a relative humidity of about 70–80% and a temperature of less than about 75°C. for proper growth. The microorganisms do not subsist on the cellulose itself, but instead utilize decomposition products of it which are formed by the action of enzymes secreted by the organisms. Hydrolysis occurs at the glucosidic linkage to yield water-soluble products that either diffuse into the microorganism to be metabolized or are further hydrolyzed to glucose by other enzymes.

Enzymatic reaction is usually associated with either a coenzyme or with a particular portion of the surface of the enzyme. The portion that is responsible for the catalytic reaction is referred to as the active site. The active site may contain groups such as —SH, —OH, —NH_2, and others. The coenzyme may be a small molecule that is closely associated with the larger protein body of the enzyme. In either case the reaction that can be catalyzed by an enzyme is specific.

Since there are two ways in which enzymes function, there are two mechanisms for preventing their activity. One is to block the active site and the other is to promote reaction of the coenzyme with some other compound. Another way of preventing damage to cellulosic textiles is chemically to modify the cellulose to make it unsuitable for enzymatic attack. Agents which are added to cellulosic textiles that are effective in controlling bacterial enzymatic action are called bactericides and bacteriostats, and those that control the fungal enzymatic action are referred to as fungicides and fungistats.

Although the exact mechanism through which the microorganisms degrade cellulose is not known, it is known that the splitting of the molecule occurs at the glucosidic linkage.

2. Test Methods

Damage to textiles caused by weathering can be measured in terms of loss in breaking and tearing strength, cuprammonium fluidity, and methylene blue number.

Results of laboratory methods of exposure of cellulosic fabrics to light do not correlate well with damage caused by weathering because weathering is a complex interaction of several factors. The degrading effects of weathering on cellulose vary depending upon the season of the year, location, latitude, humidity, temperature, and a number of other less important factors. The best and only reliable way to evaluate cellulosic textiles for weather resistance is to expose samples of the fabric to the weather in the location where the fabric is to be used. In this test, fabric is held at a 45° angle facing south (in the Northern Hemisphere) (39,40). Fabric is vulnerable to attack from sunlight, microorganisms, airborne acids, and other agents in this outdoor exposure test. In most locations light and microorganisms cause most of the damage. It is possible to differentiate between deterioration caused by sunlight or airborne acids and that caused by microbial attack. Microbial attack reduces fabric strength but does not appreciably change fluidity of the cellulose in solution, whereas sunlight and acids reduce fabric strength and also produce an increase in fluidity. Apparently, the enzymatic hydrolysis by microorganisms splits glucosidic links at or near the end of the cellulose molecules to produce water-soluble material that is leached out, while the actinic degradation occurs at random along the cellulose to produce mostly water-insoluble products of shorter chain length then the original cellulose.

Since outdoor exposure of fabrics is time-consuming and because tests are also desired on fabrics that are not intended for outdoor use, a number of laboratory tests are used to indicate resistance to either sunlight or microorganisms. The Weather-Ometer test (41–43) is used frequently to simulate deterioration from sunlight. In the test, fabric is exposed to full spectrum of the carbon arc or filters may be used. The exposure can be done with or without an intermittent water spray on the fabric. The soil burial test (44,45) is the most drastic, quickest, and probably the most commonly used method for determining resistance to microbial degradation. In this test, fabric strips are buried in warm, moist soil in which untreated fabrics are destroyed in about one week. Another frequently used test is the pure culture technique (46,47), in which the sample is placed in a culture vessel with a nutrient solution and a known organism. The inhibition of organism growth or loss in fabric breaking strength is observed.

3. Protective Finishes

No single chemical modification of cellulosic textiles provides adequate resistance to the degrading effects of both sunlight and microorganisms. Therefore, a combination of chemical agents or processes is used when such protection is desired. Some of the chemical treatments that provide protection are described below.

a. Prevention of Damage Caused by Solar Radiation

In order to protect a cellulosic fabric from its major source of actinic degradation, means must be provided either to remove photosensitizers or to prevent activation of them. This can be accomplished by the use of materials which act as screeners, light scatterers, antioxidants, and materials which utilize the solar energy themselves. These agents may also prevent or reduce photolysis. A screener is an optical filter that absorbs certain wavelengths of light, in this case the ones that would lead to degradation of the cellulose, and allows the rest of the spectrum to pass through. Certain inorganic and organic compounds, when applied to cellulosic fabrics, have the property of reducing the amount of degradation caused by sunlight exposure.

General methods for preventing actinic degradation follow.

(1) Purification

Cellulosic textiles always contain materials other than cellulose. Some of these materials are sensitizers. Scouring, mercerization, and bleaching remove a considerable part of the naturally occurring noncellulose constituents from cotton. Although scouring may make the cotton slightly more resistant to sunlight, bleaching makes cotton more susceptible by introducing carbonyl groups which absorb the light energy that acts to disrupt the cellulose molecules. It is unlikely that cellulose can be purified to the extent that it is not degraded by sunlight.

(2) Chemical Modification

Esters of cotton, such as the acetate, stearate, or the cyclohexanecarboxylate, made from saturated carboxylic acids are degraded by sunlight at about the same rate as unmodified cotton. This is to be expected since the ester group does not appreciably affect the ease of hydrolysis of the glucosidic linkage. Esters made from unsaturated carboxylic acids, such as the cinnamate, crotonate, and sorbate, degrade more rapidly than control cotton during the initial period of exposure. It appears that the unsaturated groups absorb light quanta, and, since they are effectively part of the cellulose, the absorbed energy is transmitted through the molecule to where it can initiate a reaction. The resistance of cotton can be about doubled by first dyeing the cotton with certain vat dyes then esterifying with a saturated carboxylic acid (48). If the esterification of the dyed fabric is carried out with an unsaturated acid, the increased resistance to light is not observed. Some vat dyes are strong sensitizers for cellulose, while some have little effect and others provide a very slight degree of protection. The improved resistance obtained with the combination of vat dyes and esterification is observed even though the ester or the dye alone does not provide improved resistance.

The light resistance of other cellulose derivatives has been studied, and it may be concluded that those that extend the useful life of a cellulosic fabric in outdoor use do so, at least in part, because of the resistance to microorganisms possessed by the particular derivative. Cyanoethylated cotton is an example. Also cotton finished with methylolurea, methylolmelamine, and other amidomethylol derivatives retains more strength when exposed to direct sunlight than does untreated cotton.

(3) Additive Finishes

The application of substances to cellulose that do not necessarily react with it is the most economical and efficient means known to protect cellulosic textiles from actinic degradation. Antioxidants, nonmetals, metal salts, oxides and hydroxides, pigments, polymers, and many miscellaneous compounds fall in this category. The choice of the additive will depend in many cases upon the end use of the fabric. The pigments are probably the most effective of the group named above. There are about 4000 pigments available to the coating industry. Many of them provide considerable protection for cotton even when used in quantities of only 2–4% of the weight of the cotton (49).

b. Prevention of Damage Caused by Microorganisms

Cellulosic textiles can be protected from the action of microorganisms by the addition of biocides, which include both bactericides and fungicides, and by chemical modification of the cellulose. The biocidal agents may be strictly additive chemicals, or they may be adsorbed or bound by the cellulose through secondary valence forces. They should be highly toxic to microorganisms but of low toxicity to man.

(1) Additive Finishes

The additive finishes may be divided into four groups: the phenolics, organometallics, quaternary ammonium compounds, and miscellaneous organic compounds.

(*a*) *Phenolics.* Phenol was one of the first and most widely used biocides for textiles. It is not used much now because of its volatility and toxic properties, but halogenated phenols are used extensively. Two good examples of these are pentachlorophenol and 2,2′-dihydroxy-5,5′-dichlorodiphenylmethane.

(*b*) *Organometallics.* This is the most important group of biocides in current use for protecting cellulosic textiles. Copper and mercury compounds of this group are by far the most used compounds in outdoor applications, such as for tents and tarpaulins. The commonly used copper compounds impart odor, whereas, the main disadvantage of mercurials is toxicity to man. Good examples are copper-8-quinolinolate, and copper naphthenate, and phenylmercury esters such as phenylmercury lactate.

Organotin compounds are very efficient biocides. They are colorless and have little odor but are rather susceptible to degradation to inactive forms by sunlight. A good example of this group is bis(tri-*n*-butyltin) oxide. This compound is tenaciously held in cellulose through some unknown mechanism.

(*c*) *Quaternary Ammonium Compounds.* These are ammonium compounds in which the hydrogen atoms have been replaced by alkyl, long-chain alkyl, and heterocyclic groups in the cationic portion of the molecule. They are substantive to cellulose because of their cationic property but are inactivated by anionic agents.

(*d*) *Miscellaneous Organic Compounds.* There are many organic compounds that exhibit various degrees of biocidal activity. A relationship between chemical structure and activity has not been established. Many of the effective compounds of this group contain a thio group as typified bv the thiocarbamates.

(2) Chemical Modifications to Inhibit Degradation by Microorganisms

Some derivatives of cellulose are resistant to microorganisms but are not biocidal. This type of resistance is based upon the inability of secreted enzymes to attack the modified cellulose substrate. The degree of protection provided by a given modification depends upon the degree of substitution of the cellulose, the nature of the cellulose fiber, the method of making the derivative, and the nature of the substituent group. The influence of these variables will be brought out in the discussion below. The discussion will be limited to the modifications of cotton, since the major part of research and development has been with cotton textiles.

(*a*) *Acetylation.* Cotton is acetylated by reacting it with acetic anhydride in a solution of glacial acetic acid. Perchloric acid is a good catalyst for the reaction. Trifluoroacetic acid is an effective impellent for making highly substituted derivatives. Cotton fabrics containing about 20% acetyl (degree of substitution of 1.0) are extremely resistant to microorganisms, retaining nearly 100% strength for six months in the soil burial test. Materials of higher degrees of acetylation are only slightly more resistant, whereas products of much lower substitution have greatly reduced resistance.

(*b*) *Cyanoethylation.* Cyanoethylated cotton, like acetylated cotton, has excellent resistance to cellulolytic microorganisms. It is unlike acetylated cotton in that it is produced in cellulose-swelling media. For example, one way to produce cyanoethylated fabrics is to first pad or wet the fabric with dilute (1–5%) sodium hydroxide solution, then pass the wet fabric through acrylonitrile to allow the Michael condensation to take place. Fabrics containing 3–4% nitrogen can be produced rapidly with commercial equipment. A degree of substitution of about 0.4 (3.5% nitrogen) produces modified cotton fabrics that show little or no loss in strength after six months in the soil burial test, indicating effectiveness at a lower degree of substitution than required with acetylated cotton. Cotton fabric containing a grafted polyacrylonitrile has considerable resistance although not quite as much as cyanoethylated fabric containing a comparable amount of nitrile nitrogen.

Carbamoylethyl cellulose is another derivative made by a Michael reaction of acrylamide with cellulose. This cotton derivative has substantially less resistance to rot than the cyanoethyl derivative at comparable degrees of substitution. It is also significant to note that carboxyethyl and carboxymethyl cellulose have little or no rot resistance at low degrees of substitution. These facts strongly indicate that rot resistance of cyanoethyl cotton is due to the —CN group in addition to the blocking action of the substituent group.

(*c*) *Crosslinking.* Crosslinked cotton fabrics exhibit various degrees of resistance to microorganisms. Billions of yards of cellulosic fabrics are crosslinked each year to impart crease-resistance and smooth-drying properties. The preparation of these finishes was described earlier in this chapter.

The types of chemicals used to crosslink cotton and rayon include amidomethylols, acetals, aldehydes, methylol-phenols, epoxides, aziridinyls, sulfones, sulfonium compounds, and other compounds. Although the methods used to react the various compounds with cotton differ greatly, the main thing that the crease resistant fabrics have in common is that the cellulose is crosslinked, indicating that crosslinking imparts resistance to cellulytic organisms.

Flame retardant finishes discussed above that contain either or both tetrakis(hydroxymethyl)phosphonium chloride and tris(1-aziridinyl)-phosphine oxide are very resistant to degradation in the soil burial test.

Methylolmelamine-treated cotton fabrics made by different methods vary more than three fold in the amount of rot resistance. Other physical properties, such as strength and crease resistance, are also affected by the method of application. Properly treated fabrics retain 100% strength after 15 weeks in the soil burial test (50,51).

E. THERMOPLASTIC FINISHES

Most of the man-made or synthetic textile fibers are thermoplastic at elevated temperatures, exhibiting glass transition points at or somewhat above the temperatures used for ironing cotton or viscose rayon. Although this property necessitates special care in ironing of fabrics made from some of the synthetic fibers, it is put to use in the heat-setting and annealing of such fibers and in the production of stretch yarns and fabrics. In the latter application, the yarns or filaments are heated above the transition temperature and twisted on a false twister while in a plastic condition. On cooling, the coil or crimp remains permanently, imparting a high degree of reversible stretch to fabrics made from such yarns, as illustrated by nylon stretch socks. Applications of this type have been the objective of work to impart increased thermoplastic properties to cotton and other cellulosic fibers. Although there is currently no commercial production of thermoplastic yarns from cellulosic fibers, methods for imparting thermoplasticity to cotton are of sufficient interest to warrant consideration.

Cellulosic fabrics that have been moistened with water are thermoplastic to some extent, as shown by the ironing process. The fibers that have been swollen by water are readily shaped and molded at the temperature of ironing and remain fixed in shape and position after evaporation of the water. This thermoplasticity of swollen cellulosic fibers may be accentuated by swelling with 20–25% aqueous sodium hydroxide solutions, as may be demonstrated by moistening cotton fabrics with such solutions, followed by ironing without removal of the sodium hydroxide (52). Creases ironed into the fabric in this way are durable through many launderings, but may be removed by a second treatment with the sodium hydroxide solution. Current interest, however, centers about obtaining thermoplasticity of cellulosic fibers by esterification or etherification of the cellulose.

Although partially acetylated cotton (degree of substitution about 1) shows slightly increased thermoplasticity over ordinary cotton, the thermoplastic property of so-called fully acetylated cotton (degree of substitution of 2.1–2.5) is much greater (53). The sticking temperature of fully acetylated cotton fabric in ironing is about the same as that for acetate rayon, about 250°C. Folds and pleats may be readily ironed into fully acetylated cotton fabrics. These withstand hand laundering with a neutral detergent. The pleats may be removed by ironing and relocated, if desired. The dimensional stability of acetylated cotton yarns and fabrics may be increased by heat-stressing treatments. Thermoplastic properties are also shown by cotton fabrics esterified with other aliphatic acids, such as butyric, crotonic, capric, undecenoic, oleic, and stearic acids (54).

Thermoplastic properties of partially cyanoethylated and partially benzylated cottons have been studied (55,56). In yarns cyanoethylated without longitudinal shrinkage, a glass transition temperature appears at substitutions slightly above a degree of substitution (D.S.) = 1. Annealing becomes possible at above D.S. = 2 with the development of the crystal structure of cyanoethylated cellulose as shown by x-ray diffraction. With benzylated cotton yarns having D.S. values of 0.25, 0.34, and 0.81, the observed second-order transition temperatures were 167, 160, and 125°C., respectively, indicating that the benzyl group is more effective in imparting thermoplasticity to cotton than the cyanoethyl group or ester groups. A considerable number of other fibrous partial ethers of cellulose of comparatively high degree of substitution would probably show thermoplasticity, if evaluated for this property.

F. HEAT-RESISTANT FINISHES

Unmodified cellulosic textiles exhibit substantial resistance to thermal degradation but not adequate resistance for many applications. Hot-head press covers, ironing board covers, and electrical insulation are a few end-uses that require a high degree of heat resistance.

Thermal degradation of cellulose produces water, carbon dioxide, tar, and a nonvolatile carbonaceous residue. The main constituent of the tar is levoglucosan, which is isomeric with the anhydroglucose unit of cellulose but has an oxygen bridge between the 1 and 6 carbons. These reactions have been discussed in the portion of this chapter dealing with flame resistance. It has been theorized that blocking of the primary hydroxyl groups in cellulose would increase the thermal stability. This is observed in some cases. For example, the acetate has considerably more thermal stability than unmodified cellulose. There is some evidence to indicate that cellulose triacetate decomposes through a different mechanism from that of cellulose. Oxidation of the primary hydroxyl in cellulose with nitrogen dioxide produces a modified cellulose that degrades much more rapidly than cellulose, especially in the initial stages of the reaction. Madorsky (57) has conducted extensive investigation on the thermal degradation of cellulose and some derivatives.

A number of partial esters and ethers of cotton have greater thermal stability than cotton. Acetylated cotton fabric with an acetyl content of about 20% (D.S. = 1.0) loses less than half of its strength when heated at 160°C. for 7 days, whereas control fabric loses half of its strength in one day (58). Because of this excellent resistance, the demand for acetylated cotton for use in ironing board covers has been increasing. Cyanoethylated and carbamoylethylated cottons have about the same increased thermal stability as the acetylated cotton, but carboxymethylated cotton exhibits little or no increased heat resistance. The phenylurethane derivative of cotton also exhibits considerable increased heat resistance.

G. MULTIPURPOSE FINISHES

The majority of chemical treatments applied to cellulosic textiles are multipurpose in the sense that they accomplish more than their primary objective, changing, and often improving several fabric properties. Enhancement of a number of fabric properties with a single treatment has obvious economic advantages, and for this reason there is considerable interest in such treatments. A number of multipurpose treatments, have been discussed previously in this chapter, such as certain of the durable flame-retardant treatments that also impart increased crease resistance, dimensional stability, and resistance to microorganism. These additional properties are incidental to the flame-retardant treatment, requiring no additions to the formulations. Another way to obtain multipurpose treatments is to combine several agents into a single formulation. An important property of a finishing agent is its compatibility with other finishing agents. A valuable property of a water and oil repellent, such as Quarpel, is that it may be added to wash-wear and flame-retardant formulations to obtain repellency without adverse effects on the other desired properties. Certain silicone water repellents may be similarly used. There is current interest in addition of dyes to various textile treating formulations, such as those containing difunctional agents like APO or divinyl sulfone. Very washfast colors are obtained when the dye reacts with the difunctional agent so as to become chemically linked to the cellulose. The combination of various kinds of finishing agents into multipurpose formulations is an interesting and important field of work for the practical textile finisher.

H. MISCELLANEOUS FINISHES

There are a great number of partial esters and ethers of cellulose which could be made in the form of fiber, yarn, or fabric, but for which no or very limited textile use has been found. A recent compilation covering the literature since 1948 lists 223 derivatives of cellulose (59), most of which are not in commercial use. Some, however, have been investigated and characterized sufficiently to justify consideration.

There has been considerable interest in the chemical modification of cellulosic fibers so that they could be dyed with acid dyes such as are used on wool or silk. This changed dyeing property may be brought about by attaching amino groups to the cellulose by various esterification or etherification reactions. Much of the work has involved the formation of partial aminoethyl ethers of cellulose by means of 2-aminoethylsulfuric acid, 2-aminoethyl chloride, ethylenimine or their derivatives. Although cellulosic fabrics modified in this way dye readily with wool dyes, the fastness to laundering is poor. Affinity for the ordinary substantive cotton dyes is very high, resulting in rapid exhaustion of the dyebath and poor penetration. The amino groups in these fabrics have been used experimentally as reactive centers for the attachment of other groups, but, so far as known, no commercial textile use has been made of the products.

Acidic groups have been attached to cotton cellulose by various reactions, of which the favorite is to attach carboxymethyl groups by etherification with monochloroacetic acid. The resulting chemically modified textiles dye readily with basic dyes, such as methylene blue, and take up other basic substances. There has been some interest in carboxymethylating cellulosic yarns to a high enough degree of substitution to be soluble in aqueous solutions of bases. Soluble yarns or fabrics of this type find a use as scaffolding materials in the manufacture of lace. The current way of making soluble cellulosic derivatives of this type involves the oxidation of partially carboxymethylated cotton fabrics with chromic acid or nitric acid (60). Partially cyanoethylated or aminoethylated cotton fabrics also may be oxidized to give soluble materials.

Chemically modified, fibrous cellulosic materials have been widely used as ion-exchangers and adsorbents in biochemical laboratories for the investigation of proteins, viruses, enzymes, hormones, and nucleic acids (61). The derivatives most frequently used are diethylaminoethyl cellulose of a low degree of substitution as an anion-exchange material, and carboxymethyl cellulose of a low degree of substitution as a cation-exchange material. Aminoethyl cellulose, sulfoethyl cellulose, phosphonomethyl cellulose, cellulose phosphate, cellulose citrate, and other derivatives are also used. These ion-exchange materials are usually made from purified wood pulp or cotton linters and are available also as filter paper for use in chromatography. Similar chemical modifications of dextrans are coming into use.

References

1. Tripp, V. W., A. T. Moore, I. V. deGruy, and M. L. Rollins, *Textile Res. J.*, **30**, 140 (1960).
2. Reeves, W. A., R. M. Perkins, and L. H. Chance, *Textile Res. J.*, **30**, 179 (1960).
3. "Wrinkle Resistance of Fabrics" *Technical Manual of the Am. Assoc. Textile Chemists Colorists*, **36**, 164 (1960).
4. Marsh, J. T., *An Introduction to Textile Finishing*, Chapman and Hall, London, 1947, p. 388.
5. Booth, J. F., *Principles of Textile Testing*, London Nat. Trade Press Ltd., London, 1961, p. 262.

6a. Bostwick, C., *Medd. TEFO, Svenska Textilforskningsinst. Goteborg*, **No. 23**, 1961.

6b. Bostwick, C., *Am. Dyestuff Reptr.*, **51**, 386 (1962).

7. Lako, J., and L. S. Veer, *Enka und Breda Rayon Revue*, **12**, 67 (1958).
8. Anon., *Textile Inds.*, **124** (1), 82 (1960).
9. Hunter, R. S., and C. A. Lofland, *Am. Dyestuff Reptr.*, **48** (8), 54 (1959).
10. Richardson, G. M., *Am. Dyestuff Reptr.*, **48** (16), 44 (1959).
11. Arceneaux, R. L., J. G. Frick, Jr., J. D. Reid, and G. A. Gautreaux, *Am. Dyestuff Reptr.*, **50**, 849 (1961).
12. Frick, J. G., Jr., B. A. K. Andrews, and J. D. Reid, *Am. Dyestuff Reptr.*, **51**, 45 (1962).

13. Drake, G. L., Jr., and J. D. Guthrie, *Textile Res. J.*, **29,** 155 (1959).
14. Federal Specifications CCC-T-191b, No. 5902; *Technical Manual of the Am. Assoc. Textile Chemists Colorists,* **37,** 129 (1961); British Standards 3119, 3120 (1959).
15. Reese, H. J., *Melliand Textilber.*, **41,** 1559 (1960).
16. Schuyten, H. A., J. W. Weaver, and J. D. Reid, in *Fire Retardant Paints,* Advances in Chemistry Series No. 9, American Chemical Society, 1954, p. 7.
17. Ward, F., *J. Soc. Dyers Colourists,* **71,** 569 (1955); *Chem. Abstr.*, **50,** 1324c (1956).
18. Perfect, J. R. W., *J. Soc. Dyers Colourists,* **74,** 829 (1958); *Chem. Abstr.*, **53,** 4747a (1959).
19. Little, R. W., ed., *Flameproofing Textile Fabrics,* Reinhold, New York, 1947.
20. Ford, F. M., and W. P. Hall, U. S. Patent 2,482,755 (to Joseph Bancroft and Sons Co.), Sept. 27, 1949; *Chem. Abstr.*, **44,** 1716h (1950).
21. Drake, G. L., Jr., W. A. Reeves, and J. D. Guthrie, *Textile Res. J.*, **29,** 270 (1959).
22. Guthrie, J. D., G. L. Drake, Jr., and W. A. Reeves, *Am. Dyestuff Reptr.*, **44,** 328 (1955).
23. Reid, J. D., J. G. Frick, Jr., and R. L. Arceneaux, *Textile Res. J.*, **26,** 137 (1956).
24. Hamalainen, C., W. A. Reeves, and J. D. Guthrie, *Textile Res. J.*, **26,** 145 (1956).
25. Reeves, W. A., and J. D. Guthrie, U. S. Patent 2,772,188 (to U. S. Dept. of Agriculture), Nov. 27, 1956; *Chem. Abstr.*, **51,** 7735c (1957).
26. Coates, H., U. S. Patent 2,983,623 (to Albright & Wilson, Ltd.), May 6, 1961; *Chem. Abstr.*, **55,** 17036e (1961).
27. Reeves, W. A., G. L. Drake, Jr., L. H. Chance, and J. D. Guthrie, *Textile Res. J.*, **27,** 260 (1957).
28. Rowen, J. W., and D. Gagliardi, *J. Res. Natl. Bur. Std.*, **38,** 103 (1947); *Chem. Abstr.*, **41,** 3631f (1947).
29. Graejck, E. J., and W. H. Petersen, *Textile Res. J.*, **32,** 320 (1962).
30. Schuyten, H. A., J. W. Weaver, and J. D. Reid, *Am. Dyestuff Reptr.*, **38,** 364 (1949).
31. Reid, J. D., and R. K. Worner, in *Encyclopedia of Chemical Technology,* R. E. Kirk and D. F. Othmer, eds., Vol. 14, 1st ed., Interscience, New York, 1955, pp. 962–980.
32. Schuyten, H. A., J. D. Reid, J. W. Weaver, and J. G. Frick, Jr., *Textile Res. J.*, **18,** 396–415; 490–503 (1948).
33. Conner, C. J., W. A. Reeves, and L. H. Chance, *Textile Res. J.*, **30,** 171 (1960).
34. Schuyten, H. A., J. W. Weaver, J. G. Frick, Jr., and J. D. Reid, *Textile Res. J.*, **22,** 424 (1952).
35. Berni, R. J., R. R. Benerito, and F. J. Phillips, *Textile Res. J.*, **30,** 576 (1960).
36. DeMarco, C. G., G. M. Dias, and W. F. Smith, Textile Series, Report No. 111, Quartermaster Research and Engineering Command, U. S. Army, Natick, Mass., 1960.
37. Howard, J. W., and F. A. McCord, *Textile Res. J.*, **30,** 75 (1960).
38. Robinson, H. M., and W. A. Reeves, *Am. Dyestuff Reptr.*, **50,** 1 (1961).
39. Cady, W. D., and W. D. Appel, *Proc. Am. Assoc. Textile Chem. Colorists,* **1927,** 179; *Am. Dyestuff Reptr.*, **16,** 707 (1927); *Chem. Abstr.*, **22,** 319 (1928).
40. Am. Assoc. Textile Chem. Colorists, *Am. Dyestuff Reptr.*, **36,** 705 (1947).
41. Appel, W. D., *Proc. Am. Assoc. Textile Chem. Colorists,* **1927,** 187; *Am. Dyestuff Reptr.*, **16,** 715, 1927; *Chem. Abstr.*, **22,** 319 (1928).

42. Appel, W. D., *Proc. Am. Assoc. Textile Chem. Colorists,* **1928,** 275; *Am. Dyestuff Reptr.,* **17,** 755 (1928); *Chem. Abstr.,* **23,** 709 (1929).
43. Appel, W. D., *Am. Dyestuff Reptr.,* **36,** 33 (1947).
44. Batson, D. M., D. J. Teunisson, and N. Porges, *Am. Dyestuff Reptr.,* **33,** 423, 449 (1944).
45. Bertolet, N. C., *Am. Dyestuff Reptr.,* **33,** 21 (1944).
46. Goodavage, S. E., *Am. Dyestuff Reptr.,* **32,** 265 (1943).
47. Marsh, P. B., and M. L. Butler, *Ind. Eng. Chem.,* **38,** 701 (1946).
48. Berard, W. N., S. G. Gremillion, Jr., and C. F. Goldthwait, *Textile Res. J.,* **26,** 81 (1956).
49. Brysson, R. J., G. A. Gautreaux, and W. A. Reeves, *Textile Res. J.,* **29,** 126 (1959).
50. Berard, W. N., G. A. Gautreaux, and W. A. Reeves, *Textile Res. J.,* **29,** 126 (1959).
51. Ruperti, A., U. S. Patent 2,763,574 (to CIBA, Ltd.), Sept. 25, 1956; *Chem. Abstr.,* **51,** 1622e (1957).
52. Reeves, W. A., and C. H. Mack, *Am. Dyestuff Reptr.,* **48** (21), 43 (1959).
53. Buras, E. M., Jr., S. R. Hobart, C. Hamalainen, and A. S. Cooper, Jr., *Textile Res. J.,* **27,** 214 (1957).
54. Cruz-Lagrange, M. D., C. Hamalainen, and A. S. Cooper, Jr., *Am. Dyestuff Reptr.,* **51,** 428 (1962).
55. Conrad, C. M., D. J. Stanonis, J. J. Creely, and P. Harbrink, *J. Appl. Polymer Sci.,* **5,** 163 (1961).
56. Klein, E., D. J. Stanonis, P. Harbrink, and R. J. Berni, *Textile Res. J.,* **28,** 659 (1958).
57. Madorsky, S. L., V. E. Hart, and S. Straus, *J. Res. Natl. Bur. Std.,* **60,** 343 (1958); *Chem. Abstr.,* **52,** 15902b (1958).
58. Cooper, A. S., S. T. Voorhies, Jr., E. M. Buras, Jr., and C. F. Goldthwait, *Textile Inds.,* **116** (1), 97, 194 (1952); *Chem. Abstr.,* **46,** 2302b (1952).
59. Cyrot, J., *Bull. Inst. Textile France,* **No. 85,** 29 (1959); *Chem. Abstr.,* **54,** 13648d (1960).
60. Reinhardt, R. M., J. D. Reid, and T. W. Fenner, *Ind. Eng. Chem.,* **50,** 83 (1958).
61. Guthrie, J. D., and A. L. Bullock, *Ind. Eng. Chem.,* **52,** 935 (1960).

AUTHOR INDEX*

* *Italic* numbers refer to reference pages.

B

C

D

E

G

H

I

J

K

M

N

O

P

S

U

V

W

Subject Index

H

I

T